GEOGRAPHIES FOR ADVANCED STUDY

EDITED BY PROFESSOR S. H. BEAVER, M.A., F.G.S.

NORTH AMERICA
ITS COUNTRIES AND REGIONS

GEOGRAPHIES FOR ADVANCED STUDY

Editor: Professor S. H. Beaver, M.A., F.G.S.

The Tropical World
The Soviet Union
Malaya, Indonesia, Borneo, and the Philippines
West Africa
The Scandinavian World
A Regional Geography of Western Europe
Central Europe
Geomorphology
Statistical Methods and the Geographer
Land, People and Economy in Malaya
An Historical Geography of South Africa
The Polar World
North America
The British Isles: A Geographic and Economic Survey
Western Mediterranean World
Geography of Population
Human Geography

NORTH AMERICA
ITS COUNTRIES AND REGIONS

BY

J. WREFORD WATSON
M.A. (Edin.), Ph.D. (Toronto), F.R.S.C., F.R.S.E.
Professor of Geography in the University of Edinburgh:
sometime Chief Geographer, Canada

LONGMAN

LONGMAN GROUP LIMITED
London

Associated companies, branches and representatives throughout the world

First published 1963
Second impression 1964
Second edition 1968
Fourth impression 1970

ISBN 0 582 48151 1

Printed in Great Britain by
Lowe & Brydone (Printers) Ltd., London

TO MY WIFE
FOR ENCOURAGEMENT, ADVICE, AND ASSISTANCE
AND ABOVE ALL
FOR THE CHEERFUL ENTHUSIASM WITH WHICH
SHE ENDURED THE TRIBULATIONS OF DRIVING A
GEOGRAPHER IN HIS NEVER-SATISFIED SEARCH
FOR GEOGRAPHY

Preface and Acknowledgements

The Author's Point of View

Many regional geographies march forward from structure through climate by economic zones and population belts to their ultimate regional divisions as though the final fate were in the initial foredooming, and man's last end had been shaped in nature's first beginnings. But that this book follows such an order does not imply it accepts such a concept. On the contrary, it seeks to show that the same stage may be used to portray quite different scenes according to the stories acted there. If it starts off with structure relief, climate, and vegetation, this is not to prove how these have worked themselves out through whatever dramas North America has seen, but, on the contrary, to indicate how, in Bowman's words, they have become different things with different people.

This is really, then, a regional exercise in cultural geography, to show how, in spite of the very strong and persistent influences of the terrain, taken in its fullest sense, men of different cultures, with separate aims and separate means, have come to create marked regional differences in the development of the landscape, and thus have made their own distinctive interpretation of the natural scene. This makes it important to start with structure, climate, soils, and vegetation precisely to bring out the very different way they were used by the American aborigines on the one hand and European colonizers on the other, and thereafter to stress how Europeans with quite different backgrounds and divergent aims came to make unique assessments of the several parts of the continent they called their own.

This has involved a certain amount of repetition: the physical features of North America are described as a whole, then they are discussed as they came to affect Indian cultures, they are treated again as they influenced the rise of the nation-states of Canada, the United States, and Mexico, and finally they are mentioned still again in the value they possess for the growth of the greater contemporary regions. For all its drawbacks such a reiteration does have the advantage of stressing the vital and abiding influence of the physical environment. For the fact is, although that environment receives its meaning from the different cultures that make use of it, and thus varies in significance with various stages of human development, *within any one culture it is of greatest importance*, providing the opportunities and setting the limits of what man can do with the means at his command. In the present culture it may have become more important than ever, since competition for land has never been so fierce, and this competition is driving men to respect the limits and maximize the opportunities of the region in which they live in an increasingly more significant way. There is always a balance of forces at work: the geographic sceneis both the 'environment made man', and 'man the measure of his environment'. This book therefore tries to describe both the environment in itself and in its major influences, and also man in the power of his adaptations and transformations.

That a book on North America has comparatively little to say on Mexico may seem unforgivable, but it was decided that no more should be made of this very interesting and important part of the continent since it was being dealt with at greater length by other authors in works on Latin America brought out by the publishers.

Preface to the Second Edition

The opportunity provided by revision has been mainly used to show new trends in the economy and in society within N. America, such as new methods of farming, new ways of transportation and marketing, and new patterns in the growth of settlement. In particular, the escalation of tertiary economic activities and the explosion of the city are now tremendous forces re-shaping the geography of the continent. The chance has also been taken to introduce material on new resources brought into use and new areas developed. Statistics have been brought up to date, especially in connexion with agricultural and industrial production, trade, and population. The whole of the index has been revised to provide a complete alphabetical listing as well as a subject arrangement of places and activities.

1967

Acknowledgements

The author wishes to acknowledge the help he has received from the Dominion Bureau of Statistics, Canada, and the United States Information Service; from the American Library in London; and from the many Canadian and American institutions and officials who made his wanderings on the continent more meaningful than they might otherwise have been.

Special thanks are due to the untiring interest and effort of Miss Aileen Stewart and Miss Angela Wear who typed and in other ways helped to prepare the manuscript, and to Mrs Margaret Simister for the painstaking care and discrimination with which she made the finished drawings of all the maps.

The assistance of Mr Upward in editing the proofs has also been much appreciated, while from the beginning the encouragement and advice of Mr E. W. Parker, of Messrs Longmans, Green, have been an inspiration. Throughout, Professor R. W. Steel has given of his long-accumulated skill as an editor, and the comments and suggestions he has so generously made are cordially, though inadequately, acknowledged. Finally, the author desires to thank Professor Stanley Beaver for including this work in his Advanced Study Series, and for the many pertinent and penetrating suggestions he has made.

We are grateful to the following for permission to include copyright material: Thomas Y. Crowell Co. New York for an extract from *Elements of Rural Sociology* by N. Le R. Sims; William Heinemann Ltd. and The Viking Press Inc. for an extract from *The Grapes of Wrath* by John Steinbeck; Holt, Rinehart and Winston, Inc. New York for an extract from *The Growth of the United States* by Harlow; The Macmillan Co. of Canada Ltd. for extracts from *Group Settlement, Ethnic Communities in Western Canada* by C. A. Dawson, reprinted by permission; The Ryerson Press, Toronto for an extract from *The Canadian Desert* by Duncan Stuart, and the University of Oklahoma Press for an extract from *The Great Plains in Transition* by Kraenzel.

For permission to include maps and diagrams based on copyright sources we are indebted to the following:

Figs. 6, 9 and 78 from King, *The Tectonics of Middle North America* (Princeton University Press); Figs. 8, 11 and 116 from Schuchert & Dunbar, *Outlines of Historical Geology* (John Wiley & Sons); Fig. 35 from Guérin, *Revue Canadienne de Géographie*, **IX**, No. 1, 1955, 35; Fig. 79 from Hare, *Revue Canadienne de Géographie*, **II**, No. 1, 1948, 11; Fig. 90 from Parker, *Agricultural Geography of Lower Canada, Revue Canadienne de Géographie*, 1960, 191; Fig. 36 from Johnson, *Canadian Geographer* No. 12, 1958, 5; Fig. 96 from Pearson, *Canadian Geographer*, **V**, No. 4, 1961, 11; Fig. 48 from Pattison, American Rectangular Land Survey, 189; Fig. 72 from Brouillette, *L'Actualité Economique*, 1961, 608, 633; Fig. 80*b* from Hare, *Geog. Bulletin* No. 2, 1952, 44 and Fig. 122 from Gajda, *Geog. Bulletin*, No. 15, 1960, 10 by permission of the Geographical Branch, Department of Mines and Technical Surveys, Ottawa; Fig. 85 from *Geographical Essays in Memory of Alan G. Ogilvie* (Thomas Nelson & Sons, Ltd.); Fig. 98 by permission of the Hydro-Electric Power Commission of Ontario; Fig. 126 from McGuire, *Can. Geog. Journ.*, **LIV**, No. 6, 1957; Fig. 94 from Krueger, *Can. Geog. Journ.*, **LVIII**, No. 4, 1959, 1; Fig. 134 from Fortier, *Can. Geog. Journ.*, **LVII**, No. 3, from material produced by the Geological Survey of Canada; Fig. 117 from *Economic Geography*, **37**, No. 3, 1961, 192, based on material originally prepared for the Lower Mainland Regional Planning Board; Fig. 158 from

Gottmann, *Economic Geography*, **XXXIII**, 1957; Fig. 118 from *Manufacturing Industry in the Lower Mainland of B.C.*, Lower Mainland Regional Planning Board Report, 1960, 38; Fig. 125 from *Bank of Nova Scotia Review*, June 1959; Figs. 142 and 143 from Miller, *Professional Geographer*, **XIII**, No. 3, 1961, redrawn by permission of the Association of American Geographers; Figs. 144 and 145 from Harris, *Annals. Assoc. Amer. Geographers*, **XLIV**, No. 4, 1954, 319; Fig. 166 from Borchert, *Annals. Assoc. Amer. Geographers*, **XL**, No. 1, 1950, 19; Fig. 180 from Gentilcore, *Annals. Assoc. Amer. Geographers*, **XLI**, No. 1, 52; Fig. 185 from Siddall, *Annals, Assoc. Amer. Geographers*, **XLVII**, No. 3, 1957, 277, all redrawn by permission of the Association of American Geographers; Fig. 194 from Eardley, *Structural Geology of North America* (Harper & Row, Publishers, 1951).

For permission to reproduce photographs we are indebted to the following:

Canadian Pacific Railway for Plate 6; Fairchild Aerial Surveys for Plates 8 and 67; Ewing Galloway for Plate 70; Geological Survey of Canada for Plate 4; *The Hamilton Spectator* for Plate 39; George Hunter for Plates 21, 31, 32, 36, 37, 40, 43, 44 and 46; Hunting Survey Corporation for Plate 34; Malak, Ottawa for Plate 38; National Film Board of Canada for Plates 2, 5, 9, 11–14, 29, 30, 33, 41 and 42; Paul Popper for Plates 68, 69, 71 and 72; Royal Canadian Air Force for Plate 1; Ian Taylor for Plates 15 and 16; and U.S.I.S. for Plates 3, 7, 10, 17–20, 22–28, 35, 45 and 47–66.

The copyright owners of the prints supplied by the U.S.I.S. are as follows: Gordon S. Smith for Plate 3; Boston Museum for Plate 7; North Dakota Chamber of Commerce for Plate 10; Joseph Munch for Plate 17; Museum of New Mexico for Plate 18; Smithsonian Institution for Plate 19; *Authenticated News* for Plates 20 and 58; Brown Brothers for Plate 22; I.C.S. for Plate 23; *New York Times* for Plates 24, 49 and 54; Beltman Archives for Plate 25; Association of American Railroads for Plate 26; St. Joseph Museum for Plate 27; Union Pacific Railroad for Plate 28; St. Lawrence Municipal Bureau for Plate 35; Black Star/Bill Ray for Plate 45; Drysdale-Perry Studio for Plate 47; Standard Oil Co. for Plates 48 and 61; Fairchild Aerial Surveys, Inc. for Plate 50; Samuel A. Musgrave for Plate 51; Chicago Association of Commerce & Industry for Plate 52; M. C. Mahon for Plate 53; Cities Service Co. for Plates 55 and 66; Standard Oil Co. (New Jersey) for Plate 56; Washington State Department of Commerce News Bureau for Plate 57; United Air Lines for Plate 59; Division of Highways, Sacramento, Calif. for Plate 60; International Harvester for Plate 62; Tennessee Valley Authority for Plate 63; I. E. Dupont de Nemours & Co. for Plate 64; and Southern Pacific Railroad for Plate 65.

Contents

List of Illustrations

MAPS AND DIAGRAMS

Plates

Introduction

North America: its Nature and Growth

PRESENT POSITION

The North America of today is one of the most fully developed continents of the earth. No comparable area is anything like as productive. None has a higher standard of living. In a world where so much depends upon mineral resources, North America leads with 62 per cent of the world's oil and gas yield, over 60 per cent of its silver, 55 per cent of its iron ore, 45 per cent of its coal, 42 per cent of its copper, and 40 per cent of its lead and zinc production. With the addition of 34 per cent of the world's hydro-electric production, it has the main sinews of modern industry (Fig. 1).

It possesses a wealth of agriculture to match. North America is the world's leading producer of maize, wheat, dairy goods, fruit, tobacco, and cotton. In all of these there is a surplus for export, and the continent is the outstanding exporter of wheat (38 per cent of the world exports), tobacco (45 per cent), and cotton (45 per cent). North America has also been blessed with extensive forests, ranking first in coniferous forests, with about 40 per cent of the total, and second in temperate hardwood forests, with 24 per cent of the world's total.

Thus with a preponderating position in power and fuels, in key metals, in many of the basic foods, and in forest products, it has the opportunity of developing a well-rounded economy, and of supplying its peoples with a high standard of health and prosperity. The noted survey by the Woytinskys[1] has shown that, at mid-century, the *per capita* income in the United States is nearly twice as great as that in the United Kingdom, more than three times that in France, nearly nine times that in the U.S.S.R., and eleven times the *per capita* income in Japan. When one remembers that the Japanese have by far the highest standard of living amongst Asiatic people, one realizes to the full the gap between North America and the under-developed regions of the world.

This contrast can hardly be appreciated unless one has lived both in the

---

[1] Woytinsky, W. S. and E. S., *World Population and Production*, New York, 1953 pp. 390–3.

United States and in the Old World countries. The contrast is equally as pronounced in consumption as it is in production. Thus

the people of the United States, representing but 6 per cent of the world's population are able, largely as the result of the high level of industrialization and the abundant resources with which the land was originally

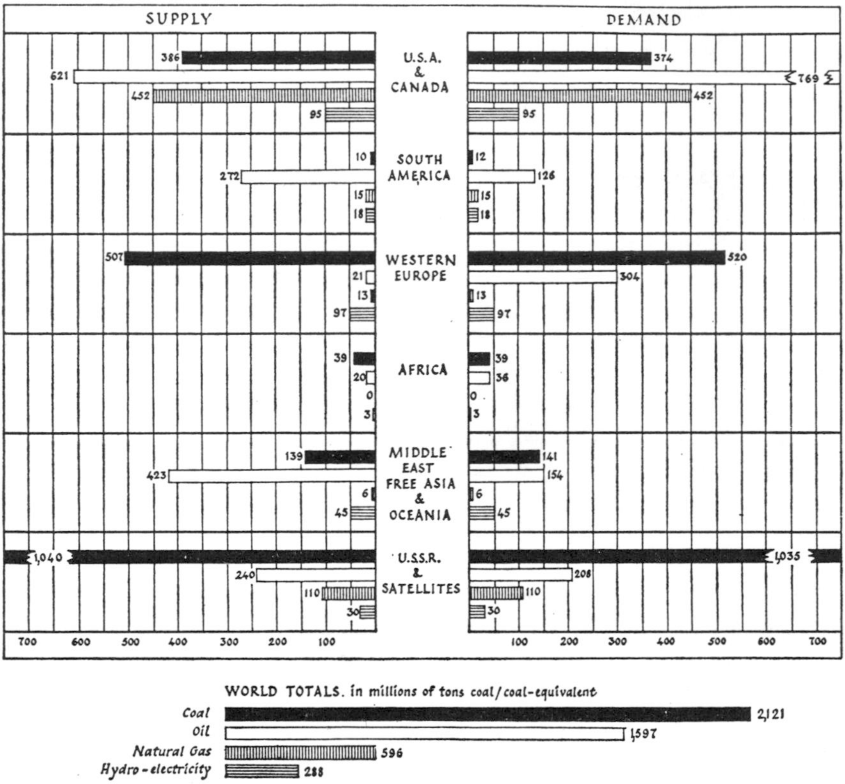

FIG. 1 North America and World Fuel and Power. Although behind West Europe and the U.S.S.R. in the production and use of coal, in all types of fuel together North America leads the world in supply and demand. Its consumption of oil and natural gas is particularly high.

endowed, to consume a major part of the goods produced in the world. We are well fed—perhaps too well fed. Each person on the average consumes food with an energy content of more than 3,100 calories each day, a daily intake which is nearly twice that of the average inhabitant of India. Indeed, fewer than 10 per cent of the inhabitants of our planet are able to live on a standard of food-intake equivalent to that enjoyed by the average American.

> On the material side, we in the United States have an automobile and a telephone for approximately every three persons. We own radios and television sets, refrigerators and washing machines, cameras and wrist-watches, toilets and bath tubs. Our gross national product *per capita* is nearly a hundred times larger than . . . that of India.[1]

Much of this is true for Canada so that the continent as a whole can be said to have, without any doubt, the highest standard of living on the earth.

THE GEOGRAPHICAL ADVANTAGES OF NORTH AMERICA

The striking development made by the North American peoples is due partly to geography and partly to history. The location of North America has been sufficiently isolated to keep it withdrawn from the major devastations of Old World conflict, and yet sufficiently central to allow it to exploit western European and east Asiatic contacts. Indeed, it possesses today those two geographical qualities—insularity and universality—which, according to Mackinder, were amongst Britain's chief assets until recently: an insularity that permitted the working out of its own way of life, and yet a universality that enabled it to profit from regions abroad.

The structure of North America has also offered advantages. It provides a remarkable balance between central shield, interior lowlands, and marginal mountains. There is not the imbalance which makes Africa mainly shield, which pre-empts the heart of Asia with mountains thrusting the plains to the perimeter, and which breaks up Europe into such highly separable units on the west or puts it under the dominance of one great region in the east. In North America, shield, plain, and mountain are about evenly matched and help to account for a varied and yet even economy.

The great shield is at the centre and forms the core of the continent; it reaches from Ellesmere Island in the north-east to Minnesota in the south-west, lying around the vast gulf of Hudson's Bay. It is an uneven plateau, tilted up to a line of heights in the east and south, dipping beneath the seas at its heart, and rising to faulted uplands in the west. Lapping its edges from the St Lawrence estuary to the Mackenzie delta are North America's huge interior lowlands. These spread south to the Gulf of Mexico. They form a series of low plains in the south and east, rising to high plains in the west and north. In the far north, in the Canadian archipelago, they have been largely drowned by the sea. Outward from the interior lowlands rise three great systems of mountains. On the eastern margin of the continent lie the Appalachians, the oldest fold belt, running from Newfoundland to Oklahoma; to the north are the Innuitians, forming a great arc facing the Arctic

---

[1] Brown, H., Bonner, J., Weir, J., *The Next Hundred Years*, London, 1957, Chap. 3, 'Some Contrasts', pp. 10–11.

Ocean; while on the western margin are the Cordilleras, a complex and massive structure including the Rocky, Nevadan, and Coast Range fold systems, with basins or long, narrow depressions between them. In the south-east and south a broad and gentle coast plain extends from the mountains to the Atlantic.

In this very varied scene the vast central plains have formed a heartland, binding the outer uplands and mountains, and the farther coasts, together.

Another advantage for man has been the relationship between structure and climate. The great elongation of the continent between Cape Columbia, 83° 10′ N., and Puerto Angel, 15° 40′ N., gives it a wide range of climates from arctic to tropical types. Possibly more significant, the greatest extent of lowland lies in the greatest spread of temperate climates. North America has appreciably more lowland in humid or subhumid temperate climates than either Europe or Asia. Most of its climates are humid; there is relatively little true desert, except for the ice deserts in the north—certainly less than in Asia or Africa.

An outstanding characteristic is the presence of very different and strongly opposed air masses. The northern half of the continent has a marked negative anomaly in its annual temperatures; places in the interior may be four to six degrees cooler, on an average, than places at the coast, at the same latitude. A polar continental air mass has emerged, with a dome of high pressure at its centre. It contrasts with troughs of low pressure over the North Pacific and North Atlantic where strong positive anomalies in temperatures occur. Here the polar maritime airs conflict with the polar continental ones, and polar fronts have evolved, swept by cyclonic storms. Meanwhile, in the south, the warm waters of the Caribbean and the marked summer warmth of the Mississippi–Ohio basin sponsor the tropical Gulf air mass. Warm, wet streams of air, blowing round the nose of the Bermuda high, sweep across the Gulf plains in the cyclones along the edge of the polar continental air over the Canadian Shield. Pacific air, streaming in above the Cordilleras, frequently generates lee depressions, along the edge of the Rockies, and these, too, move eastward, to add to the concentration of storms in the north-east. As a result, North America experiences a broader sweep of cyclones than any other continent, with the stimulating changes in weather that accompany them.

Structure and climate together have presented the continent with an unusually great concentration of economic minerals and soils. There is an extraordinary abundance of coal, oil, and natural gas. North America has more coal than the rest of the world put together. It possesses 56 per cent of the estimated iron ore reserves of the world. These two facts alone have given it an enormous industrial advantage in an age still dominated by steam-power and steel. Even when hydro-electricity and thermo-nuclear power become fully developed, its coal reserves should prove useful, while its large hydro-electrical potential and important sources of uranium should help it to hold its own in electrically driven or nuclear-powered industry. Meantime, its agricultural development should continue apace, based on the very substantial acreages of temperate grey-brown earths, black and chestnut soils, and of sub-tropical red earths, on which so much of the world's most productive cropping depends. This marriage of great industrial and agricultural potential is the most promising aspect of the continent, enabling it to meet most of its own needs and to have something to spare for those regions abroad with which its fortunes are linked.

HUMAN FACTORS IN NORTH AMERICA'S GROWTH

It is as well to recall, however, that few of these geographical advantages were made use of until the white man entered the continent. The geographical potential was there, but its historic pursuit was lacking. As Bowman remarked, the Niagara which white men harnessed meant no more than 'thundering waters' to the Indians. Geographical resources are in the last event no greater than cultural development. It is impossible to explain the inequalities of man wholly in terms of the inequalities of nature. Perhaps all one can say to explain the backwardness of the American Indians is that they were isolating themselves from civilization when they moved into North America. But this may have been less the result of geographical distance than of social distance. Their society was made up of men who had been moving away for some time; men in retreat. And when they arrived in their new home they did not look back to the civilized world behind. Indeed, there were times when they could not. Coming into the continent between glacial times, their path was cut off behind them by new glacial advances. They became completely separated.

One might nevertheless have expected them to obtain a new lease of life in the new environment. Coming from north-east Siberia into north-west North America they moved from a raw, bitter, limited region to one that, at least along the Pacific coast, was more pleasant. And the farther they moved into North America the more comfortable and stimulating the climate must have proved—that is, for all except Eskimo and Algonquin who stuck to Arctic and Boreal régimes. Yet they found this rich and fertile land as limited as their culture. There is probably no better illustration of the fact that the limitations of geography consist in the limitations of culture. With the world's greatest store of iron these people limited themselves mainly to stone-tipped tools. Even in their higher cultures, where copper and gold were worked, they did not make metals the medium of advance, but were held back by a Stone Age mentality. In plains where today the wheat farmer and cattle rancher abound they contented themselves with a nomadic life, hunting buffalo. Nomadism frequently led their paths to diverge, removing them from the challenge of competition and the chance of co-operation. In-group feelings became paramount, as witnessed by the many taboos against inter-group contacts. It was only in a few places, such as Mexico and Guatemala, that they saw something of the promise of their environment and began to exploit it. But their efforts were not sufficient and they proved no match for the white men when they came.

Actually, like their forerunners, the white settlers were glad of the insularity of the continent. Insularity developed separation, and parts of North America sought to cut themselves off from their motherlands and to resist further entanglements with the Old World. Yet the new settlers were vastly different from their forerunners in that they came to their new home not only to escape but to expand, to find a better life for themselves, to secure the resources for a progressively higher standard of living. Consequently, they early saw and began to use the unique advantages of the continent. The Spaniards started to mine silver in the 1530s and the French to work iron in the 1670s, only a few years after each had gained a footing on the land. Taking up Indian discoveries like the cultivation of tobacco and cotton the English soon developed veritable tobacco and cotton *belts*, while they transformed the interior of the continent with Indian corn.

This expansion of their well-being was linked with an expansion of their practices, and of their very hopes and ideals. In fact, expansionism became a deep-seated conviction of most of the North American peoples, and particularly of the Americans. This itself, as well as their environment—perhaps as much as their environment—led them on to bigger and better things. Few places or times offered more freedom; few peoples carried freedom so far.

THE RISE OF THE NEW GEOGRAPHY

It is in this light that the independence of America, the liberation of Mexico, and the separation of Canada as new sovereign nations must be seen. The United States of America, possessing this new sense of manifest destiny to the greatest degree, expanded faster and farther than its neighbours and secured the heartland of the continent and the lion's share of the resources for itself. The struggle between the three countries laid down the lines of the new geography. It established east–west political boundaries, east–west routes, and east–west movements of people and trade that cut across the major north–south lines of relief. This was a major reorientation of life since, in the main, previous cultures had adapted themselves to the north–south grain of the continent. The drive to the west, not unlike Russia's drive to the east—going on about the same time—was the main shaping force in political and economic geography. It reinterpreted the physical geography in terms of human geography, using the great east–west lines that did exist such as the St Lawrence–Great Lakes and the Mohawk Valley, and elevating other lines to greatness that had formerly played only a secondary role. Each country picked out and emphasized the gaps through the Appalachians or eastern Sierras, each reinforced and exaggerated the east–west rivers (mostly *tributaries*) across the Interior Lowlands or Plateaux, each seized upon and exploited the passes in the Cordilleras, building railways, and later roads and airways, to link coast to coast, and thus developed a vast and ramified system of boundaries and routes, farm belts and industrial zones, which became the main geographical axes of the New World. In this way North America was divided into three east–west regions which stand to this day as the major regional divisions of the continent.

These three first-order, architectonic regions bear witness to the tremendous importance of the human element in the geography of North America. However, within each of them there are many signs of the importance of physical factors. Once the overriding necessity of creating the great political divisions had been acknowledged, the need for adapting life to suit local conditions was recognized, and the economic geography of each country bade fair to become a reflection of relief and climate. In fact, the more advanced the economy the more stringent became the environment, economic developments competing for optimum circumstances, and thus accepting their metes and bounds. This was especially true where American ideals of freedom stressed private enterprise and the competitive system. Increasingly, competition drove entrepreneurs back to geographic factors. The capitalization of geography became a main force in American history. Thus while settlers tried to grow wheat indiscriminately in both eastern and western North America up to about 1881, thereafter the growing importance of wheat in both the Canadian and American economy led to a definite concentration west of the Appalachians, with the rise of four special centres of wheat production in highly favoured areas. Similarly, while corn was grown almost everywhere until the end of the nineteenth century, thereafter the rise of the huge pork-products industry led to the concentration of the corn-hog economy in the relatively restricted area where climate made the difference between profit and loss. Again, as long as settlers used all-purpose cows mainly for their own or highly localized needs, the raising of cows was all but ubiquitous. When cities sprang up and a vastly increased demand for dairy produce developed, then the dairy belt emerged, with a highly regional concentration of milch cattle in those districts best suited to clover, hay, and oats.

Thus broad areas arose within the three North American countries where a combination of economic specialization and natural advantages led to fairly homogeneous uses of land. These areas of relative homogeneity of resource and use have come to set their peculiar stamp upon the landscape. They have created a series of second-order, supplemental regions that fill in the outstanding features of the country.

Within each of these there are further subdivisions. But what is more important, within each there tends to be a focal-point that draws the region together, and dominates it. This is the point around which the region is organized—to which many of its products are sent, or from which money and skill, control, and direction go out. More, it is the social centre of the region, and as such becomes its heart and soul. Occasionally a super focus may arise, such as New York, Chicago, or Los Angeles, drawing several different regions together, so that homogeneity of resource and use give way to variety of stimulus and management. The rise of the city-centred region makes a third order of division helping to delineate the character of the continent.

Conclusion

The geography of North America has seen a changeful and evolving series of patterns as man has struggled to master relief, exploit climate, and make the most of the natural resources of the continent. The fundamental patterns were physical, and they long continued to play a significant part in limiting, challenging, and supporting human development. But with man's evolution, human patterns began to be more and more important, creating a man-impregnated and man-dominated landscape. This was especially true with the coming of the highly organized and technically advanced Europeans, when the whole pace of change was quickened and its scope extended, and man swiftly began to adapt the environment to his own needs and aims. In doing this, he permitted the human divisions inherited from Europe to divide the continent up in such a way that the use of relief and the development of resources were subordinated to different national interests and ambitions. Subsequently, within the national areas that came to be established, other divisions emerged, responding to the growing variety, fullness, and strength of life. Thus the changing story of settlement and development has come through time to create the character of the land—to recognize which, is to understand its present geography.

CHAPTER ONE

The Structure, Relief, and Mineral Resources of the Continent

PART 1: THE SHIELD AND THE BURIED PLATFORM

The geography of North America begins with its build. The development of the terrain throws powerful illumination on resources and their use, and on the growth of routes and settlements. It is the framework for the whole landscape, whether natural or human. It can, therefore, be hardly stressed too much, and must form the basis for any appreciation of the continent.

THE MAIN ASPECTS: PRINCIPAL STRUCTURAL REGIONS

North America, like other major land masses, has evolved around a hard central core through a series of mountain building movements and the retreat of marginal seas. Holmes[1] pictures the typical continent as a low plateau of crystalline rocks rising to marginal mountains of folded sedimentaries before falling away across continental shelves to off-shore deeps. The central mass of North America may first have crumpled its eastern edges by turning against Eurasia, and then, drifting north-westward, have buckled its northern and western margins.

On the other hand, Kay postulates a continent growing outward from a central shield, or stable area, by the consolidation of flanking geosynclines. Originally a relatively stable area emerged in what we now call the Canadian Shield. This was flanked by belts slowly subsiding under great quantities of sediments from the interior. Later, arcs of volcanic and tectonic islands developed off-shore which fed new and deeper geosynclines. These were filled up, folded, and joined to the mainland. They finally developed coastal plains (Fig. 2).

The Central Shield

The core of the continent is the Canadian Shield. It grew up around three main nuclei, near Great Bear Lake, Lake Athabasca, and northern-central Ontario. Here crystalline rocks first hardened out. Between them sedimentary rocks gathered and were then folded up and altered, masses of volcanic

[1] Holmes, A., *Principles of Physical Geology*, Edinburgh, 1945, p. 16.
[2] Kay, M., *North American Geosynclines*, Geol. Soc. Amer., Mem. **48**, 1951, p. 1.

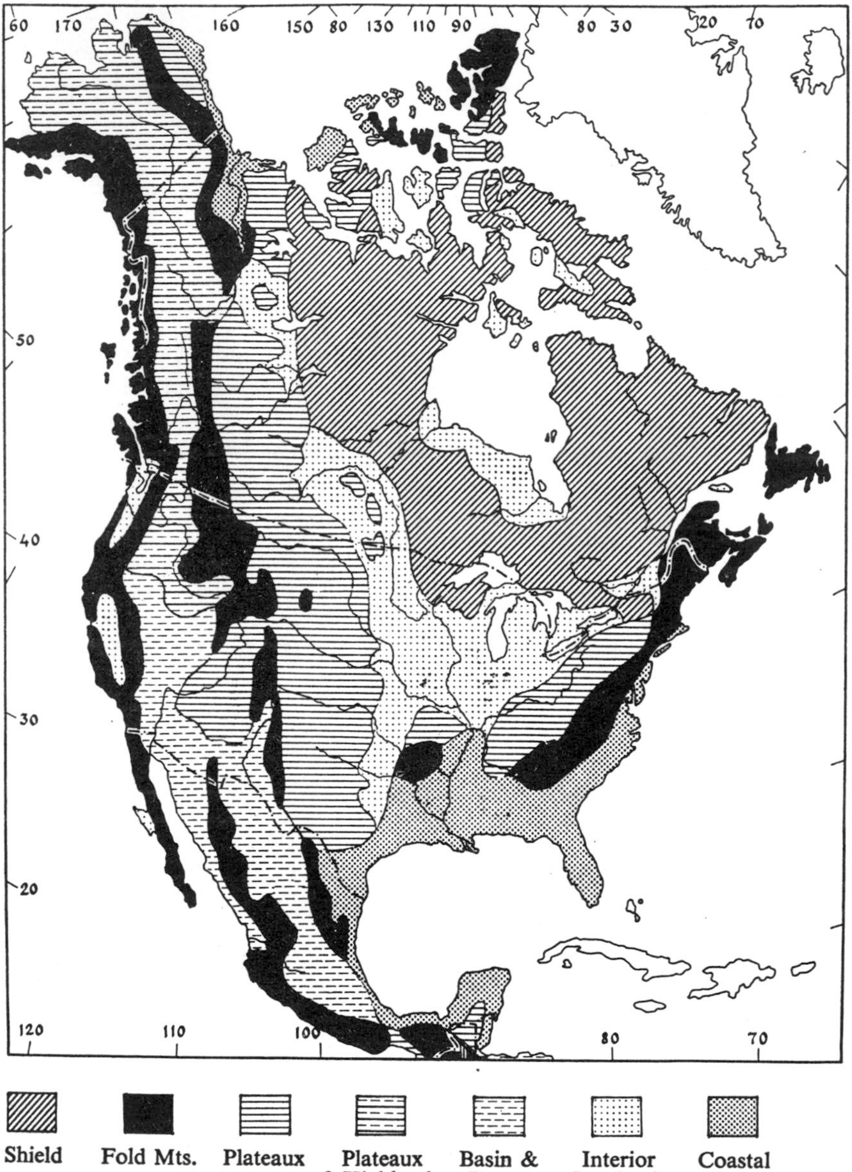

FIG. 2 The Structure of North America. The continent consists of a series of fold mountains at its margins which flank interior lowlands rising to a central shield. (Scale, 1:55 m).

rocks were extruded, and innumerable crystalline domes and dykes thrust up, until the nuclei coalesced in the form of a central shield.

The Buried Platform

This shield continues to both north and south of its visible margins as a buried platform. Such a platform underlies parts of the Arctic archipelago and also most of the Interior Lowlands of the continent. Occasional up-warpings in the hidden shield affect the overlying plains. In the south-west a portion of the buried platform was broken off by mountain-building movements and exists, as an isolated fragment, in the Colorado plateau.

The Marginal Mountains

Round the outer edges of the buried platform rise long ranges of mountains. The first of these to form were the Appalachians that rose along the Atlantic margin in Palaeozoic times. The second, the Innuitians, were thrown up along the Arctic margin in late Palaeozoic to Cenozoic times. The third, the Cordilleras, grew up on the Pacific margin in Mesozoic and Cenozoic times. The continent has, in fact, grown at the expense of the seas by the progressive immobilization of fold-mountain belts.

The Coastal Plains

A final phase of continental growth has witnessed the emergence of coastal plains, mainly along the Atlantic and Arctic slopes. They reach their maximum extent in the Gulf of Mexico, which subsided as the Appalachians rose and drew the drainage of the Interior Lowlands down to spreading deltaic flats.

There is a remarkable parallelism between the northern and southern flanks of the continent. Going in either direction from the centre of the Canadian Shield one passes first across gently dipping Palaeozoic sediments; these thicken outward and are caught up into the Appalachian folding to south and the Innuitian folding to north—both characterized by pitching anticlines and synclines, while beyond these again are coastal plains of younger rocks which are interrupted by piercement domes before dipping under the sea.

Structure and Relief

This structural parallelism is somewhat lost, however, because of the strong surface contrasts between north and south, the north having been heavily glaciated and the south having remained free of ice. Everywhere, indeed, structure has been considerably modified. Though it provides the main lines and proportions of the continent, it does not necessarily account for the detailed features. Detail has been worked out mainly by river and ice, with some wind-worked areas. Rivers have helped to produce old erosion surfaces, especially in the Shield and the Appalachians. They have also re-etched the relief of most of the continent following upon post-glacial rejuvenation.

Glaciation started about one and a quarter million years ago and altered the appearance of most of the continent as far south as the Missouri–Mississippi–Ohio line. The ice epoch saw four major advances and retreats

FIG. 3 The Glaciation of North America. From its main centre in the snow-belt of the high upland of Labrador the ice spread east, south, and west, reinforced by ice developed over Keewatin. Contact was made in the north with Greenland ice, and in the west with Cordilleran ice. The peculiar lack of ice in Alaska was due to lack of snow, not to local warmth: this is today a semi-arid area.

of ice, with a number of minor fluctuations. The main advances of ice are known as the Nebraskan, Kansan, Illinoian, and Wisconsin glaciations, separated by the Aftonian, Yarmouth, and Sangamon interglacial periods. The Nebraskan glaciation spread drift as far as eastern Nebraska and northern Missouri. Kansan drift overlies it in most regions except central Missouri. Illinoian deposits were not quite so extensive, but bury the older ones as far as Iowa. Wisconsin ice did not reach as far in the Mid-West, but buried most of the older deposits in the east (Fig. 3). Thus many of the old irregularities of relief were filled in. Many more new irregularities were created.

Wind-blown loess on the edge of the glaciated area in Nebraska heralds the domain of aeolian erosion and deposition. Wind-cut buttes and wind-filled basins are common on the southern high plains and in the arid south-west of the United States, and in rain-shadow areas of Mexico.

THE CANADIAN SHIELD

Structures of the Shield

The Canadian Shield forms the heart of the North American continent and is its most stable element. It is the largest single structural region, covering 1,850,000 square miles in the northern-central part of the continent. It takes its form from an initial Y-shaped structure which, beginning south-west of Lake Superior, split, and stretched out its arms west and east of the Hudson Bay depression. This structure was subsequently tilted up on the east, to form the high Torngat edge, faulted along the south and west, to plunge under the St Lawrence Gulf, the Great Lakes, and the Western Lakes, and broken in the north, among the straits and islands of the archipelago. It is made up mainly of Archaean and Proterozoic rocks.

In early Archaean times it began as a crescentic structure, reaching from New Quebec across the Upper Great Lakes to northern Keewatin.[1] Masses of Keewatin volcanics, interbedded with agglomerates and banded iron-stones, mark this part, along with schists and quartzites. Later they were caught up in the Laurentian orogeny, and widely intruded by granites. The Shield next added the Grenville province to south and east, mainly of limestones and sandstones, often metamorphosed into crystalline limestones and vitreous quartzites. Later, Timiskaming rocks were laid unconformably on the south and west of the growing Shield. They often contained iron laid down as a sediment.

The Keewatin–Timiskaming series lie in more or less parallel belts running west to east, with marked tilting or folding. These belts may have developed during successive mountain-building movements, ending in the Algoman

[1] Eardley, A. J., *Structural Geology of North America*, New York, 1951, p. 27.

revolution which was accompanied by widespread igneous intrusion. Thereafter, the mountains and domes were eroded down to a virtual peneplain, on top of which Proterozoic sediments were laid.

The Proterozoic era saw the Shield enlarge itself principally in the Lake Huron–Lake Superior region in the south, in the Lake Athabasca–Darnley Bay area in the north-west, and in the Labrador Peninsula–Baffin Island area in the east. It opened with the laying down of the Lower Huronian rocks along the north shore of Lake Huron in what must have been an ancient structural depression. Uplift then occurred, much of the Lower Huronian was removed, and Middle Huronian conglomerates and graywackes were deposited. A long spell of erosion followed in which the Shield was reduced to a plain. After this, the Upper Huronian sedimentaries, often associated with iron-bearing minerals, were deposited. They lay in the ancient depressions west and south of Lake Superior, south of Lake Athabasca and Great Slave Lake, and east of Great Slave Lake. Similar rocks were deposited on either flank of the great eastern arm of the Shield, in the vicinity of the Belcher Islands, and in the Mistassini depression and the Labrador trough. Subsequently, in Animikie time, the sediments were thrown up into mountain ranges—those around the Western Lakes having a south-west–north-east axis, those in the Belcher Islands region a south-south-east–north-north-west trend, and in the Labrador trough a south east–north-west axis. They came to provide a distinct 'graining' to the country.

The era ended with the laying down of Keweenawan rocks, preserved along the north shore of Lake Superior, where a major syncline had developed, also south of Lake Athabasca, and finally in the Coppermine region of the Arctic coast. Here they were involved in the downwarping that produced the Victoria Island trough in the archipelago. Keweenawan times came to a close with the Killarnean mountain-building movement which folded the rocks in the Athabasca basin and was accompanied by granitic intrusion between Sudbury and eastern Ontario.

Although the Shield did not grow further, it suffered many vicissitudes before taking on its present outline. From the end of Proterozoic times to Ordovician ones it was worn down almost to a plain. Downwarping occurred in Upper Ordovician, deepening and widening the central depression in what is now Hudson Bay. However, by the Middle Silurian the Shield had risen so high that Hudson Bay drained away! Sinking followed, but in the late Devonian the southern edge of the Shield was tilted up under the impact of near-by Appalachian folding. A long period of erosion then took place, leading to the Cretaceous Peneplain. With the elevation of the Rockies, the western edge of the Shield was tilted, but from late Eocene to Pliocene the whole region was again reduced to a peneplain. In mid-

Pliocene another major uplift occurred, accompanied by widespread faulting, but the Shield was once more depressed in Pleistocene times under the massive weight of ice. A rebound has taken place in post-glacial times, especially in the south and east, bringing the Shield to its present shape.

The result of this long evolution has been the emergence of a composite region whose overall appearance may show the evenness of an uplifted peneplain, but whose individual parts vary considerably. Variety springs from the changing trends of the old fold belts, the different axes of granite stocks, and the striking effects of fault lines and foliation patterns. These do make the difference in an otherwise rather featureless surface; strikingly linear patterns of drainage follow joints and faults; vegetation everywhere emphasizes the contrast between the bare tops of granite domes and ridges of metamorphic rock and the much greener structural depressions. In the low basins, scarps of massive limestone or conglomerate stand out, while in the Coppermine and Port Arthur plains lava flows have left mesa-like heights.

Thus structure does affect relicf to a considerable extent and may be used as a not unsatisfactory means of defining major regions within the Shield. Gill[1] describes five large units. They are: the Slave province, with a south-south-west–north-north-east trend; the Churchill one with a south-west–north-east trend; the Superior province, largest of them all, trending west–east; the Grenville region, trending south-west–north-east; and the Ungava region, with a similar trend. A Labrador Coast region should be added, with, as Douglas[2] has pointed out, markedly curved lineations, running from north-west to south-east and then swinging round from south-west to north-east (Fig. 4).

The Relief of the Canadian Shield

The main appearance of the Shield is that of an old, worn, yet still rugged upland, tilted in the east and south, broken in the north-west and north, and sinking down to a great interior basin. The upland has a general elevation of 1,200 to 1,400 feet. To the east it mounts up to 5,000 feet in the Torngats, to the south-east it rises to nearly 4,000 feet in the Laurentides, to the south it reaches 2,000 feet in the Algomas, but in the west and north it drops to 800 feet or less. Relict erosion-levels at 1,400 feet, 1,200–1,000 feet, and 800 feet often add variety to the scene. Ancient fold mountains still lift themselves above the general level, as in the Snare, Nonacho, Tazin, Cuyuna, Penokean, and Ungava ranges. In contrast to them, extensive basins occur

[1] Gill, J. E., 'Natural Divisions of the Canadian Shield', *Trans. Roy. Soc. Can.*, 43, Ser. 3, Sect. 4, pp. 61–69.

[2] Douglas, G. V., 'The Structure of Ungava', *Trans. Roy. Soc. Can.*, 43, Ser. 3, Sect. 4, pp. 53–56.

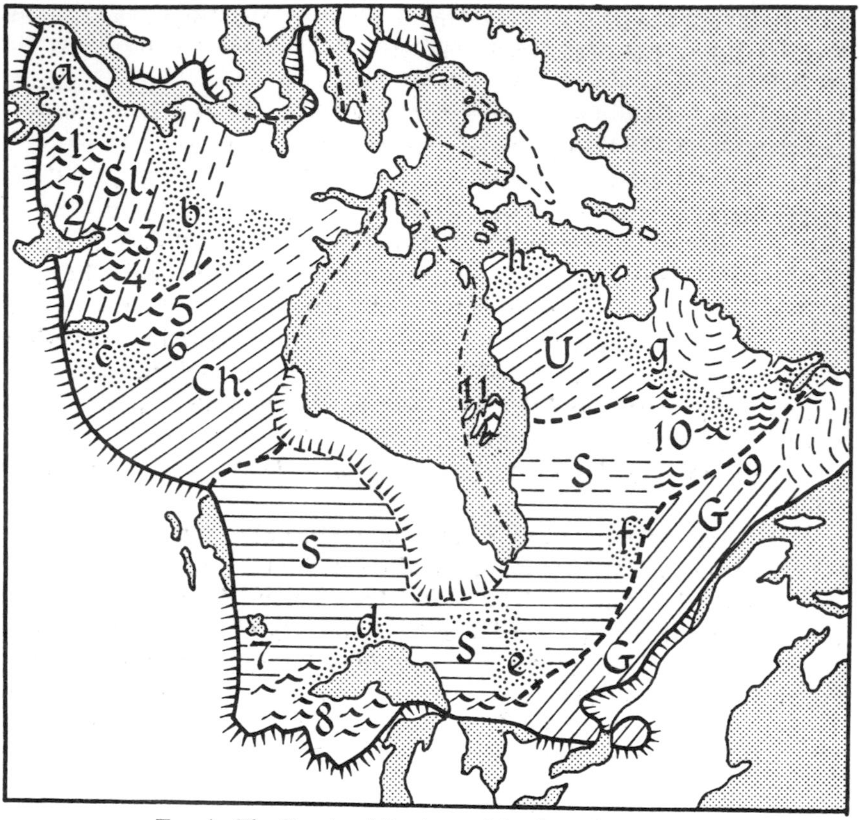

FIG. 4 The Structural Regions of the Canadian Shield.

Sl—Slave, Ch—Churchill, S—Superior, G—Grenville, U—Ungava. Chief basins or troughs in Shield: *a*, Coppermine; *b*, Dubawnt; *c*, Athabasca; *d*, Pt. Arthur; *e*, Cobalt—Gt. Clay Belt; *f*, Mistassini; *g*, Ungava trough; *h*, Wakeham B. Chief Ranges: 1, Bear Mts.; 2, Snare Mts.; 3, Slave Mts.; 4, Nonacho Mts.; 5, Athabasca Ra.; 6, Tazin Mts.; 7, Cuyuna—Mesabi Ranges; 8, Penokean—Gogebic Ranges; 9, C. Labrador Mts.; 10, Ungava Heights. (Scale, 1:35 m.)

within the upland, such as the Thelon and Dubawnt plain to the north, the Port Arthur, Cobalt, and Mistassini plains to the south, and the Labrador plain in the east, not to mention the Hudson Bay Lowlands sloping down to that great central depression.

The whole has been heavily glaciated and partially rejuvenated, so that the surface has been further roughened by ice grooving, the dumping of ground and end moraines, the spread of eskers and drumlins, and countless lake-filled hollows connected by turbulent rivers. The main centre of glaciation lay over the snowy divide of western central Labrador from whence ice swept westward to develop secondary centres of dispersion in Keewatin and, for a period, in the Patricia district. Many pro-glacial lakes were formed, some of which, like the giant Lake Ojibway, left behind wide lacustrine flats. Following upon glaciation the coastal areas rose, stranding beaches as high as 600 feet above the present sea-level, and producing extensive marine terraces. Finally, mass wastage and soil slumping have occurred on steep slopes, while solifluction stripes on the sides of drumlinoid hills, and soil polygons in broad flats, are common.

The Mineral Resources of the Shield

Since the rocks of the Shield were laid down mainly before life appeared, they are without plant or animal remains and are lacking in coal and oil. They are noted instead for metals, most of which formed in the zones of contact-metamorphism around igneous intrusions, or were deposited in sedimentary basins. As Cooke points out, the Shield is

> made up of islands of volcanic or sedimentary rocks, surrounded by a great sea of granitic rocks. Except for the minerals found in pegmatite veins, and those genetically related to bodies of basic intrusive rocks, all the ore bodies of the Shield are associated with the non-granitic 'islands'. The islands, if large, may include more than one mining camp, each with its own characteristics.[1]

Thus the Shield has come to have great significance as North America's main source of metals; it is the chief producer of uranium, gold, nickel, and iron, amongst the important metals, together with platinum and titanium, and is a major supplier of copper and zinc. It also contributes silver and lead.

There are certain well-marked mineraliferous belts; these include the Labrador trough; the western Quebec fault zone; the northern Ontario greenstone belts; the unique Sudbury intrusion; the western Ontario intruded lavas; the Superior upland; and the complex structures in or around the depressions of Lake Athabasca, Great Slave Lake, and Great Bear Lake. Other mineral-rich areas of a more local nature occur, as in the Quebec titanium, the Patricia gold, and the northern Manitoba nickel fields (Fig. 5).

The Labrador trough formed at the beginning of upper Huronian time, when local downwarping carried a long narrow strip below the sea, reaching from west of Ungava Bay down to the present Burnt Lake. This became filled with sandstone, calcareous chert, cherty dolomite, and ferruginous chert. Then it was squeezed out by mountain-building movements, and folding, metamorphism, and the intrusion of igneous bodies occurred. The iron formations were thrown into fairly large concentrations and are now being extensively worked.

In western Quebec a notable fault is found, known as the Cadillac break.

---

[1] Cooke, H. C., 'The Canadian Shield', *Geology and Economic Minerals of Canada*, Can. Geol. Surv., Econ. Geol., Ser. 1, 1947, p. 36.

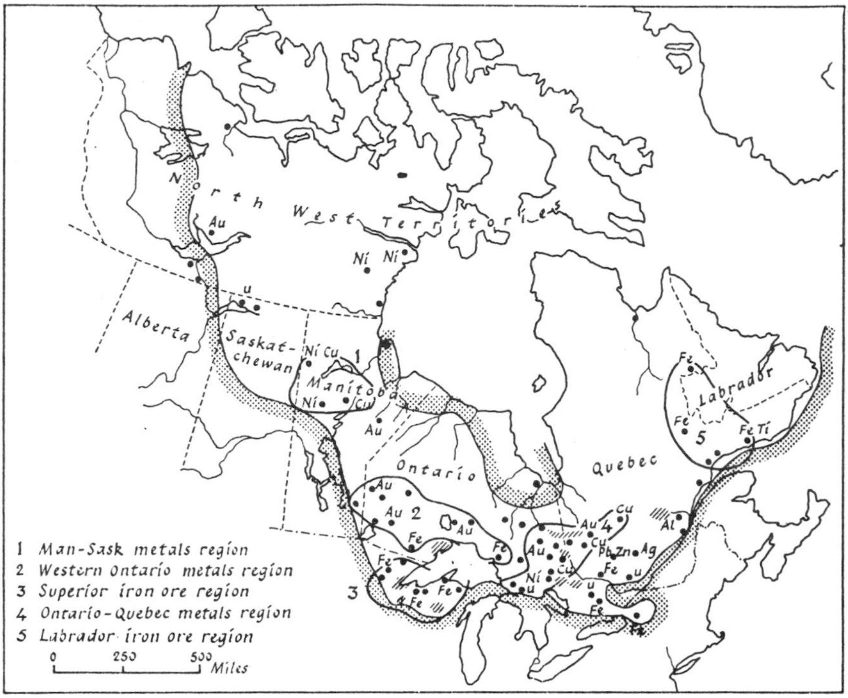

FIG. 5 The Mineral Regions of the Canadian Shield.

Fracturing broke up a series of hard, brittle rocks, into which hot solutions from rising magma escaped, there to cool and deposit their various contents. Gold is the principal ore. Farther west both gold and copper occur, in the Noranda area, where lavas of the Keewatin type have been shattered and then replaced by pyrite. This mineral-rich strip runs with only a short break into the greenstone belt of north-east Ontario, where the rocks have been altered along wide shear zones shot through with quartz and green mica, containing gold. In the famous Porcupine district lavas are intruded by porphyry, cut by many faults, where the gold-bearing solutions have hardened. In the Dome mine part of a sedimentary syncline has been infaulted into Keewatin greenstones, giving rise to rich gold veins. The Sudbury region has a unique concentration of nickel, supplying over 50 per cent of the world's total, along with copper, platinum, and zinc. The ores are associated with a very deep-seated intrusion of norite and micropegmatite, ringing a basin of volcanics. South and west of it at Elliot Lake other igneous intrusions, linked possibly with Algoman magma, have created another highly mineralized area, most important for uranium.

A good deal farther west, around Thunder Bay and in the Port Arthur plain, silver, gold, and iron have been found. Here a belt of lavas and sediments form an 'island' of mineral-bearing rocks. The Animikie iron formation of Proterozoic times runs through the Port Arthur plain into the Superior upland. No ore of consequence has been found on the Canadian side, but south of the border it exists in one of the greatest concentrations in the world in the Mesabi range. Other iron ranges run round the western end of Lake Superior. The Steep Rock iron ore is associated with volcanic action west of Lake Superior. Farther east, at Little Long Lac, arkose beds, folded into a sharp anticline, have broken in a number of shear zones into which quartz was injected, carrying much native gold.

Between Lac Seul and Lake of the Woods, in western North Ontario, there exists a mineral area, where Keewatin lavas have been altered by contact with granitic intrusives. Gold has been the chief ore. Gold is also found in the Patricia district, in small localities where hard rocks like porphyry or quartz or ironstone have been shattered, allowing ore-bearing solutions to enter the cracks and solidify. Somewhat similar conditions in northern Manitoba, where shear zones in massive basalts contain lenses of quartz, have given rise to small gold fields, and nickel-copper bodies.

The remaining mineral-rich areas of the Shield are found principally on or near the three north-western lakes, Athabasca, Great Slave, and Great Bear. These lie in highly complex faulted structures. Much-fractured edges of granitic intrusions north of Athabasca have provided gold while masses of pitchblende are mined for uranium; the lavas and tuffs of the northern and eastern arms of Great Slave Lake have been intruded by large bodies of granite to produce zones of contact-metamorphism rich in gold; while on the east shore of Great Bear Lake a narrow syncline of Proterozoic sediments has been intruded by a porphyritic sill and then faulted. Pitchblende ores, gathered in these faults, have been a rich source of radium and uranium.

Thus it is seen that in those areas of the Shield where sedimentary basins or lava fields were intruded by crystalline rocks, especially where the zones of contact were shattered by faults, ore-formation has frequently taken place to make the Shield one of the richest metal-bearing regions in the world.

THE BURIED PLATFORM

The Structures of the Buried Platform

The Shield extends outward as a buried platform under the inner Canadian archipelago, the Hudson Bay Lowlands, and the Great Interior Lowlands, reaching from the Mackenzie to the Mississippi deltas. In the *Canadian archipelago* the Shield outcrops in four long narrow prongs—forming the Paulatuk, Kent, Boothia, and Rae peninsulas—with shallow basins in between them, floored by gently dipping Palaeozoic rocks. These basins are mostly under water, but have many rocky islands where gently dipping limestone or sandstone beds provide low scarps and low flat plateaux. The rock has been split by frost action to form a wide mantle of waste, marked by stone polygons or stripes. Numerous raised beaches fringe the islands.

In the *Hudson Bay Lowlands* the Shield is buried at no great depth, but has had little effect on the landscape. The all-prevailing flatness and monotony of the scenery is, however, modified by different drainage patterns. Coombs makes out four zones.[1] These are: the dry zone, next to the exposed Shield, with a slightly undulating surface marked by morainic hills; a muskeg zone, occupying most of the region, pitted by small swamps 'as with smallpox'; the marine clay zone, a wide belt of recent marine sediments with very poor drainage; and the wet, or coastal zone, with broad tidal flats extending out for miles at low water.

These northern plains are widely separated from their southern counterparts by the broad mass of the Shield itself. Southwards the Shield thrusts out two prongs in the Adirondacks and Superior Uplands, and then becomes buried under the sedimentary strata of the Interior Lowlands. The *Adirondacks* continue a long arm of the Shield stretching south-eastward from the main mass along the Frontenac axis. They were raised in a vast, almost circular dome, which now shows a core of crystalline rocks, making broad-topped mountains over 5,000 feet in height, sticking through a broken ring of Palaeozoic rocks whose upturned edges make low surrounding scarps. Faulted surfaces overlook the Champlain trough to the east. The *Superior Upland* rises rather abruptly from the Port Arthur plain and continues as a series of old, long, narrow ranges, reaching a height of 1,600 feet, with intervening depressions. Beginning with the Cuyuna mountains on the north-west it sinks beneath the Duluth depression—edged by the Duluth and Superior escarpments, rises again in the rock-ridged Keweenaw Peninsula, dips under the down-faulted Keweenawan plain, and finally rises up to the multiple ridges of the Penokean mountains. The whole area has been peneplaned and possesses flat, even tops, but was subject to post-glacial rejuvenation, marked by beaches stranded 425 feet above the present level of Lake Superior, and by deeply incised rivers.

From its southern prongs the Shield sinks under the *Interior Lowlands* of the continent, which extend to the Appalachians, Ozarks, Rockies, and Mackenzie mountains. The underlying Precambrian rocks outcrop here and there as in the Baraboo range, the central Ozarks, and in central Texas, but in the main they lie buried under wide sheets of sedimentary deposits. Nevertheless, they do rise in a series of broad arches, and sink below great

[1] Coombs, D. B., 'The Physiographic Subdivisions of the Hudson Bay Lowlands', *Geog. Bul.*, Ottawa, **6**, pp. 1–16.

basins, which, though having little effect on the landscape, have a profound bearing on the distribution of minerals (Fig. 6).

The *Great Lakes* occupy what is probably the largest of the basins. They lie in a great long sinuous curve, which, as we have already seen, is partly due to major structural downwarps beneath Lake Superior and Lake Huron.

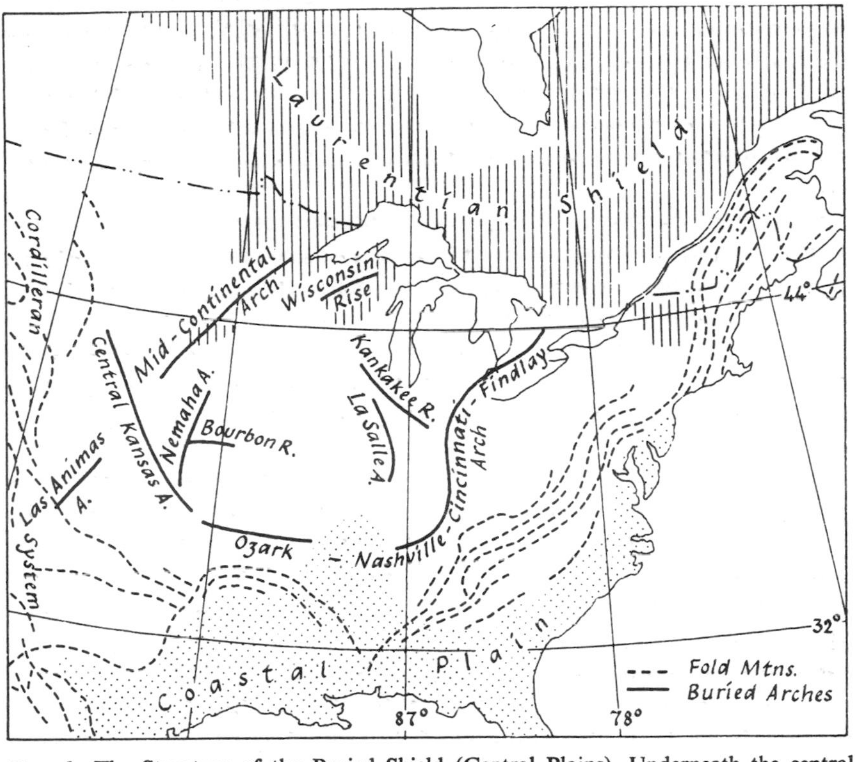

FIG. 6 The Structure of the Buried Shield (Central Plains). Underneath the central plains great upwarps and even greater down-sags of the buried portion of the Shield extend to the edges of the Appalachians and the Rockies. These are extremely important in the geography of American minerals and fuels. (Scale, 1:25 m.)

However, as Newcombe suggests,[1] the depression is also due to salt beds, running from Lake Michigan, through part of Lake Huron, to Lake Erie, the gradual solution of which resulted in the collapse of the overlying beds, subsidence, and lake formation.

Southward and westward of the Great Lakes occur relatively flat lowlands built up by the spread of great deltas from the rivers of the Appalachians and, later, of the Rockies. Although the surface of this region is largely

[1] Newcombe, R. J. B., 'Oil and Gas Fields of Michigan', *Mich. Geol. Surv. Div. Pub.*, **38**, Geol. Ser. 32.

due to river deposition and erosion, modified in part by glaciation, yet it also reflects the underlying structure. Several vast upwarps in the buried Shield produce a number of rises and sags in the heart of the continent. Southwards from the Superior Upland runs the *Wisconsin arch*, which forms a low divide between Lake Michigan and the Mississippi Valley and is marked by a number of partially exposed relics of Precambrian rocks, such as the Baraboo ranges. Two other upwarps branch off from this. They are the *Kankakee rise*, running south-east of Lake Michigan and separating the great Michigan basin from the hardly less noteworthy basin of Indiana and south-west Kentucky; and the most important *La Salle anticline*,[1] dividing the Indiana–Kentucky basin from its Illinois counterpart to the west.

An even greater system of arches occurs farther east. This begins with the *Findlay rise* which domes up the Niagara escarpment in central-southern Ontario; continues in the *Cincinnati arch*, swinging in a huge S across Ohio; extends beneath the *Nashville dome* in Tennessee, which has been partially stripped by erosion to present a ring of in-facing scarps of younger rocks about a basin of older ones, and concludes with the *Ozark dome*, standing up as a plateau some 1,000 feet in altitude, where active erosion is resurrecting the partially buried crystalline rocks.

The Ozark dome is continued along a south-south-east to north-north-west axis as the *Central Kansas arch*, which reaches as far to the north-west as the Black Hills. Most of this is buried too deep to affect the surface, and is important in the geology rather than the relief of the region. However, a parallel arch, well to the south, known as the *Llano uplift* of Texas, does bring up crystalline and early Palaeozoic rocks which are exposed at the surface through a near ring of Cretaceous formations.

Transverse to these is a deeply buried rise, the so-called *Transcontinental arch*, which runs from Minnesota into Colorado.[2] Through much of Palaeozoic time it divided the interior of the continent into two, and, though it makes no impression on the landscape today, it exerts an important control on fuel-bearing basins.

Along the Cordilleran foreland a number of structural basins exist, some of which affect the relief, and all of which are significant geologically. The *Raton basin* runs along the front of the Sangre de Cristo mountains. It terminates in a low arch, the Las Aminas uplift. North of this lies *Denver basin*, reflected in a piedmont depression along the edge of the Front range. Farther north there spreads out the vast *Williston basin*, extending from Montana and Wyoming through northern Dakota to southern Manitoba.

---

[1] Cordy, G. H., 'The Structure of the La Salle Anticline', *Ill. Geol. Surv. Bul.*, **36**, pp. 85–179.

[2] King, P. B., *The Tectonics of Middle North America*, Princeton, 1951.

Finally, still farther north is the narrow but long *Alberta basin*, paralleling the Canadian Rockies for 400 miles or more. Some of its structures would seem to have affected the surface, since sections which have not sagged as low as others have formed divides between the Bow, Saskatchewan, and Athabasca rivers.[1]

The Interior Lowlands show several contrasted landscapes; to the east and south they give way to the Interior Plateaux; they broaden out in the Ohio–Mississippi–Great Lakes region into the Central Plains; and to the west and north they climb to the Great Plains. Roughly, north of the Ohio–Missouri they have been glaciated; south of that they are drift-free.

The *Interior Plateaux* consist of two parts, one to the east of the Mississippi, the other to the west. Eastward lie the structures of the Cincinnati rise and the Nashville dome. These have been eroded for such a long time that crests have become basins ringed around with well-marked cuestas from which low plateaux dip gently away. Underlying limestones have been widely dissolved by ground-water to give a sink-and-knob surface. Westward, the Ozark dome crowns the scene. Its central part thrusts up as a hard core of crystalline rocks, forming the knob-like peaks of the St Francis mountains, about 1,800 feet in height. They are rimmed by cuestas of outward dipping Mississippian and Pennsylvanian formations. The cuestas have been bevelled off by peneplanation. Actually, the bevelling affected a wide area, known as the Salem Plateau. Subsequent doming led streams to cut deeply into their courses—gorges and entrenched meanders being the result.

The *Central Plains* extend from the flats of Lake Winnipeg to the Frontenac axis, across the middle Mississippi basin. They consist of: (i) a lake belt to the north, along the edge of the Shield, where the present lakes —Manitoba, Winnipegosis and Winnipeg, Michigan, Huron, Erie and Ontario—being but relics of still greater glacial lakes,[2] are flanked with fertile lacustrine terraces and flats; (ii) a morainic belt in the centre, where great loops of ancient terminal moraines make a gently corrugated plain, with low ridges of boulder clay separating broad flat areas of worked-over drift; (iii) a drift-free enclave within the glaciated plains, in Wisconsin; and (iv) a drift-free zone, in the Osage plains, dominated by river erosion. This zone has passed through several cycles of erosion; relict peneplains, often bevelling low cuestas or old monadnocks, occur. Late uplift has caused widespread entrenchment of the streams.

The *Great Plains* form an enormous region, stretching from the Mackenzie

[1] Rutherford, R. L., 'Regional Structural Features of the Alberta Foothills, etc.', *Trans. Roy. Soc. Can.*, **38**, Ser. 3, Sect. 4, pp. 71–77; cf. especially p. 74, structural positions of major stream valleys.

[2] Leverett, F., and Taylor, F. B., 'The Pleistocene of Indiana and Michigan and the History of the Great Lakes', *U.S. Geol. Surv. Mon.*. **53**.

delta to the Rio Grande. They are made up of relatively late sedimentary rocks lying in flat or gently folded strata. Along the edge of the Rockies the rocks are often tilted up sharply in striking hogbacks. Eastward, great stretches of marine sediments, laid down in former epicontinental seas, provide immense and sweeping horizons. On top of these were spread out large fans of gravel and sand, derived from the western mountains, which have formed a firmly cemented 'mortar bed', frequently capping the plains. The whole slopes from altitudes of 5,500 feet in the west to about 1,500 feet in the east. An eastward-facing scarp, overlooking the Central Plains, often marks the outward limits. Major differences exist between the northern glaciated portion and the southern unglaciated part.

The *Northern Great Plains* begin in the Mackenzie lowlands, and have a thin veneer of glacial debris, mostly spread by the Ungava–Keewatin ice-sheets. Large glacial-lake deposits, with sheets of deltaic sand and ribbons of post-glacial beach, mark the vicinity of the Great Bear, Great Slave and Lesser Slave lakes, and Lake Athabasca. Occasional bed-rock features rise to notice like the sharply folded Franklin Mountains, with their remarkable 'flat-irons', together with scarp-edged plateaux, like the Horn and Caribou mountains. Rejuvenated rivers cut steep-sided, deeply sunken courses.

South of the Caribou mountains the land tilts to the east rather than to the north, forming the Canadian prairies. These drop from the high plains of Alberta, at about 4,500 feet, over the Missouri Coteau, down to the Saskatchewan plains, ending along the Manitoba scarp. Two long moraines run parallel to the foothills, while other large morainic masses lie back of the crests of the great escarpments. Glacial-lake deposits have left some large fertile flats, particularly near Saskatoon and Regina. Extensive areas of sand hills derived from the deltaic sands pushed out into glacial lakes or from dune-fringed braided streams are found in the arid areas of the South Saskatchewan basin.

The *Southern Great Plains*, beginning in Montana and the Dakotas, are bounded by frequent hogbacks on their west and by the Missouri Coteau on their east. Deeply entrenched rivers in Wyoming and southern Dakota, cutting into relatively unconsolidated, flat sedimentaries, produce extensive badlands. South of these there rises the escarpment of Pine Ridge, beyond which is a broad, undulating area of sand hills in northern Nebraska. These have developed in part from the sands brought down and dropped by heavily braided rivers. In southern Nebraska widespread deposits of loess blanket the plains, cut into by numerous streams. Close to the mountains the Great Plains next sink to the Colorado Piedmont depression, an ancient structural basin partly renewed by heavy erosion of comparatively soft overlying rocks. East of this are the High Plains, a high tableland dominated by resistant cap formations. Southward the Raton basin is marked by a number of bold mesas, carved from lava flows, while the High Plains continue barred with strips of sand hills beside the Arkansas and Canadian rivers. Finally, the land widens out into a number of plateaux, with well-marked edges, stepping down from the naked Llano Estacado, or Staked Plains, some 4,000 feet high on the west, to the Edwards Plateau, at about 2,400 feet, and then again to the scalloped mesalands of the plains border, at 1,100 feet.

The Mineral Resources of the Buried Platform

While little is known about the resources of the low plains overlying the buried platform north of the Shield, widespread prospecting south of the Shield, in the Interior Lowlands, has shown a wealth of minerals. The important resources are coal, oil, and natural gas. Conditions were exceptionally favourable for their development. Shallow basins into which wide deltas were built, dense forests and marshes, vast epicontinental seas whose deposits spread over, trapped and preserved vegetative matter, and great structural arches that brought and maintained the coal beds and oil pools reasonably near the surface, all conspired to produce an unusual concentration of fuels; no other comparable area in the world has such an abundance.

Coal

North America has the greatest coal reserves in the world. Most of these lie on the western flank of the Appalachians and in the Interior Lowlands. The largest single coal field in the United States is that in western Pennsylvania, Ohio, West Virginia, and Kentucky where the Appalachians die out against the foreland of the buried platform. The seams are thick, cover a large area, are comparatively free from foreign matter, and lie at no great depth. They are good grade bituminous coals and are excellent for coking and raising steam. The Cincinnati anticline rises between this field and the eastern Interior one in western Kentucky, Indiana, and Illinois, where reasonably good bituminous coal occurs. The Kankakee rise to the north divides this from the small coal field in the centre of the Michigan basin. The La Salle arch lies between the eastern and the western Interior fields. The latter produces rather low-grade bituminous coal and is not as important as its eastern counterparts, but it covers a wide area in Iowa, Missouri, Kansas, and Oklahoma. The Llano uplift cuts this off from the south-west Interior field, again of relatively poor bituminous coal, in Texas. The mid-Continental arch forms a major divide between these Appalachian–Central Plains coal fields, of moderate to good bituminous grade, and the Great Plains deposits, of a more varied character, along the Cordilleran foreland. Tolerably good bituminous coal occurs in the Raton basin. It is cut off by the Las Animas uplift from the Denver basin field, which is sub-bituminous. Farther north extends the huge Williston basin, with very extensive beds of coal. However, apart from the sub-bituminous coal of the Powder River sub-region, the coal in the rest of the basin is mostly lignite, and is only locally important. It spreads into southern Saskatchewan where it is worked in the vicinity of Estevan. The Judith basin in Montana is another structural depression which has trapped coal, some of it of bituminous quality. Still farther north is the vast coal basin of Alberta, greater even than that of the Appalachians, though much less significant because the coal is of poorer quality and is remote from the main consumer markets of the continent. The basin divides itself into two foothills belts and two plains belts; the former have fairly good bituminous seams; the latter mainly sub-bituminous ones, pinched off on the north by the Caribou rise.

Oil and Gas

Great as is the control of the underlying structure on the coal fields, it is even more significant for oil and natural gas. The major upwarps are of paramount importance in dividing the oil fields from each other. Within the fields themselves, as Hume points out,[1] structural, stratigraphic and geomorphic traps are most significant. Structural traps have emerged where minor irregularities in the underlying platform have led to thinning or stretching of sedimentary layers deposited on top of them, and to the compaction of beds on their flanks. The stretched beds then attracted concentrations of oil and gas, which were held in by the compacted beds. Stratigraphic traps have grown up where sands and muds have been laid down in succession; sands compact much less than mud and, being more porous, have drawn gas, oil, and water into them. The muds became compacted into impervious shales and prevented the sand-trapped oil from oozing away. Geomorphic traps have proved significant where old erosion surfaces that were cut into limestone, led to leaching and solution. The ground-water circulating in the limestone then made it porous, often at considerable depth. When these porous limestones later became buried by sediments rich in organic material they grew to be reservoirs of oil and gas.

North America is possibly the richest continent in oil and natural gas. The oldest producing field has been the Pennsylvania–Ohio one on the western flanks of the Appalachian and the eastern foreland of the buried platform. Here in 1859, at Titusville, Pennsylvania, the first well started production. Gas was also, and is still, present. Gas has a wider distribution; notably in the Clinton gas belt, Ohio, the Haldimand–Norfolk field of southern Ontario, and the western New York field. Both oil and gas are still produced, though not in great quantities. The Findlay rise and Cincinnati

[1] Hume, G. S., 'The Interior Plains', *Geology and Economic Minerals of Canada*, Can. Geol. Surv. Econ. Geol., Ser. 1, Ottawa, 1947, pp. 204–5.

anticline terminate the region on the west, dividing it from the Lima, Indiana, oil field farther west. Here, too, gas is locally important. The Kankakee rise divides the small Michigan oil and gas field, in the centre of the Michigan structural basin, from that in south-west Indiana and southern Illinois. Here gas is present but is relatively insignificant. The main oil and gas field of the continent, and one of the largest in the world, is the mid-Continental one, lying between the Ozark dome and the Transcontinental arch. It spreads from Bemis-Shutz in north-west Kansas to Yates in south-west Texas. Here a whole number of low swells and shallow basins have trapped the oil and gas on their flanks. The Hugoton and Panhandle gas fields are among the largest in the world, and supply many of the central and eastern States of the U.S.A. Another major oil field is found on the Gulf Coast, where salt and sulphur domes have helped to trap oil in porous rocks above compacted, impervious ones. Gas is present, but is not very important.

Again, as with coal, the Transcontinental arch forms a major divide between the oil-producing regions of the south and east and those of the west and north. The Oregon basin in Wyoming, a small western oil field, with the Little Buffalo gas basin, and the great Williston oil basin in Montana, North Dakota, and southern Manitoba, linked with the Bowdoin, Montana, gas field, provide the western Great Plains with useful fuel reserves. In Canada the Alberta and north-west Saskatchewan oil fields, and the gas fields of the Peace river area of British Columbia, together with those of northern-central and southern Alberta, are significant. The British Columbia gas is piped to Vancouver and Seattle; Alberta gas to Ontario and the Montreal industrial district. The Athabasca tar sands, farther north, have an immense quantity of oil locked up in them, but so far it has not been economic to separate the oil from the bituminous sands with which it is associated. Should an economic method of separation be found then the tar sands should prove one of the greatest oil fields in the world. Still farther north, in a deep basin between the Franklin and Mackenzie mountains, is the small but valuable oil field of Norman Wells.

Thus it is evident that North America is extremely fortunate in the unusually large concentrations of minerals it possesses in the two basic structures of the central Shield and the surrounding platform buried under the Interior Lowlands. Some of the world's richest iron, nickel, and uranium mines in the Shield, and the world's greatest fuel resources within the Interior Lowlands, provide an unrivalled basis for industrial development and prosperity. Once the white men came into North America, with their tradition of working in iron and using coal, the continent forged ahead to become the world's leading centre of production.

CHAPTER TWO

The Structure, Relief, and Mineral Resources of the Continent

PART 2: MARGINAL MOUNTAINS AND COAST PLAINS

While the core of North America is formed by the Canadian Shield and by the buried platform of ancient rocks underneath the Interior Lowland, a large part of the continent still lies beyond. This consists of the marginal mountains, built up around the central stable area, and the coastal plains. The main highland systems are those of the Appalachians to the east and south-east, the Innuitians to the north and the Cordilleras to the west. The principal coastal plains are those of the Atlantic shore from Cape Cod to the Florida Keys, and of the Gulf of Mexico. The history of all these marginal features is probably less than one seventh as long as that of the central Shield, beginning as it does with Palaeozoic times (Fig. 7).

THE APPALACHIANS

Structure

In early Cambrian times the eastern margin of the continent began to be disturbed. A series of great geosynclines evolved from Newfoundland to Texas that were later squeezed out to give rise to the Appalachian system of mountains. Here structure has been of pre-eminent importance, for although the region has been peneplaned several times, uplift has led rivers to attack its surface vigorously and they have unearthed its ancient ridges and hollows. The structures of the initial geosynclines account for striking contrasts between the western and eastern Appalachians. The western areas rose from a comparatively shallow depression, or miogeosyncline,* following the edge of the buried platform. The eastern Appalachians rose from a deeper zone, or eugeosyncline,† out on the continental margin. The western parts now consist of more regularly folded rocks with few crystalline intrusions: the eastern parts are intensively folded and faulted and have been heavily intruded by igneous rocks.

As Kay[1] visualizes it, during the Cambrian times depressions developed

* Less than a geosyncline. † A true geosyncline.

[1] Kay, *North American Geosynclines*, p. 11.

TIME UNITS		TIME SINCE BEGINNING of PERIOD	SUCCESSION of LIFE: Animals	SUCCESSION of LIFE: Plants
CENOZOIC ERA	Recent Epoch	25,000	Age of Mammals	Age of Hardwood Forests
	Pleistocene Epoch	1,000,000		
	Pliocene Epoch	15,000,000		
	Miocene Epoch	35,000,000		
	Oligocene Epoch	50,000,000		
	Eocene Epoch	70,000,000		
	Paleocene Epoch	90,000,000		
MESOZOIC ERA	Cretaceous Period	120,000,000	Age of Reptiles	
	Jurassic Period	150,000,000		Age of Conifers
	Triassic Period	190,000,000		
PALEOZOIC ERA	Permian Period	220,000,000	Age of Fishes and Amphibia	Age of Sporebearing Forests
	Pennsylvanian Period	240,000,000		
	Mississippian Period	280,000,000		
	Devonian Period	320,000,000		
	Silurian Period	350,000,000	Age of Marine Invertebrates	Age of Seaweeds (Algae)
	Ordovician Period	400,000,000		
	Cambrian Period	500,000,000		
PRE-CAMBRIAN		4,500,000,000		

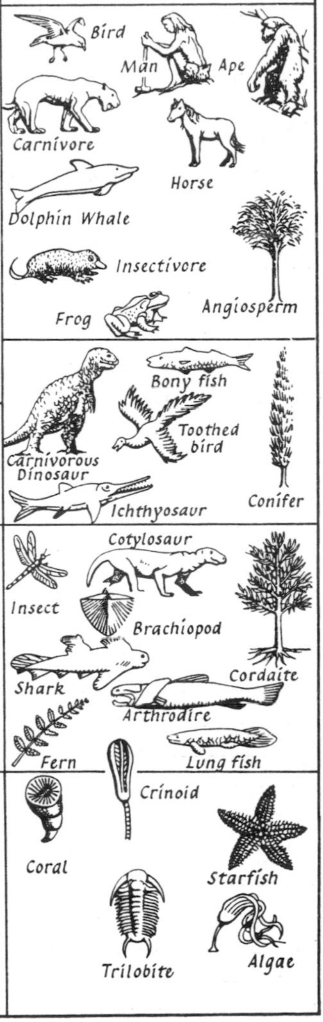

FIG. 7 The North American Geological Time Chart.

on the foreland of the central stable area, into which clastic deposits and carbonates were carried outwards from the continental interior and laid down in conditions of gentle subsidence. Later, argillaceous beds were deposited from land-swells rising up in the outer, deeper geosyncline. Along the edge of the foreland, rocks were mildly folded in what is now the

Allegheny plateau. They were faulted abruptly on the east, and a scarp created, which has now retreated to the Allegheny front. Farther east rise the much more steeply folded, though fairly regular, hills of the Ridge and Valley province. Here Palaeozoic beds have been thrown into long, steep-sided hills, which are often displaced north-westward along low-angle thrust faults. Pitching anticlines are frequent, and an alternation of canoe- and cigar-shaped mountains is typical. There are few igneous intrusions.

Still farther east extends the greatly more complex zone of the Blue Ridge and Piedmont plateau, in the southern Appalachians, and of the New England upland, in the northern. It overlies a fundamental sub-surface downfold, and is characterized by slate, cherts, and pyroclastics, interbedded with lava flows. King[1] regards it as a eugeosynclinal trough in which, however, arcs of volcanic and tectonic islands were separated by subsiding furrows. These islands, which were no doubt the crests of rising swells, provided the materials for the inner Appalachians. Possibly, too they guided the course of deformation.

This occurred in a series of mountain-building movements; the Taconian, in Ordovician times, throwing up the Taconic mountains of New York, and related ranges; the Caledonian, near the end of the Silurian, affecting central Newfoundland; the Acadian, beginning in middle Devonian times and completed in early Mississippian, raising the mountains of central New England, of the New Brunswick and Nova Scotia uplands and the mountains of eastern Newfoundland. The Appalachian orogeny proper is limited mainly to the central and southern Appalachians. Farther south and west these older orogenies may have partly affected the Ouachita mountains, but the main deformation occurred in the Wichita and Arbuckle movements, between upper Mississippian and late Pennsylvanian times, when the front part of the Ouachitas was strongly folded and thrust northward, and when the Wichita and Arbuckle mountains were formed (Fig. 8).

The relief of the Appalachians results from the peneplanation of these structures and their subsequent resurrection through repeated uplift and erosion. It sees a combination, therefore, of old-age surfaces planing mountains, of greatly modified structural features, and of structural ridges and furrows which have been fairly recently exhumed. Geographically, the region may be divided into three: the northern Appalachians reaching from Newfoundland to, in the main, the Hudson river; the southern Appalachians, running thence into Alabama; and the Ouachita–Wichita system south-west of the Mississippi.

The northern Appalachians are distinctive in that they represent the older orogenies, have been widely faulted and extensively glaciated, and, thus broken up and gouged, have been invaded by the sea. Three fairly obvious

[1] King, *Tectonics of Middle North America*, p. 74.

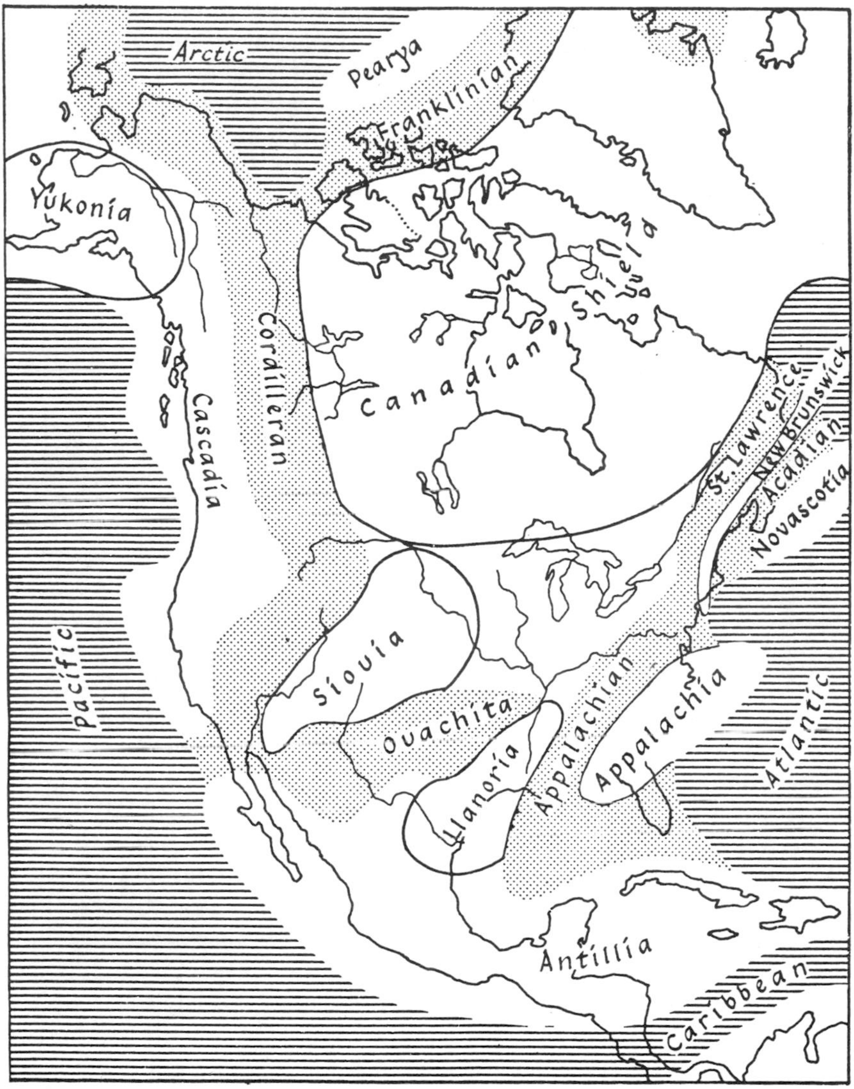

FIG. 8 The Rise of the Appalachian Geosynclines. (Late Cambrian N. America, after Schuchert and Dunbar.) A single great Appalachian geosyncline divided in the north in Laurentian and Acadian troughs. The Ouachita trough in the south was deepening, but the Cordilleran depression in the west was in an initial stage. (Scale, 1:60 m.)

belts run through the region, consisting of (i) a northern and western folded zone of well-marked ridges often thrust to the north-west, dominated by the Taconic orogeny; this runs through north-western Newfoundland, the Gaspé peninsula, and the western New England mountains; (ii) a central complex zone of plateau-like uplands, in which the Caledonian uplift to the north, and the Acadian orogeny throughout, disturbed the beds, accompanied by extensive metamorphism and plutonism; this reaches from the central upland of Newfoundland to the central uplands of New Brunswick and New England; and (iii) a southern and eastern zone, with short ridges of less disturbed sedimentaries and volcanics, and blocky or rounded uplands of intruded granites; this belt stretches from south-eastern Newfoundland to Nova Scotia and thence, after a gap, to eastern Massachusetts and Rhode Island. A special feature of the northern Appalachians is a series of troughs faulted down into the Precambrian and Palaeozoic rocks which have been filled with reddish-brown Triassic beds. Notable are the Triassic basins of Minas Bay, of the Connecticut valley, and of central New Jersey and eastern Pennsylvania.

The whole region bears the signs of peneplanation in the predominance of long, level horizons, with flat-topped or gently rounded ridges and uplands. Goldthwait[1] gave the name of the 'Atlantic Upland' to the major peneplain, and believed that it was gradually warped down so that, beginning at an elevation of over 4,000 feet in the Gaspé it slowly descended eastward to about 1,100 feet in the Bay of Fundy uplands and to 600 feet in the Nova Scotia upland. The highest level should perhaps be regarded as a separate peneplain, the Shickshock surface. It can be linked up with old-age surfaces in New England. Most of the summits of the Gaspesian mountains, together with broad benches on the sides of the Shickshocks, are about 2,000 feet high. Such benches border Mt. Carleton in central New Brunswick, continuing the 2,000-foot level eastward. This could be correlated with a pronounced bench that Fenneman[2] recognized at about 2,100 feet to be found on the flanks of the higher mountains in New England. Another bench, which is also the level of certain Vermont hills, stands at 1,600 feet. But the major level in New England, which stretches from Massachussets to Canada, is at 1,100 feet. On the other hand, Twenhofel records a series of broad-topped uplands in eastern Newfoundland, said by the people to be 'level on top, but hard to get up to', of only 800 feet.[3] This may be part of Goldthwait's tilted Atlantic upland, or a partial surface cut when the 1,100-foot peneplain was uplifted, and erosion produced a lower bench.

Glaciation has left a profound imprint on the northern Appalachians, since the Wisconsin ice spread as far as Long Island, where it laid down two parallel end-moraines. In Newfoundland the recent date of the disappearance

[1] Goldthwait, J. W., *Physiography of Nova Scotia*, Can. Dept. of Mines, Geol. Surv. Can., Mem. **140**.

[2] Fenneman, N. M., *Physiography of Eastern United States*, New York, 1938, pp. 364ff.

[3] Twenhofel, W. H., 'The Silurian of Eastern Newfoundland', *Amer. Jour. Sci.*, **245**, pp. 65–122.

1. Laurentian Shield, from the air. Grey, ice-scarred, lake-pitted, bare, eroded uplands, with little settlement, contrast markedly with well-occupied, cultivated lowland, mainly of glacial lake deposits in Ottawa valley.

2. Laurentian Shield, from the ground. The Shield, partly wooded but with many rock barrens, plunges steeply down a fault scarp to the largely cleared flats of the Ottawa basin.

3. The relief of the Appalachians, Northumberland County, Pa., shows long even horizons of the summit peneplain, wooded parallel ridges, pronounced water gaps, orchards on upper valley sides, and small grains and hay on valley floors. Strip farming helps to prevent erosion. Note large byres and barns of dairy farm in foreground.

4. Folded Triassic beds, Stor Island, in the Innuitians. Arctic barrenness is accentuated by litter of frost-shattered stone, slopes steepened by soil creep or broken by gullying.

of the ice strikes one in the freshness of the till, the rather restricted extent of delta terraces, and the small sheets of outwash. Uplands tend to have been stripped by ice; lowlands to have been plastered with an uneven veneer which has given rise to innumerable lakes and swamps. Ice-steepened fjords line the south coast. In Nova Scotia valley glaciation has left marks superimposed on the general drift; small lateral or lobate moraines lie on the sides or swing across individual valleys. Moraines are broken and scattered. Pro-glacial lakes are of importance in the middle and lower valley of the St John river in New Brunswick, and have strewn the Connecticut valley with their flats. In the Gaspé, glaciation swept over the whole region from Labrador, leaving a patchy mantle of till. Subsequently cirques were cut into the massive mountains. Fenneman shows that after the continental ice had swept over New England, streaking even the top of Mt. Washington with till, valley glaciation caused cirques in most of the higher mountains—the 'gulfs' of the White mountains—and steepened valley sides to produce U-shaped valleys here and there. End moraines have been left along the coastal islands from Long Island to Nantucket.

Since much of the northern Appalachians system is within reach of sea, marine terraces are a common feature. Twenhofel remarks on the frequency of a 50-foot terrace in Newfoundland. Goldthwait has found this around most of Nova Scotia, together with a 150-foot one. Barrell[1] claimed a multiple series of marine terraces for New England, from Long Island to the Green mountains. The higher of these might, however, be regarded as the work of rivers.[2]

The southern Appalachians show the influence of structure very pronouncedly, but are also marked by peneplanation and rejuvenation. They may be divided into four belts, namely, the Allegheny plateau, the Ridge and Valley section, the Blue Ridge, and the Piedmont zone (Fig. 9).

The Allegheny plateau, continued southward in the Cumberland plateau, is a broad area, between 2,000 and 3,000 feet in height, which shows partial ridging along its eastern front, but elsewhere remains a deeply dissected upland. Even the ridges are not sharp, but exhibit long flat horizons. A major escarpment, paralleled by a fault, marks the eastern limit of the sub-region.

The Ridge and Valley section, stretching eastward from the Allegheny front, consists, as its name implies, of a number of parallel ranges with long, narrow depressions in between. It reaches from the St Lawrence lowlands in the north to the coast plain of the Gulf of Mexico, and has a width of

---

1 Barrell, J., 'Piedmont Terraces of the Northern Appalachians . . .', *Bul. Geol. Soc. Amer.*, **24**, pp. 688–90.

2 Meyherhoff, H. A., and Hubbell, M., 'The Erosional Landforms of Eastern and Central Vermont,' *Vt. State Geol. Surv.*, **16th Ann. Rept., pp. 315–81.**

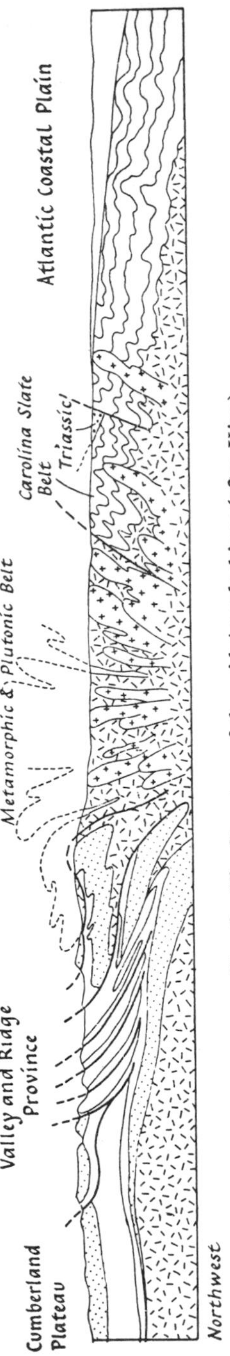

FIG. 9 The Structure of the mid-Appalachians (after King).

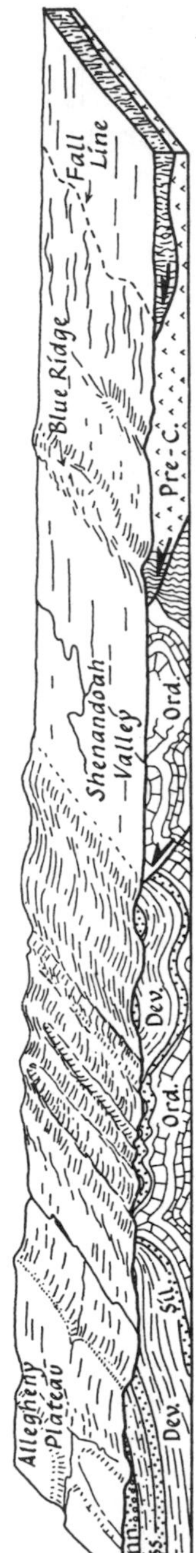

FIG. 10 The Relief of the mid-Appalachians.

from 20 to 80 miles. It is made up of Palaeozoic rocks which have been very strongly folded into sharp anticlines and synclines. Faulting is common, especially to the south, where it was accompanied by thrusting. The whole province was bevelled off and, upon being rejuvenated, saw the harder rocks stand up as ridges, even where they may have originally been synclines. Since many of the structures were pitching anticlines, they have worn into typical cigar-shaped mountains, with encircling scarps. Corresponding synclines produced canoe-shaped ridges. Zigzag ridges between these pitching structures resulted, and are very typical. The mountain crests are very even and often represent the 2,000-foot peneplanation so characteristic of the northern Appalachians. The northern section, in the Hudson-Champlain valley, is glaciated; the southern, free from drift.

Beyond the so-called Great Valley which is but the widest of the depressions in the Ridge and Valley province, rise the moderately high and massive mountains known collectively as the Blue Ridge. They continue the line of the New Jersey Prong, that extension of the northern Appalachians beyond the Hudson, and run south-westward to Alabama. They are part of the inner core of the Appalachian system, are characterized by steep folding, by pronounced uplift, by heavy metamorphism, and by extensive plutonic intrusions. They are higher in the south—with many summits of over 6,000 feet—than in the north, where they decrease to about 1,400 feet. A major break seems to be at the Roanoke valley. The northern part shows a remarkable concordance of mountain tops and also of benches and of mountain gaps. Striking peneplains are the Schooley surface at about 2,500 feet and the Harrisburg one at about 500–600 feet.[1]

East of the Blue Ridge extends the Piedmont upland, marked first by a number of monadnocks, especially in Virginia and the south, and then by a truly peneplaned surface where the gently rolling relief takes little account of structure. It ends in the fall zone, where waterfalls have partly uncovered a still older peneplain that dips steeply to, and is lost beneath, the coast plain (Fig. 10).

The Ouachita and Wichita mountains, west of the Mississippi, are like the Appalachians in many respects, being part of the great Palaeozoic orogeny along the east and south-east foreland of the continent. The rocks of the Ouachita mountains have been caught up into tightly compressed elongated folds, cut by low-angle thrust faults. They have experienced prolonged erosion and often reveal synclinal peaks. They show characteristically Appalachian pitching folds. They extend into the Wichitas which, however, diverge and swing north-westward, to include the Amarillo mountains. Many of the Wichita structures lie buried under younger rocks, but the

---

[1] Fenneman, N. M., *Physiography of Eastern United States*, New York, 1938, p. 201, Harrisburg level; p. 288, Schooley levels.

folds resemble those of the Ridge and Valley section of the Appalachians, although they are not as long, nor as parallel. They tend to lie *en echelon.* Both the Ouachitas and Wichitas show considerable bevelling, the higher ridges flattening off at between 1,500 and 2,000 feet, the lower cuestas being partially planed at some 800 to 900 feet. It is possible that these represent a single peneplain, domed at the centre, downwarped towards its margins.

The Minerals of the Appalachians

The complex structures of the Appalachians and the wide range of rocks which they possess have provided many and varied mineral deposits. The occasional exposure of Precambrian rocks, or the presence of crystalline intrusives, have given the region some of that wealth in metals associated with the Shield. At the same time the great extent of Palaeozoic rocks, especially of Carboniferous age, has offered it some of that wealth in fuels characteristic of the Interior Lowlands. The northern Appalachians are richer in metals than fuels, the southern Appalachians in fuels rather than metals, but in each section both are found.

The principal metals of the northern Appalachians are iron, lead, zinc and silver, copper and pyrite, and chromite. Non-metallic minerals of significance are asbestos, salt, and gypsum. Coal may be locally important. Scarcely any oil is found, but oil shales and natural gas are present.

The iron ore at Wabana, Newfoundland, is one of the larger single deposits in the world. It is a rich red hematite which occurs interbedded with Ordovician sandstones and shales in Bell Island. In production since 1895 it has still vast reserves, and helps to serve steel interests in near-by Nova Scotia, but mining is becoming more difficult and costly. Lead, zinc, and silver, together with copper, are found in quantity at Buchans, in the central upland of Newfoundland, where igneous bodies have been intruded into volcanic lavas, breccias, and tuffs. A large lead and zinc deposit also occurs near Bathurst, New Brunswick, where igneous intrusives have come into contact with Ordovician sedimentaries. A small but significant zinc deposit in New Jersey is likewise associated with the intrusion of igneous matter into a cone of Precambrian metamorphics.

Chromite is found in connexion with basic intrusive rocks in the Serpentine belt of the Notre Dame mountains in the Quebec Appalachians. But far more important are the unique asbestos deposits in this belt—the largest in the world. The asbestos comes from serpentinized peridotite, intruded into Cambrian and Ordovician rocks during the Taconic orogeny.

While most of these minerals are associated with igneous intrusions in upland areas, others, such as coal and oil shale, are found in sedimentary basins. Fairly extensive coal deposits occur in northern Nova Scotia and central New Brunswick. Near Moncton, New Brunswick, natural gas is locally valuable. A small coal field in Rhode Island, of near anthracite grade, makes one of New England's few mineral resources.

The southern Appalachians are especially rich in fuels, but have some metal bodies. Mention has already been made of the western Pennsylvania–Ohio coal field, lying on the west flank of the Appalachians, along the foreland of the buried platform. Its counterpart in eastern Pennsylvania is the smaller, yet still very rich anthracite field, mainly in the Lackawanna basin among highly folded rocks. It is the richest anthracite area in North America, famous for household coal. Much farther south, in the vicinity of Birmingham, Alabama, is another significant coal field, producing good coking coal. Its nearness to a small yet rich iron field, running from Birmingham to Bessemer, where Silurian sedimentary ore-beds crop out, has led to the rise of an important steel industry. Small iron fields in eastern Pennsylvania and New Jersey have been historically important, though now insignificant. Another metal area of importance is the bauxite field on the flanks of the Ouachitas, which forms the main native source for the United States.

THE INNUITIANS

Structure and Relief

As the Appalachian orogenies dwindled along the east side of the continent, new mountain-building movements took place along the northern side. These gave rise to the Parry Islands fold belt, now known as the Innuitians. Little work has as yet been done on them, but it would appear that they do form a major zone of folding. Beginning in the west in Eglinton Island they sweep through the northern parts of Melville and Bathurst Islands, include Cornwallis Island, and then change their direction, running north-east through the Grinnell peninsula of Devon Island up the west side of Ellesmere as far as Greely fjord; then they change direction again, crossing over to the east side of Ellesmere: a distance of over 800 miles. They consist mainly of folded Palaeozoic rocks, but in Ellesmere involve Cenozoic rocks as well, so that folding probably went on until the rise of the Cordilleras on the west side of the continent (Fig. 2, Chapter 1).

The Innuitians are much more like the Appalachians than the Cordilleras, however. In their western section they form a series of parallel anticlines and synclines, producing a distinct ridge and valley relief. These ridges are low, generally rising not more than the Appalachian 'summit' peneplain of 2,000 feet. They have developed from pitching structures, and show the characteristically Appalachian development of cigar-shaped and canoe-shaped forms, with zigzag patterns of relief. However, in Ellesmere they become more massive and lofty, are intruded with igneous bodies, and rise to heights of over 6,000 feet. Here they have been heavily glaciated and are cut by profound fjords.

Their mineral resources are as yet little known, but structures associated with oil and natural gas have been traced.

THE CORDILLERAS

Structure

A huge arc like the Cordilleras containing lofty mountain ranges and deep depressions, high plateaux and elevated basins, domes, and plains, has obviously had a complex structural history. Yet certain patterns stand out. There is, for example, the major difference between the eastern and the western Cordilleras; the eastern ones being composed in general of later rocks, thrown into long parallel folds, thrust far to the east, or standing up in elongated domes; the western ones showing older rocks, intruded by immense igneous bodies, or associated with numerous volcanics, and being heavily faulted, often into blocks and trenches. This difference is not unlike that between the outer and the inner Appalachians, and for the same reason —the eastern Cordilleras were miogeosynclinal in origin, the western ones, eugeosynclinal.

The eastern Cordilleras commence in the Brooks Range of Alaska, of from 5,000 to 6,000 feet high, of strongly folded rocks. These continue into the Mackenzie mountains, paralleled by the Franklin mountains, of broad open folds, occasionally broken by thrust faults. They reach from 6,000 to 8,000 feet and lie in wide arcs. The Canadian Rockies, up to over 12,000 feet high, consist of folded rocks with, however, large sections of upraised horizontal strata. They are characterized by strong thrust faulting and often rise abruptly from the plains. Similar structures continue south through the Lewis and Clark ranges. Southwards there rise a number of long elliptical domes separated by gentle parks, known as the 'dome and park' region. The Big Horn, Windriver, Uinta, and Laramie ranges are examples, rising to over 10,000 feet, with monadnocks of over 14,000. Volcanic mountains, such as the Absarokas in Wyoming, the Spanish peaks of Colorado, and parts of the San Juans, add variety to the central and southern Rockies. They are more prominent in the mountains of Mexico where they terminate the Cordilleran system in the great knot of volcanoes south of Mexico City.

The Western Cordilleras consist of four major divisions: the plateaux and intermontane basins on the east; the Cascade system in the centre; the Coast ranges of America and of the outer insular arc of Canada and Alaska on the west; and the depressions of the Pacific borderland.

The system of plateaux has its beginning in the Yukon and British Columbia, where the land is made up of fairly level strata interrupted by horsts or by lava tablelands. The Omenica batholith more or less separates them. Southwards they pass through the block-and-trench country of the Columbia mountains, into the Columbia plateau, chiefly of eroded basalt flows. This in its turn gives way to the basin-and-range province of up-faulted blocks, often sharply tilted, with intervening depressions. The Colorado plateau is like a great knot tied between two strands of the Rockies, and is really a structural feature of its own. South of it the Arizona and Mexican plateaux show a long succession of basins with fault blocks rising 2,000–3,000 feet above them.

The Cascade system begins with the Alaska range, containing the highest mountain in North America (Mt McKinley, 20,269 feet); continues through a mass of semi-volcanic peaks in the St Elias range, with heights of 16,000 to about 20,000 feet; and then broadens out in the Coast range of British Columbia, underlain for most of its length by a giant batholith. The Cascade mountains proper are made up mainly of volcanoes, of which Mt Rainier, Mt Hood, and Mt Shasta are examples, reaching over 14,000 feet. Fold rocks are, however, important, especially in the north. They appear again in the intensely folded and faulted mountains of the Sierra Nevada, with many peaks of over 12,000 feet, dominated by Mt Whitney (14,496 feet). Volcanic necks and a large number of sills and dykes are common, while long faults have produced abrupt mountain faces. Southwards a great batholith carries high land into Mexico. The Sierre Madre Occidental of Mexico is made up of a series of great anticlines broken by faults and tilted towards the east. High scarps fringe it on the west.

The Pacific border mountains extend from Alaska to the California peninsula. In Alaska and British Columbia they run through a long belt of off-shore islands. Here they are structurally related to the Cascadian system, though physiographically separate. In Vancouver Island they are underlain by a batholith. They have been much subdued by erosion and are about 3,000 feet high with monadnocks up to 7,000 feet. The Coast range of America extends from Washington to California. It is a complex system, beginning with the folded, peneplaned, and faulted Olympics (8,000 feet), and extending thence across the Klamath knot, partly batholithic, to the volcanic rocks of the Los Angeles ranges which have been subsequently caught up in folding and faulting. Here the general trend of the Cordilleras changes. Fold ranges with an east–west axis arise. Uplifted fault blocks above narrow basins are characteristic.

Separating Cascade and outer Coast systems is a belt of depressions seen in the Inner Passage of Alaska, Puget Sound, the Willamette valley, the Great Valley of California, the Salton Sea basin, and the Gulf of California.

The evolution of the Cordilleras began with the miogeosyncline known as the Millard zone. This underlay the eastern Cordilleras and was certainly an old structure. Kay refers it to the Cambrian, since it received great thickness of Cambrian rocks, but it may have existed in still earlier times. Warren[1] suggests that the Proterozoic rocks of the western Rockies and of the Selkirks probably gathered in this trough off the edge of the buried Pre-cambrian Shield. Sediments worn from the Shield were washed out, and deepened westward (Fig. 11).

They were caught up in a threefold series of movements. In upper Jurassic times the geosyncline began to be disrupted. Elevation occurred on its western margin, and it migrated eastward. It then gathered deposits from the western belt. These continued to spread eastward and thicken across what is today the high prairie, through lower Cretaceous time. In the upper Cretaceous new deposits, of feldspathic sandstone, were shed on to the prairies from the mountains rising in the western Rockies. Finally in Eocene and early Oligocene times, fresh deposits of coarse sand and boulders spread over what are today the Cypress Hills and the Swift Current plateau from the elevation of the main or eastern Rockies. The Selkirks, the western Rockies, and the eastern Rockies, thus reflect three phases of the deformation of the eastern Cordilleran trough; their trend, extent, and form being largely due to structure. Three similar uplifts occurred in the American Rockies and Front ranges, with a marked tendency for the earlier ones to be on the inside, or western part of the old miogeosyncline, and the last to be on its outer, or eastern, margin. In each case major upwarps have left major mountain crests, not as yet appreciably planed away.[2]

The later history of the Cordilleras, mainly associated with the western system, shows a more complex structure, being related to the Fraser eugeo-syncline. The rocks of this belt differ from those of the Millard zone in being extensively intruded and in having a great thickness of volcanics. Coarse sediments and marked unconformities in Palaeozoic and early Mesozoic times indicate periodic uplift when great land-topped welts rose in the geosyncline. Carboniferous rocks, embodying boulder and pebble beds, rest unconformably on older ones, thus pointing to a pre-carboniferous uplift. The main orogeny, known as Nevadan, occurred in late Jurassic times, pushing up the Sierra Nevadas and Cascades. It was accompanied by intrusions of great masses of plutonics into the Jurassic and older rocks. The largest of these is the Coast batholith underlying the Coast range of British Columbia. The geosyncline then shifted westward from the line of the Sierra Nevada to what is today the California–Oregon coast. Here detritus gathered from the Sierras to the east and also from a line of tectonic

[1] Warren, P. S., 'The Rocky Mountain Geosyncline in Canada', *Trans. Roy. Soc. Can.*, **45**, Ser. 3, Sect. 4, pp. 1–10.

[2] Russell, L. R., 'Age of the Front Range Deformation in the North American Cordilleras', *Trans. Roy. Soc. Can.*, **45**, Ser. 3, Sect. 4, pp. 47–67.

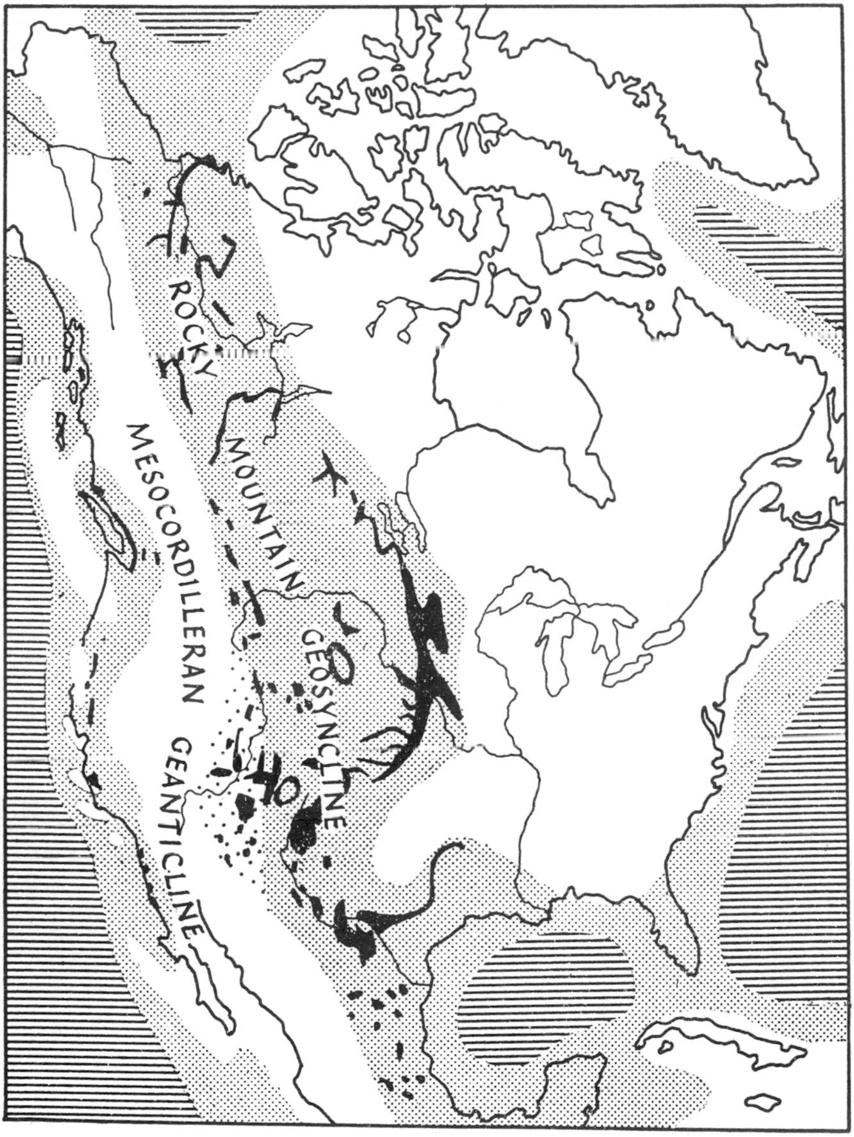

FIG. 11 The Rocky Mountain Geosyncline and the Rise of the Mesocordilleran Geanticline. (Cretaceous N. America, after Schuchert and Dunbar.) The Appalachian–Ouachita troughs having been squeezed out, deformation moved west, and began to throw up volcanoes (black areas) and buckle the rocks into fold mountains. On the Pacific coasts great depressions were forming, but between these and the Rockies lay a relatively stable mass. Here faulting rather than folding produced the main features. (Scale, 1:50 m.)

islands to the west. Its partial folding and uplift in Cretaceous times, and major deformation in the early Tertiary, threw up the Coast ranges of America, and Canada's island arc (Fig. 12).

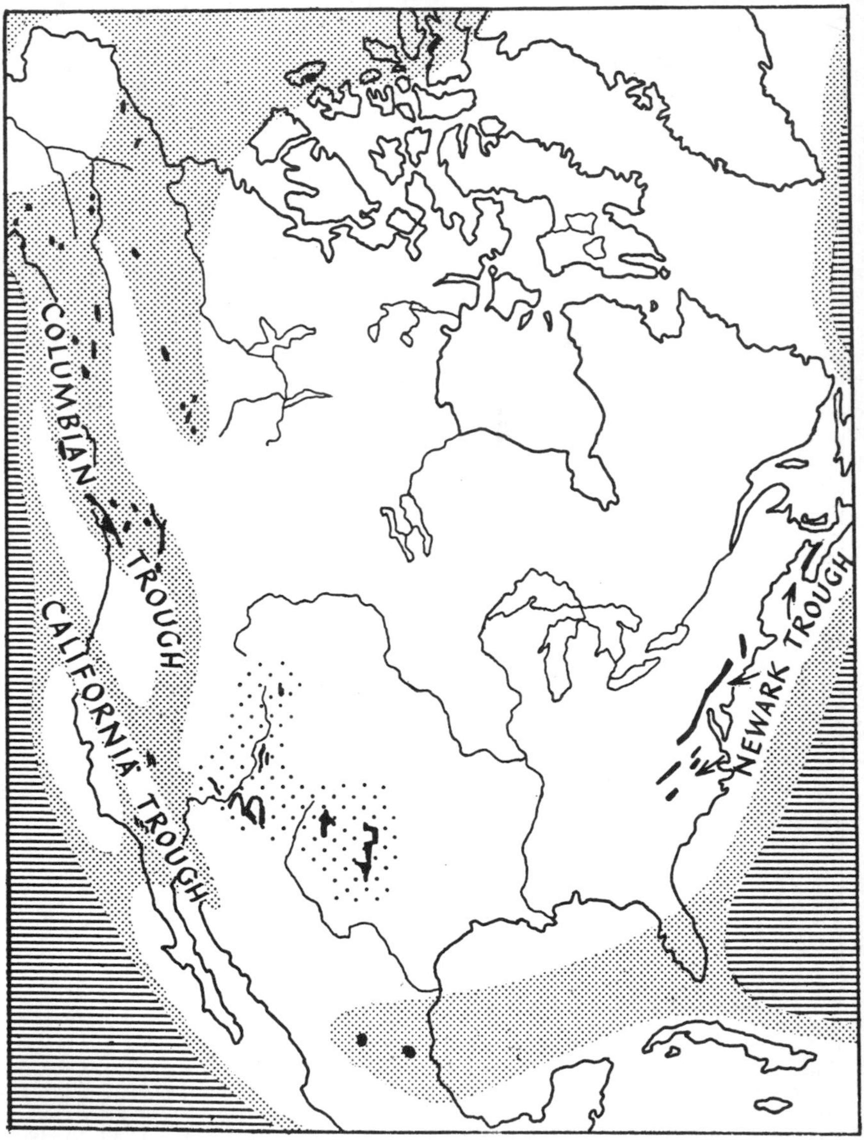

Fig. 12 The Rise of the Pacific Coast Geosynclines. With the squeezing out of the Rockies, deformation moved west again, except for volcanic outbreaks in the Appalachians and in the western intermontane plateaux. The Columbia and California troughs later gave rise to the coast ranges of British Columbia and of California. (Scale, 1:50 m.)

Between the Coast-and-Cascadian mountains and the Front-and-Rocky system lie the interior plateaux and basins. They too have had a complicated history, consisting as they do of plateaux, batholithic ranges, fault mountains, and lesser fold ranges. Great intrusions began as early as Triassic times, and continued into the early Tertiary. In Canada they form the Cassiar–Omenica and the Nelson mountains, between the Coast range and the Rockies. Farther south, large lava flows, such as those of the Columbia and Snake river basins, welled up from fissures in the interior basins and spread out to form notable tablelands. Finally, in the south-west arose a series of fold mountains and uplifted plateaux which were extensively faulted and eroded, producing the so-called basin-and-range province of south-west U.S.A. Running virtually the length of the region occur fault trenches, originating in the late Cenozoic. They are pronounced along the west edge of the Colorado plateau, and cut across the Laramide folding of Wyoming and southern British Columbia. Here they produce regular block and trench surfaces. Possibly the best known of the long, narrow faulted depressions is the Rocky mountain trench in British Columbia, followed by parts of the Columbia, Fraser, and Peace rivers.

The Colorado plateau has its own part in the Cordilleras. It began as a stable area or shelf adjacent to the Cordilleran geosynclines, and although shallow seas covered it from Mississippian to Cretaceous times, it was never depressed into the main western troughs of accumulation. It acted as a fairly resistant piece of the buried Shield severed by an eastern arm of Laramide folding from the central stable area of the continent. Another arm of Laramide folding embraced it on the west, but it escaped major deformation. The strata of the plateau were, however, caught into a series of uneven uplifts and basins. The uplifts, such as the Kaibab plateau, are frequently marked on their eastern sides by a sharp monocline. Laccolithic intrusions subsequently produced highlands such as the Henry mountains, while extensive extrusions in Pliocene time gave rise to volcanic necks and lava tablelands like the Hopi buttes. Recent elevation has led to the strong rejuvenation of the streams producing the famous Grand Canyon of the Colorado river and other gorges.[1]

The Relief of the Cordilleras

The Cordilleran region, though still strongly affected by structure, reflects major modifications made by river and ice. As Lang[2] indicates, this has happened mainly in the western parts where orographic rain is heaviest and snow- and ice-fields have been, and are, prominent. Erosion during Late

---

[1] Blackwelder, E., 'Origin of the Colorado', *Bul. Geol. Soc. Amer.*, **45**, pp. 551–66.

[2] Lang, A. H., 'The Cordilleran Region of W. Canada', *Structural Geology of Canadian Ore Deposits*, Can. Inst. Min. & Met., Montreal, 1948.

Mesozoic and Tertiary times reduced the ancestral western mountains to a mature land surface. This was, however, rejuvenated during the Laramide revolution. Relief was again lowered only to be interrupted by mid-Tertiary vulcanism. Volcanic activity was succeeded by long erosion, producing distinct erosion surfaces. However, thanks to minor uplifts, these have been disturbed, and, widely dissected, remain chiefly in broken remnants.

In the Rocky mountain system stream erosion has etched out sharp hog-back ridges from Alberta to Colorado at the foot of the main range; it has eaten back steep in-facing scarps around the igneous cores of dome-like structures; it has developed fault-line scarps, and has cut re-entrants into fault scarps, leaving 'flat-iron' interfluves between canyons; and it has carved buttes and mesas, especially from laval tablelands. Remnants of old surfaces are in evidence which, according to Wahlstrom,[1] are probably portions of a single level, the Rocky mountain peneplain.

Glaciation has attacked the northern Rockies and the higher parts of the southern Rockies. Early Pleistocene glaciation pushed out extensive lobate moraines, known as the Cerro-Buffalo series. Wisconsin glaciation left a series of higher lobate moraines and deep U-shaped valleys marked by lateral moraines or modified by mass wastage and features of slumping. The mountains have been scalloped by corries and often carved into saw-toothed ridges crowned by horn-like peaks. Glacial lakes of various sorts are common in the ice-abandoned troughs and cirques.

In the interior plateaux and basins, west of the Rockies, erosion and deposition have done much to modify the structure. In the Yukon plateau a definite old-age surface, called the Yukon peneplain, is in evidence. This was not glaciated but melt-waters from alpine glaciers in the bordering highlands poured sheets of gravel upon it. Rejuvenation led to the sharp entrenchment of the rivers and to the formation of well-marked benches. These are also striking features of the interior plateau of British Columbia, where the rivers are deeply notched between high, steep-sided kame terraces. Above them are broad remnants of an early Tertiary peneplain. At the close of the Tertiary, rejuvenation produced canyons of up to 5,000 feet in depth, such as the Fraser canyon.

Farther south in the Columbia plateau erosion created widespread 'scab-lands' across till- or loess-covered surfaces. The changing position of the Cordilleran ice front blocked the Columbia river from time to time and forced it to cut new channels which now remain as 'coulees'. Rejuvenation has developed profound canyons, particularly in the case of the Snake river. After volcanic activity in the Cascades had died down in late Pliocene times differential uplift began which, elevating the land some 2,500 feet, led to the

[1] Wahlstrom, E. E., 'Cenozoic Physiographic History of the Front Range, Colorado', *Bul. Geol. Soc. Amer.*, **58**, pp. 551–72.

cutting of the Columbia river gorge. Eustatic lowering of the sea-level during early Wisconsin glaciation resulted in downcutting by a further 600 feet. Subsequent uplift has started still more valley cutting.

In the basin-and-range province erosion, following upon heavy though short-lived showers, has eaten into fault faces and created fault-line scarps; meantime deposition of wind-blown sand has tended to fill in desert basins. The large former lakes Bonneville and Lahontan have been partially filled in and much reduced. They are strewn with ancient deltas and beach formations. Finally, in the Colorado, Arizona, and Mexico plateaux, after a summit and sub-summit peneplain had been made, very pronounced rejuvenation led to a cycle of canyon development seen in the Grand Canyon, the gorges of the Rio Grande, and in not a few Mexican canyons.

The Cascade and Canadian Coast ranges have also been greatly modified by erosion. The northern parts were heavily glaciated, the glaciers of Alaska and British Columbia producing one of the most spectacular fjord coasts of the world. Here glaciation has accentuated structure, since there is a remarkable accordance between glacial troughs or fjords and lines of jointing and faulting.[1]

The summit of the Alaska-British Columbia coastal mountains tends to show a peneplain, between 7,000 and 8,000 feet, with monadnocks rising well above. Great cirques have been cut into this by ice (much of which still covers the region). Pleistocene uplift has led to canyon cutting where antecedent streams with headwaters to the east of the range flow in profound gorges to their deltas on the west coast. Farther south the Cascades proper consist of a series of long, even ridges representing a well-marked old-age surface, with a string of lofty volcanoes rising above, clothed with snow and ice. Valley glaciers descended from these volcanoes, and have left behind great troughs, crossed by recessional moraines, together with lake-filled cirques. The trough under Lake Chelan is said to have been cut 340 feet below sea-level by the Chelan glacier.

The Sierra Nevadas, consisting of intensively folded rocks, intruded by a giant batholith, partially planed down, and then faulted and tilted westward, witnessed a long period of erosion in late Tertiary times with the formation of the Sierra peneplain. In spite of subsequent fierce erosion, leading to many cirques and knife-like ridges, there are tabular mountain-tops and an obvious accordance of main summit levels. Three other levels of erosion exist below the crest line, representing periodic uplift and prolonged downcutting. Thus plateau-like benches flank the sides of the gorges cut during and since the Pleistocene.

Finally, along the American Coast ranges erosion has actively modified

---

[1] Peacock, M. A., 'Fjord-land of British Columbia', *Bul. Geol. Soc. Amer.*, **46**, pp. 633–96.

structure. The complex foldings of the Olympic mountains have been truncated by a summit peneplain at about 5,000 feet, with monadnocks rising 3,000 feet above. Glaciation has scalloped the mountain masses and deepened and straightened the valleys. The long low anticlines of the Oregon coast range, interrupted by volcanic mountains, have been attacked, worn down to an old-age surface, and then warped from south to north. The rejuvenation of old-age streams has led to deeply incised meanders. Late Tertiary peneplanation followed by Quaternary uplift are responsible for the Klamath peneplain, and Quaternary uplift for the rejuvenated valleys of that mountain knot. The even crests of the coast ranges of California likewise suggest peneplanation, especially in view of the fact that their rocks have been strongly folded and faulted. Recent faulting has cut across the peneplain and thrown it into uneven levels, making correlation difficult from ridge to ridge. Streams that once flowed across the planed-down surface now move in deeply entrenched meanders. In the Los Angeles ranges old erosion surfaces are found which have been related to the Sierra Nevada sub-summit peneplain. Again, recent faulting has broken the mountains into unit blocks, now being vigorously attacked. All along the coast from Portland to Los Angeles well-marked sea-cut terraces have been left stranded as much as 1,500 feet above the present shore. Strong wave erosion is eating back headlands, and deposition is filling up bays, to produce a relatively even shoreline except where the mouths of canyons or of faulted basins have been drowned by the sea.

The Mineral Resources of the Cordilleras

As in the case of the Appalachians, the Cordilleras have a combination of great igneous intrusives, highly metamorphosed zones, and sedimentary basins which give it a wide range of mineral resources, including both metals and fuels. Several distinct metalliferous areas occur. These are: the Upper Yukon intrusives, the British Columbia batholith, the Vancouver batholith, the igneous intrusives and metamorphics of the Columbia mountains, intrusives in the American Rockies, the Precambrian complex of the Colorado plateau, the volcanics and intrusives of the Sierra Nevadas, and the volcanics of the Mexican Sierras. Iron is singularly lacking, except for deposits in the Yukon, in islands off Vancouver Island, and in Utah. Lead, zinc, silver, copper, and gold are the principal metals.

In the Upper Yukon rich silver-lead deposits occur in the metamorphic rocks of the Keno Hill district, intruded by greenstone dykes and sills. The Coast batholith of British Columbia is notable for its large copper deposits, mainly in metamorphics caught up into the main granitoid intrusion, as at Hidden Creek and Britannia. In Copper Mountain the ore is found in an igneous intrusion into Triassic tuffs and breccias. The Coast batholith, and also the Vancouver Island batholith, have small but valuable gold mines. The Columbia mountains are noted for lead and zinc deposits in highly faulted metamorphics where the metallic veins have been intruded into the fault fissures; such are the ores at Slocan. The Sullivan ores are replacements of argillite beds in a metamorphic zone which was faulted and then intruded by igneous bodies.

The Canadian Rockies are not highly metalliferous, but near Field is a zone of alteration in Cambrian dolomites and quartzites which has produced a considerable amount of silver, lead, and zinc. Farther south, however, the Rocky mountain system is associated with three famous metal-bearing districts at Coeur d'Alene, Idaho, known for its lead mines; at Butte, Montana, and Bingham, Utah, famous for their copper. Again, metamorphic rocks intruded by igneous ones are the main sites for these ores. The Colorado plateau, with its ancient Precambrian rocks, its intrusives, and volcanic plugs, has quite a number of metallic deposits, but is probably most significant for its big gold mines at Cripple Creek and its tungsten and molybdenum ores. The Sierra Nevadas are best known perhaps for their placer gold deposits, responsible for the California gold rush. These resulted from the erosion of a great number of gold-bearing quartz veins in the highly folded and altered rocks of the mountains, and were thence carried down into the Great Valley and other valleys where they were panned. In southern Arizona and south central New Mexico, the mountains bordering the Colorado plateau and swinging on into the Mexican Sierras are rich in copper and silver, especially at Jerome and Bisbee, Arizona; and in lead and zinc, as at Globe and Warren, Arizona, and Hanover, New Mexico. The latter are due to igneous metamorphism of calcareous rocks. Silver is the outstanding metal of the Mexican Sierras. It is found at a number of sites in the western Sierras, such as Parral, Durango, and Zacatecas, but its chief occurrence is at Pachuca, on the flanks of the southern Sierras. Here silver has been worked since 1534. The mine is still one of the leading producers! It exploits a region of Tertiary extrusives and intrusives among folded sedimentaries.

The fuel reserves of the Cordilleras are quite considerable but, apart from Californian oil, do not play a great part in the economy of the continent. They are too inaccessible as a rule. Thus the Yukon Territory and northern interior British Columbia have some quite sizeable deposits of coal, but except for the field near Carmacks, Yukon Territory, they are not used. It is only as one comes to southern British Columbia that there have been notable workings. These belong to upper Cretaceous rocks occupying a narrow plain between Nanaimo and Comox, Vancouver Island, in a downwarp on the flank of the central batholith; and also at Fernie and the Crow's Nest districts, in small basins of lower Cretaceous age: however the need for coal is much less and mines are closing. In the American Rockies there are also a number of workings, mainly on the transcontinental railway lines, but they are as nothing compared with the total reserves. Quite extensive fields occur in the Big Horn, Green river, Uinta, San Juan, and south-western Utah regions. The western coal belt in Alberta, and the coal fields of the Judith basin, Montana, the Powder river region, Wyoming, and of the Denver and Raton basins, Colorado, are often included in the Rocky Mountain coal fields, but they have already been mentioned in the treatment of the Great Plains, since they are connected with the foreland zone of the buried platform. Somewhat similar to them is Mexico's chief field, in the Sabinas district, in a wide basin on the outer flank of the eastern Sierras.

Coal is conspicuously absent from the western mountains of the American Pacific. But oil takes its place, at least in the Sacramento–San Joaquin valley, between the Coast range and the Sierra Nevadas. This is the third producing region in the United States and one of the richer oil belts of the continent. It serves most of the Pacific coast settlements from Alaska to Mexico. On the outer flank of Mexico's eastern Sierras lie its chief oil fields at Tampico and Poza Rica.

THE COAST PLAINS

Structure

On the whole, coast plains are poorly developed off North America. The main exceptions are found in the Atlantic and Gulf coastal lowlands. These reach from Cape Cod to Tampico. Narrow at first, they broaden to 100 miles in Georgia, and to 300 miles in north-east Texas, before narrowing again in Mexico. They are made up of Mesozoic and Cenozoic deposits dipping gently east or south into the sea and leaving belted lowlands along the foot of the Appalachian piedmont and the Ouachita system. It is customary to divide them into the Atlantic coastal plain, including Florida, the eastern Gulf plain, the Mississippi embayment, and the western Gulf plain; but it might be more logical to divide them into an eastern belt, correlated with Appalachian structures, and a western belt, with Ouachita ones. For the fact is they reflect the orogenic and posthumous influences of those older structures.

The eastern coastal plain began to be submerged as the Appalachians arose. The peneplanation of the highlands fed the lowlands. Great deposits, deepening seaward, were laid down over the continental shelf, from lower Cretaceous to Pleistocene times. These extend from the banks off Newfoundland and Nova Scotia to the broad lowland of Alabama. The plain they built was probably exposed to erosion over a wider area than at present since cuestas were developed on what is now Georges Bank, below the sea, and several canyons were cut, as in the Cabot Strait and off the Hudson estuary, now submarine features. The early deposits, in lower Cretaceous times, were continental and consisted of arkose sands and readily eroded clays. Upper Cretaceous and Eocene deposits were mainly marine, with clays and limestones. In Miocene times uplift in the Appalachians shed coarse gravels and sands over the coastal plains. Later deposits were principally marine, with clays, marls, and limestones. Thus rocks of harder or softer nature were laid down which, when attacked, eroded very differently, producing hollowed-out vales and upstanding, though modest, escarpments. A consequent river pattern evolved where, however, the growth of strong subsequents led to river capture, and wind gaps were formed across some of the cuestas. This characteristic landscape begins in the wold-lands of New Jersey and continues to the belted plain of Alabama. In Florida, however, the seaward dip of the beds is not pronounced and there the coast plain is made up of relatively flat marine deposits overlying an old shelf. Solution surfaces have evolved within limestone areas, dominating the scene.

Recent submergence of the land all along the coast has drowned and dismembered many of the streams. Great estuaries like Chesapeake Bay have been opened up. The Atlantic storms have thrown up bay bars and built long spits out from inspate forelands to reduce the irregularity of the shore. In bays blocked off by sand reefs, lagoons and 'dismal swamps' have developed. Several changes in shore-level must have occurred, since the coast plain is lined with old sea beaches. Cooke[1] has recognized seven marine terraces, rising to a height of 270 feet. Special coastal features are the morainic and outwash deposits reaching from Cape Cod through to Long Island, worked into remarkable hooks and off-shore bars; and the coral reefs, or cays, off the southern coast of Florida.

The western coastal plain is like the eastern one in that beds of different resistance have formed in wide belts parallel to the mountains. These different beds have, upon erosion, given several vales (or prairies as they are known in the south), and well-marked cuestas. Four of these rise one after the other in Texas. But there the resemblance ends. The western plain has had a much more complex history. Deposition began in the Jurassic with the formation of a parageosyncline off the Ouachitas. But great upwarps in this depression shed deposits towards the present coast. Later Mesozoic deposits were thus carried into the continental interior. Tertiary material, on the other hand, was mainly derived from the continent, and the Gulf was considerably reduced.

That great rivers from the interior then emptied themselves across the

[1] Cooke, C. W., 'Seven Coastal Terraces in the South-eastern States', *Washington Acad. Sci. Jour.*, **21**, pp. 503–13.

coast plain, and have continued to do so, further distinguishes the western plain from the eastern one. The Mississippi dominates the plain. It is marked by a downsag or embayment between north–south structural arches running along either side. This embayment broke down the Ouachita system and drew to itself the drainage of the greater part of the continent. Upbuilding was encouraged, to fill in this sag, and the Mississippi developed a meander plain at least 600 miles long, from Illinois to the coast. It is still actively pushing out its long-fingered delta over an area in the Gulf that may still be sagging.[1]

The western coast plain is distinguished by extensive faulting. Indeed, its north-western edge is marked by a series of fault scarps in the Balcones fault zone. Farther south a number of fault blocks with intervening troughs are common, especially in north-east Texas, southern Arkansas, and central Mississippi. These faults take the trend of the Ouachitas and are no doubt connected with the last Ouachita disturbances. Still farther south minor faults, parallel to the coast, may represent the slumping of the Gulf down monoclinal structures. They do not affect the surface but are important in the production of oil and gas.

Finally the western plain may be distinguished from its eastern counterpart in that it has a number of piercement domes in which columns of salt have pushed up from underlying salt beds to dome up, and in some cases pierce, the overlying strata. These are called 'mounds' or 'islands' in the vicinity and reveal themselves as low relief features. They are frequently associated with sulphur, oil, and gas. Their formation is well described by King,[2] who believes that the upward movement of the salt began when the overlying rocks reached such a thickness as to squeeze the basal salt beds. The salt, having a lower density than the beds above, gradually rose by flowage, concentrating at points of weakness.

The shores of the western coast plain have been considerably modified by the building of off-shore bars. The vast amount of silt carried down by rivers from the interior has offered currents a ready load for distribution along the coast. The Texas coast in particular is almost one long sand bar broken by relatively few gaps. Lagoons and marshes mark the mouths of rivers either cut off, or restricted, by sand reefs all the way round from Cape San Blas to the Laguna Madre at the Rio Grande.

The Minerals of the Coast Plains

Though poorer in minerals than the other major structures of North America, the coast plains do have significant resources. These include bauxite and thorium, phosphates, salt, sulphur, and oil. The bauxite deposits

[1] Russell, R. J., 'Quaternary History of Louisiana', *Bul. Geol. Soc. Amer.*, **51**.
[2] King, *The Tectonics of Middle North America*, p. 182.

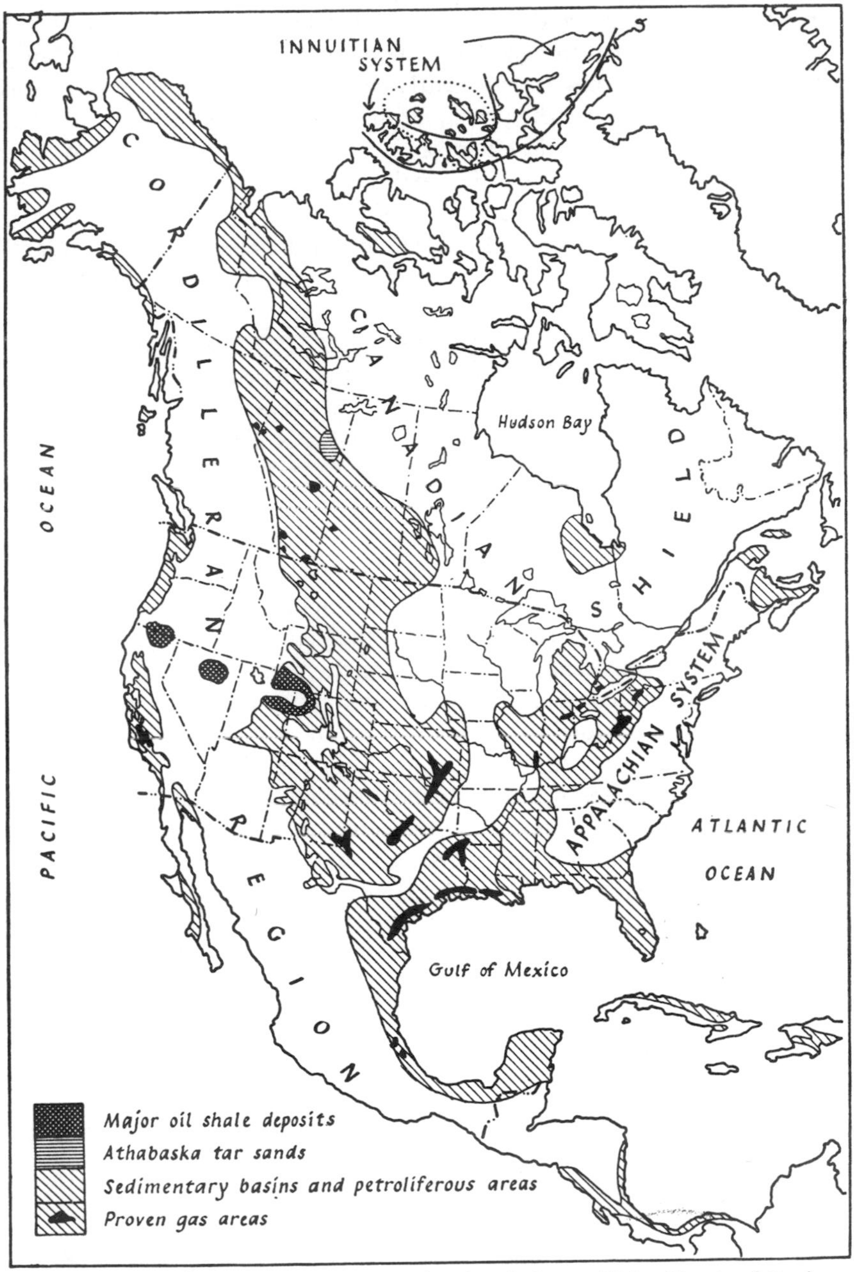

FIG. 13 The Fuel Regions of North America, in relation to Major Structural Regions. The Shield has no fuels; the flanks of the Appalachians and Cordilleras, and probably of the Innuitias, have considerable coal, oil, and gas fields. But the main wealth in fuels lies in the Interior Lowlands or southern Coastal Plains of the continent. (Scale, 1:55 m.)

are found in Georgia and Alabama, on the fringe of that world belt of lateritic weathering with which aluminous rocks are associated. Although the coast plain bauxites are not nearly as important as those of Arkansas, its thorium deposits are the principal ones in the United States. Monazite beds have developed in the dune sands of Jacksonville, Florida. Western central Florida contains one of five major deposits of phosphate rock in the United States. Actually in many parts of the coast plains phosphatic marls and limestones were deposited during slow transgressions of the Atlantic Ocean in Cretaceous and Tertiary times. In the Gulf coastal plains there is the closest association between salt, sulphur, and oil. Numerous salt domes occur, the cap rock of which contains sulphur. The domes have been buried by sands and clays, with thinning or stretched beds on their sides and compacted beds in basins in between; they have thus formed excellent structural traps for oil. The Gulf coastal plain is America's second major source of oil (Fig. 13).

Conclusion

From this brief survey it will be seen that the basic build or structure of North America has played a tremendously important role in the geography of the continent. Structure has provided the main physiographic provinces into which the continent may be divided, dominating the relief in many regions. It has thus come to dominate routeways and the siting of important settlements. It also dominates the distribution of most of the minerals of North America, concentrating the metals in the Shield, the fuels in the Interior Lowlands, and creating a wide range of metal and fuel deposits in the Appalachians and Cordilleras. Structure thus underlies much in the economy of the continent, and has special significance for mining towns and industrial areas. It therefore has fundamental value for human as well as physical geography.

CHAPTER THREE

Climate, Soils, and Vegetation

CLIMATIC ELEMENTS

The climates of a region are a very real part of its character, representing a marriage of air, sea, and land which has resulted in various kinds of soil and vegetation. The climates of North America offer a wide range of conditions, are marked by considerable extremes, show strong regional and seasonal contrasts, and are disturbed by the vigorous conflict of a few powerful air masses. They express to a marked degree the simple, but pronounced, features of structure and relief (Fig. 14).

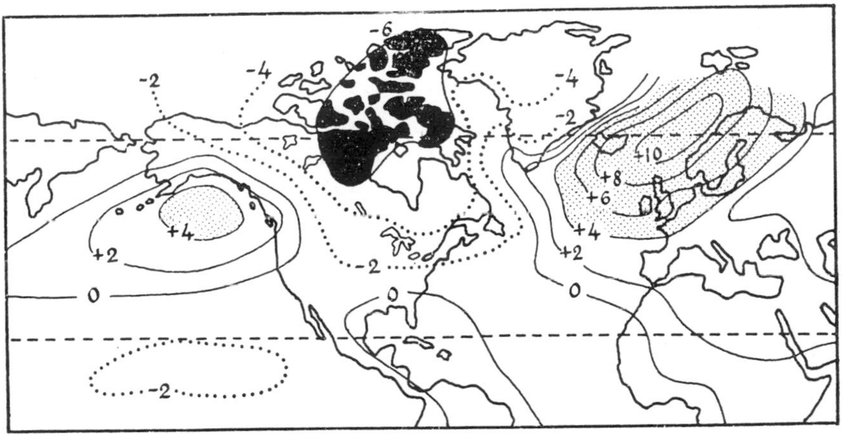

FIG. 14 Temperature Anomalies of the N. Hemisphere—major weather controls. The huge negative area in northern Canada and Greenland helps to account for the Arctic and Polar Continental Air Masses; the strong positive areas in the N. Pacific and the N. Atlantic give rise to maritime Air Masses. The zones in between the negative and positive centres are the sites of the most numerous temperate cyclones.

Climate and Relief

They show, for example, the prevalence of cool conditions corresponding with the massive spread of the continent in high latitudes. Tropical climates are not widespread since, although the continent reaches well into tropical latitudes, it narrows down there to its smallest extent. The polar air masses are the outstanding ones and rule the weather for a remarkably large part of North America.

The climates also reflect the fracturing of the northern and especially north-eastern parts of the continent, a fracturing that broke up the Innuitians and the Shield to allow the deep southward drift of pack-ice and of cold currents from the Arctic Ocean. These, and the presence of ice-caps on Ellesmere and Baffin Islands and on Greenland, have been largely responsible for the southward swing of the isotherms from the lower Mackenzie to Labrador. The north-eastern parts of North America are distinctly cool for their latitudes. On the other hand, the divergence of the west coast, north and south of sub-tropical latitudes, and the continuous sweep of the North Pacific shore, have deflected and drawn warm oceanic currents to very high latitudes, making the north-west coast singularly warm for its latitude. Thus Annette Island, in the Alaska panhandle, has a January temperature of 35°, whereas at Nain, Labrador, the average temperature is as low as −2°F. There is thus a fundamental contrast between west and east.

The western climates are very restricted, however, being held in by the thrice-ridged barrier of the Cordilleras. These still youthful and still lofty mountains, with their vast plateaux and basins, make a major climatic divide. West of them the climatic regions are narrow and elongated, running from north to south; east of them, the climatic belts are broad and extensive, running from west to east. The mountains prevent that wide penetration of south-westerly winds which is such a feature of Europe. And so, as Hare[1] points out, the largest ocean flanking North America has the least influence. Humid conditions on the coast give way rapidly to dry ones in the intermontane basins, and a great belt of arid or semi-arid climate runs well up the continent.

The west–east climatic zones, beyond the Rockies, dominate the continent. Across the Great Plains and the Central Lowlands they find no obstruction to deflect their course; but on reaching the Shield, the Great Lakes, and the Appalachians they either change their trend or experience significant local modifications. The great hollow of Hudson Bay tends to draw cold air into it, especially when winter ice forms in it. The northern climatic belts are, then, farther bent to the south-east by its intervention. The Great Lakes cause a strong local modification, reducing winter temperatures, delaying the spring, and making the hot summers very 'close' with their humidity. The Appalachians are sufficiently high to lower temperatures. They stand out on temperature maps as a distinct cold loop.

The Appalachians are not high enough, however, to produce a rain-shadow area. They are flanked by two large embayments, the Gulf of St Lawrence and the Gulf of Mexico, which introduce maritime influences to the Interior Lowlands. Consequently the climates east of the Rockies are

[1] Hare, F. K., *The Restless Atmosphere*, London, 1953, p. 125.

mainly humid or sub-humid. There are no dry climates in eastern North American corresponding to those in the west.

The trespass of water bodies actually has less effect than it might be expected to have, partly because the northern seas are frozen over much of the year, and partly because the eastern gulfs are swept by storms moving *out to sea* from the south-west. The seas which invade Europe, by contrast, are constantly feeding storms moving on to the land. Most of them are also free from ice. They intensify the maritime character of that continent. North America is marked by strong continentality. Its climates reflect the influence of one of the largest interior plains in the world.

In the summer the land at the heart of this plain heats up far more than the seas in the same latitudes, and has temperatures unknown at the coasts, while in winter the land cools down much more than the oceans and suffers from far greater extremes of cold. Thus at Winnipeg the range of temperature between the hottest and the coldest months is over 70° F., compared with a range of only 21° for Victoria. Continentality is particularly effective in winter when the rapid and extreme loss of heat in the Mackenzie basin makes that area the 'cold pole' of the continent. The coldest place is Fort Good Hope, with an absolute minimum recording of −79° F. This compares with −48° F. for Kotzebue, on the coast of Alaska at about the same latitude: a difference of 31°.

The Air Mass Geography of the Continent

The combined effects of latitude and relief help to guide the air streams and locate the air masses over North America and its surrounding seas. Each air mass has a different constitution and a different way of behaving. Over the northern half of the continent lie polar air masses, over the southern half, tropical ones. Air streams driven over the polar ice or developing in the western interior of the continent are markedly continental; but those drawn in from the north-east Pacific or north-west Atlantic, and particularly those from the south-west Atlantic and Gulf of Mexico, are strongly maritime. The interplay between these air masses forms the basis for the pronounced regional and seasonal contrasts in North American climates (Fig. 15).

Regional Characteristics

The main air streams sweeping over the surface of the land provide four major regional differences. The streams include (i) those from the north, over the Arctic or the polar parts of the continent; (ii) those from the north-east Pacific over a warm sea drift; (iii) those from the south-west Atlantic, from tropical seas; and (iv) those from the western interior of the continent itself. Mention should also be made of the jet stream that invades the

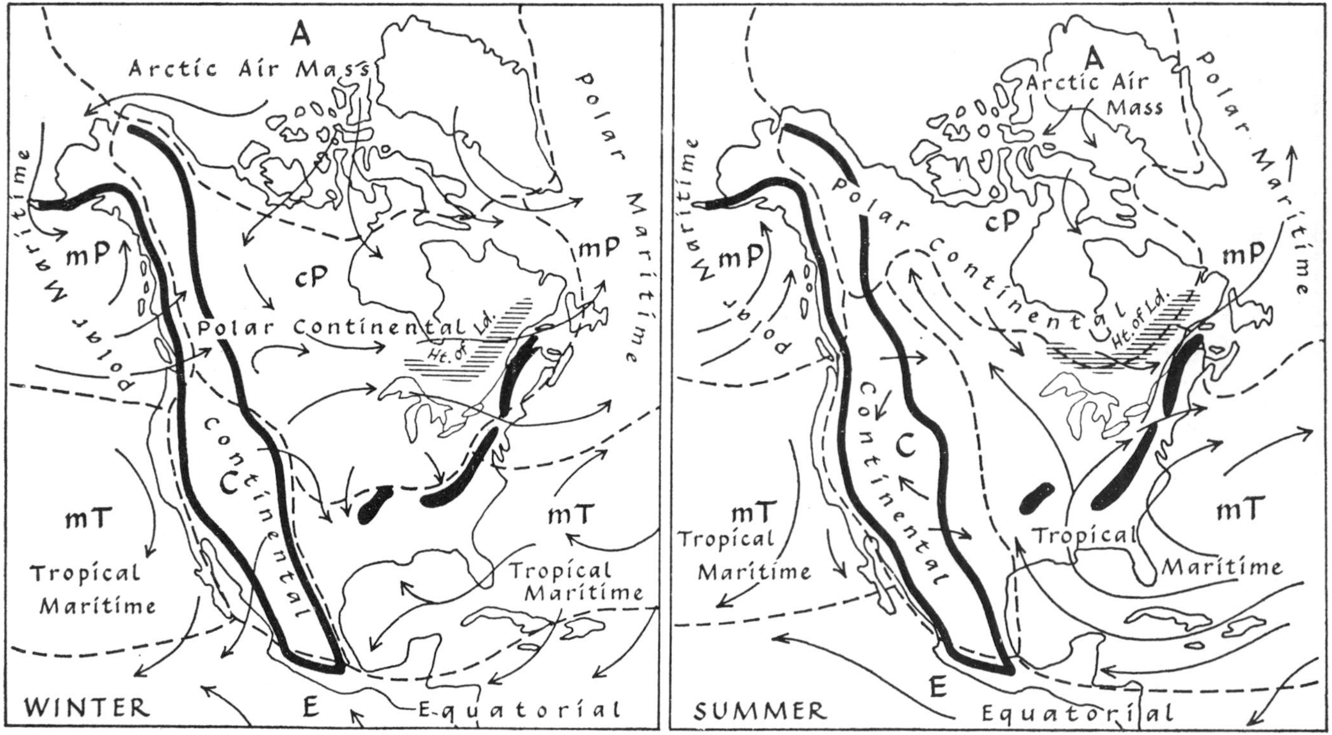

FIG. 15 Air Masses of North America, and Chief Relief Features. Both in summer and winter the Cordilleras act as a principal barrier to the invasion of Pacific air streams: their largely enclosed basins nurse a continental air mass. The Appalachians are often significant in winter as the southern boundary of the Polar continental air mass, but though they may guide they do not inhibit summer storms associated with Tropical maritime air. The Height of Land on the Canadian Shield is often the summer boundary where Polar continental air comes to rest, after having been driven back up the Mississippi–Ohio to the Great Lakes and the Mackenzie basin.

continent from high up in the atmosphere, which, although it shows oscillations from the Shield to the Gulf of Mexico, comes down mainly over the Great Plains. It tends to exaggerate continental conditions.

The northern air streams, derived either from the Arctic or the polar ice-caps and ice-filled seas of Canada, invade the broad belt of low country between the Cordilleras and Greenland. For eight months of the year the air crosses snow-covered islands and ice-packed seas and channels in the Canadian archipelago. Here, and over the northern mainland of Canada, relatively homogeneous conditions prevail. Powerful anticyclones develop and a continental Arctic air mass is generated. As Hogue indicates, the area just west of the high, ice-capped mountains of Ellesmere, Devon, and Baffin Islands has a more severe and less variable climate than the rest of the archipelago, and this may be the cradle of the cA air mass. Cold, dry surface air of a very stable kind, with a strong inversion above, settles down over the frozen land and sea, and slowly moves outward. As it does so it merges with the continental polar air mass, centred in a second area of winter severity over the north-western part of the Canadian Shield. 'Intensely cold, dry, and stable in winter, this air dominates the circulation over Canada.'[1] It is kept cold and dry in its expansion, at least as far as the Great Lakes. In winter it is chilled still further by contact with the extreme cold in the Mackenzie basin and spreads over the prairies and the St Lawrence basin; but in summer it is appreciably modified by the melting of the ice in the Great Lakes and Hudson Bay, and by the heating of the prairie plains and the Mackenzie basin.

Northern air also moves out over the northern Atlantic where it gradually changes. Contact with the sea makes it distinctly milder and more moist. The warming up of the lower layers of air, beneath upper layers that still remain cool, produces unstable conditions. The maritime polar air mass is generated, with streams of air setting in for western Europe. It conflicts with still warmer and more moist air from maritime tropical regions, giving rise to a belt of cyclones. Warm sectors in these cyclones pass over New England and the Canadian Atlantic provinces, to be followed by cold sectors bringing down continental polar air.

The north Pacific air stream moves eastward around the deep Aleutian low-pressure area and, striking the coast, is divided into two by the changing trends of the coast ranges, one part moving north or north-east over British Columbia and Alaska, the other sweeping southwards over California. The zone of divergence of the two tributary streams lies between Oregon (in the summer) and lower California (in the winter). As the air streams divide there is a certain amount of subsidence and drier air moves in from above.

---

[1] Hare, F. K., 'Weather and Climate of the Northlands', *Geography of the Northlands*, ed. Kimble, G. H. T., and Good, D., New York, 1955, p. 64.

A dry, relatively stable air mass develops over the south-west, stretching as far as the Front range. By contrast, the air stream moving north from Oregon to the Yukon marks an air mass, the maritime polar Pacific system, which is very moist and unstable. It is associated with a great number of cyclones bringing in raw moist polar air into the cold sectors and warm, wet mid-latitude air into the warm sectors. These cyclones die out over the mountains and intermontane basins of the Cordilleras.

The Atlantic tropical air stream, moving westward around the oceanic sub-tropical high-pressure cells, turns north and invades the continent in the low funnel-like region between the High Plains and the Appalachians, floods up the plains of the Mississippi–Ohio, and then flows north-eastward over the mid-Atlantic States out to the Atlantic again. It is frequently sucked into the warm sectors of cyclones on the edge of maritime polar air. Very warm over the Gulf of Mexico it tends to be cooled as it moves on to land, except in the height of summer, and is relatively stable. But in summer it may be warmed by sweeping over the excessively hot plains of the Mississippi. It then becomes quite unstable, overturning in successive convection storms, and strewing the plains with thunder-showers.

The interior continental air stream makes the fourth of the main atmospheric movements across North America. It is intimately related to the other three, being born where air from higher levels of the maritime Pacific air mass drifts east of the Cascades over that area of the interior lying beyond the normal sweep of either continental polar air or maritime tropical air. Here, as Borchert[1] shows, the Pacific air, already dried out by its movement over range after range of mountains, becomes even drier as it descends to the Great Plains. It develops into a truly continental air mass, from which air flows eastward. It thus forms a broad wedge between the northern and southern air masses, a wedge marked out along its outer edges by the Alberta and Colorado storm tracks.

It is true that some settling of air from an upper Pacific stream occurs all along the Rockies, and that in Alberta and again in Colorado and western Texas it leads to the kind of turbulence from which the Alberta and Colorado storms develop. But in these cases the air is caught up into cyclones moving along the edge of polar or Atlantic air masses, and is thus mixed with air from *northern* and *southern* sources. In the case of the interior continental air mass, the air is of a more distinctly *western* origin, and is somewhat less involved in invasions from outside centres. In the summer it frequently spreads out to form the continental tropical air mass developed over the south-western intermontane basins of the United States.

The jet stream may well strengthen the wedge of continental air lying

[1] Borchert, J. R., 'The Climate of the Central North American Grassland', *Ann. Assoc. Amer. Geogrs.*, **40** (1950).

between the polar and Atlantic air streams. Yet, paradoxically, it also assists in cyclone formation. While the vortex-like movements of air that characterize the surface tend to bring the northern and southern air streams together, producing a region of convergence in north-eastern North America that has few parallels, the strongly zonal flow of air at higher levels, moving from west to east, intensifies the drift of upper westerlies over the Cordilleras and helps to rejuvenate them above the Great Plains. Now the jet stream is concentrated mainly between latitudes 25° and 35° N.; that is, *between* the chief source areas of the tropical Atlantic air and the polar ice-cap air, in the very area of air mass continentality. As Villmow suggests,[1] the jet stream adds to the descent of air over the Rockies, and in causing subsidence at high levels further dries out the air. Behind its descent, however, turbulence occurs in a back-swirl against the Rockies that sets off Rocky Mountain cyclones travelling across the Great Plains to the Great Lakes.

In winter, as Riehl shows,[2] the jet stream has a more southerly range, of between 20° and 30° N., and affects the weather of the tropics, most significantly perhaps by blocking the normal advance of waves in the trade wind easterlies, and leading to an outbreak of cold into the tropics. In summer, on the other hand, the northward shift of the jet stream permits the wave troughs in the easterlies to intensify and to converge upon or intersect troughs in the westerlies, leading to a rush of warm air over north-eastern North America.

Storm tracks form where the different streams of air converge. They represent the conflict and interpenetration of air masses having rather different temperatures and humidities. They provide the weather typical of most of the continent, with warm moist air pushing over cold dry air, or cold salients pinching off warm sectors, to form swirling cyclones. Such cyclonic storms range the continent from south-west Texas to northern Alberta, beginning—with the exception of the Pacific coast ones—east of the Rockies and converging on the St Lawrence and Mohawk valleys. The well-marked tracks are: (i) Alberta–Great Lakes–Bay of Fundy, developed as frontal lee-depressions, drawing in cP and mP air; (ii) Rocky Mountain–Lower Great Lakes–St Lawrence Gulf, developed as lee-depressions with mP air exaggerated by upper level subsidence; (iii) Colorado–Ohio valley–Massachusetts Bay, often developed with the interior movement of the Atlantic polar front and involving mT air; (iv) the East Gulf–southern Atlantic coastal plain, developed in oscillations of the Atlantic polar front, intensifying waves in easterlies, and involving mT air; (v) the Pacific coast tracks which sweep over the western region of the continent from northern

[1] Villmow, J. R., 'The Nature and Origin of the Canadian Dry Belt', *Ann. Assoc. Amer. Geogrs.*, **46**, no. 2, June 1956, pp. 211–32.

[2] Riehl, H., *The Jet Stream*, Meteorological Monographs, **2**, no. 7 (1954).

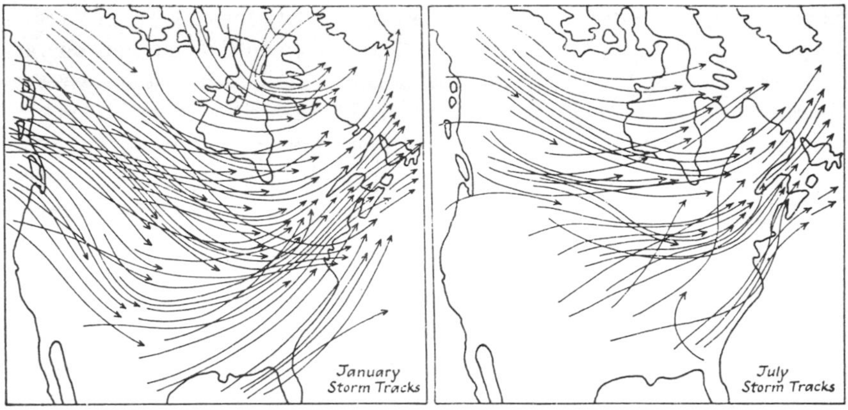

FIG. 16 The Principal Storm Tracks of North America. (Each track represents an average of four or five storms per year. Plotted from charts supplied by the Ontario Meteorological Office.) In winter there is a far greater spread of storms, and more of them come over the Cordilleras from the Pacific. Lee storms born east of the Rockies are prominent, both in winter and summer. The main 'funnels of storm' are in the Hudson Strait, James Bay and Labrador, the Great Lakes–St. Lawrence, the Ohio-Lower Lakes–St. Lawrence, the Ohio–Mohawk Gap, the Potomac–Roanoke gaps, and the east Atlantic plain and Bay of Fundy.

California to Alaska, and are developed along the Pacific polar front, involving mP air (Fig. 16).

Seasonal Characteristics of Air Masses

The air masses that develop over the continent vary considerably in size and strength with the seasons. North America generally is marked by prolonged winter and strong summer conditions with short, sharp transition periods in spring and late autumn. *In winter* the polar air masses predominate. There is then a very great negative temperature anomaly in the Mackenzie plains and very appreciable positive anomalies over the north-east Pacific and the northern central Atlantic. These anomalies are the heart and strength of the polar continental and maritime polar air masses.

The polar continental air mass spreads from the snow-covered archipelago, joined by ice to the mainland, to the cold hollows in Keewatin and the lower Mackenzie basin. In these three areas the mean January temperatures are below −20°F. As ice forms over Hudson Bay the air mass spreads farther and links up with the cold loop over the central Ungava uplands, with an average below −10°. Thereafter, in February, the air mass moves rapidly southwards over the chilled, snow-sheeted interior, flooding over the Great Plains as far as the Front range, reaching across the Central Plains to the Ozarks, and overriding the northern Appalachians to extend well out to sea. Occasional oscillations in the polar front carry great bulges of cold continental air over the Cordilleras to the Pacific coast, as far south as central California, or across the Ozarks in the southern Appalachians to the Gulf coast plain and Florida, creating havoc in the fruit-growing areas. Should the Atlantic polar front return north mT air may flood in, bringing winter thaws as far as the Great Lakes (Fig. 17).

By *the summer* the polar front has retreated, first to the Mississippi valley, then to the height of land on the Canadian Shield, and finally to the north

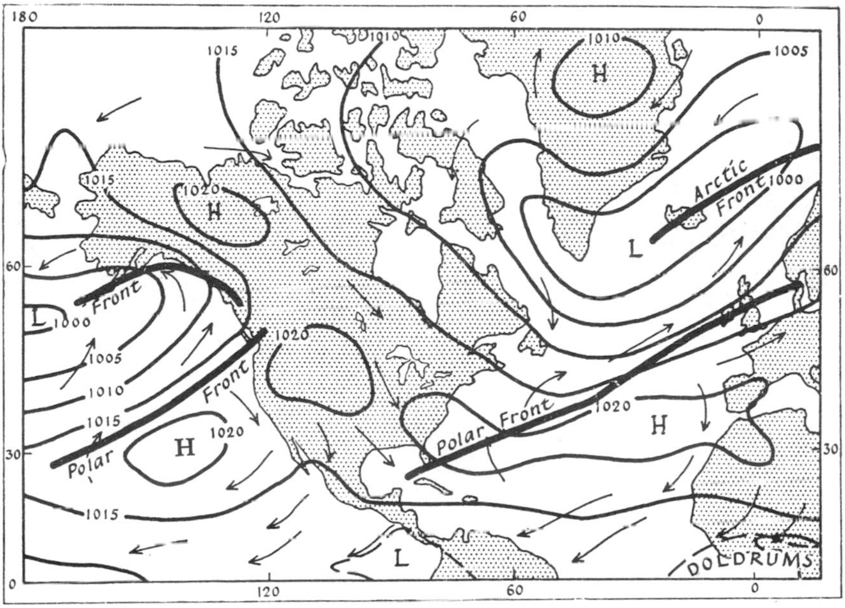

FIG. 17 January Pressure, Winds, and Fronts over North America and the adjacent seas (modified from Haurwitz and Austin). Great 'highs' over Greenland and the Mackenzie basin, together with oceanic highs over the Azores and off the coast of Mexico, dominate the weather, shedding the winds into the N. Pacific and N. Atlantic 'lows'. Here Arctic-type fronts, with strong cold sectors and a prevalence of cold north-easterlies and north-westerlies, and Polar-type fronts with strong warm sectors associated with westerlies, tend frequently to develop.

Alberta–James Bay–Labrador line. The maritime tropical air sweeps in from the Mexican Gulf, invades the Mississippi–Ohio, and then sends great warm waves over the Great Lakes–St Lawrence lowlands, and also across the prairies and upper Mackenzie basin. From June to September the main flow of air is meridional rather than zonal. Anticyclonic cells retreat to the north-west and north, or to the east, and between them very long troughs emerge, reaching from the equator to the Arctic. A great poleward movement of tropical air develops up the Mississippi–Ohio and the Mississippi–Red, especially as the interior plains become hotter than the neighbouring seas. Originally warm and moist, the air stream is then actually cooler than the continental interior, so that its surface layers are rapidly heated and become very unstable. Very muggy weather broken by violent thunderstorms prevails. Thus over areas which in winter have cold snaps of below —20°, summer heat waves develop, with temperatures well above 90° F. London, Ontario, with an absolute minimum of —26°, has an absolute maximum of 106° F. Such are the strong seasonal differences characteristic of so much of North America (Fig. 18).

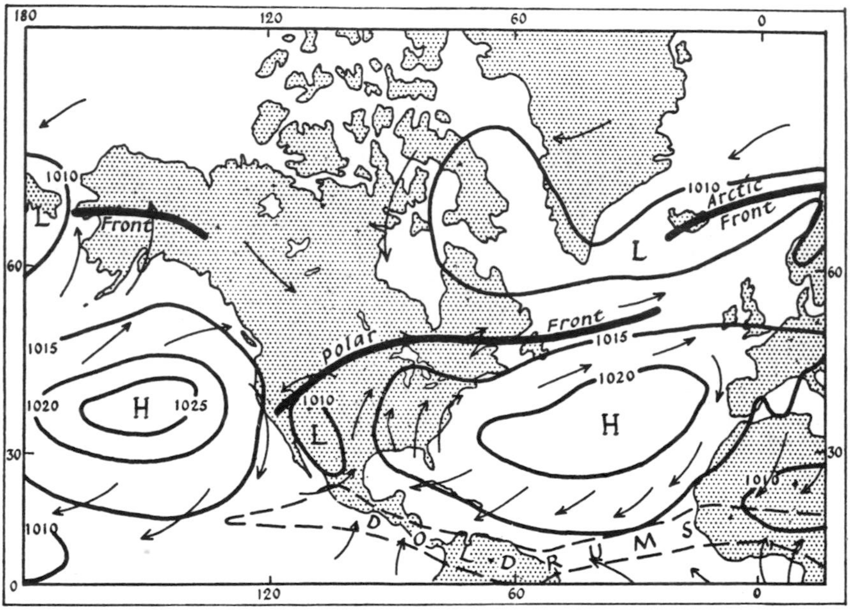

FIG. 18 July Pressures, Winds, and Fronts over North America and the adjacent seas. The oceanic highs now develop a great vortex-like movement of air over mid-Atlantic and Pacific, dominating the weather. The lows are weak by contrast.

CLIMATIC REGIONS AND VEGETATION ZONES

On the basis of the natural appearance of the continent, it is convenient to divide it into open, semi-arid or arid landscapes, and humid forested ones. The first include the cold deserts and tundras of the Arctic and then, interrupted by the boreal forest of the sub-Arctic, embrace the drier prairies and the Great Plains, and the deserts of intermontane basins. The forested regions consist of the cool temperate, warm temperate, and tropical, humid areas (Fig. 19).

The Arctic Climates

The great extent of North America that thrusts into the Arctic Ocean ensures a wide development of Arctic climate. Cape Morris Jessup on

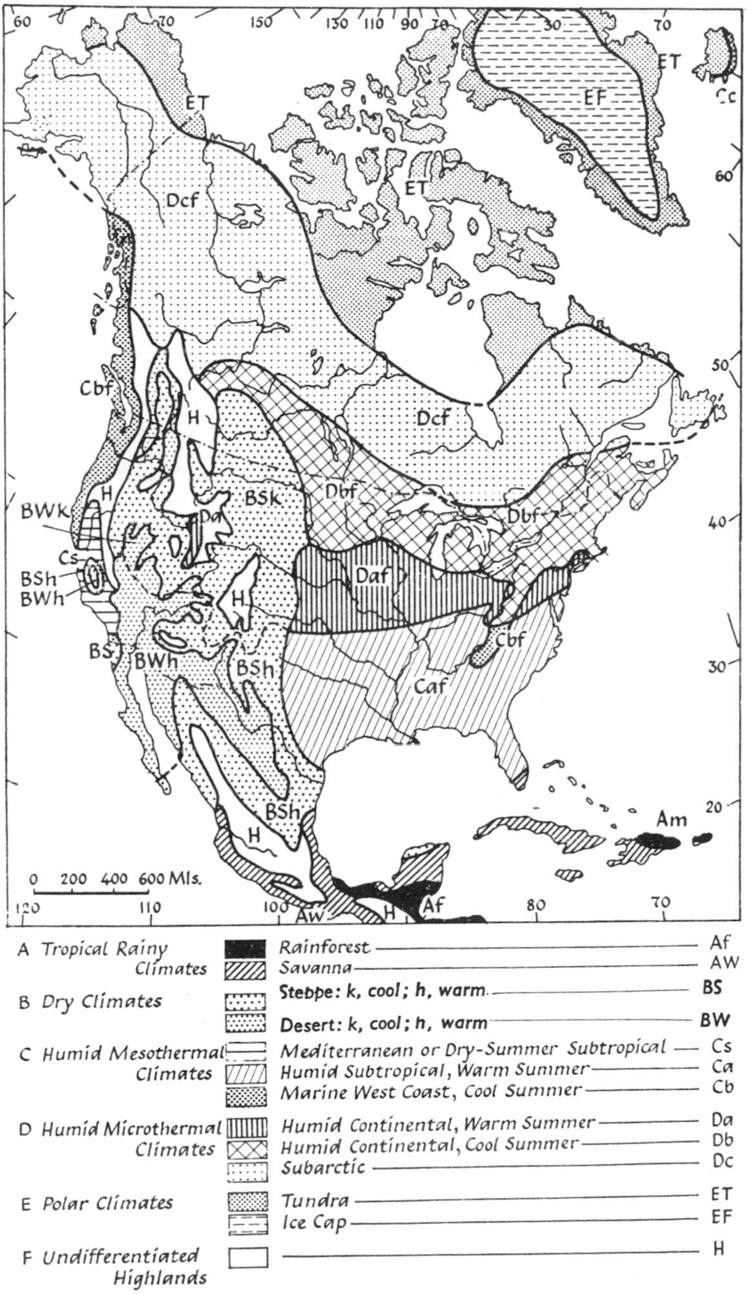

FIG. 19 Major Climatic Zones of North America. (After Trewartha.)

northern Greenland is the most northerly point of land in the world. From it the land slopes south-east to Cape Farewell and south-west to Alaska. The region has the last remaining great ice-caps in the Northern Hemisphere —those on Greenland, on Ellesmere, and on parts of Baffin Island. The high latitude, the presence of these ice-caps, and the prevalence of permanently frozen ground all make for an intensely cold air stream which, moving southward, splits into two—a smaller south-west drift, caught into the rear of the Aleutian Low, and a larger south-east flow, drawn into the front of the great Icelandic Low. This south-eastward flow is strengthened by air moving out from a pronounced ridge of high pressure over northern Alaska and the Canadian north-west.

In winter the mean January temperature is below −10° F. for all but the coast of Labrador and south-east Baffin Land. The areas with the greatest constant cold are the northern islands of the archipelago and central Keewatin, each with a January average of −30° F. or less. These are the coldest areas on the continent, although, thanks doubtless to occasional marine air, they do not suffer the extreme minima of the lower Mackenzie basin. Winter lasts long. Most of the Arctic has sub-zero weather for five to seven months, and sub-freezing weather for eight to ten months. It is only between June and September that temperatures rise above 32° F. According to Robinson,[1] Chesterfield Inlet has the longest frost-free season of any of the Arctic stations, with an average of 67 days without frost. 'But there is great variability from year to year. First autumn frosts have occurred there as early as 2 August in one year and as late as 17 September in another.' There may be frost in every month. Summer temperatures divide the Arctic climate into two subdivisions; the tundra where temperatures may average up to 50° in July, and the cold deserts where they fail to average as much as 32°.

Precipitation is everywhere low, making the Arctic one of the dry regions of the continent.[2] It is generally less than the equivalent of 10 inches of rain a year. Except for the coastal regions of Labrador, Baffin Island, and the Hudson Bay most of it falls as snow. 'In the Arctic islands', Robinson claims, 'an average of 2 to 4 inches of rain, plus 30 to 60 inches of snow, [per year] has been recorded.' Snow begins to fall in September and lasts until May.

In these conditions there is little chance for vegetation to develop. True, along the southern edge of the Arctic, and on more humid coasts—such as around Amundsen Gulf, the Hudson Bay plains, and southern Baffin Island —grass, moss, and lichens may make a fairly close, though low, cover, and on these tundra-pastures herds of caribou graze for two or three months

---

[1] Robinson, L. J., *et al.*, *The Canadian Arctic*, Ottawa, 1951, pp. 22–24.

[2] Sanderson, M., 'Drought in the Canadian Northwest', *Geog. Rev.* (April 1948), xxxviii, 2, pp. 289–99.

5. Mt Eisenhower, in the Canadian Rockies, shows rockiness of upper uplifted, frost-shattered sedimentary beds and lower scree-built slopes. Fir forests of Bow River thin out appreciably to tree-line just above screes. White scars of avalanches break higher forest front.

6. Mt Biddle shows the great height, 10,878 feet, to which here gently folded strata were lifted in the elevation of the Rocky Mountains. Relics of a glacier in a large cirque, containing a corrie lake, with frost-shattered rock walls and morainic debris are typical.

7. The Glaciated Cordilleras, the Alaska coast range, reveal great long straight U-shaped troughs, with truncated spurs, going back to cirques feeding glaciers. Lateral and median moraines are well marked.

8. The Volcanic Cordilleras, developed principally in S. Mexico, offer a variety of cones, with intervening basins. Fertile volcanic soils in extinct craters make excellent farmland, as in this double cone near Mexico City.

9. The flat, wide expanse of the Canadian prairies, pock-marked with sleughs left behind after the retreat of the ice from the till-covered plain. Note the large, square fields, recently reaped of their grain, the darker patches of summer fallow, and the long straight roads.

10. The edge of the Great Plains has been gullied into badlands in N. Dakota. Horizontal beds of harder rock stand up as cliffs, above fans of sandy talus. Bunch grass and sagebrush supply a scanty cover.

11. Eskimo making snow house.

12. Eskimo with harpooned seal.

13. Inside an Eskimo snow house, N.W.T. The trade in furs brings amenities and comforts such as clocks, Primus stoves, kettles, cups, glasses, knives, needles, sugar and tobacco.

in summer. But much of the country—as in northern Keewatin and most of the archipelago—is mainly barren land. The amount and type of vegetation depends a great deal on surface conditions and on aspect. Clay hollows are thick with cotton grass and sphagnum moss; sandy ridges are covered with heath and lichen.

There is very little chance for soil to develop. Vegetation decomposes very slowly and forms a shallow, acid, peaty layer overlying a waterlogged grey mineral zone. Beneath a narrow horizon the soil is permanently frozen.[1] The surface layer, on thawing out, becomes partly liquid and often flows slowly down slopes, leading to solifluction terracettes. Frost splits the soil with cracks that frequently form stripes or polygons, to provide a typical pattern to the ground.

The Microthermal Climates

North America reaches its maximum spread between Alaska and Labrador and consequently has a very wide development of microthermal climates. These embrace three humid types. There is: (i) a sub-humid type, with long very severe winters, which lies over the central Shield, the northern Interior Lowlands, and parts of the northern Cordilleras; (ii) a rainy type, with cold winters and cool summers, extending across the southern part of the Canadian Shield and parts of the northern Appalachians; (iii) a rainy type, with warm summers, in southernmost Canada, and the northern–central and mid-Atlantic States. All three climates are dominated by continental polar air and have comparatively long and cold winters and a high annual range of temperature. The second also feels the effect of mP air, together with mT streams, and the last comes under the strong influence of the mT air mass in summer.

The Microthermal sub-humid climate with long, severe winters lies on the southern margin of the Arctic regions and is the climate of the great coniferous forest and muskeg country of southern Alaska and northern–central Canada. It is dominated by the continental polar air mass. Winters are long and severe. They begin in October when the average temperature drops from about 45° to 35° F. Temperatures do not rise above 40° F. until mid-May. In January and February and much of March they average less than 0° F. By this time marine influences among the islands of the archipelago or the straits and bays of the Hudson Bay depression have practically disappeared; ice as good as makes these areas land. Ice-chilled air moves from the Arctic over the sub-Arctic. Extreme radiation from the Mackenzie basin lowers temperatures below −20° F., with absolute minima as low as −80° F. The dry air produces little snow and the ground is deeply frozen. Great water bodies like Great Bear and Great Slave Lake are largely, if not

[1] Jenness, J. L., 'Permafrost in Canada', *Arctic*, 1949, **2**, pp. 13–27.

entirely, frozen over. Temperatures fall beneath the coldest ones in the Arctic itself. The air is keen. Heat rapidly passes out to space. The nights are bitter in their brilliant darkness. The crunching of the snow underfoot can be heard far off, and the cracking of the ice rings through the air with sudden claps of sound.

A swift transition occurs with spring. When the continental polar air mass is broken down there is little to prevent its retreat. Vast open plains invite the rapid advance of maritime tropical air. Temperatures rise to over 50° F. by early June, to about 60° F. in July, and 55° F. in August. Summers are cool on the whole, but have one or two surprisingly warm spells with temperatures of over 80° F. Daytime hours are long, ranging from 18 to 22 hours of sunshine in June, and plant growth is rapid. Thus, in spite of the fact that freedom from frost is only from 44 to 92 days,[1] there is quite a dense vegetation. The contrast between this vigorous growth in summer and the sheer lifelessness of the winter scene is striking. Contrast dominates the climate, producing the greatest extremes in the continent, as for example at Fort Smith with a summer record of 105° F. and a winter one of −71° F., or a range of 176°.

Precipitation is medium to low, being the equivalent of from 15 to 20 inches of rainfall, but since evaporation is relatively low, most of it is effective for growth. The rain comes mainly in late summer as a result of cyclones and local convection. Winter is fairly dry. What snow falls does not blow away, however, as on the tundra, but is held by the trees, and thus piles to a depth of 2 or 3 feet. It melts very slowly in spring, and delays the coming of summer. But it supplies an excellent source of ground-water for plant growth.

Vegetation consists of a low to medium-height coniferous forest, often interspersed with reindeer moss and thick patches of lichen. This is one of the largest forest areas in the world and joins the west coast and the east coast forests of the continent in a great arc of evergreen. Its northern fringe is very irregular, with wide areas of bog, moss, or berry-bush in between the trees. Balsam, poplar, and aspen are common, along with willow in damper places. These trees grade southward into balsam fir, and white, black, and red spruces. The Boreal forest has relatively few species. Pine cling to the better drained and sandier slopes, passing down through belts of spruce to tamarack, poplar, willow, and alder in the cold, wet depressions.

The soils that grow up in these climatic and biotic conditions are thin, grey, highly leached podzols. Their upper layer has a mat of pine needles and forest duff over a shallow black zone of decayed vegetable matter. The heavy thaws of spring and the summer rains lead to a considerable leaching

---

[1] Wonders, W. C., 'Assessment [of the N.W.T.] by a Geographer', *The Canadian Northwest: Its Potentialities*, ed. Underhill, Ottawa, 1959, p. 26.

of this matter, but the greyish-white leached layer is narrow, since the period of active leaching is short. The soil is rather poor in plant nutrients and needs much liming and drainage before it becomes useful to man.

The Microthermal rainy climate with cold winters and cool, short summers lies south of the Boreal zone. It is found on the eastern edge of the Canadian prairies, the southern edge of the Canadian Shield, the St Lawrence valley proper, the Atlantic provinces, and the more rugged parts of New England. Winters are long and cold, lasting for six to seven months. By mid-November temperatures average less than freezing. In January they are usually between 20° and 0° F., with some sub-zero spells. Not until mid-April do temperatures rise above 40° F. Spring then spreads rapidly and by June temperatures have risen to 60° F. with the flooding in of mT air up the Mississippi–Red and the Mississippi–Ohio plains. Temperatures remain between 60° F. and 65° F. for July, with occasional heat waves bringing in close, muggy weather. But though days may be quite hot (Winnipeg has daily maxima of over 80° F. for thirteen days in July), the nights are cool; the July minima of Winnipeg fall below 55° F. on eighteen nights. High diurnal ranges of up to 30° are not uncommon. High annual ranges are also typical, though these are not as high as in the north-west sub-Arctic zone. In the case of Winnipeg there is a mean annual range of 70·3° between the average temperature of 66·4° F. for July and that of −3·9° F. for January.

Precipitation is moderate, being about 15 inches in the interior, and 35 inches at the coast. The summers, though short, are humid. Frequent spring cyclones bring many showers. The hot afternoons in July produce thunderstorms with a very heavy rainfall. In Winnipeg the rainfall in July (3·1 inches) is four times as great as that in January (0·9 inches). Winter is generally dry and the snowfall is light, except in the Atlantic coastal regions. Here heavy snowfalls do occur, especially where mP air is sucked over the region.

The vegetation is predominantly forest, with a mixture of coniferous softwoods and deciduous hardwoods. Black spruce and balsam fir are most prominent, with red spruce on better drained sites, and so-called cedar in the swamps. Maple, elm, basswood, and poplar are principal hardwoods. In the west, the forest opens out and mingles with tall grass prairies.

Under this mixed forest there is a greater accumulation of waste. The soil is, therefore, richer than its northern counterpart. Moreover, it is subject to both leaching and aeration for a longer period—the frost-free span is as long as 120 days—and thus is more fully developed. Nevertheless, a marked leached layer gives it a greyish tinge beneath the brown-black surface. Partially podsolized, it, too, is acid and needs drainage and liming before becoming useful.

The Microthermal rainy climate, with warm summers, is found in the upper Mississippi, the Ohio, the southern Great Lakes, and the mid-Atlantic region. In winter the cP air streams sweep over the area and temperatures fall below freezing. (The mean January temperature at St Louis is 31·8° F., at Toronto 21·1° F.) However, the winter is far from stable, particularly on the coast and in the vicinity of the Great Lakes. Alberta and Colorado type storms bring in mP or mT air, storms from south-west Texas also invade the area, sucking in mT air, and mild waves bring on sudden thaws. During spring the southern maritime air comes in much more frequently and in summer it becomes dominant. An inland city like Toronto experiences quite tropical weather (July average, 69° F.). Chicago, with 74° F., is still more typical of the region. St Louis, near its southern margin, has a July average of 78·6° F. Note that though these places lie at very different latitudes there is not a great deal of difference in the temperatures. A huge mass of hot air covers the heart of the continent. One has to go to the edge of the Canadian Shield, to the Algoma, Muskoka, or Haliburton highlands, before one finds a really cool summer.

Rainfall is on the whole ample,with 25–40 inches. Summer rains predominate. This is due to the great ind raught of mT air up the Mississippi–Ohio or up the Atlantic coastal plain. Cyclones develop along the Ohio–Lower Great Lakes–Mohawk line in late spring and early summer, and are active again in late autumn. One or two hurricanes occur in July or August, drenching the region with torrential downpours. Many convection storms occur from May to August, inducing frequent thunderstorms. These thunderstorms see a rapid massing together of the clouds, followed by their virtual disappearance when the storm is gone, so that there may be considerable sunshine along with heavy rain—an excellent combination for crops.

Winter precipitation is not so important. It is chiefly cyclonic, but though cyclones may be severe, they are not frequent. About a third of the winter precipitation is in the form of snow. The number of days with a cover of snow varies from 60 in the north to 10 in the south of the region.

The vegetation that has grown up as a response to distinct, though short, winters and long, warm wet summers has been a winter-bare, summer-green deciduous forest of oak, hickory, chestnut, and walnut, with ash, elm, and box-elder. It is the largest hardwood forest in North America. On sandier soils there are many pines, especially along the Atlantic coastal plain. Farther west forest passes into tall grass prairies. Most of the natural vegetation has been replaced by crops (Fig. 20).

The soils resulting from thick forest duff, ample rain, and a long growing season are grey-brown earths, in which organic and mineral constituents are about equally balanced. Farther west under the tall grass cover they consist of black soils, very rich in organic matter.

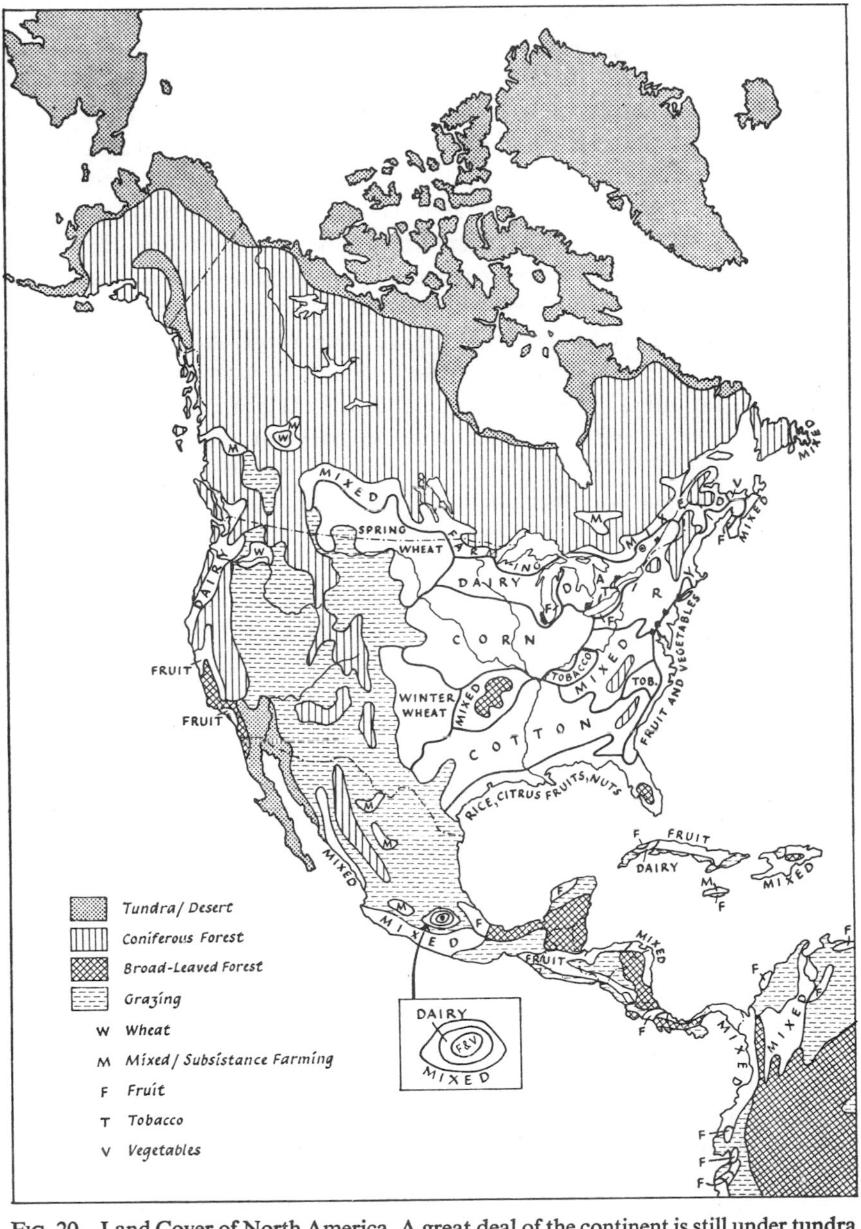

FIG. 20 Land Cover of North America. A great deal of the continent is still under tundra, forest, steppe and desert. The humid sub-tropical to cool-temperate regions have, however, been replaced by cropland or pasture, and man is making an increasing mark on the landscape. (Scale, 1:65 m.). Note, this is not a vegetation map. It indicates the closeness or openness of vegetation cover, together with the cover of crops.

The Mesothermal Climates

A very considerable part of North America lies in the sub-tropical or warm-temperate zones since, although widest in the cool latitudes, the continent does not narrow down suddenly until almost within reach of the tropics. Beneath the wide shoulders, as it were, there is a broad long trunk, before the continent narrows appreciably. There is thus an extensive mild-winter belt with warm to hot summers. Its humid portions lie on the eastern and western margins, being separated by the semi-arid or arid belt of the Great Plains and intermontane basins. On the eastern margin it is pushed well to the south by cold currents and by cP air and is confined to the area dominated by the mT air mass. On the western margin it has a much wider range, from Vancouver to Los Angeles, thanks to warm currents and the wide spread of mP air. On the other hand, the eastern type covers a much broader area, invading the interior, while the western one is confined to the coast by the Cordilleras.

The east margin Mesothermal humid climate has mild winters of about 48° F. Warm waves are drawn over the region from the Gulf of Mexico or from the western end of the Bermuda 'high'. However, cold snaps do occur when cP air spills over the Appalachians and the Ozarks. Thus New Orleans, which has an average January temperature of 54° F., has experienced a cold snap as severe as 7° F. Montgomery, Alabama, has known a cold snap of —5° F.[1] Frost even strikes into Florida, damaging the valuable citrous crops. Thus the winter, though mild, is real enough. But it is very short. The frost-free season is normally over 200 days. Spring comes in March. April temperatures of 70° F. are not uncommon. The July average is truly tropical, being as high as 81° F. Very hot muggy weather is then frequent with hot mT air blowing on shore across the warm Gulf Stream.

Rainfall averages between 40 and 60 inches. Most of it occurs in the summer with summer cyclones, in which moist unstable mTk air invades the lower Mississippi and east Gulf plain, is heated by contact with the very hot land mass, and provides close, thundery weather. Local convection storms are significant, as also are rain-thick hurricanes. Cyclonic weather continues throughout the year, and there is not inconsiderable rain in the winter.

Such a climate supports a dense forest cover, mostly of oak and chestnut, but also of sycamore, yellow poplar, the pawpaw, Kentucky coffee tree, live oak, magnolia, and crepe myrtle—typical sub-tropical species. Most of this has been replaced by crops (Fig. 20). On the sandy soils of the old stranded marine beaches loblolly, longleaf, and slash pines make up the Southern Pineries.

The soils have a fairly thick surface layer of humus, but below this show

[1] *Climate and Man*, U.S. Dept. of Agric., 1941, pp. 752, 895.

a deep leached layer. Laterization has converted iron silicates into iron hydroxides and silicic acid, thus giving the soil a red colour and making it acidic. It has a high mineral content but is low in organic nutrients.

The west margin Mesothermal climates cover a long reach of coast from southern British Columbia to southern California. This coast is swept by warm moist mP air which divides into two streams, one turning north-east across northern British Columbia into the Yukon, and the other flowing south over America's Pacific States. The northern stream blows over the warm Kuro Siwo drift and thus maintains if not augments its warmth. The southern one crosses the cold California current, bringing much fog to the coast of southern Washington and northern California. Except for winter, however, when it penetrates California, it quickly turns off and joins the easterlies around the eastern end of the mid-Pacific 'high'. In the north, not infrequent incursions of cP air westward across the Cordilleras bring cool weather in winter; in the south, very hot dry winds from the cT air mass over the intermontane basins blow down to the coast. These differences in dynamic conditions divide the Pacific shore into two main sub-types, the marine, cool summer climate of the north, and the hot summer, wet winter climate of the south.

The marine, cool-summer mild-winter region is only a Mesothermal climate because its winters are mild, with no month having a sub-freezing average. It might well be considered cool temperate on the strength of its cool summers, where July means are usually less than 65°F. The annual range of temperature is the lowest on the continent. Thus Vancouver with a January mean of 34°F. and a July mean of 64°F. has a range of only 30°. In both summer and winter marine airs sweep over the region, making for one of the most truly marine climates in the world. Rain is plentiful (40 to 100 inches) and occurs at all seasons, with a pronounced maximum in late autumn and winter.

The finest forests of the continent have grown up under these conditions, with dense stands of Douglas fir, western hemlock, red cedar, and California redwoods. A deep forest-brown soil prevails, with moderate leaching. Slightly acidic, it is quite fertile upon being drained and cultivated.

The **hot-summer wet-winter** region, in California, like its northern counterpart, has mild winters in which marine airs are important. San Francisco has a mean January temperature of 49°F., with an average rainfall of 4·9 inches. Cold snaps are very rare, and are not as severe as those in the north, nor indeed as those in similar latitudes in the east margin Mesothermal climate. Los Angeles has a record minimum of only 28°, compared with Montgomery's 5°. Mild mP air is in the ascendant, and little cold continental or mountain air has the opportunity of flooding the region. Summer conditions, however, are very different. Then mP air is very weak, and is kept out by hot dry continental air from the continental air mass lying over the intermontane basins of the Cordilleras. Temperatures become truly continental, even at the coast. Los Angeles has a July mean of 70·5°F. The air is very dry, and summer drought is pronounced.

The long summer drought has meant that vegetation is much thinner than on the northern coast. Trees are small and sparsely distributed. Patches of grass or heath divide one clump of trees from another. A xerophytic woodland of chaparral or scrub-oak mixed with laurel and holly-leafed cherry predominates, along with some sage brush passing upwards into woods of yellow pine. Red soils, not unlike the 'terra rossa' of the Mediterranean, have developed under the thin woodland litter. They have been laterized through a combination of winter rains and summer heat. Summer drought has drawn up basic salts from the mineral layer, chief of which is calcium carbonate, so that the soils are neutral. They are moderately fertile, especially when treated with organic compounds.

Tropical Climates

These are rather poorly developed in North America since the continent narrows down considerably south of latitude 30° N. Furthermore, much of this southern extension of the continent is so mountainous that temperatures are modified, and a temperate rather than a tropical system is found. The truly tropical climates are limited chiefly to the coasts of Mexico. On the rain-swept coasts of the east and of the south the climate is a humid type, in great contrast to the dry tropical climate of the west coast, which lies in the lee of the trade winds.

The **tropical rainy climate** extends across the southern tip of Florida, runs down the east coast of Mexico south of about Tampico, stretches across the isthmus of Tehuantepec, and continues to Cape Corrientes in the southwest. Here there is really no winter. Even the coldest month has an average of over 64·4°, said to be critical for the extensive growth of tropical plants. But if the winters are much warmer than those to the north, summers are not. Indeed, there are rarely the extremely high temperatures found in the Great Plains or Mississippi–Ohio lowlands. The range of temperature from the coldest to the hottest month is small—generally less than 15°.

The rain falls fairly regularly and is heavy (45 to 80 inches). In the summer convection rains, in the form of thunder-showers, come nearly every afternoon. The blue skies of the morning start to cloud over by noon. Huge piles of cloud rise on top of each other, making the horizon quite dark. Lightning begins to play around their edges. A swift wind gets up. There is a crash of thunder, and then the rains beat down in violent sheets. Actually, the storm is welcomed, because it clears the air. The oppressive mugginess of noon ceases. Skies clear, and the evening is fine and fresh.

Summer disturbances and hurricanes also bring much rain. The trade winds are far from steady. They are subject to wave-like motions, with a succession of pressure ridges and troughs that lead to sudden shifts of wind, followed by rainfall. Intense tornadoes sometimes develop behind the troughs. In winter the expansion of the mid-latitude westerlies may affect the easterlies, giving rise to rainy disturbances. At all times relief rain occurs as the trades blow on shore and are forced to rise above the coastal mountains.

Constant heat and ample rainfall produce a dense vegetation of luxuriant forests and marshes, with many species of plants. On the lower, wetter lands occur mangrove thickets, with thick interlacing branches and exuberant leafage, or groves of swamp cypress. On clay plains gum trees and quick oaks, and on the drier ground palmetto bush and palm trees, flourish. This dense vegetation supplies much forest litter for soil formation. The heavy rains wash this down and leach the soil beneath, often to considerable depths. Laterization is strong, and makes for a rather infertile soil, once the surface layers have been exhausted.

The Interior Semi-arid and South-west Arid Climates

As already indicated, although ocean-bred air streams predominate over North America, yet continental air masses prevail over the western interior and the south-west. They lie well to the west, since the Mississippi–Missouri and the Mackenzie form channels for mT and cP air respectively, bringing southern and northern streams far into the continent. But in the triangle between these north-eastern and south-eastern air streams and the maritime Pacific air on the west, lies a considerable area with mainly dry, continental air. This can be divided into a semi-arid region over the Great Plains, receiving modified Pacific air and disturbed by lee-depressions, and an arid area over the south-western basins of the Cordillera and the west coast of the tropics.

The **semi-arid interior climate** begins south and west of the sub-Arctic and the humid boreal types, and characterizes the Great Plains of the western central States and the Canadian prairie provinces. It is sometimes referred to as a steppe climate because it was associated with grassland, until the grasslands were ploughed up, and gave way to cropland. However, there are signs that woodland was once not unplentiful. The climate has possibly become rather more arid as men burned down grass and trees, particularly during the great buffalo hunts, when animals were stampeded by fire. Actually this has long been a critical zone, on the verge between aridity and humidity. The prevalence of down-sweeping air from the upper westerlies must have tipped the balance, as it now tips it, mainly in favour of dry conditions. Continentality has become the dominant characteristic. The land heats up in summer distinctly more than that to the east covered by cloudy skies or lapped by ocean currents. In Canada the range of temperatures between January and July means is appreciably greater in the prairies (65°–70°) than in the St Lawrence lowlands (45°–55°). (The extremes are greatest in the north: northern summers have temperatures almost as high as southern ones, but northern winters are much colder.) The day and night range of temperature is also high; the lack of cloud by day leading to a great intake of heat, by night to a notable loss. A rise or fall in temperatures between day and night of 20° to 30° is not uncommon.

Precipitation is low, between 10 and 17 inches. Most of this occurs in the summer when the excessive heating of the interior plains leads to local convection storms or produces a trough of low pressure up which mT air surges. While most of this mT air keeps to the Mississippi–Ohio, turning north-eastward out to the Atlantic, some of it billows across the Missouri and Saskatchewan prairies, bringing short-lived but significant showers. Rain also occurs as a result of lee-depressions that follow upon the down-drop of those westerlies that cross the Cordilleras. These Rocky Mountain cyclones bring the chief winter precipitation which, however, is scanty. cP air is then predominant, joining with winter high-pressure systems over the mountains. The sky is cloudless for days on end, and sparkles with a crisp, pale blue, letting in bright sunshine. At night, rapid radiation creates clear, dark skies, in which the stars shine out with a remarkable brilliance.

As already stated, there is some doubt as to the original natural vegetation of the region.[1] Open deciduous woodland and wide glades or parks of grass were probably typical, but conditions were so marginal that, with the intervention of man, grasses became dominant. Blue-stem sod grass, together with tall Indian grass, covered the lower Missouri prairies; farther west as rain decreased, blue-stem bunch grass prevailed, giving way to buffalo grass, grama, and wire grass on the high plains; while farther north, where the growing season was shorter, quick-growing needle grass or the tall, slender wheat grass were common. Most of these grasslands have been ploughed up and replaced by corn in the eastern prairies and wheat and barley in the western ones (Fig. 20). However, some of the Short Grass prairie has been kept as range land. Its gently rolling reaches stretching out into the distance, brilliantly green after the warm chinook has melted the snows or the spring rains have swept over it, covered with flowers in early summer which come out overnight to paint the plains with an incredible beauty, its gradual paling under the large blue skies of summer until at last it turns to a tinder brown in autumn, still give us some idea of the conditions seen by the first white settlers (Fig. 20).

[1] Shantz, H. L., 'The Natural Vegetation of the Great Plains Region', *Ann. Assoc. Amer. Geogrs.*, **13**, pp. 81–107.

The soils of the region are black on its outer, eastern margin, shared with the more humid climates, chestnut-brown in a broad central zone, and yellow-brown along its inner, western margin. The darker soils are rich in humus. A narrow leached horizon separates the dark organic layer from a yellowy-brown calcareous layer; in the lighter soils the humus layer is much shallower, the calcareous horizon thicker and nearer to the surface. These soils are neutral to alkali, and respond well to drainage and irrigation.

The **arid south-west** climate occupies the intermontane basins of the southern Cordilleras and extends down the west coast of Mexico to Cape Corrientes. It is in part a rain-shadow climate, cut off from the westerlies by the coast ranges and by the Sierra Nevadas, and from the trade winds by the Mexican Sierras, and in part the climate of a locally developed tropical continental air mass strengthened by the sub-tropical 'high'. This 'high' lies over the mid-Pacific, but is usually so close to land as to draw streams of air from land to sea on its eastern and southern flanks, aggravating if not causing coastal drought from about San Diego, California, to San Blas, Mexico. This drawing away of surface air may assist in that subsidence of the upper air over the continent which adds to the extremely high temperatures associated with cT air in summer. The region is too far south to be invaded by mP air except for the occasional winter disturbance, and at the same time it is too far north to benefit by the so-called south-west monsoons or equatorial westerlies.

For these and other reasons, which will be discussed in greater detail later, rainfall is very low generally less than 10 inches, and in some places less than 5 inches a year. Actually the average means very little. Rainfall is very variable. In some years a few extra-heavy thunderstorms or abnormal cyclones give a rainfall well above 'average'; in other years there may be no rain at all. Most of the rain that does occur comes down in heavy showers during the hot, summer days. It may be so heavy that it fills up depressions in a few hours or rushes in muddy torrents down valleys that have remained dry for years.

Under these circumstances vegetation is scanty, consisting of very sparse bunch grass or mesquite grass, strips of sage brush, and a scattered growth of cactus and similar drought-resistant trees. The soil has very little organic matter and is mainly a mineral one, with a frequent concentration of alkali salts worked up to the surface by strong evaporation.

Conclusion

Thus North American climates reflect in many of their patterns the physical disposition and structures of the continent. They are characterized by a northness that brings them principally under polar air masses. West of the western Cordilleras, north of the height of land of the Canadian Shield, and south of the Ozarks and southern Appalachians they are dominated by air streams from the Pacific, Arctic, and Atlantic oceans. In the south-west they reflect the ample spread of mountain and basin. While respecting the great divide of the Rockies, however, they boldly qualify Shield, Interior Lowland, and the Appalachians, adding further physical divisions to the existing ones. In this they supply something of their own to the strong contrasts, the broad sweeps, and the massive proportions of the continent.

CHAPTER FOUR

Native North America

PHYSICAL AND HUMAN GEOGRAPHY

The physical geography of North America, especially its relief and climate, profoundly influenced the course of settlement and the economic, social, and political geography of the continent. Yet differences in culture and stage of development prompted different reactions to physical conditions, and created a human geography that came to dominate the scene. Each group of people made a different interpretation and use of relief, climate, vegetation, and soil. This is particularly evident in the contrast between what the Indians and Eskimoes made of North America and what the Europeans did. This contrast is a most illuminating one, since it shows to what extent physical factors determined human actions, or human forces modified the natural landscape.

In general it may be said that the Indians adapted themselves to the environment while the Europeans adapted the environment to themselves. However, even quite primitive natives changed the vegetation and affected the soil of the regions they settled, while the most advanced Europeans had to settle regions by natural routeways and respond to the relief and resources they found.

A first contrast lay in the approach to North America (Fig. 21). The natives came in at the north-west apex of the continent and fanned out across it in such a way as to follow the 'grain of the country', moving south or east along the coasts, following the flanks of the Cordilleras and the edge of the Shield, advancing into the interior lowlands from north to south, and climaxing their long history of wanderings in the plateaux of Mexico, Yucatan, and Guatemala. They were able to travel up the Yukon and Mackenzie, down the St Lawrence and the Missouri–Mississippi along major natural routes. They respected the great natural divides and these, together with the frontiers of tundra, forest, grassland, and desert, became their principal boundaries.

The Europeans, on the other hand, approached North America along the broad base of the Atlantic seaboard. Already drifters to the West—the West had been their destiny since first they left Asia, their early home—they continued their westward march. Indeed, there is a sense in which, for

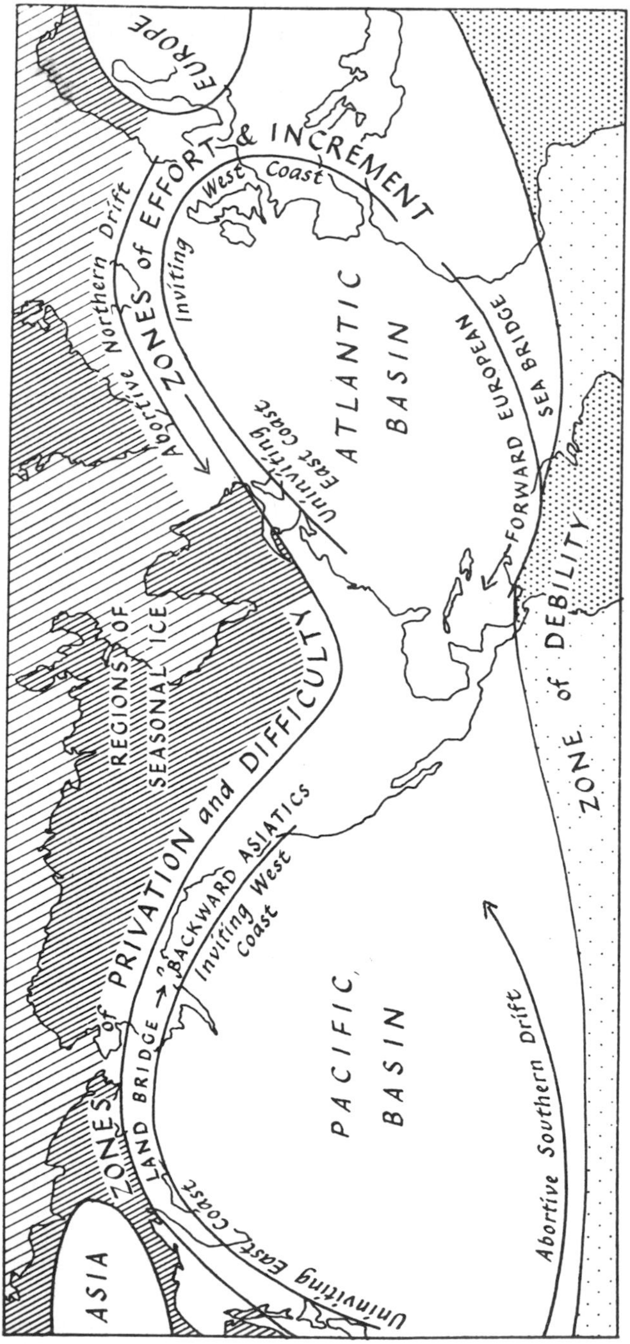

FIG. 21 Contrasted Invasions of North America. In spite of the fact that the Indians and Eskimoes left a harsh environment in eastern Siberia to find a more pleasant one in western North America, they made much less of the change than white men who, leaving pleasant conditions behind had to face sterner ones in front, at any rate in Canada and Mexico, and in western America. The more advanced culture of the Europeans was the key to their more effective use of the environment.

Europeans, the march of history has been the march to America. Arriving there they had to cut through the Appalachians, Rockies, and coast ranges, they had to move across the Shield, they had to cross the Mississippi and trek over the Interior Lowlands from east to west, finding their final goal on the Pacific shores. With few exceptions, such as going up the St Lawrence and the Great Lakes or the Hudson–Mohawk, their course was against the grain of the country. They had to challenge the great natural divides, and make their major routeways out of the tributary streams leading from the master rivers up to mountain passes. They thus took some of the secondary features of the land and turned them, for their purposes, into primary ones, reorientating the entire geography of the continent. Their boundaries were often meridians or parallels that completely transgressed relief and climate.

Other contrasts between Indian and European settlements were: (i) that the Indians moved in at the end of the Ice Age when climate was still liable to considerable change, whereas the Europeans entered when only minor fluctuations occurred—the Indians were thus very subject to climatic conditions. Although the Europeans could not escape them, they either knew how to exploit them or were able to get around them. (ii) The Indians faced nature in the raw and had the task of testing out each environment for what it was worth, finding what rivers could be 'trusted', what game was suitable to hunt, what plants could be cultivated, and so on; the Europeans had the fortune of having many of the main trails already blazed, most of the great portages already marked out, most of the usable plants already in cultivation for food or clothing, and many of the significant sites for settlement already discovered, tested, and confirmed. Finally (iii), the Indians came in with little experience and with poor equipment, and did not have the technological, economic, and political means at their disposal to take the measure of the environment; they were still Stone Age beings when they arrived and had not got much beyond the Stone Age when discovered by Columbus: only a minority had taken to agriculture, and a still smaller number dwelt in cities. The Europeans, on the other hand, had advanced to a high degree of scientific and technological skill, and economic and political organization. They had the power to measure up to the environment and either make a rational and efficient adjustment to it, or bring it under their control.

The next few chapters will consider the importance of both physical and human factors in the emergence of the main geographical regions of the continent. First, the reaction of the so-called 'native' cultures will be shown, and then that of leading European cultures. Thereafter attention will be directed to the main nation-states of today and to the economic and social regions they have developed within their borders.

Conditions at Man's Arrival

The coming of man into North America whether red, white, or black was long delayed. This was because the races of man emerged in the Old World during the Pleistocene Ice Age and, in the main, kept south of the great ice-sheets over north-west Europe and northern and north-east Asia that, along with the Labrador-Greenland and the American Cordilleran sheets, made a ring of ice about the northern lands. It was not until upper Paleolithic times, when men had learned to make tents, sew skin clothes, use harpoons and dart throwers, and had improved their techniques of hunting that they launched out with some assurance upon the tundras. In the Gotiglacial cold, Aurignacian man discovered the wealth of game in the European tundras and, about the same time, upper Paleolithic men moved out over the eastern Siberian tundras to converge upon North America.

The first arrivals came in late glacial (Wisconsin) times. Conditions were fluctuating a great deal and *challenge* or *privation* faced the intruders. The ice spread outward from the Canadian Shield or downward from the Cordilleran ranges, and then retreated again, in five great waves,[1] beginning with the Iowan advance, continuing through the Tazewell, Cary, and Mankato stages, to conclude (in the main) with the Cochrane. With the shift of ice there was a shift of the climatic belts. Big anticyclonic systems developed over the prairies and what are now the Great Lakes, driving the cyclonic storm tracks farther south. With them marched rain, grassland, forest, buffalo and deer, and, in due course, man. North of the Missouri–Ohio line, the glacial phases were hard on life. South of that line, however, they could be quite stimulating, since they were accompanied by wet, cool weather that modified the hot, dry lands of the American south-west. Immigrants began arriving in some numbers between Cary and Mankato times, and found a refuge from the cold in a broad belt from Florida to California, beloved today of escapers from the north!

Conditions continued to fluctuate after the main Ice Age had died down in Mankato times. Antevs[2] has divided the post-Mankato period into three significant stages: the *anathermal*, a cool, moist, stormy time, corresponding to the sub-Arctic and pre-Boreal periods in West European climate; followed by the *altithermal*, a warmer stage, dry in the south and south-west, not unlike Boreal and Atlantic times in Europe; this passed to the *medithermal*,

[1] Shapley, H. (ed.), *Climatic Change*, Cambridge (U.S.A.) 1960, pp. 11, 46–47, 166, 172. Glaciation continued longer in North America than in Europe, the last or Baffin re-advance occurring when the pyramids were being built in Egypt, the Minoan civilization was being founded, and Neolithic farmers and herders were beginning to settle Britain.

[2] Antevs, E., 'Wisconsin Glacial Maxima', *Amer. Jour. Sci.*, 239A, 1945, pp. 1–39; 'The Great Basin, with Emphasis on Glacial and Post-Glacial Times, Climatic Changes, and Pre-White Man', *U. of Utah Bul.*, 1948, **38**, no. 20, pp. 168–91.

a mild to cool phase, mainly wet, but fluctuating considerably, like sub-Boreal and more recent times in Europe. Fluctuations included the Cochrane readvance in Canada. The altithermal period (that avoided the extreme rawness and storminess of earlier times, brought comfort back to the continent

Chart of Glacial and Post-Glacial Times
North America and Europe

Date N/A	*Weather*	*Period N/A*	*Period Eur.*	*Maine*	*Ireland*
Present		Sub-Atlantic	Sub-Atlantic	Hemlock-Spruce Oak-Chestnut	Alder-Birch Oak
600 B.C.	Cool & moist	Medi-thermal		Oak-Beech	
2500 B.C.		Alti-thermal (Climatic Optimum)	Sub-Boreal	Spruce	
	Warm & dry		Lower Sub-Boreal	Oak-Hickory	Alder-Oak
5000 B.C.	Warm & moist		Atlantic	Oak-Beech	Alder-Oak Pine
			Upper Boreal		
6300 B.C.	Cold & moist	*Cochrane* readvance		Pine	Hazel-Pine
	Warm & dry	Ana-thermal	Boreal		
7000 B.C.	Cool & moist		Pre-Boreal	Birch	Birch
8800 B.C.	Cold	*Mankato* Advance	Fenno-Scandian Mor.	Spruce-Fir	
9500 B.C.	Mid-moist	Two-Creeks Interstadial	Alleröd Interstad	Spruce-Birch	Birch
10,000 B.C.	Cold	*Cary* Advance	Würm 3 or Pomeranian Mor.		
15.000 B.C.	Warm	Brady Interstadial	Masurian Interstad		
	Cold	*Tazewell* Advance	Würm 2 or Brandenburg Mor.		
	Cool & moist	Peorian Interval	Rixdorf Interstadial		
	Cold	*Iowan* Advance	Würm 1 or Warthe Mor.		

FIG. 22 Climatic Change—Chart of Glacial and Post-Glacial Times in North America and Europe. (Date for Cochrane readvance from J. D. Ives.)

as far as the Great Lakes, and saw the northward spread of deciduous forest and of open woodland) witnessed the rise of many new cultures. Wherever there was water, it proved to be attractive, and it is sometimes referred to by American archaeologists as the 'Climatic Optimum' (Fig. 22).

Considerable changes in the geography of land and sea occurred in post-glacial times. The huge late-glacial lakes such as Lake Lahontan, Lake

Agassiz, Lake Algonquin, and Lake Ojibway fell appreciably in level, to leave mere relics of their former selves, except in the case of the Great Lakes. Lakeside dwellers moved their camps with the shrinking shore-lines. Rivers, too, shrank. The outlets between the Great Lakes and the Mississippi, Ohio, Susquehanna, and Mohawk shrivelled to low swampy tracts. Here dwellers by the rivers had to make portages. The sea-level dropped, especially in the north-east. The Champlain Sea drained away, leaving boulder-strewn beaches and marine benches all along the lower Ottawa and St Lawrence valleys. In the Maritimes and in New England sea beaches were raised up to form narrow strips around the rugged uplands, while the rejuvenated rivers, attacking valley moraines, drained off the lakes dammed up behind them, thus creating tracts of flat land within the hills. Dwellers by the sea migrated out to and claimed the low sea beaches. Everywhere migration routes and settlements were adapting themselves to the changing geography of the continent.

Early Movements into North America

It is difficult as yet to give a picture of the first colonization of the continent, since the skeletal remains of early migrants are all too few. One of the earliest races to arrive was the so-called 'Minnesota Man', whose skeleton was found in 1931 near Pelican Rapids, Minnesota.[1] It was associated with glacial silts, believed to be late Pleistocene. Another Minnesota discovery was made two years later at Brown's Valley in a beach ridge of the declining glacial Lake Agassiz. The body was intruded into the gravels, and thus may be later than the beach, which may be dated about 12,000 years ago. But it was buried before vegetation had colonized the gravels of the beach, i.e. when glacial conditions still prevailed. The skulls of both skeletons were long and of medium breadth, the jaws rather large, and the teeth 'shovel-shaped', representing a hybrid type.

A broken pelvis, unearthed as long ago as 1845, in Natchez, Mississippi, has been found by later fluorine tests[2] to be contemporaneous with the bones of extinct mastodon and sloth, associated with the Ice Age. Human remains discovered at Melbourne, Florida,[3] have similarly been correlated with the bones of extinct horse and tapir. However, while these were Ice Age animals, they may not have become extinct in south-east America until after the Pleistocene. Orr[4] found human bones in Nevada dating back 11,000 years.

[1] Jenks, A. E., *Pleistocene Man in Minnesota*, Minneapolis, 1936; *Minnesota's Brown's Valley Man*, Mem. Amer. Anthrop. Assoc., no. 49, 1937.

[2] Richards, H. G., 'The Vindication of Natchez Man', *Frontiers*, Philadelphia, 1951, **15**, no. 5.

[3] Gidley, J. W., and Loomis, F. B., 'Fossil Man in Florida', *Amer. Jour. Sci.*, September 1926, 5th Ser., **12**, pp. 254–65.

[4] Orr, P. C., 'Pleistocene Man in Fishbone Cave, Nevada', *Bul. Nevada State, Mus.*, 1956, no. 2, 1–20.

A different strain of man, with a distinctly broader skull, began to arrive at the end of the Ice Age. Relict remains found at Tepexpan[1] in the Valley of Mexico lay in silts belonging to the anathermal period, overlain by caliche beds of the Climatic Optimum. Peat beds in the same layer of silt were dated by radio-carbon methods at 11,000±500 years old.

There is little doubt but that these races entered North America by the Bering Straits and Alaska. During the Pleistocene, Asia was a centre for great, periodic migrations of people who, as Griffith Taylor points out, moved away from the expanding ice fronts in glacial periods, or the expanding desert in interglacial ones. That some of these migrants moved north-eastward through Asia to Alaska has been shown by the finds of fossil men and stone tools. Weidenreich[2] makes out three strains in north-east China, including not only a primitive Mongoloid type, but an Eskimoid and even a Melanesoid one. These strains are represented in the early immigration into the Americas. The Lagoa Santa and Punin crania, of South America, suggest Australoid-Melanesoid relationships. Hooton[3] believes that the early incomers contained many hybrids. Thus Minnesota man was a hybrid of Australoid and an early type of evolving Mongoloid. American Indians of today, though more strongly Mongoloid, show occasional likenesses with Australoid, Melanesoid, and Caucasoid people. This may well have arisen from life in a common home, possibly the Amur basin, into which Caucasoid people from the west, Australoid folk from the south-west, and Mongoloids from the south, moved, met, and mingled. Thence they migrated to the Americas. Later people, more markedly Mongoloid, followed their tracks, and, coming to dominate the continent, gave it a strongly Mongoloid cast.

Although few skeletal remains have been left to mark their way, many stone-tipped implements were dropped by the early invaders that help to piece their story together. Strong likenesses have been found between tools in Alaska and those in eastern-central and north-east Asia, as for example between implements left at Fairbanks and those turned up by Lake Baikal. Lamellar flakes unearthed at Cape Denbigh, Alaska, are very similar to those in the Gobi. According to Giffin,[4] the woodland pottery tradition of eastern North America is reminiscent of the Neolithic pottery of northern Eurasia. Jenness[5] points to the connexions between Canadian Indians and the people of north-eastern Siberia, and states that, without doubt, they

---

[1] de Terra, H., Romero, J., Stewart, T. D., 'Tepexpan Man', *Viking Fund Pub. in Anthrop.*, New York, 1949, no. 11.

[2] Weidenreich, F., 'On the Earliest Representation of Modern Mankind . . .', *Peking Nat. Hist. Bul.*, 1939, **13**.

[3] Hooton, E. A., *Up from the Ape*, New York, 1947, pp. 405–7.

[4] Giffin, J. B., *The United States and Canada, Indigenous Period,* Mexico, 1953, p. 96.

[5] Jenness, D., 'La Traume Indienne de l'Histoire du Canada', *Nat. Mus. Can., Bul.* **86**, p. 21.

must have grown up side by side. And as for the Eskimoes of the Canadian Arctic they have had distinct affiliations with eastern Siberia up to fairly recent times (Fig. 23).

Three main racial types have resulted. These are the Paleo-Amerind,

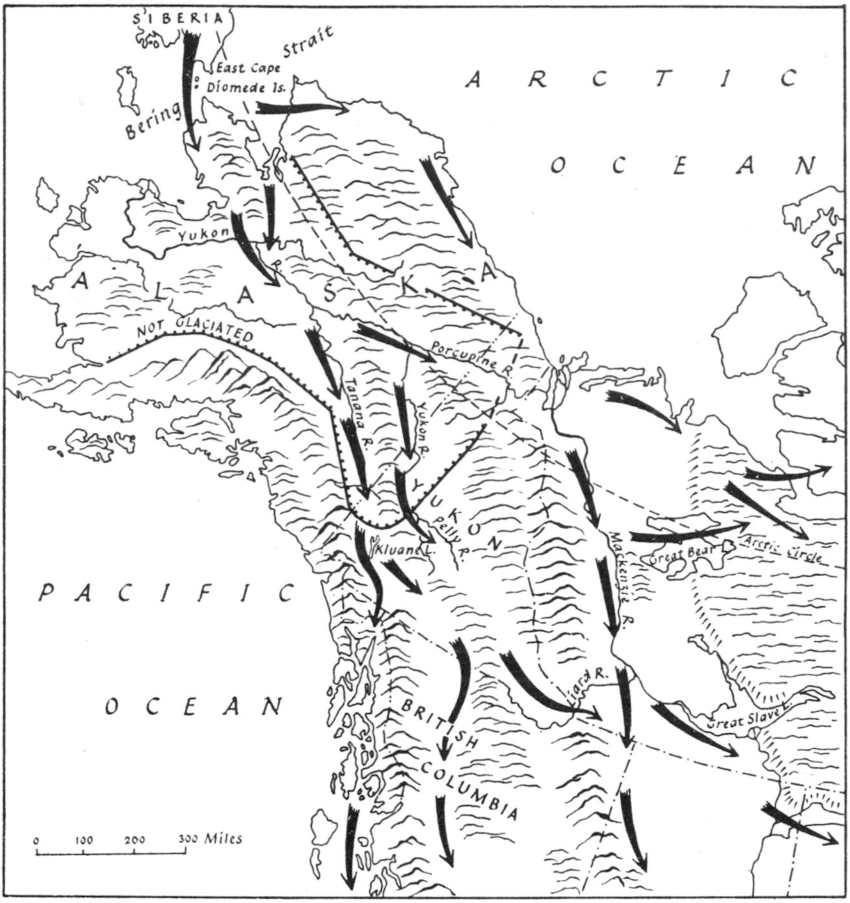

FIG. 23 The Coming of the Aborigines. The Indians moved to the south and south-east following the Yukon, the Pacific coast, and the Mackenzie. The Eskimoes migrated eastward along the Arctic coast.

Neo-Amerind, and Eskimoid stocks to which most North American natives now belong. The Paleo-Amerind are the oldest of the present native races and are characterized by a long and rather narrow head, aquiline nose, tall lithe body with narrow hips, and a deep copper colouring. They are to be found mainly along the southern part of the Canadian Shield and the St Lawrence lowlands and adjacent regions. The Neo-Amerinds came later and are represented by a well-built, broad-faced, broad-hipped people, with lighter skins, slanting eyes, high cheek-bones, and smooth black hair. When the early explorers of Canada passed from the south-east of the country where rather long-headed nations prevailed to the north-west where broad-headed groups were dominant they were struck by the differences. Hearne, who made many trips into the north-west, said that the Indian's idea of beauty there was quite different and centred in a broad flat face, small eyes, high cheek-bones, a low forehead, a large broad chin, a hook nose, and a tawny-coloured skin—reflecting strongly Mongolian characters.[1] They pushed their long-headed forerunners into the southern and eastern parts of the Canadian Shield and came to occupy the Interior Lowlands, the Appalachians, and Cordilleras, the west coast, the Atlantic and Gulf coast plains, and Mexico, thus dominating the continent. The Eskimo form a third group. They are a branch of the Paleo-Arctic race and are short and broad, with round heads, Mongolian eyes, heavy jaws, yellow skins, and straight black hair. The Eskimo kept to the far north and north-east coasts of the continent.

Late Pleistocene—Early Post-Glacial Cultures

Entering North America by the Bering Straits in late glacial times all but the Eskimo turned south and, moving up the Yukon, crossed over to the Mackenzie valley, traversed the Canadian prairies, and fanned out down the Missouri, the Mississippi, and the Great Lakes systems to the south and south-east of the continent.[2] The flanks of the Cordilleras, and the edge of the Shield, funnelled most of them into the Interior Lowlands, but gradually they spread to all parts and came to develop the first essentially American cultures.

One of the oldest of these cultures is represented by crudely flaked dart points found at Sandia Cave, near Albuquerque, New Mexico. They lie in a bed rich in the bones of extinct mastodon, mammoth, horse, and bison. This is all buried under a layer of yellowy silts, carried there by flood-waters during a change of climate in Mankato times. Above this is another fossiliferous layer which contains points similar to those found at Folsom.

In many ways Folsom man is the most famous of the early migrants into North America. He is represented by a great number of finds from northern Canada to southern U.S.A. (The name is derived from Folsom, New Mexico, where stone points of a distinctive kind were found.) 'Fifteen thousand years ago the spot was on the shores of a small lake. Now all is

---

[1] Hearne, quoted in Morton, A. S., *A History of the Canadian West to 1871*, London, 1939, p. 6.

[2] Leechman, D., 'The First Men in the New World', *Can. Geog. Jour.*, 1949, xxxix, no. 5, p. 193.

dry for miles around and the ancient camp is covered deep with soil. Lying around the old lake are pieces of bone, chiefly of an extinct buffalo. These were so abundant the Folsom people practically lived on them. Arrow points are often found stuck fast in the bones.'[1]

These points may be said to be the first American invention! They were distinct from their European counterparts. They were thin, shaped like a slender leaf, with concave bases from which two sharp projections thrust out. The edges were carefully chipped, while longitudinal grooves were flaked from each face by indirect percussion. Considerable skill was used, quite the equivalent of that of late Paleolithic men in the Old World. Along with the points were found knives, scrapers, and a primitive type of burin, i.e. the tools of hunters who shot down game, skinned and cut it up, scraped the skins clean, and made them into clothes and utensils. The chief Folsom remains actually occur at Lindenmeier, Colorado, on a river terrace of Mankato age.[2]

Another culture, possibly slightly younger, arose farther west in Nevada and California. It is known as the Pinto-Gypsum type, from the Pinto basin in California and the Gypsum Cave near Las Vegas, Nevada. Although these areas are now near-desert, they were mild and moist in late glacial and early post-glacial times, and were visited by herds of mammoth and bison. At Gypsum Cave stone dart points, broken dart shafts, and bits of basketry were found along with the dung of a giant sloth—brought into the cave for making fire—and the bones of horse and camel. The sloth dung produced radio-carbon datings of from 10,000 to 8,000 years ago.[3]

Meantime, far to the north-east, on the shores of Lake Superior, other hunting people left evidences of their wanderings. These were a more primitive folk who used heavy core-type implements rather than flaked stone tools. It is possible that they were pushed out from the more comfortable climes to their rather inhospitable site, or they may have isolated themselves to escape competition with their more advanced neighbours. In any event they left great heaps of broken tools on a hill at Shequiandah, on Manitoulin Island. This was undoubtedly one of their work places where blocks of white quartzite were quarried out and then hammered into large rough blades and scrapers together with irregularly edged knives. There were no projectile points, suggesting a people without the bow and arrow. The Manitoulin camp sites are all above the strand-line of glacial lake Nipissing. Although there was a tendency for these sites to migrate downhill, they stopped abruptly at this level, which therefore forms a time datum. Some of

---

[1] Kidd, K. E., *Canadians of Long Ago, The Story of the Canadian Indians*, Longmans, Green, Toronto, 1951, pp. 6–7.

[2] Bryan, K., and Ray, L. L., 'Geologic Antiquity of the Lindenmeier Site in Colorado' *Smithsonian Misc. Colln.*, 1940, **99**, no. 2.

[3] Harrington, M. R., 'Gypsum Cave', *S.W. Mus. Papers*, Los Angeles, 1935, **8**.

the tools were overridden by ice and partially buried under boulder clay. The age of this readvance of ice was probably Cochrane.

The cultures so far described have all been alike in that they expressed a hunting way of life. They flourished in interstadial periods between the readvance of ice, but tended to die out as the climate deteriorated. Other cultures, reflecting another way of life, existed in the more arid parts of New Mexico, Arizona, and the Mexican plateau. Here lived the seed-gatherers of the Cochise culture,[1] whose main tools were not dart points but grinding stones. Although they were remote from the threat of ice, they were challenged by the advance of the desert. Some of their earliest relics, found at Sulphur Spring, are associated with the onset of the altithermal period, when the climate began to grow warmer and drier. Game must have become much more scarce, and the people must have turned to gathering nuts, seeds and roots, and snaring snakes and lizards. Hammerstones were made to crack the nuts and dehusk the seeds. The kernels were then ground to flour between grinding stones. These were at first small and thin. But in the Chiricahua culture they developed into quite large milling stones, slightly hollowed out. In the San Pedro stage fully developed milling stones, rounded hand stones, and hammer stones were all used, along with the mortar and pestle. Farther south in rock shelters in the Sierra de Tamaulipas, Mexico, there lived seed-gatherers who in the end became corn planters. Here in the Mexican plateau agriculture was born, and spread throughout Mexico northwards to the Mississippi and Ohio valleys, as Sauer[2] has shown.

In these well-watered river plains, with their hot summers and mild winters, corn planting was adopted by hunters, who thereafter followed a dual system, hoeing and harvesting in spring and summer and hunting and trapping in autumn and winter. Their way was best represented by the Hopewell culture of Ohio, which came to dominate the central part of the continent.

The Hopewellians lived in large settlements, with fairly big houses and much household gear. The women minded their patches of corn and made delightfully decorated pottery. The men hunted with the bow and arrow, made tools, worked artistic motifs in horn and copper, and spent much time in religious festivals. One religion came to bind the various peoples from the Gulf of Mexico to Ontario. It was symbolized in serpent worship, as testified by the Great Serpent Mound, where the Little Miami river meets the Ohio. Here an enormous snake god, 1,330 feet long, was made. It was represented as swallowing a huge egg. What this signifies cannot be said, but it implies a distinct religion with symbols and holy places, and probably craftsmen,

---

[1] Sayles, E. B., and Antevs, E., 'The Cochise Culture', *Medallion Papers*, **xxiv**, Gila Pueblo, Globe, Arizona, 1941.

[2] Sauer, C. O., *Agricultural Origins and Dispersals*, New York, 1952.

priests, and rulers. Certainly much thought, planning, and organization went into the spread and maintenance of this culture.

Thus, several distinct modes of life, spurred by changes in climate and influenced by local inequalities of relief and resource, began to appear on the continent as people competed with each other for its advantages. In the forests of the north, on the high plains of the west, and the edges of the western mountains were hunting folk; in the arid south-west, seed-gatherers; in the Mexican plateau and on the Gulf coastal plain, agriculturists; and in the central interior lowlands, the Appalachian valleys, and Atlantic coast plain, planters and hunters combined—each making their own adaptation to relief, climate, vegetation, and wild life.

Culture Areas at the 'Discovery'

By the time Columbus discovered North America several well-defined cultures had emerged and had divided up the continent into fairly clearly distinguishable areas.[1] These cultures had grown up in the closest kind of relationship with the physical environment in certain *core* regions, and then had spread along distinct geographical *corridors*, to those bounds of dominance that marked their *climax*. Core, corridor, climax all had a geographical connotation. *The culture nurtured in a certain core region picked out those corridors that enabled it best to expand, and reached its climax in the wider spheres it was able to contest with other cultures.* In this development, human factors constantly entered into the picture: men might choose one region to develop in rather than another, equally good or possibly even better; two different modes of life, such as seed-gathering or corn-planting, might spring up in and divide the same environment; human vagaries might explain why one corridor of expansion was followed before or above another, as they certainly explained the extent to which the culture could reach out and master the whole of its environs, or even encroach on the environs of different cultures. Yet in all this the cultures were dependent on: (i) the attraction or challenge of places in which to develop; (ii) the limitations or opportunities of lines of contact; and (iii) the strengths and weaknesses of frontiers of conflict. 'Culture areas', places made distinctive by the response of people, thus grew up. Such areas were important in themselves, and important for the effect they had on white settlers. They left a heritage of Indian villages which have since become American cities, of Indian portages that have become American trade routes, of Indian gardens that have burgeoned to become the American corn, cotton, and tobacco belts —and thus helped to provide a framework for the present geography of the continent (Fig. 24).

[1] Kroeber, A. L., 'Cultural and Natural Areas of Native North America', U. of Cal. Pubns., *Amer. Archae. & Ethnog.*, Berkeley, 1939, **38**.

FIG. 24 Aboriginal Culture Areas—modified from Kroeber.

Region 1*a*. *Food Gatherers of the Pacific South-west*

Food; acorns, pine seeds, roots, berries; small game and reptiles; fish—particularly shell-fish.
Housing; brush structures, lean-to's, small frame huts.
Tools; sinew-backed bow; traps and snares; basketry. No pottery.
Clothing; scanty skin aprons, breech-clouts.
Art; designs worked into baskets and mats.

Region 1*b*. *Hunters and Food Gatherers of Western Plateaux*

Food; mountain deer, small game, fish, pine nuts, seeds, roots, berries.
Housing; pit dwellings (mainly in south); conical brush shelters, caves.
Tools; spears; fish-hooks, nets, weirs; snares, coiled basketry. No pottery.
Clothing; rabbit-skin robes.
Art; undeveloped.

Region 2. *Fishers and Hunters of the Arctic*

Food; arctic char and cod; seal, walrus, caribou; berries in summer.
Housing; snow houses in winter, skin tents in summer.
Tools; harpoons, bow, kayaks, dog sled, bone and sinew drill, stone kettles.
Clothing; skin parkas, trousers, and mukluks (boots).
Art; carved ivory animal-figurines.

Region 3. *Fishers and Hunters of the Pacific North-west*

Food; salmon and halibut (smoked); berries, forest deer.
Housing; large villages of plank houses with shingle-covered gabled roofs.
Tools; fish-hooks, nets and traps; bow; large dugout canoes; polished stone knives and adzes; war clubs; basketry—but no pottery.
Clothing; skin shirts and trousers, skin rain mantles, basketry hats; skin and wood-slat armour, wooden helmets.
Art; heraldic totem poles; stylized animal masks. Strong colouring.

Region 4. *Hunters of the Boreal Forest—the North-west*

Food; caribou and elk, hare; fresh-water fish; berries.
Housing; double lean-to's of brush, tipis, log cabins.
Tools; bow, spears, traps; fish-hooks and nets; bark canoes and bark vessels; snow shoes and toboggans. No pottery.
Clothing; hunting shirts and trousers, moccasins.
Art; quill decoration of hunting shirts.

Region 5. *Hunters of the Laurentian-Appalachian Woodlands*

Food; deer, fresh-water fish, water fowl; wild rice; (cultivated maize, squash and beans in south-east of region).
Housing; birch-bark tipis in north; bark longhouses over pole frames in south-east, in stockaded villages.
Tools; bow, spear, hook; bark canoes; snow shoes; war clubs; bark mats, basketry, skin bags, pottery vessels, wampum.
Clothing; skin shirts, leggings, skirt, moccasins.
Art; bead-work; human and animal masks.

Region 6. *Hunters of Prairie and Steppe—Interior Plains*

Food; buffalo, antelope, deer, rabbit, often in dried form—pemican; (maize in Missouri–Mississippi lowlands); fresh-water fish, water fowl.
Housing; skin tipis; villages of polygonal log houses roofed with sod.
Tools; travois-drawn by dog, later by horse; bow, lance, war club and shield, rawhide containers. No basketry, little or no pottery.
Clothing; skin shirt and trousers; ceremonial feathered head-dress.
Art; painting on rawhide boxes; quill and bead decoration of shirts.

Region 7. *Hunters and Farmers of the South-east Woodlands*

Food; deer, fish, turkeys, water fowl; maize, squash, beans, cane, melon, grapes, plums,
Housing; oblong or round plank houses, with thatched roofs, in palisaded villages. temples set on mounds.
Tools; cane knives and darts; blow-gun, bow, spear, fish-hooks, traps; digging sticks; dugout canoes; pottery vessels, basket ware.
Clothing; skin or woven bark clothes; shirts and leggings; dresses.
Art; decoration of clothing and houses.

Region 8. *Farmers and Hunters of the Arid South-west*

Food; maize, squash, beans; supplemented by small game, seeds, berries.
Housing; stone or ádobe 'pueblos', multi-storeyed community apartment houses, set in large villages. (Nomadic tribes, skin tipis, brush shelters.)
Tools; bow, throwing stick; hoes; basketry; weaving; decorative pottery; irrigation ditches.
Clothing; cloth shirts, trousers, breech-clouts, aprons; large decorated blankets; sandals.
Art; decorations on baskets and blankets; paintings on houses; sand paintings; silver work; turquoise jewelry.

Region 9. *Farmers and City-dwellers of the Mexican basin*

Food; maize, squash, beans, tomatoes, pumpkins, melons, peppers; cocoa; pulque (fermented cactus juice).
Housing; stone houses, one or two storeyed, built around inner courts, set in streets in cities; hospitals, schools, temples; playing-fields.
Tools; great variety of polished stone knives, axes, chisels, adzes, points, etc.; copper knives and vessels; pottery; basket ware; woven ware; bow, spear, club, shield; lever.
Clothing; finely woven cotton shirts, trousers, dresses, robes; feathered headgear; leather sandals; armour.
Art; ornate, stylized, geometric and animals motifs on religious temples and palaces; paintings on homes; decorated woven ware and pottery; fine metalwork in copper, silver and gold; fine jewelry.

Collector Communities

Desert Basin Indians. The 'worst' regions of the continent tended to be left to, or possibly were even sought out by, the most primitive peoples. These were the arid lands in the hot, closed-in basins between the Rockies and the Coast range in the American south-west. Here lowly tribes could find protection, since few other tribes wanted to live in such difficult terrain. High mountains, the deepest of gorges, low depressions cut off from rain-bearing winds, scorching summers, thin woods of stunted oak or pine, and bleak stretches of cactus-covered waste made up their home. They had few animals to hunt. Rabbits were the chief game and were caught by snares. But for the most part the people lived by collecting acorns from the oaks, seeds from the pine cones, and other types of seeds. The acorns were husked, freed from poisonous juices, pounded into flour, and made into bread. They formed the chief food. Relish was added by edible roots, fungi, and wild herbs. Sunflower seeds were popular. Some of the tribes, like the Paiute,[1] artificially flooded the gravelly fans spreading out on the edge of the desert from snow-fed gullies. Brushwood dams deflected the water into long, shallow ditches. The water then spread through wild grasses and made them spring up more quickly and densely. When the grass seeds were gathered, the dams were destroyed, and the streams allowed to flow back into their natural channels (Fig. 25).

At this point, when the benefits of even a primitive form of irrigation were evident, some of the tribes might have progressed to become seed-planters, and so to live a settled, sedentary existence, where they could have made considerable progress. However, most never met the challenge of their environment, but continued to suffer its limitations, and hardly bettered their lot in the thousands of years from Pinto times to the 'Discovery'. For them, life remained very simple. They wore few clothes, and these were of the simplest kind: an apron of milk-weed fibre for women, a breech clout of skin for the men. They never learned to spin yarn or weave cloth, although

[1] Steward, J. H., 'Ethnography of the Owens Valley Paiute', U. of Cal. Pubns. in *Amer. Archae. & Ethnog.*, Berkeley, 1933, **33**, no. 3.

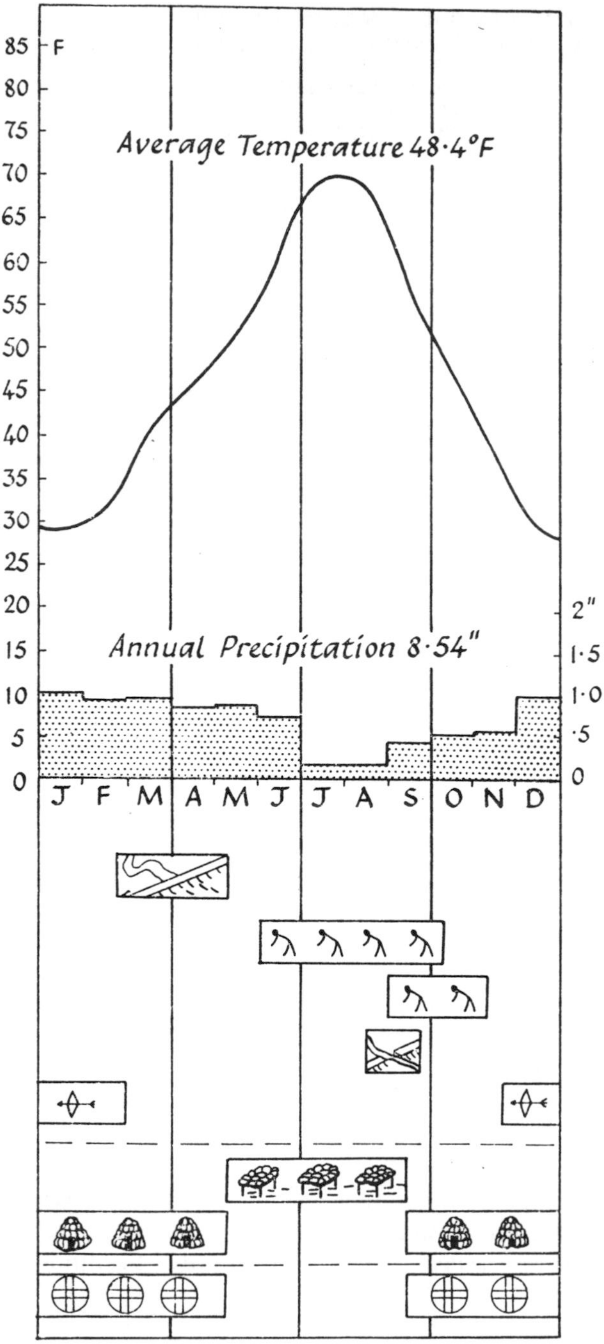

FIG. 25 Ergograph of the Paiute.

THE YEAR'S ROUND OF WORK

Damming mountain streams for primitive irrigation

Collecting and storing berries

Collecting and storing pine nuts

Pulling down dams, harvesting irrigated wild grains

Snaring rabbits

Building summer lean-to's

Building winter huts

Religious ceremonies

they did work rabbit skins into blankets and cloaks. Their homes were rudimentary, consisting of a shelter of matted reeds, or a lean-to of poles in the form of a conical tent. They never stayed long enough at one place to make permanent homes or to develop a home-loving tradition. They had to wander about from winter to summer gathering grounds, from plain to hill and back again, in search of food. They could not carry many household goods. They had no furniture, no pots or pans, and few bags or mats. Their chief equipment consisted of baskets of natural twine or of coiled wands, in which they collected their wild seeds, roots and grubs, and kept their flour. Their tools were few—pounders, scrapers, points, and chisels, with which they pounded the corn flour, scraped and cut out skins, and chiselled their digging sticks. They were very conservative and kept to their old ways for thousands of years, without change. For example, they continued to use rough, chipped stone tools, when other Indians had progressed to finely polished, sharp-pointed tools, or had begun to experiment with metal.

Their wandering habit of life, the difficulties of existence, and their limited geographical resources militated against populous settlements. Population remained low and this in turn kept down their social development. There were not enough people to support a wide division of labour, to stimulate competition, to encourage specialization, or to promote social differentiation. The people moved about in small groups. They did not feel the need for elaborate rules of political organization. Their religion was a simple form of animism and was without temple or priest. Their impact on the environment was negligible; on the contrary, they felt the full force of the environment and adapted themselves to it.

Fishing Communities

Arctic Coast Eskimo. An equally hard life, and primitive culture, characterized the Eskimoes in the cold desert of the north. At the time of the 'Discovery' these were one of two great fishing communities of the continent —the other being the dwellers of the north Pacific coast. A great difference existed between the two; the Eskimo remained poor and backward, the Pacific coast Indians had grown rich and populous. The difference may in part have been cultural; the Eskimo stemmed from Palae-Arctic people long accustomed to a primitive and arduous existence in the tundras of the north Siberian shore, whereas the west coast Indians derived from Neo-Amerind stock, used to a life in the forests beside the salmon runs of eastern Siberia. The main difference between the two fishing communities, however, lay in their physical environments: in the difference between the northern shore of the continent, gripped in ice for most of the year, barren, and inhospitable, and the western shore, swept by balmy winds, mild, moist, and densely forested. The north offered too severe a challenge. It is doubtful whether a people even with a higher culture could have made more of the snow barrens and shore ice of the Canadian Arctic coast than the Eskimoes. The probability is that, with a higher culture, they would have striven to leave the area and competed for a better one.

The Eskimo early moved across the northern shore from Siberia to Alaska and thence migrated to the Hudson Bay, Labrador, Baffin Island, and Greenland. In this long migration several cultures were evolved, as Collins has indicated.[1] These have been divided into a western group, and an eastern group, culminating in the Thule culture. This ruled the north until the recent westernization of the Eskimo peoples. Thule men were coast dwellers, who lived in semi-permanent semi-subterranean houses with whale-bone walls, and sod roofs. They hunted seals and whale, but also moved inland, in season, to catch caribou.

Although the prolonged cold, the long winter night, the lack of vegetation, and the monotony of the scene were grave disabilities, there was a wealth of fish, sea-mammals, bear, and fox at the edge of the ice that attracted (and still keeps) the Eskimo to the coast. The seal were particularly plentiful and the Eskimo soon became very dependent on the animal, following it with the onset of winter out to the edge of the ice-shelf, and returning with it, during the early summer break-up, to the skerries and rocky headlands of the shore. They fed on its flesh, made clothes and tents from its skins, used its fat and oil for their lamps and stoves, and whittled their tools from its bones. This dependence was at once the success and the failure of the Eskimo, it enabled them to survive in one of the bleakest environments in North America, but it kept them from trying out other environments, stocked with other game.

Since the seal, like other animals, was sensitive to the seasons of the Arctic, it made the life of the Eskimo highly seasonal. This was well expressed in the Eskimo calendar,[2] which began, in Ungava–Labrador, with the formation of the winter ice, when the migration from the coast to the shelf-ice started.

Sikualut, the month of the formation of young shore-ice	October
Nunalialut, the inland month (going inland for the deer)	November
Sikalut, the month of the growth of ice	December
Nelakaituk, the coldest month for frost	January
Koblut, the month when ground is cracked by frost	February
Netkalut, the month of the jar seal	March
Teyelulut, the month of the bearded seal	April

[1] Collins, H. B., 'Eskimo Archaeology and its Bearing on the Problem of Man's Antiquity in America', *Proc. Amer. Phil. Soc.*, Philadelphia, 1943, **86**, no. 2.

[2] Hawkes, E. W., 'The Labrador Eskimo', *Can. Geol. Surv.*, Mem. 91, Ottawa, 1916. The Labrador calendar, which ran from January to June, is here combined with the Ungava one, running from October.

Noyalut, the month of the fawning of seal	May
Kiniyialut, the month of the young ranger seal	June }
Munilut, the egg month	June }
Kituyialut, the mosquito month	July
Punalut, the berry month	August
Quonolilut, the month of the fading of the leaves	September

In winter, cold Arctic airs swept over the northern shores, snows descended, lakes froze over, and ice formed out to sea. Most land animals moved inland to seek refuge in the forest. The Eskimo, by contrast, left the land to venture out on the ice then forming a shelf across the bays in the shelter of the headlands. Packing their belongings on dog sleds they launched out on to the shelf-ice to make their winter homes. These were low, round snow houses, able to withstand the sweeping winds from without, and warm, although crowded, within. Sealing was carried on by making air-holes in the ice and standing over them until the seals came up to breathe. Then the seals were harpooned and drawn on to the ice. This was known as *maupok* hunting. Baited lines were also dropped down for fish (Fig. 26).

In the spring, when the ice began to break up, and 'leads' of open water developed between the floes, the Eskimo had to retreat back to the bayheads. There they built new temporary homes of snow and ice. From these they set out each day to stalk the seal, in what they called *utoq* hunting, taking advantage of the numerous ridges into which the broken ice was piled by wind and ice. The seal swam in the open leads or came up on to the ice-floes to bask. They could be speared by a successful throw of a light harpoon. This had a long leather thong attached to it, by which the Eskimo could play the seal and draw it in.

In the summer, when the shelf-ice had broken up, the Eskimo packed their goods on their backs, tied pack-sacks over their dogs, and trekked inland to a good fishing site on a river estuary. They then divided their time between sealing and whaling on the near-by sea, fishing in the river, and collecting berries and edible fungi and roots. Seals were caught by *kayak* hunting, in which individual hunters went out to the open sea, off skerries and headlands, and chased and harpooned the seal. Groups of hunters also harpooned the small Arctic white whale which, when caught, gave ample food. The heavy whale bones could be made into sledge runners or house beams. Meantime, fishing was carried on, mainly by traps at roughly made weirs in the rivers, and the fish cleaned and dried and kept for feeding the dogs in winter. It is said that an Eskimo who started the winter with less than 8,000 to 10,000 fish could look forward to lean days ahead.[1]

[1] Urquhart, J. A., 'Eskimos of the Canadian Western Arctic', in *The New North-West,* ed. Dawson, Toronto, 1947, p. 276.

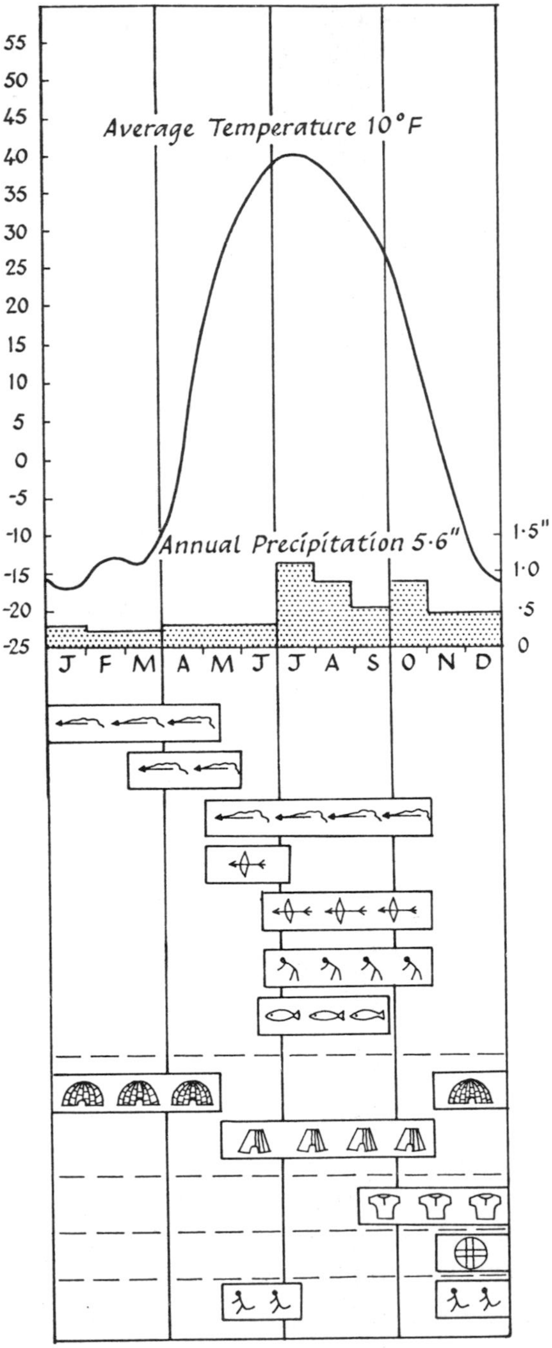

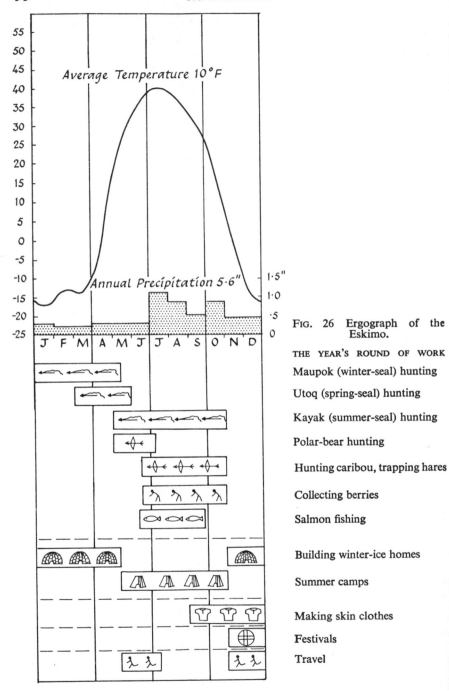

FIG. 26 Ergograph of the Eskimo.

THE YEAR'S ROUND OF WORK

Maupok (winter-seal) hunting

Utoq (spring-seal) hunting

Kayak (summer-seal) hunting

Polar-bear hunting

Hunting caribou, trapping hares

Collecting berries

Salmon fishing

Building winter-ice homes

Summer camps

Making skin clothes

Festivals

Travel

14. Totem poles at Kispiox Indian Village, near Hazelton, B.C. This village, which has church, school and shops, is a centre for interior plateau Indians, who are mainly fishermen, but also work in lumber camps in the vicinity. They have not taken to the pioneer farming which has spread to the edge of their reserve.

15. A reconstruction of a village of Huron Indians, near Midland, Ont. An Iroquois-type long house, inside a log palisade, is shown, with a common fireplace and also a fur-stretching and drying frame in front.

16. An Iroquois Indian.

17. Cliff dwelling, Mesa-Verda National Park, Col.

18. Navajo woman weaving traditional rug.

19. Homes of Zuni pueblo Indians, showing how roof-tops of the lower levels were used as dooryards for the higher storeys. Many of the household tasks such as drying corn and vegetables and cooking in outside bee-hive ovens are performed in these yards.

The Arctic came alive in the short, bright summer. It was then green with grass, lichens and mosses, and beautiful with flowers, affording excellent summer pasture for deer and caribou. Its marshes and lakes were alive with wild fowl. The rivers swarmed with fish and with muskrat. In sheltered places were masses of berries. The Eskimo made use of these many resources to vary their diet and way of life. They lived on fowl, fish, caribou flesh, berries, and edible roots. Winter equipment and sleds were safely stored away, and they took to their summer tents. Life was more comfortable. Families came together, and unions between them were often made. But soon the 'fading' month came round, the families gathered up their gear, and went out in small, isolated groups back to their icy world.

Again, as with the desert dwellers of the south-west, the people of the northern barrens experienced such difficulties, and lived under such constant strain and stress, that they never developed a large population. Their nomadic ways and sparse numbers moulded their social life. They had only the simplest division of labour, between men and women, and young and old. There were no craftsmen or merchants. Fishermen had to make their own harpoons, hooks, lines and nets, their own kayaks, and so forth. There were no specialized callings such as teachers, priests, warriors, or rulers. The Eskimo did not form themselves into tribes. Groups of related families fishing and hunting in the same district would call themselves the people of that district. But they had no officers. The enlarged family, consisting of the patriarch, his grown and married sons and their children, formed the main social and economic unit, and was governed by 'the head of the house'. The chief functions drawing people together were the family functions associated with birth, marriage, and death. Religion was very simple, consisting of a respect for the spirits of the dead, of animals, or of objects in their environment. It gave rise to no priests, buildings, or rites, though it was mediated in part by the *angekok* or medicine man. Straitened circumstances meant a straitened social and cultural life.

Pacific Coast Indians. This was not the case with North America's other great fishing community; the Pacific coast dweller. Here conditions were much more favourable. A deeply indented fjord coast gave very good harbourage and easy access at once to sea and land. The climate was much milder, with a very long growing season sponsoring a dense forest. A wealth of wood behind these settlers was matched by a wealth of fish in front of them. Salmon ran up their rivers in vast quantities, while herring and haddock were found, also in great numbers, off the neighbouring islands. Dried fish and clams early became the staple food of the Coast Indians, along with berries which they gathered in the forest.

With plenty of wood at hand, these Indians soon became skilled in making wooden structures and equipment. The houses were large, made of cedar logs, with steep roofs and wide overhanging gables. They were ornamented with fine wood-carving, and often had a splendidly carved totem pole outside. The totems symbolized the spirits which they revered, feared, or worshipped. More or less permanent villages grew up along a straight street. The Indians dug out big canoes from the thicker timbers of the coast. Sails were used to take them out quickly to the rich fisheries of the outer isles.

The bones of fish and animals were also used for making tools. A fine array of spears, harpoons, nets, and fish traps was created, along with awls and needles, for the making of clothes, and other home equipment.

The richer geographical resources of the north-west coast enabled the Indians to find a safer, more stable and richer life than the primitive fishers of the north or gatherers of the south-west.[1] Population grew. Their villages were sometimes two thousand strong. They had the wealth and the people to sponsor a reasonably wide division of labour. Different classes began to emerge. There were craftsmen, merchants, priests, and leaders, as well as fishermen and hunters. Their different tasks had to fit in with each other, and so a fairly well-knit political system grew up, with chiefs and nobles to rule the tribes. A great display of wealth was made. Slaves were generally used to serve the nobles, and costly feasts were observed. Music was fostered and art encouraged. Indeed, but for the massive ranges that shut them out from the rest of the continent, these Indians would have had much more influence than they had. However, the Cordilleras proved too great a barrier to contact between coast and interior, and east of the mountains lived somewhat less successful communities, the hunters of the boreal forests and of the high prairies.

Hunting Communities

These were settlers who occupied the boreal forest just south of the barrens and the high prairies east of the desert basins, but who had failed to colonize, or were pushed back from, the richer environments of the deciduous forests and humid prairies of the central and south-eastern parts of the continent. They certainly fared better than the Eskimo or the Paiute and made more progress; they were not content merely with trapping or harpooning individual animals or collecting wild seeds and nuts. They went after the caribou, elk, moose, and deer of the forest or the big herds of buffalo that roamed the grasslands. Naturally, this required a better system of tribal organization. They sometimes co-operated with each other in powerful groups. As a result they got more food and got it with less strain. They could support a moderate population.

Northern Forest Indians. The hunters of the northern forests were the

[1] Boas, F., 'Ethnology of the Kwakiutl', *Bul. Amer. Ethnol.*, 35th Ann. Rept Washington, 1921.

older group. Chiefly Algonquins, they were tall, long headed, and dark skinned—members of the Paleo-Amerind migration. Amongst the oldest of immigrants,[1] they came to North America before the last regressions of the ice, and spread far and wide over the Canadian Shield and the Interior Lowlands. They were later pushed to the east and north by Neo-Amerinds pouring across the Mackenzie plains and the prairies. Consequently they made their home in the boreal forests of the Laurentian upland. Here they found a rocky plateau, pock-marked with innumerable marshy depressions, with thin, leached, grey soils, bearing little but tamarack, spruce and pine, poplar, alder, and birch. Winters were long and snowy. Summers, by contrast, were short and warm. This climate of continental extremes compelled the game to migrate south in the winter and north in the summer. The Indians were forced to follow, and adopted a nomadic life.

Caribou or deer were their chief prey, which ranged the northern forests in great numbers. It was easiest to kill them in winter, when they were driven on to frozen rivers or lakes, or in the spring, when they became bogged down by sudden thaws. Thus even when the weather was severe, food was relatively plentiful. In the summer, salmon and eels were speared, seals harpooned off the coasts, or small game like hares and porcupines were hunted. Wild berries and fruits were also gathered. Where wild rice occurred it was collected in great quantities and stored away.

These northern hunters were very dependent on birch trees. They used birch bark for their canoes, for bark-covered wigwams, and for bark containers. They travelled light, abandoning one set of houses and putting up another as circumstances demanded. Utensils were kept to a minimum and were of bark or wood. Little pottery was made, except among the southern Ojibway; even there it did not supersede birch-bark containers. Clothes were of skins, and consisted of a robe, breech-cloth, leggings, and moccasins, with porcupine quills worked into them for decoration.

Spears, clubs, and bows and arrows were the chief weapons. The spears were tipped with large, heavy polished stones. Here and there tribes used copper for hooks and knives, though metalwork did not thrive because of the wandering life of the people. They were rarely able to support a class of craftsmen. Other classes, too, were poorly developed. However, their drives after game did bring people together, and clan organization was quite well represented. Tribal discipline increased latterly with wars against the Iroquois and other southern nations.

Prairie Indians. The hunters of the western prairies belonged mainly to the Neo-Amerind race and came into the continent later. Indeed the

---

[1] Spaulding, A. C., 'Northeastern Archaeology and General Trends in the Northern Forest Zone', in *Man in Northeastern North America*, ed. Johnson, Papers Peabody Foundn. of Archae., Andover, 1946, 3.

Athapascans of the wood buffalo plains in Canada were among the last migrants to North America. Avoiding the barren lands and the intermontane basins they strove with the Algonquins for the northern forests and then broke through into the prairies. Today these plains are part of the great Canadian and American wheat belt. But, though the Indians were in touch with corn-planting contemporaries from the south, they did not turn to agriculture. The great ease of hunting, and the wealth of game, kept them hunters.

It was, of course, the buffalo that attracted and held them. Buffalo ranged the open woodlands and the prairies of the western plains in vast numbers. They could be taken in vast numbers, too. The favourite way of hunting was to drive the beasts into pounds. A funnel-like structure was built of brushwood, which led to the steep edge of one of the many prairie scarps or to an entrenched river. Terror was struck into the herd by the howling of the Indians behind the brush stockade, and the animals plunged madly to their doom. Those not killed by the fall over the cliff were shot down while running in panic-stricken circles. The tribe then feasted. What flesh was not eaten right away was cut into small pieces and dried. The back-fat of the buffalo was then melted, poured on the dried meat, to make 'pemmican'—a standby when people had to travel or go to war.

Morton mentions that

> the prairies were also frequented by large herds of red deer. Moreover, in summer moose were driven by the mosquitoes out of the woods and could be caught in the park grasslands on the edge of the woods. Their hides made excellent garments.
>
> The abundance of food upon the plains made the life of their peoples a picturesque contrast to that of the timber region (to the north). Great camps were formed, in which the happy people feasted, and drummed, and danced, over a considerable portion of the year. Whole bands, under chiefs, lived in temporary villages.[1]

Since they had to follow the migrations of the buffalo, they travelled light.[2] Their dwellings were the easily movable *tipi*. The tall rods which held up the *tipi* at night were made into a *travois* by day, and served to carry the family belongings in a single large pack. The *travois* was harnessed to a dog that did the heavy work until the horse was introduced by the Europeans. There were few utensils. Little pottery was made. Containers were of buffalo skin. There was hardly anything that the buffalo did not provide. It gave them meat to live on, skin for their tents, clothes, bags, mats, and thongs for ropes

[1] Morton, A. S., *A History of the Canadian West*, pp. 14–15.

[2] Wissler, C., 'Material Culture of the Blackfoot Indians', *Anthrop. Papers, Amer. Mus Nat. Hist.*, New York, 1910, 5.

and belts. Tools were made from the bone. Indeed as Henry, the early explorer of the prairies, remarked, the buffaloes supplied them with everything they were accustomed to. The amazing numbers of the animals prevented all fear of want.

Hunting-and-Farming Communities

In the great central plains of the Mississippi–Ohio, and along the Gulf and southern Atlantic coastal plains lived Indians who developed a dual system, marrying the advantages of the hunters to the north and the agriculturists to the south. On the central and southern lowlands they had ample space, with few obstructions save for the Ozarks and southern Appalachians. Great rivers formed natural routeways. One of the 'kindest' climates in North America prevailed, with warm summers and mild winters, ample rainfall, a long growing season, deep soil, and deciduous forests having a great variety of nut- and fruit-bearing trees. Red deer were plentiful, wild turkey, duck and geese abundant, and fish ubiquitous.

Indians of the central-southern plains. Originally hunters and fishers, the Indians from the Lower Great Lakes to the Gulf of Mexico came in late altithermal times to learn the arts of planting corn and squash, beans, and tobacco. Gradually they gave up their basic dependence on hunting. This was a major step foward. It meant that their diet was richer and their food supply more secure. They did not have to wander as much in search of game. This gave them a chance to settle down. In addition to hunting-camps, they had semi-permanent villages, where they lived most of the year. There was the opportunity for arts and crafts to develop and for more advanced types of government.

These Indians usually chose a defensible site by a river or lake for their little 'town', or headquarters. They fenced it off with a protective stockade. Beyond, were the clearings where seeds were planted. There was no ploughing.

> In the Spring [Kidd writes] the women went to the clearing and heaped up the soil into little hills. Into each hill they dropped a few seeds of corn, beans, and squash. They called these plants 'The Three Sisters', because they got on very well together, as sisters should. The corn grew up tall, the beans twined round the corn stalks, and the squash vines spread out over the ground.[1]

Wild rice was gathered by the river, and maple sugar was made from the maple groves in the forest.

Their homes were quite substantial, being oblong or rounded structures covered by bark or matting and housing several families. They were quite

[1] Kidd, *Canadians of Long Ago*, p. 128.

warm in winter. There was a real home tradition. The women had many utensils, including wooden boxes and bowls, finely polished stone knives and scrapers, bone needles, awls, and combs, some copper ware, and clay pots and containers. Their pottery was often finely decorated, with geometric designs. The people had an obvious feeling for beauty. They made clothes of beautifully worked skins. The men had moccasins, leggings, a breech-cloth, and leather jerkins with long sleeves. The women wore a skirt and jacket, or sometimes a leather dress with coloured markings and a graceful fringe.

The men hunted with a variety of spears, bows, blow-guns, hooks, and nets, which were usually tipped with delicately worked flint or copper. They also had many weapons with which to wage war, especially clubs, tomahawks, spears and shields, and they developed a real military discipline. In doing so they also evolved a more advanced system of government, and the Iroquois, especially, were famous for their complex kinship relations and the federation of their nations in a League.

Farther south, where the climate was hotter and wetter, the Indians were principally planters. When De Soto[1] came upon them, in Alabama, he describes them as being thickly settled in many large towns, between which extended field upon field. The land was pleasant, and had a fertile soil with fair river margins. The woods were rich with fruit, especially plums and grapes. The Indians made use of this natural fertility. In addition to maize, squash, and tobacco, they raised millet-cane, pumpkins and melons, and gathered wild fruits, nuts, and vegetables. Their houses were quite large and consisted of rectangular rows of posts, with wickerwork walls covered with plaster. Their craftsmen manufactured good pottery, basketware, and fabrics of woven bark or hair. Their stone tools were beautifully finished. Their priests kept fires burning before their gods. The chiefs had great power and ruled strong confederations of tribes. Their social life was comparatively full, reflecting the relative success which they had made out of a comfortable and productive environment.

Agricultural Communities

Between the warm, humid south-east and the mild, well-watered valley of Mexico lies a semi-arid zone, which affords, and has afforded, rather a poor environment. Most of the tribes who dwelt there were gripped by its limitations, lived in poverty, and remained primitive. Yet this semi-arid zone did have its advantages. It was warm and had a long growing season. With water it could be fruitful. During pluvial times it must have been quite attractive. Pluvial times in Mexico led to seed planting—they may have done so in New Mexico as well. But even in dry times there were spring-fed or snow-fed streams on the edge of the steppe which, as in the intermontane

[1] Quoted in *Handbook of American Indians North of Mexico*, ed. Hodge, F. W., 2, p. 791.

basins of the south-west, drew seed-gatherers to them to collect the wild seeds that flourished in such abundance there. The larger rivers supported sufficient game for hunters. These assets must have challenged men to turn from gathering seeds to planting them and to leave a nomadic life for a settled one. This challenge was at length responded to, some of the Indians took up gardening, gave up their wandering habits, and turned sedentary. Civilized life in America began (Fig. 27).

This shift was well seen in, amongst other things, the rise of the Pueblan culture which so impressed the early Spanish explorers. Cabeza de Vaca reported in 1536 the existence of cities north of Mexico 'with houses four or five storeys high'. The thought that such a civilization might have gold led to Estevanico's and Coronado's expeditions. The narratives of the Coronado expedition describe the Pueblan Indians as an 'attractive people' whose land was 'like a garden'. They wore 'turquoise necklaces, some with five or six loops'. They made gold into 'vessels and jewels for their ears, and into little blades with which they wiped away their sweat'.[1]

Thus, although the area was arid, it could be made productive by irrigation. Seed-planting became so important that *men* did the work! This was unusual, since in most Indian tribes men went hunting and left the work to the women. Their crops were chiefly maize, beans, and cotton. These were grown in small gardens by springs or in irrigated patches at the mouths of little canyons. Great care was taken with the hoeing, planting and cultivating, and with conserving moisture in the soil. Consequently, their food was quite varied and in good supply.

The people lived in cliff dwellings, building homes several storeys in height. The families clung close together in villages or *pueblos*. Each day the men would climb down the canyon walls to their gardens, and the women and children would go to the piñon woods to collect seeds. There was enough time left over, after these duties, for making pottery and weaving cotton clothes.

In their humble way, they did develop a civilized life. This was seen in their art, their religion, and their government. Their art had rhythm and colour. Their religion was centred in efforts at rain-making, or at pleasing the spirits of summer and winter. Corn cobs or kernels played a striking part in many of their ceremonies. Government was mainly on a village basis. Each village elected its own governor and had its war chief. These governors and chiefs ruled the tribe, along with the priests. Obviously, much progress had been made.

However, the Indians who made the most progress in North America before the 'Discovery' were those who lived on the Mexican and Guatemalan plateaux. Various things conspired to stimulate and develop their talents.

---

[1] Quoted in Hammond, G. P., and Rey, A., *Narratives of the Coronado Expedition.*

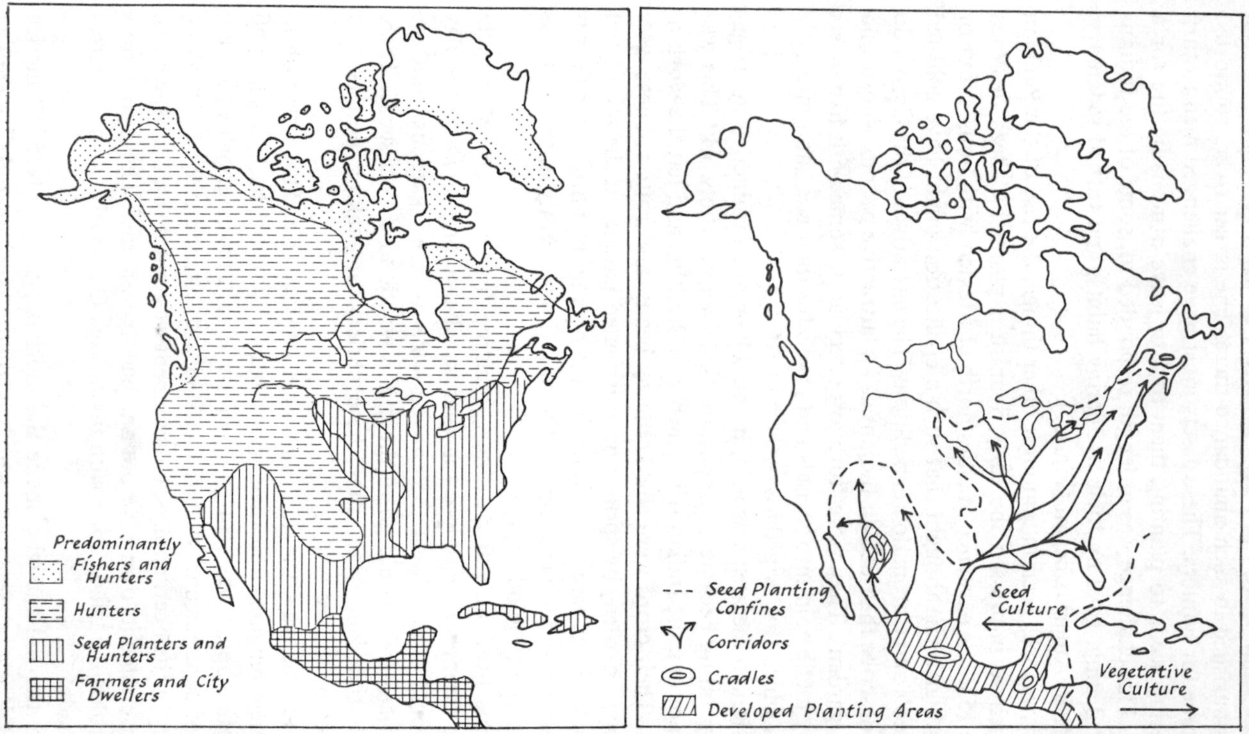

FIG. 27 Main Aboriginal Economies, and the spread of Agriculture. The cultivation of Maize is thought to have begun in Guatemala and the Mexican basin and thence to have spread north to the Colorado and Rio Grande regions, by way of the Mexican plateau, and to the Mississippi-Ohio and the Atlantic Coast plain by way of the Gulf coast of Mexico. Bean culture may have developed separately among the pueblos of north-west Mexico, and then spread north and south. Once associated with maize culture, it spread rapidly to the Mississippi and Atlantic plains. (Scale, 1:90 m.)

The continent narrowed down here, preventing that wide wandering that kept so many others in other parts from a settled existence. This narrowing down was most important as it increased contacts, called forth competition, and fostered co-operation. The area was far enough south to prevent hardship even in cool times, yet high enough to avoid discomfort even in hot periods of climatic change. It must have been one of the most pleasant regions in the continent during late glacial and early post-glacial times, wetter then than now, but still warm. A wide variety of plants occurred with the swift range of relief from coast over sierra to plateau. It was from these plants that, during an early pluvial period, corn was first planted.[1] Maize, beans, and squash soon became the basis of Mexican agriculture. As Sauer[2] points out, they formed a symbiotic complex without an equal elsewhere. The Mexican–Central American border became the hearthland of that seed-planting mode of life which changed the Americas and raised a civilization comparable in many respects to that in the Ancient World.

Indian culture reached its peak in the empires of the Mayas, Toltecs, and Aztecs. Their achievements, it is true, could not save them from the Spaniards who overthrew them. But this may have been because they devoted their arts to pomp and ceremony, rather than to adventure and trade. In any event, they progressed far beyond their contemporaries. And they did so because they saw and seized upon the opportunities in their environment. They were not content to remain seed-gatherers, fishers, or hunters, merely preying upon their environment, but stepped forward by becoming farmers, and came gradually to tame the environment. They were indeed the only Indians who gained appreciable control of climate, vegetation and soil, and made a distinct and lasting imprint on the land. Not content to use rivers and portages, they made paths; or to live in caves or camps, they built cities. They created a landscape of their own in which the works of man cut into or towered above the forest and vied with hill and stream. Their ideas spread far and wide and influenced cultures well beyond their borders.

After a long time of planting seeds, establishing villages, exploiting resources, and developing their population, the Indians of the Yucatan prepared the way for the rise of the Mayas. This first of empires emerged on the low plateau of the peninsula, between 600 and 400 B.C. Griffith Taylor claims there was a dry spell at that time which made the tropical forest less dense and difficult than it had been. The Mayans cleared much of it away and began to cultivate the soil. Gradually they obtained enough wealth to build cities, centred in wonderful pyramid-like temples. Their success led them to expand their influence over Honduras, Guatemala, and southern

[1] Sears, P. B., 'Climate and Civilization', in Shapley, *Climatic Change*, pp. 46–48.
[2] Sauer, *Agricultural Origins and Dispersals*, pp. 64, 72.

Mexico. They evolved a society of citizen-farmers, centred in separate cities with farming areas around them. Each city worked its immediate basin or valley outward to about eighteen miles, farmers going out from and returning to the nearer fields every day. Farther fields were worked from a ring of satellite villages. Maize, squash, yams, beans, peppers, tomatoes, and cacao were all cultivated, in addition to cotton.

However, the empire grew top-heavy, with too many city consumers and not enough farmers; too many priests and rulers and not enough workers. Some of the cities reached populations calculated at between 30,000 and 40,000, and required a lot of food to keep them going. Very little of this could be brought from other areas. The roads were short, linking up neighbouring cities, or joining outer villages to the inner market. Besides, there were no beasts of burden. Trade was not extensive; such of it as was carried on was in luxury goods. Cities had to rely on their immediate locality. Consequently, the soil became exhausted. The people lived on a starvation diet. They were riddled with yellow fever. Eventually conditions became critical. Cities started fighting with each other. Fierce internecine wars broke out. The Maya empire fell to pieces.

About a thousand years later a new culture rose, that of the Toltecs on the Mexican plateau. It too was based on agriculture and large villages and towns. The Toltecs were a rugged, aggressive people and, about A.D. 600, swept down on the land of the Mayas under their great leader, Quetzelcoatl. They revived the cities of the lower plateaux and brought back peace and prosperity. However, they soon faced the same problem as the Mayas. Although the wet tropical lands were very fruitful and enabled the renewed city settlements to flourish, yet the soil again became exhausted and the population subject to fever.

In A.D. 1300 when the Toltecs were very weak the Aztecs poured down from the arid north and overran southern Mexico and Central America. They were rather more successful than their predecessors. They did not make the mistake of centring their life in the humid lowlands. They built their capital, Tenochtitlán, on the site of what is today Mexico City, high up on the Mexican plateau, in a healthier and more temperate climate. The cities on the upper level were connected with those on the lower plateaux and tropical plains by trails, and all were organized in a strong empire under the great king, Montezuma.

The upper lands were rich with volcanic soils and watered by mountain-fed streams. They were well suited to maize, beans, and cotton. At the same time they were close to extensive supplies of copper, silver, gold, and turquoise in the surrounding Sierras. Geography thus conspired to provide an ideal cradle in which civilization could develop. A wider range of products occurred in the Aztec than in the Mayan empire. Indeed, the emperor's treasury overflowed with the most exotic tributes: pottery and jewels from Cholula, gold and feather robes from Azcapotzalco, fish and fruits from the Totonacs, carved stone and jade sent by the Olmecs, and baskets of flowers from Xochimilco, which were delivered daily to embellish the royal palace and temples.

When the state had requisitioned its share of these colonial tributes, the remainder went to Tenochtitlán's huge public market place to be sold along with local products. Here, in dozens of flower-arrayed booths and porticoes, one could buy or trade everything from slaves to perfumes. To market came varieties of meats, beans, squash, tomatoes, melons, avocados, pineapples, and maize. One could purchase drugs made from roots and herbs along with chocolate, cotton cloth, leather goods, mirrors, wood carvings, clay and stone sculpture and jewelry.[1]

The Aztecs became particularly proficient in manufacturing fine cloth. The Spaniards were amazed at their skill, and mistook their cotton cloth for garments of silk.

Nevertheless, it should be remembered that these fine goods were only for the rich. The Aztecs were unable to escape from the ancient Mayan tradition of building up a wealthy class at the expense of the poor. They did not try to better conditions in general. They lavished their resources on priests and nobles, temple and palace. They did not make inventions that were useful for the common people, such as would have improved agriculture, extended trade, called forth a variety of crafts and professions, raised standards and bettered health. Their working of metal, clever as it was, did not lift the people into a new age. Their culture was still an essentially Stone Age one, in which they used copper, silver, and gold for embellishment. They never equalled the scientific discoveries of the Europeans, and thus proved an easy prey to the masterful Spanish intruders.

Conclusion—the Indian Heritage

Although most of the Indians were primitive compared with their European conquerors—Cartier said of the Gaspesian folk, 'there are no people poorer than these in the world'—they nevertheless did a lot for the geography of the continent. They discovered, made use of, and gave character to the main natural regions or habitats of North America such as the desert basins of the south-west, the barren lands of the Arctic slope, the boreal forest, the open prairies, the forests of the central lowlands and south-eastern coasts, and the Mexican steppe. They tested each one of these regions, and adapted themselves and their way of life to them. They found what game

---

[1] Gallenkamp, C., 'The Cities of Ancient Mexico', *Can. Geog. Jour.*. October 1959. lix, no. 4, pp. 130–1.

was good to hunt and what plants were good to collect or to cultivate. Modern agriculture has taken up the turkey and made it the festival bird at the American Thanksgiving; far more than that, agriculture has used Indian

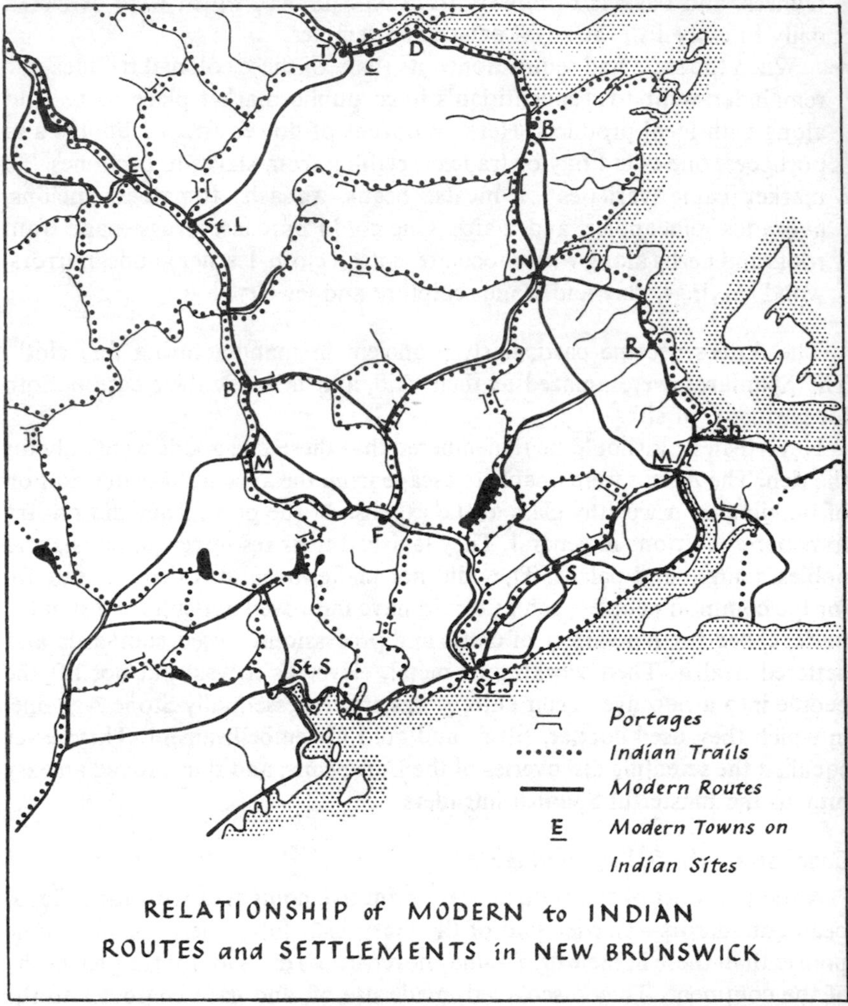

FIG. 28 Indian and Contemporary Routeways. The white men followed Indian trails wherever feasible, and even today a remarkable number of highways run along old Indian routes.

crops like maize, beans, squash, tomato, tobacco, cotton and cacao, and made them famous in the commerce of the entire world.

Indian habits, equipment, routes, and sites were particularly helpful to the early explorers and settlers. As Kidd remarks:

We should not forget that . . . the Indians helped the explorers to learn to know Canada (and the rest of North America). Some of the Indian equipment—canoes and snowshoes—proved very useful to trappers and settlers. Canoes, snowshoes, pemmican, maple syrup, tobacco and corn . . . have now become so much a part of our lives that many of us do not know where they came from. But they are truly Indian.[1]

Of great significance were the migration and trade routes that the Indians had developed, particularly the portages that linked the great river systems together. Many present-day roads and railways follow the trails that the Indians blazed. Beside these trails they built their towns or pitched their camps, and again many of the great cities of North America today are built on such sites (Fig. 28).

The Indian heritage, then, has come to its fruition in the hands of the Europeans. It helped the Europeans strike their roots firm and fast into American soil, with the result that they were able, in their turn, to introduce new crops, new uses of land, and a new geography to the continent.

---

[1] Kidd, op. cit., pp. 172–4.

CHAPTER FIVE

European Colonization and Spheres of Influence

I. SPANISH: II. FRENCH

AMERICA AND EUROPE

In spite of its long history of Indian settlement, North America remained relatively isolated from the world until 1492, when Columbus brought it into touch with Europe. Those parts which the Indians had civilized to a certain extent, in Mexico and Central America, were even more remote from the Old World than the rest of the Americas. Whatever their achievements the Indians were scarcely interested in exploration, navigation or trade, and consequently allowed the Atlantic and Pacific oceans to separate them from their more advanced contemporaries in Asia and Europe (Fig. 29).

It must be remembered that the shortest connexions between the New World and the Old, by way of the North Atlantic 'island arc', or by the Bering Straits, were also the stormiest crossings; they did not invite contacts. Moreover, Asiatic immigrants had generally been backward; they were people who had already turned their backs on progress. Ice, snow, and storm in the Bering region made the chances of their continued contact with Asia very slender; the links were soon broken. The earliest European contacts were also broken. The truly remarkable journey of Leif Ericson from southern Greenland, an outpost of the Norse, to Canada in the year A.D. 1000, might have had happier results for North America had the Norsemen not coasted such a dismal land, or, more important still, had not the Greenland colony perished some generations later. Long before Eric reached his wine-land in the more pleasant parts of the eastern seaboard, he had met the Hellu-land, or cold, waste 'stone' land, which he reported as devoid of good qualities. Doubtless the tales of this bleak and difficult approach put off other Norse adventurers.

It was not until the fifteenth century, therefore, when Europe had advanced far enough in trade, technology, and science to launch out upon the high seas, that the Americas were brought into the civilized *oikoumene*. Then Portugal and Spain were able to exploit their relative nearness to the new lands and make the first substantial conquests overseas. The desolation of the Sahara coast, and the comparatively inviting nature of Madeira and

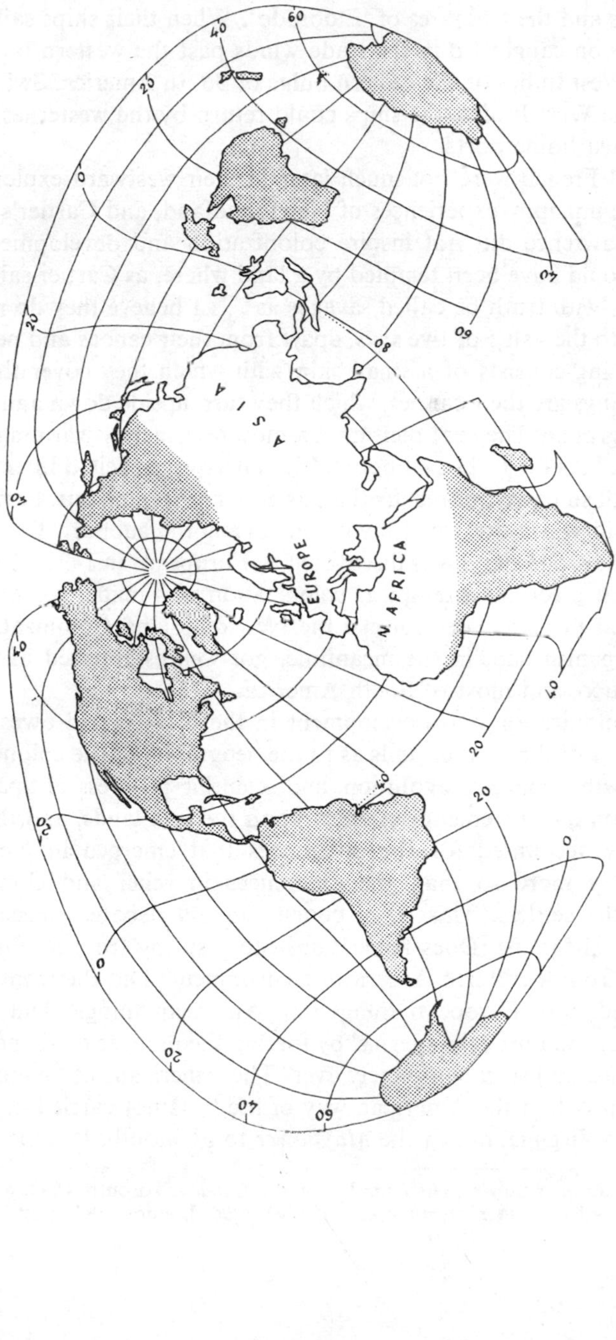

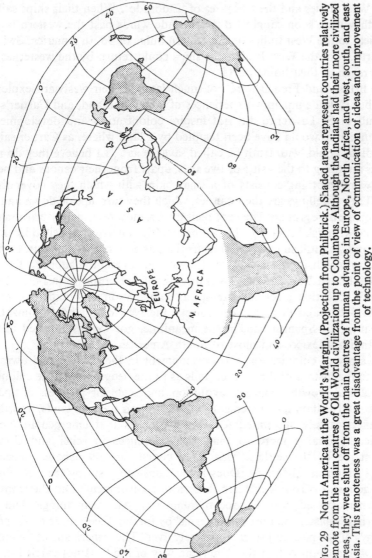

FIG. 29 North America at the World's Margin. (Projection from Philbrick.) Shaded areas represent countries relatively remote from the main centres of Old World civilization up to Columbus. Although the Indians had their more civilized areas, they were shut off from the main centres of human advance in Europe, North Africa, and west, south, and east Asia. This remoteness was a great disadvantage from the point of view of communication of ideas and improvement of technology.

the Cape Verde islands turned them westward. Moreover, the new dream of finding the Indies by sailing west, which had inspired Columbus, continued to draw them. The southern island arc led them, like stepping-stones, to the West Indies and the treasures of 'Eldorado'. When their ships sailed south they were soon caught up in the trade winds past the western bulge of Africa, to the West Indies or the eastern bulge of South America. Swinging north from the West Indies, the ships could return by the westerlies to within reach of their home ports.

The British and French were not much later in their westward explorations, but Cabot's unhappy experiences of Newfoundland, and Cartier's of the Gulf of St Lawrence did not inspire colonization and development. What monarch would have been tempted by a land where, as Cartier said,[1] the Indians could 'with truth be called savages as . . . I believe they do not possess anything to the value of five *sous*, apart from their canoes and nets. Their whole clothing consists of a small skin with which they cover their loins. Their dwellings are their canoes, which they turn upside down and lie under on the bare ground. They eat their meat almost raw, merely warming it; the same with fish.' As for Cabot, although his first voyage excited interest, his second was still so barren of results that, as Brebner[2] points out, he had little with which to win more royal favour or mercantile support. Consequently, though Newfoundland was discovered to Europeans in 1497, it was not until 1610 that a formal attempt at colonization was made, when Sir Francis Bacon and his associates formed the Newfoundland Colonization Company. The Spanish had, in the meantime, got well established in the West Indies, Mexico, and most of South America.

The story of colonization and development in the New World owes as much to the history of the motherlands as to the geography of the colonies. The political growth, economic evolution, and scientific progress of Spain, France, and Britain had a tremendous effect upon the new lands, and their differences largely accounted for the differences that emerged in North America—probably more so than the differences in relief and climate encountered by the settlers. This is, of course, an old debate, especially among American historians. Does American history spring from its European 'germs', or from the North American environment? Did the frontier, as Turner claimed, turn European things into American things? Did the 'wilderness' master the European 'germs' by forcing the pioneer to abandon the ways of the past and start completely over? The Americans of 'manifest destiny' like to think that the American way of life 'was not carried in the *Sarah Constant* to Virginia, nor in the *Mayflower* to Plymouth. It came out

[1] Stephens, H. B., *Jacques Cartier, His Four Voyages to Canada*, Toronto, 1890, p. 30.

[2] Brebner, J. B., *The Explorers of North America, 1492–1806*, London, 1933 (reprinted 1955), p. 92.

of the American forest and it gained new strength each time it touched a new frontier.'[1] Indeed many American historians are more determinedly 'geographical determinists' than the most zealous of geographers. 'Civilization in America', declares Turner, 'has followed the arteries made by geology.'[2] But in human affairs first causes, as Pierson points out, rarely lie in real estate so much as in state of mind.[3] The American adventure began, and has been again and again renewed, through West European adventuresomeness.

The fact of the matter is, both historic tradition and geographical challenge had their say. Historic tradition provided certain motives, certain habits of settlement and occupation, and certain techniques of development that shaped the whole reaction to the geographic challenge, suggesting how this should be met and, if possible, mastered. The geographic challenge, on the other hand, offered distinct opportunities or laid down distinct limitations which men could not afford to ignore, whatever their background.

The debate is a fascinating one: were the strikingly different settlements in Nova Scotia due more to local geology than to French and British traditions; was the New England township a reflection more of relief than religion, or the Virginia plantation of climate than of caste? All over America there are examples of where the same environment has given rise to quite different forms of settlement or modes of activity with different settlers and different habits. Yet there are many examples, too, of where settlers with very different backgrounds have come up with the same reaction to the same environment. Both the factors of culture and environment are important. The Europeans came with settled ways and fixed ideas. Some of these they preserved, in whatever circumstances they found themselves, others they gave up in order to adopt new ways and ideals more in keeping with their surroundings. Thus culture became at once the measure of the environment and the medium through which it acted. Environment only had as much significance as culture gave it.

As a consequence, the European background must be described and understood before the full force and majesty of the American enviroment can be valued and appreciated. Yet the European background is itself eminently geographical. Europeans had met many frontiers before they came to the American one. Indeed European history is one long struggle with, or vindication of, geography. The European was European only by reason of having let this environment of his—of land warped with sea, of mountain married with plain, of sharp defining contrasts and inextricable

[1] Pierson, G. W., 'The Frontier and American Institutions', in *The Turner Thesis concerning the Role of the Frontier in American History*, ed. Taylor, G. R., Boston, 1949, p. 77.

[2] Turner, F. J., 'The Significance of the Frontier in American History', reprinted in Taylor, *The Turner Thesis*, p. 7.

[3] Pierson, op. cit., p. 82.

blending contacts—lay hold of him, a wanderer out of Asia, and make him over. The discovery of America was only one of a long series of discoveries that had included first the discovery of the Mediterranean, then of peninsular

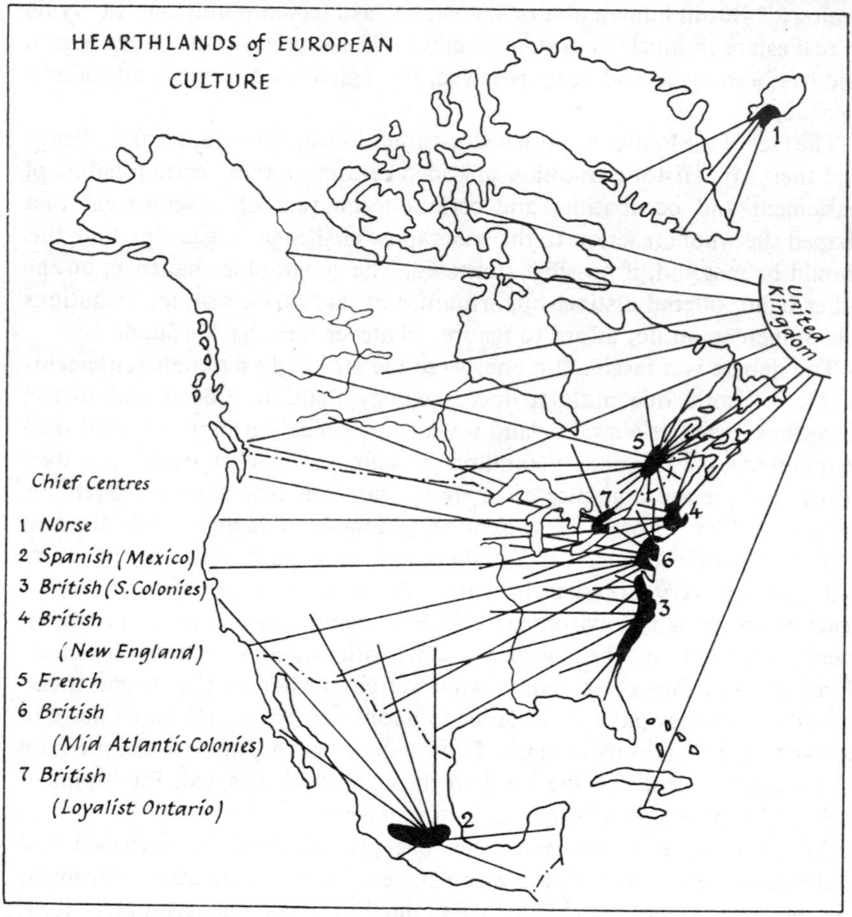

FIG. 30 Hearthlands of European Culture in North America, in order of establishment (modified from Preston James). While much of Britain's influence was mediated through Virginia, New England, the mid-Atlantic states, and Ontario, much continued to come directly from Britain herself. This was more particularly true of the West Indies, the Hudson Bay region, and Newfoundland. (Scale, 1:70 m.)

Europe, then of the Atlantic, then of Britain and the isles beyond, and so of the land beyond the isles.

What we really have in colonial America therefore is one set of geographical conditions being interpreted and used in the light of another set, the geography of America being made out of the geography of Europe. Means of transport, kinds of agriculture, and forms of settlement that had been worked out for west maritime Europe were made to do for east maritime America (and it was only a blessing that the two regions were so similar, Caledonian and Hercynian Europe being matched by Old and New Appalachia, and the divergence of westerlies across the shores of Europe being balanced by their convergence across American shores). Looked at in this way the two geographies—those of western Europe and northern America—are to a large extent but the mirror images of each other, or rather but sections of the larger geography of the Atlantic world: there is no break, but a progression; the geography of America is that of Europe in new terms (Fig. 30).

SPANISH COLONIZATION AND THE SPANISH BACKGROUND

Spain and Spanish Expansion

Spain's expansion overseas was, in this light, but the culmination of its expansion in the Iberian peninsula. The fierce struggle against the Moors having been won at last, and Aragon and Castile having been united by the marriage of Ferdinand and Isabella, Spain had reached a measure of national solidarity, confidence, and strength that enabled it, and perhaps inspired it, to launch out on new adventures, discover the Americas, and conquer the greater part of them. In this history, war and religion had been the two dominant themes, and therefore it is not surprising that the aristocratic soldier and the priest led the colonization of America. This was significant, and afforded a striking contrast to British colonization, led more often than not by the trader or the settler.

The new unity in Spain had been impressed upon the country by the Crown. This was particularly true for Castile. There, disputes between cities and strife between nobles had been overcome only by the reassertion of royal power. Since the expedition of Columbus was authorized by Queen Isabella of Castile, the laws of the new colony were based on those of her kingdom, where royal absolutism was in the ascendancy. In America the Crown became supreme. As Haring remarks:

> from the outset the Indies were treated as the direct and exclusive possession of the crown. They were not, strictly speaking, Spanish. They were not even an integral part of the Castilian kingdom. Mexico and Peru were kingdoms, combined with the kingdoms of Spain, under a common sovereign, bound to Spain only by a dynastic tie. The king possessed not only the sovereign rights but the property rights; he was the absolute proprietor, the sole political head, of his American dominions. Every

> privilege and position, economic, political, or religious, came from him It was on this basis that the Spanish conquest, occupation, and government of the New World was achieved.[1]

Various levels of local government were set up, notably in the larger towns. But although conventions of the *proctors*, or delegates of the towns, met for common action, they did so only with the consent of the Crown, for as Charles V declared, 'without our command it is not our intention or will that the cities and towns of the Indies meet in convention'.

Conditions of Colonization

The Crown pressed colonization forward by offering individuals a *capitulación* or concession in which they obtained a substantial proportion of the returns for their venture, on the understanding that they took all the risk and provided the capital and enterprise. The founders of new colonies were often given the title of *adelantado*, a title which in former days had been given to nobles who had wrested land from the Moors, and guarded border castles. The *adelantado* of the Americas was allowed a share of the revenues from the colony he set up in the king's name, obtained a large estate in it for himself, had certain rights to nominate his followers for legal or clerical positions, and could subject the Indians to the purposes of the colony. To earn these privileges he had to take settlers to America, and establish two or more fortified towns with churches.

The considerable cost involved in fitting out a military expedition to discover and conquer territory, in clearing enough common land for settlement, in transporting settlers, and in building communities, could usually be met only by the aristocratic families of Spain, supported by wealthy Jews or Moors, and could be recovered only by mining gold or silver, or establishing large sugar, cotton, or tobacco plantations. This is important to realize because it makes clear why the early Spanish colonies were so exploitive in nature, why the Spaniards turned to mining wherever possible rather than farming, why 'instead of planting corn, they rushed off in search of mines'.[2] In this they were very different from the English who, in the main, wanted land to develop, and wanted to work it on a 'homesteading' basis.

The quest for metals allowed the Spaniards to use in the New World the arts, techniques, and tools with which they had become familiar in the Old. Spain was a highly metalliferous country with many deposits of iron, copper, and mercury, and not a few of silver and gold in its highly folded and much faulted mountains. In the highly folded and much faulted chains of the

---

[1] Haring, C. H., *The Spanish Empire in America*, New York, 1947, p. 7.
[2] Ibid., p. 13.

Caribbean, Mexico, Central America, and the Andes similar conditions and opportunities were found.

Indeed Spain made much more of the mountains and mesas in America than the French or British. To the latter mountains were by and large a barrier; mountains became the backbone of the Spanish colonies. Here, then, was a marked contrast, due in very large measure to the contrasted traditions between the European geographies of the colonizing powers. Of course, American conditions were also significant. Mountains in Canada raised the French into the Arctic; in New England they lifted the British into the sub-Arctic; in tropical America they bore the Spaniards up into the temperate zone and helped them make much more of the tropics than they otherwise might have. Most of the capitals of Spanish America, within the tropics, were up on the heights; the capitals of British America were, by contrast, cities of the plain.

Where it was impossible to make money out of mining, the Spaniards turned to plantation farming. The tropical humid climate of the West Indies suited sugar production. There was a growing market for sugar in Europe. The crown agent, or his contractors, turned to sugar production on a large scale. However, the new estates were not set up with a view to colonizing the country, at least as the English understood colonization, but to earn rapid wealth for their owners. Yet in one sense they did help 'colonization'; they brought a great deal of land swiftly under Spanish rule, and led the *conquistadores* to press on in search for more. Cereal farming and stock raising were also carried on, especially on the uplands, and these too required extensive tracts of land.

Here, again, the geography of agriculture in New Spain tended to reflect that in Old. In the Iberian peninsula there were narrow, hot coastal plains or river deltas, raising tropical and sub-tropical plants. True, these were drier than the plains of the Caribbean or Gulf of Mexico but, with the use of irrigation, produced rich crops of sugar, rice, grapes, dates, peaches, and citrus fruits. Above were the tablelands and mountains, cooler but with bright sunny summers. On the tablelands great wheat farms vied with cattle ranches for the land, while sheep rearing made use of the high mountain pasture. The plateaux and uplands of Cuba, Mexico, Central and South America quite frequently resembled those of Spain, except that they were covered with a tropical savannah rather than a temperate steppe, but this was no great difference and still allowed, indeed invited, the extensive production of grain and cattle. Even though Spanish settlers did experiment with new crops, they always had the tried and trusted ways to fall back on, and could always find facets in the new environment that corresponded with the old. In this way their grasp on the New World was greatly strengthened.

Spanish Exploration

The Spaniards were much more fortunate than the French or the British in that the areas they chanced upon, in and around the Caribbean, were rich in silver, and had an unusually developed agricultural tradition. The Indians themselves mined silver and gold, and grew maize, beans, and squash, cassava, yam, potatoes, tobacco, and cotton. Such Indians were far more serviceable in Spanish mining or plantation enterprises than those, say, of New England or the Maritimes were to the British. The recognition of this opportunity spurred the Spaniards on to explore, conquer, and control the more developed regions in Mexico and Central America. Hispaniola, the base of operations in the Indies, had no great store of gold. Fragments of gold were washed out from the rivers, but the supply was exhausted in about two decades. Consequently exploration was pushed on rapidly throughout the Caribbean. La Cosa, still trying to find the legendary Cathay, sailed up the Gulf of Uraba, but though he came on no passage across Panama, he discovered gold, and so drew men west. By 1513 Balboa, seeking more gold in the isthmus, had climbed out of the fever-ridden jungles of Panama to reach the eminence from which he sighted the Pacific. This was immediately exploited. In 1514 Davila arrived at the isthmus and set up his government on the mainland. Meantime, in 1513, Ponce de Leon had sailed north from Puerto Rico and landed on North America proper, in Florida, but had not found anything worth while. In 1519 de Pineda moved round the coast from Florida to Mexico, but with no luck.

Neither Panama nor Florida offered the sort of wealth the Spaniards wanted. It was in Central America that hopes seemed best founded. Slave raids on the coast of Honduras had revealed a race of cultivated Indians familiar with gold. Cordoba's expedition of 1517 was a failure and he himself died but his followers returned to Cuba. 'Their news was electrifying,' writes Brebner.[1] 'They wrote to Velázquez, governor of Cuba, telling him that "we had discovered thickly peopled countries, with masonry houses, and people who covered their persons and went about clothed in cotton garments, and who possessed gold". Velázquez became convinced that his adventurers had touched the fringe of an established empire. Without loss of time he got together another expedition.' It was left to Cortes, however, to make the most eventful discovery in his conquest of Mexico in 1519, when he secured the treasures of the Aztecs for Spain.

Fired by their successes in Mexico the Spaniards moved rapidly into the mainland, mastering large areas before ever the French or the British landed. Between 1520 and 1522 most of southern Mexico had been explored and taken, and during 1522–4 Alvarado conquered Guatemala. By 1533 the

[1] Brebner, J. B., *The Explorers of North America, 1492–1806*, New York, 1933, pp. 28–29.

Spaniards, establishing themselves on the Pacific coast, had sailed up the Gulf of California and discovered the California peninsula. In the same year Pizarro had completed his arduous journey southwards along the Andes to Peru, in mastering which he found a wealth in excess even of that taken in Mexico. These two realms became the most opulent in overseas Spain, and there was considerable rivalry between them.

After a short pause, the drive to the north continued. De Soto, who had seen what riches the Gulf of Mexico led to in Central America, felt sure it would offer as much in North America. Returning a rich man from his earlier adventures, he persuaded the King of Spain to grant him the right to explore the northern mainland. De Vaca had described Florida, which he had visited in 1528, as the richest country of the world. De Soto was tempted by this, hoping to find Indian cities and gold. He also sought a way to the Pacific and the still greater wealth of Cathay. Landing in Florida in 1539, he explored the southern Appalachians, the lower Mississippi, and all the Ozarks region, found neither cities nor gold, and died in 1542 in the Mississippi swamps, having made a vain but not inglorious effort. Meanwhile, in 1540, Coronado had been dispatched north by the first Viceroy of New Spain to discover the fabled Seven Cities which were supposed to lie north-west of Mexico. He came upon these in the Pueblo settlements of the upper Rio Grande and Colorado basins. But they were disappointing, providing no gold or silver. Turning east he came out on the high prairies, rich in game, but ignored them for their lack of metals. On reaching the Kansas river he heard that the country to the north was cold and poorly settled, and so went back to Mexico, a disheartened man, in 1542.

An extraordinary wide area had thus become available to Spain, reaching from California to Florida, and from the Gulf of Mexico to the Kansas river (Fig. 31). Spanish exploration had made known the southern parts of the Atlantic coastal plain, the Appalachians, the Central Lowlands, the High Plains, and the Cordilleras, together with the Gulf plain and the plateau of Mexico. Unfortunately interest in gold and in plantation agriculture wrote off a lot of the discoveries as virtually useless and, although the British and later the Americans turned the plains into cotton, cattle, and wheat empires, the Spanish did virtually nothing with them. Interest swung to South America. Consequently there was little more exploration done in the north for the next generation or two.

The Development of Mexico

However, there was still a lot to attract them in southern Mexico, and many Spanish colonizers and priests poured into the country. Colonists secured the *encomiendas* of Indians in the fertile, well-watered basin and in valleys fed from snow-clad peaks where they started up their plantations;

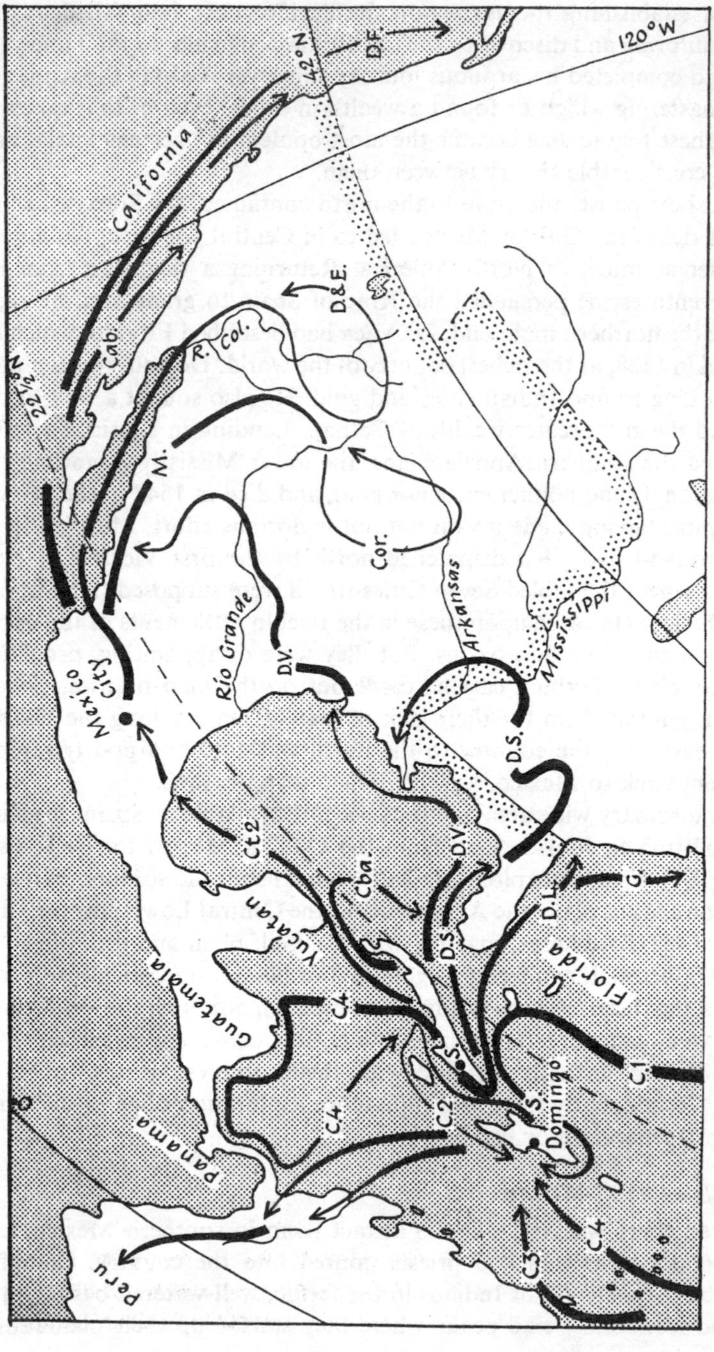

FIG. 31 Spanish Exploration and Spheres of Influence in North America. Explanation of letters: C.1, Columbus 1492; C.2, Columbus 1493–6; C.3, Columbus 1498; C.4, Columbus 1502–3; D.L., De Leon 1513; Cba. Cordoba 1517; Ct.2, Cortez 1519; G., Gomez 1524; D.V., De Vaca 1534–6; M., Marcos 1539; Cor., Coronado 1540–2; Cab., Cabrillo 1542; F., Ferrelo 1544; D.S., De Soto 1548; D. & E., Dominguez & Escalante 1776; D.F., De Fuca 1783. (Scale, 1:35 m.)

religious missions also obtained large tracts of land and began to work them; merchant guilds in Spain invested in the land or in mines and organized companies to develop them; locally successful men bought offices in government service or titles of nobility; a wealthy, aristocratic, feudal, and highly sophisticated society soon began to flourish; cities were established; markets created; imposing public edifices raised, cathedrals built and a university set up: the Castilian way of life took root in the New World.

It is important to realize that this was a full-bodied life. The new kingdom had its ruling council, or *audiencia*, and Mexico City its municipal chamber, or *cabildo*. A bishopric was established as early as 1530, and within ten years five other sees were created. The University of Mexico was founded as early as 1551, barely thirty-two years after the conquest of the city. In 1574, according to Velasco, there were 15,000 Spaniards and 150,000 Indians living in Mexico City. Soldiers, priests, lawyers, merchants, mining engineers, mill owners, landed gentry, farmers, and artisans made groups of highly competent people who ruled and developed the land to such an extent that it has remained Spanish to this day and differs radically from the Anglo-American regions to the north.

There was one drawback to this society, however; it rested on forced labour. It did not possess the manpower within itself to maintain or better itself. Although it made a Spanish nation of Mexico, it did not make Mexico a nation of Spaniards. Far from it. Even although increasing numbers of colonists were sent over, there were not enough to work the land. De Velasco claims there were 165,000 Spaniards in the Indies by 1574, but these compare ill with the five million Indians he reckoned to be there. Actually, few Spanish farmers could have wanted to migrate to a land carved up into large estates and worked by tenant labour. (By contrast the English poured into New England where freehold farming enabled them to escape the tenancy system.) Consequently, natives had to be induced, by one means or another, to work for their masters.

Under Ovando the Spaniards early took to kidnapping the less war-like of the natives. This was frowned on by the Church, and the *encomienda* system was adopted. Taken over from times of the Moorish wars when successful knights were given manorial rights over land wrested from the Infidels, rights which included the services of the peasants living on the land, the tradition permitted the New World *encomenderos* to use such Indians as came under their protection as life-long tenants. Indeed, with time, this right became heritable. Moreover, *encomenderos* could sell surplus labour to others. In 1509 Ferdinand decreed that when a region was conquered the governor could divide the Indians among his supporters, provided they undertook to christianize and protect them. While this system was attacked by some priests, it was accepted by others. Simpson quotes a Dominican report to the effect that land settlement could not be stabilized without *encomiendas* because all industry was carried on by Indian labour, and only those having Indians were able to carry on commerce. This was justified on the grounds that the Indians were offered peace and care. Las Casas, in his history, states specifically that the Indians were given in trust to the landlords, who had to protect them and provide for their religious instruction.

It was probably better than the outright slavery which many Spaniards wanted and which was, in fact, authorized in the case of Indians captured in a just war, or taken in an Indian rebellion. Such slaves were generally put to work in the mines.

Another source of labour was the commuting of the Indian tribute. In 1495 Columbus, as governor of the Indies, put down a revolt of the Indians and imposed an annual tribute on them. Those who were unable to pay were allowed to offer labour instead. This was no doubt the origin of the *repartimiento* system by which a tenth or even a quarter of every Indian community had to provide labour for a part of every year, especially for public works such as building, road-making, irrigation works, or the transport of goods, but also for mining and farming. Labour became, in effect, part of the Indian tribute. The *repartimiento* was administered by an officer in charge of Indians, who divided the Indians out to the Spanish proprietors in need of them. According to Simpson a person wishing labour on the *repartimiento* principle filed a regular form to the effect that he had a wheat farm, or cattle ranch, or plantation, whose products were necessary to the colony, and that to make sure of his crops he needed the labour of so many Indians for such a length of time. For the good of the State he was given this help, provided he treated the Indians well. Explorers and colonizers were usually rewarded with a *repartimiento*.

Forms of Settlement

These practices had their geographic implications. They emphasized the manorial system of land tenure and land use, and inhibited the rise of small independent farms in Spanish North America. The *latifundia* system of serf labour on large estates was transferred from Old Spain to New. Settlements became, if anything, more concentrated than ever. The Spaniards were used to highly nucleated villages clustered about or near to the great house of the *latifundia*. They continued to set up compact communities in New Spain. However, many Indians lived a semi-nomadic life, either leaving old villages on exhausted soils to build new ones, or combining hunting with farming. In such circumstances it was difficult to round them up for the *repartimiento*, or to use them under the *encomienda*. Therefore, they were gathered together and compelled to live in highly nucleated villages on the Spanish estates or near Spanish towns. As Haring states:

> to ensure that all the aborigines were reduced to Christian faith and governance, and that the royal tribute *and other services* were forthcoming, the crown from the days of Queen Isabella ordered that scattered Indians be concentrated in towns and villages. In New Spain some slight attempt to collect the dispersed Indians in settlements was made by the first Viceroy, Mendoza. A much more ambitious effort followed when in 1598 Monterey sent out a number of expeditions to survey all the territory of New Spain from Tampico and Guadalajara southward—i.e. all the area of the civilized Indians—and report back on the reductions or 'congregations' it seemed advisable to make. A large number were established in the next few years.[1]

De Velasco estimated in 1574 that there were eight or nine thousand such villages containing one and a half million men subject to tribute.

Special inducements were offered to Indians to come together themselves to live in villages. If they did so, they were relieved of some of their tribute, provided that, at the same time, they became Christians. Those who entered mission villages, and settled there, were exempted from tribute for ten years. Thus the Spaniards developed a highly nucleated form of settlement, with villages and towns linked together by roads and integrated in systems of district government, unique on the continent. Little if anything like it was to be found in the French or British colonies.

An interesting fact is that the Indian villages were kept separate from white settlement. When *encomiendas* were granted it was specified that 'Encomenderos must not live in their Indians' villages, nor build houses there, nor allow their slaves to go thither, nor maintain stockfarms in the neighbourhood of a village.'[2] This had its effect on the geographical distributions of the white haciendas, with houses for foremen, servants and slaves, and Indians sites, with tenants and serfs.

With the growing use of native labour, and of imported African slaves, the gold and silver mines, the cotton plantations, and the wheat and cattle haciendas of Mexico were rapidly developed and gave Mexico a lead over all other Spanish colonies, with the possible exception of Peru. Consequently, the Viceroyalty of the Indies, centred on Hispaniola, was abandoned, and a new viceroyalty created, that of New Spain, centred in Mexico and including land from Florida to Panama. It had an immense geographical range and so, to make its administration more feasible, it was divided into a number of lesser areas, each of which was governed by a captain-general, along with his *audiencia* of councillors and judges.

---

[1] Haring, op. cit., pp. 70–71.

[2] Bourne, *Spain in America*, p. 260.

Territorial Divisions

The rise of these territorial divisions reflected the geography of the times. The demotion of the Viceroyalty of Hispaniola to a province of New Spain indicated the loss of importance of the West Indies to Spain compared with the mainland. They had little gold and few of those upland steppes beloved of the Spaniard, which were, however, present in Mexico. Their climate called for a far greater adjustment than that of the Mexican plateau. Their products were sugar, yams, and cassava, not the wheat and cattle which, widely raised in Castile, could be even more widely developed in Mexico. The government of Santo Domingo, the old capital, thus shrank in control. At one time supreme over the Yucatan and Honduras, over Panama and Darien, over Venezuela and Florida, it lost these outlying areas, and had to content itself with the Antilles alone. Bourne[1] remarks on the 'rapid melting away of the population of the West Indies during the first quarter of a century of Spanish rule', from over 200,000 in 1492 to 14,000 in 1514. Mexico took over the mainland spheres north of Darien, Peru to the south.

There then occurred a tug between these two principal regions. The Viceroyalty of Mexico embraced Central America, including Panama. However, its hold on Panama was very weak, and kept up only by attenuated sea routes. Hence Panama was drawn into the Viceroyalty of Peru in 1550. In 1563 it was reunited to Mexico, but in 1567 it was again put under Peru. Somewhat similar changes affected Yucatan. Although it had historical ties with Mexico, it was geographically linked with Honduras and the rest of Central America. When it was decided to make a captaincy-general of Central America, in recognition of its geographical separation from Mexico, Yucatan was given to the new autonomous district. However, as the capital of Central America was removed from Honduras to Guatemala, that is, farther inland, Yucatan was reunited with Mexico.

The geographical separation of western Mexico also became reflected in administrative developments, giving rise to the province of New Galicia. Now when Coronado was the governor of this province he organized and led expeditions to Rio Grande and Colorado. Its frontiers were therefore carried to the Rio Grande. However, its capital, Guadalajara, was well to the south. This led to a growing pressure for the creation of a new province in northern Mexico. A wide belt of desert or sparsely populated steppe lay between the northern frontier lands and the southern, settled areas. On that northern frontier Spanish missionaries had been extremely active in setting up missions in California, New Mexico, and Texas. Indeed as Bandini, a contemporary, claimed, the missions had acquired great holdings of land from one end of the territory to the other (Fig. 32). Priests were followed by

---

[1] Bourne, op. cit., p. 211.

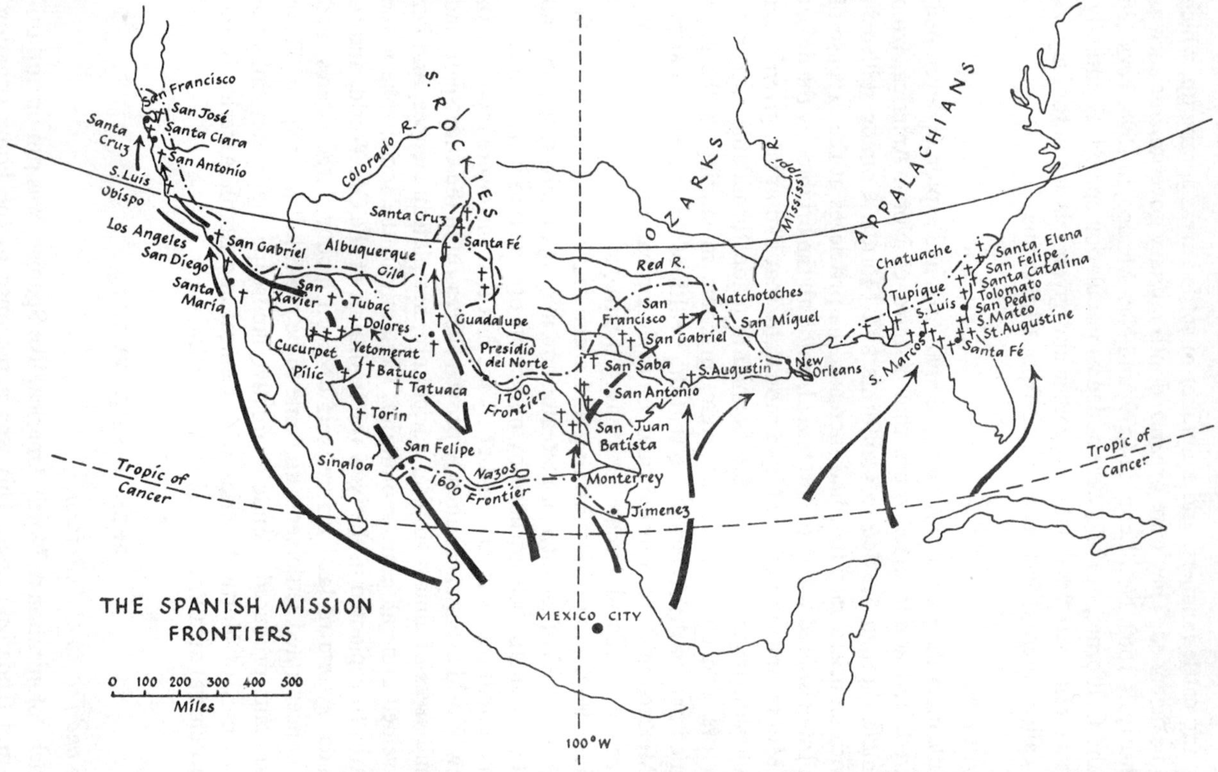

FIG. 32 The Spanish Mission Frontier, A.D. 1600–1780. Apart from Florida, most of the missions were in sparsely populated semi-desert or steppe-land territory, cut off from Mexico by distance and drought. Compare fig. 180, p. 720.

miners and cattle ranchers, and a number of settled areas sprang up, which had to be defended. They were organized into military governments such as New Biscay, in 1562, New Leon, in 1579, and New Mexico, in 1598. Texas, in 1718, and California, in 1767, were added as population spread. Eventually, these northern areas were linked together and given relative autonomy, as the so-called Internal Provinces, ruled from Chihuahua.

Conclusion

In little more than a century, then, the Spaniards had explored, developed, organized, and administered more than a third of North America, from Guatemala through Mexico to California and Florida. Coming skilled in war, with an aristocracy that had increased its privileges at the expense of beaten Infidels, fired with a religious zeal, made all the brighter by the defeat of the Moors, and strengthened by a monarchy that had at last given order and cohesion to the country, the Spaniards made formidable explorers, conquerors, and colonizers. They were fortunate in landing in the most developed part of the Americas, so that the wealth of the Indies, and above all of Mexico and Peru, spurred them on to ever greater effort. In this they made use of relief and climate, exploiting the tropical crops of the humid lowlands, developing wheat farming and sheep and cattle ranching on the semi-arid steppes of the interior plateaux, and mining the silver, copper, and gold of a mountain belt intruded by numerous ore-bearing igneous masses. To some extent this was made easier by the fact that they were repeating in the New World experiences already proved successful in the Old: Spain had her small areas of almost tropical agriculture, her plateau steppes, and her richly veined mineraliferous mountains. Certainly in the social sphere, the Spaniards transplanted in the New the traditions of the Old World, and so the feudal system of land tenure, serf or peon labour, large estates, and highly concentrated settlements all came to be typical of New Spain. These cultural traits produced a quite distinctive landscape that today links the southern part of North America with Central and South America in the greater cultural area known as Latin America.

FRENCH SETTLEMENT

France and French Colonization

French colonization in North America, like Spanish, was run on authoritarian and feudalistic lines. This was a response to the home situation. French exploration followed upon a period of internal and external war. There had been the bitter religious struggles between Huguenots and Catholics, ending in the Roman ascendancy. This ruled out the Huguenots, with their genius for trade and manufacture, from French North America, making the colonies less *bourgeois* and more hierarchic than they might otherwise have been. New France did not benefit by that considerable migration of Huguenots that brought skilled craftsmen, merchants, and professional men to Britain and thereby added to the strength of Britain's middle class and the growth of Britain's industry. The middle class were not as numerous or strong in New France as, for instance, in New England. Undoubtedly this affected settlement. It meant that there was not the same emphasis on towns, local industries, and an agricultural hinterland. Trade was concentrated in the hands of a few companies at a few centres. Land tended to be parcelled out to great concessionaires, and the feudal character of Old France thus became planted in New France.

But the power of the Canadian *seigneur* was limited to a considerable degree by the authority of the central government.[1] After all, had not the French Crown had its struggles with the greater nobles like the Duc de Guise and the Duc de Condé? The Crown, supported by the Church, particularly by the great Cardinals Richelieu and Mazarin, eventually won out and asserted its power more than ever, in a highly centralized, authoritarian government. Most people were glad when the Sun King took the rule of the land into his own hands.

'The tumultuous sixteenth century thus ended with internal peace under a strong king. The predominant desire of Frenchmen was now for harmony and order, which would presently lead to a new concept of hierarchy under Louis XIV.'[2] This hierarchy was based only in part on the feudal aristocracy, and then only on such of the nobles as found favour with the king. It rested mainly on a bureacracy of personal representatives of the king, who carried the royal power into every part of the kingdom. The country was divided up for administrative purposes into districts under royal *intendants*. These maintained the central strength of the Crown against any tendency towards marginal disaffection or weakness. The sorely tried unity of France was restored.

The kings of France from Francis I to Louis XIV were, not unnaturally, anxious to prevent the ferment in France from repeating itself in the colonies. Exploration and colonization were authorized by them in the hopes of increasing their power and wealth. Monopolies were given to trading companies that would bring back immediate profit. *Seigneuries* were granted to successful explorers, soldiers, or nobles who would support the king, and whose tenants could be levied into the royal armies. Missions were encouraged that would convert the heathen, and widen the sway of both Church and Crown. A paternalistic régime was thus set up which, while

---

[1] Trudel, M., 'Le Régime Seigneural', *Can. Hist. Assoc.*, Brochure 6, Ottawa, 1956, pp. 10ff.

[2] Brereton, G., *A Short History of French Literature*, London, 1956, p. 66.

it met the colonist's demand for new economic opportunities, gave him no greater liberty of conscience or freedom of organization than had been known at home.

French Exploration

The French were distinctly later than the Spanish and the British in turning to North America. Doubtless this was because they sought Empire in Europe, and not in the New World. Although their fishing boats left Dieppe as early as 1504 for Newfoundland, it was not until 1524 that they authorized a trip to North America.[1] This was undertaken by Verrazano, who entered New York Bay, coasted New England, Nova Scotia, and Newfoundland in the vain search for a passage to Cathay. 'The most interesting legacy of the voyage was the conjectural placing on the maps of North America of a second isthmus (in addition to Panama) in the region of the Carolinas, dividing the hemisphere into three continental masses instead of two.'[2] Since the southern two masses were mainly claimed by Spain, it may have been thought that the northern one was left for French enterprise. But nothing came of the trip, perhaps because in the next year Francis I was drastically defeated in Italy (Fig. 33).

The Italian war was still dragging on when Cartier made his interesting, but not very dramatic, journeys into the St Lawrence Gulf (1534) and up the St Lawrence estuary (1535). Sailing through the Strait of Belle Isle in late spring, Cartier coasted the foggy ice-ridden, rocky, and mountainous shore of Labrador and was so dismayed he wrote: 'I am inclined to believe this is the land God gave to Cain.' (Even today, with modern technology, the Labrador section of the Canadian Shield is inhospitable enough.) However, July in Prince Edward Island, with its red sandy-loam soils, its luxuriant forests, and natural meadows, made Cartier more hopeful. (He had come to the edge of the Appalachian country, whose many sedimentary basins are much more attractive than the uplands of the Shield.) Sailing up the Baie de Chaleur and then across to Anticosti Island made Cartier appreciate the vastness of the Gulf he had discovered. It was this, probably more than the fertility of the southern shores, that prompted him to return the following year. He was persuaded that here was either a major break-through to Cathay or a quick way into the interior of the Americas where there might be a second Mexico or Peru. He had acquired two Indians as guides and these had told him of populous kingdoms farther up the St Lawrence. (No doubt to the relatively simple Indians of the coast, the interior Indians with their agriculture, long houses, and stockaded towns seemed prosperous and advanced indeed.) Cartier's return led him, in the height of a glorious

---

[1] Hoffman, B. G., *Cabot to Cartier*, Toronto, 1961, p. 31.
[2] Bourne, op. cit., p. 144.

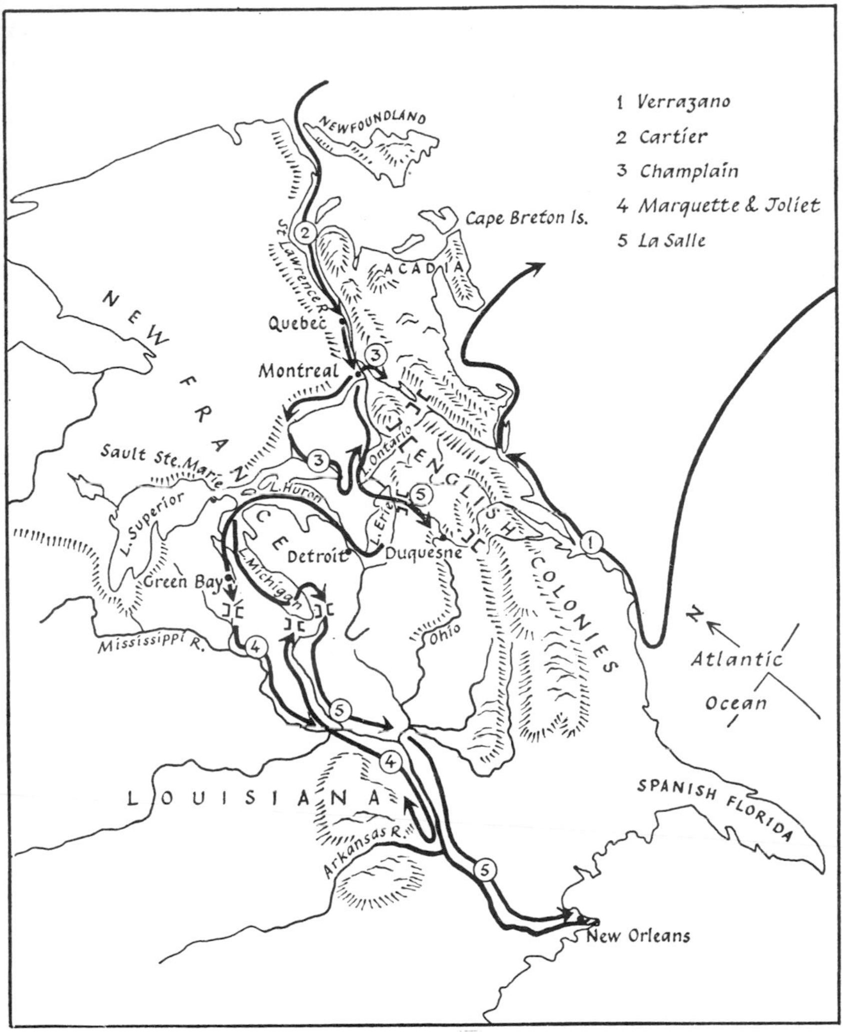

FIG. 33 Early French Colonization. Using the Gulf of St Lawrence to outflank the Shield and by-pass the Appalachians, French exploration took advantages of the highly ramified yet highly integrated waterway systems of the interior.

St Lawrence summer, past the rich woods of the Isle of Orleans, festooned with wild grapes, to the Iroquoian village of Stadacona under its great cliff. (This place, known to later French settlers by its Algonquin name, Kaybekog or the narrows, became the great fortress of Quebec.) Cartier pressed on until he came to the greater kingdom of Hochelaga, at what is now Montreal. But though this boasted a triple-stockaded town, with many large Iroquoian long-houses, and was set about with fields of corn, squash, beans, and tobacco, it was a poor place compared with the cities of the Aztecs or Incas. Disappointed, Cartier and his men turned back, with the onset of autumn, for France.

No doubt Francis I was likewise disappointed; he was not interested in land, but in wealth, or at any rate in a routeway to riches. Canada scarcely seemed worth further outlay, at least as long as European wars drained the royal coffers. Years passed and nothing was done. However, upon a brief lull in his struggles, the king commissioned the Sieur de Roberval, a nobleman of Picardy, to set up a colony in Canada, of which he was appointed Viceroy. Cartier, made commander of the fleet, returned to the St Lawrence in 1541 to prepare for this colony, and established a post at Cap Rouge, upstream from Quebec. But a bitter winter and the hostility of the Indians drove him back to France. Roberval in his turn could not stand the long, bleak winter and, although he had cleared land, sowed crops, raised buildings, and built a stockade, he abandoned Cap Rouge, leaving fifty dead of the scurvy, and returned to the homeland in 1543. The long, dark, bitter winter with keen winds blowing from off the Canadian Shield and sweeping across the ice-covered firth was too much for Frenchmen used to a much milder climate swept by warm wet south-westerly winds. The geography of the New World looked too forbidding and colonization ceased for the time being.

More than sixty years went by before the French kings again interested themselves in North America. However, in the meantime French fishermen had used the water of the Gulf, set up temporary bases on the Magdalen Islands and at Tadoussac, while French entrepreneurs had started a trade in furs. The profits of the fur trade soon came to make it

> an end in itself for European adventurers, and competition among them very rapidly became keen. As early as 1588, two nephews of Jacques Cartier sought and obtained from Henry III of France a monopoly of the trade as compensation for the unpaid accounts of their uncle. This grant provoked such an outcry among French competitors that it had to be withdrawn. The last decade of the sixteenth century revealed to France that the summer fur trade of the St Lawrence had become so valuable as to make desirable both regulation of it among Frenchmen and protection of it from encroachments by other nations. It was from this situation that there emerged Samuel Champlain of Bronage, the man who in his own person and in the activities which he initiated marked the abrupt change from mere sailors' visits along the shores of tide-water to such active exploration of the interior as necessitated actual residence in North America.[1]

---

[1] Brebner, J. B., *The Explorers of North America*, p. 121.

After a summer sailing in the St Lawrence Gulf, Champlain returned to North America with the French nobleman De Monts to establish a colony on the Bay of Fundy. Spending a bitter winter on an exposed site in the mouth of the St Croix made the two explorers choose the much more sheltered site of Annapolis Royal, in the Annapolis valley. Here in 1605 was founded the first permanent settlement of what is now Canada. The Annapolis valley, though amongst the most fertile of Appalachian depressions, was narrow and short. It did not open back to any wide fur-trading hinterland, and De Monts and Champlain therefore went beyond it and obtained a charter to trade up the St Lawrence. In 1608 they established a fortified post at Quebec, which was to become the bastion of New France.

There then occurred that alliance between the French and the Algonquin which was profoundly to affect the future not only of French exploration but of French empire on the continent. In 1609, on a fur-trading expedition up the Richelieu river, Champlain lent the strength of French arms to the Algonquin against the Iroquois. The latter were defeated and became such enemies of the French that they prevented their expansion up the St Lawrence and the Lower Great Lakes through Iroquois territory. The geography of Indian rivalry thus had a great deal to do with the geography of French discovery. With the St Lawrence river denied to them, west of Montreal, the French were forced to expand up the Ottawa and, finding an old glacial melt-water channel in the Mattawa valley, used by the Indians as a portage, they passed across to Lake Nipissing and thence, by the French river, to Georgian Bay and the Upper Great Lakes. This great journey of Champlain's in 1615, as Lower[1] has pointed out, routed the French to the Upper Great Lakes, the Upper Mississippi country, and the prairies, at the heart of the continent, and established the path that was to be used by the fur traders for more than two centuries. It linked the Hurons to the French, and in 1634 the Jesuits, under Father Brébeuf, founded a mission in Huronia, which was very successful. Allied with the Hurons, Champlain explored their lands, moving up Georgian Bay and the Trent river to cross over to Lake Ontario. Here he was turned back by the Iroquois. The fur trade of the Ottawa valley, Huronia, and Georgian Bay drew traders to the interior. Quebec was remote, and the posts of Three Rivers (1634) and Montreal (1642) were set up to strengthen the axis of empire. However, Champlain's work was seriously threatened by the war with the English, and by incursions of Iroquois, who were now English allies. The Iroquois overran Huronia in 1649, destroying the Jesuit mission, and invaded the St Maurice valley in 1651–2. In 1656 they made a startling attack upon Quebec,

[1] Lower, A. M., and Chafe, J. W., *Canada—A Nation, And How It Came To Be*, Toronto, 1948, p. 42.

plundering the lower town beneath the fort. It was not until they were defeated by De Tracey in 1666 that the threat to New France was overcome, at least for a period of years, and trade and exploration could proceed.

In 1667, after the worst of these troubles was over, René Robert Cavalier de la Salle came to Canada. He was given a large seigniory just above Montreal (which was called Lachine, apparently because he hoped that he had found, in the St Lawrence, the gateway to China). Finding it difficult to secure colonists to work his land, he decided to explore for furs and set out in 1669 for the west, following the St Lawrence up to Lake Ontario, now that the Iroquois were pacified. He then crossed to Lake Erie, which he had heard was near to the headwaters of the Ohio. In writing of the episode, Galinée claims that he was led on by the hope that the Ohio flowed into the Vermilion Sea (the Gulf of California), itself an arm of the South Seas. La Salle pressed on so as not to give anyone else the opportunity of reaching the passage to the South Sea before him, and discovering the way to China. It is possible that he gained the Ohio, but he had to turn back. Nevertheless, the dream of a western passage remained, and in 1679, having built the vessel *Griffin* on Lake Erie, he sailed west to Green Bay. He then worked his way down Lake Michigan and, coming on the glacial melt-water channels that connect that lake with the Illinois, travelled on their frozen surfaces in December 1681 until he reached open water and the Mississippi. In 1682 he reached the Gulf of Mexico, and claimed the Mississippi basin for France. Although his route had not led him to the South Sea or Cathay it had passed through the Great Central Plains that, opening out beyond the Shield and the Appalachians, offered vast resources for development. The forests of oak and chestnut, mixed with Tall Grass prairies, were rich in fur and made him realize that a centre at New Orleans might be established which could drain the trade of the southern interior into the Atlantic, as Montreal drew off that of the northern interior. Thus France would be in a position to control the core of the continent, and effectively 'contain' Britain within the Appalachians. Forts were duly established at Frontenac (Kingston), Detroit, St Joseph, Crevecœur, and New Orleans to confine the English and control the hinterland. It looked as though France had not only secured the greater share but the best share of the continent, having got the most accessible part of the Shield, the basins of the northern Appalachians, and the Mississippi–Great Lakes–St Lawrence lowlands.

France was quick to appreciate its good fortune. Another way was found from the St Lawrence to the Mississippi. In 1673 the trader Joliet joined forces with the missionary Marquette and, sailing down Green Bay, made use of the glacial outlet to the Wisconsin river which they then followed to the Mississippi. The two journeyed as far as Arkansas where, however, the fear of a clash with the Spaniards made them turn back. Their work helped to cement the connexions, a heritage of the Ice Age, between the Shield and the Plain.

About the same time (1672) Father Albanel, another intrepid missionary, had forged a link between the St Lawrence estuary and James Bay by a remarkable journey up the Saguenay and across the height of land to Lake Mistassini and thence to the northern shore. This greatly strengthened the French stake in the Shield.

The French were able to consolidate their hold on the continental heartland, where Shield met Plain, by working both west and north from the Great Lakes to the Red river. Radisson's trips to Lake Michigan and Lake Superior made the upper basin of the St Lawrence better known. By 1671 the Jesuits had followed him and had set up missions in and mapped Lake Superior. Both traders and missionaries were anxious to make northern and western areas tributary to the lakes. Forts were built at Fort William and on Lake Nipigon. The last great drive was made by Vérendrye in 1731. Leaving Fort William he found the connexion with the Rainy river and Rainy lake. Setting up Fort St Pierre, he went on to Lake of the Woods where Fort St Charles was built. The baffling country of dense woods, innumerable lakes, and low divides that stretched to the north and west provided many difficulties, but at length he reached Lake Winnipeg and in 1738 founded Fort Rouge on the Red river. Thus the eastern prairies, like James Bay, were drawn into the orbit of the St Lawrence system.

Undoubtedly this extraordinary expansion of the French had been made relatively easy by the marvellous system of natural portages left by glacial melt-water channels. Indeed the French empire in North America was very largely an empire of glacial spillways. It will be recalled that during the advance of the ice-sheets, the northern outlets of the Canadian rivers were blocked. Huge lakes were dammed up in front of the ice. At length their levels rose so high that they drained off by way of the Mississippi, Ohio, Susquehannah, and Mohawk rivers to the south. Later the truly enormous bodies of glacial lake Algonquin, glacial lake Agassiz, and glacial lake Ojibway provided spillways that sometimes connected up with each other. So an astonishingly ramified system of waterways was left by the ice which made for easy travel. The French had few of the arduous overland treks, such as the Spanish and British had to make (Fig. 34).

Thus, but a few years after founding their base in Quebec they had explored the Ottawa, portaged from the Mattawa spillway to Nipissing and Lake Huron. By 1634, only sixteen years after, they had entered Lake Michigan and used the Green Bay spillway to the Wisconsin and possibly the Mississippi. By 1671 they had explored Lake Superior. Ten years later they found the still more convenient spillways, south of Chicago, from Lake Michigan to the Illinois, and had also discovered the Maumee spillway

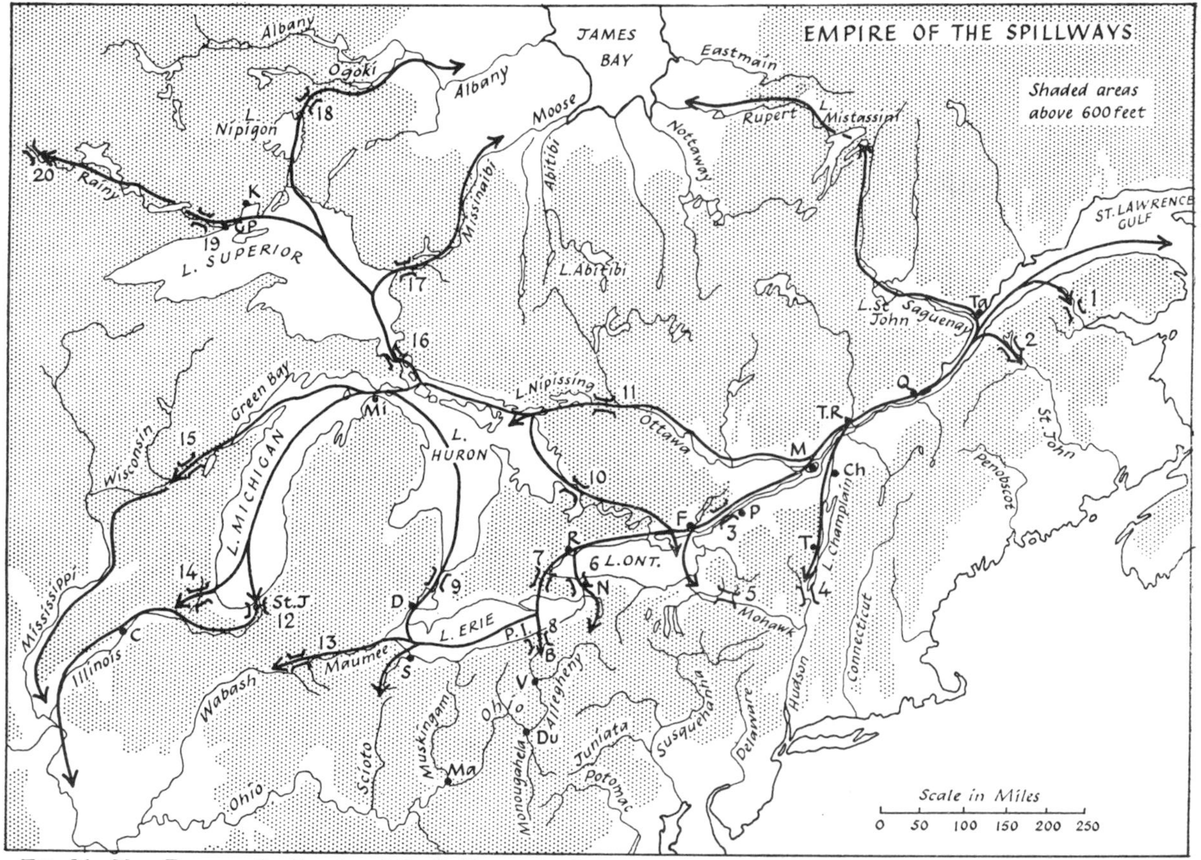

FIG. 34 New France—the Empire of the Spillways. In their advance the French were exceptionally fortunate in being able to use Indian portages that had discovered the links between the St Lawrence–Great Lakes and other river Systems.

FRENCH FORTS—READING FROM EAST TO WEST

Ta, Tadoussac; Q, Quebec; T.R, Three Rivers; Ch, Chambly; M, Montreal; T, Ticonderoga; P, Présentation; F, Frontenac; R, Rouillé; N, Niagara; P.I., Presque Isle; B, Le Boeuf; V, Venango; Du, Duquesne; Ma, Marietta; S, Sanduskey; D, Detroit; Mi, Michilimackinac; St J, St Joseph; C, Crèvecour; K, Kaministikwa; G.P., Grande Portage.

SPILLWAY PORTAGES

1 Matapedia; 2 Temiscouata; 3 St Lawrence; 4 Champlain; 5 Mohawk;

between Lake Erie, the Wabash and the Mississippi, and the Allegheny link between Lake Erie and the Ohio. Finally, by 1740 they had connected the Mississippi–St Lawrence network with James Bay and Red river–Lake Winnipeg. That is to say, within a century and a quarter they had established themselves from Louisbourg to Winnipeg and from James Bay to the Gulf of Mexico. Meanwhile, the British had just succeeded in exploring the portage from the Mohawk to Oswego on Lake Ontario and in discovering the headwaters of the Susquehanna, Potomac, and James rivers. In other words, in the time that the British took to advance about 200 miles inland from tidehead, the French had advanced at least 2,000 miles!

Thus, while the Spanish had been held back by the desert, and the British by the mountains, the French found the gateways into the interior and expanded rapidly landwards. In this they were greatly helped by geography; but their history did not let them meet the challenge. Geographical expansion was a great drain on France. The country was not really prepared, economically and socially, for what it found. It could not bring in enough settlers. Population lagged far behind discovery. The French were after easy wealth rather than pioneer lands for settlement. Their forts were built chiefly for trading purposes, not as centres of agriculture and industry, and although this gave France a great advantage in trade with the Indians, it did not populate the empire with Frenchmen. The French colonies were isolated from each other by great distances. Their lines of communication were stretched to the limit. They could easily be cut. New France was never as safe, or productive, or populous as the British colonies (Fig. 35).

Conditions of Colonization

Like other European nations of the day the French relied on four main methods of developing their colonies; namely, trade monopolies, feudal land grants, the settlement of disbanded soldiers, and the christianization of the natives. Since their introduction to the continent was in the forested hills and plateaux of the Appalachians and the Shield they found themselves dealing with an area rich in fur, but poor in farms. Consequently they stressed trade monopolies rather than land development. Furs were the only thing that offered them quick rich rewards anything at all comparable to those of the Spanish mines.

In 1599 Pontgravé and Chauvin secured a charter to trade for furs in the St Lawrence estuary, and they set up a trading post at Tadoussac. But though

> in the fur-trade they succeeded bravely enough, their colonizing zeal expended itself in leaving sixteen men, ill housed, ill clothed, and ill victualled, to endure the assaults of a Saguenay winter at wind-swept

Tadoussac. On the arrival of the trading-ship from France in the following spring, it was found that of the sixteen unhappy settlers most had died, and the rest were scattered among the wigwams of the Indians. The Tadoussac experiment was not repeated, but the fur-trade was continued with great profit.[1]

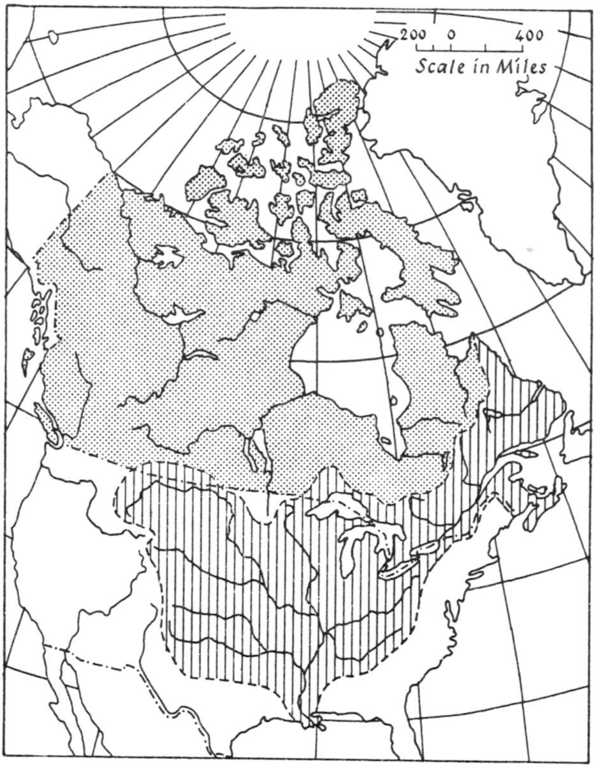

FIG. 35 The French Sphere of Influence in relation to Canada and the U.S.A. (From Guérin.) Though France's major possessions were in what is now the United States, her main influence has been felt in Canada, where the most populous relics of her empire were left and incorporated into British North America.

The fur traders were not greatly concerned about settlement as long as there were well-sited, well-defended posts to support the. trade. Unfortunately

such a rush of merchants came to the St Lawrence that not half of them could dispose of their goods, and many were ruined, while their brawling and greed frightened and disgusted the Indians. As a result a monopoly

[1] Roberts, C. G. D., *A History of Canada*, London, 1898, p. 22

> of the trade was given to a company formed in France by Champlain, under the nominal presidency of Condé, a Prince of the Blood Royal. As far as trade went, the company was very successful. In one year it carried 25,000 furs to France and is said to have paid for several years a dividend of 40 per cent. But as a colonizing agency it did nothing. Indeed, it is obvious that the company did not want settlers. The larger the expanse of ground under cultivation, the farther they had to go afield for furs; the more settled the habits of the people, the less the adventurous life of the woods appealed to them. Thus when Louis Hébert (the first Canadian farmer) came out with his family to settle, the company worried and badgered him.[1]

It must be remembered, however, that the Iroquois had denied the more fertile parts of the St Lawrence basin to the French and that the land left to develop was chiefly rocky, ice-stripped Shield, covered with thinly rooted trees or marsh. This was much better suited to furs than to farms, though doubtless more could have been made of it. For instance, the French did little to promote the lumber trade, a trade that now makes such an important use of the forest.

The Patronage of Canada next fell to the Duc de Ventadour, who used it not so much to develop the colony, either by trade or settlement, but to convert the Indians. A deeply religious man, he felt that France had an obligation to the natives whose land she had taken over. The Récollet mission had already been established at Tadoussac and Quebec. It appealed to the Jesuits for help, and Ventadour sent Brébeuf and two other priests to set up a Jesuit mission in Canada. Although this particular mission met a tragic end at the hands of the Iroquois, in Huronia, the work of the Jesuits continued. It did as much for the exploration of the country as the fur trade. The Jesuit order was powerful and well disciplined. It had the resources and the men to take advantage of the situation. Soon its missionaries had penetrated well up the Saguenay, St Maurice, and Ottawa valleys to the north, the Lower Great Lakes to the south, Lake Michigan and Lake Superior to the west, pacifying and converting the Indians. Mission stations were set up, some of which are important towns today. Indeed, Canada's most important city, Montreal, was established as an outpost of the Church, in spite of the warnings of the then governor, Montmagny, who was afraid that the mission might fall to the Iroquois. Other towns founded by the Church were Midland, in Huronia, and Sault Ste Marie.

The work of traders and missionaries had done much to open up the country, but not to settle and develop it. However, the English were starting up genuine colonies along the Atlantic coast plains, at no great distance

[1] Grant, *History of Canada*, p. 48.

to the south, and this fact may have spurred the French authorities to do more about their territories. Cardinal Richelieu was among the first to realize that to countermand England on the continent of Europe meant to challenge it in North America and elsewhere. In 1628 he organized the Company of the Hundred Associates not merely to extend the fur trade, but to colonize the country. In order to retain their fur monopoly the hundred associates had to send out three hundred colonists in the first year, and four hundred a year for the next fifteen years. The company obtained grants of land from the King on the grounds of fealty and homage, which meant calling out their settlers for military service on the King's behalf whenever required. But actual settlement was very slow. In 1661, fifty-three years after the founding of Quebec, Boucher reported that there were barely more than 2,000 Frenchmen in all Canada. A third of these were at the town of Quebec. The rest were very thinly scattered over the great land they ruled. (A similar survey in Spanish America, that of Velasco, showed a distinctly more effective colonization within the equivalent period. Thus in 1574, that is, fifty-three years after the rebuilding of Mexico, there were over 15,000 Spaniards in that city alone, and another 1,200 Spaniards in five other towns. Altogether there were 160,000 Spaniards in the Americas at that date, that is, only eighty-two years after the 'Discovery'.)

Dissatisfaction with company rule led Louis XIV to take matters into his own hands. In 1663 Canada was made a Province of France, like the metropolitan provinces, and was governed by the King, through his appointees. These were a Governor, a Bishop, and an Intendant; the first to look after military affairs, the second religious, and the third civil. These three powerful figures, assisted by twelve councillors appointed by the Governor or the King, formed the governing body and the supreme court of the colony. Louis sent out Talon to be his Intendant who, convinced that trade and settlement went hand in hand, determined to make use of and populate the land. This was done chiefly through the Seigneural system, whereby the King gave large grants of land to men to be designated *Seigneurs* on condition that they cleared the land and served him in war.

It was impossible to clear the dense forests unaided and, therefore, to meet their conditions of tenure, *seigneurs* had to subdivide their estates into small holdings and rent these out to tenants. They retained certain rights of cutting wood on tenants' land (for the erection of public buildings), of acquiring tenants' labour (chiefly for building roads), and of collecting *cens* and *rentes*. The *cens* involved a small payment on the frontage of the tenant's lot, the *rentes* a payment on his acreage. These payments were usually rendered in kind, such as a chicken or a pig. The *seigneurs* also exacted the *lods et ventes*, or a payment of one-twelfth of the value of the lot should tenants sell their lands. Finally, they had the right to insist that every tenant ground his corn in the manorial mill, for which, of course, a toll was charged.

An interesting outcome of the Seigneural system was its influence on the *forms of settlement*. The exaction of labour for building roads was much resented and the inhabitants were therefore inclined to use the rivers as their highways, in the way the Indians had done before them. It became most important for farms to secure a frontage on the river. However, they were taxed on this frontage. Consequently, they kept their frontage as narrow as possible, usually not more than 260 yards. To compensate for this, they acquired lots that went back in length ten times their width; that is, 2,600 yards. Thus a series of long, narrow farms came to line the St Lawrence and its tributaries, with the farm buildings placed very close to each other. This narrowness of the French-Canadian farm was, and still is, one of the distinctive features of Canadian settlement (see Plate 21, facing page 160).

Though doubtless social and economic in origin, it did have a sound geographical basis,[1] which is probably why it took such firm root and eventually developed a band of continuous settlement along the St Lawrence estuary and up the Ottawa. It will be recalled that this whole area had risen slowly from the sea after the Ice Age. As it did so, its rivers cut down with fresh vigour and developed long, narrow terraces along their sides. Meantime the seas cut afresh into the shore and produced shore-long narrow benches. The best use of the river terraces and raised sea-benches was to divide them into strip-like farms where each farmer could have a bit of bottomland or shore, some terrace or bench, and then some of the older, rougher, rockier, ice-scoured land above. Had terrace or bench been laid out in wide farms, parallel with and not transverse to river or sea, then fewer people could have shared their advantages. Even fewer people would have colonized the rough, rocky land behind.

Unfortunately for France, it took the land up very slowly. Talon may have had the ambition to promote dense and continuous settlement, yet he found it difficult to effect it. He tried his best. He saw to it that men, stock, and seed were sent out from France in quantity. Indeed, he had shiploads of women sent out too, mostly from religious orphanages, and, by taxing bachelors, exerted sufficient pressure on men to go to the marriage market in Quebec and get themselves a wife! New men arriving were expected to help the tenants clear the forest, or to work at a trade in a town, for a period of three years; then they had the right to claim a small hold from a local *seigneur*.

These forceful measures did help to a certain extent. Yet they were not sufficient. Talon finally suggested to the King that when the French officers and soldiers had defeated the Iroquois they should be allowed to remain as

---

[1] Trudel, M., *Le Régime Seigneural*, p. 4.

settlers, the officers to secure *seigneuries* along the frontiers of the colony, as for example in the Richelieu valley, where they could continue to offer protection. Even this policy was not effective and few Frenchmen were induced to colonize the new country. Consequently by the time that France and Britain finally contested the control of the continent, 'but eighty thousand whites constituted the semi-dependent and unprogressive population of Canada and Louisiana, over a stretch of territory above two thousand miles in length, against the million and a quarter self-supporting English colonists, who for the most part were, from Georgia to New Hampshire, massed on the narrow plain between the Appalachians and the sea'.[1]

Territorial Divisions

The low population, spread over very wide areas, made it difficult to administer the French possessions. There were very few posts at which government could be centred, and large tracts in between over which only nominal control could be exerted. The nearness of St Croix and Port Royal, on the Bay of Fundy, to New England made them vulnerable. Quebec was further removed from danger, and formed a natural centre between the Gulf of St Lawrence and the St Lawrence river. It was early chosen as the seat of government. But the areas dependent on it were remote from each other, and divided by mountains or low heights of land. Gradually they came to form separate administrative districts, if not provinces. There were four chief regions of French settlement: Acadia, Canada, Illinois, and Louisiana. The French claim over Acadia first embraced the whole coast between lat. 40° and lat. 46°, i.e. between Cape Cod and Cape Breton. But English settlements in New England and Maine and Scottish ones in Nova Scotia challenged these pretensions, and although the treaties of St Germain in 1632, Breda in 1667, and Ryswick in 1697 restored British conquests to France, the French hold steadily weakened. In 1713 the Treaty of Utrecht gave the Nova Scotian peninsula to Britain, and French Acadia contracted to northern Maine and New Brunswick, from the Kennebec to the Appalachian divide, together with Prince Edward and Cape Breton islands. Port Royal and the Annapolis valley ceased to be the centre of government, which was removed to Louisburg in 1719.

The governor, however, was responsible to the governor of Quebec, France's chief base in the New World. This was the focus of the vast colony of Canada that stretched from the mouth of the St Lawrence Gulf to the head of Lake Superior. The boundaries of this area were vague in the extreme, except in the south, where they ran along the height of land between the St Lawrence and the Bay of Fundy as far as the Connecticut

[1] Thwaites, R. G., *France in America, 1497–1763*, New York, 1905, p. 128.

valley and thence west along the 45th parallel to Lake Ontario. They were then reckoned to strike south-west to the Ohio river. The western boundary was the Mississippi river and the headwaters of Lake Superior. On the north, Canada extended to the height of land dividing the St Lawrence from Hudson Bay, although this was contested both by New France and the Hudson's Bay Company.

Obviously such a huge region could scarcely be administered from Quebec City, at its eastern end. When the Mississippi became used by the fur traders, as well as the St Lawrence, the traders and settlers of that great triangle of land between the Great Lakes, the Ohio, and the Mississippi looked to the south. Strenuous efforts were made by Quebec to control Illinois, as the district was known, but in 1721 it was made one of the districts of Louisiana. It developed quite rapidly. The Jesuits set up an Academy at Kaskaskia while the Sulpicians had developed the town of Cahokia. Fort Chartres—'the centre of life and fashion in the West'—and other forts were erected. Nearly a thousand French settlers took up land, and by 1746, when 'there was a scarcity of provisions in New Orleans the Illinois French sent thither, in one winter, upward of 800,000 weight of flour'.[1] Meantime, France had contested Spanish influence in the lower Mississippi. Iberville sailed from Brest in 1698 to plant the French flag in the Mississippi delta. Settlements were established from Biloxi to Natchez, and in 1701 Louisiana was founded as a separate French province in the New World, governed not from Quebec but directly from France. Lead-mining in the Missouri hills, plantation farming in the delta—making use of imported African slaves—and the fur trade, invited an increasing number of settlers. In 1718 Bienville established the town of New Orleans, which became the seat of government. The French extended their claims from New Mexico to Carolina to embrace the main riverways of the Mississippi, Missouri, Ohio, Wabash, and Illinois, and three years later divided this huge area into military districts, known as New Orleans, Biloxi, Mobile, and Alabama, along the Gulf; and Yazoo, Natchez, Arkansas, and Illinois up the river. Thus they provided a framework for colonization, reaching from Louisburg to New Orleans (Fig. 36).

Conclusion

The French, led by traders and missionaries, penetrated swiftly and deeply into North America. Entering by the Gulf of St Lawrence they found the old glacial melt-water channels between the St Lawrence–Great Lakes and the Ohio–Mississippi waterways and descended to the Gulf of Mexico. Thus they held the two major gateways into the continent and dominated its heartland. They possessed varied resources, from the small but fertile basins

[1] Ibid., p. 85.

in the northern Appalachians, through the great rocky stretches of the Canadian Shield, to the wide, flat, and potentially rich plains of the Interior Lowlands. However, they did little with these resources, content to use the

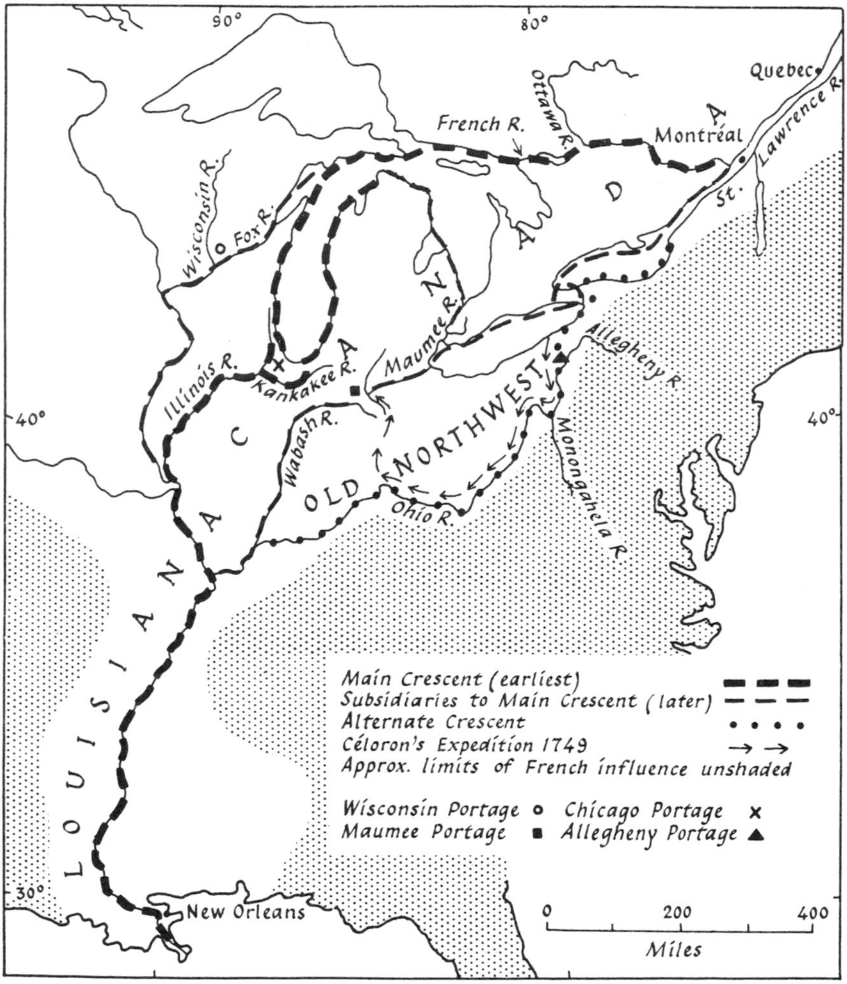

FIG. 36 The Life-lines of New France. (After Johnson.)

all-prevalent forests for the fur trade. Their highly centralized, feudalistic system of government and land tenure inhibited agriculture and they never had the large class of artisans and merchant-capitalists to develop local industries and town life. Consequently French population remained low, and France's hold on its far-flung empire was relatively weak.

While they showed considerable political and military skill in organizing their territories, they never had enough settlers to make their claims real, and consequently, when the Seven Years War broke out, they lost all of their New World empire, that west of the Mississippi falling to Spain, that to the east going to Britain. Thus Britain became, for a space of years, the major power on the continent, and the rise of Anglo-America was assured.

CHAPTER SIX

European Colonization

III. BRITAIN IN AMERICA

Geography and History

British settlement in North America, like that of Spain and France, owed its initial character to historical and social forces; yet geography was not without its importance. The Arctic to sub-Arctic climate of the Hudson Bay region prohibited agriculture and thus helped to entrench the fur trade and company rule and enterprise. The mixing of the ocean currents off the Grand Banks that is so much a part of the geography of Newfoundland gave that island colony a wealth of fish that partly compensated for its poverty of soils. The harsh climate of its interior, together with the rocky terrain, kept settlement to the coast and prevented agriculture from flourishing. Attempts by various grantees to develop the grants of land made to them failed, and encouraged other grantees to look much farther south. Virginia grew because Newfoundland stood still.

The geography of the Atlantic coast plain did much to shape its development. The warm-temperate to sub-tropical climate of Virginia, Carolina, and Georgia aided the growth of sugar, rice, indigo, tobacco, and cotton plantations. The cooler climate of New York and New England, on the other hand, favoured the raising of wheat, oats, and rye, clover and hay, and the keeping of cattle and sheep. Of course, many cereals and a large number of cattle were raised in the south, and tobacco and even cotton were attempted in the north; but in the main climate confirmed, if it did not control, the plantation system south of the Delaware, and the system of freehold farms, operated by their owners, to the north.

Once the plantation system got established, then the peculiar nature of the coast in the south, with its many great drowned inlets behind protective spits and bay-bars, did much to preserve and strengthen it. The early plantations were each able to get a share of the waterfront and thus to ship their produce out directly to Britain. There was not the need to have their goods gathered together and channelled through major ports; each large plantation had its own port. Of course this lowland of wide estuaries going back to low divides could also have been used by small-hold farmers. But the fact that it lent itself so well to large-scale plantation agriculture led the plantations to get the upper hand; small-hold farming moved up country to the rolling plains above tidewater.

In New England the coast was also indented, but between the bays were glacial ridges or rocky hills. The coastal inlets did not really lend themselves to large-scale farming. On the contrary, characterized as they were by small pockets of good land between knubbly, awkward uplands, they sponsored small, isolated, independent settlements where a scattering of little farms gathered about, and dealt through, a seaside town.

Moreover, the way in which the northern Appalachians swung down through New England in long belts of mountains—the Taconics, the Berkshires, the Green mountains, the White mountains, and the coastal uplands—produced a series of narrow, elongated valleys, separated from each other, which early encouraged the development of independent colonies; colonies of independently minded people. There was more chance for people to 'hive off' from a main waterside colony and establish separate communities in the interior, partitioned off by forested ridges from each other, than almost anywhere else. (Not until settlers had got behind the pine belt on the Carolina piedmont were southern colonists given the same sense of isolation and independence.)

Thus geography did have a vital role in affairs; climate and terrain conditioned all activity. Nevertheless, geography did not *rule* affairs; it did not put the characteristic stamp on settlement. This was done by history. It was history, not geography, that gave rise to the large companies like the Hudson's Bay Company, the London Company, and the Plymouth Company through which the first enterprises were carried on. History was responsible for the strongly feudalistic tendency in the settlement of the south and of Maryland and New York, as it was for the strongly egalitarian tendencies in Delaware, Pennsylvania, and New England. Geography may have helped to *establish* the plantations and the slavery system in the south, but it did not *create* them. Had the Plymouth Fathers landed in the Roanoke valley, bringing with them their love of small farms knit together about small towns, the face of the south would have been very different. The geography of the south could have been adapted to the township system as well as to the plantation one. There was nothing in the drowned inlets of Chesapeake Bay and Albemarle Sound that necessitated a manorial system based on the plantation.

Consequently, to understand the kinds of colonization that went on under the British, and the types of landscapes they produced, one must go back to the history of settlement. It was the history that determined the *type* of settlement; geography its growth and development, its success and extent.

Historic Conditions at the Outset of Colonization

Britain was a good deal slower than Spain and Portugal, although contemporaneous with France, in its development and use of colonies. This was no doubt due to the relatively slow evolution of unity at home. Henry VII had commissioned Cabot to sail to the New World, and Britain could have colonized Newfoundland as early as 1497, only a few years after Spain claimed Espanola and the Caribbean. But little was done to follow this up. Under Henry VIII occurred the great religious upheaval that shook Britain

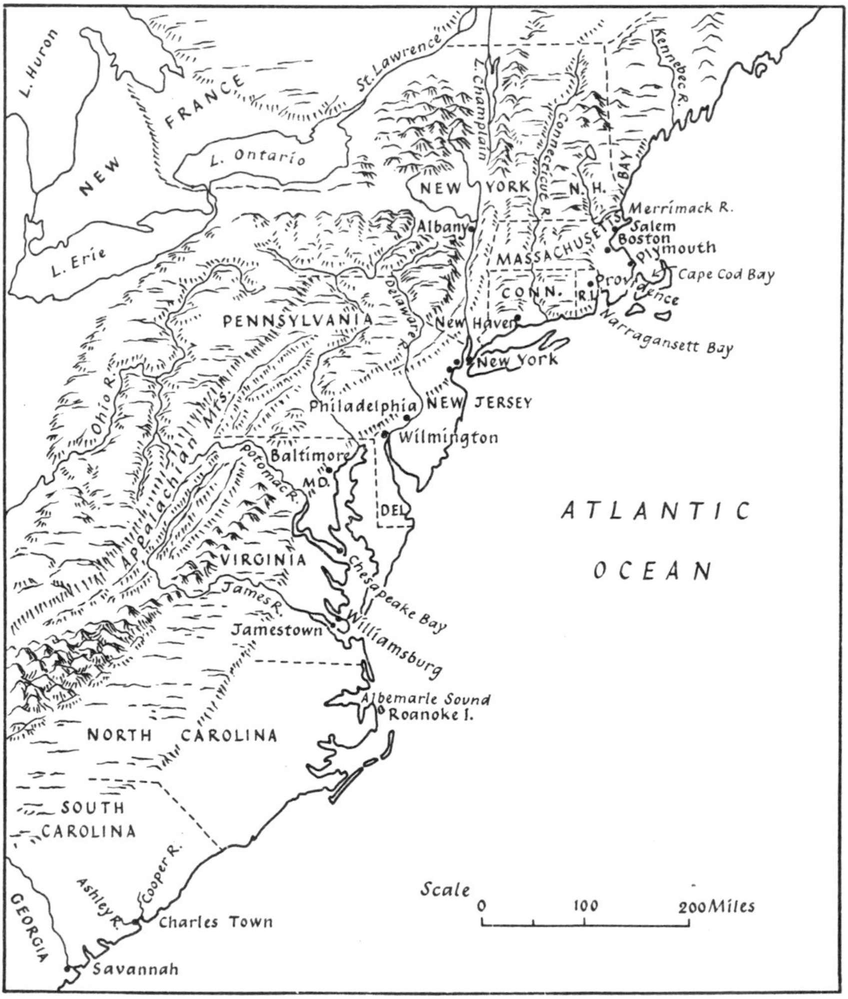

FIG. 37 The Early British Colonies, on the Atlantic coast plain, protected from the French and interior Indians by the Appalachians.

to its foundations and Elizabeth I faced the anger of the Catholic kings. Sir Humphrey Gilbert took possession of Newfoundland in the name of the Crown in 1583, but the war with Spain threatened and no formal attempt at colonization was made until a quarter of a century had passed. Although the Tudors nursed into being the sea power by which an island kingdom alone could develop an empire, it was left to the Stuarts, who first successfully united Britain, to launch out and possess new terrain (Fig. 37).

The foundation of British North America thus lay in that vexed and unequal régime that characterized the Stuarts and that witnessed a Britain torn by civil war. Obviously a king like James I, who propounded the doctrine of the 'divine right of kings', was going to develop the colonies very much as it suited him. Indeed, as Ashley[1] has pointed out, 'Through all vicissitudes it was more or less accepted that the colonies were primarily the concern of the Crown or Executive and not of parliament. King James I and King Charles I were determined not to allow parliament to interfere in colonial affairs . . . and after the Restoration the monarchy reasserted its prerogative of colonial administration.'

Britain and British Expansion

This being the case the Crown, influenced by the ideas of the time, had a good deal to say in Britain's overseas expansion. Wealth from overseas trade and the command of strategic bases were two major concerns. Concessions to royal favourites had a significant part, especially as the necessity of holding 'loyal' colonies became important. The desire to relieve England of unemployment and other social ills and to be rid of troublesome minorities also prevailed. Religious zeal, however, was notably absent, the Stuart kings having enough to do to impose their religious views upon Britain without concerning themselves with the heathen. (It was not until the Society for Promoting Christian Knowledge was formed in the reign of King William III that missionary enterprise had much bearing on colonial expansion.)

Wealth from overseas trade was probably the chief spur to colonial development. Although Cabot had found little of value in Newfoundland he had reported that the fish were so thick in the seas as almost to stop his ship! Fishermen began to use the banks in the middle sixteenth century. When Gilbert sailed into St John's harbour he was met by ships of all nations. The fisheries increased. So much so that early in the seventeenth century as many as ten thousand men earned a living there, while in the second half the numbers had grown to twenty thousand. Trade in dried fish became widespread. (It must be remembered that the agricultural revolution had scarcely advanced to the stage where it could supply most people with mutton or beef; fish was indispensable.)

---

[1] Ashley, M., *England in the Seventeenth Century*, London, 1952, p. 222.

Elizabeth and James, however, were after quicker returns, and both supported Sir Walter Raleigh in his efforts to find gold. Unfortunately Raleigh picked the very site where gold was least likely to be found—the lagoon-fringed shores of Chesapeake Bay on the Atlantic coast plain. One of Raleigh's lieutenants, Lane, made extensive explorations for gold, but found none. However, he brought back to England two products of major importance, the potato and tobacco. Raleigh gave the courtiers a taste for the latter, and the colonists in Virginia soon started to grow it. Indeed, it became so popular that at one time the governor forbade people to raise it unless they had put down at least two acres in corn, otherwise everybody would have turned to cash farming and the colony might have run short of food. Tobacco raising was even done by the townsmen along the narrow margins of the streets.

Tobacco farming really started up the plantation system. Here was a crop with great cash value that could be grown on a large scale by cheap labour on relatively light soils. It took on with remarkable speed. Twelve years after the establishment of Jamestown (1607) tobacco was being used as currency, settlers paying 120 lb. of tobacco for the privilege of marrying the young women then being shipped to the colony! The low, flat, moist, sandy-loam soils of the coast were well suited to the plant. The sub-tropical climate brought it on fast yet ripened it slowly. The many inroads of the sea made transportation cheap and speedy; indeed hardly a better site could have been found for the crop. 'Large fortunes were accumulated in a year or two by scores of planters. In 1619 twenty thousand pounds were exported, and in 1622 sixty thousand. Tobacco entered more and more into the life of the colony and the crop in 1628 amounted to upward of 500,000 pounds.' King James levied an exaction of 20 per cent from the colonial producer, and charged the Virginia Company £20,000 for a monopoly of trade in England. King Charles, in addition, levied a customs due from the English consumer!

The quest for wealth led to the rise of other plantation crops, especially as it was hoped 'to free Britain of dependence upon foreign lands'.[1] In the so-called 'dismal' swamps behind the great bay-bars through which the sluggish, meandering, muddy rivers flowed conditions were ideal for growing rice: thick clayey soils, a covering of flood water, and hot, long summers combined to favour the crop. Many difficulties did occur. It was extremely difficult to clear the swamps; negro labour was required; walls had to be built to keep in the flood waters of the river and keep out the tidal waters of the sea. But profits were good and the industry remained a flourishing one until rice from the East became competitive.

All sorts of schemes were tried to capitalize on the sub-tropical climate

[1] Brown, R. H., *Historical Geography of the United States*, New York, 1948, pp. 38, 63.

and the deep virgin soils. These included the raising of mulberries for a silk industry, and of indigo for the trade in dyes. The former soon failed, but the latter expanded and was valuable until competition from the East, in the form of the indigo planters of India, brought it down. As it declined, cotton-growing took its place. By the end of the eighteenth century cotton had established itself as a most promising crop, especially when the upland variety allowed it to escape from the coast, where sea-island cotton was in vogue, to the middle plain and then the Piedmont. The long growing season free of frost, the rains of early summer, the bright sun of late summer, and the deep forest soils all helped to make it a safe, profitable, and popular plant. The main problem in raising it was labour, since the fields required a lot of care and the plant a lot of handling, but with the introduction of slaves and, later, of cotton-ginning machines, this difficulty was overcome.

The south made so much out of plantation farming that it became unbalanced and was very subject to price fluctuations. Moreover, it was ruining the soil over considerable tracts of land. The Crown became concerned. Thus, although Charles made a good deal of money out of the tobacco trade, he warned the planters against 'building their plantation wholly on smoke', and urged them to vary their economy and, in particular, to make pitch and tar from the surrounding forests. In the same way John Guy had been advised, when starting a colony in Newfoundland, not to rely wholly on fish and cod liver oil, but also on 'the cutting of timber for export, the raising of sheep and other matters'.[1] The insistence on forest products points up another important trade, that in naval stores. The Baltic countries had had a virtual monopoly of this trade, but the wealth of oak and pine forests stretching from Carolina to Newfoundland gave Britain the hope that it could become independent of foreign powers. The import of timber, turpentine, pitch, and tar from the colonies steadily grew and greatly augmented Britain's own fast-dwindling supplies.

The forests offered still another source of gain in the fur trade. The British were rather slow in getting into this compared with the French, but soon rivalled their competitors. Initially they were in a quite advantageous position; their fur trading areas stretched all along the coast and were readily accessible to year-round open water. (The French by contrast had to strike far into the continent and then collect the furs at Montreal which was blocked by ice for six months of the year.) The British colonies could all benefit by the fur trade, and help pay off their initial costs in this way. Some men like William Claiborne, one of the first secretaries of state for Virginia, made fortunes in fur. (Indeed, friction between Virginia and Maryland brought on a miniature war over control of Kent Island, an

[1] *Newfoundland, an Introduction to Canada's New Province*, Can. Govt. Handbook, Ottawa, 1951, p. 16.

important fur trading emporium deemed by Claiborne to be in Virginia and by Lord Baltimore to belong to Maryland!)

By and large, however, the southern colonies were more interested in tobacco, rice, or cotton plantations, and it was the northern colonies that came to dominate the fur trade. The Council for New England, set up in 1620, was given a monopoly of fur trading on the northern Atlantic coast, and New England merchants rapidly developed the trade. After the Dutch were replaced by the English on the Hudson, the New York traders took the lead, since the geography of the Hudson–Mohawk enabled them to tap the fur-rich region of the Lower Great Lakes. This great natural routeway into the largest fur-catchment basin in the east rivalled even that of the St Lawrence, and enabled New York to compete with Montreal over a wide area.

Britain's initial advantage as a fur trader was soon lost. The trade was bedevilled by the fact that settlers were moving into the country in great numbers, destroying forests and wild life together, and making a better living from farming. However, there was one area for which this was not true—the Hudson Bay, that vast depression in the Canadian Shield whose shores were covered by bleak tundra or uninviting taiga. As we have seen, farming was out of the question. There was no alternative use for the region but fur trading. When Radisson and Groseilliers, the eminent French explorers who claimed—though probably falsely—to have first reached the 'Bay of the North', were repudiated by their own country and sought support in England, their account of the wealth of fur to be obtained in the north—and generally speaking northern furs had been found to be superior—attracted a good deal of attention. Consequently in 1668 two ships were sent out to Hudson Bay. One of these, the *Nonsuch*, returned under Groseilliers, heavily laden with furs. At once the London merchants became interested and through the patronage of Prince Rupert, the cousin of the King, they obtained a charter from King Charles II in 1670 to set up 'The Company of Adventurers of England trading into Hudson's Bay'.

British mercantile thought definitely regarded the colonies as part of, and tributary to, the British economic system. The whole idea was to establish plantations overseas that would supply the goods which could not be produced at home. Furthermore, the colonies were preserves for Britain's export trade. The colonists were given little freedom in starting up industries; they were permitted the purely local kind that provided them the essentials of ground corn, shoe leather, and homespun cloth. But in the main they were not allowed to develop manufactures the nature or extent of which would rival British ones. They were expected to obtain most of their finished goods from Britain. Thus the geography of industry was strictly limited. So also was that of trade. The colonies were required to export and import goods in British ships, and, in most cases, to sell to Britain only, being shut out from the other European markets. An early instance of this relates to the London Company trading with Virginia. King James I became concerned with its excessive reliance on tobacco. Far too much was being raised and there was a likelihood that the price would fall. He therefore set limits to production. The colonists replied by selling the whole of the crop to the Dutch! This was a severe blow to Britain, and the King retaliated by issuing an order, in 1621, requiring the Company to sell all its production in England. History thus dominated the geography of trade in North America.

Strategic considerations, as well as trade, influenced colonization. In fact, the two went together. So keen was the rivalry between the western nations that they offered the protection of their fleets to merchant shipping and defended the establishment of trading posts with military forts. Thus each nation was deeply implicated in trade expansion. It was thought that trade could flourish only in ratio to naval or military power—an idea that still is not altogether dead, as witness strategy and oil in the Middle East.

England's first positive claim on North America, that of Gilbert at St John's, was probably put forward as much for strategic as for economic reasons. Portuguese and French fishermen were using the Newfoundland banks and harbours almost as much as British ones. France had explored the Gulf of St Lawrence, and, with Newfoundland in its possession, would have commanded the whole of north-eastern North America. Britain's hold on St John's not only safeguarded the fishery but guarded Britain's wider rights in the region. Farther south, in Acadia, the French had established themselves in a very strategic situation at Port Royal where they could outflank the English in New England. As the years went by it became just as strategic for the English, and especially the settlers in Massachusetts, to get possession of the place. Matters came to a head in 1710, after the French had raided New England shipping and caused serious economic loss. ('In March 1709, one French privateer left winter quarters at Port Royal and in twelve days brought in four vessels loaded with wheat and corn.'[1]) A mixed British–New England force captured the port and in 1713 the French gave up their claim to Nova Scotia. Thirty-six years later Halifax was established as a naval and military base to countermand the French in Louisbourg, and, together with St John's, to enable the British to control the entrance to Canada by the Gulf of St Lawrence.

Rivalry between New England and New Amsterdam also led to the rise of certain strategic centres. The Dutch spread eastward from the Hudson and in 1633 had established a fort on the Connecticut, where Hartford now stands. The British at once replied by putting up a fort, somewhat farther

[1] Bird, W. R. (ed.), *Historic Nova Scotia*, Halifax, p. 23.

up the valley, at Windsor. Subsequently, after the British had taken over from the Dutch, they found it necessary to set up strategic centres in the Hudson–Champlain trench, such as Crown Point, and in the Mohawk–Lake Ontario gap, as at Fort Oswego. These were directed against the French, who had been the rivals of the Dutch in the St Lawrence–Lower Great Lakes region.

Royal patronage in the granting of personal concessions also promoted colonization. King James I was peculiarly addicted to 'court favourites'—even more so than Queen Elizabeth. He gave a number of large tracts of land in North America to favoured individuals on a feudal or quasi-feudal basis, securing in return, of course, certain royalties and dues. Thus in Newfoundland, James gave land to Sir William Vaughan, who founded a colony at Trepassey; to Lord Falkland, who colonized Trinity Bay; and to Lord Baltimore, who developed Ferryland. None of these colonies did very well, and in 1637 they were merged into a single grant, given to Sir David Kirke.

In Nova Scotia, King James I gave an enormous tract of land to Sir William Alexander in 1621; and, in 1624, instituted an order of baronets specifically to promote colonization. In the next ten years no less than 111 of these 'Nova Scotia baronets' were created, although few of them actually took up land. One of them, later Lord Ochiltree, tried to establish a colony at Baleine in Cape Breton Island, but it was destroyed by the French, and Ochiltree lost an investment of £20,000.

It took a good deal of wealth to prepare for, establish, and maintain a colony, and most of those to whom individual concessions were given were men of substance, willing to invest deeply in order, as they hoped, to make substantial profits. Unfortunately many had to take up a grant without really knowing what they were letting themselves in for. Thus Lord Baltimore, who had bought land from Vaughan, in Newfoundland, obtained a bare, bleak, unproductive tract. He decided to shift to a warmer zone. The mid-Atlantic coast had proved to be much more attractive, and in 1629 he asked King Charles for a 'grant of a precinct in Virginia'. The Virginians were not anxious to admit him as he was a Roman Catholic. After several years of negotiation he finally obtained (1632) a grant on the northern margin of Virginia and named the new colony Maryland, after the Queen. In the meantime Charles had granted a large tract of land south of Virginia to a court favourite, Sir Robert Heath, who named his colony Carolina, after the King.

These grants were on a semi-feudal basis, and did much to plant the English manorial system in North America. The concessionaires had the right to rent out land to tenant farmers, or, if they chose, to subdivide their estates and sell the land in separate plantations or farms. They could also charge tolls on roads or mills and issue certain kinds of licences. In Newfoundland, for example, Kirke soon started to raise money on his investment by charging rent for the platforms on which fish were dried and for the portions of the shore where fishermen erected their curing huts. He also sold tavern licences and levied certain taxes on the use of public improvements. Similar rents and levies were imposed on the manorial plantations of the south.

Social reasons for colonial expansion were also very important—probably much more so than was the case with Spain or France. Britain was going through a period of tremendous social ferment when colonization began. The agricultural revolution had started, the enclosure movement was widespread, surplus numbers of dispossessed peasants wandered about, the drift of people into the towns had begun, cities became overcrowded, new callings were followed and, above all, the Reformation was splitting up the religious life of the people into ever more and more sects. At few times in its history has England ever been so restless and divided and yet so energetic and progressive. Conflict finally broke out and the country was plunged into civil war. The land went from the extremes of royal autocracy to those of parliamentarian demagogy, from Laud's fierce uniformitarianism to the equally fierce independentism of Cromwell's colonels. It was no wonder that men cried, like Hallam, 'If these troublous times hold, we must all faine forth to Virginia.'

The agricultural revolution was particularly disturbing. During the latter half of the sixteenth century the despoiling of the monasteries and the enclosing of common lands rendered many people landless. The enclosure movement continued in the seventeenth century, with, in particular, 'those enclosures made to provide suitable residential estates, and gentlemen's seats'.[1] The number of wandering poor swelled to alarming proportions, and 'an army of idle, loitering persons and valiant beggars' went through the land. True, some of these were absorbed in the newly expanding towns, but many could find no work. The authorities were glad to be rid of them. Wastrels and offenders were committed by magistrates to the colonies; colonial development companies were glad to make use of them.

The situation was aggravated by a fairly rapid increase in population. Baker puts the population of England at the beginning of the seventeenth century at about 3,500,000. Estimates for the end of the century vary from 5,200,000 to 8,039,160. 'Accepting either the lowest or the highest estimates, it is clear that a large increase in population took place.'[2] Indeed many writers of the day claimed that Britain was seriously overpopulated. Even

[1] Baker, J. N. L., 'England in the Seventeenth Century', in *Historical Geography of England*, ed. Darby, H. C., London, 1936, p. 397.

[2] Ibid., p. 436.

the towns could not take up the surplus. England's chief industry, the manufacture of woollen goods, though witnessing a general expansion, saw some serious fluctuations. Craft guilds made it very difficult to use labour not properly apprenticed, and often opposed the rise of new crafts. There was much temporary unemployment as craftsmen tried to set up for themselves or moved from one city to another. Unemployment in England was the opportunity for overseas expansion. In 1606 when King James I gave charters to 'certain knights, gentlemen and merchants of London' and 'sundry knights and merchants in and about Plymouth' to colonize North America, both organizations turned to the unemployed for many of their settlers, and found ready emigrants.

It was, however, among religious dissidents that the companies or land concessionaires found their readiest, and possibly most numerous, emigrants. Religious differences were growing every year, and were becoming increasingly bitter and irreconcilable. During Elizabeth's reign

> no kind of nonconformity, Puritan or Separatist, was allowed to flourish in peace. Therefore, towards the end of her reign, the Puritans turned their eyes hopefully to her heir. The future James I had been brought up in Scotland where episcopacy had been abolished and the State Church had become Calvinistic and Presbyterian. James was destined to disappoint the Puritans. He kept the Calvinistic theology which he had imbibed . . . but Presbyterianism he rejected because he hated its democratic tendencies. 'No bishop, no king', he remarked, adding, 'A Scottish Presbytery as well agreeth with a Monarchy as God and the devil. Then Jack and Tom and Will and Dick shall meet, and at their pleasure censure me and my Council, and all our proceedings: then Will shall stand up and say, it must be thus; then Dick shall reply and say, nay but we will have it thus.' The Hampton Court Conference met in 1603 to give the Puritans an opportunity of discussing with the Bishops the reform of the Church. James, who prided himself on his theological learning, presided and he ended the Conference by threatening to 'make the Puritans conform, or else harry them out of the land'. In the next year no fewer than three hundred Puritan clergy were ejected, while the Separatists were constantly persecuted by the authorities.[1]

Smyth, one of the first Separatists and sometimes regarded as the father of the Baptists, left the Church of England in 1606. He formed a free-church group who covenanted 'As the Lord's free people . . . to walk in all His ways, made known or *to be made known unto them.* The ecclesiastical authorities were not long in discovering and persecuting this Separatist church which,

[1] Underwood, A. C., *A History of the English Baptists* London, 1947, p. 33.

in 1608, emigrated to Amsterdam.'[1] Ultimately, several Separatist churches moved to Holland and it was from among these dissenters that some of the 'Plymouth Fathers', the founders of New England, came. Persecution mounted under Archbishop Laud who was determined to make everyone conform to the Church of England. As a result, 'Many thousand religious refugees of all classes', Trevelyan points out, 'abandoned good prospects and loved homes in England, to camp out between the shores of a lonely ocean and forests swarming with savage tribes. *Laud was the founder of Anglo-Saxon supremacy in the new world.*'[2]

These religious settlers were passionate lovers of freedom and of democracy and therefore established colonies of farmers, artisans, merchants, and professional men who owned their own land or businesses and managed their own affairs. They formed very different colonies from those of the manorial plantations in the south. This difference was to have tremendous significance not only for the settlement pattern and the territorial organization of Anglo-America but for the whole geography of the continent. There is probably no area in the world where the social factor has been more important in shaping the course of geography than in Puritan America. Indeed, the geography of New England, and of all that part of the continent to which New Englanders carried their habits of mind, owes at least as much to the social environment as to the physical one.

Conditions of Colonization

The different purposes behind colonization, and the different methods used in colonizing, combined with differences in relief and climate, produced distinctive conditions and patterns of life. The southern and northern colonies differed considerably; the mid-Atlantic ones were transitional between them.

In the southern colonies fishing was negligible, the fur trade, though significant at first, soon declined, forest products grew in value, especially when the southern pineries were worked, but plantation agriculture in subtropical crops became dominant, principally on large manorial estates, either under great companies or individual concessionaires. In the northern colonies both fishing and the fur trade were of considerable and persistent importance, forest products were also very valuable, there was not the same dependence on agriculture but what existed was vigorous (growing out of small farms worked by individual proprietors), few large estates occurred, and most of the settlement took place in groups giving rise to small towns. In the mid-Atlantic colonies the fur trade was important up to the middle of the eighteenth century, but then declined, agriculture was the main

---

[1] Ibid., p. 34 (author's italics).
[2] Trevelyan, G. M., *England under the Stuarts*, p. 173 (our italics).

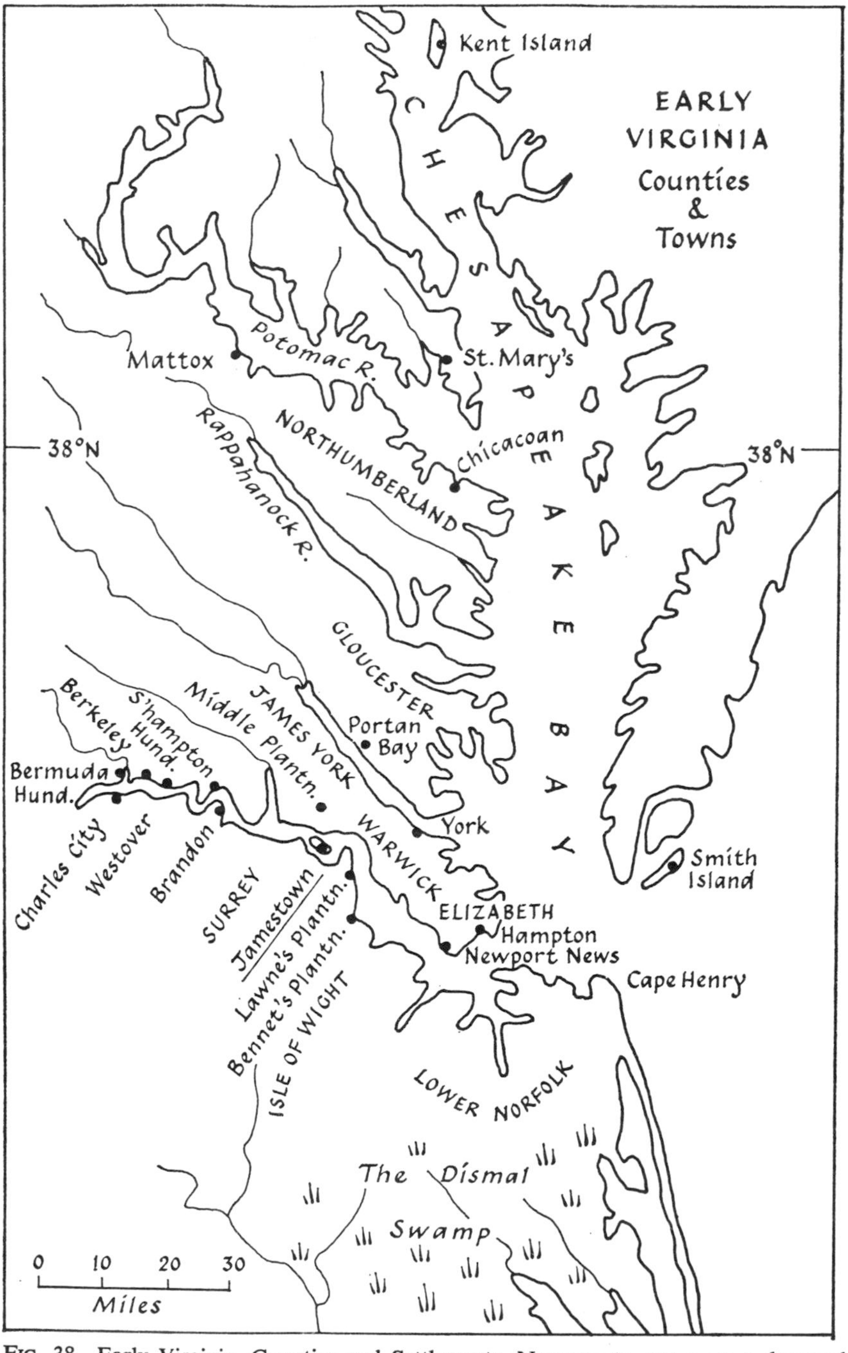

FIG. 38 Early Virginia, Counties and Settlements. Nearness to water on a drowned estuarine coast was a great advantage (in spite of nearness to fever-ridden swamps) in a sea-borne and sea-supported colony.

occupation, consisting in part of manorial plantations and in part of individual homesteads, and both the feudal estate and the freehold farm came to flourish.

The southern colonies were the first to be developed and in many ways retained the traditions of the past most firmly. They began through schemes of private colonization. In 1584 Sir Walter Raleigh, a court favourite of Queen Elizabeth I, obtained a royal patent to establish a settlement in North America. Advised by Gilbert not to try Newfoundland because of its cold climate and intractable soils, he sent his ships well south. They finally put in just below Cape Hatteras, that great prominence in the Atlantic Coast Plain (Fig. 38). The colony was named Virginia in honour of the Virgin Queen. It offered broad sheltered waters behind great off-shore bars, flat accessible land, deep tillable soil, and a climate with a long, hot, moist, productive summer. A second expedition was sent out in 1585 with two hundred men, who settled at Roanoke Island. Unfortunately, the marshy edges of the Coast Plain inlets bred disease; fevers were common, and a disheartening year was had. Notwithstanding Raleigh sent out a third party, including twenty-five women and children, in 1587. However, Britain became involved in war with Spain and it was not until 1591 that further support could be sent to Virginia. In the meanwhile Raleigh, already having spent £40,000, became short of funds. He therefore sold the right to trade in Virginia to a group of wealthy men, reserving a fifth of all the gold that might be extracted!

The burden on private funds was too great. As Hakluyt remarked, 'It required a prince's purse to have the action thoroughly followed out.' James I, unfortunately, was niggardly with money and did not directly underwrite colonial expansion. Nevertheless he was interested in it and, in 1606, he gave his patronage to two companies of private investors that decided to develop the overseas trade. These were the London and Plymouth companies. They were to hold their property in joint stock and were given powers to recover profits on their investment by renting land, opening mines, and, above all, carrying and disposing of the produce of the colonies. The emigrants went out under obligation to serve their company for a period of years before they could take up land holdings. They were supplied from a common store, and had to work the company's lands in common or do other work as required. They had no popular rights, except that they were entitled to 'all the liberties, franchises, and immunities' which they had possessed in England. But in effect they went from one highly autocratic government to another (Fig. 39).

By 1610 the London Company abolished the common store and communal labour, and parcelled out small holdings to emigrants in return for a quit rent of two and a half barrels of corn per acre and thirty days' public service in the year. The Plymouth Company adopted rather a different line. It made its settlers stockholders. The company provisioned them with supplies for the first seven years, provided that all their returns went to the company's general fund. At the end of the seven years the funds were divided up according to the shares held.

As colonization prospered, personal grants were once more sought for and given. Lord Baltimore secured land to the north of Virginia, where he

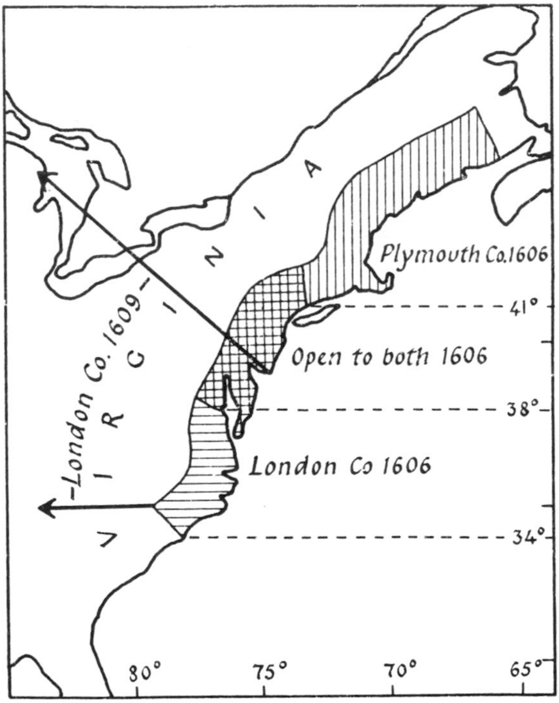

FIG. 39 The London and Plymouth Companies and their Land Grants.

established the colony of Maryland. The Carolinas were given to some eight important proprietors who had helped Charles II back to his throne. One of these was the Duke of Albemarle. Likewise Georgia was farmed out to a group of so-called 'trustees'. These grantees, together with the gentry investing in the colonizing companies, were all used to the manorial system in England, and accordingly transplanted it to America.

Many grantees were sons of merchants. They found it difficult to rise into the aristocracy at home, but through their wealth and connexions could obtain great estates and rule them like lords in the New World. Thus we are told that William Fitzhugh, the son of an English woollen draper, had come to Virginia 'with substantial capital to buy lands and servants. He aspired to the rule of a manorial estate of feudal magnificence and acquired 96,000 acres between the Rappahannock and the Potomac rivers. At his death he transmitted 55,000 acres in five family "seats" to as many sons, according to Virginian custom.'[1] He worked his plantations, to begin with, mainly with indentured labourers, i.e. servants who gave him eleven months' labour a year for three years in return for their passage to America and a home on his estate. When these men had finished their service they were apportioned land which they worked as his tenants on the payment of an annual quit rent. The fever for making money drove Fitzhugh to put as much land as he could under tobacco, although he had large acreages under corn and pasture and raised many cattle and swine. He could not get enough labour and, like many other planters, turned to negro slaves. These had been introduced by the Dutch slave traders as early as 1619, and later were sold in great numbers by slave traders from New England.

The use of slaves virtually killed the system of indentured servants, and most of the plantations became progressively less white, although it is true many white immigrants were still taken on as tradesmen or foremen on the estates or as tenant-farmers. Indeed, Virginia was settled mainly by tenant-farmers although it was led and administered principally by estate owners. 'The gulf between large planter and small farmer widened as the possession of slaves by the wealthy raised the productivity of his lands, and, consequently increased his income and heightened his social status, while these factors remained static for the non-slave-holder.'[2]

The lack of good white workers and especially of skilled craftsmen meant that industry was slow to develop in Virginia and there were few manufactures. These consisted in the main of meeting the daily needs of humbler people for food, clothes, shoes, soap, and tools. But there was little incentive for manufacturing. Southern planters were quite content to raise tobacco, rice, indigo, or cotton, as the case might be, and sell these products to Britain, or the other colonies, and buy back manufactured goods from Britain, especially the more expensive goods. They invested in land, planting, the manor house, furniture, fine clothes, carriages, and racing horses—not in factories, shipping, and trade. This mental attitude, which was typical of the landed gentry in England, kept back the industrial revolution in the south till after the American civil war, and was as responsible as anything for the very different rates of development of south and north.

Throughout the south the striking unit of settlement was the great manorial estate, with its large house surrounded by the houses of servants

[1] Wish, H., *Society and Thought in Early America*, London, 1950, p. 63.
[2] Ibid., p. 68.

and supporters, and the near-by church, inn, mill, smithy, and court-house. Since the estate, at least to begin with, was usually on, or very close to, tidewater, often having its own quays and warehouses, it traded directly with Britain. There was no great need for middlemen, merchants, merchant houses, or trading settlements.

As a result of these tendencies 'much of what became the south was shaped by the absence of cities and the lack of a middle class'.[1] This had profound results, in that it kept settlement open, encouraged large-scale production, discouraged the development of intensive agriculture usually associated with the surrounds of cities, kept roads down to a minimum, and centred the administration in the hands of leading planters. It preserved the feudal landscape, at any rate along the tidewater plains, although farther inland this broke down, under rougher conditions, and gave way to a landscape of smallholder, hunter, and frontiersman.

The other southern colonies, and in particular Carolina, took on similar traits. Indeed in Carolina the system was, if anything, even more feudalistic. Its constitution was drawn up specifically to be 'most agreeable to the monarchy'. It was to provide against 'a numerous democracy' by keeping government in the hands of the propertied class. The colony was treated as a palatinate, with very large grants to the eight 'Lord proprietors' who had promised to develop it, and considerable grants to landgraves and 'caciques'. About 40 per cent of the land went to these feudal land barons. The rest was divided up between lesser planters, their tenants, and a number of freehold farmers. The constitution insisted that the governor of the province should be at least a landgrave, the members of the legislative assembly had to be landholders possessing at least 500 acres, while the right to vote representatives in was confined to freeholders with at least 50 acres. Actually frontier conditions soon modified the constitution and, especially behind the pine belt, a more egalitarian society emerged: nevertheless the tidewater community had a distinctly feudal cast.

The northern colonies were developed along very different lines (Fig. 40). They were born of separatism and nourished on secession. They were anxious to break away from the prevailing traditions in Old England and found a New England based on the right, if not the duty, to innovate. Most of the early immigrants were dissidents, some wanting to purify the Church, others to separate out from it. Religious independence bred civil emancipation. The colonists were determined to create a new society; they were already American-minded before they came to America.

The early separatists believed that there was no succession or privilege in holy things. They looked *forward* not back. This is the essential, the distinguishing thing about them. It was put into words at the very sailing of the

[1] Wish, op. cit., p. 64.

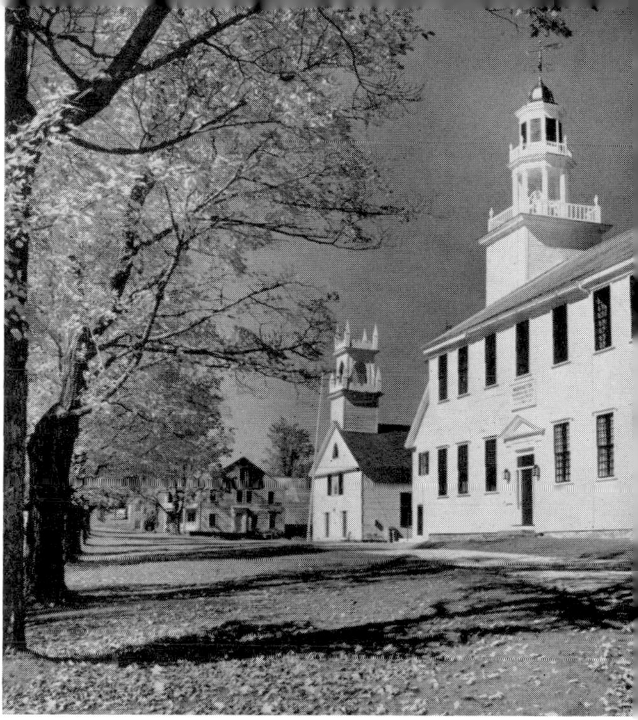

20. Many New England villages, like Washington, N.H., cluster around a central tree-lined green, fronted by the church, the township meeting-house, the inn, and spacious private dwellings.

21. French Canadian farm settlement (as on the Montreal plain) is characterized by the closeness of many narrow-fronted farms going back up long lots from roadside or river front. These streets of farms 'string out' the villages almost from one centre to another.

22. *The American Story:* a, Trading Post. Peter Minuet buys Manhattan Island from the Indians.

23. *The American Story:* b, Merchant's Emporium. Exporting and importing houses by the quays on South Street, Manhattan.

24. *The American Story:* c, Financial Hub. Financial and other business houses, lower Manhattan, that have a world influence.

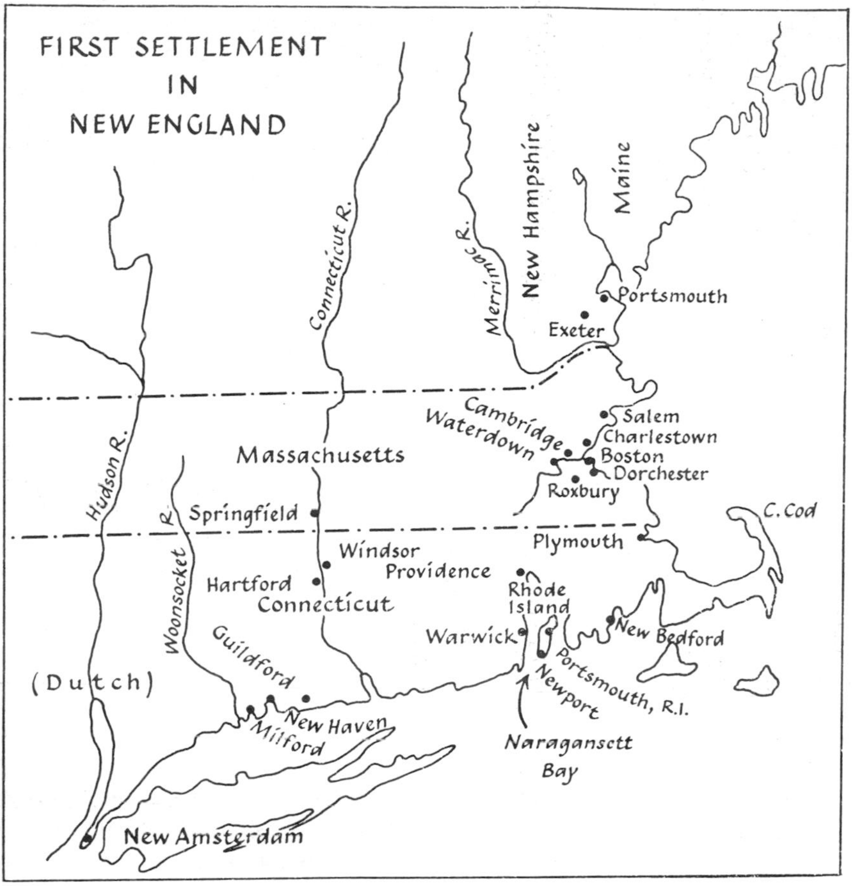

FIG. 40 Early New England Settlements. Here a drowned glaciated coast, with submerged drumlin fields and inter-morainic depressions, provided an ideal site for small independent sea-nourished colonies. (Scale, 1:4 m.)

Pilgrim Fathers when John Robinson, an associate of Smyth and Helwys in the separatist churches in Holland, bid the refugees farewell, saying:

> I charge you before God and His blessed angels that you follow me no further than you have seen me follow the Lord Jesus Christ. If God reveal anything to you by any other instrument of His, *be as ready to receive it* as you were to receive any truth by my ministry, for I am verily persuaded *the Lord hath more truth yet to break out of His Holy Word.* For my part I cannot sufficiently bewail the condition of those Reformed Churches which *are come to a period* in religion, and will at present go no further than the instruments of their reformation. The Lutherans cannot be drawn to go beyond what Luther saw. Whatever part of His will our God

> has revealed to Calvin, they will die rather than embrace; and the Calvinists, you see, stick fast where they were left by that great man of God, *who yet saw not all things. That is a misery much to be lamented.*[1]

This was the faith—the great, new faith—that launched the *Mayflower* and America upon the promise of the future.

Most of these religious refugees emigrated in groups, as congregation or part congregation. When a particular church came under the iron hand of Laud, it uprooted itself in its entirety and moved to the New World as an organized, closely knit group. This was the pattern in New England and offered a distinct contrast to the mode of settlement in the southern colonies, where companies or individual grantees had to get together odd assortments of individuals to work or take up their lands. As Truslow Adams has pointed out, the New England pattern 'operated strongly to develop a sense of unity and of corporate and community spirit. Settlements were, from their inception, closely organized bodies. The citizen lived, moved, and had his being as part of a small but tightly knit group. In church meeting and town meeting (sometimes scarce distinguishable from each other) he grew to consider organized action as normal action.'[2]

However, organized action was action among believers. Where disbelievers arose, the organization was broken, and a new start had to be made. Actually frequent discord occurred amongst the religious leaders, causing the periodic secession of splinter groups from the main body of the kirk. Indeed, colonization by secession became one of the most important aspects of New England settlement. Independence was very real since, in Wyclif's famous words, 'it was open to the Christian thinker to call in question even the most cherished dogma of the authoritative Church'. In England the Independents revolted against the State Church, in New England against each other. Their independentism went to extremes. They argued vehemently among themselves and as they claimed the right of individual conscience to guide them, there were as many types of faith as types of people. They were so vehement that, as Rodwell Jones has pointed out, 'They could not bring themselves to join in the discussion and arrangement of town affairs with those who disagreed with them in religious matters. To be a citizen one had first to be a sectarian.' *Thus religion came to have profound significance in the geography of settlement.* What split New England up into a lot of little colonies was not so much the relief of the land, rough and divided though this was, as the topography of the mind. Mental barriers were raised, that took advantage of the physical ones. People who

[1] Davies, H., *The English Free Churches*, Oxford, 1952, p. 56 (our italics).

[2] Adams, J. Truslow, 'The Historical Background', in *New England's Prospect*, ed. Wright, J. K., New York, 1933, p. 3.

thought differently had to live separately. Johnson has put it well. Practically every religious dispute produced its new township until the faintest lines of theological divergence were satisfied.

For example, shortly after Roger Williams arrived in Boston he objected to those continuing Puritans, still members of the Church of England, who had not separated themselves out. He therefore left for Salem, where the separatists were in the ascendancy. The Bay Colony leaders dissuaded Salem from sheltering him, and he went to Plymouth. He then launched an attack upon the theocratic policy of requiring civil magistrates to enforce religious practices. For this he was exiled. He fled to Narragansett Bay, where he and his followers secured land from the Narragansett Indians and set up the township of Providence. This was in 1636. In 1643 more secessionists, 'fleeing from the wrath of Massachusetts', established a town, Warwick, near to Providence. In 1644 Williams obtained a charter for the new colony of Rhode Island which allowed its settlers 'to rule themselves and such others as shall hereafter inhabit within any Part of the said Tract, by such a form of Civil Government, as by voluntary consent of all, or the greater Parte of them, they shall find most suitable'. Truly democratic government had been established in North America.

In the meantime, another controversy broke out in Boston. A Mrs Hutchison obtained followers for her belief in the efficacy of an 'inner light' to guide individuals without the need for a council of elders, or indeed the ministry. She too was exiled. She and her partisans founded Portsmouth in Rhode Island, while her brother-in-law took his flock to Exeter, New Hampshire. Further secession from Boston, by Stoughton, Brown, and Oldham—all three of whom had come under the censure of the orthodox Puritan Church—led to the rise of the Connecticut colony between Hartford and Windsor. 'The settlements well illustrate the general type of New England colonization. The emigration from Massachusetts was . . . of organized communities united in allegiance to a church and a pastor. Carrying provisions and supplies, erecting new villages, as communities they came . . . to Connecticut.'[1] In 1639 they drew up what was probably the first written constitution in the world framed by a community for that community, through its own representatives. Democracy was widening.

New England democracy produced its own landscape; it was that of the town and township, of small urban communities with individually owned and operated businesses, mills, and workshops, and of restricted rural settlements with independent, scattered farms occupied and worked by their owners. There were very few large estates with manor houses, estate offices, and slave quarters. The small town, based on the single congregation, was the unit of settlement, and the townscape consisted of a few public buildings

---

[1] Tyler, *England in America*, p. 248.

such as church, town-house, court-house, and inn, set about a central green, surrounded by private dwellings enclosed by gardens. Some grading in the size of houses as between merchants, magistrates, and artisans might have occurred, but this was less significant than the lack of strong and obvious class neighbourhoods. The independent workman, the independent farmer, the independent business man and their single workshops, farms, and offices were what shaped the landscape. New England thus became 'a land of small farms, sufficiently small to be worked by the owner and his family, and . . . a small enterprise type of life. The small farm, the town as the unit of government, the local church governed by its own congregation—all trained the New Englander to think and work in terms of the small and local group.'[1]

Undoubtedly once this trend was established it found support in the divisions, in the divisiveness, of New England relief. Through these northern colonies the older Appalachian mountains swept in ridge on ridge with long, narrow valleys in between. Some of the valleys were interrupted by volcanic sills. They were cut up into still further segments by lobate moraines thrown across them. Thus a basis for separatism existed in the land itself. The many bays behind their rocky headlands made the sea a divisive factor as well. Seceding congregations only had to circumvent an out-thrust peninsula to be in a separate little world. Thus history had the strong support of geography to justify New England's claim that: The law is our own.

In the mid-Atlantic colonies the traditions of both the south and the north were present; they therefore formed a useful link, helping to draw the earlier colonies together. The feudal tradition was present in Maryland and New York, the more independent, libertarian system in Delaware and Pennsylvania: but the different practices overlapped or interlocked. In Maryland a huge estate was granted to Lord Baltimore, who ran part of it as a proprietary feudal manor, and subdivided the rest to other moderately large landholders and small tenants. But there were few rich men to take up the land. Instead, great numbers of small farmers, attracted by the unique degree of religious tolerance afforded by Baltimore, settled the area. With indentured servants and later a few slaves they were able to make a modest living from tobacco farming. Many set up homesteading and raised corn and cattle. Town life vied with life on the estates, especially where Jews, Huguenots, and Quakers came in and started businesses and workshops.

In New York the Dutch colonists of 1624-and-after had developed the land along feudal lines. They came out under the powerful Dutch West Indies Company, which realized the importance of peopling and pacifying the country (Fig. 41). It offered large tracts of land to members of the company, provided they brought out and settled at least fifty families as permanent tenant-farmers. The landlord, or 'patroon', was given a perpetual fief

[1] Adams, J. Truslow, op. cit., p. 5.

of sixteen miles of frontage on the Hudson river—a great advantage in trading—and promised a large say in the commerce of any towns that might be established in his lands. However, the *patroonship* system tended to break down in most of the colony due to a shortage of labour and although, when

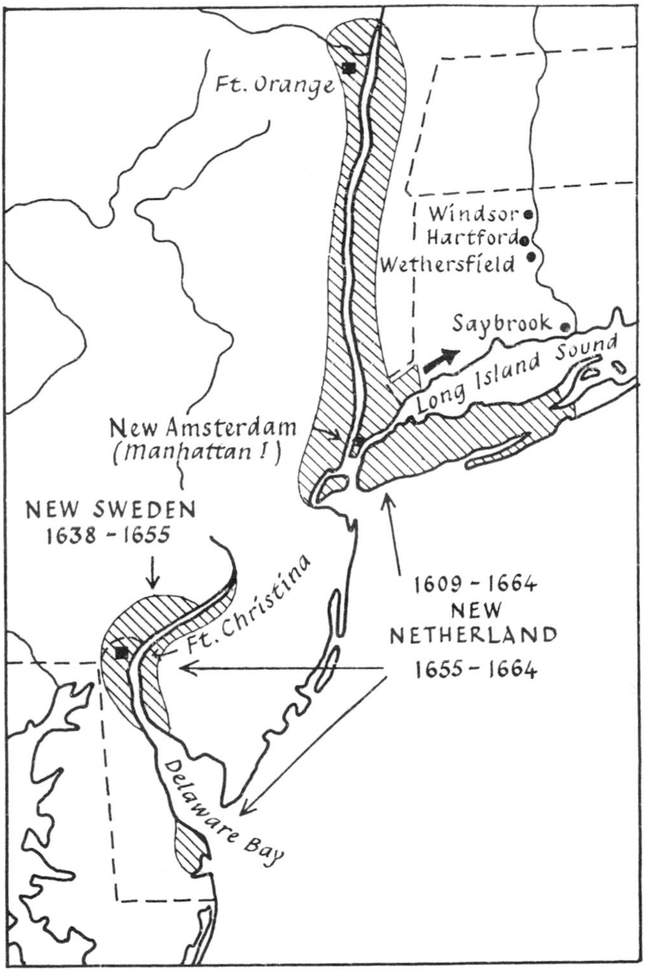

FIG. 41 Dutch and Swedish Possessions, that subsequently passed to the British, in the mid-Atlantic colonies.

the English took over, some of the feudal estates were maintained, the land became taken up increasingly by individual owner-operators. New York itself flourished under the aegis of a middle class which, having already broken guild restrictions on enterprise in the Old World, was free to adopt a highly individualistic and competitive system.

The old Swedish colony along the Delaware had been settled mainly by Finnish peasants 'possessed of a keen sense of personal independence' and anxious to have land of their own.[1] They developed a fairly varied rural economy based on farming, trapping, and fishing. When they were absorbed by the English they helped strengthen the northern tradition of independent enterprise. This was further strengthened by the founding of Pennsylvania since, although an enormous estate and considerable powers were given to Penn, they were used not so much to establish his family—although this was done—as to set up a Commonwealth for free Christians. Penn, who had written 'God hates persecution' and had asserted that 'No man, nor number of men upon earth, hath power or authority to rule over men's consciences in religious matters', was intent on encouraging persecuted Quakers to flee from England and find refuge in his colony. He offered generous terms for those who wanted to buy land, although he reserved considerable acreages for himself which he allotted to tenant-farmers on the basis of an annual quit rent. His system was in itself a compromise between those prevailing to south and north. Towns were encouraged and Philadelphia, in particular, grew to be a thriving, cosmopolitan centre.

This medley of conditions, with different patterns of settlement along the same river, or the same stretch of coast, obviously had little to do with geography. The wold-lands from New Jersey south, with their low scarps and gentle vales, did tend to favour a fairly dense colonization by small-hold farmers; but they had their estates as well—just as the wold-lands of England had. The great trench of the Hudson valley may have favoured the growth of large estates, each with a front on the water, but it attracted its freehold farmers as well. Throughout the region the accidents of history were more significant than the systems of land forms, at least in the initial stages. Ultimately as the feudal aspects of society were all but swept away and a society of farmers and townsmen took its place, local differences in relief, drainage, and soil began to play a much more significant role.

To sum up, British colonization produced three distinct modes of settlement. The rural township of freehold farms and the small town typified New England; the commercial farm, producing foodstuffs, and the commercial port typified the middle colonies; while the plantation and the tenant-farm, often dealing in industrial cash-crops, typified the southern colonies. It is evident, then, that the ideas and conditions of colonization had much to do with the forms of settlement and the types of landscape that emerged as the Old World transplanted itself in the New.

Territorial Organization

Although the British came from a kingdom recently united they set up

[1] Ward, C., *The Dutch and Swedes on the Delaware, 1609–64*, Philadelphia, 1930, p. 103.

separate colonies in the New World, some of which, like Virginia and Massachusetts, were very jealous of their lands and prerogatives. The territorial pattern was one of fragmentation. Various factors were responsible for this, amongst which geography was not least. The Atlantic coastal plain was itself fragmented by the drowning of large estuaries and the multiplication of islands and peninsulas. In New England the grain of the country ran across the path of the immigrants and separated those who pushed inland from at any rate the eastern coastal settlers. The main reasons lay, however, in the social sphere—in the whole rising tide of competitive, individualistic living that then began to characterize Britain and was most free to expand in the New World. Companies, individual concessionaires, and even congregations were out for their own rights and interests.

British territories ranged from Hudson Bay to Georgia. The oldest were Newfoundland (1583, 1610), Virginia (1606–7), and Massachusetts (1629–30). The other New England colonies and Maryland were formed during the 1630s; the first Delaware colony was founded in 1641; Carolina, New York, and the Hudson Bay territories were claimed between 1660 and 1670; Pennsylvania was set up in 1681, New Jersey in 1702, and Georgia in 1732.

Newfoundland has the proud distinction of being the oldest British colony. Discovered by Cabot in 1497, it was claimed by him in 1498 on behalf of the King of England. Cabot, who had sailed on down the North American coast as far as 34° N., also claimed the coast to this latitude on behalf of his patron, King Henry VII. However, no attempt to make good these claims occurred until 1583, when Gilbert claimed the island of Newfoundland for Queen Elizabeth I. Between 1585 and 1587 Davis sailed up the Labrador coast and penetrated the Davis Strait as far as 66° 40′ N. British fishermen began to use the Labrador fisheries, as well as those of the island of Newfoundland—but were contested in this by the French who, in 1598, claimed Newfoundland and Labrador as part of their Canadian territories. British colonies on the island began in 1610 when Sir Francis Bacon and his associates formed the Newfoundland Colonization Company. Several others followed, and all were consolidated in 1637 when Britain claimed the whole island. In 1662, 1692, and 1708 the French contested this claim, but finally recognized English sovereignty in 1713 at the Treaty of Utrecht. The coast of Labrador had likewise been disputed. Although contiguous with New France, it was fished mainly from the island of Newfoundland and was regarded by British fishermen there as an extension of their rights.

After the conquest of Quebec the whole area was indisputably British. The home government, in 1763, entrusted the administration of the Labrador coast, together with the north coast of the Gulf of St Lawrence as far west as the St Jean river, to Newfoundland. This was strongly objected to by Quebec and in 1774 it was transferred to Quebec. Just as strong objections were then put up by the Newfoundlanders and in 1809 the territory was re-annexed by Newfoundland In 1825 a compromise was reached; Quebec got the north shore of the Gulf of St Lawrence, Newfoundland the coast of Labrador east and north from Ance Sablon. Further disputes occurred, mainly about how far inland the 'coast' of Labrador should extend, which were not finally resolved until 1949 when Newfoundland was united to Canada.

Virginia, meanwhile, had begun to be settled,

> the boundaries of which had been fixed by a charter of King James I in 1606, allowing the London Company to form settlements between 34° N. and 38° N. and the Plymouth Company to form settlements between 41 and 45 degrees of latitude. It has been suggested that the southern limit of these claims can be traced back to the fact that Cabot reached 34° N. in 1497. It is also worth noting that it was in the Plymouth Company charter of 1606 that the 45th parallel [now part of the southern boundary of Canada, between Quebec Province and New York State] was mentioned for the first time as a political boundary.[1]

Actually, the original grants between the London and Plymouth companies overlapped, that to the London Company in Virginia extending to 41° N., that to the Plymouth Company commencing from 38° N., it being understood that 'in the regions where the grants overlapped, there must be a gap of at least a hundred miles between the settlements of the two companies'.[2] The boundaries were not held to. When Maryland was set up it included the northern part of Virginia up to the 40th parallel, and when Carolina was established it overlapped with southern Virginia, having a grant of land from 31° N. to 36° N. There was thus a sort of shaking down of ideas, and colonies got boundaries more nearly related to the actual territories they settled or traded in.

The Plymouth Company established an abortive colony on the Kennebec in Maine in 1607. Though this failed, the Company continued to be interested in northern expansion and obtained a new patent from King James, extending its claims to the 48th parallel. This cut right across the French colony of Acadia. In 1620 the Plymouth Company surrendered its rights to the Council for New England, which gave patents to the Pilgrims to settle in Plymouth (1621), other Puritans to found Salem (1628) in Massachusetts Bay, and other colonists to settle in New Hampshire (1629).

The Massachusetts Bay Company, in 1629, obtained its charter from

[1] Nicholson, N. L., *The Boundaries of Canada, its Provinces and Territories*, Ottawa, 1954, p. 8.

[2] Harlow, R. V., *The Growth of the United States*, New York, 1938, p. 27.

Charles I, securing the land already conveyed to the Salem settlement. This included the territory from a point three miles north of the Merrimac to one three miles south of the Charles, and thence extending westward to the Pacific! This western extension caused conflict when settlers left the Bay Colony itself to set up new colonies in Rhode Island and, above all, in Connecticut. In 1644 Roger Williams persuaded the Parliamentary Commissioners in England to establish Rhode Island and give it, 'in flat contradiction of the earlier grant to Massachusetts, the Tract of Land in the Continent of America called . . . Narragansett Bay'.[1] The settlers surging up the Connecticut river as far as Springfield were originally under the Massachusetts authority and, although they formed their southern towns into a separate colony, had to concede Springfield to Massachusetts. These divisions and others that developed in New England were less serious than they might have been, owing to the formation of the New England Confederation, 1643–4, by which most of the colonies agreed to act together in many respects, particularly against the French and the Dutch.

Against the French, New England claims were extended north to 48° by the charter of the Plymouth Company. In 1621 King James, with the consent of that company or its successors, gave the northern part of this territory to Sir William Alexander, stretching from 'the head or promontory commonly called Cape of Sable, lying near the forty-third degree of north latitude, or thereabouts . . . to the headland or point of Cape Breton, lying near latitude forty-five degrees, or thereabouts'. This became Nova Scotia, a territory which originally included all of what is today New Brunswick. In 1763, after the whole of New France passed to the British, Nova Scotia was given that part of French Acadia not claimed by New England, i.e. New Brunswick, Prince Edward Island, and Cape Breton Island, although in 1784 New Brunswick was separated from it. While these developments were going on in what is now Canada, New England was pushing across the Penobscot river into the basin of the St Croix, and even farther north, towards the St John basin. Settlers from Maine either took over vacant lands not possessed by the French or displaced French settlers, and the great northward salient of Maine began to take shape.

Against the Dutch, New England claims pushed steadily west of the Connecticut river. Massachusetts and Connecticut both pressed to the height of land overlooking the Hudson valley, although the Berkshires were not occupied until about 1760. After the fall of the New Netherlands, 1664–7, the territory of the Hudson valley, the upper Delaware, and the upper Connecticut was granted to the Duke of York, and renamed New York. The colony grew rapidly, especially along the banks of the Hudson, but waived or lost some of its claims. The southern portion, between the

[1] Tyler, op. cit., p. 235.

Delaware and the mouth of the Hudson, was given by the Duke of York to two grantees, in 1664, and became New Jersey. The northern portion formed a bone of contention between New York and New Hampshire. The 'Yorkers' moving up into the Green mountains from the Hudson met the 'Green Mountain Boys' crossing the upper Connecticut from New Hampshire. Eventually, when the War of Independence came, the settlers in this disputed zone set up the state of Vermont.

The Delaware had been divided between the Dutch and the Swedes—the latter having set up the colony of New Sweden there in 1638. But the shores of the inlet were poorly settled and in 1641 colonists from New Haven lodged themselves on the Delaware. They were harried by the Swedes but came back in force in 1651. Eventually both Dutch and Swedes gave way to British pressure, and the British took over the Delaware, the lowest portion of which finally became the small state of Delaware, the middle part the eastern entrance to Pennsylvania, and the upper section the western bounds of New Jersey.

Thus, by 1670, the British had established themselves from southern Carolina to Nova Scotia, along the coast of the mainland, and also in Newfoundland and Labrador. These formed by far the most populous and productive areas of British North America, although they were the most severely limited, being pinned to the sea by the excessively rugged and densely forested ridges of the Appalachians. In 1670, however, Britain was to claim what, although the least populous, was by far the most extensive of its territories, that about the Hudson Bay.

The Hudson's Bay Company claimed 'all the seas, straits, bays, rivers, lakes, creeks, and sounds in whatever latitude they shall be, that lie within the entrance of the straits commonly called Hudson's Straits, together with the lands and territories upon the coasts and confines of the seas, bays, etc., aforesaid' (Fig. 42). But, although the primary claim was to Hudson Bay and the lands adjoining it, up to the height of land, i.e. to the edge of the drainage basin, the Company secured the sole right of trade in those regions to which they could find passage from the Bay. Since the height of land between the Bay and the St Lawrence or the Mississippi or Mackenzie drainage systems was both low and indefinite it allowed easy passage by glacial melt-water channels into the Ungava, Great Lakes, Red river, and Saskatchewan waterways, from which the fur trade of the greater part of the continent could be reached. The French, and later, Americans, contested these claims. In 1714 the Company specified its claims as running from 'the Island called Grimington's, 58½° N., [along] a Line drawn to the Great Lake Miscosinke [Mistassini], and from the said Lake [along] a Line to Run Southwestward into 49 degree North Latitude, and that where the said Line shall cut the 49th Degree of Northern Latitude, another Line shall begin and be extended

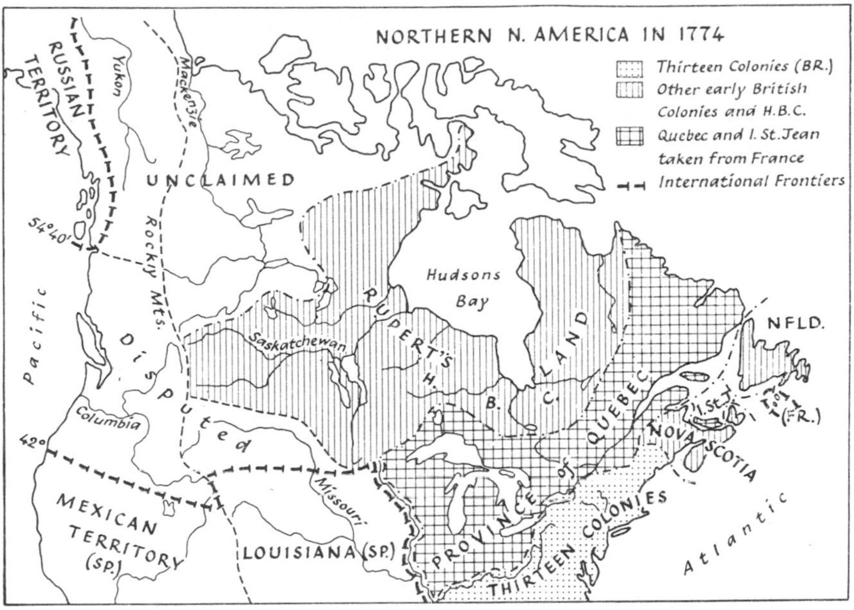

FIG. 42 The Hudson's Bay Company Lands, British Colonies in Canada, and the competition of American, Spanish, and Russian spheres of influence in the late eighteenth century. (Scale, 1:55 m.)

Westward . . . upon the 49th Degree. . . .'[1] But exactly how far west the 49th parallel was to be followed was not indicated, and, in later times, the Hudson's Bay Company claimed trading rights well to the south of it in the Columbia basin: a cause of the famous Oregon controversy with the United States.

Conclusion

Although the British were late in colonizing North America, compared with Spain, they attacked it with more vigour and enterprise than either Spain or France, finding it not merely a source for raw materials or an outlet for trade, but a home for settlement and development and, as important as anything, a sphere for new ideas and practices. They were fortunate in that their main colonies avoided the rigours of the Canadian climate or the ardours of the Mexican one and established themselves in a temperate humid zone which, though not without challenge, was rewarding and pleasant. Forced by the Appalachian mountains to keep to the coast they exploited their close contacts with each other and, for a considerable period at least, with the motherland. The colonies attracted active immigration, and

[1] Savelle, Max, *The Diplomatic History of the Canadian Boundary, 1749–63*, Toronto, 1940, p. 4.

soon became comparatively viable units. Helped by the fragmentation of the coast, but even more by the social differences that then prevailed, they developed strong individual traits. Social contrasts became reflected in unique cultural landscapes. None the less, divided by the Dutch and all but surrounded by the French, the colonies did not lack in co-operation. Eventually this co-operation joined settlements from New England to Georgia in the Thirteen States that broke the connexions with the Old World and established a new geography in the Americas.

CHAPTER SEVEN

The Rise of National Regions

By the middle of the eighteenth century the three great colonial powers of Spain, Britain, and France had firmly established themselves in North America. Spain was the dominant power in the Caribbean, in Mexico, in the Great American Desert, and in Florida; Britain had important bases in the Caribbean, it possessed the main part of the Atlantic coast from Georgia to Labrador, and held the Hudson Bay region; France had developed her empire of the waterways from the St Lawrence Gulf to the Gulf of Mexico, based on the connexions between the St Lawrence, the Great Lakes, and the Mississippi. France also owned some of the Caribbean isles.

Each of these powers was in conflict with the other; Spain had ambitions in the lower Mississippi and the lower Atlantic coast, which rivalled those of France and Britain. The latter two faced each other in Labrador, Acadia, Maine, the Hudson–Champlain trench, the Mohawk–Lake Ontario gap, and in the Ohio plains.

The struggle between these countries arose not because the chief colonial bridgeheads clashed with each other; Espanola and Mexico were far enough away from Virginia, as was Massachusetts Bay from the citadel of Quebec. The struggle grew up over conflicting hinterlands of trade and settlement. As the powers moved inland their spheres of influence overlapped; geography drew their paths across each other. Although the course of history was from east to west, the geographical grain of the continent was from north to south. As traders and settlers pressed in westward from the coast they were drawn northward or southward by the rivers and mountains.

When the Spaniards crossed Mexico they were led north by the western Sierras, and by the Gulf of California; so they came to the High Plains, the Great Basin, and the Great Valley of California. Thus although they started their westward drive south of latitude 20° N., they carried it eventually as far as 42° N.—that is, as far north as southern Canada! In the same way when the French moved westward from the Gulf of St Lawrence they were deflected south by the St Lawrence and the southern Great Lakes until they were drawn into the Mississippi–Ohio basin and thus led down to the Gulf of Mexico, south of the northern outposts of Spain! The British, too, found their western drive caught up in northward or southward drifts. The movement west from the New England shore turned north up the Penobscot and the Connecticut rivers, into the well-marked north–south grain of the country. The expansion into western New York first had to move north up the Hudson. The settlement of up-country Virginia and Carolina took place southward along the Piedmont, on the east side of the Blue Ridge, or down the Great Valley west of that ridge.

Not all this contention was serious. The conflict between Britain moving south around the Appalachians or Spain moving north from Florida and the Gulf of Mexico was not a grave one, because there were not enough traders and settlers to dispute the zone between. Similarly the clash between France and Spain in the lower Mississippi and the Ozarks region never became more than a nominal one, for the lack of real contact.

However, there was one area where contact was close and differences critical. This was in the north between Britain and France. Here, stretching from the upper Ohio to Labrador, was a major zone of rivalry, in which the two powers that had fought each other so often and for so long across the narrow waters of the English Channel, came to grips with each other on the American frontier.

The Franco-British Struggle

The conflict between France and Britain began, in part, through their involvement in Indian conflicts. As has already been pointed out, when the French sailed up the St Lawrence and moved inland up the Ottawa, they made friends with the Algonquins and the Hurons. But both these groups were at odds with the Iroquois.

The rivalry between the Indians grew when they realized they could get wealthy through the fur trade. They began increasingly to contest the fur trapping grounds of the Great Lakes–St Lawrence estuary. The Iroquois used the trapping grounds of the Champlain and Mohawk valleys, the Finger Lakes region, and the Lower Great Lakes. Rivalry grew especially keen in the mid-seventeenth century (see Fig. 59, Chapter 8).

The Algonquins and Hurons traded down the St Lawrence to Montreal; that is, through the French, while the Iroquois traded down the Mohawk to Albany. This was first a Dutch settlement, but became English in 1664, after England absorbed the Dutch colony of the Hudson. The French gradually won out, and persuaded more and more tribes to trade with them. A critical situation was reached when the Neutrals, who lived in south-west Ontario between Lake Erie and Lake Ontario, began to sell their beaver skins to the French, and not, as they had been doing, to the Iroquois, who had then sold them to the British. Unfortunately, the Iroquois had killed most of the beaver in their own territories. If they lost the western areas, held by the Neutrals and other tribes, they would be ruined. So they invaded Neutral territory in 1665, and conquered it in the so-called Beaver Wars.

When the French saw the success of the Iroquois, they were scared. They knew that behind the Iroquois were the British. Consequently, they plotted to overthrow the Iroquois. But this of course disturbed the British. So the two European countries became more and more involved in the Indian wars. As they did so, they grew more hostile to each other.

This hostility increased to the pitch of war, when British settlers at last broke through the barrier of the Appalachians into the Lower Lakes and upper Ohio region. The British pushed up the Mohawk and Susquehanna, and came face to face with the French on Lake Ontario and the Allegheny valley. The French had built forts to ring the British in. These included Duquesne (at Pittsburgh) where the Allegheny flows into the Ohio; Niagara, on the east side of the Niagara river; and Frontenac, at the entrance to the St Lawrence valley (where Kingston is today). The British decided to challenge these with forts in the Potomac, Juniata and Susquehanna valleys, and at Oswego, on Lake Ontario. They went further. They organized an attack on the French, under General Braddock. But they were unsuccessful. The expedition, aimed at Fort Duquesne, was launched from Virginia. It did not get enough volunteers or supplies. Virginia, a plantation colony, was poor in food crops and in manpower. Virginian levies were small, poorly fed, and without enough arms. They were not helped by the other colonists. The first round in the struggle between the British and the French went to the French.

The Seven Years War

The rivalry between Britain and France was not confined to North America. It flared up in India and in Europe. At last the two great powers went to war. This involved their colonies. The thirteen British colonies were now officially at war with New France. They at once became united in their efforts to break the French encirclement, and to conquer the French bases on the Gulf of St Lawrence and the Mississippi Gulf. In this they were assisted by the British Navy, with bases in the West Indies and Nova Scotia, and by Redcoats sent out from Britain (Fig. 43).

The struggle, known as the Seven Years War, was strongly influenced by geography. The French strategy lay in using Louisburg and New Orleans to outflank the British fleet, and meantime to drive in from Duquesne, Frontenac, and Montreal, cutting off the southern colonies from the central ones, and those from the north. Thus the British colonies would be separated, encircled, and defeated. In the first year's campaign, 1756, Montcalm's forces held British attacks against Ticonderoga and Duquesne and were successful in capturing Fort Oswego. The French improved their position, and appeared ready to close in.

However, in England, Pitt had come into power. He was anxious to use

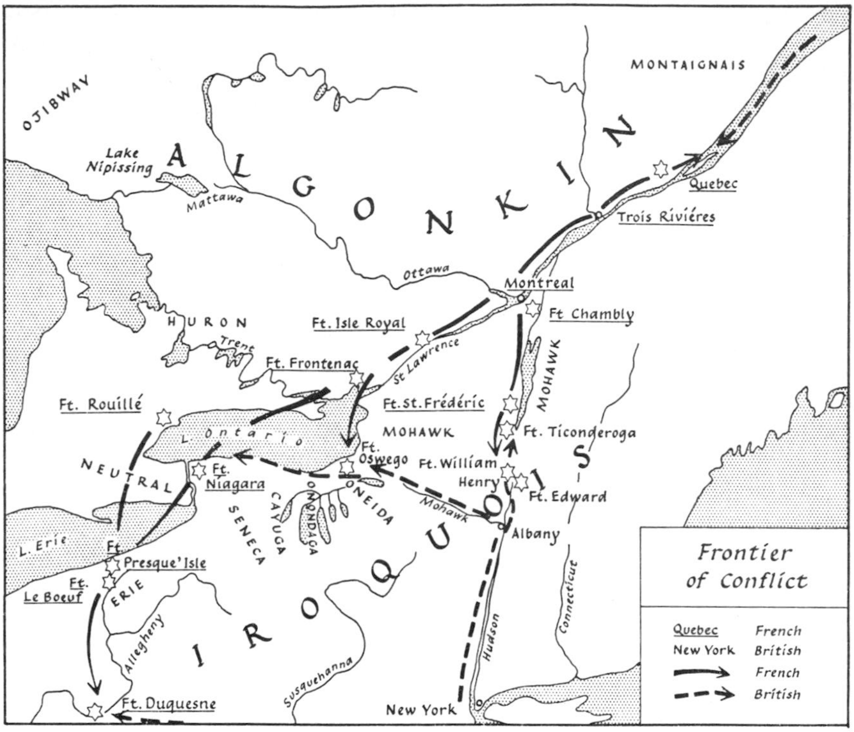

FIG. 43 The Franco-British Struggle in North America. Note the great importance of the Hudson-Mohawk, Hudson-Champlain, and Lower Lakes–Allegheny/Ohio links. Geography here made history. (Scale 1:10 m.)

the British Navy to its fullest extent, and sent increased supplies to General Braddock. The French fleet was engaged on several fronts, and could not convey enough supplies to Montcalm. Moreover, the French were putting more effort behind their campaign in India than in North America. The result was that in 1758 the British laid siege to Louisburg, and captured it. This weakened the entire French position. They had lost their northern anchor. The British controlled the Gulf of St Lawrence.

Montcalm had to fall back on Quebec. But by concentrating forces there, against the naval threat, he weakened his interior lines. This was the opportunity for the British Army. Three successful thrusts were made into the French lines, when Fort Frontenac, Fort Niagara, and Fort Duquesne were captured. The whole French front, from St Louis to Montreal, was threatened. French power on the Ohio and Lower Lakes was broken. However, the French still held the line of the Mississippi–Upper Lakes–Ottawa (see Fig. 36, Chapter 5). If they had only had more settlers in the interior, they might possibly have organized a successful counter-attack.

But their lines were extended and weak. The British meant to cut these at their most vital junction—Montreal.

In 1759 a joint Navy-Army attack was launched on Quebec, under General Wolfe. It proved a great victory, though Wolfe lost his life. General Montcalm, the genius that had held the French Empire together, was also killed. After that the British closed in, and organized a threefold thrust on Montreal, first from Quebec, up the St Lawrence; then from Albany, down the Richelieu; and finally from Fort Oswego, across Lake Ontario, and down the St Lawrence. The French capitulated.

Thus the British won by breaking the French encirclement, dividing the French front into separate sections, which could not be defended, and then concentrating on the chief French base. They did this by using the Gulf of St Lawrence, the Hudson–Champlain gap, the Mohawk gap, and the Pittsburgh gap.

The American War of Independence

The fall of New France ended the first great stage in American colonization. It decided the supremacy of Britain, and laid the foundation for the ultimate supremacy of the United States. Although Spain held Mexico and the south-west, the British had the most populous parts of the continent, while their West Indian bases enabled them to counterbalance Spain in the Gulf of Mexico. The British territory consisted of the lands around Hudson Bay, together with the newly captured 'provinces' of Acadia and Canada in the north, the Thirteen Colonies of the Atlantic coastal plain, and, for a brief space of time, the peninsula of Florida in the south.

However, the British were not to remain strong for very long. A struggle soon broke out between the Thirteen Colonies and the Motherland. For some time the colonists had held differences of opinion on matters of taxation, representation, and government, and, though they owed their victory over France, in the Seven Years War, to the Motherland, they were not willing to acknowledge her continued control in their affairs. The fact is, the two peoples were growing apart. A wide ocean lay between. In the New World the colonists adopted new ways of life. Dutch, Swedish, and German elements in the population diluted the British blood, and helped to weaken the ties with Britain. The frontier was moving rapidly west. After the fall of New France, the Ohio basin and Lower Lakes region were opened up for thousands of settlers that began to press through the mountain passes.

The colonies ceased to be a coastal fringe of settlement, hemmed in by mountains, and forced to look across to Europe. They ceased to be the extension of the European coastline. They began to look to the heartland of the continent. They turned their backs on Europe. They became American.

Thus, twelve years after Britain had sent its fleets and armies in support of the American colonists, in the vital struggle with the French, they found themselves at war with the Americans. Fortunately for the British, Canada remained loyal, and acted as a base against the revolutionaries. However, the population in Canada was small, and scattered, and could not offer much support. The British had to bring men and supplies three thousand miles to the front. The Americans had their supplies at hand, and could make local levies.

In many ways the American War of Independence followed the pattern of the Seven Years War. The British used their coastal bases to try to blockade the colonies, and to act as depots from which troops could be shipped to different vantage-points along the seaboard. At the same time they used Canada as a centre from which to launch attacks across the Appalachians. The sea and the Canadian interior were two arms of a giant pincer, to be closed around the colonies. It was the aim of the colonists to prevent encirclement, to maintain a united front, and finally to drive the British from their coasts (Fig. 44).

The Americans took the initiative by driving the British out of Boston in 1775. Lord Howe, the British commander, retreated to Halifax. The next year he set sail for New York, which he won from General Washington. Philadelphia was also captured. The British had driven a deep wedge between the northern and southern colonies. They tried to use this advantage by sending other forces down the Champlain–Hudson gap, from Montreal, meaning to surround New England, and compel it to surrender. Meantime an offer of peace was to be made to the southern colonies, which were rather lukewarm. It was Washington's genius to hold the colonies together.

In 1777 the British drove south in two columns from Canada, in the hopes of converging on New York and Philadelphia, capturing the mid-Atlantic colonies and sealing off New England. These were crucial moves. Had the British succeeded, they would probably have won. But General Burgoyne was defeated at Saratoga, and denied the use of the Hudson gap; while General St Leger was defeated in his attempt on the western gaps. Meanwhile, Washington rallied his forces, and recaptured New York, in 1778. It was the turning-point of the war.

The next year the British tried to prise the southern colonies loose. Once again they copied the French strategy of the Seven Years War. They hoped to unite the St Lawrence–Great Lakes–Ohio into a single system of defences against the Americans, while renewing pressure from the sea. General Hamilton moved across south-west Ontario into the mid-western plains, and swung south against the Ohio; but he was met and defeated by General Clark at the battle of Vincennes. At the coast, the British succeeded in capturing Charleston. They moved inland, but failed time and again to

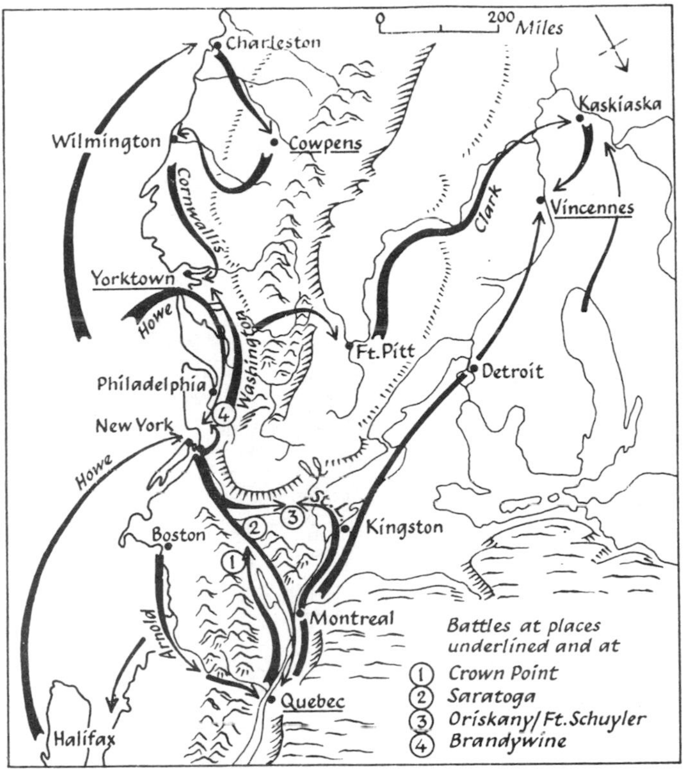

FIG. 44 The American War of Independence—chief thrusts and counter-thrusts in relation to drainage and relief. The continued importance of the Hudson–Champlain, Hudson–Mohawk, and Lower Lakes–Ohio links shows the strong influence of geography in the history of affairs.

engage the Americans, until at last, in 1781, they were defeated at Cowpens. In the interval the main British forces had been cornered in Yorktown. The Americans converged from New York, Philadelphia, and Richmond, and laid siege to Yorktown. At last, in 1781, General Cornwallis surrendered to Washington. The British encirclement was completely broken; the American colonies were more united than ever. They declared their independence as the United States of America.

The Drive to the West

With the conclusion of the Seven Years War and the War of American Independence, conditions were ripe for that great drive to the west that was to turn European colonies into American nations. Each of the three nations that evolved, Mexico, the United States, and Canada, found in the attraction of the western frontier a major spur to growth and development. Mexico had its California; the United States its Mississippi plains and the goal of Oregon; Canada its prairies and the Pacific coast.

The main drive west, however, was undoubtedly that made by the Americans of the United States. Indeed, as some of their historians claimed,

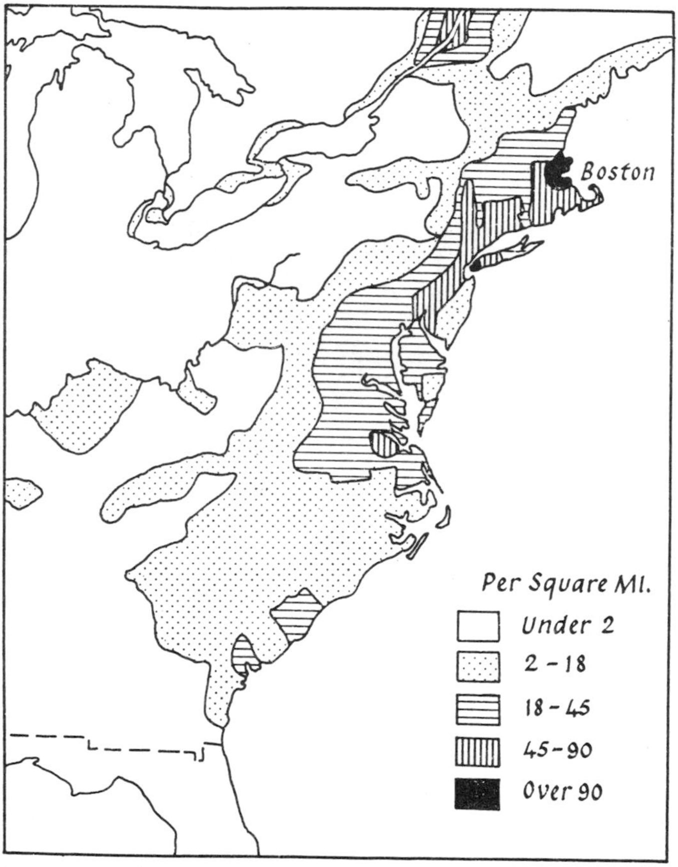

FIG. 45 The Tides of Early Population, up to the close of the eighteenth century. It was population as much as generalship that led to the defeat of the French and the success of the British in North America. (Scale, 1:17·5 m.)

they only became Americans when they turned west. Up till then they had still been European, relying on European contacts, trading with Europe, getting the finer things of life from Europe, and cherishing their European heritage. However, as they moved through the pine belt west on to the Piedmont, as they crossed the Blue Ridge west into the Great Appalachian valley, as they found the gaps in the Allegheny front and entered the blue-grass basins within the interior uplands, or the oak clearings of the Ohio valley, and as they drove westward through the Hudson–Mohawk valley to the Lower Great Lakes, they got further and further from their European past and saw their future in the western frontier (Fig. 45).

There is a good deal of truth in this, although it must be remembered that constantly new waves of immigrants from Europe repeatedly brought European ways and ideas even into the west, while there were always elements in the west that looked back to, and copied, the east. Nevertheless, one might with some justification say that it was the crossing of the Appalachians, not the American revolution, that formed the great divide in American history and geography. The American revolution was simply a separation of one Atlantic European community from another, until the winning of the west made it an American movement. While the east may have created the *revolution*, the west shaped the *evolution* of America. The frontier turned European things into American things. If the march of history was the march to America, thc march of America was the march to the west.

Conditions of Development: Social Independence

Once again history provided unique conditions for development; geography, distinct corridors of expansion. The frontier went along with, and —what is geographically more important—was advanced by, a new sense of social and economic independence. The social break was quite sharp, even before the revolution, between the coastal ways of life and the ways in what later came to be termed the Old West—the Piedmont, the Great Valley, up-state New York, and the New England back-country. The drift into these more isolated or rugged parts led to an escape from the feudalistic society of coastal Virginia and the Carolinas, from the *patroonship* system of New York, and from the theocracy of New England.

The difference between the Carolina coast and the Piedmont was so great that a virtual civil war broke out. The Carolina coast officials were scornfully called the 'gentlemen below' by the 'back-country boys'. Since there was virtually no migration from the tidewater to the Piedmont across the 'pine barrens', there was no bond between the back-country and the coast. The back-country was settled, not by aristocratic planters with their retainers, but by humble farmers and artisans. These came down from Pennsylvania and consisted mostly of 'Pennsylvania Dutch' (Deutsch, or German) and Scotch-Irish immigrants. They held small farms or workshops or mills of their own. The landscape they created was one of small farms cut out of the forest, spaced more or less evenly down long roads, serviced by small towns, where mill, smithy, general store, and inn formed a nucleus of settlement. The nearer forest was used for grazing cattle in. The farther forest was the domain of the woodsman, hunter, and fur trader.

Thus, at the close of the eighteenth century, 'the south was divided into two areas presenting contrasted types of civilization. On the one side were the planters raising their staple crops of tobacco, rice, and indigo. To this region belonged the slaves. On the other side was the area of small farmers, raising livestock, wheat, and corn. . . .'[1]

A similar difference arose between coastal and up-state New York and New England. Here there was a revolt against the rule of important New York families, the successors to the *patroons* (and their family-dominated political machines), or else against the tightly controlled and highly regulated life of the New England religious community.

Timothy Dwight, the President of Yale, complained bitterly about the frontiersmen. They were impatient of the restraints of law and morality, they grumbled about taxes, and they complained of the extortions of merchants and physicians, yet they thought themselves to be uncommonly wise. They delighted in innovation. It was, therefore, a blessing that Providence had offered them a retreat in the vast western wilderness! He was glad to see them go.

Yet of course it was this impatience at the restraints of British law, and the delight in religious innovation, that had led Dwight's pilgrim predecessors to find a retreat on the American shore, and set up New England!

In this early western movement a new geography of settlement began to emerge. In addition to the southern plantation and the northern 'town', both of which were tolerably compact, or at any rate centred in distinct nuclei dominated by social institutions, there now grew up a system of highly disseminated, independent farms, served by small, irregular centres, which were predominantly commercial. The mass of early settlers were either squatters or small landowners. Their passion was for a place of their own. Moving in as individuals, spurred by the new individualism of the frontier, they made an individual impact; the land was literally 'individualized'. It was divided into great numbers of single units of settlement, either strung out along the natural lines of rivers and coasts, or along artificial lines laid down by the surveyor. A conservative New Englander contrasted the new form of settlement with the old, reporting 'The newcomers do not fix near their neighbours and go on regularly, but take spots that please them best, though twenty or thirty miles beyond any others.'

This early, irregular form of open, disseminated settlement, particularly common in mountainous country, became modified by a more regular form, once land speculators or government land agents began to distribute land. It then became the custom to divide the land evenly by a surveyed grid and to sell off sections or lots along the roads that quartered the 'survey'. This was made possible by federal control of land.

[1] Turner, F. J., *Rise of the New West*, New York, 1906, p. 51.

The various states of the early federation had had their claims to land beyond the Appalachians. However, there was so much conflict in these claims that the idea occurred of waiving them, or rather surrendering them,

FIG. 46 Federal and State Claims in the West. Although the coastal colonies had originally received grants that gave them title to lands west of the Appalachians, they surrendered them to the Federal government, so that there might be over-all planning of the use and settlement of public lands. (Scale, 1:20 m.)

to the Federal government. Between 1780 and 1802 all the coastal states had ceded their territorial claims to the interior, and the vast area between the Appalachians and the Mississippi became public land, at the disposal of Congress (Fig. 46). Later, when the United States purchased Louisiana from France, the public lands were extended from the Mississippi to the Rockies, and thereafter, with the acquisition of Oregon and California, to the Pacific coast. In much the same way in Canada the land taken from the Indians, first by the various colonial governments, and then by the federal government of Canada, were designated Crown lands, and were sold by the Crown to land companies, development corporations, or individuals.

In the United States the problem of disposing of the public land was soon raised, as the tide of settlers poured through the gaps in the Appalachians. New Englanders pressed for a systematic, regular disposal of the land which would involve surveying it first, marking it out in geometrical blocks, and then selling these blocks off to companies or individuals who would promote group settlement. Southerners, however, had already established the 'warrant' system, by which each individual obtained a warrant to get land and then went out and got it. This was 'regularized' by subsequent survey and entitlement. Such a custom led to the indiscriminate location of settlement according to local geographical advantages, although the scattered claims were brought under a 'county' system of government. The northern system offered prior title to land and enabled the government to plan, or at least regulate, the westward advance, tier by tier. On the other hand, it slowed up immigration, it seemed to penalize the individual in favour of the group and, what was probably its most criticized aspect, it suggested that the New England way of life, as expressed in and organized under the 'township', should be the one for the whole country west of the Appalachians! The southern system was favoured by the highly individualistic frontiersman, even although it produced a great number of conflicts over titles.

Here we have, then, the first of the clashes between north and south that were to bedevil the opening up of the west. This clash lay in both history and geography. On the east coast there developed two distinct cradlelands of civilization, separated alike by social gulfs, and topographical differences; these were the New England 'hearthland' and the southern 'hearthland'. (The New England one, being the more compact and populous, centred mainly in Massachusetts Bay and Narragansett Bay, was the stronger of the two; the southern 'hearthland' was less populous and more stretched-out, extending from Richmond to Savannah.) From these cradlelands of development two 'culture streams' followed specific corridors of expansion into the opening west. The northern corridors, debouching on the Lower Great Lakes and the upper Ohio, were shorter and more direct, and soon began to carry the main weight of the westward migration. The southern corridors, through the Cumberland gap, or around the southern flank of the Appalachians, were more tortuous; and, although they were used more frequently to begin with, and distributed the stream of immigrants over a wider area, they became less effective, as northern roads, canals, and finally railroads were thrust into the interior (see Fig. 30, Chapter 5).

The North won out. In 1785 a committee of Congress proposed that the public land be developed in a systematic way, that it be divided up into townships, in the New England fashion and, as in New England, only whole townships be disposed of, and these only to united groups of settlers. The South protested in no uncertain terms; their immigrants were unwilling to have to band themselves together before moving west. Here was a clash of cultures and of cultural geography of the first order, because it involved the whole way of settlement and therefore the entire organization and appearance of the landscape. How different the geography of America would have been today had the South won out! But it did not. However, a compromise was effected, and the final Ordinance of 1785, called 'one of the most important legislative measures in American history', provided that all public lands would be divided into townships, six miles square in extent, which would in turn be subdivided into thirty-six numbered sections, each of 640 acres. Every second township would be sold as a whole as the New Englanders wanted it, or in individual lots or sections, as the Southerners demanded. The land was to be auctioned off in public roup, at an upset price of a dollar an acre (Fig. 47).

If this measure was historically important, it was geographically fundamental, because it cast the geography of settlement into an artificial grid, based on the surveyor's blueprint. Henceforth the distribution of farms and the layout of the roads were to ignore local relief, as much as this was possible. Of course major relief barriers, such as mountains or deeply entrenched rivers, drainage conditions like bogs, stretches of infertile soil, and gaps made by desert did interrupt the grid; also, favourable locations such as the convergence of natural routes, local wealth in fuels and minerals, and locally good soils, led to a greater concentration of settlement within one part of the grid than another: but the grid itself still remained. Geometry, as much as relief, controlled the geography of western settlement.

However, the surveyor could not keep ahead of the frontiersman. Settlers constantly 'leap-frogged' over the surveyed front of settlement to take up land beyond—the land they wanted. Large numbers of 'squatters' settled on land which they hoped they could retain through squatters' rights. Even if many of these individualists later had to accept and fit into the grid system, many provided local variations to the system; 'folk roads' remained, following the twists of frontier trails, even when the rectilinear network of routes was finally established. Relics of this folk geography, especially prevalent in the south, show how strong the frontier tradition was.

In actual fact, four major patterns of settlement evolved; there was first the spread of the southern plantation; second the continued though blunted advance of the southern 'warrant' system; third, the expansion of New

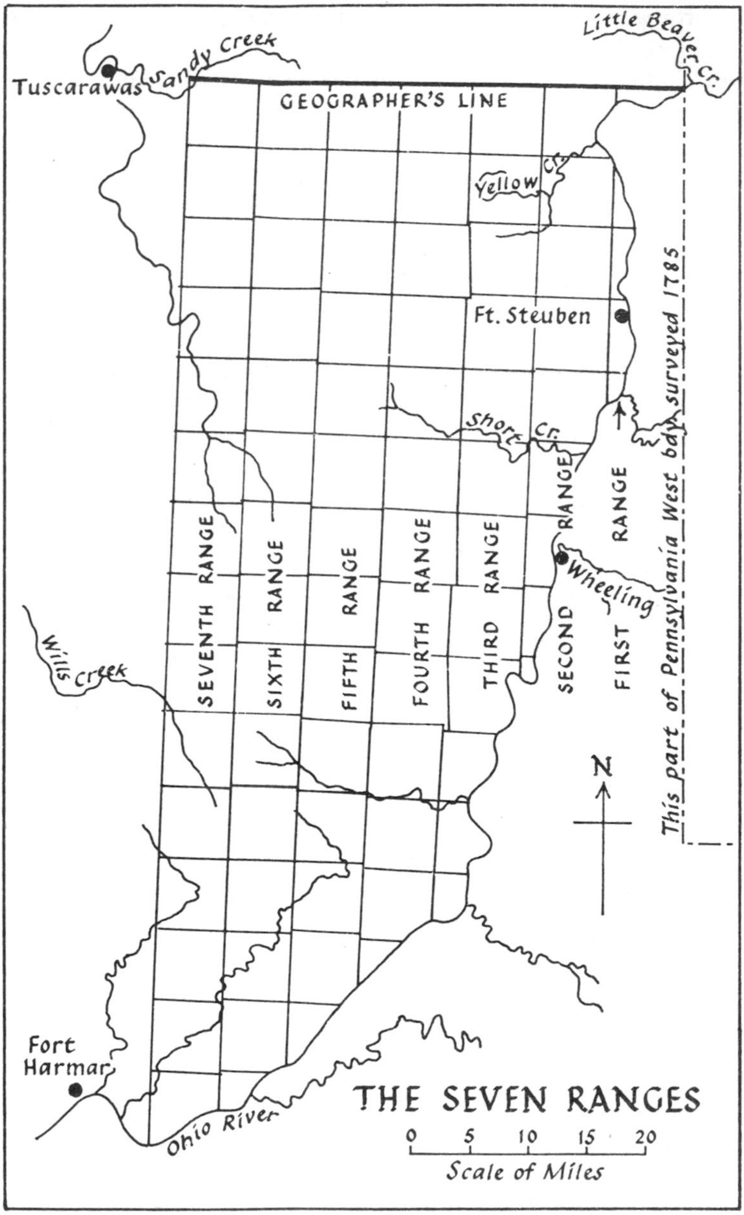

FIG. 47 The Western Land System—the initial pattern. This system led to a geometrical development of the geography of settlement in the American west.

England group-occupation; and finally, the wide and widening growth of regular but disseminated settlement.

Conditions of Development: Economic Independence

The geography of western development was shaped by economic as well as social factors. The American economy became more varied, more self-sufficient, and more buoyant. It gave ever more scope for individual initiative and enterprise. A whole succession of events was behind this, including: the replacement of tenancy by land ownership, the accessibility of 'free' land, the development of non-agricultural resources, the expansion of communications, the growth of domestic industry, the considerable enlargement of the home market, protection from foreign competition, and the rise of a so-called 'American system' in production and trade.

The replacement of leasehold by freehold land, and the rapid abandonment of the tenancy system, did an enormous amount to stimulate migration. In earlier days the quest for religious freedom had been the spur; then had come that urge for political freedom that led to the revolution; with the close of the eighteenth century came the drive for economic freedom. This was shared by Canada also. Here, too, there was a marked breakaway from tenancy. Even though seigneuries continued to be created they could find few tenants to work them; quit rents were reduced until they were only nominal—still the landlords could not get men to develop their land. In the early nineteenth century they were forced to sell their land to freeholders, and to put the capital thus acquired into lumber or flour mills, tanneries, or general stores to maintain their position as men of substance. In Ontario important pioneer families received some very large land grants. As a result they came to play a very influential part in affairs, controlling new settlement, the extension of roads, and the growth of towns. They tended, also, to control government and a veritable 'family compact' emerged, that engendered a lot of opposition. Gradually, however, they gave up land as their main means of wealth, and sold their estates to individual landholders. Today, very few of the old 'landed gentry' are left. There may be a few that still obtain some income from leasing land, but most of them maintain their positions by participation in business or industry.

Acquiring land was made much easier with the public land policy of the American government. Turner gives a vivid picture of what happened:

> Arrived on the Ohio, the emigrant either cut out a road to his new home or pushed up some tributary of that river in a keel-boat. If he was one of the poorer classes, he became a squatter, trusting to find in the profits of his farming the means of paying for his land. Not uncommonly, after clearing the land, he sold his improvements to the actual purchaser (of the

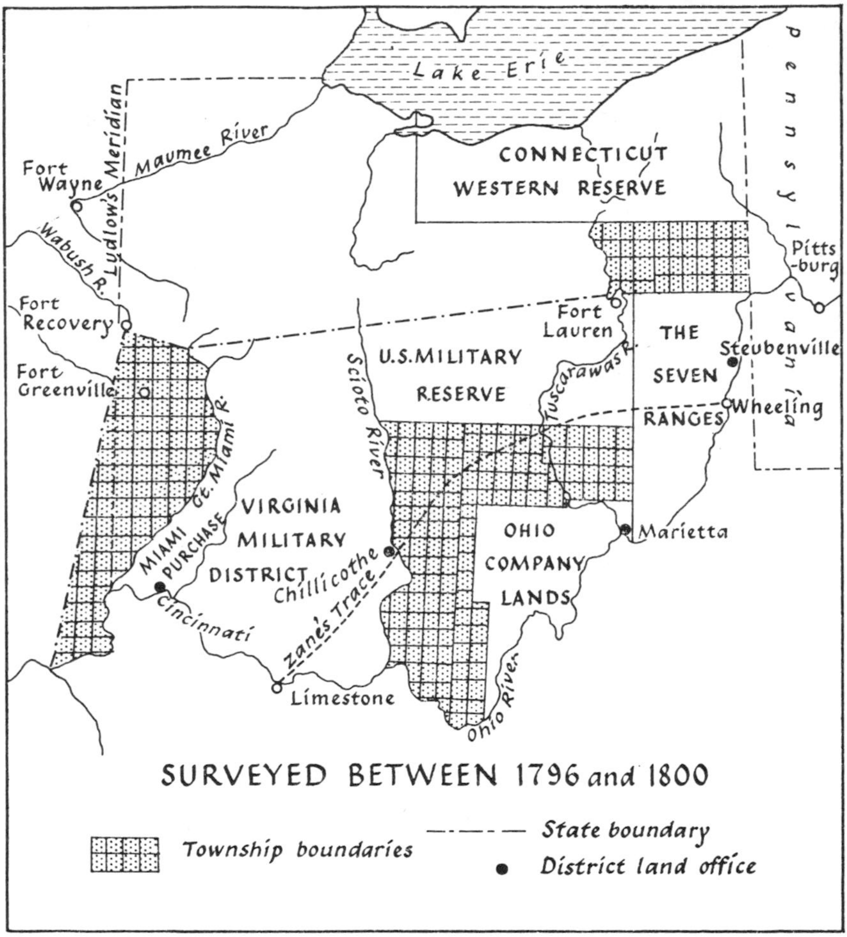

FIG. 48 Land Company and other Surveys and Military Reserves, early Mid-West. (From Pattison.)

lot or section), under the customary usage or by pre-emption laws. With the money thus secured he would purchase new land in a remoter area, and thus establish himself as an *independent land-owner*. The price of labor in the towns along the Ohio, coupled with the low cost of provisions, made it possible for even a poor day-laborer from the East to accumulate the necessary amount to make his land purchase.[1]

The drive for free, or all-but free, land was one of the greatest forces in opening up the West (Fig. 48). Since America had by far the greatest amount of suitable land, it secured by far the greatest number of immigrants. At the

[1] Turner, op. cit., p. 84.

heart of the United States lie the vast and fertile plains of the Ohio, Mississippi, and Missouri; the heart of Canada, by contrast, is taken up with a rugged, intractable, and infertile upland—the Canadian Shield; while in the centre of Mexico lies a large desert or semi-desert region. Mexico had a very restrictive land policy, based on the landlord-tenant relationship, and featured in the large 'hacienda'—at least until after the revolution. This, as well as the desert, made Mexico fall behind in the filling up of the west. America and Canada, by contrast, had equivalent land policies and systems of land subdivision. Their physical structure, however, differed so much that it made all the difference to their development. America, with soil at the heart could readily outmatch Canada, with a heart of rock!

Yet soil was not America's only wealth. As we have already seen, underneath the interior lowlands are the ancient basins and arches of the mid-continental 'stable area'. In the basins, coal and oil were preserved. Along

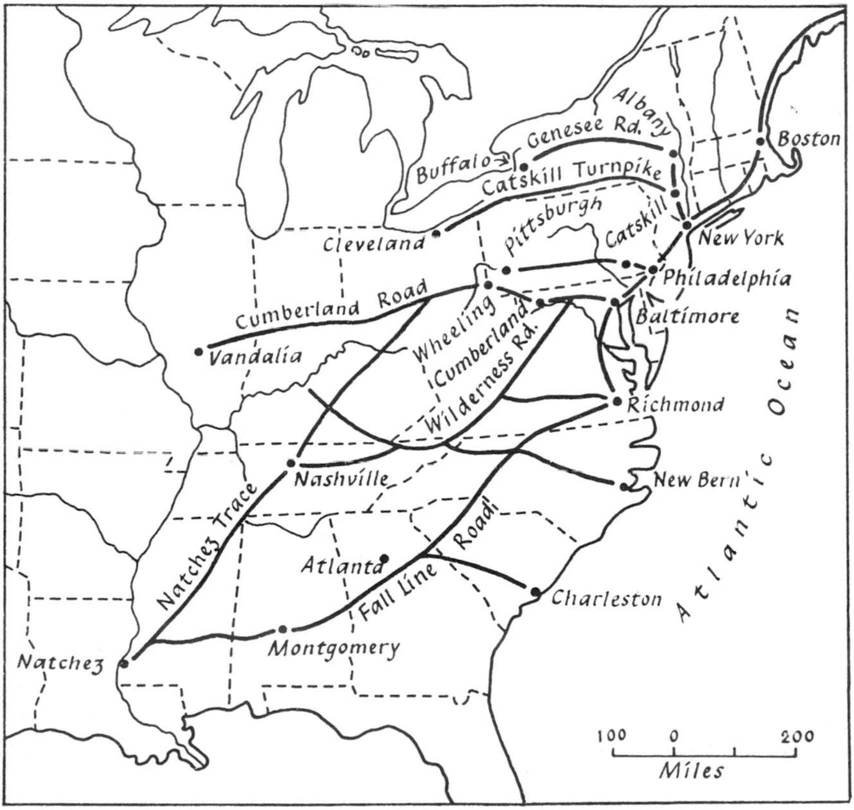

FIG. 49 Pioneer Roads in the United States. Note the importance of New York, Philadelphia, and Baltimore, commanding trans-Appalachian passes.

some of the arches, where they came to the surface, metals were presented. Where the Shield impinged on the region, around Lake Superior, was a wealth of iron. The prolongation of the Appalachian system, in the Ozarks, witnessed a wealth of lead. Thus many non-agricultural resources existed, which were more numerous and far larger west of the Appalachians than to the east. Their development gave the new-born nation new sinews of power.

Pittsburgh, amid its coal mines and with its blast-furnaces, was as much a symbol of the West as Cincinnati, with its hog pens and corn mills.

Americans soon realized that the development of all this wealth, and the filling up of the interior, depended above all on transportation. Indian trails were followed by fur traders and frontiersmen. Some of these became settlers' roads and national turnpikes (Fig. 49). The Cumberland trail, crossing the old Warrior's path of the Shawnee, opened up Kentucky. New roads were blazed and developed. Congress either developed communications or made money available to the States to develop them. The National Road, Forbes' Road, and the Catskill Turnpike opened up the Ohio. Great help though they were, these roads were costly to maintain and to use. Freight rates were very high. The war of 1812 showed up the limitations of wagon transportation and produced a demand for canals. The lack of water transportation to the Canadian frontier during the war from the north-eastern and mid-Atlantic States meant that 'every barrel of flour cost $50.00, every barrel of pork $8.00, and every cannon used there, twice as much in the cost of transporting it as in the cost of making it'.[1] Consequently, when the war was over, there was a tremendous boom with the cutting of canals (Fig. 50).

The success of the Erie canal was phenomenal. Linking the Hudson with the Great Lakes, it allowed people to travel from New York to Detroit for less than $10.00. It at once became the great highway to the west. Canals thus gave America much more freedom to move. Later, railways used the Hudson–Mohawk gap to bring the west into even closer touch with the east. Movement became much swifter; immigration and trade, more free. Other gaps were seized on; and from Boston, New York, Philadelphia, Baltimore, and Richmond railways were thrust through the Appalachian barrier to open up the interior, and the great names like the New York Central, the Pennsylvania Railroad, the Erie Railroad, and the Baltimore and Ohio started to earn their fame.

These all helped to take in manufactured goods to the west, and to take out primary products, particularly agricultural surplus, from the west. As they did so they formed a new series of bonds that bound the States together in a rapidly growing domestic trade that overshadowed, and to a certain extent actually replaced, dependence upon Europe. This was a major change

[1] Beukema, J. C., *Congressional Records*, 86th U.S. Congress, p. 1671.

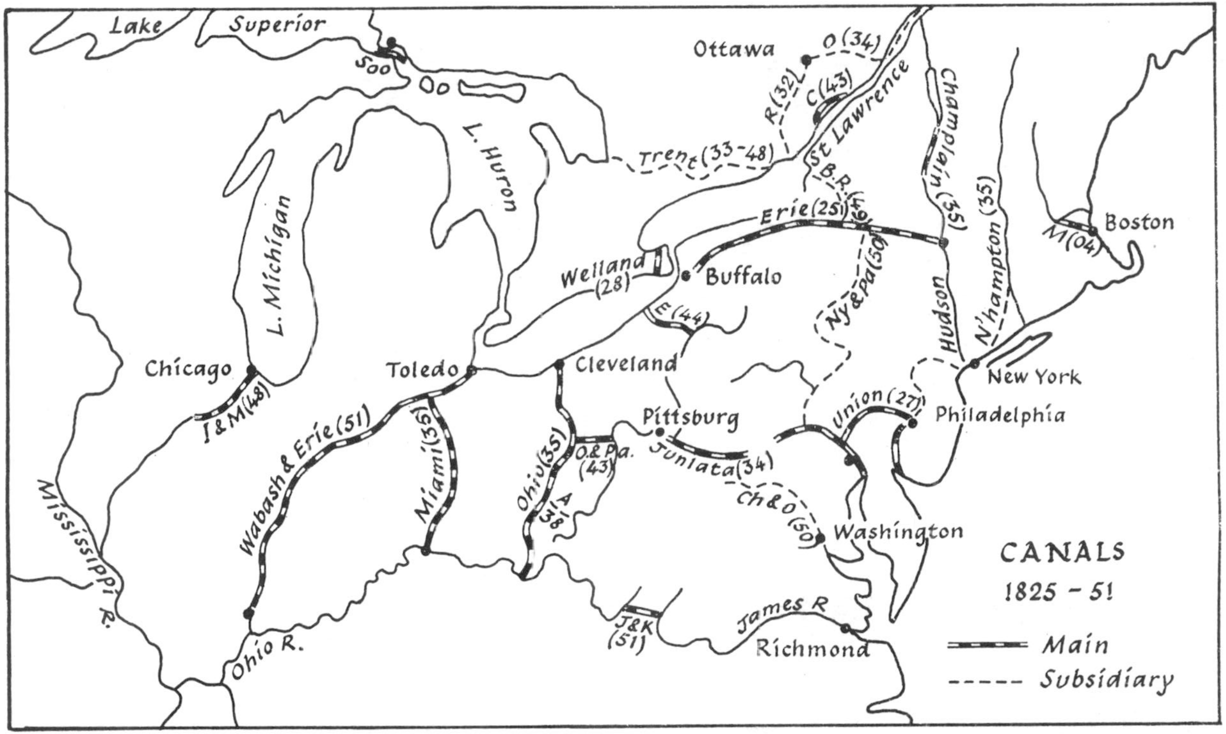

FIG. 50 Early Canals in the United States and Canada. The barrier of the Appalachians was too great for most canals to effect an uninterrupted crossing; hence the great importance of the Erie canal, from Lake Erie to the Hudson, which was able to use the low-level, open gap of the Mohawk. M, Merrimack; Ch & O, Chesapeake & Ohio; E, Erie & Allegheny; J & K, James & Kanawha; I & M, Illinois & Michigan. In Canada, R, Rideau; O, Ottawa; C, Cornwall. (Scale, 1:12·5 m.)

in the geography of the continent. America now found more across the Appalachians than across the Atlantic. The change was witnessed by the spread of communications, the rise of interior cities, and the shift of the centre of population from the coast plain to the central lowlands. Thus geographical regions were constantly being reshaped by economic regions. The rise of the west was the rise of a new American geography (Fig. 51).

The first certain sign of this was the growth of domestic industry. America was no longer obliged to buy from Europe in such quantity. It is true that the southern States still imported most of their tools and machines, their textiles, chinaware, leather goods, their books, and their luxuries from England, and did so up to the American Civil War; but the northern and western States were much less prone to do so. Pennsylvania, New York, and New England soon took on the role with the trans-Appalachian world that England formerly had with the transatlantic world. They furnished all kinds of manufactured goods for the west, rivalling Britain even in high-quality articles. What was just as important they supplied capital, management, and skill for the development of western industries. By the mid-nineteenth century lively industries had grown up between the Ohio and the Mississippi, such as iron and steel at Pittsburgh, meat-packing at Cincinnati, flour-milling at Rochester and Buffalo, salt manufacture at Syracuse, distilling in Louisville, coach-building at Detroit, and so on. Thus the west, in prospering the east, prospered itself; the east, in developing the west, entered on a new era of development. A giant home market was created which was to produce a continental economy, that is still expanding today. The home market is now so vast that it makes up some 92 per cent of American trade, leaving only about 8 per cent for trade abroad.

To nurse this home market, northern and western producers—whether manufacturers or farmers—clamoured for protection against foreign competition. Development of the interior made the economic independence of the United States possible; protection from abroad made it practicable. Yet there was a good deal of opposition to protection, from the South. The economy of the South depended on selling primary products such as tobacco and cotton for as much as possible, and buying in manufactured goods for as little as possible. The cry of the West for protection thus exacerbated the growing bitterness between north and south more than ever.

Shortly after the 1812–14 war with Canada, when the war-time boom passed into a relative recession, a tariff bill was put through Congress, in 1816, that offered limited protection to the youthful iron and steel industry, woollen and cotton manufacturers, the makers of hemp goods, and of several lesser products. A boom followed which led, however, to a worse depression than ever. In 1820 the North and West once more appealed for help from the tariff, but did not get enough support for an increase. But in

25. *Opening up America:* a, by the Mississippi Steamboat. A typical scene on the levée at New Orleans in the early nineteenth century.

26. *Opening up America:* b, by Wagon Train. After the passage of the Homestead Act in 1862 thousands of families streamed west.

27. *Opening up America:* c, by Pony Express. The arrival of the first rider in San Francisco, 1860—a notable event!

28. *Opening up America:* d, by Transcontinental Train. This historic picture, taken in 1869, shows the driving of the last spike connecting the Union Pacific and Central Pacific railways, linking West and East.

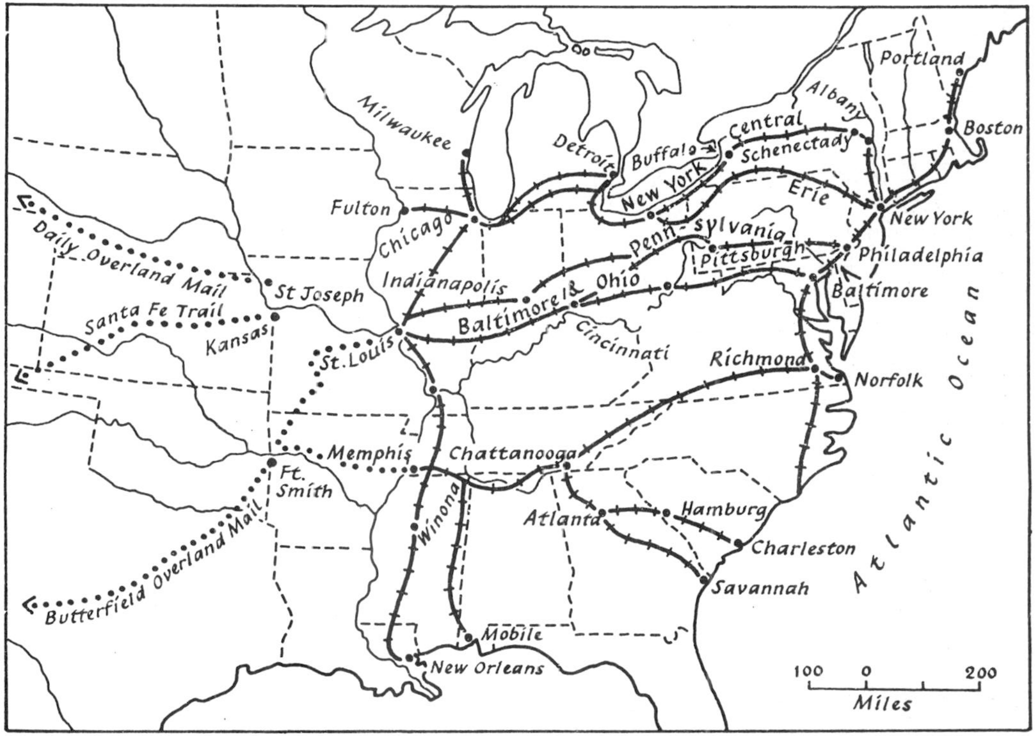

FIG. 51 Early United States Railways and Overland Mail-coach Routes. Once again the command that New York, Philadelphia, and Baltimore had of the gaps through the Appalachians gave them command of the main railways systems, the N.Y. Central and Erie, the Pennsylvania, and the Baltimore and Ohio railways. Note the comparative scarcity of N–S as compared with E–W lines.

1824 Henry Clay argued so effectively for the creation of what he called the 'American system' of development and trade, protected from European competition by a high tariff wall, that a new bill was passed. Protection became part and parcel of the American economy, and America did, in fact, begin to evolve an 'American system'. (It is interesting that in the great debate the South urged the West not to support the North, since to do so would make them tributary to the Atlantic States. The West would have

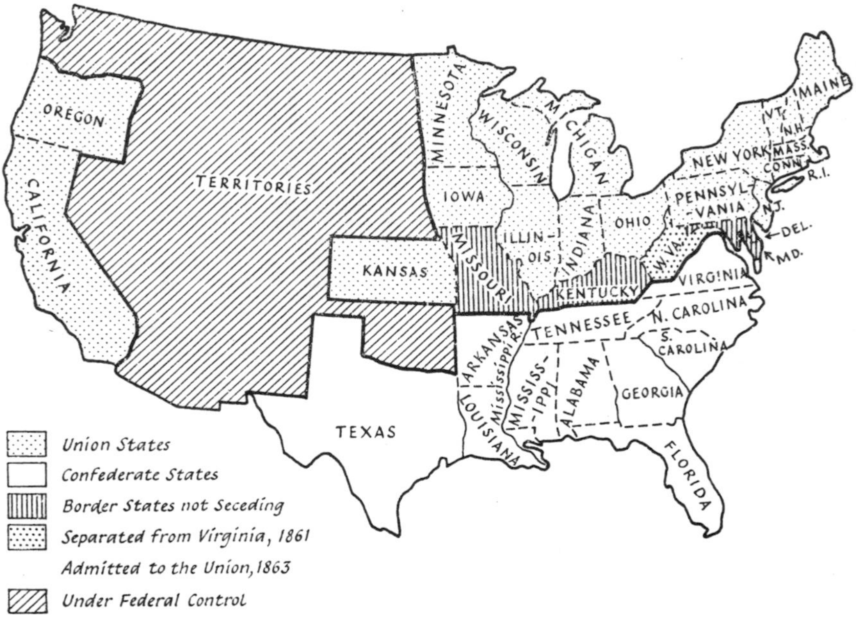

FIG. 52 The Division of the United States at the Civil War, 1861.

more to gain selling corn, meat, and mules to the South than joining up with New England manufacturers. The clash between South and North took on a more serious tone in their attempts to woo and win over the West (Fig. 52).)

Clay's system of internal improvements behind protective tariffs had great political and, in the end, geographical significance. In urging the federal government to effect internal improvements such as the building of roads and canals he was trespassing on States' rights. Nevertheless, he pointed out that the seaboard States had allowed the federal government to make coastal surveys, erect sea-walls, and build lighthouses. Was there then to be 'everything on the margin of the ocean and nothing for the great interior of the country'? He claimed that 'A new world has come into being since the Constitution was adopted. Are the narrow, limited necessities of the old thirteen states for ever to remain the rule?'[1] This appeal to let the new geography have its impact on politics did bring about a new political situation—a situation that then gave shape to yet another geography! For roads and canals were built by government aid; public enterprise augmented and strengthened and guided private initiative; and settlement went ahead at both a quicker and a steadier pace than it could otherwise have done. Thus the physical environment called forth a political appreciation which, in its turn, became the environment for a new use of the physical resources. It is in this way that geography and history constantly act and react upon each other.

Much the same story occurred in Canada. Here, the area called Canada West, or Upper Canada (what is now Ontario), pressed for protection in order to encourage infant industries. The mercantilist policy of Lower Canada was lukewarm if not hostile to the idea until the Erie canal began to make a dint on the hinterland of Montreal. Eventually, when the several British colonies united themselves within the Canadian Federation, Sir John A. Macdonald, the first Federal Prime Minister and an Upper Canada representative, established the famous 'National Policy' that protected Canadian industry from the competition of both Britain and the United States.

The West had done more than create an 'American system' of trade, however, or its Canadian counterpart; it had given these countries a new vision of themselves and of what they could be. Benton, the great protagonist of the West, was perhaps the first to see this and, concerned about British claims to Oregon, and Spanish reassertions of their claim to Texas, he urged westerners to take a part in affairs by widening America's whole horizon and view of itself. 'It is time', he cried, 'that Western men had some share in the destinies of this republic!'[2]

From this it was a short step to the concept of 'Manifest Destiny', that frame of mind which has done more to shape the geography of North America than almost any other factor, structure, relief, climate, the wealth of soil, or mineral wealth not excluded. Clay was in many respects the father of the new concept. In a speech on the ratification of the Florida Treaty he implored: 'We look too much abroad. Let us break these commercial and political fetters; let us no longer watch the nod of any European politician; let us become real and true Americans, and place ourselves at the head of the American system.'[3] Baylies, of Massachusetts, in a debate on the Oregon question, urged America to drive to the Pacific and 'anticipate the grandeur which awaited her'. Turner, whose essay on the *Frontier in American History* profoundly influenced American thinking, expressed the concept as a

[1] *Annals of Congress*, 18th Congress, 1 Session, I, 1035.
[2] Quoted in Meigs, *Thomas H. Benton*, pp. 98–99.
[3] *Annals of Congress*, 16th Congress, 1 Session, II, 2727.

necessary outcome of America's move west. 'American social development', he claimed, 'has been continually beginning over again on the frontier. This perennial rebirth, this fluidity of American life, this expansion westward with its new opportunities . . . furnish the forces dominating American character.' Time and again he returned to this idea. 'Besides its susceptibility to change, the West had generated, from its Indian fighting, forest-felling, and expansion, a belligerency and a largeness of outlook with regard to the nation's territorial destiny. As the pioneer, widening the ring-wall of his clearing in the midst of the stumps and marshes of the wilderness, had a vision of the lofty buildings and crowded streets of a future city, so the West as a whole developed ideals of the future of the common man, *and of the grandeur and expansion of the nation*.'[1] Soon the whole nation, and not only the West, was gripped by this belief, until one of its leading men, O'Sullivan, could write, in unequivocal terms: 'It is our manifest destiny to overspread the continent allotted by Providence for the free development of our multiplying millions.'[2]

Manifest Destiny and Modern Geography

This idea had a tremendous value for geography. Indeed many ideas have; ideas are as much a part of our environment as mountains, rivers, and trees. But certain ideas have a peculiar meaning for geography where they shape the use and organization of space. The ideas of the American and Mexican revolutions cut those countries from their former ties with Britain and Spain, and gave them the power to shape their own destinies, bring in what immigrants they wanted, send out their explorers, missionaries, traders, settlers, and soldiers into what territories they sought, develop their own industries, and trade where they liked. In other words, those revolutionary ideas revolutionized the geography of the two countries. Canada had a very different idea, expressed in the Crown Connexion, that had, however, just as much influence on its geography. This idea was that it would benefit an American country to maintain its ties with Europe. As Lord Tweedsmuir put it, through these ties, Canada could become for North America 'the guardian of the great Mediterranean tradition which descends from Greece and Rome, and which she [Canada] has to mould to the uses of a new world'. It was because the United States tried to stress her *difference* from Europe that the French and Loyalist traditions in Canada insisted on their *similarities*. As far as America was concerned her new-found faith was her glory; Canada's glory lay in her old and established faithfulness.* America came to regard liberty as the highest law; Canada believed in law as the

[1] Turner, *Rise of the New West*, p. 107 (our italics).

[2] O'Sullivan, J., *The U.S. Magazine and Democratic Review*, **xvii**, p. 5.

* The motto of the United Empire Loyalist expresses this well. *Ut incepit sic permanet fidelis*. 'As loyal she (Canada) began, loyal she remains.'

truest liberty. Consequently, while America went ahead and established its American system on a wave of libertarian zeal, Canada preserved a wider Atlantic system, and worked for the establishment of what Brebner called the Atlantic Triangle, linking Britain and the United States, Europe and North America together, in and through Canada itself, as much as this was possible. And this idea influenced the geography of Canadian trade, the geography of Canadian canals and railways, the geography of Canadian farming and mining, and the geography of Canadian defence. Indeed, hardly

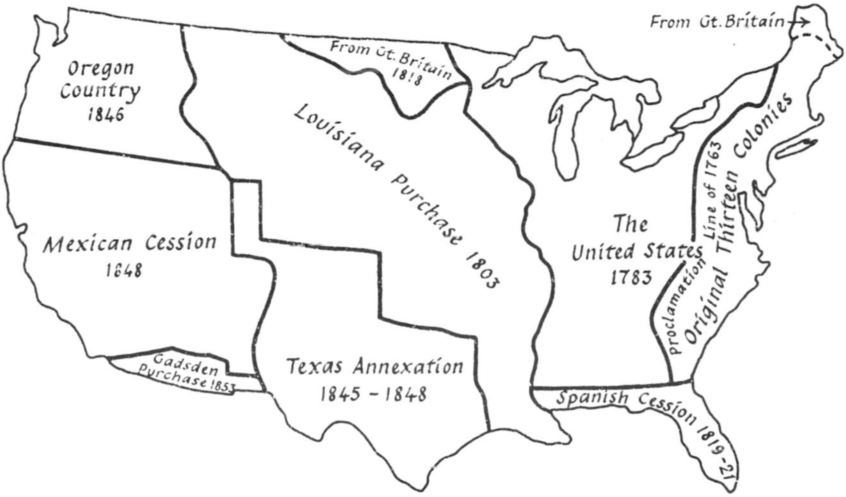

FIG. 53 Manifest Destiny—Stages of United States Growth, largely at the expense of prior claims to territory by Canada and Mexico, and often in the wake of the tide of U.S. settlers moving into already occupied but ill-established parts of the neighbouring lands.

any factor has been greater in Canadian geography than the Crown Connexion. Where the Appalachians, the Shield, and the Rockies tended to keep the original colonies apart, the Crown Connexion drew them together and eventually enabled them to form such a union between themselves as to give unity to their several geographies, and to create the geography of a united country *a mari usque ad mare.*

Of all these geographically pregnant ideas none was more forcefully held, and none exerted as great an influence as the American concept of Manifest Destiny. It made the United States the greatest expansionist power, not only in the continent, but in the Pacific and Atlantic realms as well. This chapter will conclude with a sketch of American expansionism and its geographical effects (Fig. 53).

Since its beginning American history has been characterized by territorial expansion. The United States were not content to stay within the confines of the Mississippi, the St Lawrence, and the Florida boundaries. They bought, bargained, or fought for an ever-increasing share in the continent, until their Manifest Destiny of ruling it from sea to sea, and from the Great Lakes to the Caribbean, was fulfilled. Even while the colonists were in a desperate struggle with the Motherland, explorers and traders were pushing to the west. Jefferson sent Clark and Lewis into the west to discover the possibilities of settlement. Soon the great treks to the west began, one of the spectacular movements of history, made up of adventuresome but humble people from the east and from Europe, who sought a second chance beyond the Mississippi.

However, in this great thrust to fulfil their destiny, the Americans came into competition with the Spanish and the British. The Spanish claimed Florida, and had explored and partially developed Texas, New Mexico, and California. The British had undefined claims in the north-east, and also in the west. Their fur traders had set up trading posts far in the Red river, across the prairies, and in the Columbia river basin. The Americans did not respect these claims, but urged claims of their own. Their traders or their settlers pushed northwards into New Brunswick; around to the Red river; and into the Columbia basin. Similarly thousands of settlers moved into nominally Spanish land, in Texas and California.

It was this great tide of settlement that swept aside the claims of British fur traders and immigrants, and Spanish missionaries and ranchers, and made America the dominant power in the continent. As that tide gathered strength and volume it became conscious of its Manifest Destiny, and, successfully pushing back Canada and Mexico, reached the Pacific. The tide of settlers did not set until the twentieth century; but today a new form of expansion has taken up the slack, and American business or American defence have pushed on into the Caribbean, and over the Pacific, until the American realm includes bases in remote Japan and the Philippines, Samoa, and Hawaii, the Galapagos Islands, and Panama, Puerto Rico, and the Virgin Islands. In fact, American expansion has now turned the opposite way, and is pushing into the Atlantic, back towards Europe, in bases leased from Britain, Iceland, Portugal, and Spain. America not only dominates the American continent, but also the Atlantic and Pacific oceans.

Throughout this great movement, which has had its counterparts only in the growth of the British Commonwealth and the expansion of the Russian union, the attempt has constantly been to find geographical boundaries commensurate with historical power, and to secure the geographical resources and the strategic frontiers to maintain and protect that power. It has been, in brief, to provide for an essential storehouse of wealth, to control the great gateways of contact, and assure the strategic spheres of influence on which the security, strength, and freedom of the country rest. These are the great geographical necessities that guide any nation with a respect for its own destiny; and for these basic geographical needs America, Canada, and Mexico struggled with each other until eventually, faced with far wider struggles, they interpreted these needs not in terms of national ambitions but of continental imperatives. Then, joining together in truly continental solidarity, they applied these needs to the world situation and, to make the vast storehouse of the continent itself secure, had to make safe the great oceanic approaches of the Pacific, Atlantic, and Arctic, and seek to preserve friendly spheres in Latin America, Western Europe, and East and South-east Asia.

The American-Canadian Boundary

In the American advance to the west, there was often the temptation to move north, because Canadian rivers or lakes made openings from the north into American territory. It was essential for the United States to protect these openings, and thus hold the gateways into the country. British claims had been large and they had been vague. Many of them antedated the rise of the United States, and made for misunderstanding when the States arose. By the Treaty of Paris, in 1763, Britain had obtained all the land east of the Mississippi. Through the activities of the Hudson's Bay Company, it claimed the prairies as well, at least down to the 49th parallel. The Selkirk Grant extended part of the prairie sphere to the upper Red river. In 1778 the Oregon territory, from the Skeena to the Columbia rivers, was claimed. When America defeated Britain, and took over the Thirteen Colonies, in 1783, it was difficult to say with precision what was American and what was British territory. The British held firmly to the Maritimes, the St Lawrence Lowlands, and the Hudson Bay. But there was a lot of unsettled land between the two countries, which invited boundary disputes. Britain organized its eastern Canadian territories, outside the lands of the Hudson's Bay Company, into four colonies: those of Nova Scotia and New Brunswick in 1783, and of Lower and Upper Canada (Quebec and Ontario) in 1791.

It was between New Brunswick and Maine, in densely forested and largely unsettled uplands, that the first real dispute between Canada and America took place. Canada had to protect the greatest of all its gateways, the St Lawrence estuary, which led straight to its chief storehouse of wealth in the St Lawrence–Ottawa valley–Lower Great Lakes region. At the same time Canada had to link this vital, central area with the Maritime Provinces, by means of the passes through the Appalachians between Quebec and New Brunswick. Therefore it wanted to push the boundary as far south as possible. It claimed a height of land between the St John and the Penobscot, which would have given it the broad east–west basin of the upper St John and the Aroostook valleys to connect New Brunswick and Quebec. On the other hand, the Americans had begun to settle in the region. Many Scotch-Irish immigrants, driven from lower New England by 'the hostility of Puritan clergy who feared the corrupting effects of Presbyterianism'[1] drifted first west and then north. They were followed by other pioneers. They gave some substance to the American attempt to push its claim northward to a boundary along the crest of the Notre Dame mountains. This would have protected the gateway down through the Aroostook valley to the Penobscot. But the frontier would then have come to within twenty miles of the St Lawrence estuary, and would have threatened that main gateway into Canada. Finally, after a quarrel, called the Aroostook War, a treaty was signed in 1842 accepting a compromise position, which followed the St John valley for part of its course. This left the fertile Aroostook valley in America, but gave Canada adequate, though slender, connexions between Quebec and New Brunswick, by way of the Madawaska and Matapedia passes between the middle St John and the St Lawrence estuary.

In the meantime, the Americans had spread west along the Hudson–Mohawk route and debouched upon the Lower Great Lakes. Here was an extremely fertile area, directly in line with the old Mohawk trail to the west, and forming an ideal bridge between New York-and-New England and the territories west of Lake Erie and south of Lake Michigan on which many migrants had their eyes. By the Quebec Act of 1774 all this territory right down to the Ohio and across to the Mississippi had been claimed by Britain. This claim offended the sea-coast colonies that had interior pretentions. Virginia denied Britain's right to give away her western territories, and, once the War of Independence had been won, claimed them back. The United States went further and laid claim to the Lower Great Lakes region, as well as Lakes Huron and Michigan, by wanting to extend the use of the 45th parallel westward. This had been the traditional boundary between Quebec and New York, and before that between French and British territory in this general region.

However, many loyal American colonists had by then moved into the Lower Great Lakes region. As the 'United Empire Loyalists', they were determined to hold on to the territory, which was now their new homeland, and Britain was adamant in their support. Eventually a compromise was reached, in 1792–3, by which Britain retained this vital area—which, along with the Montreal plain, is the real 'hearthland' of Canada—but gave up its claims to the area west of Lake Huron over to the Mississippi. The frontier ran along the 45th parallel to the St Lawrence river, thence through the middle of the Great Lakes, from there to the Lake of the Woods, and from the north-west corner of this 'due west to the Mississippi'.

[1] Billington, R. A., *Westward Expansion*, New York, 1949, p. 95.

Unfortunately, the western end of this boundary was so vague as to create more trouble than it settled. What was the line from the Great Lakes to the Lake of the Woods? The Americans demanded the line of the Rainy river, the main portage between the two lakes; but this would have meant the loss to Canada of a part of upper Lake Superior. Had Britain known that this part contained the famous Mesabi iron-ore deposits—the greatest in the world—it would doubtless have made every effort to keep the area for Canada. As it was, Britain pressed for a line from Duluth to Rainy Lake and thence to Lake of the Woods. But the Americans, anxious to develop the fur trade in the Upper Great Lakes region, insisted on the old fur-trade portage. Consequently, in 1826 they claimed a northern frontier running from the Mississippi to Rainy Lake and thence to Thunder Bay. Again, a compromise was reached, and Pigeon river was chosen as the border, giving Canada the harbours of Thunder Bay, and a good portage route from Lake Superior to Rainy Lake, Lake of the Woods, and Lake Winnipeg. America obtained the Head of the Lakes, which was later to be developed into the greatest iron field in the world.

Still another dispute occurred west of Lake of the Woods, for it was found that the line agreed on, which was to run due west until it cut the Mississippi river, ran well to the north and cut the Red river. But this had been claimed by the Hudson's Bay Company on behalf of Britain, and part of it had been given to Lord Selkirk, in which he founded a colony. The Red river was also used by the North-west Company trading out of Montreal. Unfortunately, hardly any settlements had been built, except at Fort Gary. The Americans had been operating in the southern part of the valley from St. Paul, and claimed it for their own. They were anxious to use it for their rapidly expanding fur trade. Once more a compromise was effected and the 49th parallel, running from Lake of the Woods to the Rockies, was chosen as the frontier.

The Americans pushed westward and came to the Oregon country (Fig. 54). This was very debatable land. It lay between Spanish territory in the south (California) and Russian territory in the north (Alaska). In 1778 Cook had explored it from the Pacific, and in 1792–4 Vancouver followed, and sailed from the mouth of the Columbia river to Prince of Wales Island. That was roughly the stretch which the British claimed, extending eastward to the Rockies. In 1793 Mackenzie explored the northern half in an adventurous trip from the Peace river across the Rockies to the sea at Bella Coola inlet where he all but met Vancouver. Finally, between 1807 and 1811, Thompson made extensive explorations in the Columbia basin to the south.

However, the Americans had not been inactive. New England traders had sailed to the mouth of the Columbia at the end of the eighteenth century to buy the coast otter whose pelts fetched such fabulous prices in China.

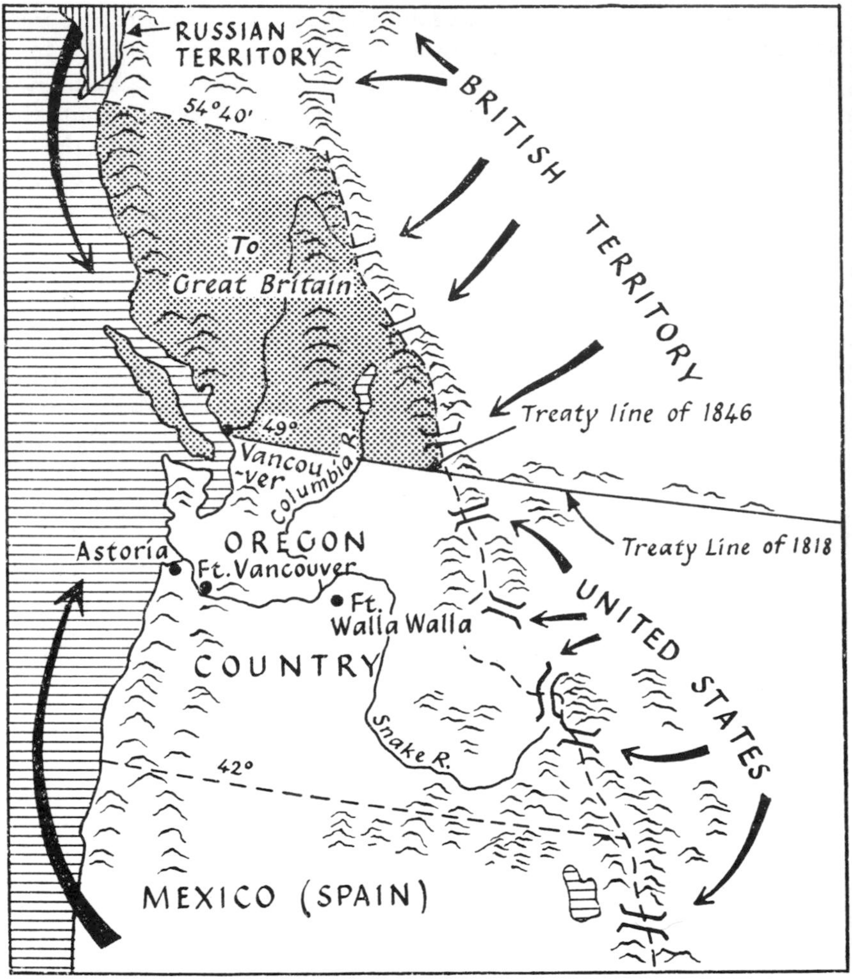

FIG. 54 The Oregon Question—a clash of British, American, Spanish, and Russian claims. The United States received the lion's share because it settled and developed the region most rapidly. (Scale 1: 20 m.)

Jefferson was most anxious to know more about the region, and when he became President sent the famous American adventurers, Clark and Lewis, across the plains and mountains on their historic trip from St Louis to the mouth of the Columbia river and back. This occurred between 1803 and 1806 and was used to establish American claims to the territory. The British had the advantage of prior discovery; there is no doubt but that they were in there first. They had also set up the first fur-trading posts, and were thus the first to begin to use the area. Yet they were unable to settle it. Oregon was too far from England by sea, or from Ontario by land. On the other hand, it was not too remote from the Mississippi, to which the tide of American immigration had swept. The Americans, therefore, started to move in, finding it an all but empty land.

The strange situation then occurred in which the territory was occupied by both British and Americans, until in 1846 an agreement on its future was reached. This lost Canada the lower part of the Columbia basin, where most of the Americans lived, but gave it the upper half, in which the Canadian fur trade was well established. The dividing line became the 49th parallel, which was continued across the Rockies from the interior and carried to the coast. Thus Canada kept the Fraser valley, and also the passes in the Rockies which allowed it to connect Vancouver with Winnipeg. One last problem was the gateway to Vancouver itself. Had the 49th parallel been extended to the ocean, across Vancouver Island, it would have given America sole use of the Straits of San Juan da Fuca. The boundary was bent south to run down the length of the straits and thus give both Vancouver and Seattle direct access to the Pacific.

Thus in the march of the American people from the Atlantic to the Pacific, the United States and Canada often found themselves in disagreement over their frontiers. The disagreements were serious, but only on one occasion, during the 1812–14 struggle, did the two countries go to war with each other. They took the wiser course of settling matters by treaty. And although Canada lost much territory, she at least straightened out her border. This had the advantage of strengthening the east–west forces in Canadian geography, and so of overcoming the north–south pull to America. The Canadian frontier tended to use or to parallel the St John–St Lawrence–Great Lakes–Saskatchewan–Fraser waterways, and keep the nation self-contained. Thus, with the removal of pre-existing Canadian salients into America, there ceased to be any major cause of friction between the two States, and they have now enjoyed over a century and a half of peace (Fig. 55).

The United States, Spanish America, and Mexico

In its expansion to the west the United States came into conflict with Spain, as well as with Britain. This was along its southern frontier, principally opposite Mexico. Spain had huge possessions in the Caribbean Isles, Florida, Mexico, and Central and South America. However, as in the case of Britain, her claims were greater than her achievements. The frontiers of New Spain in 1763 included Florida, the huge territory of Louisiana (reaching up the Mississippi–Missouri and sweeping across to the Rockies), Texas, and all the western states, up to the border of the Oregon territory. This made Spain the chief power on the continent. Nevertheless Spain had by no means

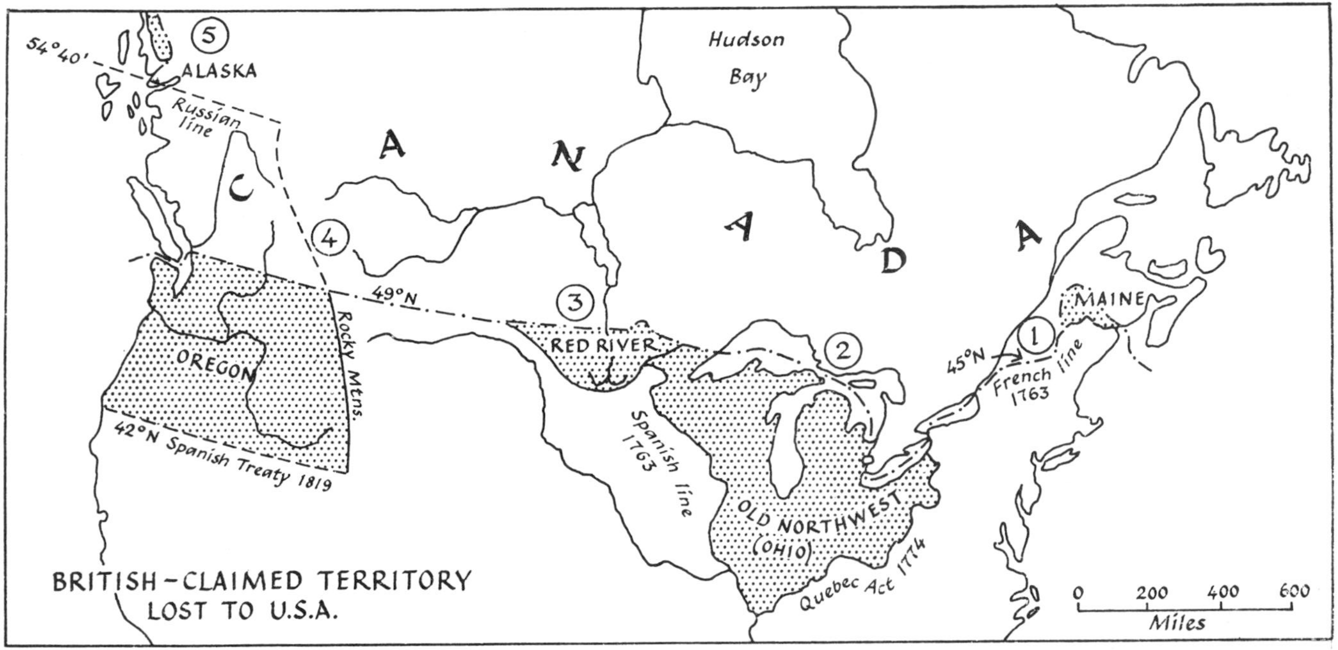

FIG. 55 The Straightening of the Canadian Frontier by Losses to the United States. This strengthened the East-West trend in national development. The chief losses were in: 1, Maine; 2, Upper Quebec (or what Americans called the Old Northwest); 3, the Upper Red River (a portion of the Selkirk Grant); 4, the lower Columbia basin, or Oregon; and 5, the fjord-head strip of the Alaska Panhandle.

settled or developed all this area. The frontier of Spanish settlement was roughly from Jacksonville to Pensacola; from the Sabine river to the head of the Rio Grande (Santa Fé); thence to the Gila river; and beyond that to the San Joaquin river, California. The immense area of Spanish Louisiana and the Mountain States was to all intents and purposes without settlement.

Spain had been weakened by a long series of wars in Europe, in which she lost possessions to Britain and other European powers. These wars affected her position in North America. For instance, she lost Florida to England in 1763. When, in 1783, Britain gave Florida back to Spain, there was a quarrel over its northern frontier, which now bordered the United States. Britain had lost its war with America, and America claimed a large share of British West Florida. In the treaty of 1796, America carried the boundary as far south as the parallel of 31° N. (Fig. 56).

Two years later occurred the French Revolution and the extraordinary expansion of France as the greatest power in the world under Napoleon. Spain was overrun, and in 1800 was forced to give back Louisiana to the French. Then France began to feel the pressure of Britain, and as the two great nations entered into a death-struggle with each other, France looked around for help. The United States was a likely ally. A deal was made in 1803 to sell Louisiana to America in return for money to support Napoleon's dream of empire. Thus America received the immense area of land, north of Texas, stretching from the Mississippi to the Rockies, and from the Gulf of Mexico to the Red river. This was to add enormously to its storehouse of wealth, and change it from a middling to a great country, with tremendous resources and possibilities.

French Louisiana, before it was ceded to Spain in 1763, had included a part of western Florida. The United States claimed that the transfer of Louisiana in 1803 gave it a right to West Florida, which it demanded. This strip of the Gulf coast blocked off the upper Alabama from its lower course, and prevented the westward expansion of the south from having its natural outlets to the sea. America felt so strongly about its need for gateways of access it finally annexed the area between 1810 and 1813, when Spain, involved in the Napoleonic wars, was not in a position to dispute the matter. This gave America much more of the Gulf coast and, what was more important, complete command of the Mississippi delta, which could otherwise have been threatened by a foreign power. In this way, America secured its main southern gateway to the sea, and opened up the Atlantic to direct trade from Ohio river settlements. Then a claim was made to eastern Florida, which a much weakened Spain gave up in 1819–21. At length the whole coast was American, from the Mississippi to the St Croix. The danger of any Atlantic power using part of the American mainland, such as Florida, to dominate American seaways, was over.

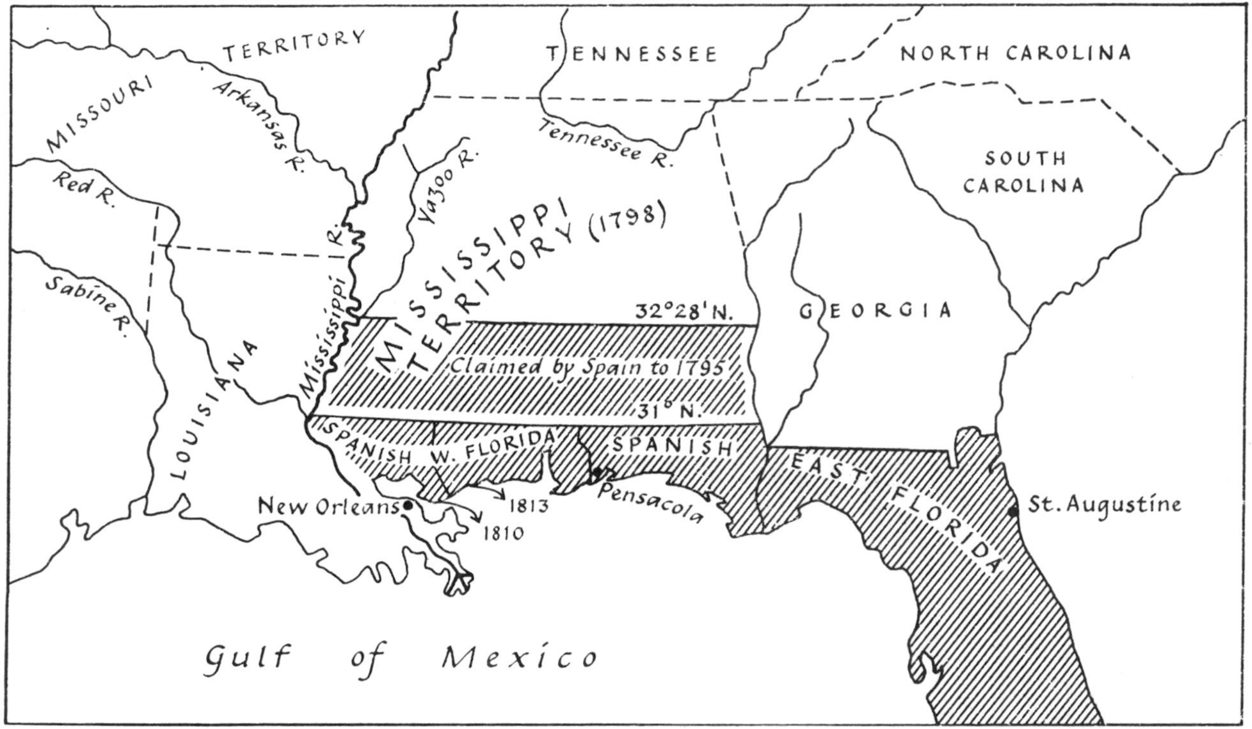

FIG. 56 The Florida Question. This was particularly irksome to the United States because West Florida controlled the outlet to the sea of the Mississippi–Ohio waterway and of lesser southern rivers like the Alabama. The peninsula of Florida was a threat to America's southern flank. (Scale, 1:10 m.)

The Americans moved rapidly into Louisiana, following their explorers, such as Lewis and Clark into Oregon, and Pike into Colorado and the upper Rio Grande. Many of them crossed the border into Texas, and later into California. This led to friction between America and Mexico.

Texas was peculiarly susceptible to American invasion. Its physical geography shut it off from Mexico and opened it to the United States. It consisted of two parts: the high, stripped plains of the Llano Estacado, semi-arid, with burning summers, and a thin Short Grass range; and the eastern lowlands, beneath the protection of great scarps having belts of clay vales and low limestone hills sinking down to the Gulf coast. The upper part was hardly inhabited, save for a scattering of Indian tribes only partly pacified by Spanish missions. A number of ranches were set up in the early nineteenth century, but most of the Mexican population lay well to the west in the upper Rio Grande basin. The lower part of Texas lay very close to the peopled plain of the new-won and newly developed Mississippi. Moreover, the belts of lowland, known as black waxy prairies, which were extraordinarily fertile, were continuous with similar belts running eastward up into the lower Mississippi. The American settlers who were moving in so rapidly into the eastern end of these belts, east of the Sabine, could hardly be expected to let the western end, west of the Sabine, stand empty. Where geography invited, history was not long in following. Permission to settle the Texan portion of the Gulf prairies was soon obtained from Mexico, and American settlers moved in, willing even to become Mexican citizens if need be, to enjoy the opportunities before them.

The situation was very difficult for Mexico. Mexicans themselves were too remote from lowland Texas to settle it, yet the area called out for settlement. To have forbidden the Americans would undoubtedly have provoked them. All Mexico could do was to allow them in, and hope they would accept their Mexican citizenship. Yet Mexico did not make this easy. It would not allow any Protestant churches to be built; Protestants had to worship informally, if at all. Also, it was opposed to slavery; yet most of the planters wanted to come with their slaves. Ill-feeling developed. Mexico was very slow in giving land grants. Americans retaliated by entering illegally and squatting on the land they wanted. Actual forays were made into Mexican territory. In 1812 Magee, moved by rumours of a Mexican revolution, led a sizeable force deep into Texas to liberate it from the Spanish yoke. In 1819 James Long and a group of settlers proclaimed an independent Republic of Texas and set up a provisional capital of Nacogdoches. When the Mexican revolution did break out, in 1821, hopes ran high that Texas would at least be granted local autonomy. The revolutionaries, however, were more anti-American than their Spanish predecessors. They threw out Long and, instead of giving Texas more autonomy, tried to tie it more securely to Mexico proper; national powers were increased at the expense of provincial ones.

The United States government took a correct attitude to all this at first, and the Adams-Onis Treaty of 1819 recognized the Sabine river as the frontier. But 'even then a force was in motion which was speedily to make amends for the failure of American diplomacy. The fate of Texas, as of the entire Far West, was decided not by government officials but by the expansive forces of the American frontier which were soon to bring the vanguard of American settlement into Mexico.'[1]

The Mexican government tried to hold back the tide. In 1830 a law was passed forbidding further American immigration. The Americans in Mexican Texas revolted, and in 1836 defeated the Mexican army. An independent Republic of Texas was set up in 1837, recognized by the United States, Great Britain, and France.

The Mexicans lost out in this struggle mainly because their capital and their settled areas were far to the south. Between the populous part of the country and their borderland provinces lay the Mexican deserts and steppes. The wide belt of unsettled, arid land made it extremely difficult for the Mexicans to keep in close touch with their border provinces. These provinces were in much closer contact with the United States. They were reached more easily by American trails, and American settlers, and traded more easily with American traders or through American ports. Thus it seemed natural and indeed logical for the Americans to develop them and to take them over.

The Lone Star State of Texas did not remain independent for long. Americans were anxious to annex it, and although Washington at first demurred, in 1845 it offered Texas statehood in the Union. This was accepted, and carried the American frontier to the old administrative border of the Mexican state of Texas. But since the Texans had claimed beyond this line to the Rio Grande, the United States supported them, and regarded the Rio Grande as it southern boundary. The Mexican government considered this an act of war, and the two countries fought a short but severe war in 1846–7. Three American expeditions entered Mexico. Kearney drove west from Santa Fé down the Gila river to San Diego, on the California coast, and split the country in two. Taylor moved inland from Brownsville, and Scott from Vera Cruz in a great pincers attack on Mexico City. The Mexicans were defeated and gave up all the land east of the Rio Grande, and from the head of that river to the boundary of the Oregon territory.

This disastrous war also lost Mexico all the land north of the Gila river, including New Mexico and Colorado, Utah and Nevada, Arizona and upper California. At last America had achieved its Manifest Destiny of

[1] Billington, op. cit., p. 484.

ruling the continent from sea to sea, and from the Mexican desert to the Canadian divide.

The United States and the World

Yet this was not the end. Although America was dominant by land, it still felt threatened by sea. The boundaries it had got, at the expense of Canada and Mexico, gave it security on land; the Hudson estuary, the Mississippi delta, Puget Sound, and San Francisco Bay were in its hands—the chief gateways to the continent (except for the St Lawrence estuary and the Fraser valley). The vast Mississippi–Ohio–Missouri plains were put at a safe distance from Canada and Mexico. They formed an immense storehouse of wealth, augmented by the wealth of the flanking mountains and coastal plains. America had all it wanted by land, with the exception of Alaska, bought from Russia in 1867. But by sea, America was rather weak. It had no naval bases off-shore to protect the approaches to its great harbours, and no overseas territories from which it could prevent remote affairs from coming near at hand to endanger its prospects. It had, in fact, no established spheres of influence; strong and independent, it could not use its power or its freedom to shape world events.

This was remedied by the Spanish-American War, and the First and Second World Wars, during which America became an important overseas power, with far-flung possessions in the Atlantic and the Pacific. Indeed, the Pacific may now be regarded as an American lake. There is no other power to dispute its dominant position.

The rivalry with Spain continued even after peace had been made with Mexico. The chief Spanish colony in the Caribbean was Cuba. It had a very strategic position, controlling the Gulf of Mexico. Its possession by a foreign power was thought dangerous to America. Therefore, when the Cubans started to rebel against Spanish rule. America helped them. In 1898 America demanded that Spain recognize Cuban independence, and leave the island. Spain refused, and a war followed, which led to the destruction of the Atlantic and Pacific fleets of Spain. Cuba and Puerto Rico were given up, Cuba to become a virtual protectorate, Puerto Rico to be drawn into the American Commonwealth. Meanwhile the Philippine Islands and Guam were handed over as colonies to the United States. America became a Caribbean and a Pacific power.

America now began to rival Britain and France by sea, as she had done by land. This rivalry led to American possession of Hawaii. These strategic islands dominated the Pacific. They were claimed by the United States, Britain, and France at various times, yet kept an uneasy independence. When the Spanish-American War showed America how necessary it was to control Hawaii, the islands were at last annexed, in 1898. The use of

Honolulu and Manila gave America excellent harbours to develop Pacific trade with the Far East, and with Australia and New Zealand.

On becoming both an Atlantic and Pacific power, America sought to connect these two oceans by the Panama Canal, so as to be able to operate in both areas, and switch her fleets from one sea to the other.[1] The narrowest neck of land between the two oceans was in the state of Panama. Another possible connecting link was Nicaragua. In 1903 America obtained from Panama the right to build a canal, and to protect it by the acquisition of a canal zone on a permanent basis. In return, America guaranteed the independence of Panama that had more than once been threatened by Colombia. The canal at once created its own problems—the main one being its defence. To help protect its immediate approaches the United States secured the right to build a naval base in Nicaragua and, if necessary, construct an alternative canal through that State. But there remained the problem of guarding the farther approaches; Puerto Rico and Florida were sufficient to shield the canal from the east, but there was no western shield. In 1942, however, an air base was built in the Galapagos Islands, by agreement with Ecuador.

Farther approaches became more critical with submarine warfare, aerial attack and, above all, missile war. Outer bastions of defence became a prime necessity, to give America the defence in depth so necessary in modern geography. In the Second World War the Japanese naval and air attack on Pearl Harbour showed how vital mid-Pacific defences were. At the same time the threat of German U-boat attacks made the Americans want a defence line well out in the Atlantic. The famous 'Destroyer Deal' with Britain gave American naval bases in Newfoundland, Bermuda, the Bahamas, and Trinidad, in return for desperately needed destroyers. This great outward advance of America in the Atlantic was matched by another great outward step in the Pacific. At the end of the war America obtained the Japanese-mandated islands of the West Pacific and the strategic island-base of Okinawa. The alliance between Nationalist China and the United States gave it naval and air bases in Formosa.

Thus America came at length to make its sea approaches safe. It had thrown an inner ring of bases around the Panama Canal, which was tied in with its own coastal defences. It had thrown up a line of mid-ocean defences in the Pacific, with Hawaii and Guam, and in the Atlantic, with Iceland, Bermuda, and the Cape Verde Islands. And it had developed an outermost arc of defence in Japan, Okinawa, and Formosa on the one hand, and in defences which it jointly manned in Britain, Germany, Spain, North Africa, and Turkey.[2] As a result it had built up a triple-zoned defence that gave it

[1] Whittlesey, D., 'The United States: Expansion and Consolidation', in *The Changing World*, ed. East, G., and Moodie, A. E., London, 1956, p. 284.

[2] Mainly through its participation in the North Atlantic Treaty Organization.

ample protection from across the seas. More than that it had secured spheres of influence in Western Europe and the Mediterranean, and in East and South-east Asia that enabled it to play a major role in shaping world affairs so as to make them conform as much as possible to the American ideals of widening human liberty and strengthening peace.

Starting as a series of small British colonies crowded around inlets between the Appalachians and the Atlantic shore, America has, over the course of the years, successfully broken its initial encirclement, rolled back the Canadian and Mexican borders, dominated the heart of the continent, spread from sea to sea, and then launched out upon a hemispheric order of expansion that has made it the great power of the Western World. In each case it has moved forward to make the most of its geographic opportunities, to gain a fully rounded geographic base for prosperity, to secure the geographic approaches to power, and to use this prosperity and this power in ever wider spheres, not only for itself, but for the continent as a whole, for the Americas, and for the Pacific and Atlantic realms.

CHAPTER EIGHT

Regionalism: National Areas, Sections, Sub-regions

Once European colonization had spread across the continent it came to divide it on lines that were far clearer and more meaningful than those in the past. This was perhaps because the new lines of division tended to transgress and transcend natural ones, and thus came to create a new geography. Not that the boundaries were independent of natural ones; but they produced a new arrangement, a new balance, of natural features, giving them significance where they had value for the political, strategic, historical, cultural, and economic aims and ambitions of the European settlers.

Thus the nation-states themselves, and then groups of states within these, grew to have a powerful say over how mountains and plains, how coasts and rivers, or how forests and prairies came to be used. And as the power of the nation, or of sections of the nation, has increased, as participation, not to say guidance or control, in the development and consolidation of the land has widened, the effect on the landscape—that is, the geographical impact—has grown enormously.

THE IMPORTANCE OF POLITICAL FRONTIERS

Geographers have not always realized this, but have been prone to stress physiographic or economic divisions, taking *them* to be the shaping forces in the regional geography of the continent. These are, of course, important; and in many cases may shape affairs—but only where man has accepted them into his scheme of things. Thus some mountains and rivers may have been used as divides, but only where historical forces accepted them as such. A great many more 'natural frontiers' were ignored, while artificial frontiers were set up that then came to shape settlement and development. In Catholic Quebec the Church has played an active part in colonization, and church-centred villages dominate the landscape. In Ontario, although the churches had their significance, struggles between Protestant denominations ended the granting of church lands, and a highly secular system of settlement emerged where commercial institutions took over the village or town centre. In Saskatchewan socialist government at mid-century had its effect in the rise of several provincially owned operations and in the spread of co-operative farming. Similarly, in the United States, the beliefs in social freedom in the northern States, as contrasted with a view of racial caste in the South, have profoundly influenced land use and settlement in these great sections of the nation.

The divisions of North America, then, present themselves not only in different kinds of terrain, produced by relief and climate, nor in different countrysides, stamped by agriculture and industry, but also in different human regions, existing (as Louis Wirth claims) each as a distinct 'state of mind, a way of life, a mode of collective consciousness'.[1]

Unfortunately this has not been widely enough recognized and some geographers, stopping short at questions of collective consciousness, custom, belief, and loyalty, have divided the continent into regions as though political and cultural frontiers did not exist. Indeed a leading geographer of the early twentieth century specifically urged that, in attempting to recognize regions, boundaries should be chosen which resulted 'from the work of the cosmic forces that make climate, surface, soil, mineral deposits, land, lake and sea'. Political frontiers were to be ignored since 'Political units such as Canada, Maryland, or California have their present boundaries because of the whims of chance and the accidents of history'. Consequently, the Maritime Provinces of Canada were grouped with New England; southern Ontario with those parts of the Great Lakes States lying in the dairy belt; the Canadian prairies with those areas of the Dakotas and Minnesota comprising the spring wheat belt; and southern British Columbia with the Pacific north-west. Canada was thus treated as merely the physical attenuation and economic extension of regions in America!

At first this seems plausible enough. There is often no physiographic break between a region in the United States and its counterpart in Canada. There may even be no break in land use. Would it not be proper, therefore, to describe the two regions as one? Such was Russell Smith's proposal. Taking America's spring wheat region, he wrote: 'This region extends [from Minnesota] into South Dakota and North Dakota and into Canada where it stretches across the three prairie provinces of Manitoba, Saskatchewan, and Alberta. How foolish it would be to describe the Spring Wheat Region three times for each of the three American states and three times more for each of the three Canadian provinces'[2] (Figs. 57 and 58).

This may be true, but it would be equally foolish to pretend that Canada and the United States were irrelevant merely because their boundary happened to interrupt the wheat belt!

Superficially there may not be much to distinguish the two parts of the prairie. They both consist of a series of flats divided by low escarpments, they have both suffered glaciation and are strewn with glacial moraines and

---

[1] Wirth, L., 'The Limits of Regionalism', in *Regionalism in America*, ed. Jensen, M., Madison, 1951, p. 391.

[2] Smith, J. Russell, *Men and Resources*, pp. vi–vii.

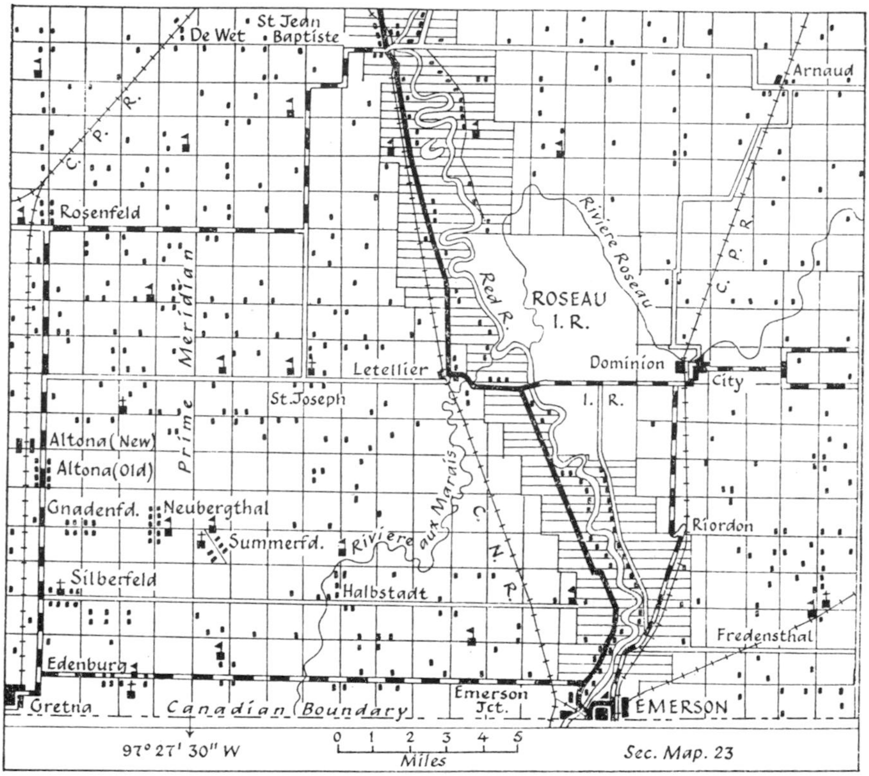

FIG. 57 The United States–Canadian West: the Canadian Pattern of Settlement. This includes French villages and strip farms, and German and other ethnic group bloc-settlements, as well as the open grid established by the British. Even in a rich plain land was still left for an Indian reservation.

glacial lake deposits, part of the American prairie is drained by the Canadian Red river, and on both sides of the boundary wheat is the predominant crop.

But are the landscapes identical? Starting at the customs houses, do we not find features eloquent of their differences? At first the signs may seem small—the flags are different, the pillar-boxes are in different colours, the shop headings have 'Ltd.' after them in one and 'Inc.' in the other country. But the signs soon take on greater significance. There are different kinds of administrative buildings—due to different levels of government—which make for appreciable differences in the towns. Institutional geography is also different. There are more episcopalian churches north of the border, they take a more prominent part, and their notice-boards proclaim them to be units of the Anglican Church in Canada. There are also more Presbyterian churches, relics of the Selkirk settlement that early gave a Scotch

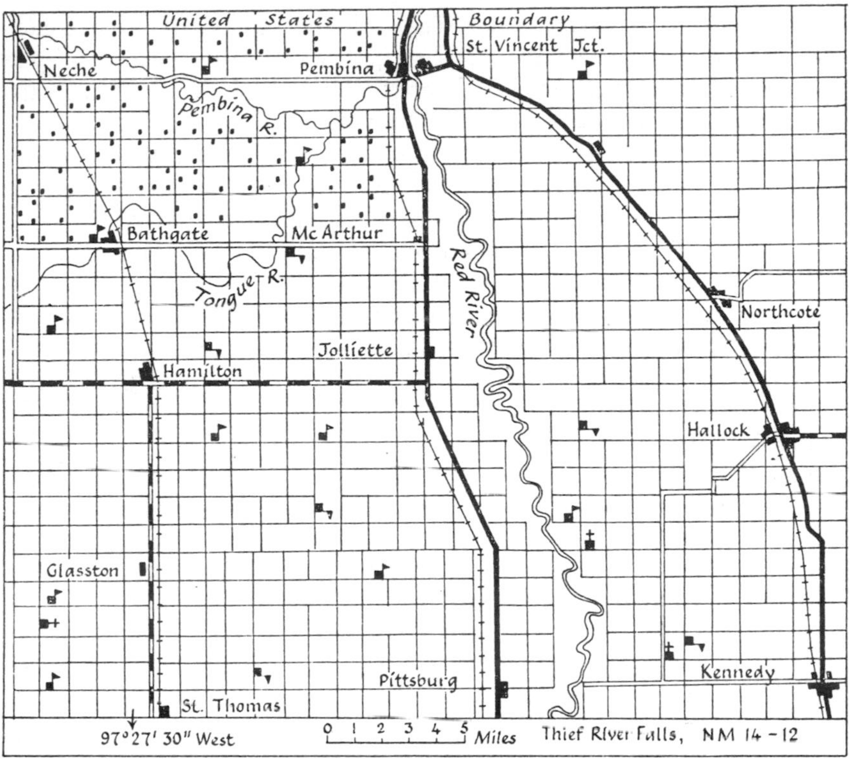

FIG. 58 The United States–Canadian West: the American Pattern of Settlement. (Only the upper left section of the diagram has been filled in with farms; but a similar even scattering occurs throughout.) Here the grid-system dominates. French names, denoting former French influence, are not associated with the French-Canadian system of land division. The melting-pot theory of colonization has left no room for highly compact ethnic communities and nucleated villages. The isolated single farm and country church and school are the main features of the rural landscape. Main settlements are essentially commercial groupings of warehouses, shops, garages, and other 'services', in a region devoted to highly commercialized agriculture. Such a region has little room for the Indian, pushed west into the badlands.

flavour to the Canadian plains. Farther north rise the silver spires of Roman Catholic churches that surprise one with their un-American supremacy over the settlements they crown. Next to them are nunneries, alms houses, church schools, and other church buildings. These are often so prominent that they push the shops out of the centre. (But has one heard of an American town without its Central *Business* District?) Beyond the houses are rows of farms, each on a long, narrow lot. This system of land division is, again, quite different from the quarter section of the American rural scene (Fig. 57).

The French-Canadian communities thus come to add a distinctive element to the landscape. Is not the French belt, then, as significant, geographically, as the wheat belt? French shop signs and road signs and French radio stations remind one that the northern prairies are the venue of a great bi-cultural experiment that is fundamentally opposed to the uni-centred culture south of the border. This is important.

Also of importance is the main west–east trend of routes. While the roads and railways north or south along the Red river are much in evidence at the border, they are but links between two great transcontinental systems, the Canadian Pacific and Canadian National railways on the one hand and the Great Northern and Northern Pacific on the other. What gives Winnipeg its power is not its connexions with Minneapolis–St Paul, but its links with western and eastern Canada. It is, in a sense, the king-pin of the whole Canadian system, as can be seen in the tremendous development of railway yards, round-houses, repair shops, and factories.

Beside these are large wheat elevators, flour mills, and meat-packing plants—which are mute reminders that what is done with the wheat grown north of the 49th parallel is quite different from what happens to it to the south. The collection of the wheat, the marketing organization, the policies controlling price and production, the movement of wheat and flour to Canadian or American ports, and the trade abroad* give rise to a quite different commercial geography—a geography which has relatively little to do with the supposed unity of the wheat belt, or, behind it, the unity of the Red river basin, or of the Canadian and American prairie, but has everything to do with the political frontier.

That frontier, then, does have its significance; it is as real a divide as mountain, river, vegetation-break, or soil. It sponsors real differences, and to the observer who is willing to take *all* the facts into account, and to look for the imprint of racial, religious, and political beliefs in the land, such differences are valid. And this is so, because they are valid in the consciousness of the people. The Canadians, it may be remembered, have come of age in *competition* with the United States. Frequently it has been the pressure, challenge, and even provocation of the larger country, both in political issues like boundary questions and frontier wars, and also in economic and cultural measures, such as tariffs, and the intervention of American ways of life, that have shown Canada its own profile, and discovered for the smaller country its own soul. As Patterson Smith[1] says, it was because Americans assumed that the absorption of British North America was an inevitability which time would consummate, that they begot a sense of nationality in Canada which ultimately destroyed any notion of union.

Therefore, let us beware of the specious geographical argument that a

* 'Red' China is now Canada's third most important wheat-buying customer, in strong contrast to the U.S.A. which opposes trade with the Communist régime.

1 Smith, J. Patterson, 'A United States of America', *Can. Hist. Rev.*, June 1945, p. 110.

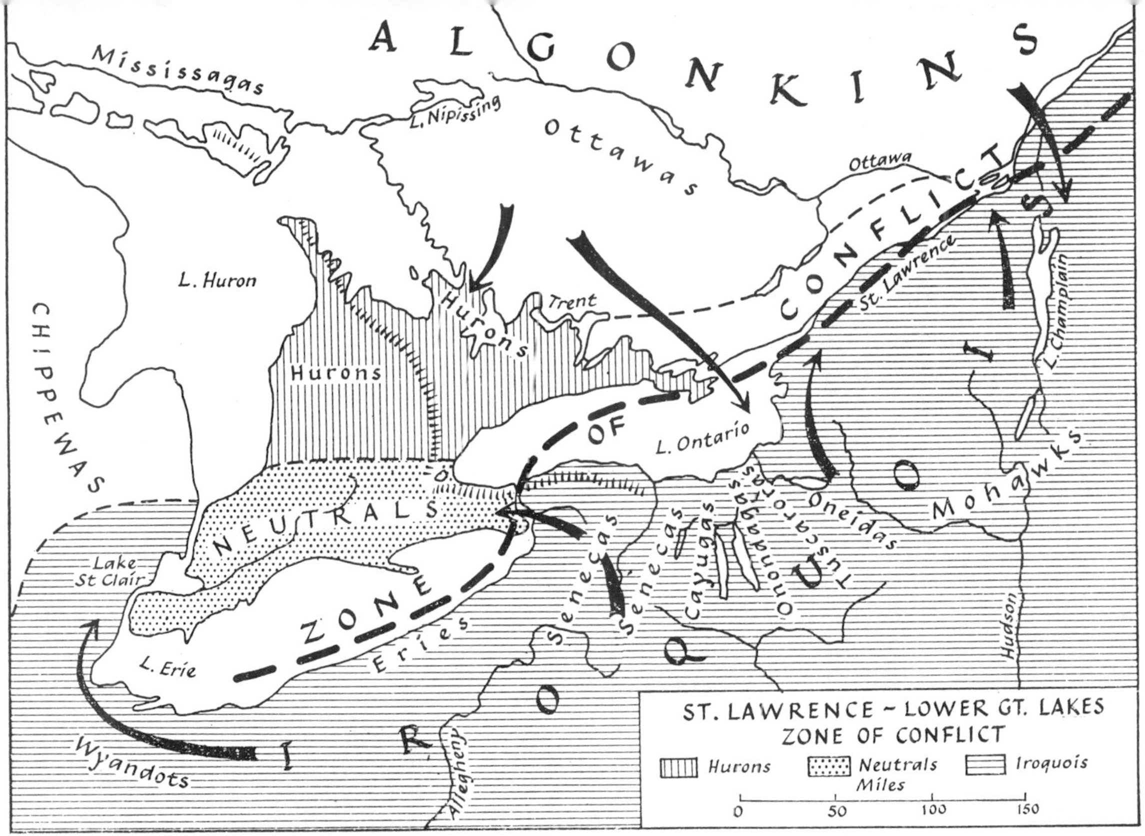

FIG. 59 The St Lawrence–Great Lakes, a Zone of Conflict: (*a*) in Indian Times. Before the white man came the Indians had been locked in conflict in this area, the Iroquois south of the Lower Lakes and the St Lawrence river invading the Algonkins of the Ottowa valley and the St Lawrence estuary. The Neutrals tried to follow a policy of non-commitment, while the Hurons, though of Iroquois culture, allied themselves to the Algonquins. French support for Algonquin and Huron led to strong reprisals from the Iroquois, supported by the British, and thus early rivalries became entrenched.

In the Beaver Wars the Iroquois over-ran the Neutrals and extended their power to the Lower Lakes area.

common environment gives rise to a uniform reaction, and produces its corresponding geographic region. It does not. The Canadian prairies have been seen to be a good example of this. An even clearer illustration is the St Lawrence basin. Here is a major natural region if ever there was one. But men have made of it a zone of conflict. This was evident in the bitter struggle of Algonquin against Iroquois, referred to earlier (Fig. 59)—a struggle which the French inherited against the British, and Canadians against Americans. Even if Canada subsequently made the region a basis of co-operation with the United States, this was done through an independent appraisal of its value for man. Thus Canada has done a great thing for the human spirit, if it has done nothing else, in showing that a natural environment can be so surcharged with human endeavour as to become a different thing with different ideals. Increasingly, there are in geography only the patterns which we select.

The Canadian–United States Frontier

Thus the Crown Connexion came to have a great deal of influence in the geography of Canada (as it did in Mexico until the revolution). In Canada it had the effect of keeping the country firmly linked with Europe when all other major regions in the Americas had severed their ties with their motherlands; it reinterpreted rivers and portages to create a new set of routeways that assisted in the internal integration of the country; and, in offering the French Canadian way of life a bulwark against Americanization, it helped French Canada to become, in turn, a bulwark of Canadian independence. These three things have been of prime importance in Canadian life.

External Connexions

They are—and have always been—especially influential in Canada's external relations. They have created a distinct resistance to the pull or push of continental geography. The geographical similarities with the United States have served simply to accentuate the historical differences; it is because of the geographical tug to the south that the historical counter-pull to the north and to Europe has been so strong, and so significant. It is as well to remember that, because of its European connexion, Canada is in a unique position in North America.[1] Respect for its ties with its European past, especially those linking it with Britain and France, kept Canada on a separate path and mapped out a separate destiny. It is the faithfulness to the past, by which even her faith in the future is measured, that has distinguished Canada from the United States. Canada is the weft of the Old World in the warp of the New.

---

[1] Trotter, R., 'Overseas connections have not been deemed by Canadians inconsistent with national existence and liberty, but rather the condition making possible their survival and growth', *Queen's Quarterly*, Kingston, Ontario, summer 1940, p. 135.

In Canada's case, then, geography has little meaning outside of history. Indeed, this is generally true. 'L'état, ce n'est pas donné, c'est forgé.' The nation is a country together with its people. Its physical geography will, of course, impose certain limitations. But it will suggest certain opportunities. And eventually it is the opportunities that have been seen and exploited which make their mark upon the country.

North America was both sufficiently far from Europe to allow the United States to separate itself off, yet near enough to permit Canada to maintain its European ties. The continent provided both alternatives; it was Canada's choice to keep itself in the European culture area, while the United States created a new sphere for itself. This is fundamental. The land offers a whole series of possible developments, but does not equip us with a ready-made character. That is something we forge out of our intimate association with, and at times from our bitter struggle against, the land. It is man who gives geography character by moulding it to his own uses. He chooses which forces within the environment to release, and which to suppress; he creates his own sort of connexions between features otherwise unrelated; he substitutes for the chance pull of different influences, his own pattern of associations.

Although natural characteristics had much to do with the rise of present-day geographical regions, they did not determine them. The regional geography of North America is not simply the natural region spelled out in terms of man—not, at any rate, after the coming of the White Man. Since Europeans had come at a high enough level of technology and organization to adapt nature to their purposes, they were able to interpret natural regions, more and more, in human terms. It is most important to remember that Europeans had already attempted to transcend, and in some cases had transcended, natural divides, in the frontiers of their empire-states. Rome and the Holy Roman Empire had tried to knit together Mediterranean and transalpine lands and cultures. France had sought to marry continental and maritime differences; England, upland and lowland ones. Through repeated clashes of race and religion, of trade and politics, Europeans had come to establish the importance, if not superiority, of human regions compared with natural ones, and had begun to adapt nature to their own ends. This meant concentrating on 'advantageous' natural conditions, and avoiding, or at least minimizing the effects of, 'hostile' ones. The environment was charged with meaning and given human orientation and value.

In such a way Canadian history came to put its own interpretation on coasts and riverways, on upland and lowland, on forest zones and soil belts, until at length these things began to express, over and above the general similarities with their American counterparts, a specific character, differentiating them from others, and making them without question Canadian.

Internal Integration

Basically, these things were interpreted in terms of Canadian aims and needs. It was the desire to maintain Canada's distinctive way of life, and, in doing so, to knit its own several regions more closely together, that led Canada to match the sea-lanes, the canals, the railways, the trunk roads, and the airways developed by the United States with parallel, competitive, and independent systems (Fig. 60). Thus when the Erie barge canal was built to connect the Lower Great Lakes and the whole of the old north-west with the Hudson–Mohawk and the Atlantic world, Canada at once built the Welland and the St Lawrence canals to provide its own water connexion between the interior and the sea. A whole new series of Canadian towns resulted which, in due course, developed new industries and other activities for the country. Here was the Crown Connection in terms of bricks and mortar, of something concrete in the landscape and, because the bricks and mortar were put up by people anxious to marry European styles with American needs, something distinctive.

The canals in the Ottawa valley, on the Severn and Trent and associated waterways, soon augmented the St Lawrence–Great Lakes system, and further strengthened the west–east ties between the interior and the Gulf of St Lawrence, indeed between Canada and Britain.

Roads, too, were significant—especially the Matapedia trail in the east, built to circumvent the great bulge of Maine; and the Dewdney trail in the west, made to ensure that the gold of the interior of British Columbia should be exported by an all-British route.

Similarly during the railway era, when the Erie, New York Central, Pennsylvania, and the Baltimore and Ohio railways, and other American routes, were opened, linking up the Ohio, the Great Lakes, and eventually the Mississippi with the mid-Atlantic coast, Canada replied by building its Inter-Colonial and other railway lines to ensure a Canadian outlet for Canadian goods. The railways did what the canals could not do; they gave a winter outlet through ice-free ports by lengthening the Canadian system of routes to the ports of the Maritimes. The further lengthening of the transportation net westwards across the prairies and the Rockies to the Pacific coast was an even greater triumph and at last drew and knotted together all the parts of Canada into a single steel-bound entity.

In this the railways created a new interpretation and orientation to Canadian routes. They picked out the east–west rivers that flowed down from the divides of the Appalachians, the Shield, and the Rockies, and connected them up across portages and passes until they became the main thoroughfares for immigration, traffic, and trade. They came to displace

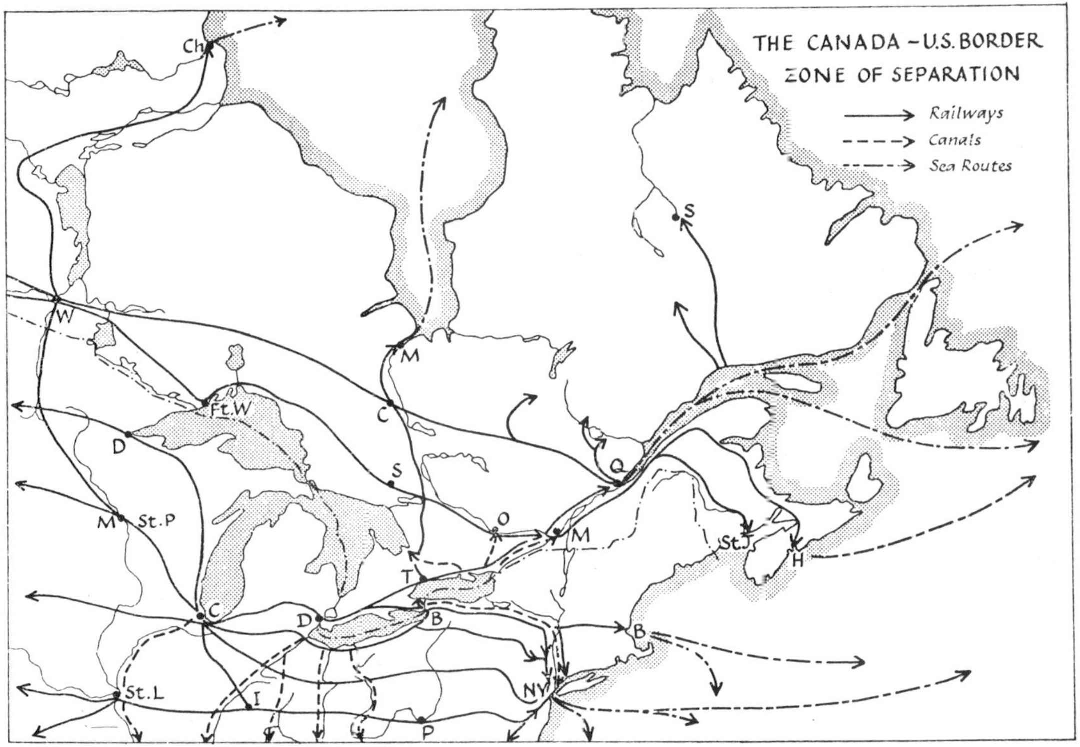

FIG. 60 The St Lawrence–Great Lakes, a Zone of Conflict: (*b*) in Commercial Rivalry. Competitive systems of canals and railways developed by separate Canadian and American interests effectively divided a single great natural basin into two opposing commercial regions. Montreal and New York soon came to struggle as principal outlets for the great St Lawrence–Lakes hinterland. Montreal had the advantage of being on the St Lawrence, but its harbour was frozen over in the winter. New York, an ice-free port, commanded the Hudson–Mohawk gap to the Lower Lakes, and thus to the Upper Great Lakes as well. National policies on both sides of the border favoured their own outlets and thus made the border a very real zone of commercial competition and conflict. New York's objection to the St Lawrence Seaway reflected that conflict right up to mid-twentieth century. (1:20m.)

(though not completely to replace) the old north–south connexions of the Bay of Fundy, the Champlain–Hudson, Mohawk–Hudson, the St Lawrence–Great Lakes–Ohio, the Upper Great Lakes–Mississippi, the Red river–Mississippi, the Missouri, and the Columbia river systems which, had they not been beheaded by the Crown Connexion, would doubtless have exerted a much more powerful sway. In this way, *lesser* linkages in Canadian relief were built up into *major* ones, and *major* ones were made *minor*: surely a factor of utmost importance in any geographical appraisal of the continent. Again, whole new lines of towns, new markets, new industries were built up, all serving the overall needs of Canada, or Canada's ties with Britain, or other overseas lands.

Although the trade contacts abroad are not now as important as they used to be, the east–west trade contacts within Canada are of the greatest national value and undoubtedly have been assisted by the reorientation of its routeways. Internal trade has also been greatly assisted by the so-called 'national policy', inaugurated by Sir John A. Macdonald in the late nineteenth century, by which Canada built up tariff, fiscal, and other barriers to protect its growing industries. These barriers have at times been far more significant for the deflection of trade than the mightiest of mountains or bleakest of barrens (Fig. 61).

The Cultural Factor

The fact is, Canada has sought to keep itself separate and so has worked out its separate alignment. Perhaps nowhere is this sense of separation greater than in Quebec, where all the old French traditions have been allowed to continue and, indeed, to flourish. Here again the Crown Connexion has been of the utmost significance, as Brown insists in his study of Canadian Nationalism,[1] since Britain agreed to cultural autonomy for Quebec, and wrote into its charter (as a part of British North America) the protection of the French language, of the Roman Catholic religion, and of the Franco-Roman code of law.

It is because French Canadians have been allowed to stay loyal to their customs that they still remain a homogeneous human group, and have developed a way of life that makes its own distinctive impress on the landscape. The Crown is here a geographical factor itself. It has done what the local environment, linked as it is with the Champlain–Hudson plains, could probably not have done, namely, maintained the old patterns of settlement and, in Brouillette's words, allowed 'the usage and tradition of France' to survive more vigorously in Canada than in the old country. As a result Canada does not, like the United States, try to fuse things into what is

[1] Brown, G. W., 'Canadian Nationalism', *International Affairs*, xxx, 2, p. 167.

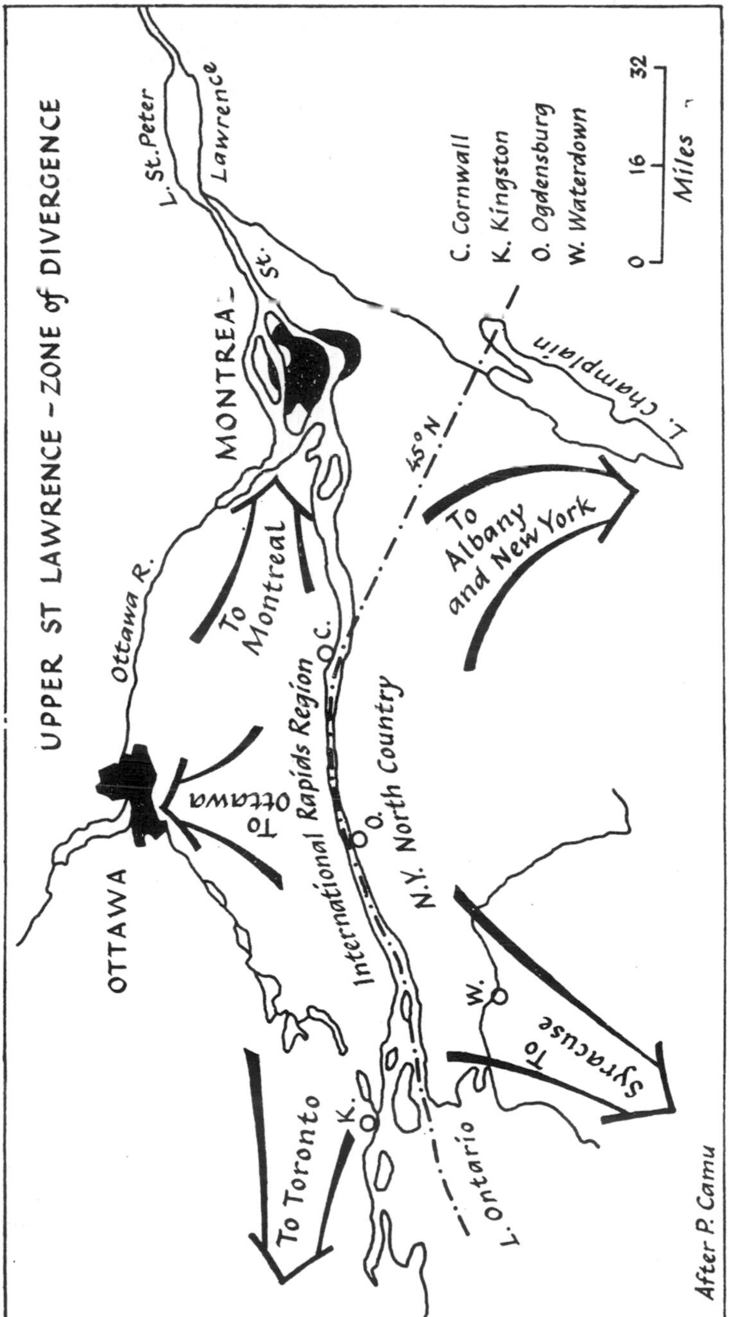

FIG. 61 The St Lawrence–Great Lakes, a Zone of Conflict: (*c*) in Riparian Development. The divergent way in which the frontier zone has been settled has meant that riparian growth has been slow. The river, instead of bringing people together, has witnessed a pulling apart, as the areas deeper in each bordering country have been developed.

essentially an Anglo-American mould. Its geography is not, strictly speaking, that of Anglo-America. It is not the geography of the melting-pot. It is the geography of the loom, in which differences are accepted, are valued indeed, and made use of, for the patterns they create. Thus although the French may form but a small part of the country, they exert a great deal of influence, not only in and by themselves, but through the principles of cultural diversity and political autonomy for which they stand. They have created a great bi-cultural area in northern North America of the first importance.

The Mexican United States Frontier

If the presence of the French in Canada is enough to mark Canada out as a distinctive area in North America (and it should be remembered that the French are quite strong in New Brunswick, in eastern and northern Ontario, in Manitoba, and in the northern parts of Saskatchewan and Alberta; they are by no means confined to Quebec, but form a whole belt across the country), the prevalence of Spanish descendants in Mexico must mark that out as a separate region. And in fact it is. Here the Latin tradition is stronger than ever—so much so that in not a few geography books Mexico is included in Latin America, along with Central and South America, almost as though it were not a North American country.

This is perhaps going too far: Mexico is a part of North America with important commercial ties with the United States, and pledged with it and Canada to the defence of the North American continent. Nevertheless, behind the barrier of its frontier—a notable geographical 'break'—it was able to maintain those barriers of language, religion, law, land economy, and outlook that prevented it from being 'Americanized' and allowed it, like Quebec, to pursue its separate and treasured ways.

THE RELATIVITY OF REGIONALISM

From all this it should be evident that the task of recognizing regions in North America, as in any continent, is far from simple. Physiographic, climatic, economic, cultural, and political divisions rarely coincide. The main physiographic regions run north–south, providing a longitudinal 'grain' to the continent. Climatic belts follow these in the strongly mountainous west, but from the Rockies east they run in roughly west–east tiers, giving the continent a latitudinal 'grain'. The agricultural belts tend to respond to climatic ones; but political considerations often affect agricultural geography, leading to greater or lesser specialization, influencing production, and orienting the trade in agricultural products. Industry is, possibly, even more affected by national policies. Culture is, thus, of increasing importance, and culture areas have developed with their peculiar systems of land tenure, land development, settlement patterns, and social conditions, sometimes closely attached to economic zones, but at other times forming independent and unique divisions.

Thus a whole series of regions exists, some of which coincide, but many of which overlap, depending on the degree of relatedness of the elements that go to shape them. In earlier days the physical elements dominated; today the human elements are growing more powerful. This being so, the geography of North America is a different thing at different ages and stages. In the present age it would seem to be dominated by: (i) national areas; (ii) sections of national areas composed of groups of states or provinces; and (iii) subdivisions of sections, based on economic districts, especially those centred in great metropoli. However, it should be pointed out that changes are taking place evolving: (i) an awareness of inter-sectional relationship and dependence; (ii) a sense of continental solidarity, involving continent-wide movements and agreements; and (iii) a recognition of world connexions and commitments that are already having their effect on internal divisions and external ties. Regions have, then, only a relative significance; they are true only of and for their times.

The Rise of the Sections

Yet for their times they have a very real value, they produce areas where particular physical elements and human forces arrive at unique relationships with each other to create a distinctive landscape where a distinct community of existence may be sensed. When European colonization had divided North America into the three great national spheres of Canada, the United States, and Mexico, the expansion of these countries themselves led to further divisions into broad sections, and greater or lesser regions. The sections were areas where major political, cultural, and economic differences came to be felt. Already by the end of the eighteenth century 'that bugbear—a *sectional* man' was beginning to appear; that is to say, a person who believed himself to share a way of life and owe a loyalty distinct from, and even at variance with, what proved to be the case in other sectors and in the nation as a whole.

Sections came to be thought of as major areas where the idea of separate needs, traditions, and interests took hold of the people living there and gave them a sense of being separate. Sections thus grew up as vital entities. This is important; they are not mere formal concepts. They depend on how people feel and behave, as well as how the area looks and is made up. Morse, the 'father of American geography', divided the United States of his day (1819) into three eastern sections: New England, the Middle States, and the South, and a fourth grand division, the West, taking into account (i) situation, relief, climate, and soils; (ii) agriculture, industry, and trade;

and (iii) races, religions, and political beliefs. The last of these considerations was as important as the first—because it conditioned the awareness and use of the first. The emergence of major sections, and of their several divisions, was due to what people thought and believed about the land, and to their concept of how the land should be used. Thus the sections were subjectively realized, and grew and even changed with the aims and objects of the people who settled them. This was especially true of the West, which, as it was developed, came to be divided into many Wests—as will be seen.

The fact is, physical and human factors were both important and both played their part. This has been well expressed by Billington in his *Westward Expansion.* As the European settler

> moved westward he found awaiting him in the American wilderness a variety of geographic conditions destined to exert a modifying influence on his ways of life and thought. A series of differing physiographic provinces lay before him, each with a distinct soil, topography, and climate. In this checkerboard of unique environments occurred an *interplay of migrating stocks and geographic forces*, to produce in each a distinctive type of enterprise best suited to the natural conditions and imported habits of the settlers. In many ways these sections resembled the countries of Europe, each had its own history of occupation and development, and each was so conscious of its differences that it possessed a sense of distinction from other parts of the country. Thus, as specialization developed, each section demanded from the national government laws beneficial to its own interests; hence the sectional concept. . . .[1]

As we have seen, the United States was first split into three sections: New England, the Middle Atlantic States, and the South. The Middle States then expanded west to the Ohio and Lower Great Lakes—the 'old' North-west. A 'new' North-west developed in the Upper Great Lakes region, while the South extended its system of plantation into the South-west. For a time three main sections vied with each other, the North-east—including New England and the Middle States—the South, embracing the South-west, and the West, centred on the Mississippi–Great Lakes. Eventually the West was drawn into, and divided in two by, the growing divergence between North and South. The differences between these two sections grew so great as to lead at last to civil war. The Constitution was reasserted but, as Desmond[2] points out, came to be less a contract between the several states than 'a

---

[1] Billington, R. A., *Westward Expansion, A History of the American Frontier*, New York (2nd edn.), 1960, p. 11.

[2] Desmond, H. J., 'The Sectional Feature in American Politics', *Trans. Wisc. Acad. Sci. & Arts*, viii, p. 7.

treaty of alliance between two great sections having opposite civilizations and diverse interests' (see Fig. 52, Chapter 7).

If this seems strong, refer to Cash.

> There exists among us [he writes]—both North and South—a profound conviction that the South is another land, sharply differentiated from the rest of the American nation, and exhibiting within itself a remarkable homogeneity.
>
> As to what its singularity may consist in, there is, of course, much conflict of opinion, and especially between Northerner and Southerner. But that it is different and that it is solid—on these things nearly everybody is agreed. Now and then, to be sure, there have arisen people, to tell us that it is all a figment of the imagination, that the South really exists only as a geographical division of the United States and is distinguishable from New England or the Middle West only by such matters as the greater heat and the presence of a larger body of Negroes. Nobody, however, has ever taken them seriously. And rightly.
>
> For the popular conviction is indubitably accurate; the South is, in Allen Tate's phrase, 'Uncle Sam's other province'. And when Carl Carmer said of Alabama that, 'The Congo is not more different' [from Massachusetts] he fashioned a hyperbole that is applicable in one measure or another to the entire section.[1]

While this section may have become the most singular one, other sections have grown as the country has developed. From Morse's simple fourfold scheme, geographers and statisticians developed more complex systems, principally to take account of the rise of the West, and, later, of industrial America.

Mood and Carstensen have given an excellent survey of the growth of the sectional concept in the United States. They point out that after the revolution, the U.S. Government set about administering the country through sectional divisions. Thus there were Eastern (New England), Middle, and Southern divisions of the Department of Indian Affairs; there were Eastern and Middle divisions of the Navy; and Eastern, Middle, and Southern commands of the Army. Similarly three judicial circuits were set up, known as the Eastern, Middle, and Southern—although here New York was included with the Eastern, and Virginia with the Middle. At the beginning of the nineteenth century, when the West began to be opened up, a Western circuit, including Ohio, Kentucky, and Tennessee, was instituted. By the mid-nineteenth century the Western circuit was split into three: the Northwest, made up of Ohio, Michigan, Indiana, and Illinois; a Western-Middle,

[1] Cash, W. J., *The Mind of the South*, New York, 1941, p. 1.

of Kentucky, Tennessee, and Missouri; and the South-west, of Alabama, Mississippi, Louisiana, and Arkansas. Subsequently a 'Deep South' circuit was set up from Florida to Texas; a Mid-West circuit for the lands opening up on the west side of the Mississippi, from Arkansas to Minnesota; and a Far-West circuit for California, which was subsequently extended to Oregon. At the end of the century the Great Plains and nearer Mountain States came within the Mid-West, while the farther Mountain States were allocated to the Far-West.[1]

The West changed in character and meaning on being 'unrolled', as has been well brought out by Turner, in his *Rise of the New West*. Actually, the first West—often referred to as the Old West—does not come into what we now think of as the West at all; it was the western fringe of the Seaboard States. The trans-Allegheny West, or New West, replaced this, as people streamed across the mountains, after the revolution. Then there was the North-west. But this term had to be changed several times. The Old North-west consisted of Ohio and Michigan; the New North-west, of Wisconsin and Minnesota. Eventually the Pacific North-west came into being with the American occupation of lower Oregon. In the same way the South-west once signified the area between Alabama and Arkansas, but was later expanded to include Texas. The Far-West came to include Oregon, California, and Nevada. The term Mid-West was generally used of the lands from the Ohio to the Rockies, but was sometimes confined to those west of the Mississippi river. In 1875 Swinton proposed that the term 'Western' should be reserved for the Rocky Mountain, Plateau, and Pacific States, and that the designation 'Central' should be used of the Mississippi basin States. Later, he suggested dividing these States into an Eastern Central and a Western Central group.

The Census Bureau since its inception has tabulated statistics by groups of States as well as by individual States. A widely used system was that first proposed in the Census for 1910 which divided the country up into nine major sections: (i) New England; (ii) the Mid-Atlantic States; (iii) the East North-Central States (the Ohio–Wisconsin region); (iv) the West North-Central States (the Missouri–Red river region); (v) the South Atlantic States; (vi) the East South-Central States (lower Mississippi, east); (vii) the West South-Central States (lower Mississippi, west, and Texas); (viii) the Mountain States (Rockies and intermontane basins); and (ix) the Pacific Coast States. This system, with occasional modifications, is still frequently followed (Fig. 62).

---

[1] Mood, F., 'The Origin, Evolution, and Application of the Sectional Concept, 1750–1900', in *Regionalism in America*, ed. Jensen, M., Madison, 1951, pp. 5–98.
Carstensen, V., 'The Development and Application of Regional-Sectional Concepts, 1900–1950', in *Regionalism in America*, pp. 99–118.

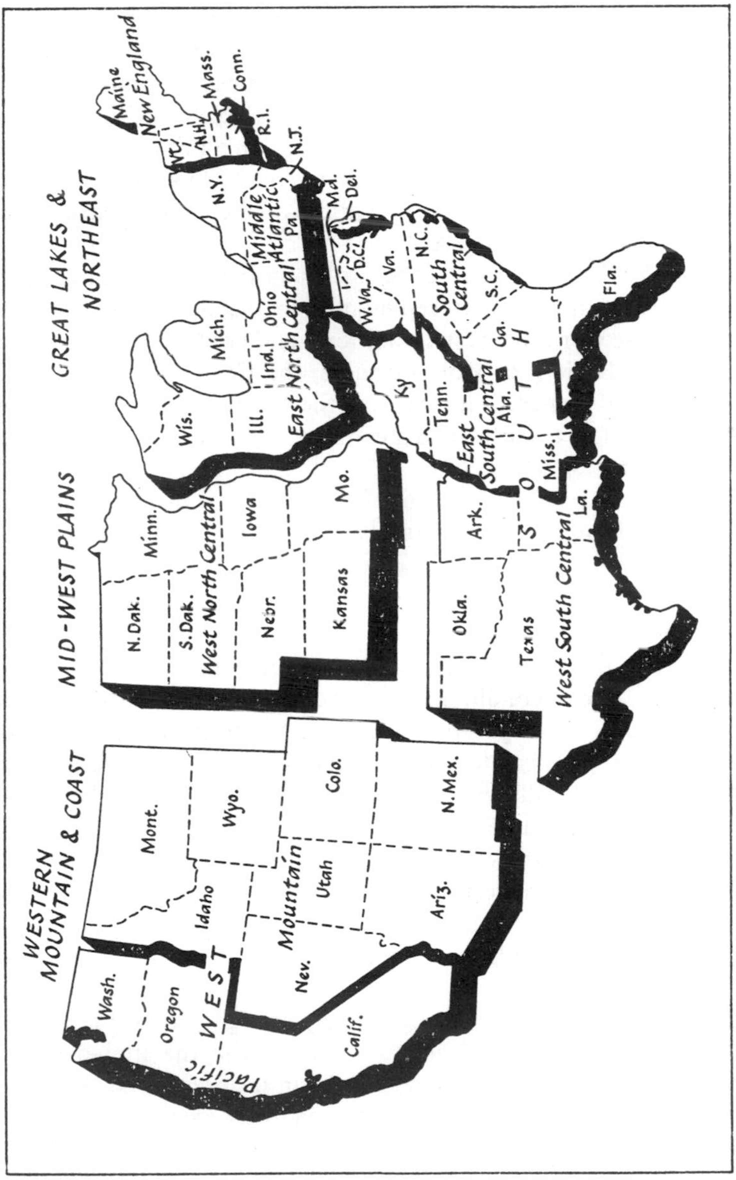

FIG. 62 Major United States Sections. Note that the East North Central States are often included with the West North Central, as the American Mid-West. They are here included with the American Northeast because, like the Middle Atlantic and the New England States, they are fundamentally industrial and not agricultural. Four great sections have emerged, with some distinct sub-sections, as shown.

The Census emphasized the economic and social factors that lay behind regional realities. As such it prompted definitions of sections based on the occupational habits of the people. The most important of these has been the 'Manufacturing Section', a major division of the continent which gathers into itself groups of States that, in earlier times, formed separate regions. This great section may be said to include the New England, Mid-Atlantic, and East North-Central States of the United States. In all of these, industry and commerce have come so to dominate their way of life as to have made less significant those cultural, political, and historical factors that once made them distinctive regions in themselves.

Although sectionalism may have gone further in the United States than elsewhere in North America, it is represented in the other countries. In Canada significant sectional interests, traditions, and needs have divided the country[1] into an Atlantic group of provinces, the Central Provinces, the Prairie Provinces, and British Columbia and the Yukon. Northern Canada is beginning to develop a sense of distinctness, as an area with its own pioneer problems and aims (Fig. 63).

In Mexico, also, the northern section of the country is distinct from the south, and the mainland from the peninsula of Yucatan, and from the lands round the Gulf of California.

Economic and Social Sub-regions

Within the great sections of each nation are numbers of lesser regions, where economic or social conditions of a special kind produce local but significant variations. These generally go back to strong physical forces (like prominent relief, peculiar structure, special patterns of climate or soil), which, in turn, sponsor locally important economic adaptations. They may, however, reflect strong cultural traits, leading to distinct social situations. In either case, they qualify the general conditions prevailing in any section. Often, indeed, they transgress sections, carrying one use of land or form of settlement from a part of one section to another. These sub-regions are, principally, agricultural or industrial areas, or the spheres of influence of great cities.

Take the South, for example; although it may be regarded as one section because of the way it was settled and developed (with the spread of the plantation system, the dependence on negro labour, the prevalence of cotton. and the absence of widespread and intensive industrialization), yet it has distinct subdivisions in it, as judged by different economic and social traits.

---

[1] Nicholson, N. L., 'The Boundaries of Canada, its Provinces and Territories', *Geog. Branch*, Mem. 2, Ottawa, 1954; cf. *Sectionalism and Administration*, pp. 114–15. 'Sections have, unofficially, taken shape in Canada . . . and have become part of Canadian thinking and organization.'

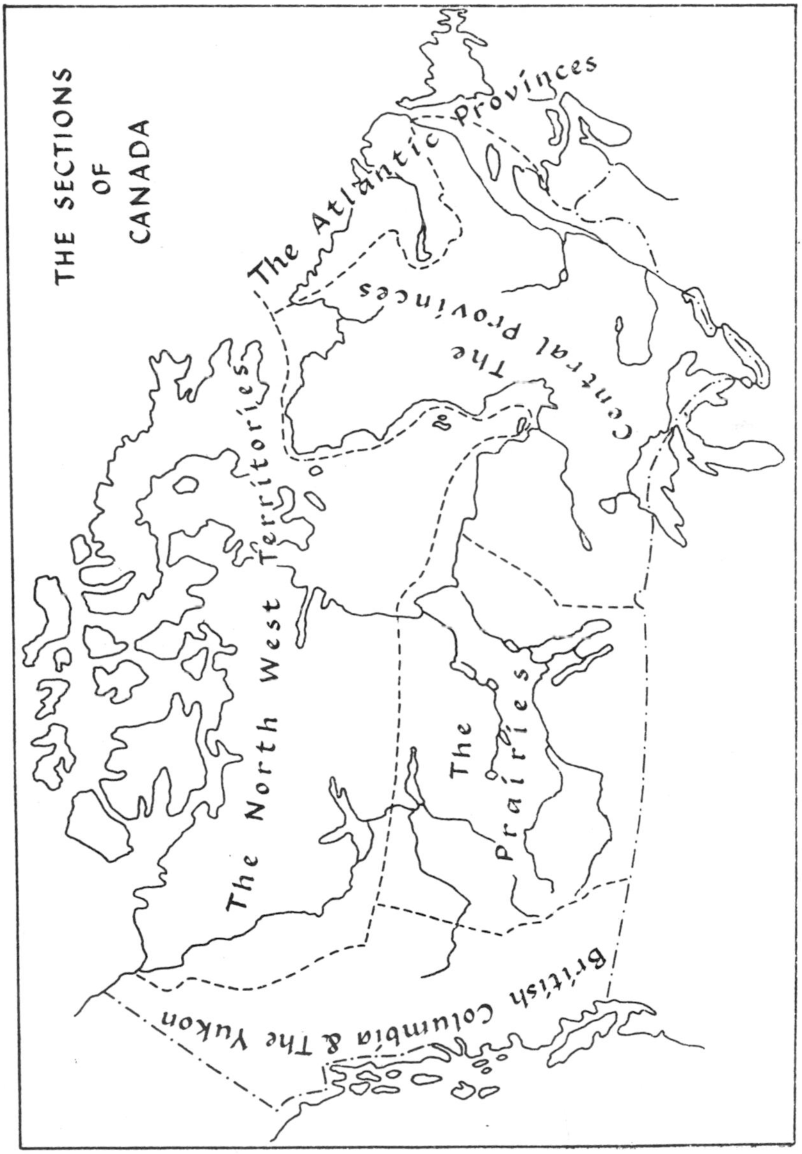

FIG. 63 **Sectionalism in Canada.**

There is the South of the Virginia and Carolina tobacco belt; the South of the Georgia peach district; the South of the Florida and Texas citrus industries; the South of the rice-lands of Louisiana; the South of the Alabama coal fields, and of the Texan oil fields; there is the South of the great seaboard trading cities, and the 'hillbilly' South of the mountainous interior; there is the old South of landed-gentry and agricultural estates; and the new South of financial tycoons and modern factories (Fig. 64).

In the Middle-Atlantic States there is a similar sort of subdivision. Characterized though the area is, as a whole, by highly commercialized agriculture and by massive commercial and industrial developments in its coastal cities, it has its separate features. There is the coastal strip where truck-farming is concentrated; there is the belt of transportation terminals where great seaports have grown up, surrounded by industry; there are the mining zones on the eastern and western flanks of the Appalachians; the fruit-raising valleys and lake plains of the interior; and the route-crammed gaps through the mountains, linking coast and hinterland.

Again, in New England, though the section everywhere feels the pulse of industry and trade, there are the back-state areas of forest, or cut-over and burned-over 'barrens'; there are the upland interfluves where declining farms are being bought out and transformed into country estates or summer retreats; there is the potato farming of the Aroostook and tobacco farming of the lower Connecticut; while the industrialized areas themselves have become highly specialized and differ one from the other—there is still the old New England of textile mills and tanneries, but there is also the new New England of precision tools and scientific equipment.

Canadian and Mexican sections may, in the same way, be seen to have distinct sub-regions, where social and economic conditions vary from place to place, often in response to local changes in geology, relief, or climate.

In the Atlantic Provinces, for instance, there are the cod-fishing, salmon-fishing, and shell-fishing communities; vying with them are log camps and lumber towns by heavily forested hills; contrasted with these are coal and iron mining towns; then there are the orchards of the Annapolis valley and the potato farms of Prince Edward Island; while, unique to the area are Canada's winter ports and terminals.

In the industrial section of the Central Provinces, linked together and made one by canal, railway, and road, and by manufacturing and trade—in spite of older historical and cultural divisions—there are sub-regions based on specialized industrial areas, and also on very different, highly commercialized farming districts. Pulp and paper-making in the St Lawrence estuary and the Ottawa valley, the building of ships, railways, and aircraft in the Montreal region, the production of iron and steel in the Hamilton area, the proliferation of engineering, automobile, and petro-chemical

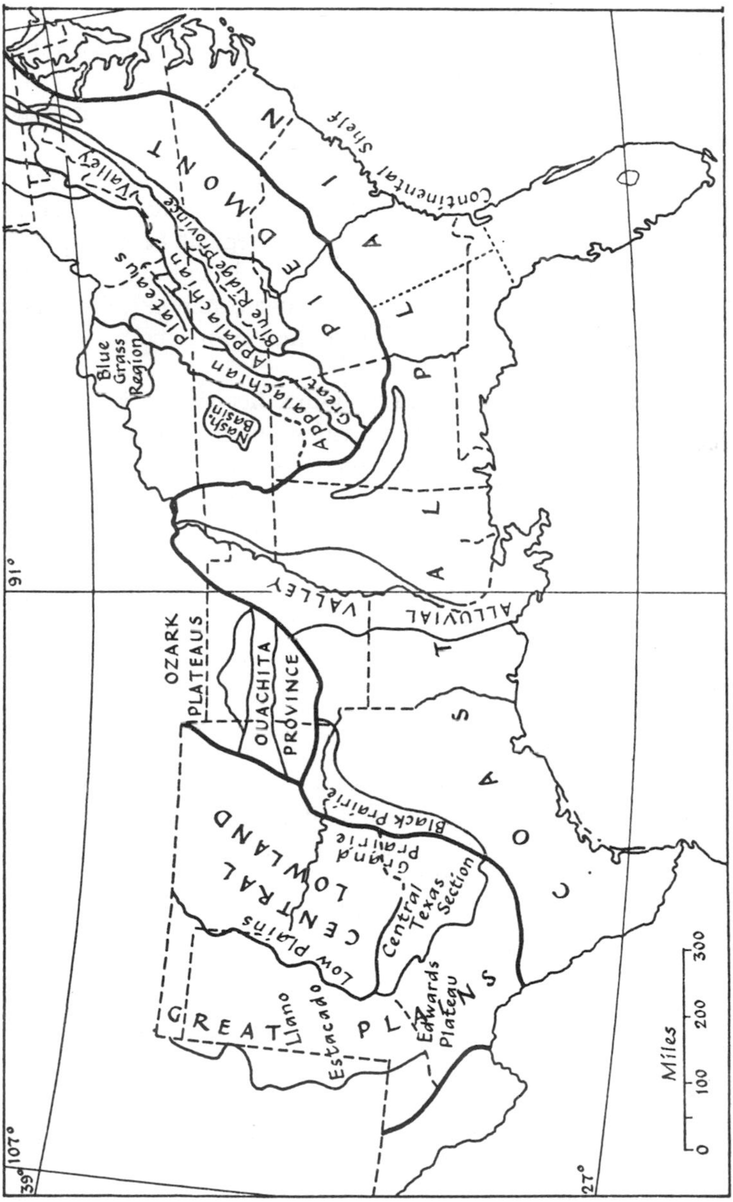

FIG. 64 Section and Sub-region: the South and its Divisions. Although forming one of America's great sections, the South is divided into many sub-regions, of which the most abiding are the physiographic ones. These tend to be reflected in economic divisions, and provided considerable variety within the section as a whole.

industries around Toronto, the rise of brewing and baking industries in the agriculturally rich area about London—these all give variety to the section, marking off distinctive spheres.

The above examples should be sufficient, at this stage, to demonstrate the kinds or orders of sub-regions with which the great sections of each of the national areas are marked out. They should also show how these sub-regions have arisen and on what they are based.

Some sub-regions correspond to zones of a more or less *homogeneous* economy or use of land; they are the fruit belts, tobacco belts, and transportation belts described above. They form *specific* regions based on special distributions and relationships. While they are usually subsumed in a major section, to which they are connected by one or two common traits, they are often distinct from it, with peculiarities of their own, due to local considerations.

Other sub-regions develop through a tying-together of quite *heterogeneous* uses of land, and economic and social activities, about *great foci* of integration; they are the spheres of influence of seaports, gap towns, route centres, and commercial and industrial nuclei. These sub-regions have tended to transgress the regions of homogeneous production, and make them subordinate to the growing power of the regional focus.

Indeed, where the focus is a truly great metropolis, its sphere may extend well beyond the section in which it is located, and may, in fact, be well on the way to creating a new section—although this has not been consciously acknowledged in North America as yet. Still, the sphere of New York is, in certain respects, far greater than that of a sub-region of the Mid-Atlantic States. In terms of financial control and cultural leadership it has the whole nation—indeed, continent—for its hinterland.

With the increasing urbanization of American life—and by that is meant something much more than the increasing concentration of population in cities: the commercialization, mechanization, integration, and standardization of life—the rapidly growing power of the city has come to dominate the geography of the country. One aspect of this is its domination of regional geography. 'The city', Mumford says, 'is the region in human expression.' More and more the city extends its influence outward and gathers in more and more of the countryside into its sphere, until it creates its own region, focusing the life and activity and thought and loyalty of an area recognizably on itself (Fig. 65).

Dawson expresses this trend in his discussion of North American society.

> In each physiographic region [he writes] a major city emerges. The expanse of territory tributary to each city depends on transportation advantages, the resources of its hinterland, and the stage reached in its

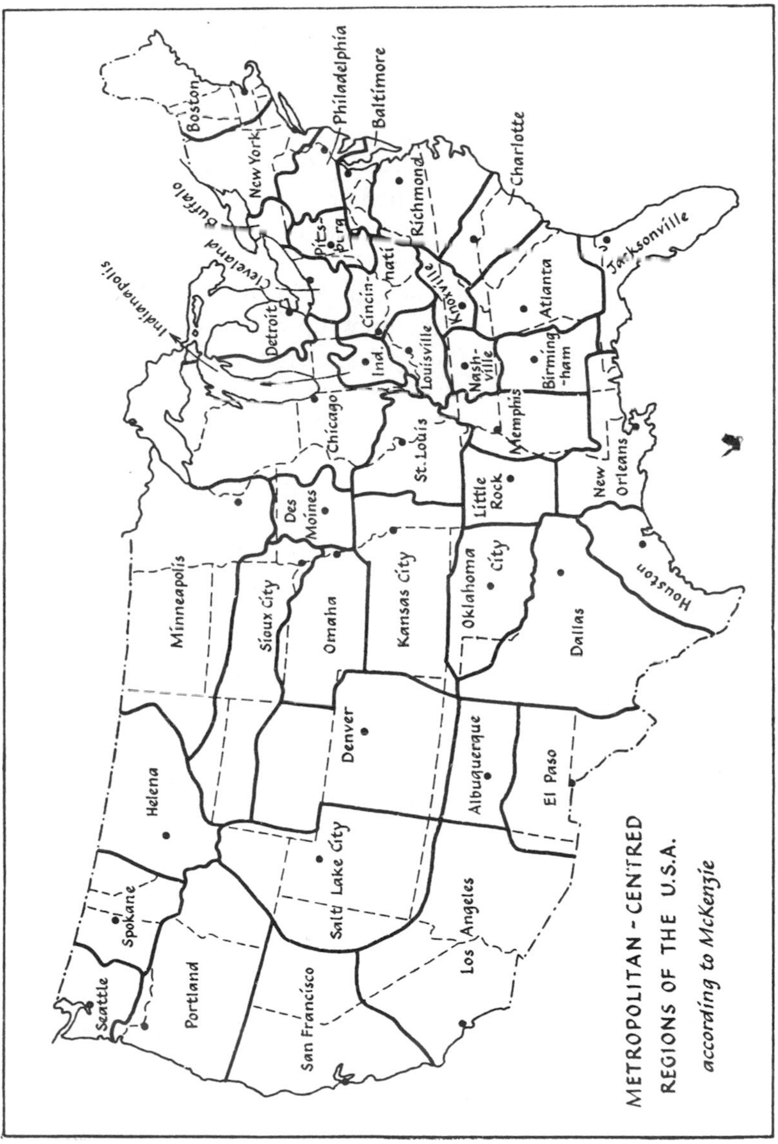

Fig. 65 The United States and the growth of City-dominated Metropolitan regions. (Scale, 1:25 m.)

> development. Its cycle of development links it in increasing intensity with a widening hinterland. If such a city has distinct advantages it tends to become the center of a metropolitan region which extends beyond its original physiographic area. The city becomes increasingly the point of dominance about which the hinterland develops its natural organization. Each of the region's subsidiary cities, towns, and villages . . . finds a more or less specialized place . . . competitively.
>
> These metropolitan regions in turn compete with each other with regard to position and function. In this fashion the whole of North America is in process of being organized into a constellation of metropolitan regions.[1]

This was at length recognized when, in 1935, the National Resources Committee of the U.S. Government drew up a scheme of metropolitan regions as a basis for regional planning. Some of these regions were as large as the historic 'sections' that had given their great cities birth. Others divided the sections into what were considered to be significant 'areas of integration'. New England was almost swallowed up in Boston's sphere; the Mid-Atlantic States were divided between New York and Philadelphia, with the former getting the lion's share; the South was difficult to divide because of the lack of great metropolitan centres—but three city-focused regions were recognized around Baltimore, Atlanta, and Dallas. The East Central States were divided into the spheres of influence of Detroit, Cleveland, and Cincinnati; the West Central States into those of Minneapolis–St Paul, Chicago, and St Louis. The Great Plains were devoid of city-centred regions of any significance, except around Denver, and were thought to come mainly under the control of Chicago and St Louis. Salt Lake City was recognized as the only outstanding centre in the zone of intermontane plateaux and basins, while Portland, San Francisco, and Los Angeles marked out the divisions of the Far-West. In much the same way Canada, too, has its great metropolitan regions[2] (Fig. 66).

Conclusion

It is difficult to create a clear, simple, or final scheme of geographical regions in any continent. Regions come into being only as the result of the interplay of many forces. They should not be considered to have a fixed, unchanging, definite, objective reality in themselves. On the contrary, they are growing and changing entities. Above all, they are relative things—relative to the aims and objects that govern the use to which men put them and the way in which men organize them. Early thinking was inclined to visualize them as essentially natural regions whose forces then shaped the

[1] Dawson, C. A., *Essays in Society*, Toronto, 1940, pp. 30–31.
[2] Watson, J. W., 'Canada and its Regions', *Scottish Geog. Mag.*, Dec. 1962.

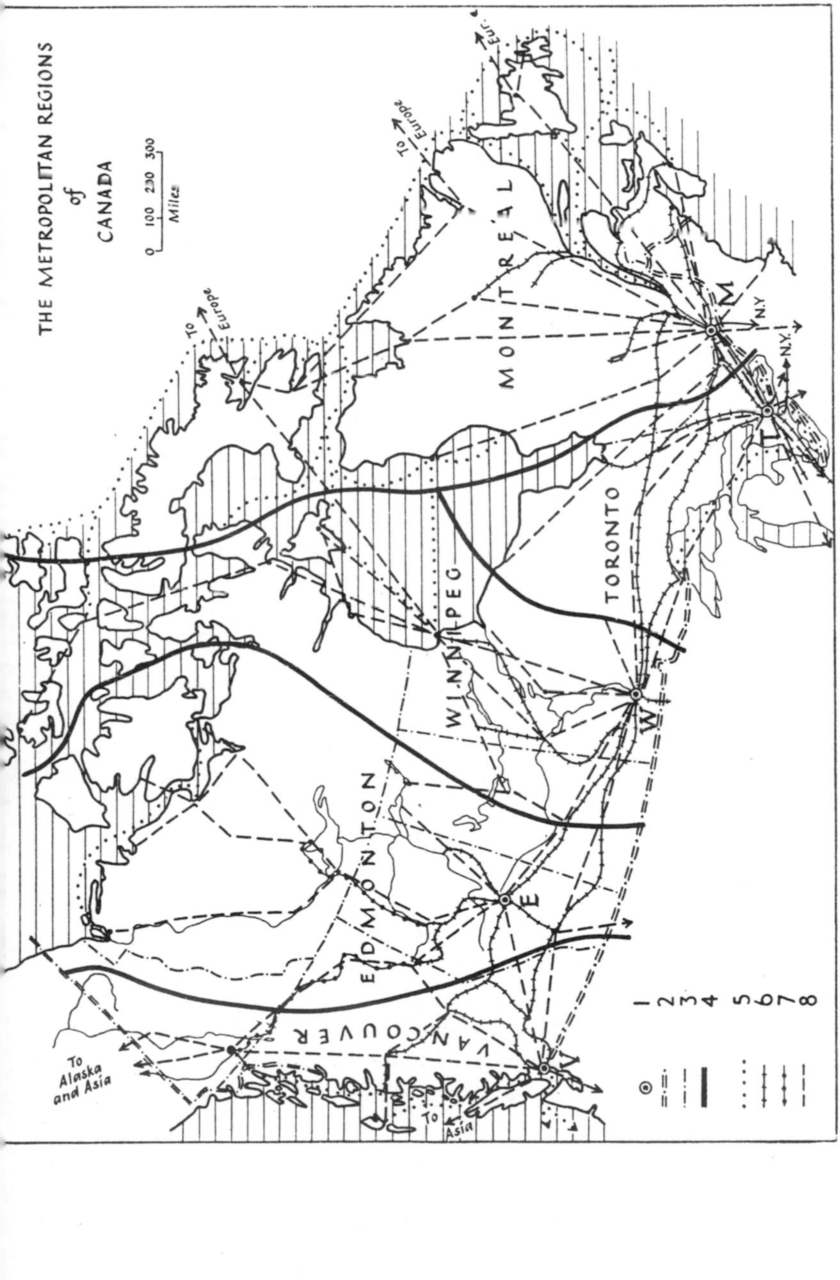

FIG. 66 Canadian Metropolitan-Centred Regions. (Reprinted from a review of the author, 'Canada and Its Regions', *S.G.M.*, Dec. 1962, by kind permission of the *Scottish Geographical Magazine*.)
1, Metropolitan centres; 2, International frontier; 3, Provincial frontier; 4, Boundaries of Metropolitan Regions; 5, Ocean and Lake shipping; 6, Railways; 7, Highways beyond railhead; 8, Airways.

destinies of the men who settled them. But since it came to be shown that, with the European conquest, men increasingly subordinated the landscape and shaped it to their own ends, regions were considered in terms of culture areas.

This concept treated Mexico as essentially a part of Latin America, and stressed the importance of the Mexican frontier as a divide quite the equal of Appalachians or Rockies. The rest of North America was considered to form the Anglo-American culture area. However, the distinct (though perhaps not great) differences between a bi-cultural Canada, still linked with Europe, and a mono-cultural America, centred in itself, have been great enough to divide these two national areas from each other. Cultural differences have been crystallized, strengthened, and defended by political ones, and there seems good justification for using at least the major political frontiers as principal geographical divisions. They are of first importance in defining areas of contrasted tradition and custom, and are fundamental to an understanding of the administrative, institutional, linguistic, religious, and social geographies of the continent, and of the impact these have made on land tenure, the operation of land, patterns of settlement, orientation of transportation and trade—indeed, on the landscape as a whole.

Within the larger cultural-political areas are sections where people have come to feel a division of interest or ideals between themselves and others. Again, because this feeling has been nurtured, historically, through connexions with province or states, it has tended to express itself in divisions based on groups of states. This is how the sectional sense or awareness of the people evolved, and although such divisions often failed to coincide even with the physiographic, economic, or social areas from which they were presumed to have sprung, nevertheless, as group-of-states regions, they came into common use. Such regions have a special attraction in forming clear-cut statistical units. However, states became divided—like Virginia —or they changed their sectional allegiance, and so the actual groupings of states shifted from time to time. Ohio was at one time considered to be in the Middle Section along with New York; Delaware was once thought of as part of the South. When West Virginia 'seceded from secession' it was linked with the North-east—and so on.

Sections themselves were seen to possess many variations within them, even if these were 'variations upon a theme'. Thus sub-regions came into being which, because they were very largely functional in character (depending either on an area of like habit of work or on a sweep of different activities organized about an integrating centre), changed quite considerably with time and circumstance.

Regions then, as Hartshorne has rightly insisted, can scarcely be considered to be 'closed objects'. Even where they exist in the consciousness of those living in them, they cannot always be clearly recognized or defined. Their definition will vary with the changing emphasis which history puts upon the values that go into the creation of geography. Today's regions are often yesterday's dreams; they may be only tomorrow's memories. It is with this *caveat* that the following regional descriptions are presented.

CHAPTER NINE

Canada: Physical

Canada is size and ruggedness, northness and marginality; it is, also, competition, conflict, tolerance, and accommodation; the physical environment is one of challenge, if not frustration, to which the human response has been one of unremitting effort, courage, and ingenuity.

PHYSIOGRAPHY[1]

Canada's size was one of the first things that struck the early explorers. Cartier took the greater part of July and August 1535 to sail from side to side of the Gulf of St Lawrence, and he then had a twelve-day trip up the estuary to make, let alone the St Lawrence river. As he moved inland he became increasingly impressed by the vastness of the country, as were the soldiers and settlers of later days; a vastness that was both a handicap, making it difficult and costly for people to keep in touch with each other, and also an opportunity, offering ample living room.

Modern Canada, with an area of 3,845,744 sq. miles, is the second largest country in the world. This dubious distinction has created real problems for economic integration and social cohesion. But it has given Canada ample scope for expansion. It has also encouraged a largeness of thought and boldness of action that have, from time to time, marked its history. Its largest province, Quebec (594,860 sq. miles), is more than twice as large as Texas (263,644 sq. miles) and is larger than Great Britain, Germany, France, the Low Countries, and Denmark put together!

The geographical shape of Canada has emerged very largely out of its history. At one time it was given great length from the Gulf of St Lawrence to the Gulf of Mexico, but the country subsequently lost everything south of the Great Lakes and contented itself with its westward prolongation from Atlantic to Pacific. As settlers moved up the St Lawrence and the Great Lakes to Lake Winnipeg and the Saskatchewan, and as, piercing the Rockies, they joined up with settlers moving in from the coast, they began to realize the enormous width of the country. Today, along the International Frontier, Canada stretches for nearly 4,000 miles, and at its widest, between Cape Spear (Newfoundland) and Mt St Elias (Yukon Territory), spans 5,781 miles. This great width has drawn out the climatic, vegetation, and soil zones into

[1] Watson, J. W., 'The Land of Canada', *Can. Geog. Jour.*, April 1956.

vast east–west belts. It has also had its influence on the east–west development of the country, the east–west lie of the routes, spread of the population, and alignment of the main boundary.

Actually, the shape of Canada is rather like a flattened diamond. Cabot and Cartier testified to the importance of an eastward salient, commanding the shortest crossing between Europe and North America; La Salle discovered the great southward probe of the country, in peninsular Ontario, that carries it far into the hearthland of the continent: a southern thrust that was to involve it deeply in the challenge from the United States. Davis, Mackenzie, Franklin, and others were to sketch out the huge northward bulge of the land, a bulge that reaches far out towards the U.S.S.R.; while Vancouver, and then Fraser and Thompson, came to delineate the western coast, which faces the teeming populations of the east.

Structure

The largeness of Canada, and its strategic position, have not proved as advantageous as they might, because of the ruggedness of the country. Almost two-thirds of the area is uninhabited, since it consists of inaccessible upland and inhospitable mountain. (And in Canada's latitudes it does not take much increase in altitude to lift a place into sub-Arctic or Arctic weather.) Structurally, Canada consists of a huge central upland bordered by plains which are flanked in turn by mountains.

The fact that settlers moving in from the Atlantic and Pacific had to cross ranges of mountains and that, on coming to the heart of the country, they came on a rocky plateau, made settlement difficult, costly, and slow. Champlain early realized the confinement of the Appalachians in the east, and decided to by-pass them by using the St Lawrence estuary and the Ottawa. Soon, however, his footsteps brought him to the rugged edge of the Canadian Shield. It took many years before Le Vérendrye found his way across that Shield to the interior lowlands. In the same way almost two centuries were to pass before white men moved over the Shield from Hudson Bay to settle in the Red river valley. Likewise the Rockies formed a major barrier from the time Mackenzie explored them to the building of the Canadian Pacific Railway almost a century later.

The occupation of the country tended to follow, stage by stage, the westward discovery and penetration of the major physiographic regions. These were: (i) the Canadian Appalachians; (ii) the St Lawrence–Great Lakes Lowland; (iii) the Canadian Shield; (iv) the Prairies; (v) the western Cordilleras; and (vi) the Canadian north (Fig. 67).

The Canadian Appalachians cradled the first permanent white settlement in Canada, that at Annapolis Royal, in the Annapolis basin. But the numerous mountain ranges with intervening depressions, often drowned by

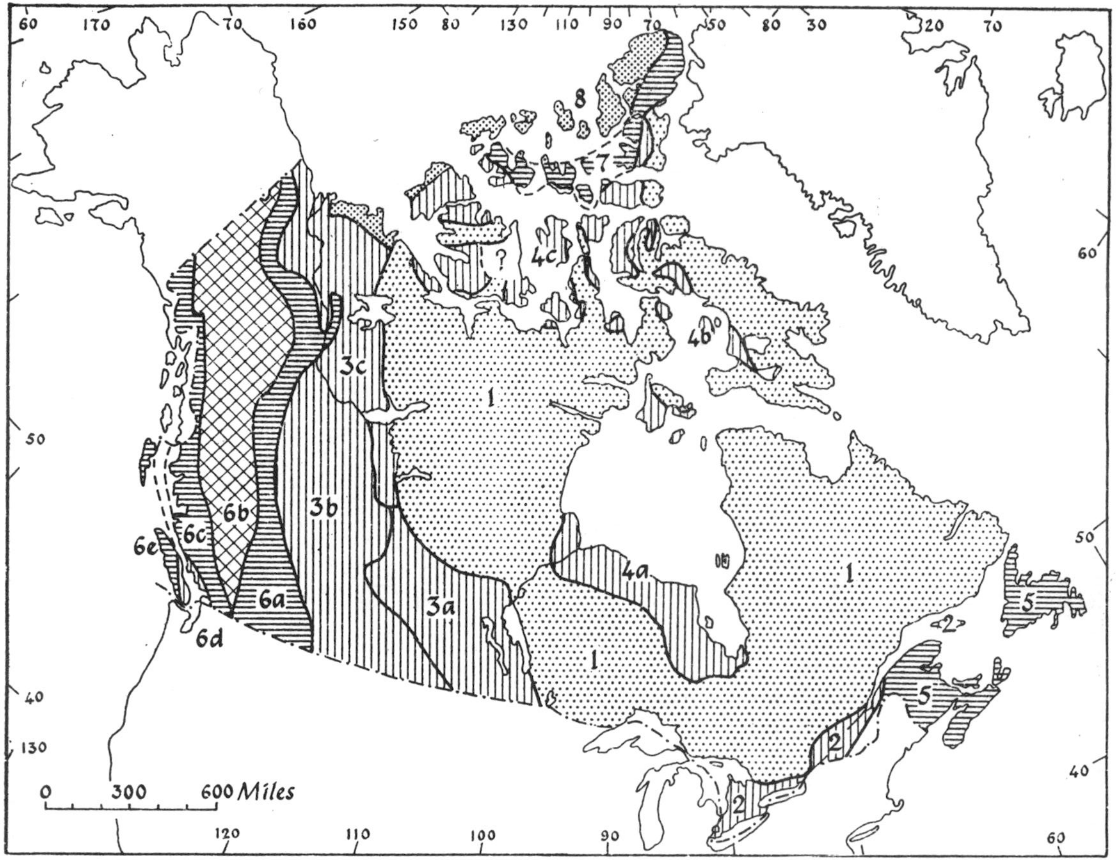

1, Canadian Shield; 2, Lower Great Lakes–St Lawrence lowland; 3, Western Interior lowlands, (*a*) Central plains, (*b*) High plains, (*c*) Mackenzie lowlands; 4, Northern Interior lowlands, (*a*) Hudson Bay lowlands (*b*) Foxe basin plains. (*c*) Southern Archipelago plains; 5, Canadian Appalachians; 6, Western Cordilleras, (*a*) Rockies, (*b*) Interior

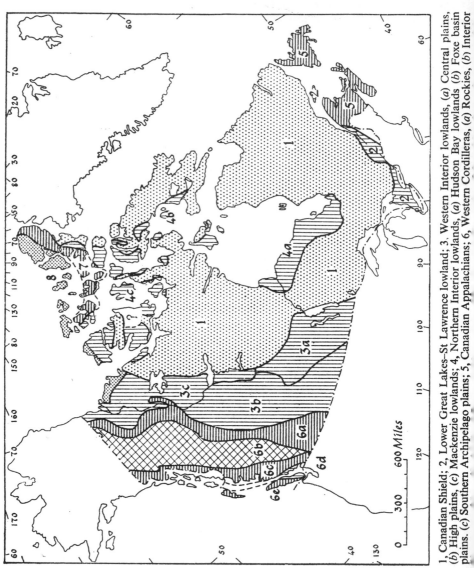

FIG. 67 The Physiographic Regions of Canada.

the sea, made occupation very slow and broke it up into a number of small independent efforts. A measure of the difficulty of the region may be seen in the fact that though Champlain was the first to set up European settlement there, he soon abandoned it, 'having decided that the St Lawrence offered more possibilities than the Bay of Fundy'.[1]

The fact is the Appalachians form an extensive and complex belt of old fold mountains, beginning in the island of Newfoundland and continuing through New Brunswick and Nova Scotia into the New England uplands. Three main zones occur:

(*a*) To the north and west there is a group of long, parallel ridges, with the folds often thrust to the north-west. This begins in the Long range of western Newfoundland isle, continues in the mountains of the Gaspé peninsula, and extends through the Notre Dame mountains to the Taconic and Green mountains of the U.S.A.

(*b*) Through the centre of the Canadian Appalachians stretches a number of broad plateau-like uplands in which domes of crystalline rocks often show through folded sedimentaries, as is the case in central Newfoundland and central New Brunswick. Extensive plutonism and metamorphism are associated with base-metal reserves.

(*c*) To the east and south, from the Avalon peninsula, Newfoundland, through Cape Breton Island to southern Nova Scotia, the Canadian Appalachians are made up of a number of rather short but intensively folded ridges into which small bodies of cross-cut granite have been intruded. Volcanic features, such as the trap ridges of Nova Scotia, make striking, sharp-edged mountains. This eastern zone contains important iron ores and coal basins.

The whole Appalachian region has been eroded since upper Palaeozoic times with the result that its mountains have been planed to a virtual level on more than one occasion. Relics of former erosion surfaces are seen in the Shickshocks at about 4,000 feet, in the Fundy highlands at 1,100 feet, and in the Nova Scotia uplands at 800 feet. Glaciation has affected the whole landscape, having swept across it from the north-west. Many ice-scraped steeps are to be found, while valleys are frequently lined by, or terminate in, hummocky moraines. In post-glacial times changes in land- and sea-levels stranded a number of sea-beaches and terraces 150 feet and 50 feet above the present shore. Rivers have been rejuvenated and not a few rapids and waterfalls have been used for hydro-electric power.

Although the Appalachians have often been regarded as a barrier in Canadian geography and history, it has always been relatively easy to

[1] Chafe, J. W., and Lower, A. R. M., *Canada—A Nation*, London, 1948, p. 35.

by-pass them by way of the St Lawrence Gulf, except in winter when the waters of the St Lawrence are frozen over. Consequently, the St Lawrence early came to play the major role in Canadian settlement and development.

The St Lawrence–Great Lakes Lowland is, in fact, the real heart of Canada, even if not the geographical centre. This is boldly presented by Dr Newbigin, who entitled her book on the country, *Canada—the Great River*. The St Lawrence was in effect the making of Canada and it was because the French and British became so firmly established there and built up their bi-cultural pattern of life that they were able to unite the other colonies into a nation stretching from coast to coast.

One secret of its strength has been its variety. In spite of its mild relief it shows considerable differences, due partly to structure and partly to glacial and post-glacial erosion and deposition. The area is underlain by a natural trough, interrupted in the vicinity of the Thousand Islands by a spur of the Shield reaching south to the Adirondacks. It thus falls into two basins, the eastern one of which forms the Montreal plain, the Ottawa valley, and the lowlands of the St Lawrence estuary. This basin was flooded by the glacial Lake Champlain, and later by the Champlain sea, to levels of up to 650 feet. When these waters receded, lacustrine terraces, glacial beach ridges, and glacial lake bottoms were left which have greatly influenced occupation and settlement. The western part of the trough early formed the basin of the Lower Great Lakes. Here there evolved a belted lowland in which softer rocks, mostly shales, were eaten out into hollows, and harder rocks, chiefly limestones, stood up as escarpments. The depressions, no doubt deepened by glaciation, were filled by ice-front waters. In this way the Great Lakes were formed. With the recession of the ice the lakes fell in level, leaving behind wide expanses of lacustrine flats and old lake beaches, like long fluttering ribbons, that again have been of the first importance for farms, roads, and towns.

The Canadian Shield was early encountered in Europe's conquest of Canada, but it long remained a barrier to colonization. Cartier, sailing along the edge of it, thought it a land to avoid and turned into the interior lowlands. Though it was used by fur traders, its rocky nature, thin acidic soils, and inclement weather made it a sparsely populated region, known as 'the barrens', whose empty spaces were to become a major 'zone of separation' between the older Canada of the east and the newer Canada of the west. It was not until modern times when its vast mineral wealth, its reserves of lumber, and its power potential were realized that it ceased to play a negative role, but took a positive part in the development of the country.

The Canadian Shield is the central structure around which Canada, and indeed the continent, has been built. Lying around Hudson Bay and abutting both on eastern and western Canada, it covers 1,850,000 sq. miles, or more than half the country. It is made up of very ancient rocks mostly in the form of great, rounded granite domes and belts of twisted metamorphics. Occasional sedimentary basins or lava uplands occur. The domes, veined with quartz, and glinting a pale white, often lie in lines to produce series of granite ridges. Many of the metamorphics, with dark grey bands of highly compressed rocks running through them, are relics of ancient mountains. These still stand up above the general level of the Shield. The sedimentary plains, though few, are wide and sometimes of importance where climate permits them to be settled. They usually stand out a vivid green in their mantle of forest.

Some of these structures are rich in minerals, particularly the highly metamorphosed edges of the granite domes, the exposed cores of the ancient fold mountain systems, and those basins which have collected beds of iron. The Canadian Shield is the richest mineral-bearing region in North America and one of the richest in the world.

In spite of its varied elements the Shield looks mainly like a low plateau. The fact is, it has been eroded for such a long time its domes and mountains have been largely planed off, and its depressions partially filled in. Its general level has been reduced to a height of about 1,200 feet. It has, however, suffered considerable deformation, having been tilted up on its eastern edge in the Torngats (5,000 feet), and on its southern edge in the Laurentides (2,400 feet); warped down in the centre under Hudson Bay; fractured along its western margin, from Lake Winnipeg to Great Bear Lake; and fragmented in the north, in the inner archipelago. The Shield also suffered extensive glaciation. Moraines frequently ponded up melt-water into great lakes in front of the ice. Such lakes fell in level after the ice disappeared, leaving behind sheets of lake-bottom clays and winding ridges of beach gravel and sand. The Great Clay Belt is a relic of the glacial lake of Ojibway. Drainage is very irregular, consisting of innumerable lakes linked by youthful rivers, often plunging down rapids or waterfalls.

The western plains were slow in being developed by both French and British largely because of the obstruction of the Shield. Many settlers in moving to the west were deflected by the rugged barrier of the Shield into the Central Plains of the United States. Canada has thus lost between one-in-ten and one-in-five of its immigrants to the more favoured country to the south. However, there were good portages between Lake Superior, Lake of the Woods, and Lake Winnipeg, while the Nelson river led back from Hudson Bay to the Canadian prairies, so that the more adventurous fur-traders and settlers were able to push through to the west. Here they found immense areas of plain and plateau filling in the expanse between the Shield and the Rockies. Although these were shown to be comparatively level they came to offer important differences in relief and drainage.

Their southern portion, known as the Prairies, descends in three major steps from the foothills of the Rockies to the front of the Shield, shedding the drainage eastward to Hudson Bay. Their northern part, the Mackenzie basin, drops gently from a broad west–east divide to the north, shedding its rivers into the Arctic Both regions are really the buried margin of the Shield and are influenced by rises and sags in the underlying Precambrian rocks. Underlying the lower two levels, at least along their southern border, is the Williston structural basin, an important source of natural gas and oil for Saskatchewan and Manitoba. Under the uppermost level lies the elongated Alberta structural basin, Canada's chief source of natural gas and oil.

The various Prairie levels are united by a common glaciation and a common drainage system. Ice moved down from the Rockies and was met by lobes pushing out from the Canadian Shield. A long, narrow series of moraines runs from Edmonton to Calgary. Southwards a number of west–east moraines create strongly rolling country along much of the Canadian frontier, forming a divide between the Saskatchewan and Missouri drainage basins. Most of the Prairie flats have been grooved by ice and thrown into countless small hills and hollows, or sleughs, where glacial till was deposited. At times moraines dammed back melt-waters into large ice-front lakes, such as those which have left such extensive sheets of flat-lying clays in the Regina, Saskatoon, and Winnipeg plains. Glacial-lake Agassiz filled most of the Red river valley and left a rich heritage of clay bottoms and sandy beaches.

The Mackenzie plain not only slopes north, but has, also, a west–east tilt, which makes it quite asymmetrical. The major tributaries such as the Athabasca, Peace, Liard, and Peel come in from the west. Towards the eastern margin of the basin are large depressions, associated with the faulting of the edge of the Canadian Shield. Here have developed the important water bodies of lakes Athabasca, Great Slave, and Great Bear. These lakes were much larger in late-glacial times. Their recession has stranded huge deltaic flats in lakes Athabasca and Great Slave, together with many beach ridges, particularly noticeable round Great Bear Lake. Glaciation spread a thin veneer of till over the whole basin, leaving behind countless swampy or lake-filled depressions. The oil resources of the Mackenzie basin are probably considerable: a very large amount of oil is locked up in the Athabasca tar sands of northern Alberta, while a significant oil field has been developed in the Norman Wells region. The upper Peace river basin has important natural gas reserves, together with some oil.

These and other mineral resources may help to offset the agricultural limitations. One of the great disappointments in Canada has been that the vast plains and tablelands of the west, suited as they well might be by their level horizons to massive use and development, are by reason of climate on the razor's edge of habitability, with the larger part of them suffering from a short growing season, frost, or frozen soils. Nevertheless, there is a narrow but fertile strip that carries settlement on westward to the Rockies and the Pacific.

The Canadian Cordilleras were one of the last regions to be reached by Europeans. The enjoyment of the Mississippi plains to the south and the quest of the North-west Passage to the north, long drew off settlers and explorers. But the urge to strike through to the far bounds of the continent was irresistible and in the early nineteenth century fur traders and settlers began to stream across the mountains.

Progress was slow because it was found that the Cordilleras form one of the most complex systems in the world. They comprise six distinct geographical zones: namely, the Rocky Mountains, the Rocky Mountain Trench, the Interior Upland, the Coast Mountains, the depression of the Inner Passage and an Outer Insular Arc.

(*a*) The Rocky Mountains, as their name implies, stand up like a wall of rock abruptly above the plains. Although they include folded structures they also contain great lengths of relatively horizontal strata lifted bodily to elevations of 12,000 feet. In Alberta they are strongly faulted and have been thrust forward over a notable thrust fault. The Rocky Mountain folds have caught up into their midst narrow coal basins, particularly in Alberta, and also some formations rich in oil and natural gas.

(*b*) The Rocky Mountain Trench is a remarkable feature, forming one of the longest depressions in the hemisphere, reaching from Oregon to the Yukon, and containing long stretches of the Columbia, Thompson, Fraser, Peace, and Liard rivers. It greatly assisted Thompson in his exploration of the west, and has since linked Rocky Mountain passes with coastal rivers.

(*c*) The Interior Upland is at the heart of the Cordilleras, lying between the Rockies to the east and the Coast Mountains to the west. It extends from the central plateau of Alaska, through the Yukon plateau and the plateau of central British Columbia to the Columbia plateau in the U.S.A. It is a wide as well as a long region and has a varied surface made up of blocky mountains, usually of fold rocks pushed up by batholiths and then sharply faulted, together with lava tablelands and elevated sedimentary strata. The whole complex was bevelled by prolonged erosion, then vigorously attacked by ice, and finally cut deeply into by rejuvenated rivers. The southern portion was heavily faulted to give rise to a block and trench relief where the Purcell, Selkirk, Monashee, and Okanagan blocks rise above trenches partially filled by lakes. The blocks have proved rich in copper, lead, and zinc, while the terraced lowlands by the lakes are excellent for agriculture, particularly for fruit ranching.

(*d*) The Coast Mountains of British Columbia begin in a magnificent mass of semi-volcanic peaks in the St Elias range, where Mt Logan, Canada's highest mountain, 19,850 feet, lies. Southward the ridges are underlain by a giant batholith, one of the longest in the world. This has produced a great arching of overlying rocks, with broad-shouldered mountains which have, however, been cut into sharp horns and knife-like edges by extensive glaciation, relics of which still occur among heights clothed with eternal snows, in small ice-fields and valley glaciers. The British Columbia batholith is associated with rich bodies of copper and base metals.

(*e*) The Inner Passage from Puget Sound to Alaska is made up of a line of ancient basins, similar to the Great Valley of California and the Willamette valley, which have here become drowned by the sea. It is flanked by magnificent fjords, and presents some of the finest scenery in the country. If affords a relatively sheltered route, much frequented by shipping, from Seattle and Vancouver to Juneau and Skagway.

(*f*) The Outer Insular Arc, made up principally of Vancouver Island, the Queen Charlotte Isles, and the islands of Alaska, evolved as a series of folded rocks lifted up to heights of 4,000 to 6,000 feet by the intrusion of igneous domes or batholiths. These masses in Vancouver Island are often flanked by ore bodies. Copper and iron are important. The folds also caught up narrow basins of coal-bearing rocks, especially round Nanaimo, British Columbia.

The greater part of the Cordilleras has been glaciated. In Quaternary times there grew a Cordilleran ice-sheet that not only lay over the mountains and plateaux but also extended eastward down to the prairies and westward into the Pacific. On melting away from the mountains the ice left dead portions in the valleys, around whose edges great kame terraces were developed. Very active erosion has subsequently produced deeply entrenched rivers, some of which, like the Fraser, flow in profound canyons. Many sites exist for hydro-electric power development.

The Canadian archipelago was the last region to be exploited, although it was by no means the last to be explored. Its long reaches of water between the many islands invited probe after probe as men from Frobisher's time to Amundsen sought a north-west passage to the Pacific. Eventually this was discovered but because of the prevalence of ice, even in summer, it was found to be of little use.

The Canadian archipelago is dominated by the Innuitian mountain system and by remnants of the Canadian Shield. It is divided into an inner and an outer zone by the great water break of Lancaster sound. The inner archipelago is made up of four prongs of the Canadian Shield, with intervening basins of Palaeozoic rock. The outer archipelago shows a wide arc of folding in the Parry Islands and in Ellesmere Island, running for over 800 miles. In the Parry Islands are a number of narrow, parallel ridges with pitching anticlines and synclines which are very similar to the ridge and valley section of the American Appalachians. In Ellesmere the mountains are more complex and massive, rising to altitudes of 10,000 feet. Ice-caps still exist on the higher mountains. Glaciation covered most of the region, but may not have affected the very arid islands of the extreme north-west. Here in Isachsen and Elef Ringnes isles remarkable piercement domes are found, rising above otherwise rather featureless plains. It is possible that oil is associated with these structures.

It may be seen from all this that the structure and relief of that part of North America that has become Canada are on a grand but relatively simple scale. Each of the features forms a large region in itself. Some of these, like the Appalachians, Shield, and Cordilleras, have proved severe barriers; others, like the gulfs of the east and west coasts, and the great plains of the St Lawrence and the Prairies, have attracted settlement and development. The combination of challenge and opportunity, the necessity for struggle but the chance of achievement, have together entered into the whole pattern of Canadian life. The struggle has been rather greater than has been the case in the United States, and the chances more limited; hence the more northern nation has less than a tenth of the population of its southern neighbour. Nevertheless sea-coast, lakeside lowland, and great river plain have provided a basis to overcome the upland barriers and make them yield their wealth of forest, power, and minerals to the well-being of the whole.

CLIMATE[1]

In all this, climate has been as important as relief. It plays both a complementary and a conflicting role. Along the west coast and in the Cordilleras, climate accentuates relief; elsewhere it tends to transgress or counterbalance it. In the Prairies, for example, the threefold belts of arid, semi-arid, and sub-humid climates, running in the west–east arcs, are in many ways more important than the three Prairie steps, running north to south. In the Canadian Shield such unity as is based on physiography is offset by the divisions between Arctic, sub-Arctic, and cool temperate climates which traverse that great structure. The St Lawrence valley west of the Appalachians and Fundy lowlands to the east, though different in structure, have much the same climates. In general, apart from a few exceptions, the relief of Canada is longitudinal, the climate latitudinal. The two influences form the warp and weft of Canadian landscape and life.

The climate of Canada is characterized by its northness, which means to say its winterness. Canada reaches as far north as 83° 07′ in Cape Columbia.

[1] Connor, A. J., 'The Climate of Canada', *Can. Yr. Bk.*, 1948–9, pp. 41–62; Thomas, M. K., *Climatological Atlas of Canada*, National Research Council, Canada, 1953.

Northness dominates the great cold loops of temperature, the prevalence of polar air masses, and the length and severity of the winter which form major aspects of the environment. This northness has been of greatest significance. It has slowed down development and settlement and so allowed Canada to mature slowly; it has offered a constant challenge, keeping men (as has been said) on the razor's edge of habitability; it has produced a hardy breed of settlers; it has sponsored many ingenious adaptations, calling for inventiveness and skill; it has sharpened conflict and yet, at the same time, widened co-operation; it has become, in fact, part of the very character of the Canadian people. Northness is one of the chief distinguishing features of Canada—'the true north, strong and free'.

Air Masses

Northness dominates the air masses. Over the high Arctic prevails the cold, dense, relatively stable Arctic air mass. Its occasional extensions across the inner archipelago and the northern mainland may lead to bitter blizzards. The heart of Canada, the Canadian Shield, cradles the polar continental air mass, a vast system whose advance and retreat play a very significant role. In winter it spreads far and wide to invade the Cordilleras, sweep over the interior lowlands, and override the Appalachians. It is a mass of cold, relatively dry air, clear and scintillating at the centre, though raw and cloudy at the edge. Its advance is marked by storms and pronounced cold snaps. To east of it is a cool, moist air mass, known as the maritime polar (Atlantic) which, when it invades the coast, brings heavy cloud or fog, and copious rain or snow. Its western counterpart is the polar Pacific air mass. This is even more moist, but is not as raw. On the contrary, it brings mild, humid unstable air over the Coast ranges. Its mildness is particularly beneficial in winter and helps to account for a long frost-free season on the Pacific coast.

Canada is on the northern fringe of the warmer, mid-latitude air masses. The chief invader from the south is the tropical gulf air mass, a warm, wet air stream that moves up from the Gulf of Mexico in the late spring and floods over the St Lawrence plains, the Prairies, and the Mackenzie basin during the summer, bringing extensive heat waves.

These various air masses, with very different conditions of temperature, pressure, and humidity, come into constant conflict with each other, a conflict that creates an exhilarating change of conditions from month to month. Storms tend to concentrate along certain tracks, as, for example, the lower Fraser, the Mackenzie basin, the northern Prairies, the Great Lakes–St Lawrence depression, James Bay, and the Bay of Fundy (Fig. 16, Chapter 3).

There is an unusual concentration of these storms in the region of the Lower Great Lakes, the St Lawrence and Ottawa valleys, and the St Lawrence estuary and gulf. Here the cyclones born in the Canadian Prairies or in the Great Plains of America, together with those moving southward from James Bay, or—more important—those sweeping northward up the Mississippi and Ohio, converge on southern Ontario and Quebec almost as though they were being sucked into a vast funnel. Undoubtedly this gives the St Lawrence region, together with the Canadian Maritimes, one of the most stimulating climates in the country, if not in the world. Here is, in fact, the 'zone of stimulus' in Canada.

Climatic Contrasts in Canada

As a result of these general distributions of temperature and pressure, air masses, and cyclonic tracks, certain contrasts emerge between one part of Canada and another. There are, for example, the contrasts between the west-coast climate, with its north–south orientation, and all the other climates, which tend to lie in great east–west belts. Then there is the contrast between the Arctic and the temperate climates, between the death-zone and the life-zone of Canada, between areas where stillness grips the land for the greater part of the year and areas where growth and activity have a sufficient lease of summer to dominate the scene. There is, furthermore, the contrast between the humid temperate climate, dense with forest, and the semi-arid ones, with an open covering of grass. Finally, there are the special contrasts between areas threatened by frost or drought, and those with a long growing season and verdant with rains (Fig. 19, Chapter 3).

The West Maritime climate differs more sharply from the interior and eastern seaboard climates than is the case in Europe and Asia, because the Cordilleras shut it off abruptly and keep it to a narrow coastal strip; it does not have the chance of penetrating deep into the continent. It is much less variable or extreme than other Canadian climates. Controlled by Pacific airs, it experiences warm, wet winds which blow over the Kuro Siwo drift—the Pacific counterpart of the Gulf Stream. Winters are far milder than the average of their latitude, January means being above 40° F. On the other hand, the foggy weather of spring and the cloudy skies of summer keep the temperatures cooler than average. July means are rarely over 65° F. and more commonly in the upper fifties. The annual range of temperature is very low. At Victoria, British Columbia, it is only 21° F. (between 61° F. July and 40° F. January). Day and night extremes are also uncommon, the clouds which tend to keep excessive heat out by day, prevent the excessive loss of heat by night. At Victoria most days in the summer have a difference of less than 15° between their maximum and minimum temperatures.

The West Maritime climate is a very rainy one with from 30 to 120 inches of rain between lowlands and highlands. Much of the rain is orographic, i.e. rain caused by the updraught of humid air over the coastal mountains. Consequently, it is very unevenly distributed. However, a lot is also cyclonic.

It falls at all seasons, but is most plentiful in winter, when the low-pressure systems over the Aleutians, within the polar Pacific air mass, are most intense. Snowfall is not abundant, except on the mountains. At the coast it quickly melts away.

Such a climate is green all the year round, except on the mountains; it is dressed out in forested slopes and meadow-rich flats; it hums with business most of the time—the cropping season is long, and cattle are out in the fields far longer than in the east; rivers do not freeze up, and traffic is scarcely impeded by the weather, unless there is an exceptional flood; industries are able to draw upon fuels and raw materials and to ship out goods without any major seasonal hindrance; and people find the mild winters almost as uninterrupted and full of activity as the long, pleasant summers.

The Arctic and sub-Arctic climates form the major contrast to this. They are bound in silence and inactivity for much, if not most, of the year. *The sub-Arctic climate* prevails over the northern part of the coniferous forest belt, where the trees are short, and where they thin out to give place, more and more, to bushes, moss, and lichen. The whole area is marked by very short, very cool summers, with July averages in the fifties. Weather is very changeable. Occasional eddies of warm Gulf air may produce surprisingly warm summer days of from 70° to 80° F., but these may be followed, with a swift veer of the wind, by polar air and sub-freezing temperatures. Summer does have its long days with 18 to 22 hours of sunshine in June, but it is soon over, and there is a drop of 20° to 30° in average temperatures in October, when winter begins. This is a long season continuing to the end of the following April. Extremely low minima, down to −80° F., make the region the 'cold pole' of North America. Polar continental air dominates the year. It is dry as well as cold, and consequently semi-arid conditions prevail.

The Arctic climate of Canada covers a huge area north of the tree-line, including north-east Mackenzie District, north and east Keewatin District, the northern fringe of Manitoba and Ontario, northern Ungava and the Labrador coast, as well as the whole of Franklin District. It is much wider than the region bounded by the Arctic Circle. This is because the relief of the Shield, and particularly of the north-eastern straits and Hudson Bay, conspires to draw the polar continental air deep into the heart of the country, letting Arctic conditions spread well south of the Circle to the southern shores of Hudson Bay and the Labrador coast. July averages are between 40° and 50° F., but are not enough to prevent the summers from being raw and uncomfortable. The growing season is very short—less than 60 days, but frost may occur at any time, even in the height of summer. Precipitation is low, with an equivalent of less than 10 inches of rain per annum. Most of this is snow. Since evaporation is low and little melting takes place, the snow lies a long time, and on the highlands and northern plains is permanent. Even where the snow may melt off for one or two months the soil below is permanently frozen.

The Sub-humid Continental Microthermal climate, with severe winters, holds very wide sway in Canada, reaching from Labrador to the upper Mackenzie District. On the east it is the climate of the height of land between the St Lawrence and the Hudson Bay. On the west it extends over the northern Prairies down part of the Mackenzie basin, with outliers in the Yukon. It is controlled by the polar continental air mass. Even in summer this mass is not far removed and prevents the tropical Gulf air mass from residing over the region. A series of warm waves of air may bring days of unusual heat with temperatures climbing to the upper seventies, but July averages are usually between 60° and 65° F. In the north, where the climate passes into a sub-Arctic phase, July averages are as low as 50° F. The growing season does not provide much more than 120 days free of frost, and often not more than 90 days. Winter sees the swift advance of polar continental air until a huge dome of cold dense air lies over the area which, with its cloudless nights when ex-radiation is considerable, helps to reduce temperatures to well below zero by January and February. Intense cold snaps then take place, with the thermometer falling to —40° F. or lower. The climate is most extreme, with an annual range of over 65°.

Precipitation is moderate to low, 12 to 15 inches. Most of this occurs in the late spring and early summer, when convection showers and cyclonic rains abound. Evaporation, however, is not high, thanks to the low temperatures. Winter snowfall, contrary to popular opinion, is light—lighter than in the St Lawrence type of climate. Nevertheless it lasts long, and covers the region with a mantle of white from November to April.

The East Maritime Microthermal climate, with a cool summer and with snowy winters, is found in southern Newfoundland, the Maritimes, the St Lawrence estuary, and the edge of the Shield in central Quebec and northern Ontario. Although maritime, this is a strongly seasonal climate, with an annual range of from 35° to 45°. The July average is generally between 60° and 67° F. There are usually one or two heat waves in the summer, with temperatures of over 80° F., but they are not long-lived. The growing season has up to 165 days free of frost. In winter, raw blustery weather occurs with an alternation of polar continental and polar Atlantic air masses. Precipitation is very heavy, most of it in snow. The annual precipitation is equal to 35–45 inches of rainfall.

The Humid Continental type of Microthermal climate, with a hot summer phase, is found in southern Ontario and southern Quebec. Although the average temperature may be described as a 'temperate' one, it includes an annual range of from 40° to 50°, being typical, in this, of continental régimes. In the summer a huge mass of tropical gulf air covers the heart of the continent. July averages are from 69° F. (Toronto) to 71° F. (Leamington). Several heat waves occur when temperatures climb above 90° F. There is a long, warm fall. The growing season is marked by up to 190 days free of frost. Then winter returns and the whole region is overrun by cold polar continental air. Cold snaps with sub-zero weather take place. The struggle between the two air masses, or vagaries in their behaviour, lead to a high incidence of storm and considerable precipitation, equal to 30 inches of rain.

The unusual warmth of the summer, the comparative length of the growing season, and the coming together of many storm tracks, make this one of the most productive and exhilarating parts of Canada—a fact seen in the great variety of agriculture, the concentration of industry, and the density of population. Here is the real heart of Canada, where the early lead in national affairs has been continued and indeed strengthened.

The Semi-arid Continental Microthermal climate, found in the southern Prairies, is distinctly different. While it has the warm summers of much of southern Canada, with July temperatures of 65° F. and mean July maxima of 80° F., it is seriously affected by drought. The rainy season is shorter, and evaporation more conspicuous. As a result precipitation is reduced to an equivalent of 10 to 15 inches of rain. Winter snows are quite light. The winter is long, intense, and bleak. The frost-free period is about 120 days. In spring, warm winds falling from the Rocky Mountains, known as *chinooks*, help to thaw the land rapidly, but in summer these may intensify the drought.

Canada—Land of Winter

It is obvious from this brief description that, except on the extreme west coast, winter dominates the Canadian climate. In fact, as Stephen Leacock once said, life in Canada consists of preparing for, suffering, and recovering from winter. With its near approach agricultural activity either stops or radically changes, many grain farmers leave their farms to winter in the city, while dairy farmers bring in their cattle into winterized barns; houses and cars are winterized; the central-heating plants are switched on; people get into winter clothes, eat warmth-giving foods, and turn to winter sports. Industry may close down for the winter season, or, to see itself through, may lay in great stocks of lumber, ore, coal, and oil. Most industrial cities are mounded with such stocks—whose rising piles often crown the roof lines and even vie with the towers of church and school. During the winter enormous efforts are required to keep roads and railways open, and to maintain the flow of traffic from suburb to city centre, and from one town to another. Many people are laid off work, or have to change their occupation; in some cases this means that men have to leave their families or commute great distances to their winter jobs.

When spring eventually returns, storm windows and doors are removed from housing, people shed their overboots and heavy clothes, and relief is found in summer sports. Ships begin to sail on lakes and canals again, and the whole land swings into the most intense activity, so as to make the most of the short verdant summers. Farmers work long hours, in a concentrated effort to get their crops started in the all-too-brief spring. Cities take on a different aspect; they are no longer snowbound, bleak, and bare, dominated by great heaps of coal or mountains of logs, but are green and bosky, and filled with the joy of people returning to their gardens. Industry is so active it often finds itself short of labour and optimistically takes on the many immigrants that begin to stream in through the newly opened and ice-free ports. As summer strengthens there is a great week-end exodus out into the forests and up into the hills or down to lake and sea, and everywhere the summer chalets are opened up once more, screen doors and windows fitted on to keep out flies and mosquitoes, and people in their hundreds of thousands relax in the welcome warmth.

Thus it is clear that the northness of Canadian climate dominates almost all activities, occupations, and interests, causing, amongst other things, a marked rhythm in existence that is one of the most typical things about the country.

SOILS AND VEGETATION[1]

These are affected by both relief and climate, and in their turn have a great effect on men. In the Cordilleran region they form north–south belts that closely correspond to the relief. In the higher parts of the Shield and in the Appalachians relief causes strong local modifications. Elsewhere, soil and vegetation form belts that coincide with the major climatic belts. The main regions include: (i) the Lower Great Lakes; (ii) the Upper Great Lakes–St Lawrence; (iii) Acadia (the Maritimes); (iv) southern Laurentia and the Mackenzie and Yukon valleys; (v) northern, central, and western Laurentia; (vi) the northern Prairies; (vii) the varied conditions special to the Cordilleras; and the arid areas of (viii) the southern Prairies; and (ix) northern Laurentia and the Canadian archipelago (Figs. 68 and 69).

The Lower Great Lakes region is one of low, flat glacial-lake beds, varied by old glacial beaches, clays, and gravels that readily weather. In addition it has the hottest Canadian summer and a fairly long growing season. It has developed a forest of hardwoods, mainly oak, hickory, and elm, along with walnut and chestnut. Maple is also common, with white pine on sandy ridges. Members of the Carolinian forest, dominant much farther south, are found in sheltered localities, including the magnolia and Kentucky

---

[1] Halliday, W. E. D., *A Forest Classification for Canada*, Canada Forest Service, Bul. 89, Ottawa, 1937; Putnam, D. F., *Pedogeography of Canada*, Geog. Bul. no. 1, Ottawa, 1951, pp. 57–85.

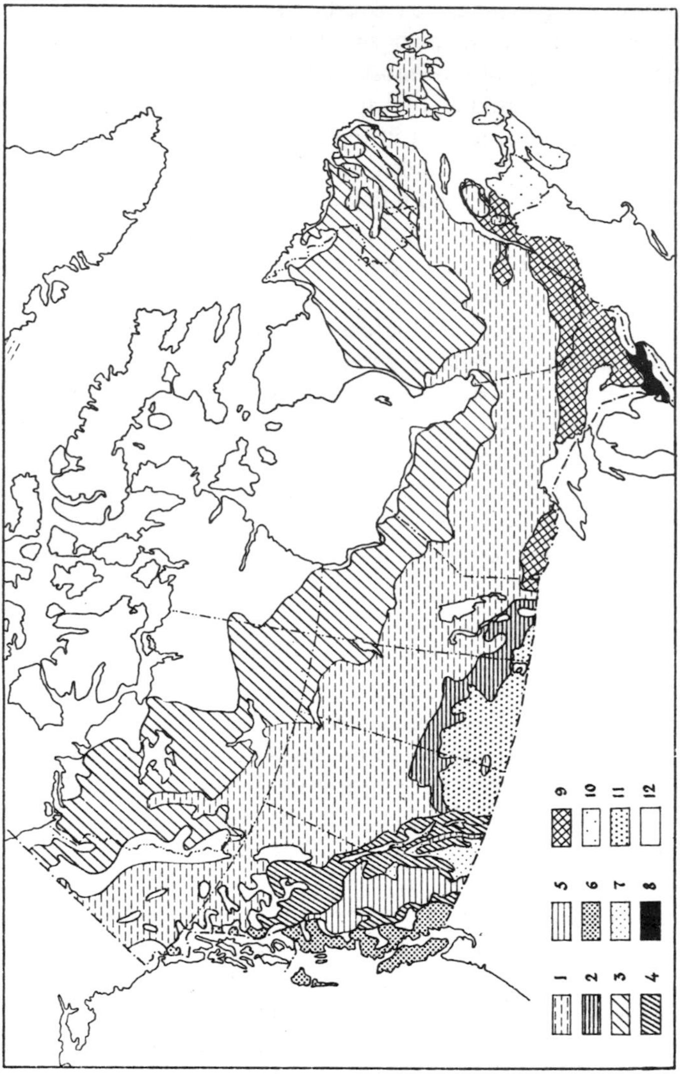

FIG. 68 The Vegetation Regions of Canada.

1–10, Forest Formations; 11, Grassland Formations; 12, Tundra (Arctic and Alpine) Formations. The Forest Formations are: 1, Boreal or Laurentian forest, predominantly in trees; 2, Aspen-grove southern fringe of boreal forest; 3, Barren and scrub northern fringe of boreal forest; 4, Sub-alpine forest; 5, Montane forest; 6, Coast forest; 7, Columbia forest; 8, Carolinian forest; 9, Great Lakes–St Lawrence mixed forest; 10, Acadian forest. (Scale, 1: 40 m.)

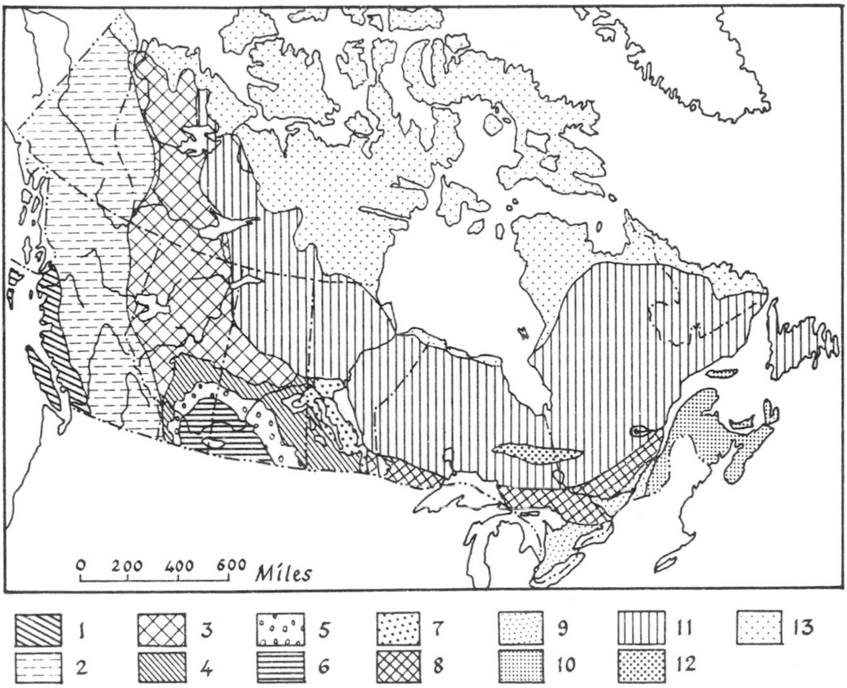

FIG. 69 The Soil Regions of Canada.
1, Pacific Coast; 2, Cordilleran; 3, Grey-wooded; 4, Black and degraded black; 5, Dark brown; 6, Brown; 7, High lime: 8, Brown podsolic; 9, Grey-brown podsolic; 10, Eastern podsols; 11, Canadian Shield podsols; 12, Clay Belt podsolic; 13, Tundra soils.

coffee tree. A thick mantle of leaves on the ground has provided an ample supply of humus and the soil is a fairly rich, deep grey-brown earth. It is well suited to corn, hay, and small grains. Agriculture has replaced most of the forest cover.

The glacial-lake lowlands bordering the **Upper Great Lakes**, together with the plains of the Ottawa and the St Lawrence, are clothed with a mixed deciduous-coniferous forest. Sugar maple, beech and yellow birch are widely found, along with white and red pine, and also hemlock. The soil has a thick brown layer of forest duff with a strongly leached greyish layer beneath. It is transitional between the grey podsols of the Shield proper and the grey-brown earths of the St Lawrence plains.

The Acadian region, which comprises all but the higher points of the Maritime provinces, has a mixed forest of hardwoods and softwoods, with a high proportion of maple and of red spruce. There is a considerable fall of leaf, and the soils have a fairly high organic content. However, leaching is strong, especially during the melting of the heavy winter snows, and in the spring and autumn rains. A brownish podsol is the result which is rather acid and has to be well drained and limed before it becomes really productive.

The southern-central and the western parts of the **Canadian Shield** also have podsols, but here the soils are still more leached, and are thinner and more acid. Under a shallow layer of decaying vegetation is a deep leached zone that lends a characteristically grey colour to the soil. Similar grey leached soils are found in the Mackenzie basin and the Yukon valley. The forest associated with these soils, known as the boreal type, is made up principally of quick-growing coniferous softwoods and hardier deciduous trees which can make the most of the very short, cool summer; white and black spruce, jack pine, and tamarack are common, together with balsam, poplar, aspen, and birch. The boreal forest is characterized by large stands of a few species; it is easy to cut out, and is highly prized as the hemisphere's largest reserve of pulp and other softwood products.

It merges without any appreciable break into the **sub-Arctic forest**, where spruce, birch, and willow predominate, but where the trees are shorter, and wide spaces, full of reindeer moss and lichens, occur. This zone has relatively little commercial value, although it serves its purpose as the winter feeding ground of the caribou on which so many northern Indians and Eskimoes depend.

Transitional between the boreal forest and the grasslands of the southern prairies is a broad belt of **mixed woods and parkland**. Spruce and poplar are common, together with the western maple and cottonwood. But the woodland is patchy and opens out into many wide spaces covered with grass and bushes. The soils of the region are known as grey wooded ones, which are more fertile than the grey leached soils, though not as productive as the grey-brown earths.

The forests and soils of the **Cordilleran region** differ markedly in trend, responding to the north–south lay of relief, rather than to any latitudinal alignment. As a consequence, they are very complex and show marked contrasts as between valley and ridge, and also between windward and leeward slopes. Four forest types may be distinguished. The sub-alpine forest, found on the higher slopes of the Rockies, is made up mainly of white spruce, Engelmann spruce, and lodgepole pine. Farther west is the Columbia forest, found in the Selkirk and Purcell mountains, with Engelmann spruce and western hemlock. Western red cedar also occurs. On the ranges of the interior plateau is the montane forest, with yellow pine predominating, together with aspen, Douglas fir, and lodgepole pine. Finally, on the Pacific coast, clothing the Coast Range and the outer isles, is the coast forest, which is very dense and is made up of extensive stands of tall timber. The chief trees are Douglas fir and western red cedar, with western hemlock, western white pine, maple, cottonwood, and alder. This forest forms Canada's chief source of construction lumber. The soils of the Cordilleras also vary greatly. Under the sub-alpine forest they are chiefly podsolized types, acid and rather infertile; in the more open woodlands of the interior plateau, and in the grasslands of the interior valleys, they range from a brown podsolic to a dark brown type, which, with irrigation, can be very fertile. On the coast they are mainly a forest-brown soil, rich in humus. When cleared of trees, these soils make good farm land.

The remaining soil and vegetation zones of Canada are those of the arid interior and the cold and arid north; that is, on the flanks of the forested regions.

The Prairie Provinces are so called because of the considerable area of grassland or prairie that was found there by the early settlers. Some of this still exists as range land, though most of it has been ploughed up and sown to wheat or hay. Two belts of grassland exist; the northern one, consisting of the Tall Grass prairies, has now been largely replaced by crops; the southern one, known as the Short Grass prairie, is still partly intact, with spear grass and buffalo grass mixed with rye grass and wheat grass. Soils have responded closely to vegetation. Under the tall grasses of the sub-humid zone of the prairies, black or dark brown soils have evolved, high in organic matter, with virtually no leaching, and neutral in chemical reaction. These are amongst the richest soils on the continent and underlie Canada's chief wheatlands and its western dairy belt. The soils of the semi-arid short-grass prairie are a paler brown to yellow in colour, have less organic matter, and possess a high lime content. Where the climate permits they too have given rise to extensive wheat farming. Often they are rather arid. In that event they have been left unploughed, except where irrigation has been possible.

Over a large part of northern Canada lies the **Canadian tundra**, a region of short grasses, heaths, lichens, and mosses, together with strips of very stunted trees by river or lake. The soils are frozen most of the year. Even in summer, whereas the surface layer thaws down to perhaps a foot, the sub-surface layer remains frozen. Great frost cracks and other features of thawing and freezing pattern the ground, often in regular stripes or polygons. The region pastures caribou in summer and a few herds of musk-ox, but is otherwise of little use.

Over vast areas the soils of Canada are of marginal value or may prove of no value for human use. Thus marginality is a Canadian characteristic. Yet when acidity has been combated by drainage and liming, or aridity by irrigation or dry farming, the soils are rewarding enough. This promise of reward is an exciting element in Canadian life, especially when won only by effort and enterprise.

CHAPTER TEN

Canada: Human

THE HUMAN RESPONSE

Although Canada has been rather inaccessible and forbidding, through its position, relief, and climate, it has nevertheless had sufficient to offer, by way of river and plain, forest, fuel, and mineral wealth, to attract to it people who have had the vision to see the possibilities there and the courage and ability to exploit them. Since opportunities were at first confined to a narrow southern fringe they led to sharp and often bitter conflict between the French and British anxious to discover and exploit them. Conflict eventually turned to co-operation, and, in a united, bi-cultural effort, the early conquerors opened up the country to wave on wave of immigration from many parts of Europe. The new-comers greatly enriched the nation's life until, with a fund of skills and ideas, with a growing home market, and with widening contacts overseas, Canada was able to develop a fully fledged economy and establish a distinct way of life (Fig. 70).

Economic Development

At present, development is still limited in scope, though noteworthy in degree. With great spaces and resources but with as yet relatively few people, Canada has tended to go in for primary production rather than for manufacturing. Industrial goods account for only two-fifths of the value of all goods produced in the country. Canada's wealth still lies in its fisheries and forests, its soil, water-power, and minerals. It has come to develop these resources by highly scientific, mechanized, and commercialized methods, thus making the most of them in view of the comparative lack of man-power. Home consumption, though high enough on a *per capita* basis, is relatively low in terms of totals, and there is a large surplus for export. The sale of primary products abroad enables Canada to buy in the goods it cannot, for reasons of geology and climate, produce itself or which, for economic reasons, it does not manufacture. Since Western Europe and the U.S.A. have exhausted many of their own raw materials, or depleted them below their own needs, they are anxious to buy from Canada. They thus afford good markets. In return, the very development of her resources makes Canada a good market for the manufactured goods of the U.S.A., Britain, and other highly industrialized nations.

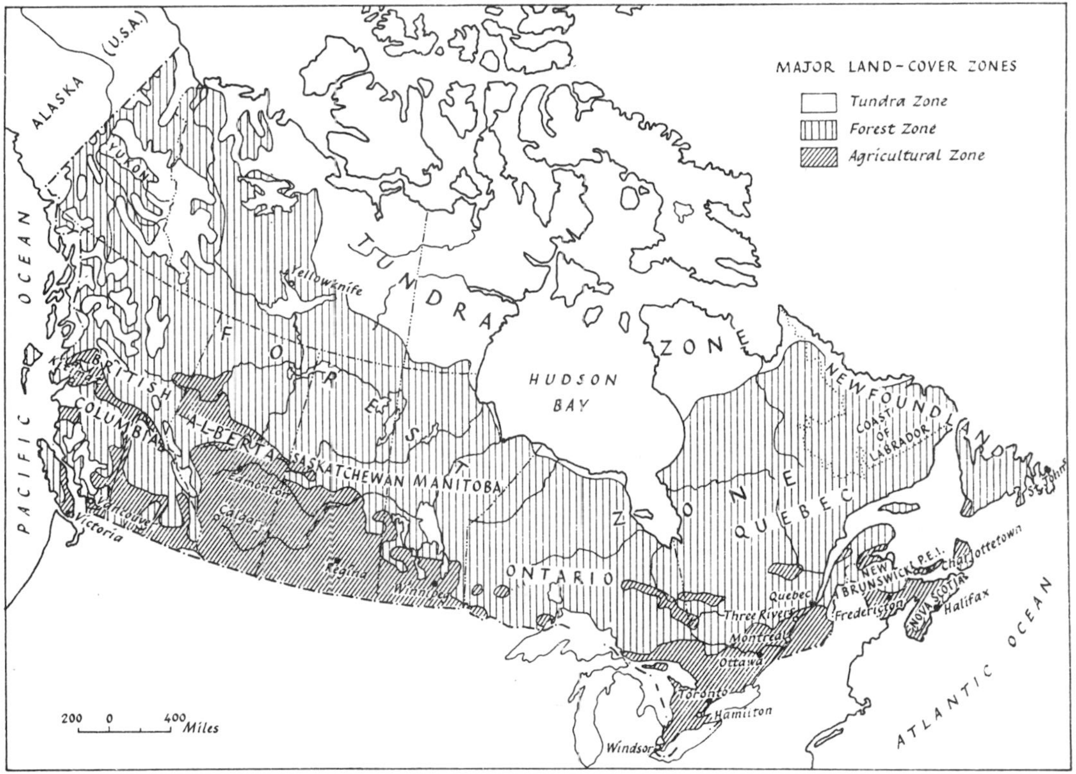

Fig. 70 The Land-Cover Zones of Canada. The greater part of the country is under Tundra and Forest. Agricultural zone is broken by the Appalachians, Shield, and Cordilleras, and is extensive only in the St. Lawrence–Lower Lakes and the Prairies.

The fisheries of Canada probably form her oldest resources. For nearly a hundred years before the British and French settled in the country these people, and others, fished off the Newfoundland Banks and other east-coast fishing grounds. Canada has one of the longest coasts of any country in the world; much of this coast is indented by great estuaries, by faulted depressions, and by fjords; most of it leads back to great rivers with many lakes. Such conditions are ideal for fishing and Canada has some of the most prolific fisheries in the world. Chief amongst these are: (i) the Atlantic Banks; (ii) the fjords and canyons of British Columbia; and (iii) the Great Lakes and other large inland water bodies.

The banks lying off the Atlantic provinces cover an area of over 70,000 sq. miles or well over the area of England. Here the relatively shallow water is stirred up by the mingling of two contrasted currents, the warm Gulf Stream from the south, and the cold Labrador current from the north. This mixing apparently stimulates many forms of marine life and results in an ample supply of food for herring, halibut, cod, and haddock. Meanwhile the glaciated and drowned shores of Newfoundland and the Maritimes offer excellent fishing coves and harbours. The dense forests of the near-by uplands have made the building of boats cheap and easy. Over the last thirty years, with a yield of more than 1,100 million pounds of cod alone, the Canadian Atlantic fisheries have proved to be the greatest cod and haddock areas of the world. The inshore fisheries, at the same time, provide large quantities of oysters, lobsters, and sardines. Salmon is important up the Restigouche, off the Gulf of St Lawrence.

The main salmon fisheries, however, are in British Columbia, where natural conditions have conspired to create the largest salmon fishery in the world. Numerous deep glaciated fjords invite an annual swarm up the rivers to their heads. The salmon swim upstream and spawn in the freshwater lakes among the mountains. Salmon traps on the rivers, and the netting of salmon at the mouths of the fjords, provide an annual catch of about 150 million pounds. Herring are caught in quantity off the Pacific isles.

On the Great Lakes and around Lake Winnipeg and Great Slave Lake are many small fishing ports that take in large catches of whitefish, lake trout, and pickerel. A ready market is found in the large cities such as Toronto, Detroit, and Chicago, near at hand.

Altogether Canada lands a total annual catch of over 400 million pounds of fish, most of which is exported.

The fur trade is another very old Canadian industry, dating back to the beginning of the seventeenth century. Indeed, it was responsible for much of the exploration and discovery of the country. It, too, is closely connected with the geography of the land, reflecting the great extent of northern latitude, the dominance of winter, the prevalence of fur-bearing animals, and the need for warm clothing. Its importance, relative to other occupations, is declining, particularly in southern Canada where the hardwood forests have been cleared. However, along the northern fringe of the coniferous forest and in the tundra, it is frequently the only activity making use of large tracts of land, and therefore has great significance. This is true in northern Quebec and Ontario, northern Manitoba and Saskatchewan, and in the North-west Territories. In recent years Canada has pioneered mink and fox farms, notably in Prince Edward Island and northern Alberta.

The forest products of Canada are among its most important. Relief and climate combine to make this a forest land. Each of the forest types has its peculiar value.

The eastern hardwoods, used for building the pioneer homes and early cities of the Maritimes, lowland Quebec, and southern Ontario, also gave rise to implement and furniture industries. Birch and maple are still used extensively for hardwood flooring and furniture, oak and ash for the handles or frames of agricultural and other implements.

The northern forest has been used pre-eminently for logging and the manufacture of pulp and paper from softwood coniferous trees. Traditionally the trees are cut down and trimmed in the winter, the logs hauled out on the snow to the edge of a lake or a river, they are floated downstream after the spring break-up and boomed at the mills for processing during the summer and fall. Huge piles of logs, accumulated each spring, usually keep the pulp-mills going until the next year's supply. Both relief and climate favour these activities. The prevalence of plateaux, the glaciated nature of the land surface causing many lakes and chutes, the heavy snows, the summer rains, the large volume of water, and its swift current, all assist in the assembly and floating of the logs, and in providing adequate water and hydro-electric power for purposes of the mill. In Newfoundland, New Brunswick, Quebec, and northern Ontario, uplands tend to predominate, and logging is a principal activity. In the Prairies the forest fringe is rather remote from the settled areas, but logging and lumbering are of increasing importance.

The Cordilleran forests have gone in mainly for lumbering. This is especially true of the dense, tall timbers of the coastal ranges of British Columbia. Here very durable woods have been obtained in large trunks that lend themselves to sawing, rather than pulping. Thus the larger constructional shapes can be cut from the tree and used for the basic beams of house and office construction, the building of sheds and warehouses, railway yards, and ships' quays, etc. Since, in many cases, the forests are the only adjustment to the steep slopes and heavy rainfall of the coast, their presence gives a sound economic basis for otherwise unusable land. Consequently, their conservation is a prime consideration.

Canada's **agriculture** is one of its most extensive industries. In spite of the narrowness of the agricultural belt from south to north—it is rarely more than 250 miles broad—its great extent from east to west provides an ample basis for development. Three main areas may be distinguished: the eastern, mid-western, and Pacific (Fig. 71).

Canadian agriculture began in the microthermal climate of the Maritimes, Quebec, and Ontario, in lowlands with deep soil, a fairly long growing season, and a moist, warm summer. This was the natural habitat of the hardwood forest, and agriculture prospered largely at the expense of the woodlands. However, in some places, like the Annapolis valley and the Niagara peninsula, it replaced timber by fruit farms and so did little to change the scenery except to put the trees in line. Elsewhere it burned off the tree altogether and opened up the scenery to wide fields of pasture or of crops. Clovers, hay and oats, winter wheat or rye, and turnips were introduced and found to flourish. Indian corn, tobacco, potatoes, and squash, the gifts of the natives, were greatly expanded. The moderately severe climate and podsolized soils tended to limit activities to general farming or dairying. But in favoured areas, such as Georgian Bay, the Lake Erie shore, the Niagara peninsula, the Bay of Quinte, the Montreal plain, and the Annapolis valley, specialized crops developed, including fruit and tobacco farming and market gardening.

With the opening of the west, after the Canadian Pacific Railway was put through to the Rockies in 1885, an immense expansion in Canadian agriculture took place. Here the small grains, like wheat, rye, oats, and barley, were replacing wheat-grass and rye-grass and other seed-bearing grasses. In other words, grain farming was a natural adjustment to the environment. It maximized all its advantages, while suffering fewest disadvantages. Like the grasses, the small grains could spring up and come to seed in a short growing season, unaffected by the extreme severity and length of the winter. Like the grasses, they could make do with the rather scanty rainfall and, perhaps more important still, adjust to the variability of rainfall. With the breeding of drought-resistant and frost-resistant grains, the two principal hazards were cut down. The soils were ideal for shallow-rooted grains, supplying a wealth of nitrates and of phosphates and calcium, from the mode of their formation.

Furthermore, the western lands were relatively easy to farm and manage. They were wide and open, gently rolling or even flat; they were not interrupted by forest and hill as were the farm lands of the east. Consequently, they invited large-scale, mechanical methods of farming that produced the maximum yield for the minimum outlay of human labour. This has been important in as thinly settled an area as the Prairies. As a result the grasslands of the Prairies largely disappeared, except in the driest regions, and

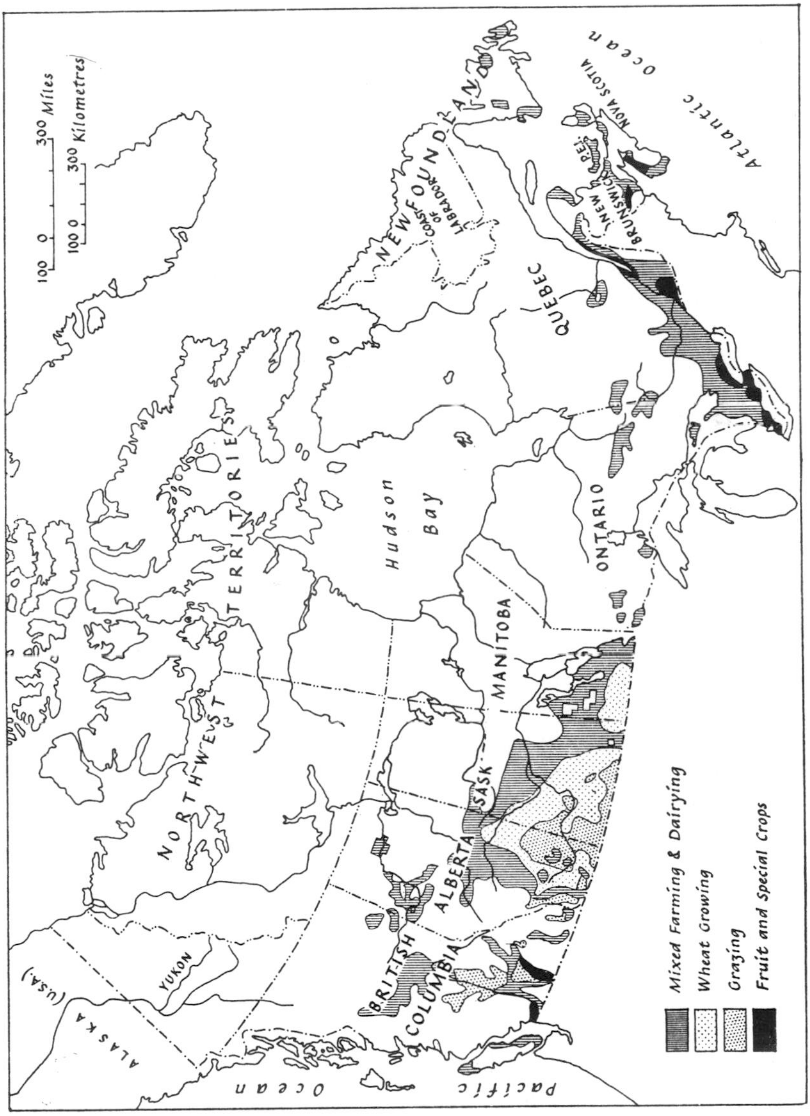

FIG. 71 The main types of agriculture in Canada.

wheat farming became widespread. Rye on the cooler margins and silage corn on the humid margins were also significant. With time, a more varied agriculture has grown up in the Prairies, as the special values of local relief, drainage, and soil-geography have become recognized.

It is in British Columbia, however, that variety becomes the keynote. In the interior valleys, particularly, there is a marked zonation of terraces, soils, and climate that makes for a wide range of farming, from fruit to cattle ranching, in a relatively short range of distance. Where the land widens out in the Fraser delta, on the more humid coast, dairy farming and market gardening are more common.

Mining production in Canada has rapidly forged ahead to compete with agriculture and forest products for a foremost place in the country's economy. Unfortunately, the difficulty of getting at Canadian fuels and metals compared with the comparative ease of securing supplies from the United States, long held the industry back. But, as supplies started to dwindle in the United States or became more costly to mine and to distribute, especially as the high-grade ores began to be used up, there developed a growing demand for Canadian products and it came to be seen that Canada was singularly well endowed with mineral wealth.

Fuels. The geographical distribution of Canadian fuels has been somewhat unfortunate in the light of the peopling of the country. By the middle of the nineteenth century Ontario and Quebec had become the most populous regions. Their proportion of the total population grew with the twentieth century, far surpassing the Maritimes or the Prairies. Thus the coal that was being mined in Nova Scotia and New Brunswick was remote from the bursting cities and thriving industries between Montreal and Windsor. The coal later discovered and mined in Alberta was even more remote. Consequently, the Central Provinces found it more economic to import coal from the huge coal fields of near-by Pennsylvania, West Virginia, and Kentucky. This has continued in spite of growing efforts to use more Canadian coal. Nevertheless, the coal of Nova Scotia has been very useful for factories, railways, and ships along the eastern seaboard; that of Nanaimo for the western seaboard; and that of Macleod, Drumheller and Lethbridge in Alberta, and at Fernie, British Columbia, for the trains and for domestic use out west. Use on trains has, however, now ceased.

Oil and gas have been much easier to transport than coal, and here the situation is more favourable. Canada's oil resources, at first thought to be confined to the Turner valley, Alberta, and to amount to not more than about 50 million barrels, are now known to lie in reefs all along the Rocky foothills as far north as St John, while oil wells on the northern margin of the Williston basin in U.S.A. have come into production in southern Saskatchewan and south-west Manitoba. Reserves are now put at several

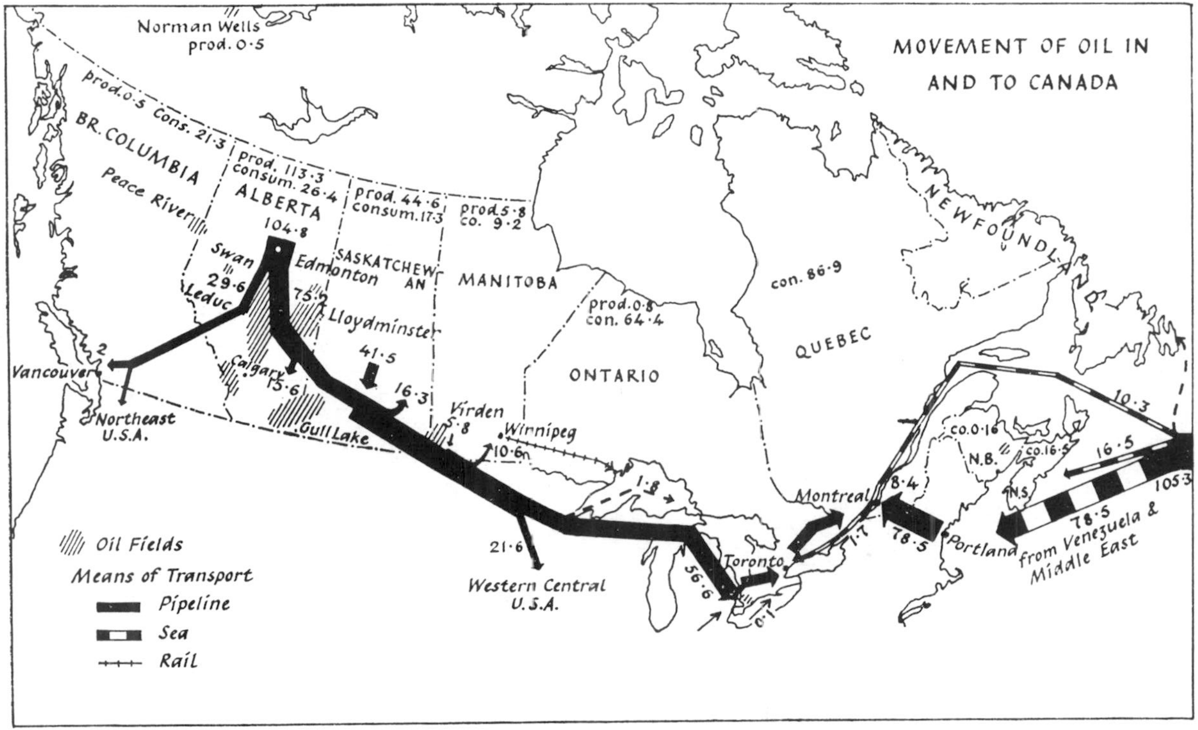

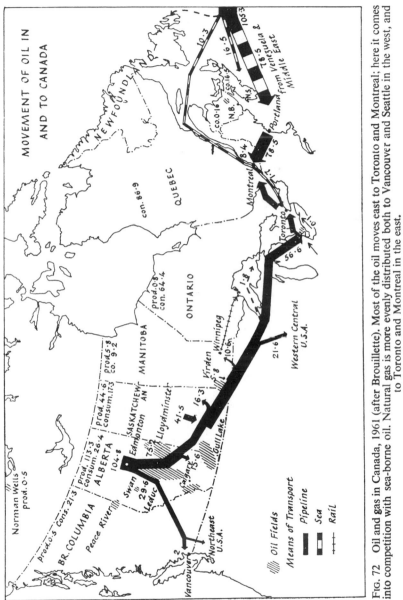

FIG. 72 Oil and gas in Canada, 1961 (after Brouillette). Most of the oil moves east to Toronto and Montreal; here it comes into competition with sea-borne oil. Natural gas is more evenly distributed both to Vancouver and Seattle in the west, and to Toronto and Montreal in the east.

thousand million barrels. The oil is piped to the industrial cities in southern Ontario at competitive rates (Fig. 72).

Natural gas is also found in abundance along the foothill fringe of western Alberta and in the Peace river area. It, too, can be transported easily and pipe-lines occur west to Vancouver and east to Toronto and Montreal. Natural gas should be an immense boon to many metallurgical, ceramic, glass, and chemical industries.

The ease of transportation of these fuels has meant that there has not been a mass movement of industry to the fields of production. Certain oil-refining, metal-concentrating, and chemical industries have grown up in the Prairies, as a result of the wealth of cheap fuel, but, in the main, oil and gas have moved to the existing industrial areas of Ontario and Quebec.

Metals and other minerals. While metallic ores and other minerals are fairly widely found in Canada, they tend to be concentrated in the Central Provinces which have long held the lead in Canadian mining, with nickel and copper at Sudbury, silver and cobalt at Cobalt, gold at Timmins, gold and copper at Rouyn-Noranda, and asbestos in the Eastern Townships. More recently iron at Steep Rock and also in the Ottawa valley, and along the great Labrador trough, together with quantities of titanium in eastern Quebec, have further strengthened this historic leadership (Fig. 73).

A rapid extension of mining, however, has occurred through northern Manitoba and Saskatchewan and in the North-west Territories, along the western edge of the Shield, while there has been much activity in New Brunswick and central Newfoundland in base-metal deposits in Appalachian structures.

Next to the Shield, the other great metalliferous structure in Canada is that of the Cordilleras. Gold in the Yukon and the Caribou mountains of British Columbia did much to open up the country. Today, silver is more important in the Yukon, and copper, lead, and zinc in British Columbia, in those regions already designated. Even more might be mined were it not for the general inaccessibility, rough terrain, and low population of much of this area.

Manufacturing in Canada has increased greatly in the last fifteen years to make Canada one of the twelve leading industrial countries of the world. There is still much room for expansion.

The vast quantities of machinery needed in the fishing, logging, lumbering, mining, and farming operations of today require either a large industrial output at home or good trading contacts abroad, or both.

To begin with, Canada was more or less content to import the machinery required, together with the many other articles needed, from Great Britain, France, Germany, or the United States, in exchange for the export of raw materials. This policy worked well enough as long as the population was so

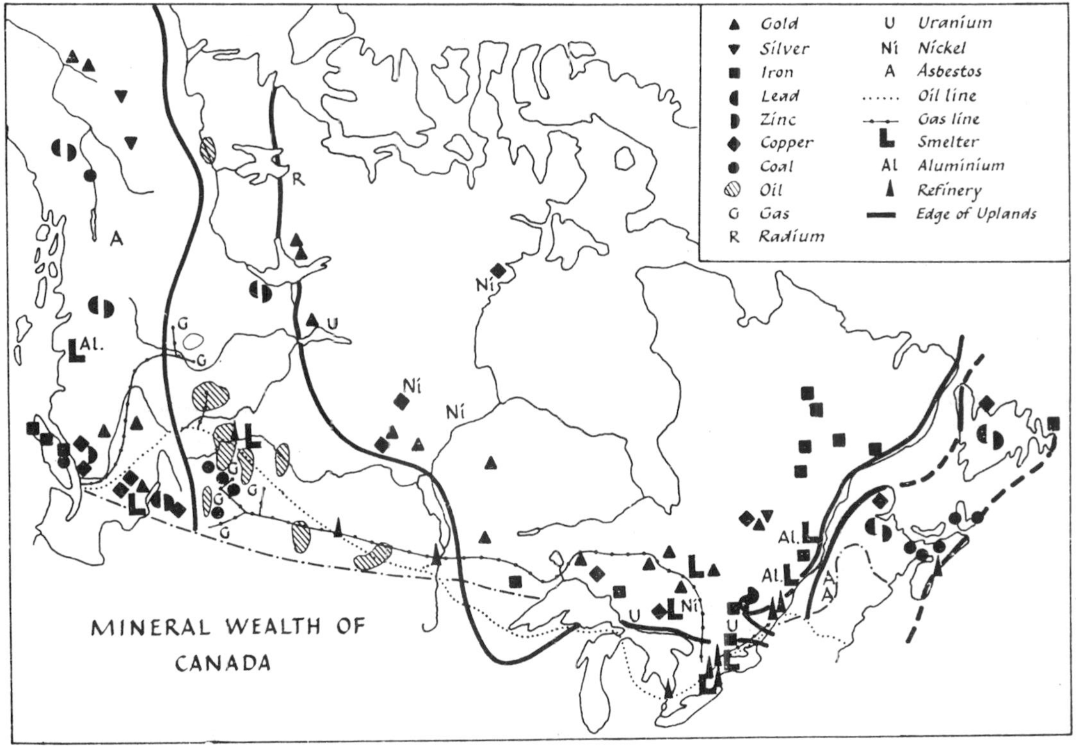

FIG. 73 The Mineral Wealth of Canada. The Shield is rich in metals; the Lowlands in fuels; the Appalachians and Cordilleras in both fuels and metals. The edge of the Shield and of the Cordilleras, with much hydro-electric power, are metal-refining areas. Oil refineries dot the Prairies and the Lower Lakes–St Lawrence plains. (Scale, 1:269 m.)

scarce that there was not the capital or labour to devote to secondary production. The country was opened up by producing fish, furs, wheat, meat, wood, and metals for sale in the great cities of western Europe or north-eastern United States.

However, as population grew, as savings were accumulated, as a pool of labour was formed, local initiative started to develop home industries that gradually competed with those from abroad and enabled Canadian mills to furnish the machines, tools, clothing, and housing required by the communities engaged in primary production. This at the same time enlarged the home market for Canadian raw materials. Eventually Canada came to process many of these materials and to send them out, in semi-finished form, or as consumer products, to the nations of the world. Its industry advanced beyond fulfilling its own needs to the stage of competing in world markets with those of Europe or the United States. In turn, this has strengthened Canadian trade, until Canada has become one of the great exporters, and is now the world's fourth trading nation.

Through this whole development Canada has learned what it could best produce itself and what it should best import. There has been a concentration on types of industry which, for one reason or another, proved most advantageous. Geographically, this has led to a concentration on the most advantageous sites for production. Canada does not try to make everything, everywhere; it capitalizes on optimum activities in optimum localities.

The *chief Canadian manufactures* are, in order of importance: (i) pulp and paper; (ii) slaughtering and packing of meat; (iii) smelting and refining of non-ferrous metals; (iv) motor vehicles; (v) petroleum products; (vi) saw mill products; (vii) butter and cheese; (viii) primary iron and steel; (ix) rolling stock; (x) flour mills. Items (i) pulp and paper and (vi) saw mills, represent the vast importance of Canada's forests; items (ii) meat packing, (vii) butter and cheese making, and (x) flour milling, point up the value of agriculture. Items (iii) non-ferrous products, (viii) ferrous products, and (v) petroleum, show the great significance of mining and allied activities. Items (iv) motor vehicles and (ix) rolling stock, show the large part that transportation plays in a country so huge in its proportions.

The manufacture of *forest products* is carried on chiefly in Quebec and Ontario, together with British Columbia, New Brunswick, and Newfoundland. Quebec is ideal for such activity, lying as it does across the Appalachians and the Canadian Shield. These forested areas experience little or no competition from agriculture; they lie in river basins with an ample water supply which also generates great quantities of hydro-electricity; they have the snowy winters to facilitate logging and the steep slopes that take the logs down to the mill; and they are very near the large markets in Montreal and other cities. Quebec manufactures about 45 per cent of the Canadian total of pulp and paper products and also has a fairly important saw mill industry.

Ontario is likewise important, with a large area of forest-covered Shield bordering on the Great Lakes, well supplied with logging streams and hydro-electric sites, and near to the great industrial centres of Toronto and Hamilton. In addition, thanks to Ontario's position, deep in the heart of the United States, it has access to even greater markets in New York, Buffalo, Detroit, and Chicago.

New Brunswick and Newfoundland have relatively little rich agricultural land to compete with forests and so devote a high proportion of their energies to logging and pulp and paper manufacturing. With heavy winter snows, numerous lakes and rivers, good hydro-electric sites, and a seaboard location, they possess both the facilities for logging and milling and the opportunity to contact rich overseas markets.

British Columbia, too, with much more mountain than plain, has a great area whose main, if not sole, potential is lumbering or logging. The fact that most of the economic forest is on the mountains of the coast, flanking the numerous fjords that penetrate far into the land, makes access to it relatively cheap and easy; timber can be boomed all up the coast and brought by tug to Vancouver and other milling centres. Most of the trees are tall evergreens with very tough wood. Consequently, saw-milling and the preparation or construction timber are the chief activities, surpassing pulp and paper manufacturing. Indeed, British Columbia accounts for 42 per cent of all the saw mill products of Canada.

The manufacture of *agricultural products*, though it might be thought to be widespread, is by no means as widely distributed as agriculture itself. Indeed, its chief activities, meat-packing, flour-making, and the preparation of cheese and butter are concentrated, to a remarkable extent, in Ontario and Quebec. For example, the Central Provinces account for about 69 per cent of the butter and cheese making, 55 per cent of the slaughtering and meat-packing, and 50 per cent of the flour-milling. This is due in part to the southerly latitude and great fertility of the Lower Great Lakes–St Lawrence lowlands, which have produced a local agriculture of high standing, specializing in dairying and the fattening of beef cattle. At one time, too, they were noted for their winter wheat, which still is an important cash crop. Yet, by and large, the region has been surpassed in its agriculture by the Prairies. Thus it contributes only 8 per cent of Canada's wheat crop today, compared with 91 per cent for the Prairies.

Industrial momentum helps to explain the lead of the Central Provinces. When they were still the agricultural heartland of Canada they established flour mills, packing houses, creameries, and cheese factories that were so efficient they continued to attract raw materials to them even after the west was opened up. So the greater part of western grain continued to be milled in central flour mills.

The chief reason, however, for the concentration of agricultural manufactures in the Central Provinces is the presence of the great market which exists there for food products. Not only this, but there are the widest commercial contacts possible with United States and European markets to dispose of the surplus that Ontario and Quebec cannot consume. The western and Atlantic provinces have, by comparison, a limited local market and fewer financial connexions overseas.

It should be pointed out, nevertheless, that since the Prairies have comparatively few other industries, meat-packing, butter and cheese making, and flour-milling are important for them. They are respectively the first, third, and fourth industries of Manitoba and of Alberta; and the third, fourth, and first industries of Saskatchewan. They are concentrated in the larger cities, such as Winnipeg, Edmonton, and Calgary.

Other *food* industries of importance are the canning of fruit and vegetables, concentrated at or near the Niagara peninsula, Ontario, the Annapolis valley, Nova Scotia, and the Okanagan valley, British Columbia; and the curing and canning of fish in Newfoundland, Nova Scotia, and British Columbia. Local geographical advantages explain their particular distribution.

The manufacturing of *mineral products* is another great field of Canadian activity. It is centred chiefly in the smelting and refining of gold, nickel, copper, lead, and zinc; in the making of iron and steel; and in the refining of petroleum and making of coal by-products.

Again the Central Provinces are in the front, accounting for 76 per cent of the refining of non-ferrous metals; 81 per cent of the primary iron and steel production; and 80 per cent of the products of petroleum and coal.

Once more this is partly due to a very favourable start, to industrial momentum maintaining the initial lead, to the presence of the biggest local market, and to widespread commercial connexions. Ontario and Quebec are fortunate in having the metal-bearing rocks of the Shield so close to their fertile and populous plains—all the way from Atikokan to Burnt Creek, from Red Lake to Chibougamou. Here the Shield comes nearest to the heartland of North America. Its products are closest to the great industrial cities which consume them in such quantity. Around the west end of Lake Superior are the iron ores of Steep Rock and the Minnesota ranges; these are more than matched by the iron of the Ungava trough, in Quebec–Labrador; the enormous nickel deposits of Sudbury are unique; and farther north is the gold and copper belt of northern Ontario and Quebec.

Being on the edge of the Shield these minerals are near to rivers with great catchment basins in the lake-riddled upland and with many cataracts in their descent to the plain. This, and a humid climate, provide large amounts of hydro-electric power for smelting. Ontario and Quebec are also near to the vast coal fields of Pennsylvania and so can readily obtain coking coal for smelting purposes. Limestone flux is secured from south-west Ontario. Thus the chief ingredients of a great metal industry are at hand. They can be brought together relatively cheaply by the Great Lakes–St Lawrence waterway, a fact accounting for the distribution of many of the refineries and metal mills at lake or river ports, such as Sault Ste Marie, Port Colborne, Hamilton, Toronto, Port Hope, and Montreal.

The chief asset of the St Lawrence area, however, is its position. On the east, from Montreal to Sept Iles, it commands the sea gates to the trade of Europe and the Atlantic States of U.S.A. On the west, from Toronto to Windsor, it commands the land gates to the vast plains and industrial might of the northern-central and mid-west States of the U.S.A. The area is linked by ancient glacial spillways such as the Champlain gap, the Mohawk valley, and the Maumee portage, with the Hudson, Ohio, and Mississippi rivers and all their thriving communities.

The chief metal industries outside of the Central Provinces are the iron and steel mills at Sydney, Nova Scotia, the base-metal smelter at Edmonton, and the base-metal smelter at Trail, British Columbia. These are strategically situated to make use of local iron and coal resources in Nova Scotia; natural gas in Alberta; nickel and copper from northern Manitoba and possibly lead and zinc from Great Slave Lake; and copper, lead, and zinc from the rich mines of southern interior British Columbia.

In addition, Canada has developed a great aluminium industry, making about a third of the world's aluminium, mainly in the basins of the Saguenay, Quebec, and Nechako–Kitimat, British Columbia. This has been done on the basis of a huge supply of cheap electricity and the ease of shipping materials to Canada and the finished product to Europe or the United States. Canada has no bauxite, the raw material from which aluminium is made: this is imported from British Guiana and Jamaica. It is Canada's plentiful power that is responsible for the industry.

The refining of petroleum and the making of by-products from petroleum and coal are also largely concentrated in the Central Provinces, even although these lack both petroleum and coal. They have the cities and the industries which use the products, however, and have long imported coal and oil from the near-by states of the U.S.A. or, in the case of oil, from the Caribbean and the Middle East. Here again the St Lawrence–Great Lakes waterway has been a boon in this regard, enabling the cheap assembly of raw materials in the heart of the country. More recently oil and natural gas have been piped in from the west.

However, with the opening up of western petroleum fields, the refining of petroleum products at Edmonton and Calgary and, to a lesser extent, at Regina and Winnipeg, has given rise to an important section of the industry in the Prairies. Refining at the coastal ports on the Pacific and Atlantic is important for their hinterlands.

The *chemical industry* of Canada has had a great impetus given it through the demands of the wood-products, agricultural, metal, and petroleum industries. Increasingly the world is in need of what are frequently called *ersatz* goods, such as rayon from wood or nylon from coal, plastics from wood, milk, or petroleum, and so forth. These are made through chemical processes. Meanwhile the strengthening, refinement, artificial amalgamation or preservation of metal, petroleum, wood, paper, fruit, and vegetable products require the use of many chemicals. Since such a large number of these industries is already established in the zone between Quebec City and Windsor, it is not surprising to find the chief chemical plants there, mainly at Montreal and Toronto, the Niagara peninsula, and at Sarnia.

The manufacture of *vehicles, rolling stock, ships, and transportation equipment* is another major Canadian enterprise. This is only to be expected in a country which is 3,500 miles wide. The unity and strength of the land depend to an unusual degree on its railways, internal and coastal shipping, its airways, and its trucking facilities. Canadians are also a very mobile people, travelling in great numbers, either on work or for recreation, and one of every three or four families has a car. The development of the north through freight-carrying planes has been one of the truly great Canadian epics and is unmatched anywhere else.

Not unnaturally the factories turning out planes, cars, engines, ships, rails, and related goods tend to cluster near the iron and steel centres, or where steel ingots, bars, or plates can be assembled cheaply. So we find them at Hamilton, Toronto, and Montreal, Windsor and Sorel, and associated points; mostly on the St Lawrence–Great Lakes waterway. From these central sites their products can be sent both west and east to other parts of Canada and to foreign markets.

The *industrial heartland* of Canada can be seen to be the lowlands of the St Lawrence and Lower Great Lakes. Their fundamental advantages include Place, Power, and People (Fig. 74). They are the most southerly parts of Canada and thus have the warmest and longest summers, with a fertile agriculture and a dense rural population. They are placed between the metal-rich Shield and the coal-rich Appalachians. They border the greatest forest area of the continent. They lie between overseas markets in the east (Europe and Atlantic America) and continental ones in the west (the Prairies and mid-west States). Southern Ontario is particularly well placed, thrusting a deep salient into the heart of America, to assure itself of U.S. supplies and to contact U.S. markets. River, canal, railway, and road are all concentrated in a narrow belt and thus maximize the advantages of good transportation.

The power resources of the region are derived from the vast amount of water in the Great Lakes basin feeding the waterfalls and rapids of the mighty St Lawrence. Moreover, the region lies along the edge of the Shield and of the Canadian Appalachians whence lake-fed, youthful rivers plunge down to the lowlands, over falls and cataracts. Thus a steady head of power stored up in big and numerous lakes, accompanied often by a high head of

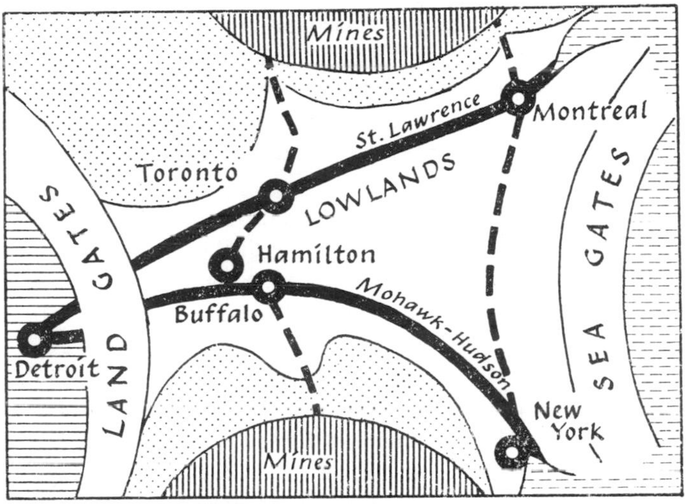

FIG. 74 The Advantages of southern Central Canada–athwart the two great gateways of eastern North America. A lowland, centred on a great waterway, with access both to the ocean and the continental interior, the region lies next to the forests and to the metal mines of the Canadian Shield, just north of it, and to the rich coal mines of the Appalachians, just to the south.

power, at waterfalls like those of Niagara, Shawinigan, and Shipshaw, make for cheap and plentiful hydro-electric power. The development of the International Rapids by Ontario and New York has assured still greater power supplies.

The people are the chief and final resource of the region. They consist of thrifty and industrious French Canadians, responsible and courageous United Empire Loyalist stock, adventurous and ambitious immigrants from Britain, the Low Countries, Germany, Italy, and Slavic lands. The result has been a most effective blending of many traditions and a high concentration of skill. The population is denser than in any other part of Canada. Indeed, over half the people of Canada live in the comparatively small triangle between Quebec City, Ottawa, and Windsor. One out of every ten Canadians lives in Montreal alone. Densities of over 200 people per square mile occur in nine counties along the St Lawrence–Great Lakes line.

Ontario and Quebec produce 81 per cent of all the goods made in Canada; Ontario making 53 per cent, Quebec 28 per cent. In fact, within the Commonwealth, this region ranks second only to the United Kingdom in manufacturing.

The *foreign trade* of Canada reflects both primary and secondary production. Until the Second World War, the main trade was in primary products, most of them to Great Britain. The United States still produced a surplus of most of the things that Canada raised, and therefore was not in a position to be a major customer. Canada bought much more from the U.S.A. than it sold to it. A three-way trade occurred in which Canada sold its wheat, fish, forest products, furs, and some metals to Britain, obtained dollars from Britain's earnings in the United States, and bought manufactured goods from the U.S.A.

After the Second World War the situation changed radically. Britain reduced its import of Canadian goods; sterling was not easily convertible; and the old triangular trade was disrupted. However, the U.S.A. began to be in need of the very products Canada had for sale. Great though U.S. resources were, they were no longer sufficient for the enormously expanding U.S. market. The U.S.A. became an importer of forest and mining products and even of agricultural goods. Nothing was more natural than that it should obtain these close at hand in Canada. Soon the U.S.A. replaced Britain as Canada's chief market. At the same time Canada's rapidly expanding economy has led it to widen its range of imports, both from the United States and Western Europe, and to sell its manufactured goods abroad. Canada's share of world trade is considerable for a country with its population and amounts to about 6 per cent, or just over half of that of the United Kingdom and about a third of that of the U.S.A.

The chief countries to which it exports its goods are, in order of importance: (i) the U.S.A.; (ii) the United Kingdom; (iii) Japan; (iv) Germany; (v) Australia; (vi) South Africa; (vii) Belgium, Luxembourg, and the Netherlands; (viii) Norway; (ix) France; and (x) Mexico. Those from which it imports most of its goods are: (i) U.S.A.; (ii) the United Kingdom; (iii) Venezuela; (iv) Germany; (v) Japan; (vi) India; (vii) Brazil; (viii) Netherlands West Indies; (ix) Belgium and Luxembourg; (x) Mexico.

The People of Canada

These outstanding economic developments, that so changed the geography of Canada, have been due in large measure to its people, and particularly to the white people, and, from amongst them, to the French and the British. That the transformation really was the work of Western culture may be seen by looking at what the aborigines were able to do with the land. This was not a great deal, although it played its part in the ultimate 'humanizing of the wilderness' (Fig. 75).

The *native races* of Canada consist of the American Indians and the Eskimoes. They are supposed to have entered the continent in early post-glacial times by the Bering Strait from the north-east Asia, and to have fanned out from Alaska across North America. Some of them followed the

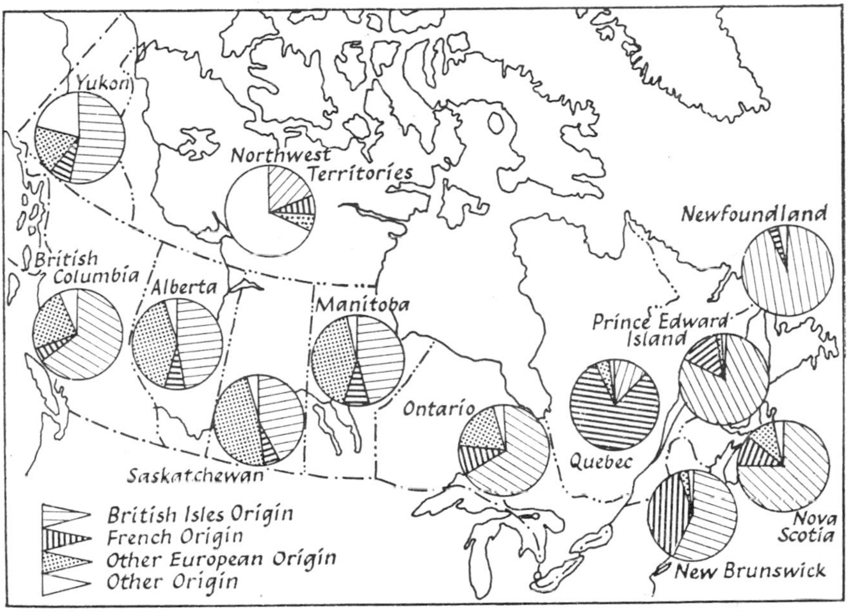

FIG. 75 The Ethnic Composition of the Canadian Population. In every Province are British and French; in most are other Europeans. This last group is most prominent in the Prairies, and in the cities of Ontario and British Columbia. Indian and Eskimo are unimportant save in the north.

Pacific and Arctic coasts and lived as fishermen. Some moved along the edge of the Rockies and, debouching on the grasslands of the Prairies, became buffalo hunters. Others followed the edge of the Shield, moving from one great lake to another by natural portages left by glacial spillways, and hunted deer in the boreal forest. Eventually these eastern hunters moved down into the warmer clime of the hardwood forests in whose glades they built towns and planted crops.

Moving into North America from the narrow apex of the continent, the incomers found more and more space for themselves, the farther they migrated. This tempted them to buy security with space and to continue in an extensive economy. As a result there was little incentive to use resources more efficiently and to change from hunting to herding or farming. Few

Indians settled down. They remained semi-nomadic down through the centuries.

Moreover, the farther they went into the continent the more isolated they became. The barriers of relief and climate gradually cut them off from each other. The Cordilleras cut off the Coast Indians from the Plains Indians. The forest reduced the contact between the Plains Indians and those of the Shield and the St Lawrence valley. The Appalachians tended to separate the latter from the tribes in the Maritimes, and the St Lawrence gulf cut off these from tribes in Newfoundland. The tundra separated the Indian from the Eskimo world. Thus there were not many trade or cultural exchanges, at any rate such as radically affected ways of life, and the peoples lived very much within the limits of their particular environment. It was not until the French, Dutch, and British came that the great tradeways developed and widespread changes in culture occurred.

Consequently, nomadism, an extensive economy, and comparative isolation, maintained a generally primitive mode of living right up to the fifteenth century when the white men first came to the land.

The impact of the Europeans was tremendous. It much improved methods of farming, hunting, or fishing; led to greater ease and comfort; and provided a wider division of labour and more opportunity for the individual. On the other hand, the ravages of the white man's diseases were considerable, while warfare became more lethal. In Newfoundland the whites destroyed the Indian (Beothuk) race.

For historic reasons, the whites and natives tended not to mix. By treaty the Indians were left with certain portions of the land to themselves, and to this day the bulk of them live in these 'reservations'. The Europeans came, on the whole, to work the land on their own and to supply the labour for their factories from their own ranks, and so did not draw upon the Indians for these tasks. Indians could leave their reservations and live, work, and move freely amongst the whites, marry with them, and adopt their ways if they liked; and, over the course of years, many have done this. Nevertheless, most of them have themselves maintained their separateness, carrying on as many of their old ways of life as were commensurate with living in a modern society.

European discovery long preceded settlement. The Norse have been credited with the discovery of Canada in the eleventh century, but they never colonized it. The British sponsored Cabot, an Italian adventurer, in his discovery of Newfoundland in 1497. Yet it was not until 1563 that fishing crews from Europe wintered on the island, and the first colony was not established until 1610. The first white child was not born until 1613. Similarly, although Cartier had explored part of the Labrador coast and the shores of the Gulf of St Lawrence, between 1534 and 1536, Quebec was not founded until 1608. Davis's exploration to Baffin Island in 1585, and Hudson's remarkable voyage of 1610–11 into and around Hudson Bay, were also abortive of settlement.

The reasons why colonization was so slow were partly the backwardness of the Indians, who did not have gold and silver to offer the British or the French, like their counterparts in the Caribbean; the severity of the environment, especially along the Newfoundland, Labrador, and Gulf of St Lawrence coasts—fog and winter ice were not very prepossessing, the mountainous or upland interior was frequently forbidding; and the psychology of the times—men explored Canada really to by-pass Canada. They were seeking the North-west Passage to the fabulous riches of the Far East. Whether they sailed up the coasts of Labrador, entered Hudson Bay and pierced Davis Strait, or whether they moved up the St Lawrence and finally burst upon the Great Lakes, they were seeking the western or southern sea, on which they hoped to launch their real fortunes. It was quite some time before the wealth of fish and fur, of farm and mine made men satisfied, and, indeed, anxious to settle the new land and make it theirs.

Initial European settlement was dominated by the French and the British, and early marked Canada out for that dualism of cultural development that has come to permeate its whole history, and set it off from other areas of the continent (Fig. 75). The way in which the British Isles extended out into the Atlantic from western Europe, as did Newfoundland from eastern North America, formed the geographical basis for the link between the motherland and its oldest colony. The westward thrust of France from the European mainland into the Atlantic also enabled it to take full part in the overseas expansion of Europe. This was matched, to a certain extent, by the outthrust of Nova Scotia from the mainland of North America, and the first French settlements were on that peninsula. Spirited rivalry did much to stimulate the exploration and early development of Canada; the British moved into it from Nova Scotia and New England, in the south, and from Hudson Bay, in the north; the French reached to its heart up the St Lawrence–Great Lakes route.

First impressions were of a land much colder, harsher, and more demanding than those which had been left. The fishing fleets from western England and from Brittany visited Newfoundland for nearly seventy years, took their catch and returned to Europe, before thinking of establishing permanent fishing communities in the New World.

It is to be remembered that there was, indeed, a considerable difference between the comparatively equable and mild west-maritime climates and the more extreme east-maritime ones in the northern latitudes. Nevertheless, after the initial *contrasts* were measured they became less significant than the essential *similarities*. Both western Europe and eastern Canada were glaciated regions; their daily weather, compounded of an everlasting flux between warm and cold fronts, was remarkably alike; they were covered with a mixture of hardwood deciduous and softwood coniferous forests, in which many of the species—pine, fir, oak, beech, elm—were the same; and they had not unsimilar, podsolized soil. The crops grown in western Europe could easily be transplanted to Canada and there be quickly acclimatized.

The British and French people had shown themselves to be amongst the most adaptive and progressive peoples of Europe, and so they very soon learned to adjust to the new environment. This adjustment was helped by the fact that the Indians had already mastered many of its elements and the whites, by using birch-bark canoes and snowshoes, planting corn, tobacco, and squash soon felt at home, by river and field.

Since most of the French settled beyond the Appalachians in the plains of the St Lawrence estuary and lower St Lawrence river, while most of the British were on the other side of the mountains, along the shores of Fundy and the Atlantic, the two peoples found separate cradlelands for development. In other wards, the geography of the New World reinforced that of the Old in keeping the two cultures distinct and competitive. This was all the more true after the expulsion of the Acadian French and their replacement by the British in the Maritimes.

The French found a relatively secluded area along the St Lawrence estuary and in the Montreal plain, protected to north and south by the Shield and the Appalachians. They rooted themselves so firmly in this that they soon felt a *national* attachment for their new homeland. They gradually spread outward—up the Richelieu, the St Lawrence, and the Ottawa valleys, making use of this web of rivers to extend their trade connexions, particularly into the interior.

Their outward spread, however, came into conflict with the inward movement of the British, as these at length crossed the Appalachians and began to debouch upon the interior lowlands. The British were led up the Hudson to Lake Champlain and up the Mohawk to Lake Ontario, thus converging on the St Lawrence lowlands. At the same time they began to move into the lower St John valley to challenge the French who were drifting through the Matapedia into its upper reaches.

Soon the incursions of the British were much increased and accelerated by the thronging of the United Empire Loyalists into the Maritimes, the Eastern Townships, the upper St Lawrence, and the Lake Ontario plains. Their footsteps were led very largely by geography. In the interior they had to move round the Adirondacks, or around Lake Ontario. Stopped by the French in the Richelieu valley, they found little opposition in the upper St Lawrence and Ottawa valleys and virtually none in the terrace lands fringing Lakes Ontario and Erie.

The British thus came to flank the French on the west, south, and east. In order, however, for the scattered British groups to carry on relations with each other, they depended on the good graces of the French. Thus the two peoples, interpenetrating each other in the way they did, and coming to rely on each other in the desperate struggle to create and assure Canadian identity against the expansionist tendencies of their southern neighbour, were no longer able to remain separate, but began that marriage of blood, mind, and effort which was to give birth to the Canadian nation.

In the north and west similarly, competition and conflict grew into co-mingling and co-operation. The swift spread west and north of French trade connexions by the Ottawa–Mattawa–Upper Great Lakes–Rainy river–Lake Winnipeg–Saskatchewan rivers impinged upon the spread south and west of British connexions up the Albany, or up the Nelson to Lake Winnipeg and the Red river, or west by Assiniboine and Saskatchewan. The historic struggles of the North-west Company and the Hudson's Bay Company which represented these ancient rivalries in a new way, did not end until their merger in 1821, and after that French and British lived side by side in growing dependence. This was particularly the case in the Red river valley. Their relations were disturbed by the Riel Rebellion but were cemented again by the threat of American expansion from the Great Plains into the Red river and the Short Grass prairies. Thus in the Prairie Provinces, as in the central ones and the Maritimes, the two peoples had to learn to make adjustments to each other.

Even in the far west, in British Columbia, British and French came together and developed the land side by side. The British had begun the settlement of this region, not from Ontario or Hudson Bay, but from fresh and independent bases on Vancouver Island and in the Fraser delta. Moving inland, they were met by other British on the long trek across the continent, and it seemed as if they would, together, make an essentially British colony. However, land-hungry French Canadians, moving across the northern pioneer fringe, entered the Peace river and there came to form a substantial element in British Columbia's tramontane lowland.

The question of British–French relations is too often considered in terms of Ontario and Quebec. It should be remembered, however, that in each of the provinces the two peoples live together. It should also be noted that each is a minority in some area or other (Fig. 75). In Quebec the British form a minority; in the other provinces, the French. Thus each has to learn the responsibilities and opportunities of being majority and minority groups. The result has been a gradual growing together until, instead of living in a state of coexistence, juxtaposed but separate, they have come a long way towards developing real unity, albeit respecting diversity. Undoubtedly geography has had a lot to do with this by preventing the physical separation of the two but, undoubtedly, a new geography has risen from this, enriched by both traditions.

The *mature settlement* of Canada, however, awaited the introduction of a third force, the immigration of new Canadians from other countries than the original motherlands. By far the greater proportion of these have been continental Europeans; but a few are Asiatics. Europeans other than French and British were not lacking in the initial peopling of the country. Many Pennsylvania Dutch, mostly Germans who had settled in Pennsylvania, came over shortly after the American revolution, settling in southern Ontario, on their way out west. Germans, too, peopled parts of Nova Scotia and made a great contribution to the fishing industry there. Nevertheless the main tides swept in with the opening up of the West, or more recently with the vast industrial and urban expansion in the Central Provinces.

The Prairies were very slow in being settled. This was partly the result of their remoteness, but it was also due to their comparative aridity and to the fact that they formed a new environment. Would-be settlers from the east found the summers distinctly shorter and drier and the winters longer and more severe. Eastern grains, grasses and clovers, the eastern rotation of crops and eastern fruits either failed or did not do too well. Drought- and frost-resistant crops had to be developed and the arts of conserving surface moisture and of summer fallowing had to be learned. Moreover, there was a scarcity of wood for building homes, barns, and fences, for fuel and other purposes.

It was not till the railways crossed the Prairies in the early 'eighties that extensive settlement was attracted. Then all kinds of goods could be brought in, to overcome the limitations mentioned, and produce might be shipped out; isolation was at an end, and cheap or even free land was available. In the late 'nineties and the first decade of this century world prices for agricultural produce were high. European industry could not absorb all the surplus population of that teeming continent. A great influx of immigrants occurred, reaching a peak in 1913 when 400,000 people entered Canada.

A large number of these settled in the Prairie Provinces. Since there were comparatively few British and French, the new-comers soon bulked very large in the population and altered its whole composition. They swamped the French, becoming the second force in the region. In Saskatchewan they came almost to equal the British.

Many also settled in the cities of Ontario, but here British immigration and the natural increase in the basic British stock kept in pace, so that the balance of the population was not affected as much. The presence of the new-comers in cities and camps in British Columbia and the Atlantic Provinces, though less important, has not been without significance. The 'old' Canadian, in every part of the nation, has had to accept the 'new' Canadian into full and equal partnership.

In terms of dominant stock, Canada is British at the Atlantic and Pacific coasts and in the centre of the country, French in Quebec, and cosmopolitan in the Prairies. Such a geographical distribution prevents a grossly unequal division of the nation but, on the contrary, keeps the several ethnic groups dependent on each other. This is all the more true when it is realized that

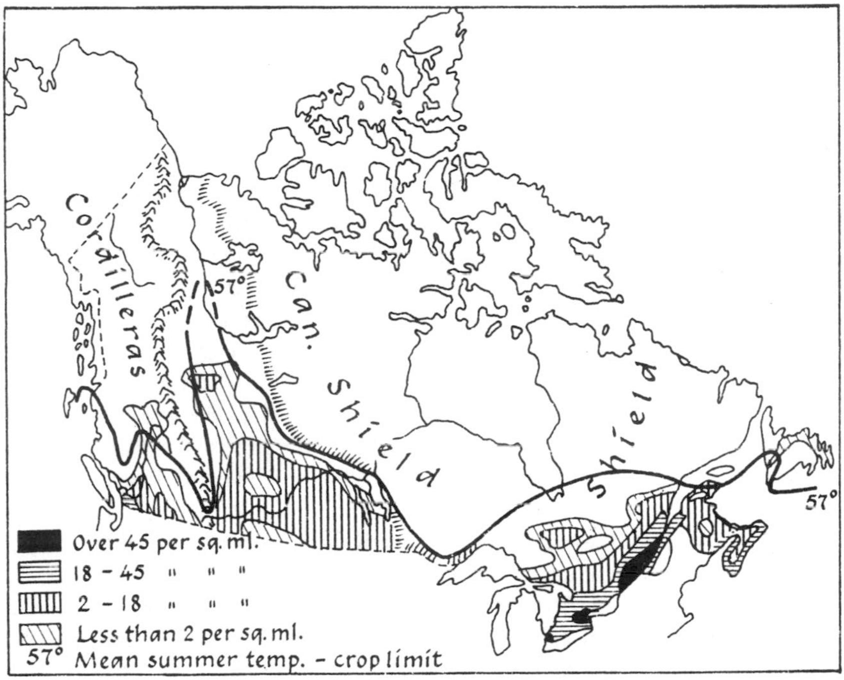

FIG. 76 The distribution of population densities in Canada, in relation to major physical controls. Most of the population lies in the warm-summer zone. The Shield and the Cordilleras make great breaches in the continuity of dense settlement. (Scale, 1: 55 m.)

representatives of each of the three great forces—British, French, and other Europeans—are to be found in significant numbers in most of the provinces.

Other characteristics of the population show Canada to be a predominantly youthful, male, and urban nation, in active growth. About two-thirds of the Canadian people are under thirty-five years of age. There is, thus, a higher than usual number of active, productive, and ambitious individuals. This is particularly apparent in the expanding north and in some of the rapidly growing cities, across the country (Fig. 76).

Although for long a rural nation, engaged chiefly in primary production, Canada has recently become a predominantly urban community, engaged more in industry and trade. The farm population now constitutes only about 12 per cent of the total; other rural population, 18 per cent; leaving 70 per cent urban. Actually, these figures do not show the real picture because much of rural Canada has adopted essentially urban standards and ways. In fact, that is the great reason for the increasing urbanization. Canadians are everywhere mechanizing their production, concentrating their efforts, developing more specialized skills and forms of labour, and adopting more efficient and comfortable standards of living.

The result has been that the rural areas develop with the least compatible amount of manpower: this is multiplied by machines and services made and developed in the city. Medical, legal, insurance, banking, and other services, once scattered in small and possibly inefficient units over wide areas, tend to be concentrated at the city; and the same is true of engineering, construction, repair and maintenance services. Consequently as farming and other rural occupations improve they favour a greater emphasis on the city. That is why even in provinces like British Columbia, or Manitoba, where the general prosperity springs from primary production in mining and lumbering and farming, about half the total population reside in a single large centre. Even in Quebec, which many think of as a typically rural province, one out of every three people lives in the one centre, greater Montreal.

On a provincial basis, the Atlantic and Prairie Provinces are still the most rural; the Central Provinces and British Columbia the most urban. Actually Newfoundland, Prince Edward Island, and New Brunswick are still predominantly rural; as is Saskatchewan in the West. But even in these there is a rapid growth of the major cities. Ontario and Quebec, as one would expect from their key position at the centre of Canada's transportation system, and from the way in which they dominate Canadian manufacturing, are the most highly urbanized centres. Greater Montreal, now over 2 millions, and greater Toronto, nearing that mark, are amongst the major cities of the continent. More and more, the metropolis is guiding and dominating the geographical development of the country.

As a matter of fact, in Canada, metropolitan growth has been greater than that of the frontier, at least since the beginning of the century. Even in the first decade, when, with the opening of the West, the agricultural population grew as it never had before—indeed, literally exploded—

> as many people were added to the aggregate population of Montreal, Toronto, and Winnipeg as to all the rural areas of Saskatchewan and Alberta combined. Manufacturing plants as far east as the Sydney steel mills hummed with activity, turning out goods to build the rail lines and equip the farms of the new wheat economy. In the 'twenties when development had shifted to the northern forest and mining frontier, and a score

> of communities such as Flinflon, Noranda, and Kapuskasing were appearing on the map, the *big* additions nevertheless took place in the industrial and commercial centres.
>
> In the period since the war, when the development of natural resources has been more widespread than ever before, the story is the same. New settlements have boomed all across the frontier—Murdochville in the Gaspé, Schefferville and Seven Islands in Quebec, Manitouwodge in northern Ontario, Lynn Lake in Manitoba, Uranium City in northern Saskatchewan, and Kitimat on the British Columbia coast, to name only some of the better known. In addition pulp and paper towns in both east and west have grown rapidly, and numerous small communities in Alberta that had stood still for twenty years have doubled in size since the oil boom. But much as it fires the imagination, this population growth on the frontier bulks very small beside that in the metropolitan communities.[1]

By mid-century about one out of every four people in Canada lived in the greater urban areas of Montreal, Toronto, Vancouver, and Winnipeg; one out of every three in cities of over 100,000; and three out of every four in cities of over 50,000 (see Fig. 66, Chapter 8).

Finally, it should be pointed out that, as a result of Canada's great social and economic progress, and of the physical possibilities for even further advance, the country as a whole is growing very rapidly. Its current rate of increase is 2·1 per cent per annum, one of the highest overall rates. This compares with a rate of 1·7 per cent for India, 1·35 per cent for the U.S.A., and 0·6 per cent for Great Britain. Indeed, few nations are expanding more rapidly. This derives from the great natural resources of the land, and the way they have been used, not only through expanding systems of primary production, but also through marked developments in manufacturing and trade. It represents a stage of national growth in which at last Canada can be said to have overcome its major limitations, and shown itself ready to exploit to the full its many advantages.

Conclusion

Although Canada is a small nation, its geography will not let it alone, but having tested it with a severe climate, with a formidable terrain, and the strain of sheer distance, has brought it into the forefront of events, given it a strategic position of the first order, challenged it with its emptiness and girded it about with opportunity. And the people have responded; they have

[1] *The Trend to Bigger Cities*, Monthly Review of the Bank of Nova Scotia, Toronto, July 1955. Also *Recent Population Changes*, Rev. B. of N.S., May–June, 1962. '60% of Canadian population growth in 1951–61 has accrued to the large metropolitan centres', p. 3.

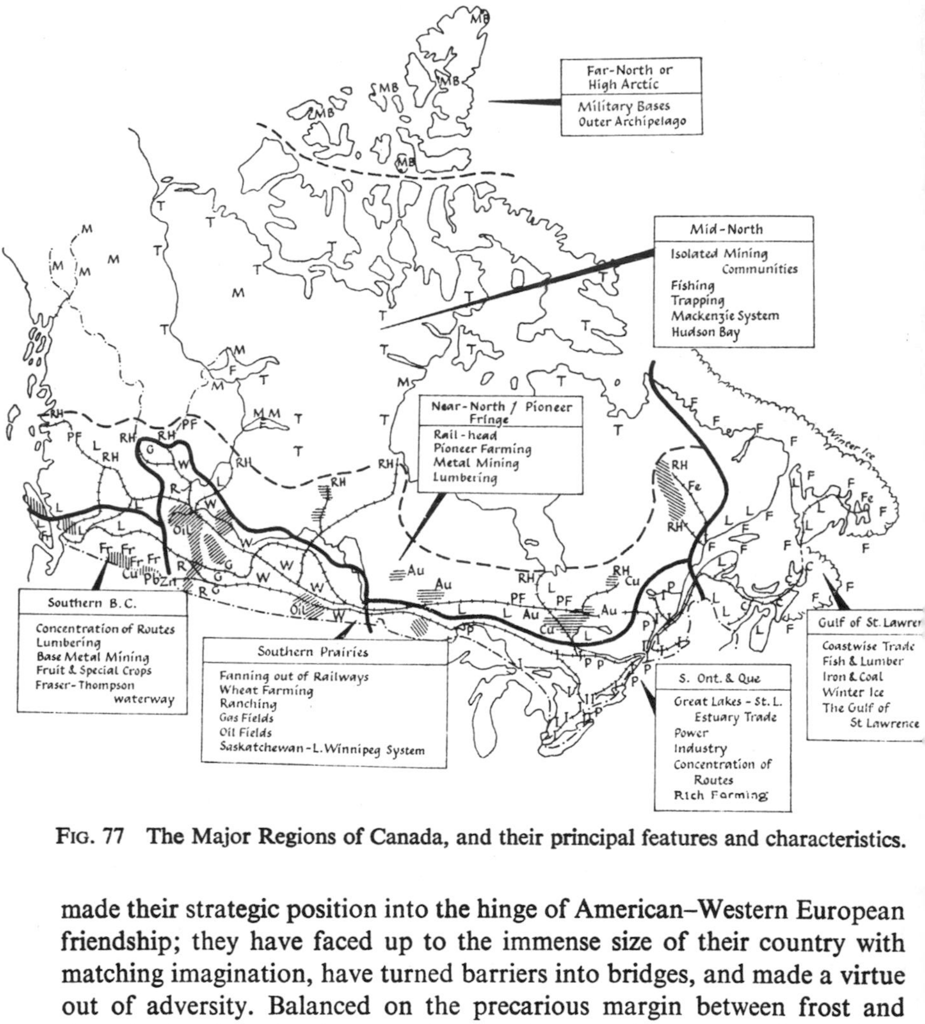

FIG. 77 The Major Regions of Canada, and their principal features and characteristics.

made their strategic position into the hinge of American–Western European friendship; they have faced up to the immense size of their country with matching imagination, have turned barriers into bridges, and made a virtue out of adversity. Balanced on the precarious margin between frost and drought they have bred new grains to take care of the one, and organized new farming methods to defeat the other. With nothing but rock for their heartland they have turned it into such wealth that it bids fair to become the core of their economy. Divided by blood and belief they have nevertheless achieved a unity, based on a bi-cultural way of life, which has set their own particular stamp upon the land; a country made rich by its difficulties, and strong by its differences. Place and people have become fused at last into a reality that testifies, by its vigorous growth, its birth to power (Fig. 77).

CHAPTER ELEVEN

Canada: The Atlantic Region

The section of Canada first settled and developed by Europeans was the Atlantic region; in 1497 Cabot discovered Newfoundland for the British, and in 1534 Cartier sailed into the St Lawrence Gulf and claimed its shores for France. The French hold was further strengthened by Champlain's work in the Bay of Fundy, where he discovered the mouth of what is now the St Croix river, in 1604, and, with de Monts, established the first European settlement in Canada at Port Royal (now Annapolis Royal) at the mouth of the Annapolis river, in 1605. The two nations made separate inroads on the region and, indeed, contested it bitterly between them. In the main the French settled the inner side, fringing the Gulf of St Lawrence, while the British occupied the outer edge, from Nova Scotia, through eastern Newfoundland, to the coast of Labrador. But in the eighteenth century they began to interpenetrate each other's spheres;[1] the British displaced the Acadian French around the Minas basin and moved inland, up the St John river, into New Brunswick. The French built Louisburg, Cape Breton Island, on the Atlantic coast, and tried to lay claim to Labrador, or at any rate the southern part of it.

With the conquest of New France by the British, internal strife virtually ceased (except for the claims and counterclaims of Quebec and Newfoundland for lower Labrador). Gradually the two great peoples turned their faces to becoming one. This was made somewhat easier by the threat from the United States during the American Revolution and later during the war of 1812–14. The challenge from without helped to create unity within, and soon British and French settled down to a life of mutual respect, tolerance, and co-operation that, in the Maritimes and Quebec, was different from anything else on the Atlantic coast, and developed something typically Canadian.

Cultural diversity and unity were matched by physical variety and integration. Variety is present in the different structures, air masses, ocean currents, soils, and types of vegetation found in the region. Integration is provided by the common history of glaciation, by the convergence of storm tracks on the area, and, above all, by the ubiquitous seas and the mingling of their waters.

---

[1] Bird, J. B., 'Settlement Patterns in Maritime Canada, 1687–1756', *Geog. Rev.*, 1955, xlv, no. 3, pp. 385–404.

In the main, the physical environment is a marginal or difficult one, dominated as it is by rugged uplands; and by polar air masses giving rise to a raw climate with heavy winter snows; by the dominance of cold currents and ice-cluttered coasts; and by acid soils. However, the uplands have considerabje mineral wealth, the climate provides a good supply of water for hydro-electric schemes, the currents, where they mix, stimulate marine life, and the soils have a wide range of texture that, where limed and drained, support a varied agriculture. Thus there are not a few opportunities with which to offset the limitations.

THE PHYSICAL ENVIRONMENT

The structure of the region brings together three of the principal features of the continent, the Canadian Shield, the Interior Lowlands, and the Appalachian mountains. The Shield runs from the coast of Labrador (Newfoundland) through to the north shore of the Gulf of St Lawrence (Quebec). That Gulf consists in part of the drowned trough of the Interior Lowlands, of which Anticosti Island is a surface survival. In part, the Gulf is made up of drowned lowlands belonging to the Appalachians. This system sweeps through the Maritime Provinces to the Island of Newfoundland. The whole area has been shattered by faulting, depressed, and invaded by the sea, and it is the sea, particularly in the Gulf of St Lawrence, that links all its parts together, and has helped man to make this into a distinctive region.(Indeed the importance of the Gulf made Hewelcke, in his discussion of the Regions of Canada, refer to this as the Gulf Region.)[1] (Fig. 2, Chapter 1.)

In the north the area is marked by the great Ungava trough, extending southward from Ungava Bay to the divide between Atlantic and gulf rivers. This is a deep, wide depression which began as a geosyncline in upper Huronian time. At first accumulating great depths of sediments—in which iron-rich formations occur—it later experienced moderate folding, the intrusion of granites, and extensive faulting. At the end of Animikie time ranges of low mountains flanked the trough, but these became worn to a rough-topped plateau, about 2,000 feet in height. The whole plateau was tilted up eastward to end in a high, abrupt edge facing the sea. At its highest the up-tilt has produced the Torngat mountains, rising to 5,500 feet. These have been cut by cirques and valley glaciers into sharp ridges divided by profound valleys, often flooded by the sea to form long, steep-sided fjords. Southwards the Shield drops in height (Kaumajet mountains, 4,000 feet; Mealy mountains, 3,700 feet; the Labrador Height of Land, 2,000 to 2,400 feet) until, overlooking the Gulf of St Lawrence (Bradore hills), it is little more than 1,500 feet. But throughout, it breaks in a sharp, though much indented

[1] Hewelcke, G., 'Eleven Regions of Canada', *Can. Geog. Jour.*, 1950, xli, pp. 84–89.

scarp, and is very rocky and rugged. In Palaeozoic times, when the Appalachians were being folded up against it, the Shield was involved in warping and faulting, often along west–east trends that cut across the older south-south-east to north-north-west trends.

It is thought that in Cretaceous times the Shield was reduced to a peneplain, but in mid-Pliocene it was uplifted and once again warped and faulted. A major west–east depression was created in the Lake Melville–Double Mer 'graben', or down-faulted trough, which opens out into the Hamilton inlet. Above it rises the fault-faced 'horst' of the Mealy mountains. The sharp southern scarp of the Shield, towering above the St Lawrence Gulf, is due, in many sections, to faulting, where movement was renewed probably several times.

A number of the larger rivers, and in particular the Hamilton, maintained their courses as the Shield slowly rose; this meant that they cut down very deeply. In post-glacial times the slow upward movement of the Shield has led to further down-cutting, with the result that most streams flow in deep, narrow valleys, often interrupted by waterfalls. Grand Falls, on the Hamilton river, sees a spectacular plunge of water, 245 feet high, into a profound gorge. Although the lower ends of many rivers are drowned, the estuaries are lined by recent raised beaches.

The Shield ends abruptly at the waters of the Gulf. These all but bury the structure known as the Interior Lowlands stretching, farther west, between Shield and Appalachians. But a relic remains in Anticosti Island, a long, narrow cigar-shaped feature, low at the sides but rising to a broad-backed upland of about 800 feet in the centre. It is made up of relatively flat sedimentary beds of limestone interbedded with shale and some conglomerates—Ordovician in the north, and Silurian in the south.

Southward rise the mountains, basins, and plateaux of the Canadian Appalachians, cut into islands and peninsulas by the deep invasion of the seas (Fig. 78).

Formed in two great geosynclines, the Caledonian and the Acadian, with a broad mass in between pierced by crystalline instrusives, the area consists of a complex series of ridges and depressions. A major arc of folded highlands, in part of Cambrian but mainly of Ordovician rock, sweeps through the Eastern Townships of Quebec and the Gaspé peninsula. Its trend is carried on and then changed in a sinuous curve through the upper Long Range of western Newfoundland Island. In the Eastern Townships the fold belt consists of three parallel ridges; the Sutton Mountain anticline (rising to Round Top Mountain, 3,175 feet), a continuation of the Green mountains of Vermont; the Stoke Mountain anticline; and the Megantic anticline, part of the White Mountain system of New Hampshire. These all rise out of a broad plateau, called the Eastern Quebec Upland, of from 900 to 1,000 feet,

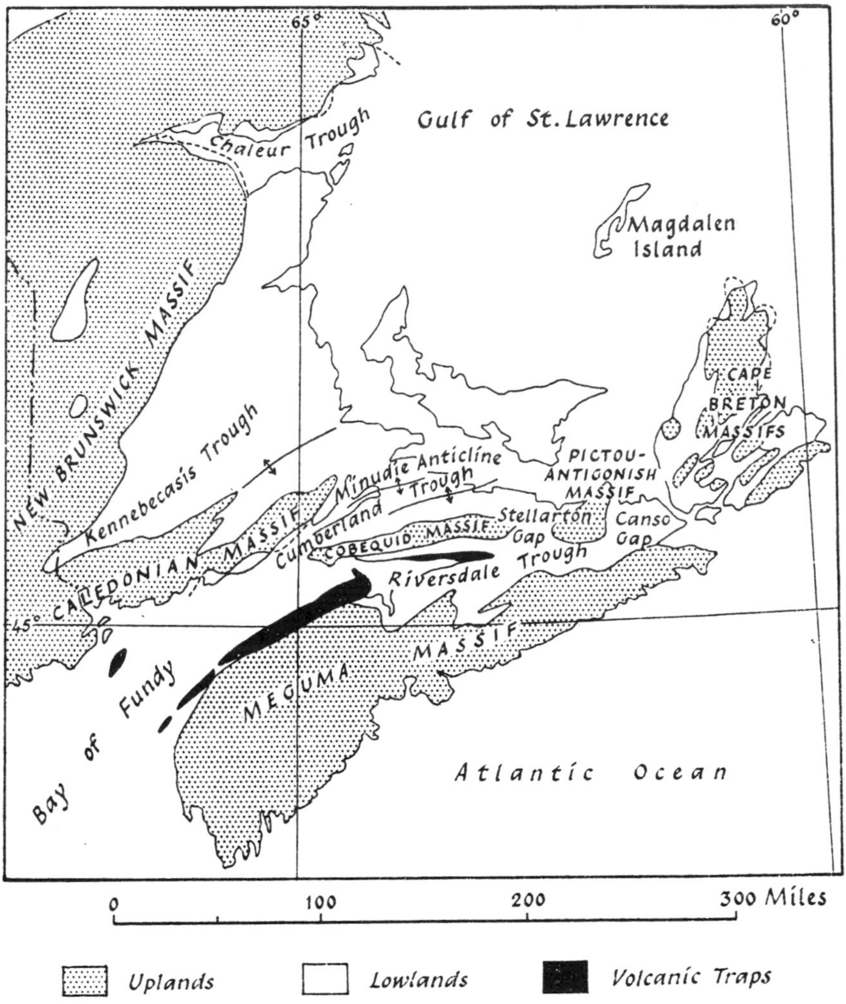

FIG. 78 The Structure of the Maritimes. (From King.)

and themselves have flattish summits, of over 3,000 feet, which appear to be relics of former peneplains. North-eastward, a single great belt of folding occurs in the Notre Dame range of the Gaspé peninsula, rising to 4,160 feet in Mt Jacques Cartier, in the flat peneplaned mass of the Shickshock mountains. The extraordinary evenness of some of the summits, notably of Tabletop Mountain, is eloquent of the prolonged erosion suffered since Ordovician times. Roughnesses are now due principally to ice action in the Pleistocene, or to post-glacial frost action which has produced large stone circles and stripes.

In the western peninsula of the Island of Newfoundland the Caledonian fold belt continues, between Cape St George and Bauld Cape. In the south, between St George's Bay and Bonne Bay, it comprises a number of igneous intrusions thrusting through uplands of Ordovician rock. These form blocky, steep-sided, flat-topped, isolated masses, such as Table Mountain (2,300 feet) and the Blow-me-Down mountains (2,135 feet). Northwards is a continuous narrow strip of highlands, the Long Range, which is rather higher in elevation (Gros Morne, 2,666 feet). It rises very steeply on the west side along a major thrust-line where older metamorphic rocks were pushed westward over younger Palaeozoic beds. Dipping gently to the east, it is terminated abruptly at a parallel fault along the coast of White Bay, marked by steep rocky cliffs of up to 500 feet.

This western, outer line of highlands (from the Eastern Townships to Newfoundland's north-west peninsula) is cut off from a central group of highlands by a well-marked depression followed by the Restigouche river, the Baie de Chaleur, the waters of the Gulf, and by the trough of Grand Lake and White Bay.

Southward rise a series of uplands or highlands enclosing notable basins. First and largest of these are the highlands of New Brunswick which form a V-shaped mass, running from south of the Restigouche to the Bay of Fundy and thence along the north Fundy shore. In the main they consist of great granitic or other igneous domes pushing up through surrounding sandstones, limestones, and shales. The largest of these is the Mt Carleton (2,690 feet) dome, from which the tributaries of the Restigouche, St John, and Miramichi rivers drain away in an outstandingly radial pattern. The Fundy highlands are composed of highly folded metamorphosed rocks—some of them late Proterozoic and Cambrian, as well as the prevailing Ordovician—together with igneous intrusions.

In the centre of the V of highlands lies the chief plain of New Brunswick, a basin of Pennsylvanian rocks, opening out, across the shallow interruption of Northumberland Strait, to the gently rolling lowland of Carboniferous-Permian beds of Prince Edward Island. This considerable basin forms the main basis for any extensive development of farming in the Atlantic provinces. It also contains small coal fields.

East and south of it are the principal ridges and depressions of the Acadian system, in places mountainous, but on the whole bevelled off to make an Atlantic upland. A sinuous string of highlands, of from 1,000 to 2,000 feet, runs from the upper end of the Bay of Fundy to Confusion Bay (Newfoundland). It is interrupted by the Strait of Canso and by Cabot Strait. It is made up of the steep-sided but round-topped Cobequid mountains; the Antigonish highlands, broken into isolated groups; the northern tableland of Cape Breton Island, which offers a fairly even surface of about

1,200 feet cut across a variety of Mississippian-Pennsylvanian rocks; and the lower Long Range and Annieopsquotch highlands of Newfoundland, continued northward into the Dunamagon highlands about Baie Verte. The higher points of these, Table Mountain (1,700 feet), Main Topsail (1,822 feet), and Hinds Hill (2,158 feet), slope up to a peneplain that is little inferior in height to that of the upper Long Range.

Associated with this long string of highlands are numerous small basins or troughs, such as the Cumberland lowland, the Inverness basin, the Bras d'Or basin, and, in Newfoundland, the Cape St John plain. The first two of these have significant though small coal fields.

East and south again lies the Atlantic upland which, though it includes some of the most varied rocks and formations, from the Precambrian schists and quartzites of eastern Newfoundland and Cape Breton islands, through the Cambrian, Ordovician, and Silurian sandstones, quartzites, shales, and slates of central Newfoundland and eastern Nova Scotia, nevertheless presents a remarkably even-topped appearance, averaging about 800 feet in height. In Nova Scotia the region comprises the Triassic volcanics of North Mountain, the highly metamorphosed fold ridges of South Mountain, with the fertile Annapolis valley and Minas basin between them; and the Precambrian granitic domes, dolomitic limestones, and gneisses of the eastern hills of Cape Breton, going down to the coal-rich basin of Glace Bay. In the Island of Newfoundland the region embraces the central high plateau, reaching up to 1,200 feet (Mt McCormack), and also the low rocky uplands of the Burin and Avalon peninsulas of from 800 to 600 feet. It passes beneath the sedimentary plain of the Grand and Gander estuaries and island-thick Notre Dame Bay.

A striking aspect of the Atlantic region is the unity of structure which, providing a remarkable parallelism in trend from the Eastern Townships to southern Labrador, and from southern Nova Scotia to the eastern peninsulas of Newfoundland, and giving rise to a basic similarity of relief, has afforded a strong foundation for the regional consciousness it now enjoys. The interlocking of great plateaux and down-folded or faulted basins and the interpenetration of land and sea, assist each part of the region to repeat conditions experienced in every other part. (This has helped to explain the interleaving of French and British traditions as their settlements were grooved one into another. Here then history and geography supported and reinforced each other.)

Another striking thing about the region, from Labrador to Nova Scotia, is the dominance of flat or round-topped summits; there are very few sharp peaks or edges, and these are mainly due to the erosion of the tablelands by ice in Quaternary times. The widespread occurrence of long, even summits led Goldthwait to postulate the presence of a great Atlantic peneplain which once gave unity to the whole area. He considered this to have become warped and then broken up by faulting and by the invasion of the sea, but visualized a broad unitary surface sloping from the 3,700 to 4,200 feet summits of Labrador and the Shickshock mountains, through the 2,400 to 2,600 feet summits of central New Brunswick and western Newfoundland Island, to the 1,200 feet plateau of Cape Breton, and the 800 foot upland of South Mountain and of the Avalon peninsula.[1] It may, however, be more appropriate to think of these levels as relics of a series of peneplains. Alcock speaks of the flat surfaces of the Cape Breton tableland, the Caledonian mountains (Fundy highlands) of southern New Brunswick, and the Shickshock mountains as 'parts of an uplifted peneplain that may have been formed as early as Cretaceous time. This was later uplifted and a second erosion level was produced in Tertiary time on the area underlain by softer rocks. The lowland belts of Nova Scotia and New Brunswick and the lower upland surface of Gaspé, known as the Gaspé peneplain to distinguish it from the higher upland or Shickshock peneplain, are parts of this younger erosion surface.'[2]

Yet another characteristic of the section, which gives it a certain unity, is the common glaciation it experienced from an ice-sheet moving south and eastward from central Labrador. All the highlands and uplands are grooved, striated, and plucked by ice; most of the uplands and lowlands are plastered by till and are often pocked with kettles or mounded with drumlins; while many of the valleys have been deepened and widened by glaciers and then ridged with kame terraces or festooned with kame moraines where the dead ice rotted away. Sandy deltas pushed into glacial lakes or seas, while outwash plains, spreading beyond valley moraines, are also typical, especially of the lower eastern fringe.

The ice seems to have pushed outward from a great glacial divide, roughly between lakes Michikamau and Kaniapiskau, and to have sent vast streams or lobes eastward over the coast of Labrador, south-eastward across Newfoundland Island, south-south-east over Nova Scotia, and southwards to south-south-east over the tops of the Shickshocks across the uplands and plains of New Brunswick. As the major ice-sheet waned, local ice-caps emerged, as for example in central Newfoundland, the Long Range peninsula, the central highlands of New Brunswick, and in the Notre Dame mountains.

Finally, there is the unity given to the region by the marine terraces which fringe all its coasts from the Labrador Sea to the Bay of Fundy. Wherever

---

[1] Goldthwait, J. W., *The Physiography of Nova Scotia*, Mem. **140**, Geol. Surv. of Canada, Ottawa, 1924.

[2] Alcock, F. J., 'The Appalachian Region', *Geology and Economic Minerals of Canada*, Econ. Geol., Ser. **1**, Geol. Surv. of Canada, Ottawa, 1947, p. 134.

soft rocks or glacial debris occur along the shore these stranded, wave-cut benches form outstanding features. The main beach terrace is usually at 50 to 75 feet, but Tanner in Labrador and Campbell in Nova Scotia describe a well-marked 150-foot level, particularly in evidence where it cuts across the soft sand beds of old deltas (like that of the Hamilton river) or of glacial kames or outwash (as in the Minas basin).[1] Actually, strand lines at 250 or even 300 feet are found all along the Atlantic coast; while in the Gulf of St Lawrence and the St Lawrence estuary even higher ones, from 400 to 600 feet, have been noted.[2] The use of the lower sea beaches for the siting of settlements is still another thing that the region has in common.

The Climate. Although the climate of the section is one of conflict, indeed of the concentration of conflict, this fact in itself gives character and unity to the region. Here is a clash of polar continental and maritime air masses, together with the invasion of Tropical Gulf or Atlantic air streams, which is different from most in that it draws together the leading storm tracks of the continent and concentrates them in a unique way. The polar continental air mass dominates the scene. In doing so it spreads out from Labrador across the whole region for a large part of the year to make it distinctly more cool and much more continental than it might be considered to be, having regard to its latitude, and to its maritime position.

The maritime air masses are, in the main, less effective. The polar Atlantic air, associated with the Icelandic Low, is generally well off the east coast. Air streams blowing into the Low are moving *away* from the Atlantic region. Meanwhile, air streams from the Tropical Gulf air mass, which move up the Mississippi–Ohio, often tend to die out before reaching the Gulf. The movement of tropical Atlantic air around the nose of the Bermuda High, which can bring such hot, muggy, oppressive weather to the Atlantic coast plain, likewise frequently fails to reach the Maritimes. All these air masses do help to create disturbances around the edge of the polar continental system, but it is this last that forms the key to the situation (Fig. 79).

As a result coolness is marked. Labrador, for instance, which has a latitudinal span of roughly between London and Lerwick, in Britain, has average January temperatures of about 10° F. in the south (51° 30′ N.) and −10° F. in the north (60° N.), compared with 39° F. and 34° F. for similar places in Britain. January averages for southern Nova Scotia, 30° F., are 17 degrees below those for southern France, 47° F., in the same latitude. This is due, of course, not only to the prominence of Pc air, but also to

---

[1] Tanner, V., 'Outline of the Geography, Life, and Customs of Newfoundland–Labrador', *Acta Geographica*, **8**, no. 1, Helsinki, 1944, p. 245.

[2] Cooke, H. C., 'The Canadian Shield', *Geology and Economic Minerals of Canada*, Econ. Geol., Ser. **1**, Geol. Surv. of Canada, Ottawa, 1947, p. 35.

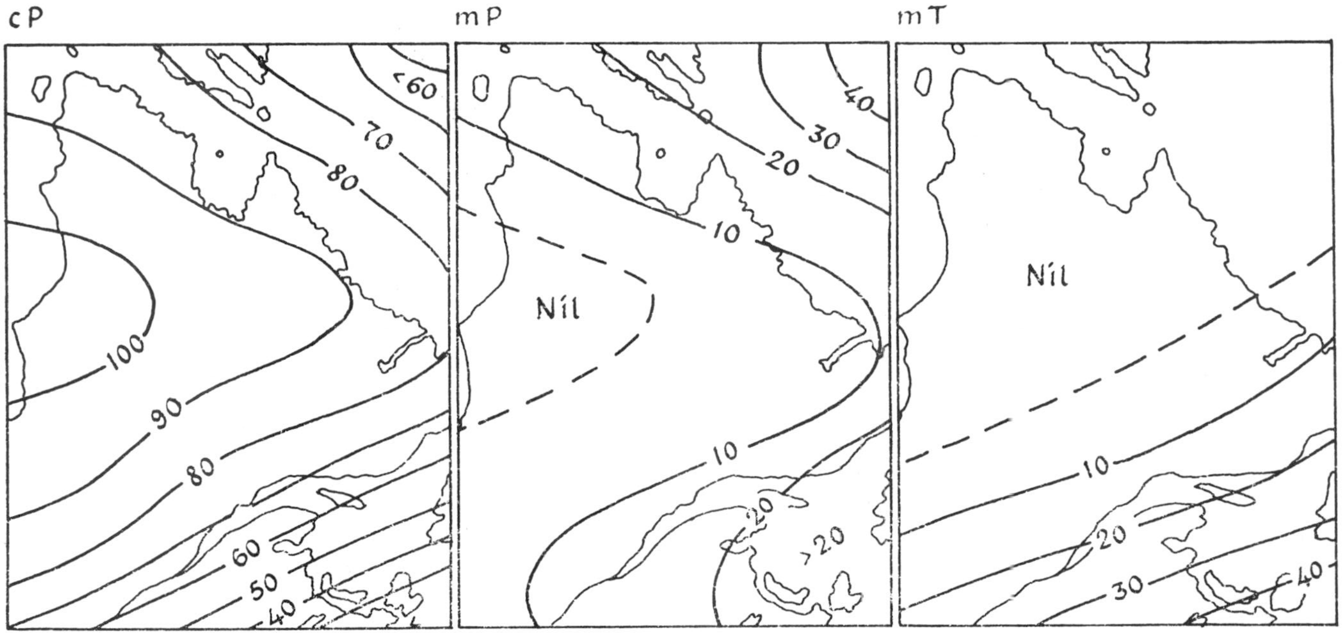

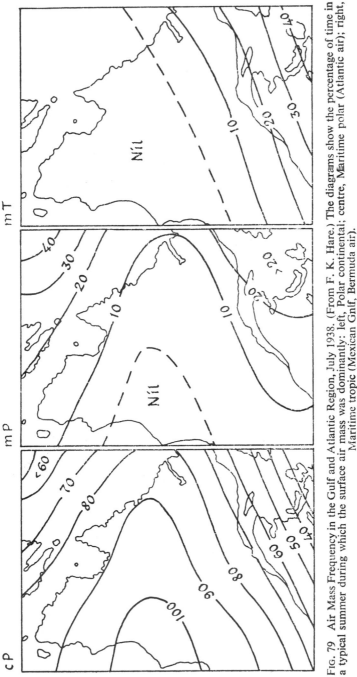

FIG. 79 Air Mass Frequency in the Gulf and Atlantic Region, July 1938. (From F. K. Hare.) The diagrams show the percentage of time in a typical summer during which the surface air mass was dominantly: left, Polar continental; centre, Maritime polar (Atlantic air); right, Maritime tropic (Mexican Gnlf, Bermuda air).

the presence of cold currents off the shore, where the cold Labrador drift prevails. All the year the coast of Labrador and the island of Newfoundland are bathed by ice-cold waters carried south from Arctic seas. These waters also enter the gulf where they spread their chilling effects. It is only in the south-east that warmer conditions occur, due to the partial influence of the near-by Gulf Stream.

Continentality is also marked. The climate of Labrador is quite extreme, with summer maxima in the interior of over 80° F. and winter minima of −60° F. Winters are long and summers short. Precipitation is mostly in the summer. Even in the peninsula of New Brunswick, or, more surprising, in the central part of the Island of Newfoundland, semi-continental conditions obtain. It is to be remembered that these areas are joined on to the mainland in winter by a sheet of ice across Belle Isle Strait and the inner Gulf. Such ice chills the air above it, invites the descent and spread of continental air from Labrador, and thus widens the sphere of the continental climate.

The semi-continental climate of New Brunswick has warm summers (July average, 60°–65° F.) when the air is heated over the central lowland and the broad St John valley, and thunderstorm rains occur. Of the total precipitation (35–40 inches) more than half falls during the summer. The winters are cold (January averages, 8°–13° F.) and raw, with heavy snows. They are also long. The frost-free season does not begin until mid May, and only lasts for 90–115 days. The range of temperature between the coldest and warmest months is considerable—usually around 65°–70°. Thus seasonal contrasts are great.

In the centre of Newfoundland summers, though short, are also quite warm (July average, 60°–63° F.), with occasional hot spells (Buchans, July maximum 87° F.), but winters are long and bleak (January average, 15° F.), with several cold snaps well below zero (January mean minimum, −15° F.). Thus the seasonal range of up to 48° is surprisingly high (Fig. 80).

Truly maritime climates only occur in the Bay of Fundy, and along the Atlantic coast as far as the Avalon peninsula. These are the only regions free of ice. The influence of the warm Atlantic current is quite noticeable in the Bay of Fundy, helping to advance the summer. The movement of the tides, which are strong in these confined waters, assists in keeping down the frosts. In the Annapolis valley and Minas basin quite warm summers (July average, 65°–66° F.) and a fairly long frost-free season (140–160 days) obtain. Summers are not very stormy and most of the rain occurs in autumn and winter. The annual precipitation averages 40 inches. Winters are snowy but raw rather than severe. January averages are about 20°–21° F. These still show a considerable range of 45°—which is more than twice the range of seasonal temperatures on Vancouver Island. Compared with the west coast, the east is *not* typically maritime; yet compared with the interior parts of

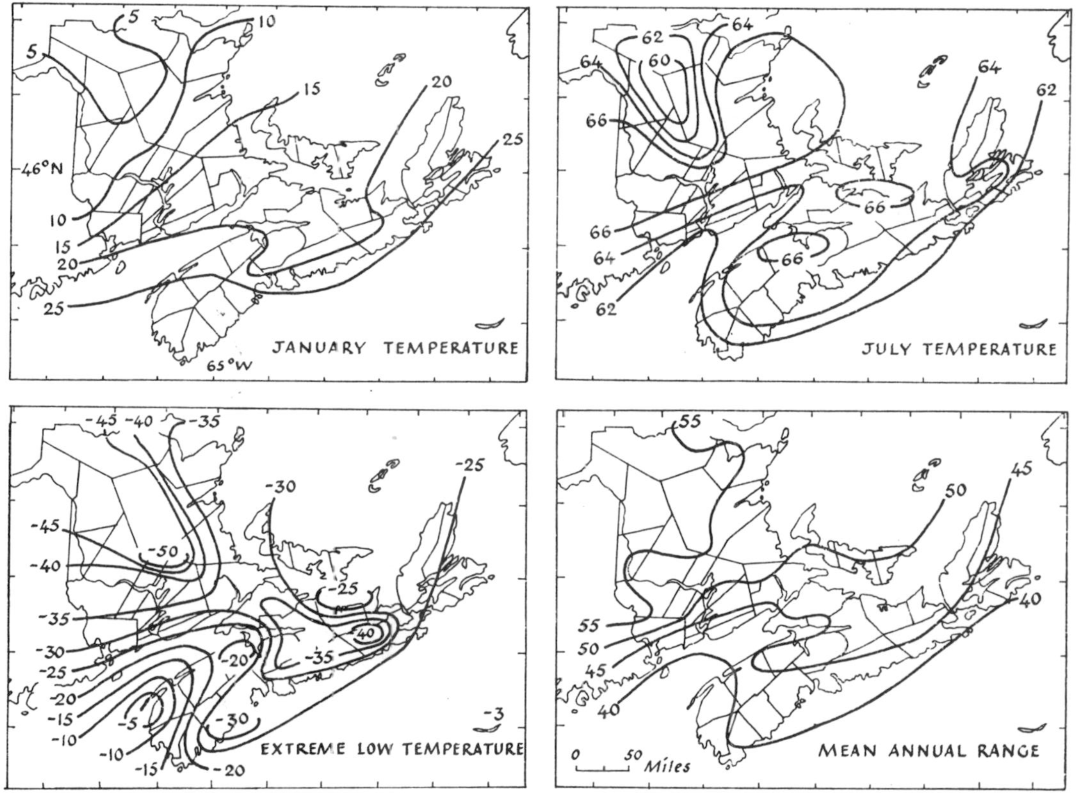

FIG. 80(*a*) The Continental and Maritime aspects of the climate of the Maritimes. (From Putnam.) Only the eastern rim of the region is truly maritime and even here the annual range of temperature is twice that of Victoria, B.C. (Degrees F.)

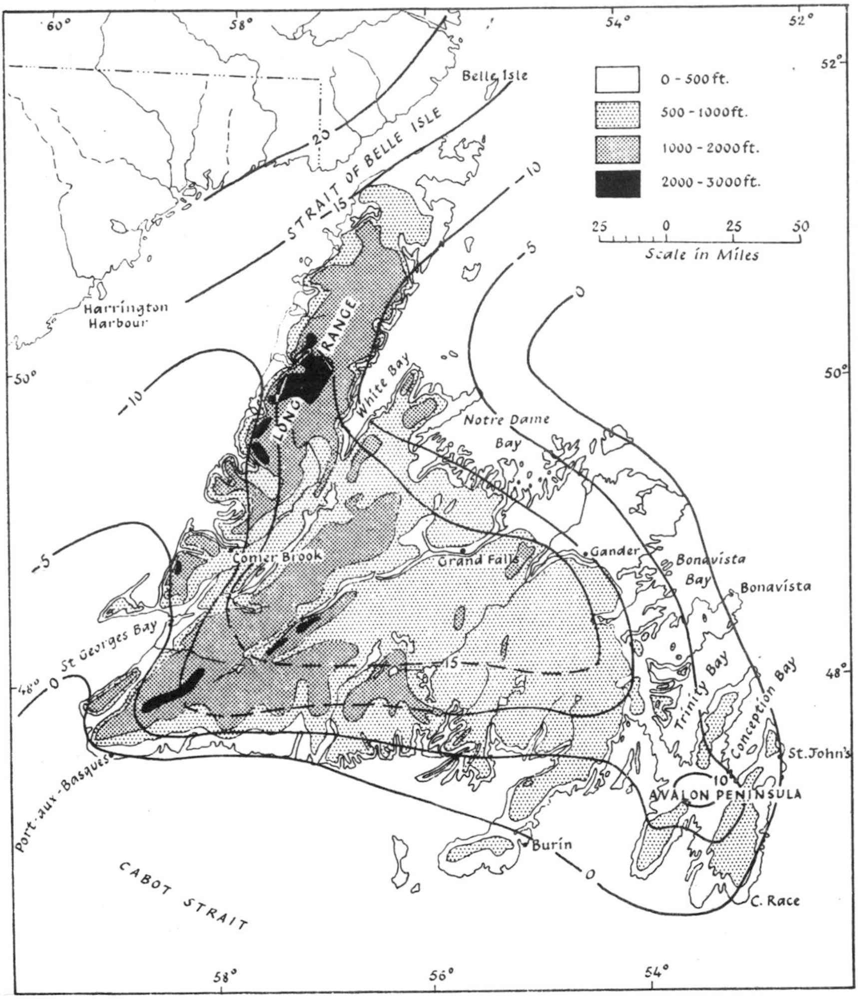

FIG. 80(*b*) The Continental and Maritime aspects of the climate of Newfoundland Isle. (From Hare.) These January temperatures show how little is the effect of the sea in winter, when it is generally at a maximum, as in Britain. The distinctly low average temperatures over most of the Island are a continental feature, reflecting the spread of Polar continental air from the adjacent mainland. (Degrees F.)

New Brunswick, Newfoundland, the Gaspé, or Labrador, this south-eastern sector is appreciably less extreme.

Farther north, along the upland rim of Nova Scotia, Cape Breton Island, and eastern Newfoundland a cooler type of maritime climate is found, more subject to ice rounding Cape Bonavista or moving out of Cabot Strait and, also, more subject to salients of cold Pc air. This whole sector is characterized by cool, short summers (July average, 62·5°), followed by very wet, raw winters (January averages, 20°–25°). Winter maxima (January, 45°) are quite high, and, according to Hare, there is marked day-to-day variability of temperature. Precipitation is heavy, about 50 inches, and most of it falls during winter cyclones. The winters are long, but mainly because spring is remarkably slow. In Newfoundland 'the stream of pack-ice that almost encircles the island keeps sea temperatures close to the freezing-point until late May'.[1] The frost-free season is short and ranges from 143 in the south to 100 days in the north. There is much foggy weather, particularly when the warmer airs of the Atlantic air mass override the cold land in winter and spring, or when the ice is drifting in to shore. The east coast has over 90 days of fog a year (or 1 out of every 4 days).

Throughout the whole climatic story the sea, sea-currents, and sea-ice have played a major role. Although the sea presses far into the land and is, in fact, at the land's centre, in the Gulf of St Lawrence, it does not modify continental conditions spreading off the land as much as it might. This is because it is very cold, except in the south-east, being stirred by the Arctic Labrador current, a current that flows in a wide sweep down the coast of Labrador, splits at Cape Bauld, pushes into the Strait of Belle Isle down the west side of the Island of Newfoundland, and presses down the east side of the island into its wide north-facing bays. Indeed, the current moves right round the island, up the Cabot Strait. Here it comes into conflict with the somewhat less chilly, but none the less cool, Gaspé current. Even in summer the waters off Labrador and north-east Newfoundland are only 45°, and only 50° in the Belle Isle Strait. Not until one comes to the south-east coast of the region—off Nova Scotia and the Newfoundland Banks—do warmer waters occur (65°), where eddies of the Gulf Stream make for a more maritime régime.

Sea-ice, even more than cold currents, keeps the region cool. During the winter the coastline of most of the Gulf, and of the Atlantic north of the Avalon peninsula, is sealed by ice (Fig. 81). As Gutsell shows:

> During the Fall (October–November) coastal waters are subject to severe cooling and this chilling effect spreads southwards over the shallow waters covering the Labrador and Newfoundland Banks, and allows the formation of 'field' ice. In addition, there is Arctic ice which originates in Davis Strait and Hudson Strait and moves southwards to reach Cape Chidley, in north Labrador, early in November. The ice sweeps down the Labrador coast and reaches Belle Isle during December, often extending as far as 100 miles to the east of Belle Isle Strait. It enters the strait and rapidly fills it, sealing up this northern channel. By January or early February the

[1] Hare, F. K., 'The Climate of the Island of Newfoundland', *Geographical Bulletin*, no. 2, Ottawa, 1952, p. 43.

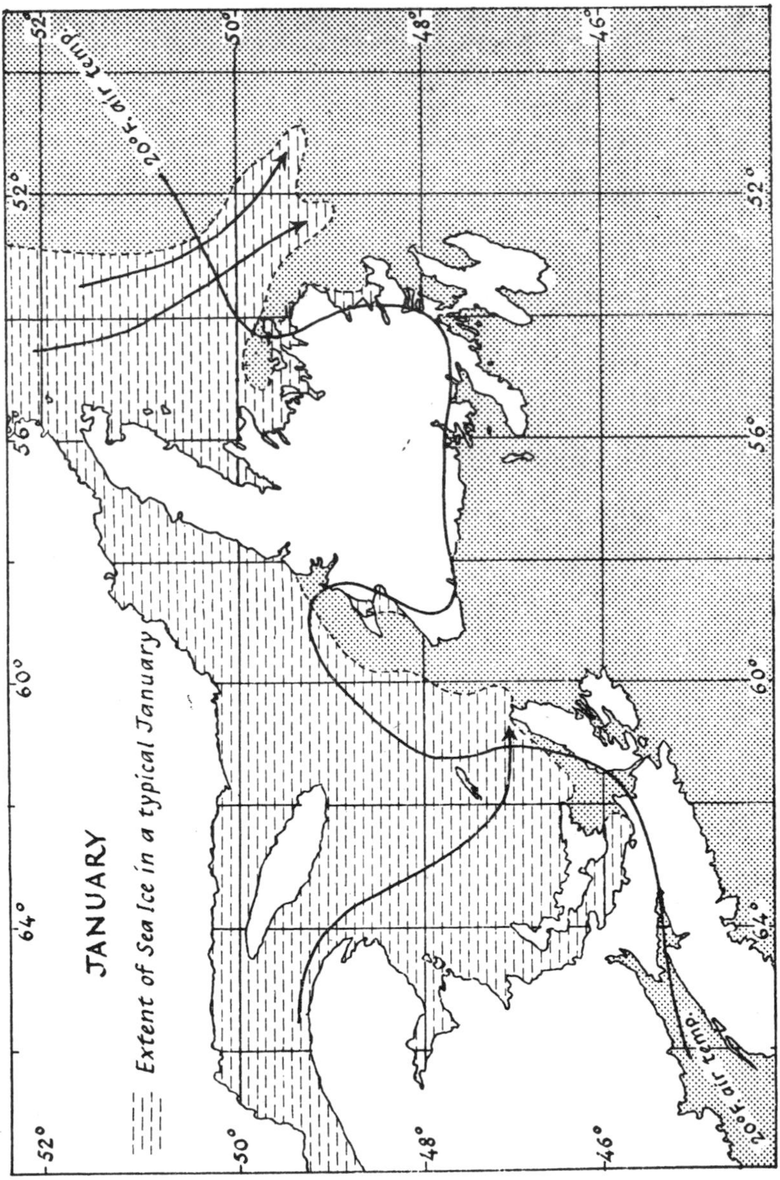

FIG. 81 Winter ice in the Gulf and Atlantic Region. (From the Ice Atlas of the Northern Hemisphere.)

ice reaches the northern edge of the Grand Banks and closes the east coast of the island. In March it reaches its maximum extent and spreads south to latitude 45°, where it is normally open pack-ice but is dangerous to navigation.

Break up begins during April with the opening of Cabot Strait, though frequently a rush of ice from the Gulf of St Lawrence (which has also become filled by ice between January and March) causes a block between Cape Race and Cape Breton Island. [Ice delays the coming of Spring until late May or early June, although] by June, most of the coast is open. The Labrador coast is not freed until late July.[1]

The blocking of Belle Isle Strait, of the Gulf, and of the estuary of St Lawrence, by winter ice is one of the great deterrents to Canadian trade and development; on the other hand, this blockage gives the open-water ports of St John's (Newfoundland), Halifax (Nova Scotia), and Saint John (New Brunswick) opportunities which they might otherwise not have enjoyed. From December to April they become the gateways to the region, and, in the case of the last two, to the whole of eastern and central Canada.

Vegetation and Soils

Climate and relief both affect the kinds of vegetation and soil that have emerged. The northern and the highland parts lift themselves up into the Arctic tundra; those central-southern parts of intermediate relief are under sub-Arctic or boreal coniferous forest; while in southern–south-eastern lowlands, occur mixed hardwood and coniferous forests.

In the Cape Chidley peninsula and along the coastal strip of mid-Labrador, barren lands are widespread, along with a patchy tundra of scrub willow, Labrador 'tea', moss, lichen, and sedge. Inland, a thin forest forms ribbons of green up rivers like the Koksoak, with small, open growth of black spruce and larch, thickening through white spruce, white birch, and balsam fir to the denser and taller forest of southern Labrador. Hustich[2] distinguishes three kinds of vegetation, depending on the moisture of the soils. A wet series of plants, on badly drained ground, gives rise to string bogs, muskegs, alder and willow bush, and swamp forest. A moist series, usually on steeper slopes, is made up of close-crowned coniferous forest, mainly of black spruce and balsam fir. A dry series, found on sandy deltas, outwash plains, or eskers, forms an open-crowned lichen-woodland, with widely spread spruce, a shrub layer of dwarf birch, and a thick carpet of reindeer moss.

---

[1] Gutsell, B. V., *An Introduction to the Geography of Newfoundland*, Geographical Branch, Dept. of Mines and Technical Surveys, Ottawa, 1949, p. 22.

[2] Hustich, I., 'On the Forest Geography of the Labrador Peninsula', *Acta Geographica*, **vol. 10**, no. 2, cf. pp. 36–42.

Higher land in the Island of Newfoundland, the Gaspé, and Cape Breton Island is mostly under bog, wet moor, or moss-barren. But the slopes of the valleys are covered with a moderately dense coniferous forest, usually of spruce and pine; ill-drained slopes are predominantly under black spruce and balsam, the better-drained ones spring to the eye clothed in white birch, with groups of white spruce.

On the southern uplands of New Brunswick and Nova Scotia red and white pine are common, along with spruce and balsam.

In the central basins and southern plains, as for example in Prince Edward Island and the lowlands bordering Northumberland Sound, in the Chignecto isthmus, the Annapolis valley, and the lower St John, sugar maple, beech, and birch are the commonest trees. Elm, basswood, red oak, bur oak, and butternut also form fine deciduous woods. Evergreens are not as numerous, and are mostly red and black spruce.

The soil over much of the area, perhaps as much as four-fifths of it, is acid and infertile, immature, and not suited to agriculture. Over the northern part of Labrador it is underlain by a permanently frozen layer, at from 6 to 9 inches below the surface. The surface layer itself is frozen for about eight months of the year. When it thaws out in the summer it becomes waterlogged, and is very acid. In southern Labrador and on the highlands and most of the uplands of Newfoundland Island, the Gaspé, and the Maritimes, the soils are thin, immature, highly leached, grey, siliceous podsols. The heavy snowfalls produce meltwaters that saturate the soil. Cool, stormy, wet summers, with relatively low evaporation, continue to keep the soil wet and acidic, and see considerable and strong leaching of organic matter from the sub-surface horizon. Even on the plains, soils are by no means well developed. On heavy till or Carboniferous sandstone plains they are coarse and infertile. It is really only on the red sandstone lowlands, or on warm, well-drained drumlins, or gravelly beach ridges, that they have developed in depth to produce a brown podsolic type, which, though slightly acid, can be fairly easily neutralized by liming and made agriculturally productive.

The manner in which the different kinds of vegetation and soil interpenetrate each other, and the similar way in which they repeat each other from lowland through to highland, have again helped to give unity to the Atlantic region, albeit a unity based on variety.

THE HUMAN RESPONSE

Settlement

Unity based on variety has come to characterize the human response. To begin with, however, variety, not to say difference and division, held sway. When Gilbert sailed into the Bay of St John's in Newfoundland, in 1583, he found there fishing vessels of the leading nations of seaboard Europe. Place-names like English Harbour, French Bay, Portugal Cove are eloquent of the many peoples who, through the 460 years since Cabot's discovery, have contributed to the region's story.

Conflict dominated the early scene. As MacNutt remarks:

> The Maritime Provinces were born of war. They formed a natural theatre of contention for the two great powers of the time. To the north-west was the French empire of the St Lawrence. To the south were the energetic and commercially minded inhabitants of New England. The area was a strategic one. From it could be dominated the approaches to either Quebec or Boston. Before the struggle for the control of the interior of North America could be decided a conflict would be necessary here.[1]

The rivals struggled fiercely with each other for over 150 years and in that struggle first picked out and exploited the differences and divisions of the environment. Eventually, coming together, they came upon and stressed the togetherness of forces and features in the region, so that, during the last 150 years they have created an area of remarkable unity along the Atlantic coast.

It was not unnatural that the French and British should have early become rivals in the northern coasts of North America, since their history had made them rivals in the northern coasts of Europe. The French established themselves at Port Royal on the Annapolis basin, and at St Croix Island in Passamaquoddy Bay. The English, meantime, had colonized the Avalon peninsula of Newfoundland to the north and New England to the south, thus bracketing the French position. Friction between the colonies soon broke out, as their ships crossed each other's paths on the ocean, as they competed for the fishing banks and the fur-rich forests, and as they fortified strategic spots which would give one nation or the other the advantage.

At first it seemed obvious that the French had the advantage. Their posts in the Annapolis basin and in Cape Breton could endanger the life-lines of the British colonies, both to north and south. The situation became very critical and warfare broke out. In 1628 Port Royal was seized by the British, but was handed back when the boundary between Acadia (the French sphere in the Maritimes) and New England became the Penobscot river. Then in 1654, under Cromwell's orders, the British captured Acadia, which remained British until 1667, when it was again restored to France by the Treaty of Breda. Thus the fate of North America changed with the fate of Europe; the geography of North American settlement varied as the history of European conflict.

---

[1] MacNutt, W. S., *The Making of the Maritime Provinces, 1713–1784*, Can. Hist. Assoc. Hist. Booklets, no. 4, Ottawa, 1955, p. 3.

From 1667 to 1713, when Acadia was again French, immigrants began to pour in, as tales of the fertility and beauty of the region reached France. The French population increased from 392 to 2,500. It kept on growing even after Acadia finally became British, and in 1755 was 16,000. By this time it seemed firmly rooted in the soil; villages and farms, fishing hamlets and hunting camps were scattered in six important districts: (i) in the Yarmouth–Cape Sable area; (ii) at the mouth of the Annapolis valley; (iii) around Minas Bay; (iv) around the coasts of Cape Breton Island; (v) on the coasts of Prince Edward Island and the Magdalen Islands; and (vi) around Chignecto Bay and up the Saint John in New Brunswick. Meanwhile, the French had secured a hold on the southern and western shores of the Island of Newfoundland (Fig. 82).

The British authorities were worried about the success of the French colonists, and in 1755 they decided to 'evict' the Acadians from the Maritimes, and settle the region with British stock (many of whom were Scottish Highlanders, being 'evicted' from their homes after the last great Jacobean rebellion), or with New Englanders. About 7,000 French were deported. However, the British realized the mistake they made in thinking they could solve problems in this way. A much better method was to work for the close co-operation of the French and British, so that they could live side by side, and exchange goods and ideas, and thus help each other develop the land. So about a decade later the Acadians were allowed to drift back to their old homes.

In the meantime Quebec had become a British province and settlers from Quebec began to move along the east coast of New Brunswick. Later still they moved down the Matapedia and the St John rivers into northern New Brunswick. (This movement is in full swing today, and as a result New Brunswick is the most French of the Maritime provinces, with 164,000, or 35 per cent of the population. Here, more than one out of every three persons is French. Indeed, they form a significant element in each of the Maritime provinces, accounting for about 16 per cent of Nova Scotia's population, and 20 per cent of that of Prince Edward Island. There are over 10,000 of them in Newfoundland.)

The British settlers came in rather haphazardly, but four important movements can be distinguished, over and above the early establishment of military posts. First, there was the northward drift of New Englanders after 1755 to replace the deported Acadians. They settled around Yarmouth, Digby, the Annapolis valley, Minas Bay, and Chignecto Bay. Then came the evicted Scottish highlanders who found homes in Cape Breton Island, the north shore of Nova Scotia, parts of Prince Edward Island, and of Chaleur Bay. Thirdly, in 1777, the Loyalists poured in from the United States, taking up land along the south shore of Nova Scotia (from Shelburne

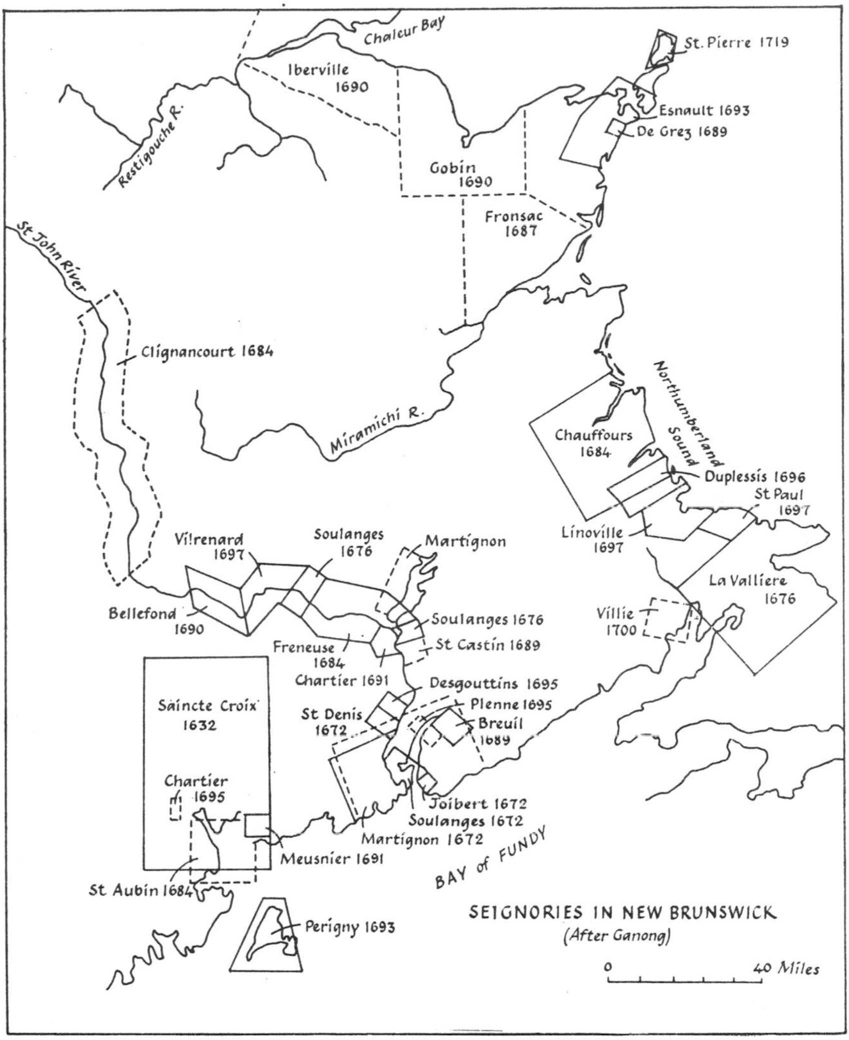

FIG. 82 Historical Geography of Settlement—Seignories of New Brunswick. These differed considerably in size but were the same in having boundaries going back at right angles to coast and river.

to Guysborough) and in the valleys of the St Croix, Saint John, and Kenebecasis rivers, in New Brunswick. A few obtained lands in the south of Prince Edward Island. Finally, after 1788 a slow but steady trickle of settlers arrived from Britain, augmented in the 1840s by groups of Irish that escaped the potato famine by settling in southern New Brunswick.

It is interesting to note that the early New England settlers moved into adjacent territory bordering the Bay of Fundy; the Scots settled in the northern parts, nearest to Scotland; while the Loyalists chose either the Atlantic coast (the refugee fishermen) or the wide river plains of New Brunswick (the refugee farmers). Thus each group found something that reminded them of home, or that came nearest to hand, or suited their particular occupation, and were able to preserve their traditions even while adjusting to each other, to the French, and to the new environment.

The New Englanders played a valuable role, as Clark points out,[1] pressing for democratic reforms, which would enable them more readily to meet the new situation. Many of them were 'cottars', or tenant-farmers, and were not given many rights in New England. The British authorities were anxious to attract them to the Maritimes, and promised them more privileges, until on 2 October 1758 they obtained representation in an elective assembly. Thus they secured the right to vote before their fellow colonists to the south, and so, when the American rebellion occurred, they saw little reason to join with the Americans, but remained loyal to Britain. *The United Empire Loyalists* who streamed in after the war emphasized that spirit of loyalty still more. As a result, liberty together with loyalty have been two of the great contributions of the Maritimes to Canada.

A third great contribution has been to preserve diversity in unity. The mistake of the Acadian evictions had taught people not to try to uproot different groups possessing different ideas, but to accept them and, in the end, benefit from them. In this way people came to feel proud of their language, their religion, and other aspects of their culture, and yet grew to acknowledge the value of other cultures as well. So we find today that the French Canadians are devout followers of their own religion, retain their own language, have separate schools, and develop their distinctive arts and crafts. The Scottish settlers have kept their historic clannishness. Many of them still live as groups of related families in the glens of Cape Breton Island; they cherish the Gaelic; hold annual Gaelic Mods (singing, oratorical, and poetry competitions); and sport their Highland Games. Religious denominations are strongly represented, and have kept up their own schools and universities. Nova Scotia has its historic Baptist University in Acadia, its Anglican foundation in King's College, its Presbyterian one in Dalhousie, and its Roman Catholic centre at Francis Xavier. The United Church of Canada supports Mt Allison University at Sackville, New Brunswick. These strong religious differences have nevertheless bred a notable sense of mutual respect and tolerance.

---

[1] Clark, S. D., *The Social History of Canada*, Toronto, 1942, p. 101. 'The New England Migration brought new sources of strength to the social organization of Nova Scotia. The New Englanders were pioneers from a pioneer community and possessed all the advantages of familiarity with the environment.'

Undoubtedly, the varied landscapes of the Maritimes have helped groups to find separate valleys or basins to settle in, and kept them rather isolated from each other. But there have been other geographical factors to draw them together. The sea has no barriers. It knows no frontiers. French, Scottish, English, Irish—all meet together as equals on the seas, and mingle at the fishing ports and bustling harbours. The forest, too, has drawn them together. Lumber camps collect young men from many different villages to go back into the bush, and work and eat and sleep together. Finally, the cities have brought them together, and made them mix with and respect and depend on each other in the factories, at the railway yards, on the streets, and in the shops. And since the Maritimes are becoming more urban than ever (Nova Scotia is 46 per cent urban) this process of mixing will gather and grow, until people think of each other, not as French, or Scotch, or Germans, but as Canadians all.

ECONOMIC OCCUPATIONS

Fishing

From the very first the sea predominated in the life of the Atlantic region. This early meant fishing; later it meant transportation and trade, in addition. Fishing has been especially important, since so much of the land, being mountainous or barren, is relatively unusable, and forces men to look to the sea. Thus fishing still competes with farming as the chief occupation of the people. In the western plains of Nova Scotia, the central ones of New Brunswick, and the lowlands of Prince Edward Island farming is no doubt more important; but from Yarmouth to Cape North, along the east shore, fishing predominates, as it does in the Magdalen Isles, in the Gaspé, around most of the Island of Newfoundland, and up the Labrador coast. So important is fishing that it forms a major part of the history and character of the Canadian Atlantic. As Dr Innis has shown, the fishing industry kept the section apart, gave it a unique role to play in Canadian affairs, and prompted a healthy spirit of self-reliance and self-respect. In particular, it accentuated the contrast between the Maritimes and the mainland.

On the continental mainland, where the trade in furs was the chief early occupation, 'the pull of the fur trade was to the interior in pursuit of a steadily exhausting resource, whereas in the Maritimes the pull was towards the sea in pursuit of its relatively inexhaustible resources. The fur trade was characterized by centralization, the fishing industry by decentralization.'[1] Fur trading fell into the hands of a few large monopolistic companies, and as a consequence it was easy for a few dominant men to direct the affairs of

[1] Innis, H. A., Editor's Preface in *The Canadian Atlantic Fishery*, Grant, R. F., Toronto, 1934, p. vii.

the colony: this helped to perpetuate the feudal tradition in the interior. But fishing was carried on in small boats by individuals or families, and nourished a sturdy independence amongst the seaboard population, who have always been noted for their democratic ways.

The fishing industry is closely dependent on geography. Fish gather in large numbers off the Newfoundland and Nova Scotia Banks because of the great amount of food that there is for them there. They feed on tiny animals, which in turn feed on water algae or diatoms. These are so small that six million may live together in one quart of water! They require cool, shallow water, penetrated by the sunlight, and mixed up by currents. Now there is an enormous area of fairly shallow water in the Gulf of St Lawrence and the continental shelf, where the Maritimes and Newfoundland lie. The continental shelf swells upward in a series of low submarine ridges which come nearly to the surface, and offer still shallower water. These are the famous 'Banks'. The Grand Bank covers an area of 36,000 sq. miles, or seventeen times the size of Prince Edward Island. It is the most important cod-fishing ground in the world. South-westward are other large banks,

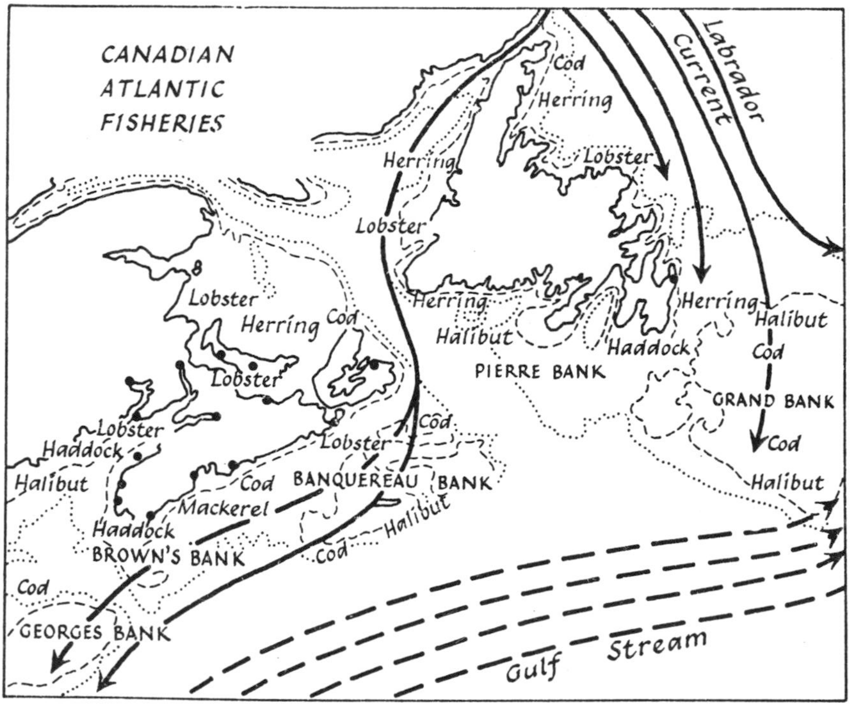

FIG. 83 Fishing in the St Lawrence Gulf and on the Atlantic Coast is closely associated with the Labrador and Gulf Stream currents and the off-shore banks. (Scale, 1:15 m.)

including the St Pierre Bank (4,800 sq. miles), a cod and halibut fishing ground; Banquereau Bank (3,000 sq. miles), noted for halibut, hake, and haddock; Sable Island or Western Bank (6,320 sq. miles) with cod, halibut and haddock; Le Havre Ridge (1,575 sq. miles), with cod and haddock; and Georges Bank (8,498 sq. miles) where cod and haddock abound. There are eight other smaller Banks in addition (Fig. 83).

The fishing grounds are rarely more than fifty fathoms below the surface of the sea. Therefore they are easily reached by the sun's rays. The water over them is kept cool by the drift southward of the cold Labrador current which comes from within the Arctic Circle. Also drift ice and icebergs for eight or nine months of the year help to keep the temperatures down. Yet the waters are not too cold, because they also feel the effects of the warm Gulf Stream which drifts north from the Caribbean gulf. The meeting of the two currents keeps the waters constantly stirred up. This is very good, because it carries up minerals from the deeper layers of the sea to feed the plants and animals in the shallower layers. Thus there is an inexhaustible food supply for the fish, which swarm in great numbers.

Climatic and other factors further aid the fishing industry. Low temperatures, even in summer, prevent the quick decay of the fish, once it has been caught, and make it easier for the catch to be salted before spoiling. The long, cold winters provide great quantities of ice which can be cut and stored away, and then used cheaply by trawlers or freight companies in packing and transporting fresh-frozen fish to the market. The near-by forests supply cheap wood for boats, oars, tackle, storage sheds, casks, etc., while large salt deposits in Nova Scotia allow the sailors to salt down their catch at a relatively low cost.

The fishing industry is divided into two classes: inshore fishing, where smacks are commonly used; and Banks fishing, in which trawlers and schooners are resorted to. During recent years there has been a decline in trawling the Banks because the market for dried cod in Italy, Spain, France, and Latin America has been declining. The number of fishermen employed in inshore fishing, on the other hand, has increased, because the demand for fresh fish in Canada has grown. Better transportation contacts with the inland markets have also done much to help the inshore fisheries. As a result, there has been a great development of lobster and oyster beds, scallop, smelt, and sardine-fishing, along the coasts. Oysters are most important on the New Brunswick shore and the north shore of Nova Scotia. The Maritimes' lobster fishery is the largest in the world. Nova Scotia is the chief herring centre in the Western Hemisphere. Even during the war, when many fishermen were in the Armed Forces or serving with the Merchant Marine, the catch of fish steadily increased. Newfoundland takes the lead, especially in cod-fishing; it is followed fairly closely by Nova Scotia, where the principal catch is herring, followed by cod, lobsters, sardines, and halibut. New Brunswick comes a poor third, with about half the Nova Scotia catch, and is followed by the Gaspé, and by Prince Edward Island. The Atlantic region accounts for well over half of all the fish taken in Canada.

The present prosperity is different, however, from the comparative poverty of the pre-war depression. Nevertheless, some good came out of the depression. The fishermen tried co-operative methods which brought them together. They purchased supplies in groups and distributed them at cost; they took up shares in boats and worked them co-operatively; at length they built co-operative canneries, and shared the profits amongst the members. At the same time, the women took a new interest in domestic handicrafts and sold them through co-operative agencies. Much of this fine work must be attributed to the Roman Catholic university of St Xavier at Antigonish, Nova Scotia, which encouraged the co-operative movement and brought new hope to the people.

Today, co-operative fishing takes place chiefly in the inshore fisheries, where men go out in small sailing smacks or motor-boats and fish with lines or traps. The fishing on the Banks is still largely in the hands of companies. The smaller companies tend to rely on schooners which are sent out from the middle of March to the end of September. These make three or more trips a season, each lasting about a month. The boats search for large 'schools' of fish, where cod, halibut, or herring swarm in great numbers. From each schooner several small 'dories', with two men in them, are put out daily. One man rows for a while, and his partner pays out a line which has been baited with bits of frozen mackerel, or with capelin and squid. The line has many side-lines or 'ganglings', spliced at even intervals, which end in a baited hook. Some of the longer lines will have a thousand hooks on them. They are put over the side in various directions, so as to cover as wide an area as possible. From time to time they are pulled in, the fish removed, and the lines rebaited and payed out once more. When the fish are transferred from the dories to the schooner they are cleaned. The head and fins are removed. The liver is kept for making cod or halibut liver oil. The fish are washed thoroughly and sprinkled with salt. They are then packed in the hold until the ship reaches port. The final curing of the fish, or its canning, is then undertaken by the curing and canning companies on shore.

Larger companies tend to rely on the motor trawler, which is changing the methods of fishing. The industry is becoming concentrated at a few larger ports, which are properly equipped for trawlers and have large drying, salting, and curing plants. Such ports are St John's, Newfoundland, and Halifax, Yarmouth, North Sydney, Canso, and Lunenburg, Nova Scotia.

Trawlers go out to the Banks about every two weeks. They catch the fish by hauling a large 'trawl' net through the waters. The net is emptied into a tank and then the commercial fish are sorted out from the rest, cleaned, and packed in ice. Trawlers can operate in stormy weather and in winter, when it is impossible for the dories to be put out. Thus trawlers give a regular supply of fish throughout the year, and are consequently displacing schooners on the Banks.

However, as yet trawling is not used as much as it might be and only accounts for a fifth of the catch. This is a drawback and is due, as Miss Grant points out, to failure to adopt modern methods. 'With the geographic advantage of proximity to prolific fishing grounds, coal at tide water, and its use as a cheap source of dry-ice refrigerant, the possibility of a modernly equipped trawler fishery, and the development of a floating-factory fisher, warrant serious consideration.'[1] But the immense amount of capital needed may not be forthcoming while the market for dried or salted fish in the Caribbean and Latin America continues to decline, and the chief near-by market for fresh-frozen fish, in the United States, is largely denied by high tariffs. Outside markets are crucial factors in the problem of reorganizing the fisheries, and at present are distinctly limited.

Another crucial factor is the slowness with which fishermen and their families are willing to give up the many small villages in which they live and where they have both a great deal of personal freedom and also of social co-operation, in order to concentrate in large numbers at major fishing ports. Social inertia keeps the geography of the fishing industry an eighteenth-century affair in a twentieth-century situation.

This is particularly true of Newfoundland and Labrador, notwithstanding the fact that sea-ice hinders operations for so much of the year and the people, as Black reminds us, have to 'make the income derived from two or three months of the summer fishery provide for the whole year'.[2] But although Government and private industry have encouraged a concentration at favoured areas, particularly where there is all-year fishing, people still cling to their little coves where they can carry on their rugged, but very independent, lives unchanged. Here social geography and economic geography are at loggerheads.

Forestry, Pulp and Paper Making

Early on in the history of Newfoundland, as we have seen (p. 149), the people were urged not to devote themselves wholly or even mainly to fishing, but to broaden out their economy by, amongst other things, using the wealth of the woods. This great wealth, taken with the fact that there are rather

---

[1] Grant, R. F., *The Canadian Atlantic Fishery*, p. 139.

[2] Black, W. A., 'Population Distribution of the Labrador Coast, Newfoundland', *Geol. Bul.*, no. 9, Ottawa, 1956, p. 54.

limited opportunities for agriculture, makes the Atlantic region largely a lumber country. The cool, moist climate, and the thin, leached soils, are generally better fitted for forests than farms. The chief exceptions are the central plains, where the deciduous forest has largely disappeared and given way to excellent farm lands in the lower St John, the Gulf plains of New Brunswick and Prince Edward Island, and in the Annapolis valley and the Minas basin.

In Newfoundland, forests are second only to fish as a source of revenue. Actually, forestry is rapidly overtaking fishing, especially in that it is becoming swiftly modernized and is being run on a large-scale mechanized basis. Although less than half the area is forested, about 83 per cent of this is exploitable. So far, cutting is balanced by annual increment, and a programme of forest management should ensure a satisfactory balance. Up to the beginning of the century logs were exported, but from 1909 when the Anglo-Newfoundland Development Company started a paper mill at Grand Falls, on the Exploits river, logs were consumed within the province for pulp and paper making, and these products exported. This company holds land with about 29 per cent of Newfoundland's usable forest; the giant Bowater firm, about 52 per cent. The former have their chief holdings in the Exploits river–Red Indian Lake basin, and the Terra Nova valley; the latter in the Humber river–Grand Lake basin and the Gander valley. The Bowater Mill at Corner Brook on the estuary of the Humber is one of the largest in North America, and has sponsored a whole complex of actively growing settlements.[1]

In New Brunswick the forests cover about 13 million acres, or 73 per cent of the total area of the province. The value of their products is about one-third as much again as the value of agricultural products. Half the cut is for pulp and paper, and only about one-sixth for sawn timber. This is due to the wide extent of spruce and balsam, well suited to pulp making; the great demand for paper in the near-by New England market; and the rather poor demand for construction timber in the Maritimes, which lacks the industrial or urban market. Nearly four-fifths of the production is for export outside the province, either to Montreal or to New England. The larger pulp and paper mills are close to the upland balsam-spruce forests, on large or swiftly flowing rivers which bring down the logs, and on railway or shipping lines, that carry the pulp away. Important mills occur at Edmundston, Fredericton, Bathurst, Campbellton, and Dalhousie. There are over two hundred saw mills in other parts of the province, but many of these are quite small, and are moved from place to place.

In northern New Brunswick there are little settlements where both farming

[1] Wonders, W. C., 'The Corner Brook Area, Nfd.', *Geog. Bul.*, no. 5, 1954, p. 35. 'The effects of the mill, company, and town are island-wide in scope.'

and lumbering are carried on. The settlers cut out the wood individually, and it is trucked to the saw mills. They farm the cut-over land, raising milk, eggs and vegetables for their own use. This pioneer development is being copied in Quebec, and elsewhere. It is of great significance in areas on the northern or upland margin of farming possibility.

The forest area in Nova Scotia is proportionately as great as in New Brunswick (71 per cent), though the value of forest production is not as important, and is only two-thirds that of farm production. That is because the farm area, though comparatively just as small as in New Brunswick, produces more valuable crops. The lumber industry does not seem to be as well organized in Nova Scotia: there are few large mills, but many more small portable ones (about 400). This is perhaps because the forests are broken up by the relief into several small units, and there is no large continuous forest cover as in northern New Brunswick.

In Prince Edward Island the forest is almost all cut off. The farms have their small woodlots, and there is some wood cut for fuel, but there is little natural bush for lumbering purposes. Actually, the land is too valuable to be left in forest. Being one of the few fertile lowlands in the Atlantic region, it has long been cleared and turned into good farm land.

Farming

Farming country is at a premium in the Gulf basin. It is a small part of the landscape, being confined to restricted areas of fairly small plains which are sheltered from frost, well watered, and relatively fertile. The largest exploitable plain is that of Prince Edward Isle; others are: the Annapolis valley, the lowlands facing the Northumberland Strait, and the central and northern plains of the Saint John, in New Brunswick. There is really no significant plain, suited to agriculture, in Newfoundland. The northern-central lowland is used chiefly for forestry.

Prince Edward Island is a low, rolling, sandstone region, with short rivers, in close touch with the sea. The summers are warm (65° F. July), but the winters fairly cold (17° F. January). The rainfall averages about 40 inches a year, with a marked autumn maximum. The frost-free period is as long as 145 days. These conditions suit hay, oats, and root crops, and consequently the island is noted for its dairy produce and potatoes. Bacon, poultry, butter, and cheese are exported, particularly to near-by mining cities in the Maritimes. During recent years a rich trade has sprung up with the United States in seed potatoes. The farms are fairly small—averaging 93 acres in size, and most of them are individually owned and operated. They go in for specialized products. One of these—fur farming—has become quite famous. Some of the earliest attempts at domesticating the silver fox were made in Prince Edward Island, and over two thousand live foxes for foundation-stock are exported annually to the United States. In addition, many furs are sent to the great fur markets at Montreal, New York, and London.

While 760,000 acres out of 1,200,000 acres of farm land in Prince Edward Island are cultivated, in Nova Scotia only 850,000 acres are cultivated, out of a total of 4,300,000 acres occupied as farm land. In other words, farming is much less *intensive* in Nova Scotia than in the island. This is shown by the fact that farms are bigger (about 110 acres each) and contain a lot of woodland on them, together with natural pasture. Farming is confined largely to the north shore, the Minas basin, and the Annapolis valley.

The north shore has rather a short growing season, since the ice stays late in the spring, and it is therefore suited chiefly to hay, oats, and potatoes, and the production of poultry and dairy products. Around New Glasgow and Sydney local demand for 'whole' milk has helped farmers to make a success of dairying. The Truro district of the Minas basin is also important for its dairy farms, though from Truro south, orchards increase in number. Between Windsor and Digby they crowd the warmer, sandier soils on the floor and sides of Annapolis valley. Here the frost-free span is somewhat longer (143 to 160 days), the summers are warmer than anywhere else in the Maritimes (66° F. July) and best suited for ripening fruit, while the winters are relatively mild (22° F. January). In the spring, the waters of the near-by bay remain cool and spring is delayed. The opening of the buds is therefore kept back until the danger of frost is gone. In the fall the bay remains warm, after the land has begun to cool off. Therefore, it helps to keep frosts away until after the harvest is gathered. The mountains to north and south of the valley protect it from cold continental air in winter, which spreads from the north-west or from the raw easterly winds that blow off the Atlantic in spring. It is no wonder, then, that farmers have gone in for fruit farming in a very *intensive* way, and that, in good years, over five million bushels of apples are exported from the region. They go chiefly to England. Plums, cherries, and strawberries are also raised. Here over 40 per cent of the land is improved, as compared with 10 per cent for the more rugged southern half of the province.[1]

New Brunswick is the least agricultural of the Maritime provinces. There are large areas without any farms on the northern mountains, central plateau, and southern uplands. Even large parts of the central plain are rendered useless because of the widespread marshes. The chief farming areas are restricted to the St John and Kennebecasis rivers, and to the shore plains. Field crops occupy only 23 per cent of the total farm land, the rest is in grass or woodland (Fig. 84). The most important crop is hay, which accounts for nearly two-thirds of the cropped land, and is the basis for a flourishing dairy industry, especially around Saint John and Moncton. The climate is

[1] Putnam, D. F., 'Farm Distribution in Nova Scotia', *Econ. Geog.*, **15**, no. 1, p. 50.

too severe for much fruit-growing, with a short growing season and long, cold winters. However, it is adequate for root crops, and New Brunswick is famous for its seed potatoes. They are grown chiefly in the middle St John valley, between Woodstock and Grand Falls, and are exported to the United States

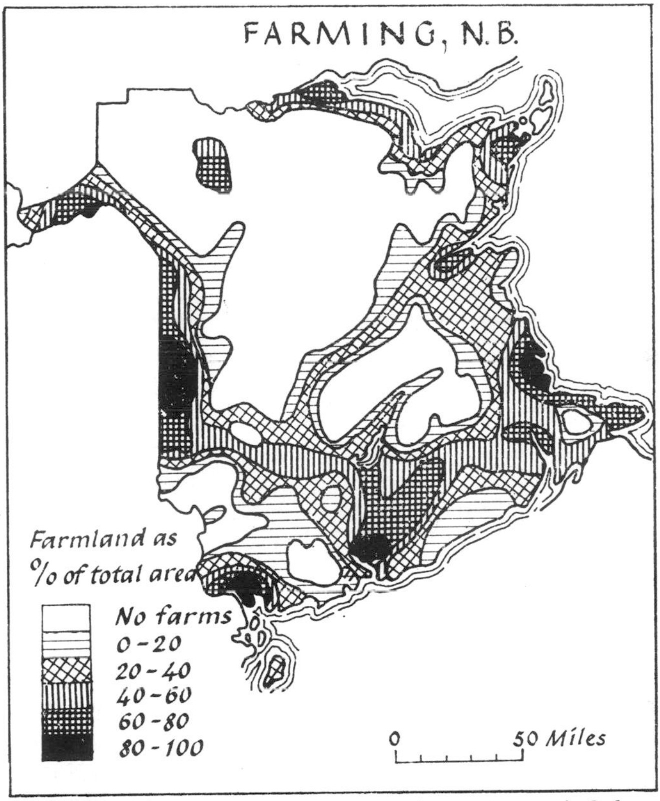

FIG. 84 Farming in New Brunswick. (From Putnam.) Only a relatively small amount of the Province has more than two-thirds of the surface under farms; most of the area is still forest. Much of the farm land is not improved, but remains cut-over bush and grazing. The amount of improved land decreased by 22·8 per cent in the quinquennium before the last census, which was the highest decrease registered in Canada. By contrast the Prairies and southern British Columbia showed an increase in farm land and especially in improved farm land.

and overseas. Potatoes for food are sent in large quantities to Montreal and Toronto. The cool summer climate and friable loam soils are ideally suited to potatoes, and the yield per acre, about 200 to 250 bushels, is much higher than elsewhere in Canada. (Compare Ontario, with 90 to 100 bushels per acre.)

Agriculture is even less significant in the Gaspé peninsula where it is confined to the very narrow belt of marine terraces beneath the steep, thickly wooded sides of the Notre Dame mountains. It is often of a fairly primitive kind of general farming, raising 'store' sheep or cattle to be fattened elsewhere, together with fields of peas as a cash crop.

Farming has least significance in Newfoundland, where it accounts for less than 5 per cent of the occupied population (as compared with 32 per cent for fishing). Rough relief, even on the lowlands, sour and immature soils, and low summer temperatures (57°–63° F.) on the very verge of those needed for agriculture, are all inimical, and there are little more than 150 sq. miles of cropland in a total of 155,364 sq. miles! However, it is not the physical but the mental background that is the basic factor. Traditionally, as Gutsell points out, the outlook of the people has been away from the land towards the sea. When they turned to the land it was to take up lumbering, a winter occupation that did not compete with fishing. But since the call of the field came in the same summer months when the seaboard dwellers heard the call of the Banks, it was without much effect. It is a source of constant wonder to visitors how a land which has been occupied for 350 years could still look so unoccupied and unused. Everywhere, still, the forests or the barrens greet the eye. It is only around the Avalon peninsula and in the south-west and up the Humber valley that fields often come into view, where, near St John's or Cornerbrook, large local markets have induced dairy or truck farmers to wrestle a living from beach terraces or glacial outwash fans.

Mining

In Newfoundland, mining is much more important than farming, and in the Atlantic region as a whole mining plays an increasing part. According to the structure, it may be divided into two types: the mining of small ore bodies but quite rich coal fields in the Canadian Appalachians; and the mining of the ore-rich areas of the Shield. The Appalachian ores were the first to be discovered and worked. In the Meguma formations of Nova Scotia, and in river-bed gravels in the Eastern Townships, gold was found to occur. Gold mining along veins between beds of slate began in 1862, and reached its height in 1939, but even in that year it only just topped an annual production of $1,000,000—which is insignificant. About three times as much came from the placer workings of the Chaudière river, in the Eastern Townships, but even this was unimportant.

Nevertheless, gold set prospectors on the trail, and copper and iron, and, later, lead and zinc were found. In the Sutton and Stoke mountain district in the Eastern Townships copper was worked from 1865 to 1939. In 1942 new finds were made, but developments have continued to be small. Many small bodies of magnetitic or haematitic iron were discovered in the southern ridges of the Eastern Townships, in the crystalline massif south of Bathurst, New Brunswick, in the hills of Pictou and Antigonish, and among Cambrian strata in Cape Breton Island, but with the exception of the Bathurst mine none was really economic. Even the Bathurst mine was profitable only during the First and Second World Wars.

A major source of iron was discovered in the Wabana deposit at Bell Island, Newfoundland, in 1892. Rich in haematite, it began to be worked the very next year, and continues to produce at the rate of about one and a half million tons a year. The beds dip under Conception Bay and, within the limits of present-day submarine mining, have reserves of 2,500 million tons of ore. Total reserves are tremendous if we include low-grade as well as high-grade ore. Most of the ore goes to Sydney, Nova Scotia, to be made into steel, but much is exported to the 'American Ruhr' (or the lower Delaware). Because of difficulties mining is on the decline.

Lead and zinc mines, of considerable importance, were opened up at Buchans, Newfoundland, in 1905, and have maintained production since, although the difficulties of building a railway into the bleak, rocky plateau, west of Red Indian Lake, and of erecting a company town there, were very considerable. A big lead and zinc mining area near Bathurst, New Brunswick, has been opened up, and is now an important producer.

The Canadian Appalachians are more noted for coal, however, than metals. It will be recalled that the central part of the Maritimes has been folded or faulted into a number of basins floored by Carboniferous rocks. These basins spread from eastern New Brunswick across to northern Nova Scotia. In them are bituminous-rich beds, well suited to the production of gas and coke. The largest and best coal fields are in Nova Scotia, the chief mines being at and around Sydney, at Inverness, in Cape Breton Island, and in the counties of Pictou and Cumberland, on the north shore. The coal lies in fairly thick seams close to the surface on the edge of the uplands. It slopes down to the sea. Therefore it can be easily mined and cheaply exported. Although it has been mined since 1749, there is still a large reserve, which has been estimated at about 36,000 million tons. The present rate of production is about 8 million tons a year, or nearly half that for all Canada.

About three-quarters of the production comes from the Sydney district, which covers 200 sq. miles, and extends up to three miles under the Atlantic. The chief centres of operation are at Sidney, Glace Bay, and New Waterford. The coal is a good quality bituminous and suitable for gas, steam, and coke. In New Brunswick, coal is the most important mining product. It comes from the Minto field. It is largely for local consumption, whereas Nova Scotia coal is mostly for the local steel mills or for export, and is shipped to Montreal or to Boston. Coal mining is, however, in decline.

Gypsum is, next to coal, the most plentiful mineral in the Maritimes, and occurs in the Windsor, Dingwall, Walton, and Cape Breton districts of Nova Scotia and at Hillsboro in New Brunswick. It is mined largely for export to New England, where it is used in the plaster, insulation, and paint industries. Natural gas, often found near gypsum, is used in the vicinity of Moncton.

The only other mining product of great value is salt. The oldest salt mine in Canada occurs at Malagash, where over 50,000 tons of salt a year used to be produced. Production has fallen, but is still important locally in the fish-curing industry.

In the division of the Atlantic region floored by the Shield, mining has been much more recent, but promises to be much greater, and to have a much wider impact on Canada as a whole. Here in the Labrador trough, partly in Quebec and partly in Labrador, lies one of the world's greatest deposits of iron. Although these iron beds were noted in geological reports last century, they were thought to be too remote and of too low a grade to be worth developing. But as the high-grade ores of Mesabi and elsewhere have been used up, low-grade ores have been turned to and, by the process of 'beneficiation', that is, roasting or magnetic concentration, have been brought up to a grade suitable for smelting. Actually, there are large bodies of high-grade ore within the Labrador iron zone, in an area of about 20,000 sq. miles around Schefferville, and also farther south in another extensive area around Gagnonville. These two centres are rapidly developing now that they have been connected to the harbours of Sept Iles and Port Cartier on the Gulf of St Lawrence. Already about 15 million tons of ore a year are being sent up the St Lawrence seaway to the great steel centres at Hamilton, Ontario; Cleveland, Ohio; and Gary, Indiana. An interesting thing about the Schefferville development is that although the town and much of the mining is in Quebec, the railway passes, for a considerable part of its way, through Labrador, thus involving, yet again, the closest co-operation between French and British Canada.

This brief outline of fishing, forestry, farming, and mining will have shown just how dependent the Atlantic region is on primary production. Indeed this is one of the chief things that distinguishes it from the Central Provinces. This also distinguishes it from New England so that, although older geographers may have lumped the Maritimes in with New England because of their similarity of geology, structure, and climate, the two areas can very well be considered to be separate. They are very different in the kind, rate, and intensity of their economic development. They are also different in the social traditions which have guided and guarded that development.

Amongst themselves the Atlantic Provinces also show notable differences: Newfoundland–Labrador is very dependent on mining and forestry; New Brunswick on forestry; and Prince Edward Island on farming. Nova Scotia presents the most balanced development, although mining is the major primary occupation. But agriculture, fishing, and forestry are about equally developed.

Province	*Mining*	*Fishing*	*Forestry*	*Agriculture*
Newfoundland	**24%**	7%	11%	1%
Prince Edward Island	—	10%	—	**44%**
New Brunswick	4%	2·5%	**14%**	10%
Nova Scotia	13%	6%	4·5%	6%

(Figures are the proportions of the total production of each province made by the main primary occupations.)

Manufacturing and Trade

Since the Atlantic region has concentrated on primary production, it does not offer much scope for manufacturing. In this it makes a striking contrast with the Central Provinces, accounting for only 4 per cent of Canada's total, as compared with 81 per cent by Ontario and Quebec. Manufacturing is less important than primary production in two of the provinces—Prince Edward Island and Newfoundland—and nowhere does it count for more than other occupations put together. Thus in Prince Edward Island it is responsible for only 16 per cent of the total production of the province; in Newfoundland, for about 30 per cent; in New Brunswick, for 49 per cent; and in Nova Scotia, for 45 per cent.

Prince Edward Island lacks any of the requirements of large-scale industry, such as fuel and metal resources, population and capital. Its industries are small and are mainly agricultural, processing the local produce for sale in wider markets in Canada and Britain. The making of butter and cheese, fish-curing and packing, slaughtering and meat-packing, and the canning of vegetables and fruits are the chief concerns. But they are very small concerns. There are about 200 plants, but they employ in all scarcely 1,800 men, or less than nine each! Compare this with New Brunswick, where about 1,000 plants employ over 22,000 people; or Nova Scotia, whose 1,400 plants employ 32,000 workers.

In Newfoundland, manufacturing consists in the main of processing raw materials, and is closely associated with fishing, forestry, or mining. There is very little production of secondary manufactured goods. However, the curing and canning of fish, the making of fertilizers from fish, and the manufacture of paper are all quite important—certainly for their district. They add considerably to the value of the primary product. (Thus the value of the fish catch varies from $11 to $14 millions a year; that of the fish processing industry is over $16 millions.) Most of the plants are small; there are only two employing more than 500 men each: on an average they employ less than a dozen workers each. Manufacturing actually accounts for barely 10 per cent of the province's work force. Corner Brook and Grand Falls are the chief manufacturing towns, making pulp and paper. St John's has a number of small fish-processing plants and ships' chandleries, but they are scattered and unimportant compared with the commercial establishments. They have not produced any marked industrial area.

St John's (95,000) dominates Newfoundland. It is one of the oldest cities in Canada, having been founded towards the close of the sixteenth century. It grew up about a remarkably sheltered and extensive harbour, in the ice-free section of the Avalon peninsula, opening on to a small plain, let into the rocky, ice-scraped upland. There is a long waterfront with numerous small quays, lined by warehouses. The fishing and coastwise trades use the central part of the port, the docks for ocean-going boats, and the rail and road terminals lying to north and south—facing gaps in the surrounding hills. A large naval dockyard occurs on the southern arm of the bay. The town lifts itself in tier on tier of streets, taking the contour of the steeply ascending land. The wooden box-like houses rise above the two short rows of shops found between harbour and hill.

In New Brunswick over three-quarters of the factories depend on local raw materials, such as lumber and pulp, fish, and agricultural and mineral products, but there is more opportunity than in Prince Edward Island for bringing in foreign raw materials, because the province is an important shipping and railway terminus. There is also some local production of coal. Moreover, since the rivers are long and uneven, with waterfalls and rapids, it has been possible to develop considerable hydro-electric power. Three large plants occur at Grand Falls, on the upper St John; Grand Fall, on the Nipisquit; and Aroostook Falls, on the Aroostook.

There are twelve towns each with an annual production of that of Prince Edward Island. But actually a great amount of the production is concentrated at Saint John and at Moncton, the important transportation centres. Both of these have risen out of their local environments as 'natural' centres of communication, Moncton at the head of the Bay of Fundy tidal bore, Saint John at the great reversing falls where tides and river currents rip alternately over a rocky bar at the mouth of the St John river. Yet both cities have extended their influence far beyond their immediate localities and have made other localities tributary to them. Thus they have become focal-points for new social regions, built up on railway and road, on market demands for milk and vegetables, and on services for a wide ring of rural communities. These social regions are now the predominant ones in south-east and east New Brunswick.

Moncton is a busy little city at the head of navigation in the Chignecto

29. Cornerbrook, Nfd. Here rugged terrain and a cold raw climate so common to the region have made for forests and lumbering.

The Atlantic and St Lawrence Gulf Region of Canada

30. Salmonhurst, N.B. The low sedimentary plains of the Maritimes are the site of potato and dairy farming.

31. Transcontinental railway terminal, Montreal.

32. The St Lawrence Seaway, new canals on former International Rapids section of the waterway.

33. Main multiple-lane highway from Montreal, P.Q., to Windsor, Ont., here seen near Galt.

branch of the Bay of Fundy. It is also the busiest railway junction in the Maritimes, where the three chief lines of New Brunswick come together before spreading out again in Nova Scotia. Moncton is the headquarters of the Atlantic division of the Canadian National Railway system, and has large repair shops and railway works. Foundries, transportation machinery, glass-making, and textiles are important industries. Natural gas from Stoney Creek is used for the glass industry and also for domestic lighting and heating. The city serves as the chief shopping centre for the east shore of New Brunswick and also for the north-west angle of Nova Scotia.

Of much greater importance is **Saint John** (98,000) which has come to dominate not only the lower St John and its main tributary the Kennebecasis but the lower St Croix as well. Indeed, its influence extends over the whole province, of which it is the commercial capital, while as one of Canada's two principal winter ports its influence extends right back to the Prairies.[1]

Although chiefly a trading centre, it has become a significant focus for industry. Not having been a great fortress town, like Halifax—which has much of its land tied up in military and naval establishments—it has had the freedom (where there has been the opportunity) to grow along industrial lines. It does not rank as one of Canada's main manufacturing cities—indeed no Atlantic city comes within the group of 'leading industrial centres'; that is, those shipping out more than $100 millions of manufactured goods, but it is important for its region, being the largest manufacturing city in the Atlantic Provinces.

What are some of its advantages? (*a*) It lies at the head of a large inlet, which provides shelter for shipping. (*b*) It commands the second shortest crossing between Canada and Britain, and is the nearest large port to the United States. (*c*) It is an open-water port, and therefore remains in operation after Quebec and Montreal are closed by ice. (*d*) It serves as an excellent transportation centre for New Brunswick itself, commanding the rich hinterland of the St John and Kennebecasis rivers, with direct connexions to Fredericton (the capital) and Moncton. (*e*) It is the eastern terminal of the vast, transcontinental C.P.R. system, and thus has good rail connexions with Montreal and Toronto and the rest of interior Canada. It can also use the C.N.R. line through Edmundston.

Thanks to these transportation advantages it may assemble raw materials and fuels at relatively low costs, and distribute its finished articles over a wide hinterland. Important industries are saw-milling and the manufacture of pulp and paper—making use of the great forest reserves of the province; sugar refining and the packing of coffee, tea, and spices—making use of overseas raw materials, needed in the interior markets; the spinning of

---

[1] Matheson, M. H., 'The Hinterlands of Saint John', *Geol. Bul.*, no. 7, 1955, p. 70. 'The Prairies Provinces . . . produce the greatest volume of Saint John's exports.'

cotton, depending on American sea connexions; the canning of fish, depending on the rich fisheries near by; and the manufacture of transportation equipment.

The city spreads out on either side of the Reversing Falls, on to points of land that jut out into the Bay of Fundy. At the centre lies beautiful King's Square Park, laid out like the Union Jack, with the old Court House (1830) facing it. Shops, large hotels, and business blocks crowd around. The streets then run south and west to another busy district of offices, factories, and warehouses by the port. Large C.N.R. and C.P.R. elevators stand east and west of the harbour entrance. The sugar refineries rise on the side of the bay, the pulp and paper mills farther north, on the edge of the river. Suburbs sweep up to low hills, looking out to the Atlantic or up the calm reaches of the St John.

A number of northern towns are famous for their forest products: Edmundston on the upper St John; Newcastle on the Miramichi; Bathurst on the Nipisquit; and Dalhousie on Chaleur Bay. They are on logging rivers that come down from the forested upland, or else on shores to which the forests reach. St Stephen and Milltown, using local water-power, and with good sea connexions, manufacture a variety of products, including lumber, pulp, and textiles. Sackville and the capital, Fredericton, are also noted for their variety of manufactures (such as pulp and paper, textiles, boots and shoes) carried on in small plants, using local materials or cheaply imported ones. At Fredericton is the University of New Brunswick.

In Nova Scotia manufacturing is more important in total output than in the other Atlantic Provinces. The deposits of coal are much larger; they are near to large deposits of iron in Newfoundland; other mineral products, such as gypsum and salt are available; while in addition there are extensive forests and fisheries, and regions of specialized agriculture, to supply raw materials. Nova Scotia is also nearer to foreign markets and is a main gateway for imports to the rest of Canada.

The nature of its industry differs from that in New Brunswick. Iron and steel manufacturing is first in importance; it is not important at all in New Brunswick. Fish-curing and packing is second in Nova Scotia, but fifth in New Brunswick. Ship-building is the third industry of Nova Scotia, but few ships are made in New Brunswick. On the other hand, saw mills and pulp and paper mills are fourth and fifth in Nova Scotia, but first and second in New Brunswick. Thus Nova Scotia has continued in the historic role of ship-building and fishing, which first brought prosperity to the Maritimes, and in addition has developed large-scale heavy industries.

There are thirteen towns producing over $1 million in manufactures every year. Of these the most important are Sydney and Halifax.

Sydney may be thought of as the most industrial city in the Atlantic region. It owes its development to the small but rich coal field, of which it is the centre. This stretches from Glace Bay in the east to Sydney Mines in the west and has given rise to five thriving towns. Sydney became the chief of these. Situated at the head of a long sheltered arm of the sea in the heart of the coal basin and at a focus of routes on the eastern peninsula of Cape Breton, it was able: (i) to import iron cheaply and easily from Bell Isle in Newfoundland; (ii) make ample amounts of coke and gas for smelting the iron ore and creating an important steel industry; and (iii) draw in milk and vegetables from quite a wide area to help feed its growing population and at the same time provide vital commercial and social services for this low and accessible district. The large harbour has given plenty of room for assembling and storing raw materials, and for plant expansion. Cheap water transportation allows for competitive marketing as far west as Montreal. Other important iron and steel towns are Pictou, Trenton, and New Glasgow, also on a coal field round a large, land-locked bay. Amherst, at the gateway to the province, is well known for its machine shops, making every component of a railway carriage, and also for its aeroplane industry. Stoves, furnaces, and engineering supplies are made at this good distribution centre.

Truro is a busy manufacturing town in the heart of the province. It is often called the hub of Nova Scotia, because railways and roads from north, south, and east converge there before going west. It is at the heart of a rich agricultural area, and goods can be brought in from a wide variety of farms. Truro has large condenseries and creameries, flour and feed mills, and knitting mills. Other centres of agricultural industries are Windsor, with a fertilizer plant and textile mills, and Middleton, with its canneries. Lunenburg and Yarmouth are important for fish canning and curing and building boats. Liverpool has several pulp and paper concerns.

Halifax (188,000—including Dartmouth) is, however, without question, the main industrial centre in Nova Scotia, though, as has been pointed out, manufacturing is not its chief role. It is fundamentally an administrative hub and a defence base, and is dominated by its naval dockyard, military fort and barracks, and government buildings. But dockyard and fort early called for supplies, repairs, and equipment, and so mills grew up. The main industries today consist of making naval supplies and machinery, boat making and repair, refining oil imported from Venezuela, brewing beer using British hops, making sugar from imported Caribbean and Latin American materials, manufacturing chocolates with cocoa from West Africa, weaving wool originally obtained locally but now principally from Uruguay and Australia, and canning and curing fish taken from the Nova Scotia Banks.

In nearly all cases industry is dependent on imported raw materials and fuels; that is, on sea contacts. The harbour is, then, of tremendous importance. It is a truly magnificent one, consisting of a deep-water 'narrows', where the port has developed, and the wide stretch of Bedford basin behind, where railways, coal dumps, and oil depots have found room for expansion. Halifax is one of Canada's leading ports and the chief winter port on the east coast. It is the eastern terminal of the great Canadian National Railway transcontinental system. It handles about 6–7 million tons of shipping annually, with an average of 2,500 ships entering and leaving every year. Saint John handles about 3 million tons, and less than 1,000 ships. It is interesting to compare the two ports:

Comparison of Port Facilities	*Halifax*	*Saint John*
Minimum depth	51 ft.	30 ft.
Number of piers	88	34
Length of berthing	35,416 ft.	24,175 ft.
Transit shed floor space	1,464,804 sq. ft.	1,000,000 sq. ft.
Cold storage capacity	1,750,000 cu. ft.	900,000 cu. ft.
Grain elevator capacity	4,200,000 bu.	3,000,000 bu.
Coal-dock storage capacity	115,000 tons	34,000 tons
Oil tank storage capacity	200,000,000 gal.	35,000,000 gal.

Its main imports are oil and petroleum, coal and coke, salt, wool, molasses, cocoa, tea, and coffee; and its main exports, wheat (from western Canada) and gypsum (a Nova Scotia product). During the winter its hinterland expands to the Prairies and the port is extremely busy; but in summer, when the ice in the St Lawrence melts away, it faces the competition of Montreal, and much of its business lapses.

The city is a very striking one. It has grown up on a small rocky peninsula between two narrow arms of the sea—one a cul-de-sac used by yacht clubs, the other, Chebucto Bay, offering a long waterfront, crowded with shipping. The town was laid out in 1749 on a well-marked marine bench under the shelter of a massive drumlin and above a steeply shelving beach. The drumlin was crowned by a huge fort—Halifax Citadel. The marine bench gave rise to a town square—now flanked by cathedral and town hall, with beneath it a business square, partly taken up by Parliament Building, and partly by banks, insurance offices, and trading concerns. The lower beach was transformed by a long line of quays from the naval dockyard at the north end, past the fishing jetties, to the great commercial terminal in the south, where transoceanic and transcontinental traffic meets. The universities and schools have now mainly moved from the old crowded part of the peninsula, just behind the port, to quieter and more open parts, facing the mainland (Fig. 85).

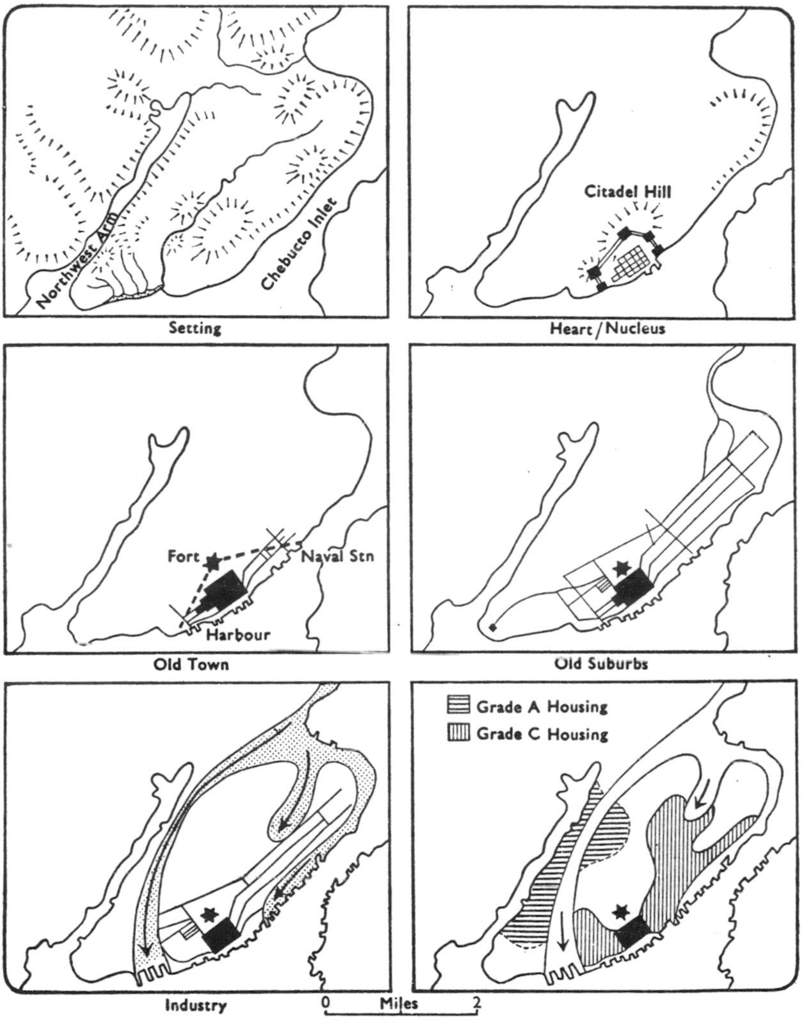

FIG. 85 Significant patterns in the growth of Halifax. The city grew up on a rocky peninsula, ridged with drumlins. The nucleus was established between the Citadel, on the largest drumlin, and the Harbour on the coast. The old town spread along the shore as a Naval Base developed to the north, and a transatlantic terminal to the south. Suburban growth then moved farther north and south along Chebucto Inlet. Industry advanced into the city in three prongs following the advent of the railways, and better housing moved across the peninsula to the shelter of Northwest Arm.

Halifax has come to dominate a very wide area and to create a city-centred region which now engulfs most of central and southern Nova Scotia. It draws its milk, butter, and eggs from farms in isolated bays along the east coast from Sheet Harbour to Mahone Bay, as well as from farms in the Minas basin. Its green market regularly obtains vegetables and fruit from the Annapolis valley. Its daily paper has a wide circulation from Canso Strait south—and, indeed, throughout the province, and east of Springhill it forms the chief insurance and banking centre. One of its banks, the Bank of Nova Scotia, has nation-wide significance. Halifax is indeed the metropolis of the east and is rapidly becoming a favoured centre for residential, commercial, and industrial expansion.

Conclusion: Problems and Opportunities

The Atlantic region is fairly rich in resources, and has an industrious and educated population. It is able to produce well above its own needs. Nevertheless, it has not developed as fully as neighbouring regions in the United States or as the Central Provinces of Canada. It has remained in a primary stage of production, depending on agriculture, forestry, mining, and fishing. Its manufactures are small, and consist chiefly of processing raw materials rather than making a large number of finished goods.

The region depends on primary products chiefly: (*a*) because of the excellent markets for them in the U.S.A. and Great Britain, and (*b*) because of the difficulty of finding markets for its industrial products. The great shortage of wood in the United States and Britain, and particularly of wood-pulp, provides a ready demand for sawn timber, pulp, and paper. The need for dairy products and fruit in Britain stimulates farming in the Maritimes. America buys large quantities of oysters and lobsters from the inshore fisheries. Other markets for fish are found in southern Europe, the West Indies, and Latin America. The United States also takes most of the gypsum mined in the Maritimes.

Thus there are good opportunities for primary production, with cheap transport to markets; but secondary production meets with serious problems. In the first place, both Britain and America have protective tariffs to keep out Canadian manufactured goods. At the same time, Canadian tariffs on foreign goods have worked against the sea-borne trade of the Atlantic region. Ships cannot go out laden with manufactured goods and count on paying their way home by bringing in foreign goods. The foreign markets raise high barriers against Canadian industries (except factories processing needed raw materials), while Canada keeps out both manufactured goods and raw materials (except those it cannot itself produce).

Unfortunately, the interior Canadian market is as limited as the foreign one. Although the Atlantic region has a great, natural gateway to the interior, the cheap and easy water connexions by way of the St Lawrence gulf to Quebec and Montreal are shut off for six months of the year by the winter freeze. The overland railway haul is long and costly, and raises the price of Maritimes products. (Should the same products be made in the Central Provinces they could be distributed and sold at a lower cost.) The Atlantic region is not the only gateway to the interior. Imported raw materials may come into Canada by other routes than the Maritimes; for example, by the Gulf of St Lawrence and Montreal, during the summer, or by the Hudson–Mohawk gap and the Niagara peninsula. Therefore, the Maritimes cannot monopolize the industries, such as packing coffee and tea, refining sugar, molasses and oil, making leather and textile goods, and distributing consumer goods, which characterize importing centres. Montreal can share in these industries and then redistribute the processed products more cheaply. Then again, the Maritimes are too remote from the interior to act as the chief exporting regions of Canada; Montreal and New York are much closer to the heart of Canada and compete in the export of Canadian wheat and other products. Of course, when Montreal is closed, then the Maritime ports are the chief eastern outlets of Canada; but they cannot monopolize the export trade. Finally, the goods which the Atlantic region manufactures are mostly from agricultural and forest materials, which are in abundance in interior Canada. The only goods for which there is a ready demand are fish, seed potatoes, and farm-bred furs. Iron and steel have a limited market in Quebec province, but scarcely west of Montreal.

As a result of all these factors, the Atlantic region has failed to develop as rapidly as other parts of Canada. In 1871, shortly after Confederation, the Maritimes accounted for 13 per cent by value of all Canadian production; today, even including Newfoundland, the Atlantic region barely contributes 4 per cent. The total volume of business has grown, but the relative position of the section has declined.

Here again we see how history affects geography, since new discoveries or new economic policies have constantly altered the location of industry, and changed the relative importance of one industrial area compared with another. When Canada was first occupied by the British, the Maritimes led because they dominated a trade-economy which was closely linked with the Motherland. But as Canada expanded into the interior, and especially when it developed an industrial economy, in rivalry with Great Britain, then the Central Provinces became most important, and the Maritimes became, in Newbigin's pregnant phrase, 'the land that was passed by'.

CHAPTER TWELVE

Central Settled Canada

A key section of Canada consists of the continuously settled portion of the Central Provinces. It is a key section in that here the two chief English-speaking and French-speaking groups in the land live and work together; here is the natural link between the coast and the interior, between the Eastern and the Western Provinces, a link made all the more effective by the St Lawrence seaway; here is the nation's greatest development of finance, trade, and industry; here is Canada's chief concentration of population; and here the capital of the country.

The section is based on the joint occupation by the French and the British of the St Lawrence–Lower Great Lakes lowland, and tributary valleys, and the highly integrated and distinctive use to which that lowland has been put (see Fig. 77, Chapter 10).

Although part of a single physiographic unit, the St Lawrence basin, it is not to be treated as one with the remainder of that unit which lies in the United States. Unity of landform does not necessarily produce unity of landscape. Different uses of landform create landscapes different enough to express a sense of regional difference. This is important. Russell Smith recognizes it, to the extent of treating the lower part of the basin—the St Lawrence valley proper, where French influences predominate—as at least separate from the remainder. His inclusion of the Ontario portion of the Lower Great Lakes plain with the Lakes plain of the American Dairy Belt shows less regard for the significance of culture. White and Foscue's assumption that the dominance of industrialism in southern Quebec and Ontario necessarily places them in the American Manufacturing Belt, while true enough within this limited context, ignores other cultural factors, although these factors may be *felt* to be more significant by the people living in the region. Unity in dairy production or industrial output has not been regarded by Canadians as outweighing divisions of history, land settlement, law, language, and loyalty—in a word, ideology.

Actually the northern part of the basin, now in Canada, has differed from the southern part, now in the United States, for hundreds of years. In terms of cultural geography, it is doubtful whether there has ever been a period in which the area was united. Certainly in late Indian times it was a region divided. The Algonquins lived all along its northern part, the Iroquois along its southern fringe. In between were the Hurons, and the Neutrals. Reference has already been made to the way in which the arrival of the French and British exacerbated the bitter rivalries that existed, and further split the region. The French alliance with the Algonquins and Hurons led to fierce retaliation by the Iroquois, supported by the British. The Iroquois overran the Hurons and then, in the sharp struggle of the Beaver Wars, conquered the Neutrals. The French made a determined effort to throw back the Iroquois and cleared the St Lawrence–Lower Great Lakes route to the west.

The first period of white domination saw anything but peace and unity; the area was split from end to end. However, after 1666 the valleys of the Richelieu, St Lawrence, and Ottawa rivers, together with the north shore of Ontario and the basin of Lake Erie became unified by the French and was given the name of Canada, or Quebec Province.

Conflict and division soon broke out again as the French and British came into direct collision (mainly in the Champlain and Ontario plains), in their contest for the continent. The British won, and in taking over from the French, more or less accepted the former boundaries, although they enlarged Quebec Province to the south-west and west. They had not the time to develop it, however, before they were themselves divided and plunged into civil war. The Republican British, who became the Americans, took over the southern fringe of the area, leaving Loyalist British and the French the lands along the north shores of Lake Champlain, of the St Lawrence, and of the Great Lakes (see Figures 43, 44, 59).

Many United Empire Loyalists entered the area, moving into the Eastern Townships of Quebec, crossing the St Lawrence, and settling the northern shore of lakes Ontario and Erie. They emphatically thought of this new home as different from America. Most of them poured through the Champlain and Mohawk gaps, but swiftly spread out, once on the St Lawrence and lakeshore lowlands. As a result, British now vied with French for the use of the area.

However, they did so without conflict. The fact that, after the conquest of Quebec, the British had secured to the French their religion, language, and laws, established a basis for mutual respect and co-operation. Furthermore, the fact that the French had fought with the Loyalists against the Americans, in the American revolution, and later joined their English-speaking compatriots to fight the Americans with equal fervour in the war of 1812–14, further cemented the two groups together. Consequently, an *Anglo-French bi-cultural* development began which was to make the northern or Canadian part of the St Lawrence–Great Lakes basin something quite different from the southern, American part. A new 'culture area' was established, producing a new cultural landscape, that made a distinctly Canadian region north of the frontier.

Once again, a so-called natural region, the St Lawrence basin, gave way to human divisions, first along the borders of national areas, and then along the sectional bounds within the nations. Not unnaturally there were differences of outlook and approach as between English- and French-speaking Canadians, but these were submerged beneath the common resistance to a common threat. The American support of Canadian dissident groups, notably of the 1837 rebels, the talk of war during the Oregon Crisis (54° 40′ or fight!), and the Fenian raids of the 'sixties and 'seventies did much to bring and keep English and French together in Canada. Thereafter, although

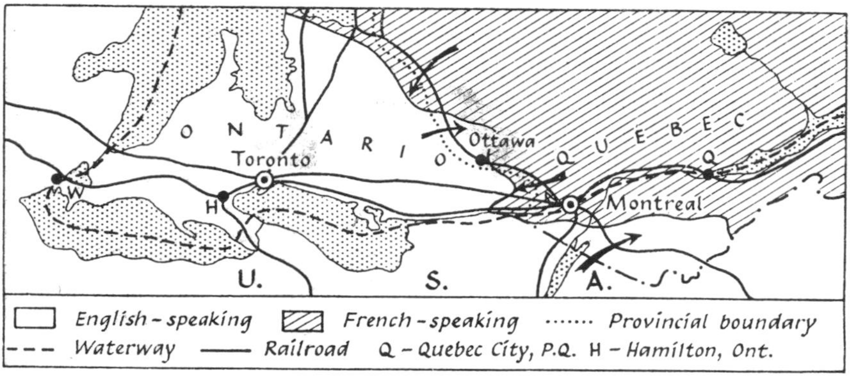

FIG. 86 Southern Ontario and Quebec, diverse yet unified. Although Ontario is often thought of as English-speaking, and Quebec as French-speaking, each has important minority groups from the other—a basis for bi-cultural development. Each is tied to the other by canals, railways, and roads, and by an economy jointly dependent on the Lower Lakes–St Lawrence System.

pressure from outside came to an end, the groups inside the frontier continued to work together, and became more and more bound to each other by transportation and trade and other aspects of the Canadian economy (Fig. 86).

Actually, the French Canadian and the Loyalist traditions are strangely alike, although they differ in many details. Both go back to Europe before the French Revolution or the British Civil War. Both carry forward ideals repudiated by the Americans. Both are influenced by a profound respect for the past. 'One cannot exaggerate the cult of the past', claims Michel, 'in French Canadian life.' In Ontario, too, it is ever present, protected by many societies formed specifically to revere and protect the European heritage, societies whose buildings often dominate village and town. (How different from America which, according to Turner, grew by a 'necessary and deliberate abandonment of what was old'.[1]) Both British and French have

[1] Taylor, G. R., *The Turner Thesis concerning the role of the Frontier in American History*, Boston, 1949, p. 69.

also shown the strongest loyalty to the Church, particularly to the Anglican and the Roman Catholic branches, i.e. to the 'establishment'. They have originated few new faiths. These, such as Mormonism, Christian Science, Seventh Day Adventism, Pentecostalism, Jehovah's Witnesses, tend to spring up in, or become characteristic of, regions south of the border.

Both Canadian groups have a strong patriotic sense. This is particularly marked among the French who are so conscious of their uniqueness in a continent which, north of the Rio Grande, is predominantly English-speaking, that they have come to regard themselves as, in some ways, a race apart. Loyalty to 'race' is tremendously important to them, and is a major factor in their survival as an ethnic group. As Foisy has maintained, 'quand la race ne veut pas mourir, on ne peut la tuer'. This loyalty to the race entails respect for the family. 'La famille, le sol, et le travail', are three essentials of French-Canadian faith. In French-Canadian life, Quebec is no more than the family, enlarged.

Both Loyalists and French have a deep attachment to the soil, and to the rural virtues. They are still rural by nature and mentality, even where they have become townsmen. As Hertel remarks, they are integrated with the countryside. (This is especially true of Quebec which, though highly industrialized, seems rooted into the soil.) Consequently, both people are conservative, even while they adapt themselves to changing circumstances. Each has a profound sense of duty, of dignity, of respect for self and for others, and a feeling for the 'rightness of things', which go back to the need of a life balanced with nature.

Consequently, in spite of their initial rivalries and the differences that still remain, both groups have an understanding of each other that has given them a working unity and thus given unity to the section in which they live. As a result, natural features common to the region have been picked out and exploited, and diverse elements brought into a general interdependence, in a quite unique way (see Fig. 86).

THE PHYSICAL ENVIRONMENT

The section is made up of three elements, the southern part of the Canadian Shield, the interior lowlands of the St Lawrence and Great Lakes, and the western slope of the Canadian Appalachians. Essentially, it is based on the lowland, and is tied into the uplands of the Shield and to the Appalachian mountains by rivers caught up within the St Lawrence system. It has a continental climate where the luxurious growth of brief hot summers becomes mantled under thick winter snows. Hardwood forests are conspicuous, but rapidly give way on morainic hill or rocky upland to coniferous woods. Good soils in the southern parts and marginal ones in the north further contribute to the diversity of conditions. The great river of the St Lawrence threads all these things together.

The Relief of the Land

The relief varies mainly as the structure, but is also markedly affected by glaciation and by post-glacial changes in land- and sea-level.

In the Appalachian division moderately high but steep mountains form a triple barrier between Canada and America. The rocks have been hardened by long and intensive folding, and also strengthened by granitic intrusions. They form rolling plateau country, mainly about 2,000 feet, deeply cut into by rivers. The drainage is very complex because of the parallel folds, the faulting, and the long history of erosion. A rather typical 'rectilinear' pattern has developed, in which parts of the rivers flow in south-west to north-east paths, along the line of the folds, and other parts form deep, gorge-like sections, across the folds. Thus, although the air-line distance from head-water to mouth is quite short, the length of the rivers may be considerable. The youthful sections, with their deep valleys, rushing currents and waterfalls offer sites for power plants. The hydro power is used by many mills in southern Quebec.

Farther east the mountains are higher, until in the Shickshocks they reach over 4,000 feet. Here a massive granite intrusion appears through the surrounding sedimentaries. Yet the plateau likeness has not disappeared. The top of the Shickshocks consists of a flat surface, which is part of the great Summit peneplain that, as has been seen, stretches across most of the Appalachians. This peneplain is probably the same one which is met again in the Shield, and is evident in the flat tops of uplands such as the Laurentides, Mt Tremblant, and the heights north of the Saguenay.

The Shield forms a large but marginal part of the region, reaching from the Upper Great Lakes eastwards to the St Lawrence estuary. It makes a broad warp, with hard crystalline rocks in the centre sloping down to sedimentaries in the Hudson Bay and the St Lawrence lowlands. Small areas of sedimentary rocks are found in hollows in the Shield around Lac St Jean and Lake Temiskaming. A pronounced spur of Shield country, known as the Frontenac axis, runs southward through Ontario to cut the region in two, in the vicinity of Kingston. Relics of it make up the Thousand Islands at the foot of Lake Ontario, beyond which it is continued into the Adirondacks.

The surface of the Shield is remarkably uniform. Erosion has proceeded for such a long time that the great mountain ranges of the past have disappeared; only their stumps remain. The landscape varies little from place to place. Everywhere it appears as a series of broad, flat-topped, but knubbly hills, sweeping down rather abruptly to wide valleys or lake-filled basins. The ridges of old rock thrusting through the glacial clays and sands are like the giant ribs of the country, showing its essential build.

During the last Ice Age, vast sheets of ice moved southwards from the Patricia district and from Labrador, to cover the whole region. The ice scoured the upland, flattening the hills and deepening the valleys. It left morainic deposits, and created lakes and outwash channels which have made very irregular drainage patterns. When the ice-front retreated northward it gave rise to glacial lakes. In these lakes were deposited thick beds of clay. Long sandy beaches formed which became exposed when the waters shrank to their present level. Lake-bottom plains and lake-beach terraces form very characteristic features in the Shield. Glacial Lake Algonquin, which spread north of Lake Superior and Lake Huron, has left clay plains around Fort William and Nipigon and in the Sault Ste Marie–North Bay districts. The last of the glacial lakes was Ojibway, which filled a depression in the Shield right across north-central Ontario into Quebec. This now forms the Great Clay Belt. These clay plains, left behind by the ice, compose the chief agricultural areas of the north. They are islands of cultivation in a sea of forest and waste.

As soon as the ice melted, rivers began their attack. They tended to take over from ice-gouged valleys and depressions and, as a result, their courses are very irregular. Here they are dammed up into shallow freshwater lakes by moraines; there they fill rock-cut basins with much deeper lakes; or again, their courses have been deflected by the ice, and they wind in a seemingly haphazard fashion; or they follow ice-deepened gorges in swift currents and waterfalls. Where they flow into the Gulf of St Lawrence their mouths have been drowned. Thus rivers start in rather ill-drained marshy divides on the Laurentian plateau, flow through lake sections, meander over peneplain surfaces, roar down glacial gorges, fall in rapids or waterfalls over rock ledges, and in some cases enter the sea in long, deep fjords. These characteristics make them ideal both for logging purposes, and the development of hydro-electricity. Famous power developments are those at Cameron Falls, Des Joachims, Gatineau, Shawinigan, and Shipshaw.

Both the Appalachian upland and the Shield are rich in minerals. They offer raw materials for the industries of the St Lawrence lowland, and also buy food and fish from the lowland villages. Asbestos is the most important product of the Appalachian uplands; nickel, copper, and gold of the Shield. When the Algoman mountains were evolving, they buckled up the Keewatin lavas and Timiskaming sandstones into sharp folds. The folds often broke into a number of fractures, up which gold was forced. The chief gold mines of today are therefore associated with these ancient veins. The fundamental structure seems to be a basin of Keewatin and Timiskaming rocks intruded by Algoman granite. This is found at all the great gold camps such as Porcupine, Kirkland Lake, Larder Lake, and Little Long Lac. Similarly, the iron deposits of Steep Rock Lake are preserved in folds in Keewatin and Timiskaming rocks.

The later Killarnean folds are also important because they are filled with veins of nickel and copper, and with lesser amounts of gold, silver, and platinum. The enormous nickel deposits at Sudbury are of this age; as are the silver deposits of Cobalt, South Lorrain, and Gowganda.

The Shield abuts on the Rainy river and on Lakes Superior and Huron as far south as Georgian Bay, and then swings east to Mattawa, and so to Quebec. However, it sends a long finger south-east to Kingston, and to the Adirondacks. In this south-eastern portion Grenville limestones contain a variety of small mineral deposits.

The St Lawrence–Great Lakes lowland forms the heart of the section. It makes a great depression, often bounded by faults, between Shield and Appalachians. It is divided into two distinct districts by the hard rocks of the Frontenac axis, coming to the surface in the Rideau hills. To the east lie a series of basins; the St Lawrence estuary below the rock of Quebec, the middle St Lawrence plains below the former International Rapids, and the Ottawa valley, between the Rideau and Gatineau hills—all united by the St Lawrence system. The estuary is marked by pronounced raised sea-beaches. The middle plains, which were once covered by the Champlain Sea, also witness strand-lines, marked by boulder-strewn beaches, as well as wide terraces—former beach platforms. A remnant of the glacial seas is Lac St Pierre, which lies in an area of weak rocks deeply gouged by ice. Morainic deposits extend east of the lake towards Quebec. Tributaries, such as the Richelieu and the St Maurice, flow into the Lac St Pierre depression across sandy deltas. The whole area from the lake to Montreal is very flat, and, as Vézina says, gives the strange impression of limitless horizons.[1] Here the Monteregian hills occur, stretching south from Mt Royal (that crowns Montreal). These are exhumed ancient igneous stocks. A stretch of hard rock west of Montreal has checked the river and is responsible for the famous Lachine rapids. These have been got around by the Lachine canal, the first in the great system of canals making up the St Lawrence seaway. The swift waters of the river supply power for the Beauharnois power plant. Farther west the plain becomes constricted by limestone rocks, sloping down from the Frontenac axis. It passes over a low scarp into the Ottawa basin, a wide valley bounded on the north by the Laurentian fault scarp. Here old glacial lake terraces give a step-like landscape, descending from the arms of the Shield. The Ottawa itself, and a number of its tributaries,

[1] Vézina, F., 'La Région du Saint-Laurent', in *Notre Milieu*, ed. Minville, E., Montreal, 1942, p. 62.

like the Petawawa, Rideau, and Nation, built up large sandy deltas into the receding waters of the former glacial seas (Fig. 87).

West of the Frontenac axis lie the plains of central and south-west Ontario. These consist of a belted lowland of sedimentary rocks worn into scarp and vale by prolonged river erosion. The earliest rivers probably flowed south-west, across all the different belts of rock. Tributaries developed from the north-west and the south-east. These attacked the weaker shales and wore them into vales, like the Ontario plain, or the Erie plain. They left the harder limestones standing up between as escarpments, like the famous Niagara escarpment, and the much less conspicuous Onondaga scarp. The region has a soft, gently moulded outline of wide vales, across which meandering rivers wind, deep in water meadows, dominated by the forested slopes of the escarpments. Rich farms and busy cities dot the plains.

During the Ice Age, the drainage of southern Ontario was completely altered. For example, the river flowing from Georgian Bay to Toronto was buried. So was that flowing from the Erie basin to the Ontario basin by the Dundas valley. The Great Lakes gradually evolved, drowning most of the dales. New channels were made between the lakes. The Niagara river displaced the Dundas valley; the Trent river drained Georgian Bay into Lake Ontario; at one time the Mattawa river carried the waters of Lake Huron and Lake Nipissing into the Ottawa valley. The Grand river and the Thames had their courses altered by moraines and outwash channels. These lakes and old channels form a marvellous network of natural routes, which have been followed by canal, road, and railway, to make southern Ontario one of the most accessible parts of Canada. Indeed, these routeways are the basis of its industrial growth and prosperity.

In some places the ice has exaggerated features, in others it has masked them. It has, for example, exposed rocky limestone uplands by stripping them of soil, so that in many parts the rock is revealed to form a jagged surface. Such limestone plains occur along the north and south edges of the Frontenac axis, and along parts of the Niagara escarpment from the Bruce peninsula to the Niagara peninsula (see Fig. 87).

The ice deposited masses of ground moraine, to form rolling till plains, together with long, uneven morainic ridges. The most conspicuous are the Horseshoe moraine in south-west Ontario, and the Oak Ridges moraine in Central Ontario. The ice also left many small drumlins and eskers, which fan out from Georgian Bay and Lake Ontario. In eastern Ontario there is a large scattering of drumlins, suggesting a sweep of ice from the north and north-east.

The glacial lakes also left many deposits of lacustrine clays which extend over the coastal regions of Georgian Bay, Lake Huron, Lake Erie and Lake Ontario, and also reach into the Lake Simcoe and Kawartha Lakes

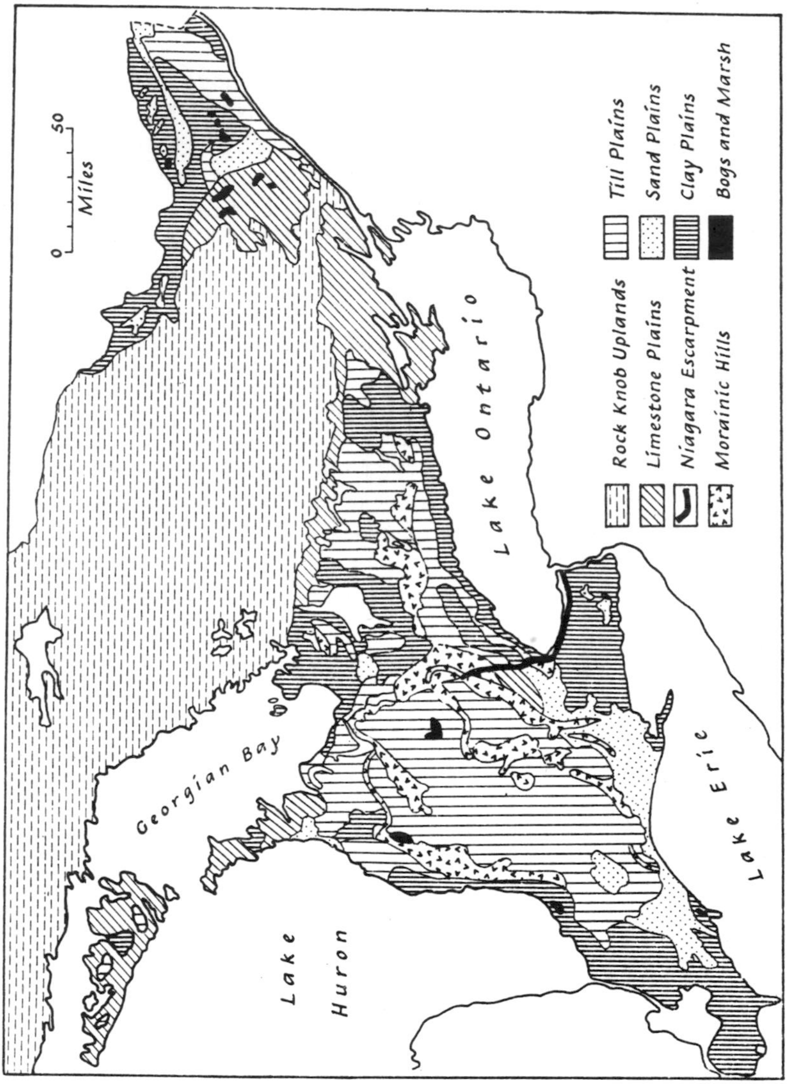

FIG. 87 The Physiography of southern Ontario. (After Putnam and Chapman.)

depression, and up the Ottawa valley. The various levels through which the lakes shrank are marked by stranded beaches. Finally, as the lakes receded, the rivers advanced steadily and formed deltas, spreading sheets of sand over the lacustrine clays. The largest areas of deltaic sand lie between the Middle Thames and the Middle and Lower Grand river. They add variety to the flat plains; some of them are very fertile and form good farm land, some are relatively barren and have been left in forest (see Fig. 87).

Thus, although the St Lawrence–Great Lakes lowland may not have strong relief, it is very varied, and this variety of landscape helps to produce an extremely varied agriculture. This is all to the good, because the structure of the region does not sponsor mineral development. About the only mineral products of any value are small oil deposits and some natural gas under the Erie plain, quantities of gypsum in the Niagara peninsula, and building stone from the Niagara escarpment. It is the rich agriculture, and, above all, the natural routeways of the lowland, that have made it the hub of the country.

Climate, Soils, and Vegetation

The climates of the region can be divided into three major zones. The northern parts, roughly equated with the Shield, have a cool-to-cold, very snowy climate, with a short cool summer, and a long severe winter. The northern-central and eastern valleys have a microthermal climate with a short warm summer, and a less severe winter. In the Montreal plain and south-western Ontario a distinctly more temperate climate occurs, with comparatively long warm summers.

Along the edge of the Shield the climate is controlled very largely by the polar continental air mass. It has long severe winters, with at least four months of weather below freezing, and short cool summers, with less than four months over 50° F. A mass of cold, rather dry air covers the region the entire winter, and since relatively few cyclones occur there is little relief from the cold. (The main cyclone track is farther south, across the Great Lakes.) Spring is delayed because a large part of the sun's heat is used in thawing the snow and the frozen ground. Therefore the summers are short. However, compensating for this are the long summer days, which stimulate growth. In sheltered localities it is even possible to raise good crops. Nevertheless, widespread agriculture is out of the question. The growing season is too short, and the soils are too poor. Frost varies so much and the rains at the harvest-time are so heavy that only the hardier crops find it possible to flourish. In the months of August and September, when the crops are ready for harvest, cool, drizzly weather happens, with an overcast sky. As a result, harvesting is often spoiled and the crops ruined.

Consequently, the high hopes for extensive agricultural settlement, as for example in the Clay Belt, have subsided. Most of the basins in the Shield will continue to remain chiefly under balsam and black spruce mixed with aspen and white birch. As Dagenais remarks, the Shield, though so rich in many other respects, is, from the point of view of climate, the least attractive region in Quebec for settlement.[1]

The valleys sloping down from the Shield have a moderately cool climate. Compared with the Clay Belt the winters are milder (14°–18° F.) as a result of more frequent cyclones, which draw in air from the lake districts; the springs are warmer and shorter—the soil is not so difficult to thaw; and the growing season is longer, there being 100 to 120 frost-free days. Summer frost is very rare, while summers, though cool (64°–66° F.), are bright and sunny. The annual precipitation is from 30 to 40 inches, of which 10 to 12 inches fall as snow. Thus conditions are more favourable to growth. The original forest consisted of magnificent stands of white pine along with fir, hemlock, and maple. Most of the pine has been cut out, and replaced by second-growth hardwoods like maple, bass, poplar, and birch. The soils are a weak podsol or brown podsolic type, with only a thin leached layer, and they require expert management to be made agriculturally successful. 'Inherent acidity has to be corrected by the application of lime, and the lack of phosphorus by fertilizer. Coarse sandy areas are useless for agriculture. Areas of gentle relief, such as the clay and sand plains, are frequently poorly drained.'[2]

The climates of the Middle St Lawrence and the Lower Great Lakes are the most productive in the region, with cold but not bitter winters and with distinctly warm summers. The Montreal plain is quite protected, and in summer is much warmer (70° July average) than the lowlands bordering the St Lawrence estuary (63°). It opens westward to the Lower Lakes and Ohio valley, and south and eastward to the Atlantic coast. Thus it attracts warm, moist tropical gulf and moist Atlantic air. Only in the depth of winter is it absolutely dominated by the polar continental air mass, when temperatures, normally 12°–15° F. (January), may drop to −30° F.

Climatically, the plain is the only region in Quebec suited to intensive land use and dense settlement. With the highest temperatures and longest growing season, it also has the heaviest and most regular rainfall. An average of over 40 inches a year falls in the strip between Montreal and Quebec. This is due to the cyclonic storms of winter and spring, and to the thunderstorm rain of summer. The autumn is fairly dry, and good for harvests. There is a heavy winter snowfall of over 8 feet, which protects the soil

[1] Dagenais, P., 'La Région des Laurentides', in *Notre Milieu*, ed. Minville, E., p. 108.

[2] Richards, J. H., 'Land Types in the Precambrian Shield Area of S. Ontario', *Geog. Bul.*, no. 13, 1959, p. 58.

from really penetrating frosts, yet melts away quickly enough in spring to allow for spring sowing.

Originally, the plain was covered with a hardwood forest of maple and beech, along with elm, oak, hickory, and butternut. This was floored with a fairly deep-brown forest soil.

South-west Ontario is even warmer than the plain of Montreal and is, in fact, one of the warmest regions in Canada. This is due to a combination of low latitude, low altitude, the presence of large bodies of water, and shelter from the polar airs. Winters are comparatively mild, 24°–27° F., with minima of —25° to —15° F. The protecting effects of the lake waters, and the numerous cyclones bringing warm air from the south, prevent excessive cold, and consequently orchards and winter wheat are at a high premium. The Leamington and Niagara fruit belts are famous. In the summer, the low latitude ensures comparatively high average temperatures (68°–71° F.), while the invasion of heat waves from the Mississippi–Ohio raises the maxima to 105°. The long, hot summer days are very good for vegetables and fruit, sweet corn, and tobacco. They account for the many sub-tropic or Carolinian types of plants—the Kentucky coffee tree, pawpaw, gum tree, magnolias, and sassafras—which may be found. Above all, there is a relatively long growing season, including 140 to 170 days free of frost, giving the farmer a great advantage over competitors in other parts of Canada. A water surplus built up from winter snows and early summer rains more than offsets rainfall deficiency in the autumn (Fig. 88).

The forest originally consisted of a thick growth of tall hardwoods, such as maple, oak, hickory, butternut, and walnut. From the rich humus they supplied, there developed grey-brown earths. These are fairly deep, and have a lot of organic matter, which is well mixed with the soil minerals. The organic matter (the A1 horizon) is well decomposed (the result of plenty of leaf mould and a warm, wet climate). There is a leached layer (A2) beneath, but it does not show the intensive leaching of the podsols. Beneath this is a well-formed layer (B) of accumulation of iron and aluminium salts. The extent to which the organic matter has been mixed in with the mineral soil helps agriculture. No lime is needed on 80 per cent of these soils. After the prairie soils, they are probably the richest in Canada.

THE HUMAN RESPONSE

The St Lawrence–Great Lakes lowland is favoured by a great diversity of relief, climate, and soil, and also by a diversity of peoples and their cultures. On one of the great immigration routes, that of the St Lawrence estuary, it is close to the metal mines and lumber camps of the Shield and to the wealth of fuel in the (American) Appalachians, while in itself it possesses considerable

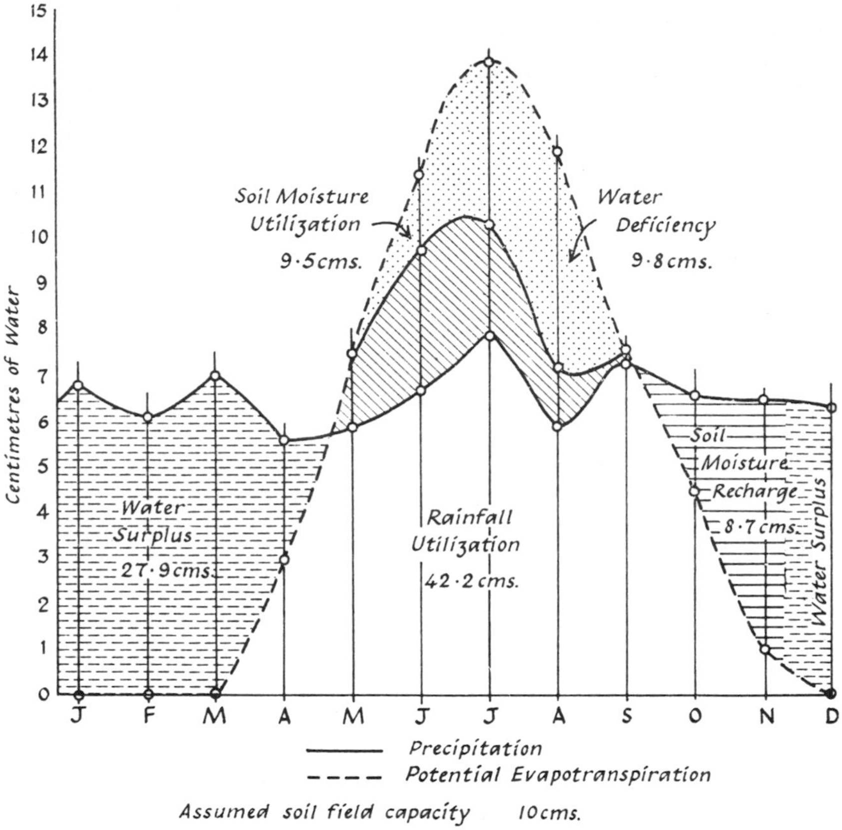

FIG. 88 Typical climatic features of southern Ontario—water surplus and deficiency with the seasons; Hamilton, Ontario. Although late summer droughts are common, they are usually compensated for by soil moisture built up in the periods of water surplus.

agricultural potential (see Fig. 74, Chapter 10). These facts have helped to make it the chief section of economic development and population growth in Canada. Indeed, one is astonished to find to what extent it has concentrated the country's prosperity within its bounds. As has been pointed out, Ontario and Quebec produce 81 per cent of all the goods made in Canada; Ontario making 53 per cent, Quebec 28 per cent. In fact, this region ranks as one of the continent's major manufacturing centres.

It is interesting to note that Ontario manufactures 96 per cent of Canada's automobiles, 96 per cent of its agricultural machinery, 88 per cent of its leather goods, 81 per cent of its rubber goods, 76 per cent of its electrical appliances, 70 per cent of its canned goods, 68 per cent of its refined metal and iron and steel products, 60 per cent of its woollen goods, 60 per cent of its hosiery, and 60 per cent of its flour and bread products. Quebec is responsible for 68 per cent of the cotton goods, 68 per cent of women's finished clothing and 58 per cent of men's, and over 50 per cent of Canada's wood products.

This outstanding development has been made largely by capitalizing on local geographical advantages. The adjustment to the land has nowhere been finer or more effective. As a result local differences have made themselves very apparent in the landscape. This has continued to be the case; in fact, has increasingly become the case, as farming has grown to be more scientific, and industry more efficient (Fig. 89).

In addition to the local differences, there are some overall contrasts, as between French and British forms of land survey and patterns of settlement and, above all, as between rural and urban development and population. Thus the whole sector is full of interest and has pronounced characteristics of its own.

The exploitation of natural advantages has concentrated activity in the St Lawrence–Great Lakes plain and tributary lowlands. Although this area has only moderate relief, it has a great variety of drainage and soil conditions. These have been seized on by white men and made to produce their local geographies. Altogether some ten significant districts have emerged. They are (i) the Estuarine terraces; (ii) the Quebec–Lac St Pierre plain; (iii) the plain of Montreal and the Eastern Townships; (iv) the St Maurice basin; (v) the Ottawa valley; (vi) the upper St Lawrence lowland; (vii) the Ontario shoreland; (viii) the Lake Erie shoreland and the Windsor peninsula; (ix) the chief moraine lands; (x) the Georgian Bay plain.

The Estuarine terraces form a narrow fringe of habitable land from Tadoussac to Quebec in the north and Rimouski to Levis in the south. These terraces are old sea-beaches, which have been left stranded above the present gulf as the land slowly rose after the passing of the ice. The terraces slope from salt-water marshes on the edge of the St Lawrence estuary, across fairly fertile fields, where, however, boulders are a great agricultural nuisance, to the wooded steeps of the Appalachian plateau, or of the Shield. Fishing and navigation were the chief occupations from 1608 to 1830. Then lumbering offered attractive profits. Today agriculture is the main interest. Fine, though small, dairy farms produce milk and cream for sale to the cities and creameries. Potatoes and peas are paying cash crops, suited to the cool, short summer. They are in great demand in near-by Quebec city. (Pea-soup is almost a national dish of the French Canadians!) Rivière-du-Loup and Rimouski are the largest towns, commanding passes across the Appalachians to the Maritimes. North-east of Quebec, Montmorency Falls, Murray Bay Spa, and St Anne de Beaupré are tourist resorts, or centres of pilgrimage, or nuclei of rapidly expanding industry.

The Quebec–Lac St Pierre plain unites the north and south shores of the

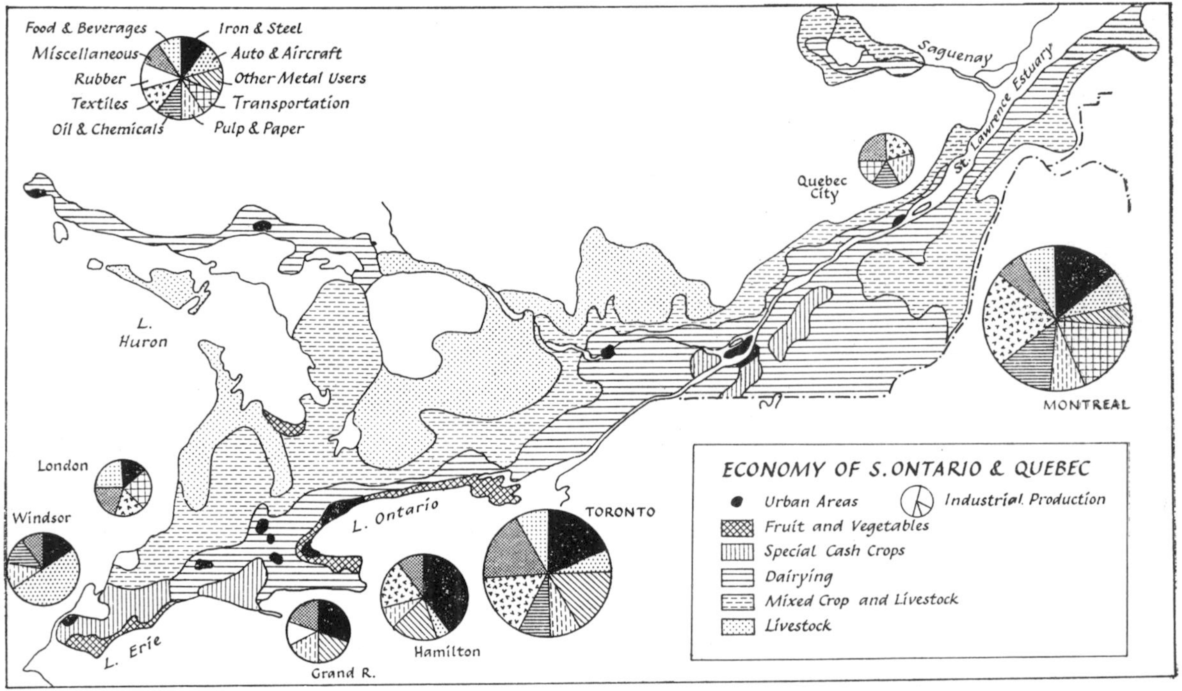

FIG. 89 Farming and Industry in southern Ontario and southern Quebec. The southern lake-shore plains and the low-lands at the confluence of the Ottawa and St Lawrence are particularly rich in warmth, soil moisture, soil, and crop development. These are the same regions most suited to urban growth, and there is the most intense competition for land between city and country. (Circles proportional to value of production.) (Scale, 1:8·5 m.)

St Lawrence gulf, and forms the historic gateway to Canada. The Lac St Pierre district is very flat, and productive, and early attracted settlement. By the end of the eighteenth century marshes had been drained, much of the forest cleared, and by the middle nineteenth century the whole area was colonized and had begun to show signs of overpopulation. Hunting and fishing were important until 1760, then agriculture became the chief occupation. Wheat growing was common until about 1875, after which dairying took over. Today, the district is festooned with villages, consisting of lines of farms growing outward from a central church and several stores. However, the population is falling, and is nearly 20 per cent less than it was in 1891. This is due to the drift of the rural people to the cities, and to the modernization of farming which uses machines instead of family labour, Small industrial towns like Sorel and Donnacona have grown up, making use of the abundant labour supply, and also of the good communications of the district. **Sorel** is an active port, and has important ship-building yards with steel, textile and lumber industries, and grain elevators.

Rising about 400 feet above the St Lawrence plain is a low platform that stretches eastward from Lac St Pierre to Quebec. It is called 'the Quebec Platform', and is rather poor, with a severe climate, ill-drained soils, and large marshes. The rivers cut deeply into the platform and are too swift or narrow to act as lines of transportation. Roads are poor and inadequate. The area was late in being settled and once the forest was cut off it became a belt of abandoned saw mill settlements. No modern industrial development has occurred to keep the people there, and over twenty thousand of them have migrated, since 1891, either to the cities or to the United States. Many that remain are transient labourers, and leave for Montreal every winter to work in the factories of Beauharnois. The farmers have a hard time, and are relatively backward. As Blanchard remarks, with only twenty-seven people per square mile and the impossibility of maintaining these, here is a tragic area![1] (See fig. 89.)

The narrow, low plain of Quebec offers a marked contrast. Here, 'une vie fluviale' has been created, where each village is linked by the river to the other, like beads on a rosary. The river dominates, but railway and highway have also brought many contacts to the villages that line the plain. The district passed through the usual progression of fishing, lumbering, subsistence farming, and specialized farming. Some of the specialities are poultry (particularly turkey farms), dairying, orchards, and fox ranching. The estuary divides around the Island of Orleans, which is intensively cultivated and densely settled. It was colonized as early as 1641. It has a mild climate, with warm, sunny slopes on the south banks of its many ravines. Here

[1] Blanchard, R., 'La Région du fleuve Saint-Laurent entre Québec et Montréal', *Revue de géographie alpine*, 1936, p. 129.

apple orchards, small fruits and vegetables do very well. There is an excellent market in Quebec. However, the population has been decreasing. Farms are getting smaller; there is no more land available for colonization; and no employment for all the members of the large farm families. Many are leaving for the cities.

Quebec City (395,000) is the outstanding site of the district. It was discovered and claimed by the French more than three centuries ago, in 1608, and became the centre of their vast empire of waterways. Situated at the head of the St Lawrence gulf, the largest inlet on the Atlantic coast, it completely by-passed the barrier of the Appalachian mountains. Thus it gave the French direct access to the interior. (By contrast, the British were hemmed in to their small coastal colonies in America, without the chance of expansion, until after the American Revolution.) The estuary led to the wide hinterland of the St Lawrence–Ohio plains, the Great Lakes, and the Canadian Shield, and thus provided a vast area for exploration, conquest, and development.

Quebec has served different purposes at different times, when different elements in its geography have been used. From 1608 to 1763 its chief use was as a fortress. The French made it their key base to link Louisburg on the Atlantic coast with Frontenac, Niagara, and Duquesne in the interior. Here they rallied Algonquin resistance to the Iroquois; here they protected their great hinterland from the British. Later, in the American Revolution, the British used the site to defend Canada from the Revolutionaries. Indeed there was a time, as Wellington said, when British America hinged on Quebec! No better location for a fortress could be found. A high rock, 300 feet high, overlooks the narrows where the estuary passes into the river of the St Lawrence: it commands both sea-ways and river-ways. At the same time, the rich plain around provides room for settlement, agriculture and trade, and allowed the fortress to be more or less self-supporting. It also allowed the site to develop peaceful functions, once its purpose as a fortress had been served.

From 1763 to 1871, Quebec expanded as a busy commercial centre and port. It had a thriving locality to serve. As Blanchard remarks:

> C'est à Québec que se chargent les goélettes distribuant leurs marchandises *le long de l'estuaire*, dans les petits ports des deux rives et *jusqu'à l'extrémité de la lointaine Gaspésie*; de là que partent les vapeurs desservant *les havres de golfe du* Saint-Laurent *jusqu'au détroit de Belle-Isle et à Terre-Neuve*; à Québec que les uns et les autres rapportent les chargements du bois, du beurre, et du poisson, destinés à la vente. De même Québec est la tête de ligne de voies ferrées desservant les comtés de la côte sud de la Gaspésie, de celles qui pénètrent dans Montmorency, Charlevoix, Chicoutimi et le Lac St Jean. A travers tous ces territoires, si l'exportation

des produits s'effectue en partie au profit de Montréal, c'est en tout cas à Québec que l'on achète.

Quebec also developed as an important overseas harbour. It was the point of landing of the early French immigrants, and even more so, of the great tide of British settlers who entered Canada in the nineteenth century. In the thirty-six years between 1829 and 1865 over one million people landed at Quebec. When the head of navigation moved to Montreal, Quebec lost some of this traffic, but since the river journey from Quebec to Montreal is tortuous and slow, many people prefer to leave the boat at Quebec and then travel swiftly into the interior by train. It is, therefore, still an important port for express passenger and mail-boat service.

Until Montreal developed as an ocean port, Quebec also handled much of the imports and exports of Canada. It began by exporting timber cut in the St Lawrence and Ottawa valleys. Handling wood in great quantities, it started to make wooden ships and developed a small merchant marine which carried its trade throughout the Atlantic. When railways were built, it was chosen as a terminal of the northern Trans-Canada railroad, and built elevators for the export of wheat. The building of the great Quebec suspension bridge across the river enabled it to connect the railway systems of both the south and north shores of the estuary and gulf of the St Lawrence. However, its importance as a harbour has diminished in the last eighty years, to give way to Montreal.

Nevertheless, Quebec has obtained a new lease on life through its industrial expansion. Being a centre of the storage and exchange of supplies, it has many raw materials to draw upon. Also, being in a rich and densely populated plain, it has an abundant supply of relatively cheap labour. Finally, it is sufficiently close to hydro-electric plants in the Appalachians and Shield to secure low-cost and ample power. Its earliest industry was ship-building, but this lost its importance when iron ships replaced wooden ones. Quebec has no large iron foundries to support a modern ship-building programme. Tanneries were the next industry to develop, based on the export of hides from the livestock regions of the St Lawrence. Then textiles were added, based on the cheap import of cotton and silk from abroad, and the use of French-Canadian women long trained in home crafts such as weaving, rug-making, and knitting. Paper and metal industries are further developments, using the raw materials of the hinterland and the cheap transportation by sea to foreign markets. Quebec is strategically situated for the paper industry because: (*a*) it commands huge forest reserves to the north of it, in the Shield; (*b*) it has sufficient electric power; (*c*) it is on water transport for coal and sulphur, additional materials; and (*d*) it has cheap water communications with U.S.A. and Great Britain, its chief markets.

Quebec is a well-balanced city. Not only has it important commercial, industrial, and transportation services, but also tourist, governmental, and cultural ones. Although manufacturing dominates, employing over 17,000 people, the tourist trade is significant, employing about 4,000, while there are 3,200 government employees, and over 2,000 priests and nuns. Quebec is the religious capital of the French Catholics, and has several seminaries and nunneries. It is also the site of the famous old Laval University. This institution is widely known for its theology faculty and law school. It also has an established science faculty housed on a suburban campus.

The result of the various stages of development that Quebec has gone through is seen in several well-marked zones, into which the city may now be divided. Citadel Hill, the site of fortress, government buildings, and old residences, is being crowded more and more with fashionable shops, hotels, and business and professional offices. Below this lies the harbour, with its warehouses and closely packed tenements. Newer industrial expansion has found room to grow on the north slopes or along the river flats, especially by the St Charles river. This newer town has drawn to it large multiple stores and offices, and sponsors a business district the rival of the old.

The Montreal plain is the most productive, most highly industrialized, and densely populated part of Quebec province. As we have seen, it is flat, except for the Monteregian hills, and is floored largely with clays. It has a milder climate and hotter summer than any other part of the province. It is at a meeting place of natural routeways. Thus it provides the basis for intensive agriculture on a commercial basis. Until the mid-nineteenth century it was the granary of Canada, but as Montreal grew, the local demand for milk, eggs, vegetables, and fruit led to a more specialized and varied farming. (Meantime the West had become Canada's 'wheat basket'.) (Fig. 90.) The different types of farming use different soils. Market gardeners, producing vegetables and small fruit, together with tobacco farms, use the sandy soils, which make for quick growth, and are easy to cultivate. Orchards cover the hill slopes, where they find more sun, less frost, and have good drainage. Dairies spread across the clay flats, where fine crops of hay and oats are grown, particularly around the volcanic stumps of the Monteregians.

The plain began to be cleared as early as 1641, and was soon divided into parishes, each with a central village, and long narrow farms going down to the river, or up to the hills. By the beginning of the nineteenth century some of these villages were crowded with surplus rural population, and there were hundreds of men and women who could no longer find employment on the land. This was the opportunity for wealthy merchants to employ the excess rural labour in mills, warehouses, railways, canals, and industries. A number of towns developed, of which Montreal became the most important, because

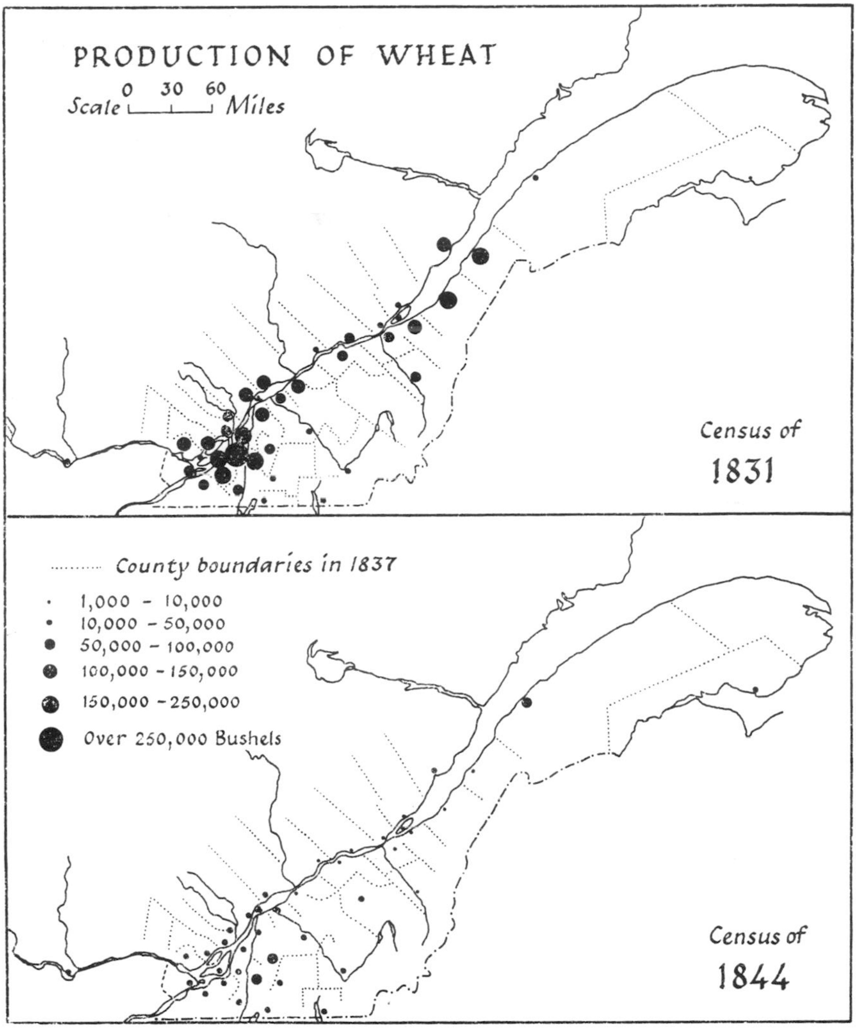

FIG. 90 Wheat production in the Montreal plain, early nineteenth century, and its subsequent decline. This decline was due to the local competition of market gardening and dairy farming as the urban market grew, and to the remote competition of the Prairies which was a region better suited to the raising of wheat. From Lower Canada production first migrated to Upper Canada, where it went into decline in the 1880s with the opening of the railways to the Prairies—now the bread basket of Canada. (From W. H. Parker.)

of its commanding site. As it grew, it gave birth to many industrial suburbs, or satellite towns. Consequently, the region is a dense network of settlements and routes, including large villages like Terrebonne, Ste Thérèse, and Marieville; medium-sized mill towns like Beauharnois, Farnham, Jolliette, Valleyfield, St Hyacinthe, and St John; and the great metropolis of Montreal, with its numerous industrial suburbs such as Lachine, Verdun, and Outremont. Indeed, on Montreal island there were once as many as forty municipalities, though many of these have now been incorporated into greater Montreal.

The Eastern Townships form a southern and eastern extension of the Montreal plain, linking it with the Appalachians. However, they have much stronger relief, made up of four principal elements—the Appalachian peneplains, the lines of mountains rising above them, the deep valleys cut down into these, and a foothill platform sloping down to the St Lawrence plain. The peneplains form rather monotonous uplands. The mountains run in three more or less parallel arcs, known as West Range, the Serpentine Belt, and Centre Range. The Serpentine Belt is particularly rich in minerals. The valleys are deep and form a rectilinear pattern, with long headstreams flowing along north-east–south-west lines, and shorter, more rapid middle sectors across the ranges, and then more mature parts winding over the St Lawrence lowlands. Lakes in the long headstreams keep up a steady volume, while rapids or waterfalls in the middle sectors supply good sites for power. Valley terraces provide soils suitable for cultivation. The foothill platform extends to the north and west of West Range, and has been heavily glaciated. The rivers are interrupted by falls and rapids. The Champlain Sea left sheets of clay, which now form important agricultural land.

Forty per cent of the area is still in forest, while another 20 per cent is under farm woods and rough pasture. The remainder of the land is covered with field crops and meadows. Oats and hay are the primary crops. Wheat has been tried but is not important. That is perhaps because the tradition has been to raise livestock. The first settlers came from New England and raised cattle and sheep in natural beaver meadows. Sheep provided a market for wool as well as meat, and local woollen mills sprang up. Sheep are still kept on the hillier land. Cattle became more important as the market for milk, butter, and cheese expanded with the expanding mill towns. Today the Eastern Townships are a famous dairying district (see Fig. 89). The French settlers, who now predominate, took over the livestock tradition and, indeed, improved on it by the organization of co-operative creameries, which manufacture butter and cheese in great quantities both for the Montreal market and also for abroad. Large numbers of poultry farms have recently appeared, to take advantage of the cheap transportation to Montreal, New York, and Great Britain. Fox farms are another recent innovation which supply the great fur markets of Montreal, New York, and London. In the more sheltered area of Huntingdon, along the New York border, where the growing season lengthens, fruit farming is a specialization that makes use of milder climate and better soils.

The industrial development of the Eastern Townships is today their most striking feature. The region offers lumber, minerals, and water-power, and is on important railways and highways, linking Montreal to New York. The first settlers were U.E. Loyalists who brought with them an active tradition in crafts. As early as 1850 they had developed large lumber mills, and were delivering sawn timber to the United States and to Montreal. Lumbering is still important, especially in the hilly interior, and has given rise to the furniture industry of Scottstown, and to many pulp and paper mills. Woollen mills were running as early as 1851 at Sherbrooke and Granby. These depended on local supplies of wool and used local water-power. The textile tradition has grown. Cotton weaving was introduced after 1871 and there are now three large centres of manufacture at Sherbrooke, Drummondville, and Magog. Silk mills were added later at Drummondville, and have proved very successful. Industry was first in the hands of the British. However, by the beginning of the twentieth century, the French had largely displaced them. Some American-owned plants occur. Thus American, British, and French interests meet and interlock in the Eastern Townships, which form an excellent example of 'racial' goodwill and co-operation.

Mining and metallurgical industries have begun to be important. In the Serpentine Belt there are large deposits of asbestos, and smaller deposits of copper, zinc, and lead. Copper has been worked for nearly a century now, and is still in production. Asbestos was discovered in 1876 at Asbestos, Black Lake, and Thetford, and Quebec now supplies about 70 per cent of the world's total. These mines require a lot of wood, and the mining settlements need milk, butter, eggs, and vegetables. Thus they stimulate agriculture and lumbering. Indeed, one of the chief characteristics of the Eastern Townships is the way in which occupations depend on each other.

Sherbrooke, with a population of about 72,000, is the chief town. It stands at crossroads in the valley of the St Francis, at the site of a waterfall, 117 feet high. It is thus both a transportation and power centre. The first mill was built as early as 1794. Lumbering was the principal industry at first, but in 1842 the railway came, connecting the town with Portland and Montreal. Later, lines were built to Quebec, and also to connect with New York. Industrial expansion was very active between 1871 and 1900 when many French Canadians, the surplus rural population, flocked into the town, and provided plentiful and cheap labour. However, competition with Montreal itself, and with industrial New England, prevented further growth until the First World War. The war boom in textiles and machinery was followed by an influx of new international industries in metals, paper, and rubber. The town expanded downstream from the falls, and room has been found for the mills on the well-marked river terraces.

The City of Montreal (2,200,000) binds the Eastern Townships and the

Montreal plain into one, through its radiating roads and railways, its extensive financial controls, and its cultural and administrative services. Along with its satellites, it has grown into a vast conurbation which not only monopolizes the greater part of the total production of Quebec, as Riou shows, but represents the most densely populated and highly industrialized area in Canada.[1] Undoubtedly, this is due to its historical importance at a rich site in a strategic situation, and to the way in which both British and French joined in its development. Standing on an island, splitting the St Lawrence at the confluence of the Ottawa, it commands the historie riverways of Canada. It is also north of the Champlain gap, and the way to New York. Thus it is ideal for entry into the interior, or exit to the coast, for contacts northward to Ottawa and the raw materials of the Shield, or southward to New York and the industries of America. These have been useful advantages at each stage of its development.

In Indian days it was an Indian fort, controlling the junction of the riverways. This was important when trade or conquest followed the rivers. The near-by Caughnawaga Indian Reserve forms a relict link with Hochelaga of the past, whose reputation as a considerable town drew Cartier to the site. Though the French were disappointed in the town, they soon realized the importance of the site. They used it as an important fortress to defend themselves and the Algonquins from the Iroquois. The fortress played a significant role in the Seven Years War between the British and the French; in the American Revolution; and in the War of 1812 between America and Canada. It was a link between sea-coast (Quebec) and interior (Niagara), the seizure of which, either by way of the Champlain or Lake Ontario, would have broken the chain that kept Canada together. Commercially, the French developed Montreal as the centre of the fur and timber trade. French traders went up the Ottawa and Mattawa valleys to the Upper Great Lakes and the West, and opened this enormous hinterland to Montreal. The site had its difficulties, particularly in the Lachine rapids, at the head of the island. This was the first major barrier to ocean boats on their way up the St Lawrence. The French disembarked people and goods at this point, and then transferred them to canoes or river-going scows. Montreal broke their journey inland, and here they found it necessary to build docks, warehouses, supply shops, and homes.

However, the large-scale business and industrial growth of the city was left to the British. Settling there in small numbers as soldiers and administrators, they soon saw the business value of Montreal. They were especially interested in making Montreal the hub of Canadian routes, and developed canals, highways, and railways. The Lachine Canal, which had been built as early as 1700, was widened and deepened. Montreal money was largely

[1] Riou. P. 'Les Industries Manufacturières' in *Notre Milieu*, ed. Minville, pp. 282–4.

responsible for the Welland Canal in 1829. Thus the Great Lakes region was made tributary to the city. In 1830 a Port Commission was formed, and in 1856 the approach to the port was deepened to permit large ocean-going vessels to berth there. The river was bridged in 1860, and Montreal was made a highway junction for the main east–west (Quebec–Windsor) road, and the main north–south one (Ottawa–New York). Montreal also became the terminal for the Canadian Pacific Railway and Steamship Company, thus linking trans-Canada with transatlantic lines. It is today the terminal of the transatlantic airplane flights from Britain and Western Europe.

These developments in transportation went hand-in-hand with hydro-electric developments and growth in industry. Pioneer industries, using water-power and the canal system, witnessed the rise of flour mills, saw mills, and tanneries. Water-power, and later hydro-electricity plants at near-by Beauharnois and not too distant Shawinigan, came to provide cheap electricity for a great number of industries, such as textile, canning, milling, and the making of electrical appliances.

As coal became needed, it was shipped up the gulf from Nova Scotia or down the Welland Canal and the St Lawrence from Pennsylvania. Iron was also cheaply carried by water from Scotland, Nova Scotia, or Ontario. After the Second World War, steel mills and steel-using industries flourished. First, large railway works and ship-building yards sprang up. Later, many engineering plants and particularly airplane and aero-engine factories developed.

When ocean navigation by modern liners reached the port, it became the centre of oil and sugar refining, the manufacture of textiles, dyes, chemicals, rubber goods, chocolates, cocoa, distilling and brewing, and the packing of coffee and tea—all making use of overseas imports. Canadian raw materials were also processed, such as flour, malt, tobacco, fruit, and meat—brought by canal or railway from Ontario and the Prairies, for export to Britain and elsewhere.

The development of transportation, the growth of a huge import and export trade, and the rise of industry have all made Montreal a major financial centre. The financial ability of the British, and the artistic skills of the French combined to make a site without coal, oil, or iron—which are usually regarded as the prerequisites of industry—the greatest manufacturing centre in Canada. Montreal makes 75 per cent of the tobacco products of Canada, 60 per cent of its railway rolling stock, 45 per cent of its men's clothing, 35 per cent of its shoes, 35 per cent of its furs, 35 per cent of its flour, 35 per cent of its beers and ales, 33 per cent of its gasolene, and 32 per cent of its drugs. Altogether, Montreal has some 5,500 factories which make about 20 per cent of all the manufactured goods in Canada. This is a very high concentration, and shows the unique value of its geography. With its satellite cities, it forms a conurbation of two and a quarter millions, in other words one-ninth of the Canadian population.

In the city itself there is a very close relationship between geography and settlement (Fig. 91). The city slopes from the summit of Mt Royal down to where the river is at its narrowest. At the narrowing of the river occur the highway and railway bridges. The railway stations lie on the terraces above the river flats: below are the canal basin and the main docks. Thus road, rail, ocean, and inland-waterway terminals are brought close together, so as to serve each other. By the Harbour and the canal basin are grouped large warehouses, huge grain elevators, coal piles, and ship-yards. Large steel mills and railway shops occur where the freight lines and canal come together. Big meat-packing plants, tanneries, and various food industries crowd the waterfront between the freight terminal and harbour. Eastward, a variety of industries extends to the riverfront suburb of Verdun. The chief business centre lies where the highway from the road-bridge strikes between the old Canadian Pacific Railway and Canadian National Railway railway stations. In this central area, on a terrace above the industrial belt, are the Cathedral, hotels, offices, and theatres. North of the railway tracks, the land slopes upward to a line of large shops and then to a belt of schools and colleges. Here is famous McGill University, while the Université de Montréal crowns a neighbouring city height. Thus each level of the city has given rise to a different zone; the river flats to the industrial belt, the river terraces to the business sector, and the hillside to the cultural and residential areas.

Certain areas are marked by English architecture and parks. Although Montreal is the second largest French city in the world it has English towns like Westmount embedded in it. This makes it singularly representative of the bi-cultural nature of Canada.

House types reflect these differences. In the lower, older parts are row-houses, three storeys high, known as 'triplexes'. Usually faced with brick, some have grey-stone fronts. Very frequently winding outside stairways, with decorative iron railings, rise to the second or third flats, demanding from the tenants 'l'agilité d'acrobates en hiver pour sortir ou entrer de leur logement'.[1] Two-storey blocks, or duplexes, characterize the intermediate terraces, except close to the town centre, where they are displaced by luxury apartments in multi-storey, towering construction. Large single mansion houses show through the woods of the mountain slopes, with magnificent views over the river to the Monteregian hills. Outer suburbs, on lesser and less central heights, are filled with two-storey villas or low bungalows.

While the Quebec–Montreal plains form the core of the lower part of the St Lawrence basin, they derive much wealth from two tributary regions,

[1] Camu, P., 'Types de Maisons dans la Région Suburbaine de Montréal', *The Canadian Geographer*, no. 9, 1957, p. 21.

34. Quebec City, showing Citadel, Château Frontenac, passenger quays in foreground, and industrialized harbour at St Charles estuary.

35. Montreal Harbour, with industrialized quarter round Lachine Canal, international passenger terminals in mid-distance, and lower part of business district. St Lawrence River is on right.

36. The Montreal business district, where banks, insurance offices, hotel, and railway terminals crowd in around the Cathedral fronting on Dominion Square.

Urban Canada, City Scenes from Ontario

37. Skyscraper townscape shows importance of central business district, Toronto.

38. Suburban shopping centre, Ottawa, and the importance of the car.

39. Bungalow sprawl, Hamilton, eating into valuable agricultural land at the city edge.

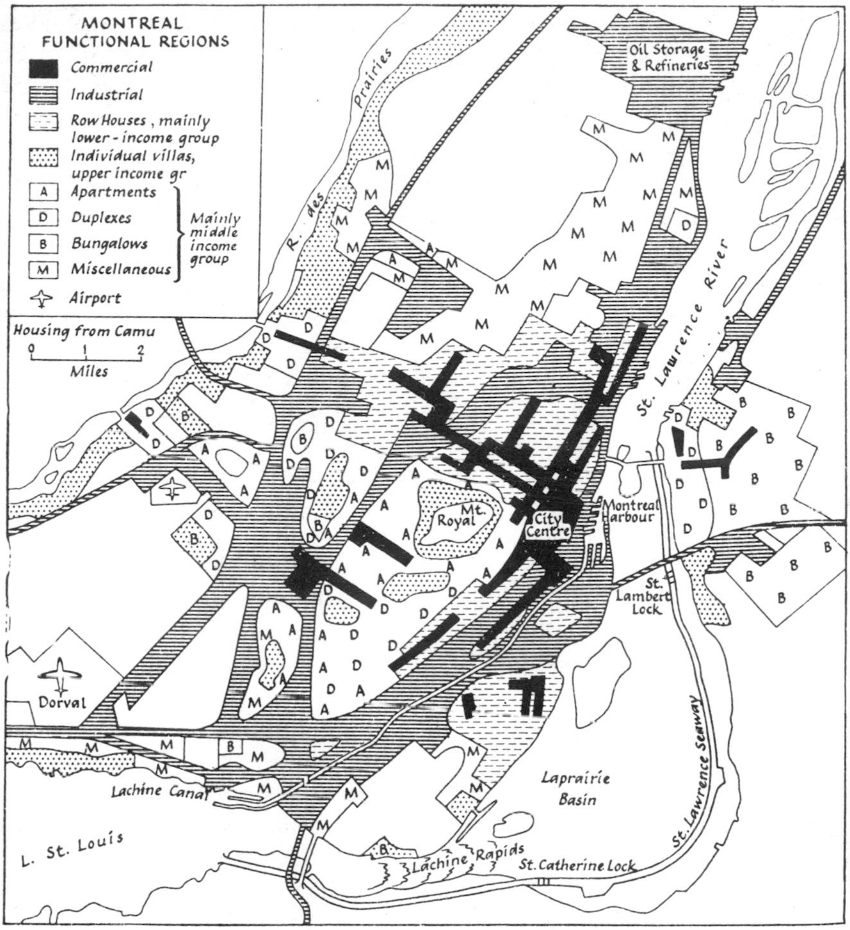

FIG. 91 Greater Montreal—its chief urban features. The harbour developed at the head of tidewater below the Lachine rapids. On the low terrace behind it are the main railway and industrial belts. Business has climbed to a middle terrace where shops and offices have spread north-east and south-west. Various types of houses grade themselves out from the multiple apartments among business and industrial quarters in mid-town to stately private homes on the high slopes of the central mountains. Modern industry, housing, and air terminals have spread over the northern flats, with suburbs along the back channels of the St Lawrence.

the St Maurice and Ottawa valleys that, formed in the Shield, debouch on the St Lawrence lowlands.

The St Maurice basin lies mainly in the Shield, but is oriented to the St Lawrence. It drains some 17,000 sq. miles of upland into the plain of Lac St Pierre. A little pioneer farming is carried on, but the soils are too acid and the climate too severe for successful colonization. The chief wealth of the St Maurice region is its forests, together with its water-power. The river starts high up on the Laurentian peneplain, draining several large lakes which give it a steady and ample flow. Logs are cut and sent down the river and its tributaries to mill towns which are situated at waterfalls that offer abundant power. Such towns are La Tuque and Grand'Mère. The largest towns are Shawinigan, with fifty establishments, and Three Rivers, with over a hundred. Shawinigan occurs at the Falls of that name, and, together with its satellites, has a population of 45,000. Cheap electricity, developed in enormous quantity from the Falls (150 feet high), supplies the power for textile, chemical, paper, and aluminium industries.

Three Rivers, with a population of 58,000, grew up where the St Maurice joins the St Lawrence waterway. It is a half-way point between Montreal and Quebec, with excellent road, railway, and river communications. It rules the logging 'empire' of the St Maurice. It is near enough to the mighty Shawinigan power plant to obtain cheap electricity, and so is an excellent industrial site—able to assemble its raw materials at a low cost, to use cheap power, and to distribute its goods inland to Canada or overseas to Britain.

The Ottawa valley, although also tributary to the St Lawrence, is a major basin in itself. It runs along a zone of weakness between the crystalline rocks of the Gatineau and Algonquin districts. In its upper course, it escapes from the Temiskaming basin through a rather narrow section, flanked by rocky uplands; but below Arnprior it opens out into a much broader vale, floored with sedimentary rocks. The whole valley has been altered by glaciation.[1] At one time it was connected with the Great Lakes by way of the Mattawa valley, and was used as a northern outlet. Then the Champlain Sea invaded the valley. When the sea retreated, the Mattawa, Petawawa, and upper Ottawa waters laid down huge sheets of sand, which are over 100 feet thick in the vicinity of Petawawa. The sea stayed long enough in the lower Ottawa valley to deposit stretches of clay, and leave behind beach terraces. When it finally retreated, the Ottawa river transported some of the sand from its upper course and spread it over its newly developed valley. These sandy and clay terraces, lining the sides of the river, give a variety of soils, which produce a varied agriculture (see Fig. 87).

As we have seen, the Ottawa valley was once connected with the Great Lakes by the Mattawa river. When Champlain canoed up the Ottawa he discovered that by a short portage he could get through the Mattawa valley and so proceed to the Great Lakes. Champlain's route was widely used. It offered a direct way to the fur-rich interior from Montreal, and saved the much longer and more roundabout journey by the Lower Lakes. Therefore, the Ottawa valley early became an important routeway; and has remained

[1] Mackay, J. Ross, 'Physiography of the Lower Ottawa Valley', *Rev. Can. de Géog.*, III, nos. 1–4, pp. 53–96.

so ever since. Today it is used by the great northern highway linking Quebec, Montreal, Ottawa, North Bay, Sudbury, and Winnipeg (the Trans-Canada Highway); and is also followed by the Canadian Pacific Railway from Montreal to the Prairies and British Columbia. The upper Ottawa affords a low gap, via Lake Temiskaming, to the Great Clay Belt and James Bay, and is followed by a connexion with the Trans-Canada network of the Canadian National Railway. Thus the Ottawa valley plays an important part in linking east and west, north and south, and perhaps for that reason it was chosen as the site for the capital of Canada—Ottawa City.

It is also important, however, in extending the agricultural area northward, and in attracting industry northward into the Canadian Shield, which is the core of Canada. The upper Ottawa valley is still a zone of pioneer farming, or of general farming engaged in the raising of cattle and sheep. It has no significant cash crop, largely because the season is too short, and the soil rather poor. Only about one-fifth of the land is under field crops. In the lower Ottawa valley the soils are better, the climate milder, and hay, oats, silage corn, and clover are produced in quantity to feed large herds of dairy cattle. Potatoes are an important crop. Most farms also raise poultry and hogs, and have a small vegetable garden. The farming is rich enough to support the large cities of Ottawa and Hull, together with many small towns.

The industrial development of the valley has been slow, partly because the valley was long used for commerce, and commercial interests came first before industrial ones, and partly because Ottawa remained an administrative centre, and did not attract factories. Moreover, there are not many raw materials in the locality, and American sources of supply are remote. At the same time the population was rather scanty, and did not offer a good labour market. Nevertheless, in the upper Ottawa are immense, readily available supplies of lumber. In the middle Ottawa are large water-power resources. The lumber was cut in the upper Ottawa and the tributaries, and floated down to Ottawa and Hull. There it was sawn into dressed timber or crushed into pulp and paper. The Chaudière and Gatineau falls produce ample power. There are today four large pulp and paper concerns—one at Gatineau, yielding 1,700 tons a day and others at Hull, Buckingham, and at Lachute. In addition, paper products are turned out at Hull and Ottawa. Various by-products of wood are also made.

More recently, metal and machine industries have appeared, refining magnesite at Grenville, making electro-metallurgical products at Brownsville, and manufacturing steel at Hull. **Hull** is the largest industrial centre, with a population of 60,000. It was founded when the Ottawa valley was predominantly a British district. (Indeed, the British remained more numerous than the French until 1825; now the French are numerically superior.) Hull was a lumber town until the twentieth century, and is still the site of

Canada's largest paper factory. However, textiles (the making of woollen socks and knitwear) and metal industries (steel and electrical appliances) have grown in importance, and there is also a huge cement plant, using local stone. There are today over fifty plants, employing about 4,000 people. But the city is also growing as a service centre. Much of its present prosperity is due to Ottawa, on the opposite bank of the river, from which Government offices have spread out into Hull.

The City of Ottawa, from which one may see the forested edge of the Shield, or look down on rivers plunging over a rock-ridged plain, or face across to terraces cut in deltaic sands, or gaze on alluvial bottomlands, is as typical of the Ottawa basin as any place in it. With 475,000 in the 'greater city' area, it dominates the valley, where the valley widens out from the Shield, and makes it possible for routes to fan to Montreal, Kingston, and Toronto. It thus connects Quebec and Ontario at the end of the long route across the Shield from western Canada. This position makes it the linch-pin of the nation, a fact which was recognized in 1858 when it became the capital of Canada.

It lies at the head of navigation on the Ottawa. Just above it are the Chaudière Falls. Its early growth depended on the junction of rivers (Ottawa and Gatineau) and canal (Rideau) (Fig. 92). The rivers were used for floating down fur and timber. But it was not until the 1870s, when there was extensive railway-building, that it grew quickly. It was then able to distribute sawn lumber very rapidly to the growing cities of Montreal and Toronto. It became 'the lumber capital of the world'. But by 1900 the pine timber, associated with the valley's wide spread of deltaic sands, was gone. There came a changeover to pulp and paper which could use the balsam and spruce of the uplands to west and east. (Large reserves of spruce still occur in the upper Ottawa and Gatineau basins, especially where the rivers widen out into lakes.) The change to paper was easily made because of the vast quantities of hydro-electric power. Ottawa has a potential of about 10 million horse-power within fifty miles! Large amounts are used in the pulp and paper mills, and in newer industries such as metal and machine works, food, textile and leather products, printing and publishing.

Altogether there are over 300 manufacturing establishments in Ottawa, yet the industrial wage earners are only 12 per cent of the total. Sixteen per cent are engaged in the retail trade, and 25 per cent in Government services. The rather limited labour supply of the region is drawn off into Government work, of one kind or another, and Ottawa has never attracted immigrants enough to furnish a large labour force. It has the fewest immigrants of any large city in Canada.

Yet it has enough of these to make it a quite representative Canadian city, although the Canadian quality of its life is derived more, perhaps, from the strong blending of British and French peoples, traditions, and ways. Public architecture had a distinctly French cast, private building is very English. There is both a French-speaking and an English-speaking university. Anglican and Roman Catholic cathedrals are prominent, along with a central Presbyterian church. French restaurants vie with English inns. Cricket is played on the lawns of the Governor-General's residence, while

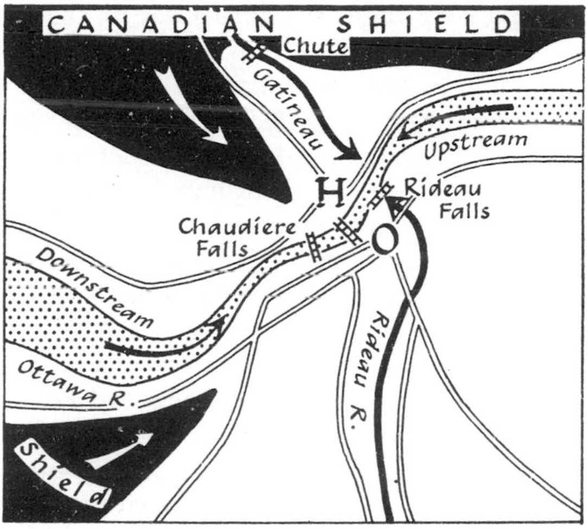

FIG. 92 Ottawa and its Site. Two prongs of the Shield constrict the middle Ottawa valley. Around them hard sandstones and limestones bar the course of the river, causing it to break into rapids and falls. Tributary rivers join the main one down additional sharp unevennesses. Portages and a break in journeys up or down stream were thus necessitated. An abundance of water-power led to grist and lumber mills, and later to pulp and paper plants. Uniting Quebec and Ontario at a good bridging place at a point of power in a valley rich in farms, the site has proved most effective for Canada's capital.

curling is everywhere popular. French Canadians dominate the ice-hockey arenas. Bilingual signs appear on all the streets and in the main edifices. Statues to both French and British heroes grace the squares and parks. English and French place-names cross and recross, weaving the memories of the homelands into the dreams of the new-born nation.

The city is well laid out, and has made a striking use of local relief. Parliament Buildings are on a high point, thrusting its rocky bluffs out into the river. Across the road from them are tall shops and business blocks. Upstream is the Chaudière, and the interprovincial bridge, connecting Ottawa and Hull. Here are some of the saw and paper mills. Downstream is the opening of the disused Rideau Canal. It is flanked by the railway station and famous Laurier Hotel. Farther downstream are Government offices. The suburban areas lie to the south and south-west.

The main problem facing Ottawa has been to make room for more Government offices, and yet at the same time not have them pre-empt the centre of the city or the waterfront. A National Capital Planning Commission has been formed, and plans are in effect to desegregate Government bureaux, and permit normal neighbourhoods to grow up between and around them. Several large industrial enterprises on the waterfront have been bought out and parks developed. New industries have been kept to the outskirts. Ottawa is in process of becoming a 'show' capital.

The upper St Lawrence river—that is, the river proper, flowing out from the Great Lakes—is separated from the Ottawa valley by a very narrow, probably youthful, divide. The district runs from swift waters cutting through the Frontenac axis in a spectacular section of rock and forest known as the Thousand Islands, past the formerly turbulent International Rapids, down to the once white rapids of Beauharnois, where it merges with the Montreal plain (see Fig. 87).

The area, though low, is stony, with either limestone scarp or an upwarp of crystalline rock sweeping across it. A no-man's land in Indian times, it became a sharp divide in colonial days, and remained as such virtually up to the meeting of Roosevelt and Mackenzie King that resulted in the Ogdensburg Agreement. Loyalist British streamed across the river, with Republicans hard on their heels. The plains on either side of the mighty stream became separated and were developed along separate lines (see Fig. 61, Chapter 8).

The Canadian division, marked by the swell and sag of glacial mound and marsh, often interrupted by stretches of infertile rock, and with a raw-to-severe climate, is characterized by a rather poor agriculture and small agricultural towns. It has been, and is, a region to pass through, and is significant mainly for the St Lawrence canals that by-pass the cataracts and link the Great Lakes waterway with the waters of the St Lawrence estuary and gulf. Winter minima of −40° F. occur. There is a heavy snowfall of over 100 inches, and the annual precipitation is from 35 to 40 inches. These conditions suit fodder crops, but are not ideal for winter wheat or orchard crops, which are lacking. Dual purpose cattle are raised, both for milk and beef, since there is a good market for both in Ottawa and Montreal. Sheep are also raised, and there is a small local market for the wool. The towns act as milling, marketing, and distribution centres.

The chief places are Prescott and Cornwall. These grew up as transhipment centres. Prescott is at the downstream limit of lake-boat navigation. The larger grain ships had to lighter here, and let the grain be transferred to 'canalers', which took it down the rather narrow, and shallow St Lawrence canals. Large flour mills arose at the site to use the grain; and then the flour was exported by rail. A great new lease of life has been gained with the building of the St Lawrence seaway and associated power projects. New towns have sprung up and old ones been revived; and new industries, using the hydro-electric power produced in such abundance locally, and making the most of the cheap transportation provided by the seaway, have literally mushroomed. Cornwall, especially, with its large paper mills and its hydro-electric offices, has boomed.

The St Lawrence seaway has wrought this big transformation (Fig. 93). It seems surprising now that there should have been so much opposition to it. But when it became all but imperative to facilitate the passage of iron from Labrador to the interior, the opposition of Montreal and New York was overcome. Steel brought about the change.

> The rapid depletion of the high-grade ore of the Mesabi caused concern among all the steel companies of the U.S. leading the U.S. Steel Co. to acquire 3,800 acres of land on the Delaware river near Philadelphia for the establishment of an integrated steel mill and the Bethlehem Steel Co. to extend its Baltimore plant, both firms using the newly discovered ore in Venezuela, while Hannah of Cleveland and the Hollinger interests of Canada determined to exploit the recently discovered Labrador ore, 10 per cent richer than that being shipped from Mesabi. But if the Labrador ores were to be fully exploited with success, the St Lawrence seaway had to be constructed.[1]

Hence the old Cornwall canals were replaced by both a U.S. and Canadian seaway along the

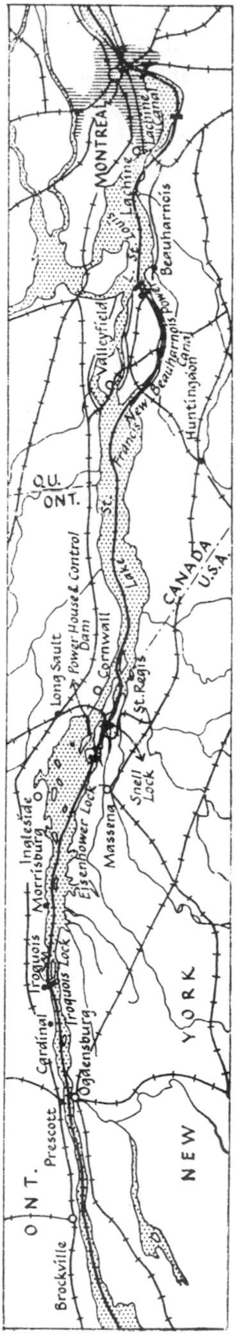

FIG. 93 The New St Lawrence Canals—the International Section of the Seaway—have brought great changes, not only with new links at Iroquois and Massena, but with new power plants, and new towns such as Ingleside and Long Sault.

[1] Walles, M. J., *The St Lawrence Seaway Development*, London Univ. Ph.D. Thesis, 1958, p. 190.

International Rapids section of the St Lawrence. Much power was developed at the same time.

The Ontario shorelands which run westward from the Rideau hills, marking the Frontenac axis, to the foot of the Niagara escarpment, form the central part of the central section of Canada. They are thus at the very heart of the country. As Coleman early showed, they consist of two level lowlands, an upper one, the old beach and beach platform of glacial Lake Iroquois, and a lower one, the plain bordering Lake Ontario. Lacustrine clays, with spreads of sand washed out from glacial beaches, together with strips of alluvium along the rivers flowing into the lake, give a wide variety of usable and often fertile soils. The climate is relatively warm, and rarely produces a cold snap of lower than −32° F. (This is about the critical winter-killing temperature for apple and cherry, and also for winter wheat.) The frost-free period is of medium-long duration, 140 to 165 days, and although it is hardly enough for sweet-corn and early vegetables, it is sufficient for the hardier fruits, asparagus, tomatoes, and strawberries. Consequently most of the townships of the Ontario shore go in for market gardening, apple, cherry, and peach orchards, small fruits, dairy and poultry products.

They show their most intensive development in the famed Niagara Fruit Belt (Fig. 94). The major part of the belt lies on the scarp-foot plain between the Niagara escarpment and Lake Ontario. Protected by the scarp and warmed by the lake, the fruit belt has the mildest winters of any region in eastern Canada. The minimum temperatures do not exceed —15° F. Thus there is very little danger of winter killing, and plants like apricots and peaches are rarely damaged. The frost-free span is between 160 and 170 days, and the summer warmth considerable (July, 68° F.), so that fruits have ample time and heat for ripening. Moreover, the frosts are not as variable as elsewhere, and so there is less risk of buds being nipped or the fruit blighted. To this extent the Niagara fruit belt is safer than the fruit areas of Leamington and Norfolk. Many canning crops are also grown, and grapes are extensively raised. Canning and wine-making are prominent at Niagara Falls, St Catharines, and Hamilton. Indeed, at Hamilton is the headquarters of Canadian Canners Ltd, the largest canning industry in the Commonwealth.

The farms are very small as a rule (5 to 20 acres) and are intensively cultivated, vegetables and small fruits being grown as cover crops between the rows of orchard trees. Farmers are so close to the cities that they use city services—garages, plumbers, carpenters, bankers, insurance agents, and lawyers. They also patronize city shops, places of amusement, and clubs. They occasionally send their children into city high schools, and sometimes attend city churches. Thus village life in the fruit belt is being weakened, and village churches, schools, and clubs are keenly feeling the impact of urbanization.

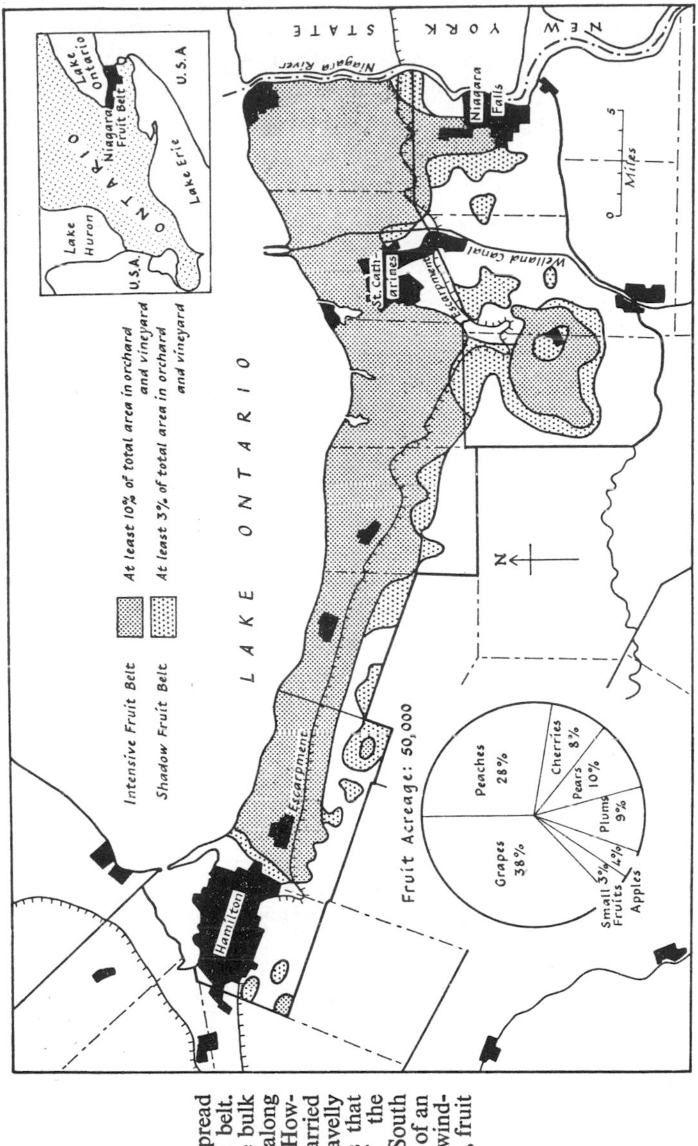

FIG. 94 Rise and spread of the Niagara fruit belt. (From Krueger.) The bulk of the production is along the scarp-foot plains. However, expansion has carried the orchards to the gravelly moraines and kames that fringe the top of the Niagara Escarpment. South of these, on the clays of an open, frost-bitten and wind-swept dip-slope plain, fruit culture ceases.

Another factor disturbing the local communities is the great influx of foreign-born, and the emigration of the old Loyalist families. This is quite natural, the older families selling off their farms and moving into the cities, and such foreign immigrants as have a fruit-growing tradition drifting to a familiar landscape in Canada. When they arrive they try to take up land near each other and keep together as a *bloc*, so as to worship in their old faiths and speak their old languages. Thus there is a Ukrainian Catholic

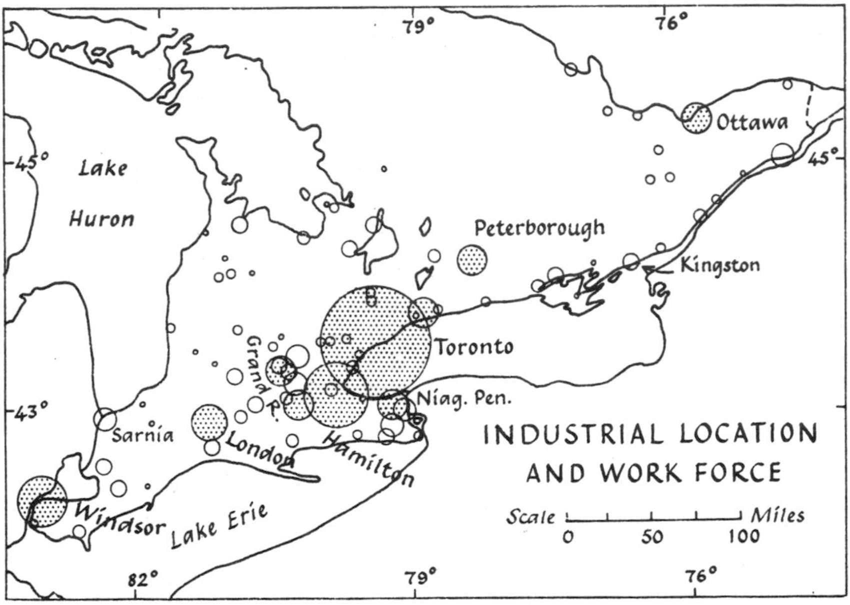

FIG. 95 Industry in Ontario. (From Kerr and Spelt.) Note the extraordinary concentration in the Toronto–Hamilton area. (Circles proportional to production; stippled circles, main centres.)

community south of Grimsby, a German Mennonite community at Vineland, and a Russian Mennonite village at Virgil. They carry their community spirit into business, and support strong growers' co-operatives. Their example has been followed by many Canadian-born residents who have taken up the co-operative ideal with enthusiasm.

The Ontario shore, though long noted for its agricultural wealth, is now thought of as one of Canada's leading industrial areas. The landscape is dominated by factory and town, by four- or six-lane highways, railway belts, and high-tension electric cables swinging from pylon to pylon. Agriculture has adjusted itself to industry, forming rings of market gardens and dairies about every city (Fig. 95).

There is, however, a marked difference between the eastern end of the plain, backed by the rough, rocky hills of the Frontenac axis, and the western end, leading into the heart of the belted lowland of southern Ontario. The eastern end is characterized by fairly small, though busy, towns such as Kingston, Brockville, Belleville, and Trenton, with varied milling, canning, textile, and light machine industries; the western end forms the chief manufacturing region of Ontario, if not of Canada.

The eastern end had early historic significance, after the American Revolution, because it stood opposite the great Hudson–Mohawk gap, which was America's chief route from the seaboard to the interior. **Kingston** (60,000) grew up about the old French fort, Frontenac, and was for a time the capital of Upper Canada. The city, with both French and British people, sprang up where the St Lawrence leaves Lake Ontario, and the Rideau river goes inland to Ottawa. Under the dominating height of Fort Henry, by the wide harbour of the Rideau estuary, the town evolved as a fortress and a harbour. It is still the site of the Royal Military College. Its industries are small—railway shops, agricultural implements, metal works, ship-building, and textiles. There never has been a big enough labour market to support large-scale industry. The countryside is dominated by the infertile Frontenac axis, and has a sparse population. The city is most famous as a university centre, where Queen's University and the Ontario School of Mines are situated.

The most highly developed region of Ontario lies at the western end of Lake Ontario between Oshawa, Toronto, and Hamilton. This has been called Canada's 'golden hinge', on which so much of the prosperity of the country depends (Fig. 96). At Toronto the Canadian Pacific Railway and Canadian National Railway and the Temiskaming and Northern Ontario Railway have large terminals from the Prairies, Sudbury, and the Haileybury–Hearst regions, bringing wheat, meat, metals, timber, and pulp. Through Hamilton the Canadian National Railway and Canadian Pacific Railway carry anthracite, coking coal, cotton, chemicals, machine parts, and other products from America. Both cities also obtain a lot of raw material by water. They have the best natural harbours on Lake Ontario, and draw materials such as sugar, cocoa, coffee, salt, metals, oil, rubber, and building material through the St Lawrence or the Welland canals. The same routeways make it possible to distribute manufactured products throughout Canada and abroad. Then, too, both cities are centres of rich agricultural areas, and can draw on surplus rural population for labour, and buy plenty of milk, butter, eggs, and fresh vegetables. In addition they attract immigrants. They lie at the meeting of the two chief immigration routes of the continent, the Hudson–Mohawk valley, and the St Lawrence–Lower Lakes. Finally they are near enough to the Niagara Falls and Queenston power-houses to secure cheap and plentiful electricity. Hamilton gets natural gas piped from the

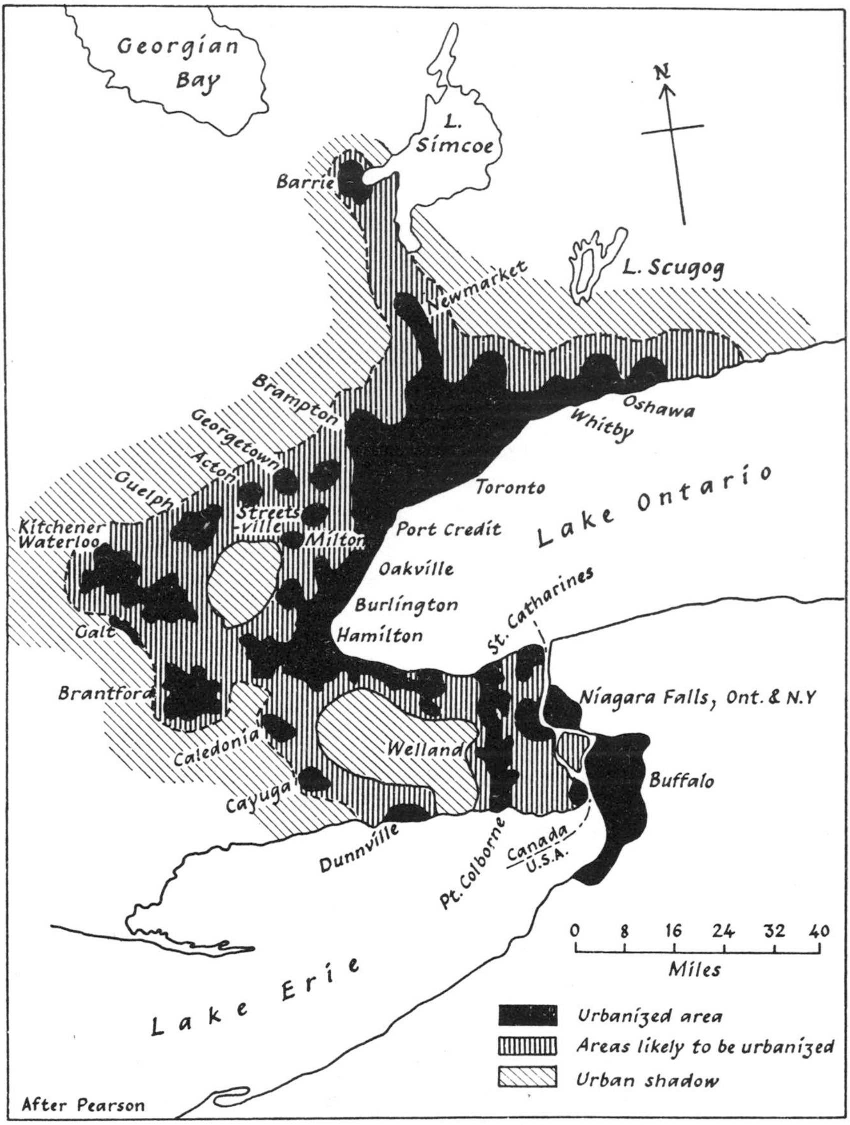

FIG. 96 The Canadian Megalopolis—Canada's 'Golden Hinge'. One of the fastest-growing urban areas in North America, this is rapidly subduing country to town in one immense urban sprawl—now being subjected to planning control in its individual parts.

Lake Erie fields, and both cities are now on the oil and gas pipe-lines from the Canadian west.

The industrial area has grown so rapidly that many satellite cities occur, which share these same advantages. **Oshawa** (70,000), lying well to the east of Toronto, is the Canadian centre of General Motors and Dunlop tyres, and turns out automobiles and trucks; Pickering is the site of the General Engineering Corporation. Mimico, lying to the west of Toronto, makes electrical equipment and food products; while at Port Credit are two of Canada's largest oil refineries. Oakville has a huge plant for making Ford cars, and Burlington, north of Hamilton, manufactures food products and insecticides. Dundas, in the cleft of the Niagara escarpment, is a textile and machinery centre, while St Catharines, at the mouth of the Welland Canal, makes automobile and electrical equipment. So great is the industrial activity that town practically runs into town for a distance of about 120 miles.

Hamilton, with a population of 450,000, is at the head of the lake, and commands the Dundas valley to South-western Ontario and the Niagara peninsula (Fig. 97(*a*)). It is the shopping centre and conference town for the

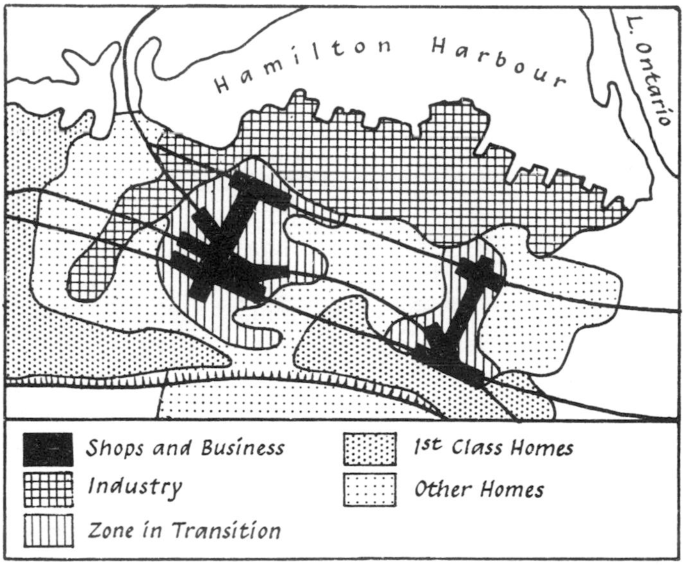

FIG. 97(*a*) Functional Plan of Hamilton. The main shopping, office, and administration centre of the town developed in the west end, between harbour and escarpment. Its opportunities for expansion being limited, it grew by budding off another centre to the east. Marked zonation occurs from these central business districts through transition zones of warehouses, small factories, and apartment blocks, to zones of middle-cost duplexes, and thence to suburbs of higher-cost single homes. Heavy industry is concentrated at the lake front.

peninsula, and also for the Grand river. It lies on a land-locked bay, across the upper and lower part of which great sand and shingle bars have been thrown. These enable road and railway to approach it directly. A canal in the lower bay-bar lets ships into the harbour. A large expanse of flat clay plain gives ample room for industries, which have big railway sidings next to their private quays. Rising ground to the south carries the shopping district up to and across the glacial Lake Iroquois terrace. Above this are residential districts, which are crowned by the Niagara escarpment. Westward are 'commuter' settlements, and the magnificent campus of McMaster University. The chief industries are iron and steel and steel products, electrical appliances, textiles, agricultural machines and preparations, tobacco, canning and meat packing, and the making of rubber tyres and chemicals. Note how these show the use of American supplies (coal, iron, cotton, rubber, chemicals) and of great quantities of cheap power (electrical appliances) and of farm produce from the fruit, tobacco, and stock belts in Ontario (canning and packing). There are 600 establishments, employing 60,000 people. The annual production is about a tenth of Canada's.

Toronto (2,000,000) is the second largest manufacturing city in Canada with a present output of both primary industrial and consumer goods equal to a fifth of the total output of the Dominion. The chief industries are metal foundries and machine shops, ship-building, and agricultural implements—all heavy industries; together with meat packing, flour-milling and canning; textiles, automobile furnishings, and clothing; paper products, printing, and publishing. Notice the reliance on Shield products (metals and paper) and on the Prairies (meat and flour) and also on the ease with which consumer products (cars, clothes, books, canned goods) can be distributed across Canada. There are over 3,500 establishments, and more than 150,000 employees (Fig. 97(*b*)).

Some interesting comparisons with Hamilton occur. Whereas Hamilton employs four men for every woman (as one would expect of an iron and steel centre), Toronto employs not quite two to one. Why? Because Toronto has many light industries such as clothing, canning, furnishings, bookbinding, etc., which are able to employ women. Another unusual thing is that Toronto employs one salaried person for every five wage earners; in Hamilton the figures are one in eight. In other words, there are bigger office staffs in Toronto, where a great number of the head offices occur of industries all over the country. Finally, in Hamilton, industry employs about a third of the working population but only a quarter in Toronto. Hamilton is more dependent on industry than any other large Canadian city, but Toronto has great commercial, financial, and professional interests as well. Its lofty Bay Street offices and palatial Yonge Street stores dominate the business and shopping of the province and beyond. Its social life is more

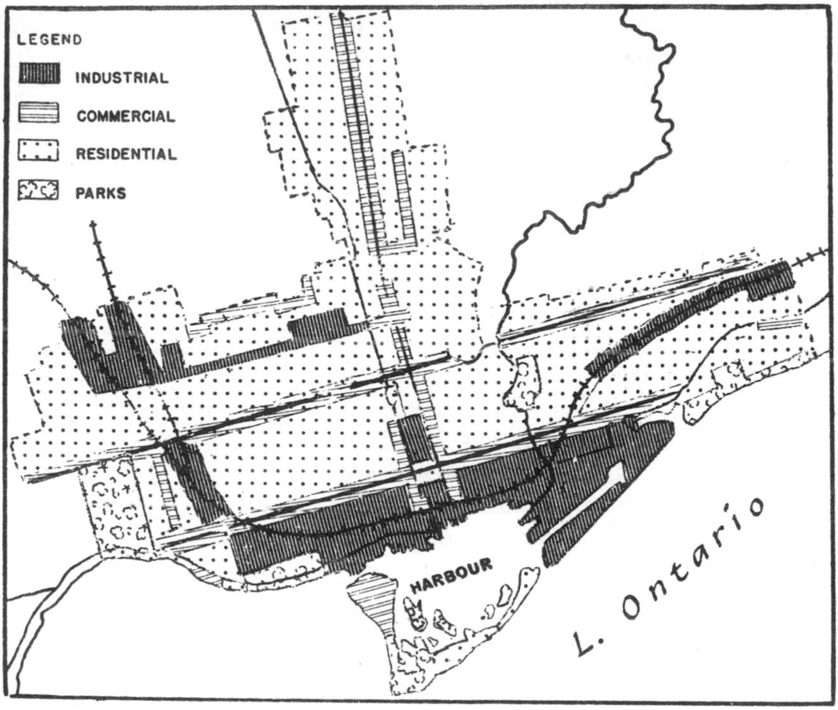

FIG. 97(*b*) Simplified Plan of the Functional Zones of Toronto. The shore front, especially in the spit-enclosed harbour, is crowded with industry. Where Front Street is crossed by the main road from the north, Yonge Street, the main financial and hotel nucleus occurs. The city has expanded more or less west and east along the old shore-line of glacial lake Iroquois, and northward down the great interfluve between the Humber and Don valleys to west and east. (Suburbs in contiguous townships not shown.)

balanced, because occupations are fully represented. Consequently, Toronto plays a leading role in the cultural development of Ontario. It is the seat of Anglican and Catholic archbishoprics, and has the Provincial Parliament, not far from which are the classical collonades of the Provincial Law Courts.

Toronto was chosen as the provincial capital over earlier sites like Niagara-on-the-Lake and Kingston, because it was much more centrally located. It is the centre between eastern and south-western Ontario at a point where they can be joined with northern Ontario. The command of the old Dundas Road, between Windsor and Montreal, and of Yonge Street, leading to Lake Simcoe, the Shield, and the Prairies, was followed by control of the railways, linking Canada's industrial axis to transcontinental routes. The site is good for government, business, and industry alike. Toronto has a large low plain opposite the great hooked spit which protects its harbour. Industries have direct access to rail and water transport, and room to expand. The Humber and the Don valleys carry roads and railways inland, and also invite the spread of industry. The station and railway tracks mark off the industrial front from the business and shopping section, which passes north to the central block of government buildings, law courts, and the provincial university. Thereafter, the land rises over the old Lake Iroquois shore beach, and residential suburbs stretch as far as Richmond Hill.

The rapid industrialization of Toronto and Hamilton has created major urban problems. The heavy industry of the shore is crowding back and invading former commercial and residential sites; smaller industries are moving well up the valleys from the lake, all but into the suburbs. New, lighter industries have been established on the city outskirts. At the same time, the central business and shopping areas are expanding outwards from the old city nuclei. Caught between the advance of factory and office, the residential areas are squeezed out, or else squeezed into slums. Old houses are turned into flats. Gardens disappear and are built over. Small factories and offices transform old mansion houses. The better-off families move out, farther and farther, into ever-extending suburbs. The poorer families put up with smaller and more crowded quarters in the midst of shops and factories.

Very often it is the poor immigrants who occupy these 'shatter belts' between 'invading' factories and shops. They have no means; they must be near their work; they are willing to put up with conditions for the sake of living in Canada; they cannot speak English; often they are kept out of the better suburbs. Thus little 'foreign' quarters emerge—an Italian area, a Jewish area, or Hungarian, and so on. In these 'homes from home' the foreign-born[1] can speak their language together, wear the clothes and eat the foods they are used to, have their churches and clubs, and feel secure. Nevertheless, by doing so they are making it difficult for themselves to become Canadians. Consequently, movements like the Toronto Settlement, and district community centres, town planning and so forth, have sprung up to try to overcome 'racial' segregation and prevent 'racial' discrimination, and to create in their place a richer Canadian society where all groups contribute what they have to the common culture. These large industrial cities, therefore, present some of the gravest problems, but offer golden opportunities to Canadian citizenship.

The Lake Erie shoreland and the Windsor peninsula, together with the tributary basins of the Grand and Thames, also form a highly commercialized area, with very specialized agriculture, and with a considerable amount of industry. As Putnam[2] has shown, most of the district lay under

---

[1] At the last census, 31 per cent of Hamilton's population and 31·4 per cent of Toronto's had been born outside the country. These are very high proportions—almost 1 in 3.

[2] Chapman, L. J., and Putnam, D. F., *The Physiography of Southern Ontario*, Toronto, 1951.

glacial lakes, and it steps up from the present lake level in a number of wide lacustrine terraces, often edged with stranded beaches. One striking feature is the huge spread of sand formed as deltas of the Thames and Grand pushing out into glacial lakes. Northward, the district passes into the strongly rolling land of the Ontario moraines (see Fig. 87).

The area extends far south for Canada and has a relatively short winter, a frost-free span of from 160 to 170 days, and hot, moist summers (July, 68°–71° F.). It is thus climatically favoured and has developed some highly specialized crops, including tobacco, sweet corn, and sugar-beets, peach orchards, and canning crops. Throughout, dairying is important, with large farms and pedigree herds. The farm regions form a close response to local variations in climate, soil, relief, and market (see Fig. 89).

In the counties of Elgin and Norfolk is Canada's chief tobacco belt. Canning crops, winter wheat and malting barley, apple orchards and poultry are also plentiful. They take advantage of well-drained wide, sandy plains, the former deltas of the Thames and the Grand. The soil warms up quickly, and remains hot throughout the summer, thus stimulating plant growth. Tobacco, particularly, likes a sandy soil. The farmers start the plants in steam-heated seed-beds, and transplant the shoots from the hot-houses into the fields, once the danger of frost has passed. The tobacco needs a lot of cultivation. At harvest, thousands of transient labourers are attracted to the district from all over Ontario and from the neighbouring States. The leaves of the plants are cut in order as they ripen, and are then hung on rafters of large drying kilns to be cured. After that they go to the tobacco factories. The farms need a lot of capital and equipment—seeding beds, hot-houses, kilns, transplanting machines, and cultivators—but can supply a profitable living from a small area (5 to 25 acres). Many continental European immigrants, such as Belgians, Czechs, and Hungarians, have settled in the district, carrying over their love of tobacco farming from their homelands. St Thomas (55 establishments), Simcoe and Tillsonburg are the chief towns. Agricultural machinery, canning, brewing, and tobacco-curing constitute the principal industries.

Farther south and west, in the Windsor peninsula, the counties of Essex and Kent are also noted for highly specialized crops such as sweet-corn, tobacco, peaches, sugar-beet, tomatoes, onions and other garden crops, early potatoes and winter wheat. These products reflect the long frost-free season (170 days or more) and high summer temperatures (68°–71° F.), and also the relatively high winter minima (—20° to —25° F.). Soils are clay loams, developed on lake-bevelled till plains, and sandy loams, associated with beach ridges and outwash. The heavier soils are ideal for corn, wheat and sugar-beet, and the lighter ones for peaches, tobacco, and canning crops. The land is nearly flat, and all of it can be used for cultivation. Good roads and railways exist which put it in touch with the large urban markets of Windsor, Chatham, London, and St Thomas, and beyond. Farms are quite small—many of them only 5 acres—but they are intensively cultivated. Close proximity to the city encourages a high standard of living, since the farmers use city services, enjoy city recreation, and try to maintain city-looking homes. Leamington, the chief agricultural market, is the most southerly town in Canada. It has tobacco and canning factories and provides baskets, insecticides, and agricultural equipment for a wide region. The Heinz Company of Canada has a large canning factory near by.

The prosperous agriculture of the region has helped industry forward by providing raw materials, excess capital, and surplus labour, for manufacturing; and also by affording a good market for farm machines and consumer goods. The towns have not sprung up along the lake, which for much of its length has strong cliffs cut into the prevailing till plain, but have emerged in the river basins behind.

The Grand river towns, Dunnville, Brantford, Paris, Galt, Guelph, Kitchener-Waterloo, were founded to make use of the water-power supplied by the river, to draw on the raw materials of a rich agricultural area, and to benefit from the connexions with U.S.A. provided by the Windsor and Niagara gateways. They also have easy access to the Canadian market. They produce a wide variety of goods, including furniture, woollens, rubber, agricultural machinery, and chemical plants. Kitchener-Waterloo, the chief node, has become one of Canada's significant insurance centres. **The Thames valley towns,** Woodstock, Stratford, Ingersoll, and London, rely largely on local agricultural raw materials and are noted for their dairy products, beer, leather, cereals and biscuits, and agricultural implements (see Fig. 95).

London (200,000) is the routeway centre for south-western Ontario, and as such is far more than an industrial town; it is also a thriving agricultural market, a transportation hub, a shopping centre, a business exchange, and the cultural capital of the whole busy and densely populated region. Indeed it is second to Toronto as a financial and insurance centre, and its mortgage and life insurance companies are known throughout Canada. Its industries are tied up closely with the agriculture and transportation of the region (breakfast foods, flour, biscuits, wines and beer, and railway machinery being its chief products). The University of Western Ontario is situated there, on a high hill, overlooking the winding Thames.

The Grand river and Thames river towns owe their development to water-power and natural routeways. However, though water has turned their mills it has also flooded their streets. Thus a major problem has arisen, that of flood control. This is not simply an engineering problem. It is also a social one. At first one imagines that all that is required is a dam. But where is the dam to be built? How many dams should be built? Who is to plan them? Who is to pay for them? Who will buy the farms that must be drowned out, and resettle the farmer? How much water is to be released and at what times? The answer to these questions differs with the different towns. But a river knows nothing of municipal limits. One part cannot be dammed, without affecting every other. Consequently, its use must be planned and paid for *as a region.* Towns must be willing to put the interests of the region first. Something along this line has been done in the Grand valley, and a new departure in Canadian provincial government was made when Ontario established a ministry of Planning and Development. This is now actively at work in the Thames and other river basins, throughout the province.

The Niagara and Windsor peninsulas form special divisions of the Lake Erie plain. They are noteworthy as Canada's chief gateways to America. Here the Canadian manufacturing belt feeds into and from the American one. Both frontiers lie on the Great Lakes waterways (St Clair river and Welland Canal) and share in the flow of the seaway trade. American industries have found convenient sites for building Canadian branches, including American automobile works at Fort Erie opposite Buffalo; large paper factories at Thorold; carborundum works at Niagara Falls; and American chemical, steel, and automotive interests at Welland and St Catharines. In fact, at one time, these plants were largely staffed and managed by Americans. The Canadian towns have thus become counterparts or satellites of the much larger cities on the opposite frontier. Canadians shop, do business, visit the theatre, and go to college in the near-by American cities. This has undoubtedly meant their absorption in the American way of life.

Such is especially the case with the foreign-born immigrant. More than a quarter of the population are New Canadians, ignorant of the Canadian tradition. Many of them have relatives in America. They easily adopt American ways. Therefore, the frontier cities have a problem of maintaining their Canadian identity. But their strong sense of history, and the reminders they have of the past in Fort George, Fort Erie, and Amherstburg, enable them to do this. Nevertheless, their more important function is to interpret their own country to the other, and so to create a respect for both traditions in their citizens.

The Niagara industries make use of the enormous quantities of cheap electricity released at Niagara and Queenston (Fig. 98). Typical industries are electro-chemicals at Niagara Falls and Welland; electro-metallurgical industries and refineries at Welland and Port Colborne; electrical appliances at St Catharines; and paper-making (which uses a lot of electricity) at Thorold. **Windsor** (205,000) is one of the larger cities of Canada, and dominates the St Clair and lower Thames lowland, opposite to Detroit. Undoubtedly it owes much of its prosperity to Detroit and it is dominated by the automobile industry, in association with Ford and Chrysler. Cars can be sent to both

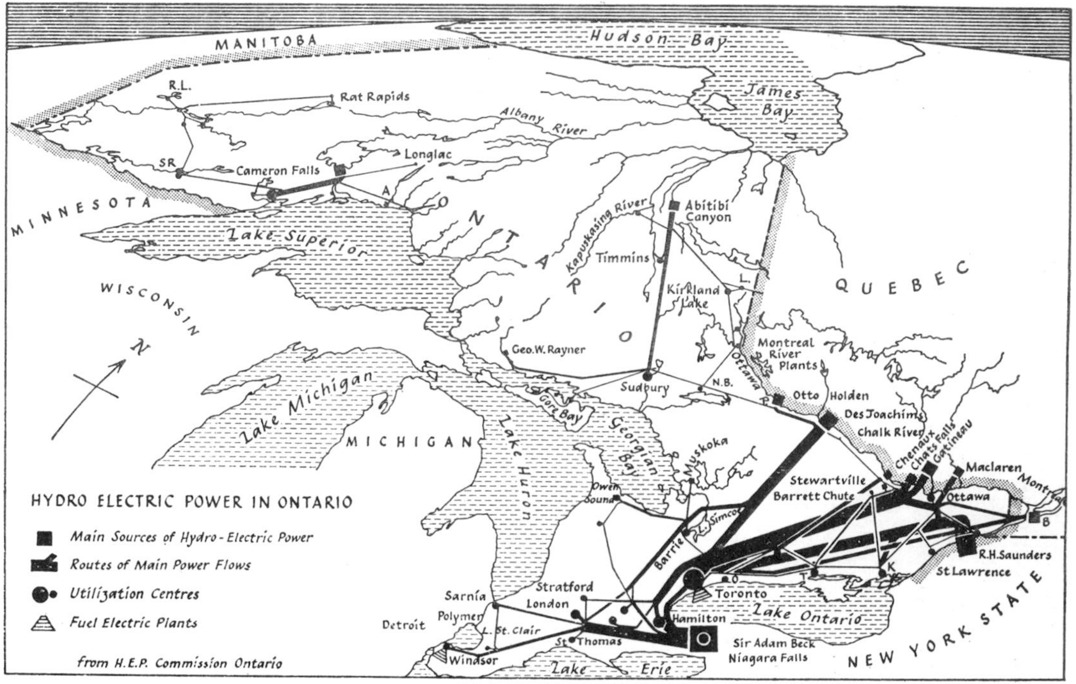

FIG. 98 Power resources of Ontario. (From the Ont. H.E.P. Commission.) Note the dominance of Niagara Falls and the St Lawrence River (International Rapids) sectors. A, Agnasabon; B, Beauharnois; K, Kingston; L, Larder Lake; NB, North Bay; O, Oshawa; RL, Red Lake; SR, Steep Rock; T, Trenton.

West and East Canada with equal ease. Walkerville and Amherstburg are known for their whiskeys (on the grain-route); and Sarnia for oil refineries (on the pipe-line from Alberta) and for chemical works (linked with large local salt deposits). It is also a centre for rubber production.

The Georgian Bay fruit belt forms the third of the lakeshore districts of peninsular Ontario. Here a narrow glacial lake terrace thrusts out from beneath the scarp of Bruce peninsula, to give scope for farm and village. The south shore, from Owen Sound to Collingwood, is noted for its apple orchards. This is decidedly an outlier of warmth in northern-central Ontario. The lowest temperature recorded is −30° F., which is above the critical temperature for the winter killing of apples. The open water of Georgian Bay warms up the northern winds that otherwise would slide off the cold Shield and bring severe cold snaps (as in the rest of northern-central Ontario). The area is also given some protection by the Niagara scarp. The cold air does not stand on the fields but drains off down the scarp-face and across the scarp-foot plain. The frost-free period, 150 days, is above the average for the latitude.

The plain widens eastward into the Huronia where the French fathers first won the Huron Indians over to Christianity. Today far more than the corn and beans of the Huron tribes are raised, and silage, root crops, and hay form the basis of beef and dairy farming. Midland is the main market town, and Owen Sound the chief port for the district.

The Morainic uplands of south-western and southern central Ontario show a gradual change from the highly commercialized agriculture, and from the industrialization and urbanization of the lakeshore plains, to more generalized pursuits. They have much more woodland, their farms are larger and depend mainly on animal products, and their towns are smaller and farther apart than lakeside counterparts. The land is rough, with the swell and sag surface associated with moraines. The complex series of moraines, known as the Horseshoe system, in western peninsular Ontario, gives a wide variety of relief, drainage, and soil. The more massive Oak Ridge moraine offers a whole series of boulder-clay hills that rise and fall across central Ontario. Much of the land should have remained under forest since, with the widespread destruction of the trees, the steep slopes have become subject to pronounced soil erosion. This has increased with time and impoverished much of the farming. However, the climate is not unkind and is suitable for fodder crops, clover, winter wheat, and potatoes, but not for orchards or canning crops. The frost-free season is from 130 to 145 days, and the mean July temperature is about 66°. The soils of the region are mainly a stony, clay loam.

A large acreage of rough pasture is typical. This has tended to develop beef production along with sheep-raising. Hay and coarse grains are the principal crops, and are fed to the livestock. The Lake Huron Counties, the Simcoe-Kawartha and Renfrew areas, are not suited to intensive cultivation, except where they open out here and there, as in the Lindsay and Peterborough basins, into flatter and more fertile patches (see Fig. 89).

Farms are farther away from the large cities than in any other zone in southern Ontario. Land is comparatively cheap, and the farms average 120 to 150 acres, much of which is left in bush. They are worked on a family basis, and there are few day labourers or even seasonal labourers employed. In the busy seasons the families co-operate with each other to get the work done. They are very dependent on their local market towns, which, as a result, are relatively large and varied. These have good shopping and business facilities, and farm-supply and equipment stores. They also have large creameries, feed mills, and sometimes breweries and woollen mills. They usually sponsor country fairs of note, and have cinemas, skating rinks, bowling alleys, and saloons to entertain the farmer and his family. Their high schools serve a wide area beyond the town and compare very favourably with city ones. Such towns are Walkerton and Durham, in the Western uplands; Barrie and Orillia on the shores of Lake Simcoe; Lindsay, Campbellford, and Tweed between the Oak Ridges and Frontenac axis. **Peterborough** (50,000) has developed into a thriving industrial city, with important machine, agricultural, and tourist industries and Trent University.

The area north of Lake Simcoe, including Muskoka, Haliburton, and Nipissing districts, is a transition zone between southern and northern Ontario, where farming has tried to establish itself on the edge of the Shield, but has generally failed. Small lacustrine plains are farmed, and produce hay and oats as fodder crops for beef cattle; but much of the land is left in rough pasture, or is returning rapidly to forest. The farm population of these districts is declining. Lumbering has revived with the remarkable boom in the furniture veneer trade. But the chief occupation is the tourist trade. Towns like Bracebridge are gradually changing from market and mill centres. Gift shops, restaurants, tourist lodges, hotels, and tourist-supply shops are becoming more prominent in the streets. Many of the farmers are selling off lake-front lots, and turning themselves into guides or caretakers, or confining their work to raising sheep and yearling beef on the rough pasture. Those that have suitable land are raising vegetables and dairy produce for the tourist hotels and camps.

SUMMARY

The southern settled areas of the Central Provinces form the most intensively farmed and highly industrialized section of Canada. The section is rich in local differences based on relief, and soil, and has produced an astonishingly wide range of occupations and activities. Previous reference has been made to differences in historical geography which stamp the predominantly French-Canadian area in Quebec as different from the British-Canadian sector in Ontario. But though variety is rife, it is caught up into an over-all unity. The split between French and British is not clear or deep enough to permit a separate treatment of Quebec and Ontario, because there is an appreciable British element in Quebec City, Montreal, and the Quebec side of the Ottawa valley; while many French live in Ottawa and eastern and northern Ontario. But aside from the ethnic integration that has been going on, there is the economic integration of the two districts. Montreal depends to a considerable extent on the St Lawrence, Welland, and Soo canals, and on roads and railways from the interior to the coast; while Toronto secures many goods and people from Europe sent through Quebec. As a result, a large commercial and industrial complex has been built up, organized along an east–west Canadian axis, that has drawn the whole region, from Lake Huron to the St Lawrence estuary, into a single, vital entity. With this growth the region has become the keystone to the Canadian economy, uniting the eastern seaboard with the western interior plains and basins.

CHAPTER THIRTEEN

The Southern Prairies

The Prairie Provinces form another of the major sections of Canada. Lying between the Shield and the Rocky mountains they are clearly bounded on east and west. To north and south, however, they pass without any appreciable break into the Mackenzie and Missouri–Mississippi basins. Nevertheless, even here the fact that they are essentially the plains of the Saskatchewan-Nelson waterway, and that this is the only major west–east drainage system in the western interior lowlands of North America, helps to set off the section from regions to north and south. But, as has been pointed out, where nature failed to provide any marked divide, man created one in the International Boundary, with the result that north of the forty-ninth parallel the history and nature of settlement, the growth of institutions, and the development of trade went on in a distinctive way.

The Prairie Provinces play an important role in Canada, both as a physical link between the Pacific and western Cordilleras on the one hand, and the Great Lakes–St Lawrence and Atlantic on the other, and also as Canada's main source of food and fuel. They form quite a large section, covering over 750,000 sq. miles. It is true that this is only about three-quarters the size of the Central Provinces. However, most of Ontario and Quebec is an inhospitable shield, whereas most of the Prairies is level plain. Consequently, it has much more land available for farm settlement, and is the granary of Canada. Its welfare is bound up with agriculture. Although the population is no longer predominantly rural, except in Saskatchewan, the cities flourish on agriculture, distributing supplies to the farmer, and using farm materials in their industries, so that rural interests prevail (Fig. 99).

The opportunities and the problems of the Prairies, therefore, are chiefly those of the farmer. His main problems are the location of his farm, its drainage and soil, the weather, the cost of transportation, the hire of help, foreign markets, the price of wheat, and the competition of other wheat-growing districts in the world. Some of these are geographical factors, and others are economic and political. All are important. However, there is a special importance in the geographical ones, because frost and drought are very real hazards. Agriculture is a great deal more dependent on the local environment than industry. Ontario can afford to import coal, iron, cotton, and other raw materials from a great distance because it makes a good

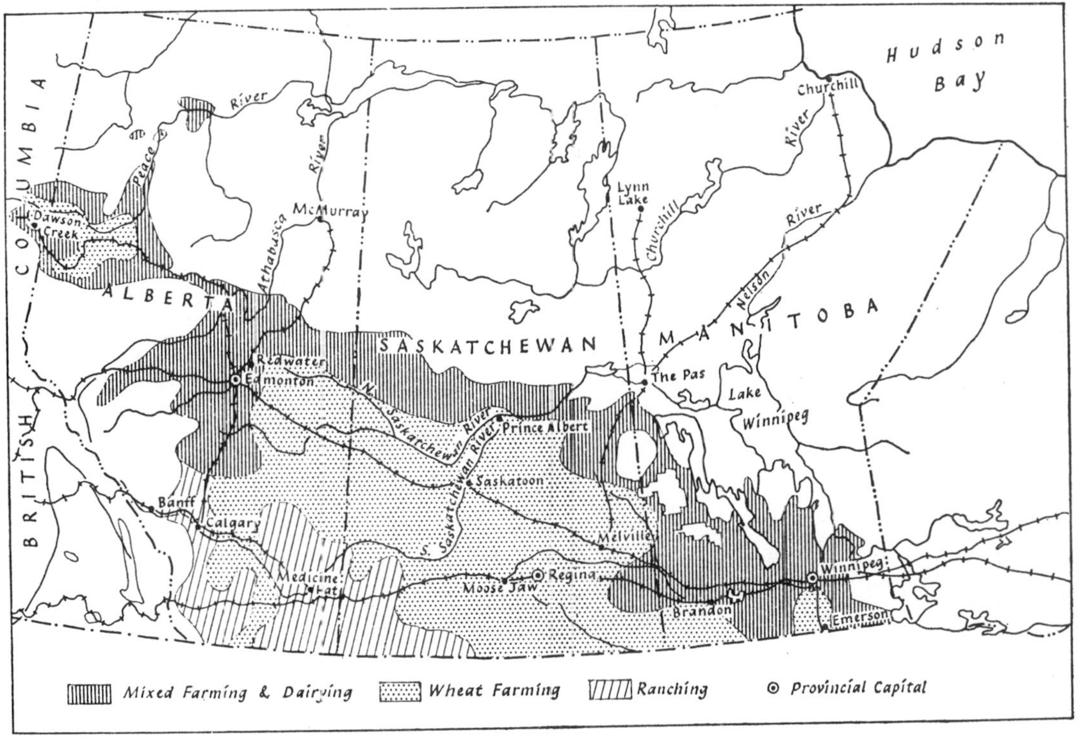

FIG. 99 Land Use in the Canadian Prairies—chief agricultural zones and urban centres. The unshaded portions are mainly under coniferous forest. Wheat is at the core; dairying and mixed farming are on the cooler more humid northern front; ranching on the drier southern or hillier south-western front. (Scale, 1:15 m.)

profit by manufacturing them, and distributing the finished goods far and wide. The Prairies depend to a much greater degree on their own local resources because they rely largely on exporting farm products and not finished goods. This makes relief, climate, vegetation, and soil of special importance.

THE ENVIRONMENT

Relief

People often imagine the Prairies as an endless, monotonous plain. Yet many relief features do occur, which, because of their influence on drainage and climate, railways and settlement, are very significant.

The Prairies form a wide basin between the Shield and the Rockies. In the east, old sedimentary rocks slope from the Shield. They have been attacked so long by erosion that they make a series of low scarps and gentle vales in Manitoba, not unlike southern Ontario. In the west, along the Rocky foothills, the old rocks have been folded, along with younger sedimentaries, and turned sharply upwards. They create long, narrow ridges in Alberta parallel to the Rocky ranges, some of which are virtually 'hogbacks'. In between the Manitoba lowlands and the Alberta hogbacks are fairly level beds of sedimentaries.

During Cretaceous times large rivers flowing east from the mountains smoothed the area down to almost a peneplain. However, a new uplift occurred in the Rockies. Streams were rejuvenated. They brought down masses of sand and gravel, which were dropped when they came to the flat peneplain surface. Then the waters would overflow the banks and make new river channels. Thus quantities of gravel and sand were deposited, which hardened and formed what is called the Eocene mantle—an uneven upland above the older surfaces.

Still another uplift occurred. The Eocene mantle was carved up into separate uplands, including the Edmonton–Calgary plateau, the Cypress hills, Moose mountain, Wood mountain, and Turtle mountain. The present drainage pattern took shape with reinvigorated streams cutting sharp water-gaps through the hogback ridges, and then flowing eastward in deep depressions until they emerged on the Manitoba vale. They are bordered by high terraces, which are the remains of older valley sides.

As a result of this long history of change, the Prairies form three distinct levels or steps. The first level is the Manitoba vale, which extends from the edge of the Shield to the edge of the Cretaceous rocks. It is 715 feet above sea-level at Lake Winnipeg. The Cretaceous edge rises sharply like a great wall, known as the Manitoba escarpment. It has been cut into different blocks by swift, active rivers. These blocks are the Pembina mountain

(1,600 feet), in the south, and Riding (2,200 feet), Duck (2,500 feet), and Porcupine (2,200 feet) mountains, in the centre of the province.

The next level stretches across Saskatchewan, and has a rather more uneven character, with patches of Eocene and Oligocene rocks forming hills above the Cretaceous plain. It ends against another escarpment known as the Missouri Coteau. Once more, the rivers have cut up the scarp into a number of separate uplands, about 2,500 feet high. These are Wood mountain, in the south—a great cap of Eocene rock; the Coteau, Bad, and Bear hills in the centre, and the hills north of Battleford.

The third level forms rolling country rising from the Coteau to the deeply scalloped Cypress hills and the Calgary plateau of Eocene rock. The level passes into the Rocky mountains through a belt of steeply inclined ridges, 4,000 to 5,000 feet high. The rivers have cut deeply into the surface.

Important minor features, due to glaciation or to desert conditions, vary the Prairie landscape. The ice swept south and west across most of the Prairies. It left a sweeping arc of moraines from the Red Deer river south to the Saskatchewan South Branch, along the top of the Coteau, and also along the brow of the Manitoba scarp—producing strongly rolling country, with small lakes in glacial hollows. Undulating ground-moraine is found everywhere, but especially in the south. As the ice retreated, glacial lakes and melt-water channels formed in front of it. One of the largest lakes in North America was glacial Lake Agassiz. It covered almost the whole of the Manitoba vale, and extended up the Saskatchewan river and the Assiniboine and Souris rivers to the foot of the Coteau. Lake Winnipeg is a small remnant of this vast sheet of water. So are Lakes Manitoba and Winnepegosis. The glacial lakes have left wide, flat deposits of clay in the Saskatoon, Regina, Brandon, and Winnipeg plains, which are invaluable for agriculture. The plains are varied by sandy beach ridges and deltas, especially along the foot of the Manitoba scarp.

The chief melt-water channels on the Prairies are found between the Oldman and Milk rivers and from the South Saskatchewan around the flanks of the Cypress hills. Eastward, in the Chin and Etzikom depressions, 'coulee' lakes have formed. Where semi-desert is found, between Swift Current and Lethbridge, alkali flats and saline lakes are common.

Across all three Prairie levels flows the Saskatchewan river, from the Rocky front to Lake Winnipeg. It gives the Prairie region an essential unity. It also provides a west–east axis that parallels the International Frontier. This is very important. Although the main relief features run across that frontier—the Rockies, the Coteau, the Cretaceous scarp, and the Red river basin—the Saskatchewan and its tributaries offer a latitudinal strike and east–west alignment, from the Upper Great Lakes to the Rocky passes, keeping the Prairies a Canadian region. The railways later followed and strengthened the line of the rivers.

Climate, Soil, and Vegetation

The interior location of the Prairies stamps their climate with two characteristics: continentality and aridity. The climate is very continental, and therefore extreme and variable. In summer it heats up to as high as 100° F., and in winter cools to as low as −50° F. It lacks the moderation of a seaside climate, where the water remains cool in summer and warm in winter, thus moderating the temperatures of the near-by land. The Manitoba lakes do modify temperatures to a certain extent, but their influence does not spread far. The average range of temperature from winter cold to summer heat in the Prairies is from 75° to 100° F.

This means that the Prairies are very much under the action of conflicting cold and hot air masses. From November to March the polar continental air mass prevails; from June to August the gulf air invades the region; and streams from the Pacific are not infrequent, especially in winter and early spring. As a result, cyclones are common, particularly in the early and late winter. These are often born in Alberta in the lee of the mountains, and sweep eastwards across the plains to the Great Lakes.

There are no outstanding physical barriers in the Prairies themselves, and so the air masses surge back and forth with more than usual freedom. A very cold wave may break out of the Mackenzie basin and sweep right down to Texas before it has spent itself. Similarly, a hot wave of Gulf air might press right to the Arctic. The area of conflict is large and open. In some winters the main cyclone track may be farther north, in which case there will be many mild spells, with temperatures of up to 20 degrees above normal. In other years, the tracks may be far south; the Prairies then come under the keen rule of polar air masses, and temperatures may fall 20 degrees below the normal. Quite often warm and cold spells follow each other quickly, and the temperatures rise or fall 50 degrees within a few hours. This is especially true near the Rockies where the warm Chinook winds blow down the valleys, and raise the temperature very high in a matter of hours.

Changeable weather of this sort is always trying, but it is more trying during the growing season. It can affect the crops in several ways: it may bring sudden frosts which blight them; or unusual droughts which kill them; or sudden hailstorms, or duststorms; or a spell of great heat along with the drought; or warm moist weather, in which plants are forced ahead, followed by hot, dry weather, in which they shrivel and die. The Prairies know all these vagaries—and more. The most serious dangers are frost and drought. For the Prairies are on the border between boreal forest and desert. The northern farmers constantly fear frost; the south-western ones, drought.

It is only along a narrow zone in between that there is tolerably steady weather.

The areas with an average of over 120 days free from frost are moderately safe for agriculture. If the weather varies 25 per cent from normal, they still have a chance (90 days) in which to raise their wheat. But where the average warm season is less than 90 days, then the risk from frost is great. A long-growing-season loop extends from Alberta into Saskatchewan as far as the junction of the North and South Saskatchewan rivers. Here the longer season is due in part to the Chinook, and also to the mild Pacific air drawn in at the front of spring lows. Another long-growing-season loop extends from the Red river, across the Manitoba plains to the Assiniboine valley in Saskatchewan. It is due to the influence of the Manitoba lakes, and to the path of the 'lows' on their way to the Great Lakes. The early recognition of this warm loop, in 1856, led people to think of the Prairies as suitable for farming.[1]

Between the warm loops is a cold one, which spreads over the whole of the northern Prairies and sends a long arm from the Pasquia hills south-westward by the Beaver hills and Moose mountain to the Cypress hills. This is the *Frost Belt*. It lies in the area most remote from the Rocky foot-hills and the Manitoba lakes, and bounds the agricultural frontier on the north where it cuts across the central plains. Here quickly growing or hardy crops, like hay and rye, replace wheat.

The *Drought Belt* lies to the south and south-west (Fig. 100). It is called Palliser's Triangle, after Captain John Palliser, who explored the region between 1857 and 1860. He came to the belief that between longitudes 100° and 114° W., and south of latitude 52° N., there is a triangle of land unfit for cultivation because of its infertile soil and arid climate.[2] This great triangle lies in the 'rain shadow' of the Rockies, and outside most of the storm tracks which converge on the Great Lakes. Therefore it is cut off from moisture-laden airs. Like the rest of the Prairies it is dominated in winter by the dry, keen polar continental air mass. But in summer, when the western foothills are getting rain from Pacific airs, and the eastern plains from the gulf airs up the Mississippi–Red river depression, Palliser's triangle is dry and hot. Rains do occur. Generally they are violent, short-lived thunderstorm rains. They do not sink slowly into the soil, but run off quickly into gullies. The average rainfall is less than 15 inches a year. In two districts, between Lethbridge and Medicine Hat, and south-east of Regina, the annual average is 13 inches or less. However, the hilly parts have more rain, and are clothed with wood or grass. Thus, the Sweet Grass hills rise clad in green above the

---

1 Morton, W. L., *The West and Confederation, 1857–71*, Can. Hist. Soc. Booklet, no. 9, Ottawa, 1958, p. 4.

2 Kerr, D. G. G., *A Historical Atlas of Canada*, Toronto, 1961, map 86, p. 60.

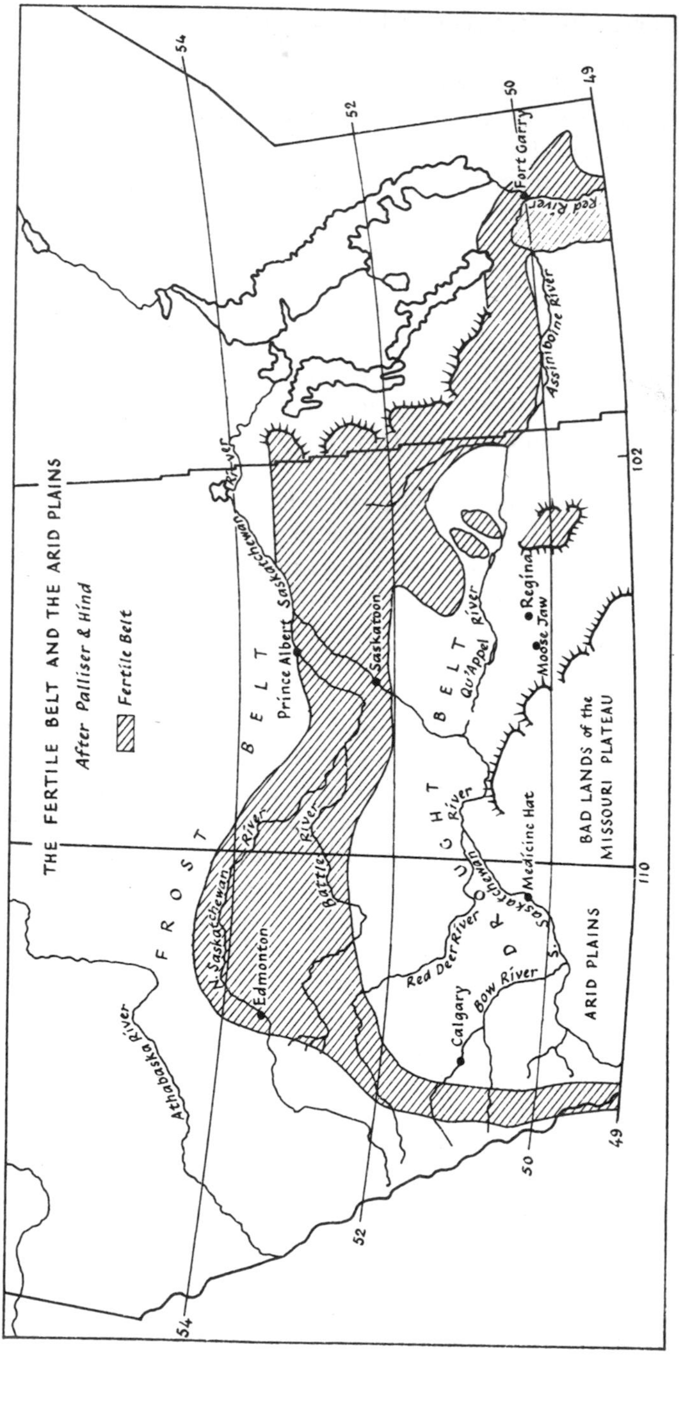

FIG. 100 The fertile and the arid belts, the Canadian Prairies. The fertile belt is relatively narrow, and lies as on a razor's edge, between the hazards of the frost belt to the north and of the drought belt to the south. (Scale, 1:11 m.)

sands and cactus scrubs that border the Milk river. The Cypress hills used to be covered with a thin forest, until the jack pine was cut off.

It is not the mere dryness of weather, however, that is a drawback to agriculture. It is its extreme variability. A farmer might successfully use dry-farming methods if he could rely on the rainfall, even if it were low; but where it is both low and unreliable he has little chance[1]—outside of irrigation. For example, at Medicine Hat the average growing-season rainfall is 9·3 inches; yet in some years the farmer gets only 4·5 inches; in other years he might get as much as 16 inches. It has been calculated that in any year he can expect a deviation of at least 34 per cent from the normal. This could mean an occasional bumper crop; it could also mean famine. The yield of non-irrigated wheat has varied from forty bushels an acre to as low as three. The average deviation from the 'normal' crop is as great as 47 per cent. This presents a real risk for the ordinary farmer, especially if he has a large mortgage to pay off, high costs of labour, and other charges to meet.

Moreover, he has to compete with farmers in other and more favoured parts of the Prairies. The element of competition makes climatic variability still more risky. If wheat prices were to fall, and in the same year the crop yield were reduced by excessive drought the farmer would suffer a double loss which would make it almost impossible to carry on. Other farmers could withstand the fall in prices, where their yields were still high. In Edmonton, for example, the average deviation from the 'normal' crop is only 16 per cent, or three times less than in the Drought Belt. Other things being equal, the Edmonton farmer has three times less risk than his competitor in Medicine Hat.

There are two comparatively wet regions in the Prairies. They are the Alberta plateau and the lower Manitoba plain. The foothills of the Rockies and the high plains from about Calgary to Edmonton have over 20 inches of rainfall a year. This is partly due to their high altitude, but mainly to the influences of the Pacific air mass, and of lows born in the lee of the Rocky mountains. The hot valleys often produce convection rain in early summer. As for the Manitoba lowlands, they are invaded by moist gulf airs in late spring and summer. The local lakes also help to maintain the humidity of the atmosphere and increase the likelihood of rain. Summer thunderstorm rain is valuable.

Thus we see that although frost and drought are hazards in the north and south, the climate of the greater part of the Prairies is well suited to agriculture. The growing season, with an average of 100 to 120 days free from frost,

[1] Waines, W. J., *Prairie Population Possibilities*, Ottawa, 1939, p. 7. 'Rainfall deficiency is less significant than variability. An economy can adjust itself more easily to a stable situation, even though at a low level, than to one where fluctuations are extreme yet costs are relatively fixed.'

is adequate for all cool-temperate crops. Daily the summer temperatures rise to over 70° F. for a period of eight weeks, which is sufficient for ripening wheat. The rainfall occurs chiefly in the spring and early summer, when it is most needed for growth, and is followed by a sunny autumn, ideal for harvest. The bright sunshine assists in developing high vitamin and protein content in the grain for which the Prairies are noted.

The Vegetation of the Prairies

Differences in Prairie rainfall do not seem great, when measured in inches of rainfall; nevertheless they are very critical, especially for vegetation. The rainfall fluctuates about the margin where forests thin out and grasses take their place. Thus, slight changes in rainfall may lead to quite striking differences in vegetation.

The word 'prairie' means a meadow, and the Prairies are the grasslands of Canada. However, it is important to realize that they have large areas under forest. The northern parts of each of the provinces are covered with the *boreal forest*, of black spruce and tamarack. Jack pines flourish on the lighter soils. These evergreen trees can withstand the cold winters and start growth immediately upon spring. Their quick rate of growth uses the short growing season. Though rainfall is low (15 to 20 inches), evaporation is also low and there is enough moisture supply. The melting of the winter snows also helps to keep the soil moist.

Along the Alberta foothills a mixed *boreal and sub-alpine* forest occurs. Here the growing season is also short, but the rainfall is greater, and evergreen stands of tall lodgepole pine are found mixed with white and black spruce and also with aspens and birches. Jack pine and poplar abound on the sandy knolls.

On the edges of the Shield in Manitoba stretches a thick forest of black spruce and tamarack (on swampy ground) and jack pine (on higher areas). Jack pine has spread very rapidly because it is first to spring up after forest fires. It then forms pure 'stands'. In the wetter and warmer parts of southern Manitoba *hardwoods* are numerous, along with conifers. Balm of Gilead and western birch are plentiful, and extend in patches westward to southern Alberta. Actually, the trees are never far from river valleys or the rainier prairie bluffs. They do not form a close, extensive forest, but are separated by wide stretches of grass.

The forests thin out eastwards from the Rockies, westwards from the Shield and southwards from the sub-Arctic towards the grasslands of the interior, and as they do so give rise to a transitional vegetation of open woodland and grassy parks. This is the Park Belt. Large natural meadows, several hundreds of acres in extent, open out in the midst of trees, verdant with tall grasses and beautiful with flowers. The river valleys are clothed with elm, basswood, and ash. In the warmer valleys maple and cottonwood appear. In the rougher country groves of aspen or black poplar stretch in ragged patches to the 'bluffs' which have a mixed hardwood and coniferous forest.

The *grasslands*, where they occur, widen out in the central and southern dry prairies until they predominate, and trees are only found in the river courses, or edging the prairie buttes. Most of the grassland has now been replaced by wheatlands or has been modified by irrigated pasture.

In the truly arid region of Palliser's Triangle the vegetation is a mixture of desert bush and short grass. Vegetation is scanty, and does not form a continuous cover. It leaves bare patches between the clumps of sagebrush and grass. Grama and buffalo grass grow in short tufts, sometimes interspersed with low cactus. Around the glistening alkali flats are the greyish-green alkali grasses, along with wild barley, rushes, and gumweed. The better sections are covered with a carpet of western wheat-grass, June-, spear-, and meadow-grasses, which make good grazing.

Between Palliser's Triangle and the Park Belt is a zone often called the Central Prairies. Here the grasses make a denser cover, and increase in length. Short grasses like blue grama, western wheat, and western needle grass are mixed with longer ones such as fescue, couch, blue-stem, and Indian grass. These make up the Tall Grass prairies in which many berry bushes grow, including the cranberry, Saskatoon berry, and snowberry.

The Soils of the Prairies

Changes in soil go along with changes in vegetation and climate. Palliser's Triangle with its semi-arid climate and short-grass, sage-brush vegetation has a light brown soil; the Central Prairies, with more rainfall and longer grasses, have a dark brown (chestnut) soil; the Manitoba steppe, which is sub-humid and has a mixed tall grass and woodland vegetation, possesses a black meadow soil; the Park Belt, also sub-humid, with parkland forest, has a black park soil; while the northern sub-Arctic climate, with its coniferous forest, has a grey timber (podsol) soil. A transitional soil zone lies between the park-black and the timber-grey soils (Fig. 101).

There are many local variations, within these broad zones, due to the rocks from which the soils have been weathered or due to altitude, relief, and drainage. These are locally important, but do not alter the general picture. All the brown soil types have a low to medium content of organic matter (sparse vegetation covering) and a high concentration of lime and other carbonates. The black earths have a high organic matter content (thicker vegetation) and a medium concentration of carbonates. The grey soils have a leached layer, with an accumulation of iron and aluminium salts. The lime concentration is unimportant.

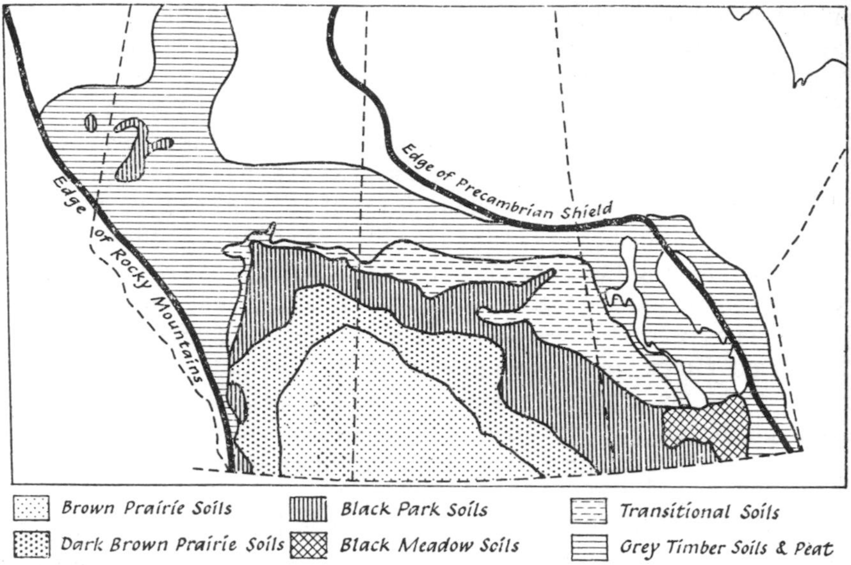

FIG. 101 The Soil Zones of the Canadian Prairies. (Scale 1: 17 m.)

The light brown soils are found within the drier parts of Palliser's Triangle, on the southern Alberta and Saskatchewan prairies. They include the districts of Lethbridge, Medicine Hat, and Swift Current, and reach as far north as the junction of the Saskatchewan South Branch and Red Deer rivers. The light brown colour is due to the low organic content of the soil, which, in its turn, results from the sparse vegetation of the semi-arid climate. Plants in such a climate reduce the amount of leaf to a minimum, and grow in separate clumps. Thus there is not much leaf mould, and what little there is has a scattered distribution. The low content of organic matter makes the soil poor in nitrogen and phosphorus. It is, however, rich in calcium and magnesium. Light solutions of calcium and magnesium carbonate occur in the soil. They are drawn up towards the surface through evaporation, and make the soil slightly alkaline. The application of phosphates and nitrates is needed for satisfactory crop yields.

The dark brown soil zone, called the chestnut soil belt, forms a transition from the brown (semi-arid) to the black (sub-humid) prairie soils. It occurs in the outer part of Palliser's Triangle and the inner edge of the Central Prairies, and corresponds to the gradual change from short grass to tall grass vegetation. Blue grama, western wheat and western needle grass, and the taller oat grasses are common and under natural conditions make a fairly close and even cover to the soil. There is more leaf mould, decayed root, and stem material, and therefore a higher organic-matter content.

Rainfall is higher (15 to 20 inches) and evaporation lower. There is less accumulation of lime, and it is at a lower level beneath the surface. The soil is only slightly alkaline. It is one of the best agricultural soils, with enough plant nutrients and soil moisture for small grains.

The black soils encircle the brown ones from southern Manitoba to northern Alberta, and then to south-western Alberta. The black colour is due to the large amount of organic matter in the upper soil horizon. This in its turn comes from the decaying vegetation of a tall grass sod and a mixed hardwood and coniferous forest. The rainfall throughout most of the belt is over 20 inches. Evaporation is comparatively low. The layer of lime accumulation is 16 to 22 inches below the surface. It is enough to make the soil neutral. With their good moisture supply, a naturally high content of nitrates and phosphates and sufficient lime, the black soils are very productive and form the best farming lands in Canada. 'The excellence of these soils is shown by the fact that whereas the average size of farm in the Brown Soil zone is about 1,000 acres, most of the farms in the Black Soil zone have an area of about 320 acres.'[1] The danger from drought is not serious. However, on the northern edges the danger from frost is recurrent.

This is still more so in **the timber-grey soil zone** where a long winter occurs in which the frost freezes the ground. In the spring the snow and ice thaw, and the land is waterlogged. As the water drains away it tends to leach the soil of the organic matter and soluble salts at the upper levels. Summer rains continue the leaching process. Thus beneath the grey-black, crumbly loam of the surface layer (rich in forest decay) is an ashen grey, rather sandy layer which has been heavily leached. The soil is slightly acid, and unless well drained and limed is not very fertile. In the Peace river district occurs a park-black and timber-grey transitional soil where leaching is not so pronounced. It is fairly fertile and suited to grain and fodder crops.

THE HUMAN RESPONSE

The History of Agricultural Development

The history of Prairie development has been influenced by location, relief, climate, and soil in turn. The interior isolation of the Prairies was their first problem; finding the easiest routes across, the next; discovering the boundaries of successful agriculture, the third; and adapting farm types to soil regions has been the final task. Each phase was an adventure in itself, and showed the courage of the people as well as the wealth of the country.

The Prairies were first reached by river from the Great Lakes and from Hudson Bay. The Rainy and Nelson rivers were like antennae of the east feeling into the west. Up the Pigeon river to Rainy lake came Le Vérendrye,

[1] Putnam, 'The Pedogeography of Canada', *Geographical Bulletin*, no. 1, 1951, p. 67.

who passed from Lake of the Woods into the Winnipeg river and thence to Lake Winnipeg. In his expeditions of 1731 and 1743 he discovered Lake Winnipeg, the Red river, the Assiniboine, Lakes Manitoba and Winnipegosis, and went as far as the great fork of the Saskatchewan river. However, no settlers followed in his wake. The prairies were too remote. There was still enough land in the east.

Nevertheless, fur trading became important. The Hudson's Bay Company, organized in 1670, slowly opened up the region from the north; while the North-west Company, formed in 1784, gave them keen competition from the south. The rivers of the Prairies make long west-to-east festoons which were soon drawn up into a network of fur posts. The upper Athabaska-Churchill net used McMurray and Prince of Wales, the Saskatchewan-Red-Nelson system centred on Fort Garry, and stretched from Edmonton to York Factory. The Nor'westers used the still longer waterway of the Assiniboine-Winnipeg-Rainy-Upper Lakes-Mattawa system from Rocky Mountain House to Montreal!

Gradually the Prairies were made accessible to the outer world. Land-hungry settlers, hearing of the sweeping, level plains, were prepared to venture into the interior. In 1804 discharged servants of the Hudson's Bay Company, mostly French Canadians, settled on the banks of the Pembina river (one of the warmest parts of the Canadian Prairies, with fertile sandy-loam, black meadow soils). They started to raise crops, got their meat by hunting, and thus became self-sufficient.

Their effort attracted the notice of the Earl of Selkirk, a Scottish landlord who was interested in settling dispossessed clansmen in the colonies. He bought up stock in the Hudson's Bay Company, for which he obtained about 70,000 sq. miles of the Red river valley. It was the best of western Canada. In 1811 he sent ninety settlers under Miles Macdonald to found the Selkirk settlement. From 1812 to 1816 four other groups of settlers arrived. In 1821 Swiss immigrants came out. However, conditions were severe. The Nor'westers, interested in fur trading and not farming, opposed the settlement. None of the settlers was used to the hard winters. Grasshoppers destroyed their grain. A flood swept down the Red river and carried buildings away. Above all, the expense and delay in getting in supplies made the venture a hard test of endurance. Nevertheless, more settlers arrived. Livestock and equipment got through, and by 1825 the colony was well established.

The difficulty still remained of making contact with Britain by way of Hudson Bay, or with eastern Canada by the Great Lakes. As long as the colonists were willing to live on a subsistence basis, merely getting a living without any of the comforts of life, it was possible to develop; but many wanted to improve their circusmtances by trade. This was impossible because of the high cost of river transportation, which isolated the Prairies from the market. Therefore, in 1857, the colonists petitioned for direct communication with the rest of Canada. This was soon obtained.

Just as early developments grew out of the competition between the Hudson's Bay Company and the North-west Company, so land settlement quickened with competition between American and Canadian transport companies. In 1862 an American steamboat company sailed the Red river and helped to draw the Canadian Prairies into the American sphere. In 1878 a railway was built down the valley from the United States, and American settlers began to stream in. The Canadian government realized the serious consequences of this and helped Canadian interests to develop a counter system of transportation. But it was not until 1885 that the Canadian Pacific completed its transcontinental line, and at last brought western and eastern Canada closely together. Then western farmers were able to import modern equipment and to get out their surplus grain, meat, wool, and hides.

In the building of the railways, relief was an important factor. The confluence of the Red river and the Assiniboine was a natural meeting-place of routes, and there, at Winnipeg, the Canadian lines from across the Shield met the American line from the Mississippi. Railways then fanned out over the Prairies, using gaps in the Manitoba scarp and the Missouri Coteau. Their final task was to find good passes across the Rockies to the Pacific coast. There are four naturally good passes through the Rockies. From south to north they are the Crow's Nest pass, where the South Saskatchewan meets the headwaters of the Kootenay; the Kicking Horse pass, where the Bow river eats back through the divide to the Columbia river; the Yellowhead pass, where the upper Athabaska contacts the upper Thompson valley; and Finlay Forks, where the Peace river leads back to the upper Fraser.

The first railroad used the Kicking Horse pass, because it offered the most direct crossing to Vancouver. The line followed the Assiniboine from Winnipeg to Brandon through a wide breach in the Manitoba escarpment. It then bent north of Moose mountain but south of the Beaver hills, to reach Regina. From Regina it crossed to Moose Jaw and then climbed the Coteau where a tributary of the Assiniboine made a useful re-entrant. Passing south of a line of morainic hills it struck the South Saskatchewan at Medicine Hat. Then it turned north-west, taking the high plain above the Bow river canyon until it reached Calgary. Climbing the Rocky foothills it kept close to the Bow, and so went through the pass. An early branch was built from Medicine Hat to Lethbridge, which was continued to the Crow's Nest pass up a tributary of the South Saskatchewan.

Other railway companies, such as the Canadian Northern and the Grand Trunk, started to build transcontinental lines in competition with the Canadian Pacific. These were completed between 1913 and 1915. They took the northern routes to Yellowhead pass. The Canadian Northern then turned south to Vancouver, using the Thompson-Fraser valley; while the Grand Trunk Pacific continued north via the Fraser-Skeena to Prince Rupert. Eventually these two lines were merged, with several others, into the Canadian National Railway. After the Canadian National Railway leaves Winnipeg it crosses the Manitoba scarp by way of the Assiniboine breach, skirts the Beaver hills to arive at Saskatoon, boldly climbs the Coteau, making directly for Edmonton. It then crosses the low divide between the North Saskatchewan and the upper Athabaska and so enters the Yellowhead pass. Branch lines extend south down the Alberta plateau to Calgary, and northward by the Athabaska and Lesser Slave Lake to the Peace river.

Thus the railways flung a net over the Prairies, making the most of the west-to-east grain of relief. They picked out those features which oriented the Prairies to the British east rather than the American south. Population followed the railways, and took up the west-to-east pattern. The Prairies were saved for Canada.

Modern developments began about 1900, when hundreds of thousands of immigrants poured into the Prairies. An unprecedented demand arose for wheat, meat, hides, and wool in Britain, then at the height of its economic expansion. Competition between railway companies steadily reduced the costs of transportation. Prices for wheat rose, and between 1914 and 1918 there was a golden boom.

In people's anxiety to make money quickly, new lands were bought up wherever accessible. Farmers even risked going into the Frost Belt and also moved into Palliser's Triangle. They could afford the risk of poor yields because of high profits. However, in the early 'twenties business fell off. Prices declined. Semi-arid land was rendered economically marginal. Thousands of acres were abandoned, in some sections amounting to 50 per cent of the occupied land.

In this expensive way the problem of climate came very much to the fore. It was not enough that the settlers had successfully adjusted themselves to their location in the interior, and to the relief of the land; they still had to adjust themselves to the climate.

They did not do this at first. Another boom, 1927 to 1929, led them to expand the wheat acreage once again, with the result that when prices fell in 1929–30, and the Great Drought struck in 1930–1 and continued to intensify to its peak in 1934, thousands of farmers were faced with ruin. 'The drought reduced farm income over the eight-year period (1930–37) by $580 millions.'[1] Still more abandonment of land took place, on a large scale. Farms sagged into wasteland. Villages became deserted. Many

[1] Waines, *Prairie Population Possibilities*, p. 50.

Americans trekked back to the United States. There was also a flight to the Eastern Provinces of Canadian immigrants.

It was then realized that the mass settlement of the Prairies and the war-time boom of the First World War had corresponded more or less with wet phases in the climate. Settlers had come to think that the weather they first experienced was normal. It was not. It was abnormally wet. It could not continue, like that. In the 'thirties it became abnormally dry.

These long-term changes in Prairie weather repeat themselves. They have happened in the past and will continue to happen. Therefore farming must adjust itself to them. In 1857 to 1860 Palliser and Hind claimed that 100,000 sq. miles in the south was waste. Macoun, in 1880, believed only 20,000 sq. miles were uncultivable. The differences in these claims were due to the fact that they were made in dry and wet cycles of weather. When the Prairies were settled, from 1900 to 1910, it was again wet and Macoun's estimate seemed justified. But the drought of 1930–7 proved Palliser's fears. The Canadian 'dust bowl' almost exactly coincided with the area he called waste. Now it so happened that during the wetter-than-normal years when the Prairies were being settled there were good prices. They spurred people to plant too much land. It also happened that the Great Drought struck at a time of low prices. In 1929, prices had fallen by 60 per cent. In 1930 the terrible drought began. Farmers raised 2·6 bushels an acre for 50 cents a bushel! This led to widespread farm abandonment.

It is just this combination of weather-cycle hazards and of business cycle difficulties that forms the heart of the Prairies problem, and Canada came to realize that if it were to save itself the untold miseries of another 1930–1 it had to learn to adjust settlement to both these factors. In other words, it had to guard against over-expansion when wet years or high prices happened, or, above all, when both these conditions took place together. It also had to prepare for dry spells which might come along in depression years. This required the careful adaptation of farm methods and crops to the local situation. It also entailed co-operation on a large scale. Political guidance and economic planning were therefore stressed, coupled with individual adaptation.

During the hard times of the 'thirties attention turned increasingly to the soil. The sudden expansion of settlement, followed by the sudden abandonment of land, meant that many areas were ploughed and then left fallow. Rainstorms lashed the top soil, washing sheets of it away. Windstorms carried the fine particles into the air until they blew about in clouds of dust, rising off the barren fields and blanketing the tilled ones. Soil drifting took place. The whole landscape changed. Grass became scantier and often died out. The water-level in the soil fell. A Canadian desert was formed—a man-made desert.[1]

[1] Stuart, D., *The Canadian Desert*, Toronto, 1938, Chaps. 6, 10, 12.

The causes of desert-making are many. Farmers hopefully plough up fields in wet years that cannot be cultivated in dry, but are then abandoned and attacked by erosion. Ranchers overstock their land when prices are high. As a result, it becomes overgrazed. Then there is not enough grass to hold the soil together. When dry years return it drifts away. Speculators buy up land cheap in a depression and over-sell it in a boom, getting rid of land-lots that in normal times would be 'sub-marginal'. They tempt more settlers to take up land than the land can bear. Thus 'in the West, speculative holding of lands becomes nothing short of a blight'.[1] When prices fall people cannot meet their payments on the farms they bought at boom prices. Those who own sub-marginal lots are ruined. Fields are abandoned. Soil erosion begins. In good years salesmen sell a lot of farm equipment and home improvements, and force up the standard of living to levels which cannot be maintained through a sequence of frost-ridden or droughty seasons. Communities become over-ambitious in wet cycles and boom years and put themselves into debt for roads, bridges, drains, halls, and schools that cannot be kept up in unfavourable times. Then, teachers are not paid. Schools close. Roads go into disrepair. The population drifts away. The soil drifts after them. The desert spreads.

It is obvious that individuals alone could not meet these trying conditions. Large-scale hazards, over which the individual had no control, demanded large-scale measures. These were supplied by private corporations, by co-operative societies, and by the Provincial and Dominion government. The railways developed large irrigation schemes. The wheat 'pools' stored surplus grain in good years to make up for low yields in bad ones. The provincial governments developed conservation programmes to halt erosion and to regrass wasted areas, and also to assist farmers burdened with debt. Yet the Prairie problem remained so big it could not be solved by the Prairies themselves. And thus the Dominion was called in. For what affects the Prairies affects the prosperity of the entire nation.

Consequently, in 1935, the Dominion government passed the Prairie Farm Rehabilitation Act (the P.F.R.A.). Under the terms of the Act the Minister of Agriculture was given power to promote new systems of farm practice, tree culture, water development, and land settlement, so as to give the Prairie farmers more security and to restore the natural resources of the region. Dominion experimental farms were to advance research into soil, water, and land-use problems. District demonstration stations were set up to illustrate the best methods of farming. Reclamation stations were built to show how abandoned land might be regrassed or brought back into cultivation. Agricultural improvement associations were formed in over two hundred communities. Finally, regional improvement plans were drawn up

[1] MacDougall, J., *Rural Life in Canada*, Toronto, 1913, p. 87.

to guide farmers in water development, tree planting, and the best use of the land. Soil surveys were financed and carried through with the aid of the provincial universities, and the breeding of drought- and frost-resisting plants was furthered. Forestation, regrassing, strip farming, and, above all,

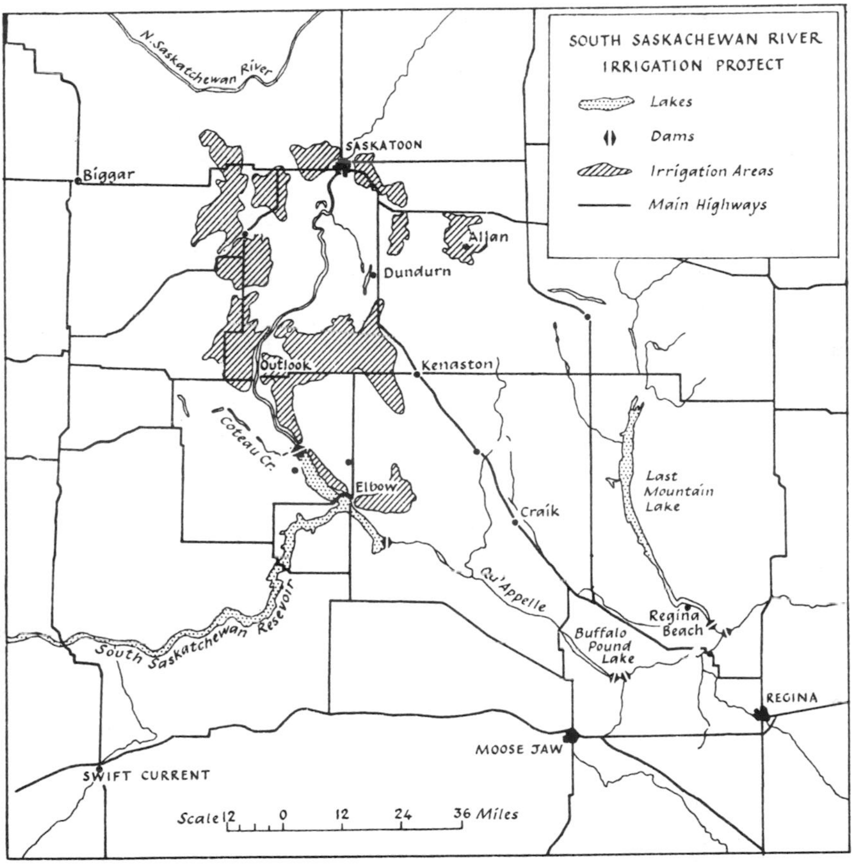

FIG. 102 Western Irrigation—the South Saskatchewan Scheme.

irrigation were all encouraged. Forty large irrigation projects were started, together with over eight hundred smaller ones. These have done a lot, in addition to private projects, to remove the fear of drought. The most spectacular of these schemes has been the South Saskatchewan Dam[1] (Fig. 102). The 1961 Agricultural Rehabilitation and Development Act has further strengthened conservation and made a better use of marginal land.

[1] MacNeill, P., 'They Are Changing the Face of Saskatchewan', *Canad. Geog. Jour.*, lx, 5, May 1960, p. 171.

Farm Types and Farming Regions of the Prairies

The chief types of farming in the Prairies are pioneer farming, ranching, wheat farming, mixed-grain production, mixed stock and crop farming, and dairy farming. These broadly correspond to the great soil zones. Pioneer farming is advancing into the timber-grey soil belt. Wheat-growing is concentrated on the dark brown soils, though farmers on the light brown and black soils also grow a lot. Mixed farming occupies the park-black soils and mixed farming and dairy farming the meadow-black soils. Ranching is common to the light brown soil zone, but also occurs in hilly areas in the other zones (see Fig. 99).

The difference between these regions has grown up through increasing competition. As the wheatlands of America developed along with those of Argentina, India, and Australia, the Prairie farmer had to keep his costs down to compete in the foreign market. This meant he could not afford to grow wheat where the likelihood of drought or frost would recur. It is possible to raise wheat anywhere on the Prairies where there are more than a hundred days free from frost, and more than 12 inches of rainfall. Yet it is only when the frostless season is longer than 130 days that the danger from frost is overcome. The danger from drought is not passed unless the rainfall is over 15 inches a year.

Therefore, the limits of *profitable* wheat farming are much narrower than those where wheat farming is possible. The area bounded by these limits (130 days frost-free season and over 15 inches annual rainfall) is the *optimum* wheat region. It is in the optimum region that the farmer reduces his risks to a minimum and has the best chance of competing for markets.

The optimum wheat region straddles **the dark brown soil zone**, from the wetter parts of the light brown zone to the warmer parts of the park-black zone. It runs from just east of Calgary and south of Saskatoon to the Regina plains. Moose Jaw is a typical location. It has reasonable freedom from frost and drought. The weather is extreme and variable, but not as variable as in the light brown zone. The range between the highest rain record (20·8 inches) and the lowest (10·1 inches) is only 71 per cent of the average, as compared with Medicine Hat, where the range is 147 per cent of average. The soil has a medium amount of nitrate and phosphate, and readily available lime. It is watered by melting snows in the spring and by early summer rains, and retains the moisture until the fall. It is well suited to grain crops.

Sixty-two per cent of the Prairie Wheat Belt is improved; the rest is chiefly grazing land, on rougher parts or patches of lighter soil. Of the improved area 61 per cent is under grain crops, and of this amount 80 per cent is under wheat. This is a very high concentration. The value of wheat is six times the value of livestock in the zone, and is higher per acre than anywhere else. The wheat has a very high protein content, and sells well.

The farms are of a medium-large size, with an average of 485 acres. The wheatfields are very big, and have no fences or hedges between. Small amounts of barley and oats are raised, especially on poorer ground. Fallow fields are rotated with the grain. Large-scale methods are used, with multiple-furrow ploughs, drawn by tractors, and large reaping, threshing, and bagging combines. This saves labour, though it requires heavy expenditures. Transient labour is used during the harvest-time, although by no means on the scale that used to prevail.

After the harvest, farm activity dwindles. There is little if any stock to keep. Not a few of the richer farmers spend the winter in California or Florida. The fact that farming is highly commercialized and mechanized has produced an unusually high rural living standard in good years, but severe depression in bad years. The farmers are not self-subsisting. Most of them buy their food and clothes from near-by towns, on the strength of their cash returns. They have telephones to keep them in touch with stores, offices, and workshops in the towns, and cars to cover the long distances between themselves, their neighbours, and their agents. Consequently, when the Great Drought struck and the depression came, farmers found themselves with large debts and expensive living habits, but a sadly reduced income.

Some of them switched over to cattle farming, and let the land go back to pasture. Others took to subsistence farming. Others bought up two or three farms and by putting them together managed to get a saleable crop. Many sold out or otherwise abandoned their farms, and retired on what was left of their savings, or drifted into the city for work. Over a million acres were thus abandoned in this soil belt during 1936. The grouping together of farms in larger holdings, the spread of grazing areas, and the abandonment of farms led to a decline in the rural population. This is still continuing. The density of population is about 4–5 people per square mile (Fig. 103).

The density of population in the **light brown soil zone** is less than 3. Here is the really dry part of the Prairies, with a mean annual rainfall of 10 to 15 inches. It also has the most variable rainfall; the maximum range, between wettest and driest years is, according to Hopkins, 147 per cent of average.[1] Over a considerable part, the growing-season rainfall is inadequate (less than 7½ inches) for the production of crops in four to six years out of every ten. The vegetation has responded to these conditions by growing in bunches, and by remaining stunted. It used to graze herds of buffalo before the white man came. Grazing is the natural use of the land. Nevertheless, settlers soon turned to cultivation, since, by dry-farming methods, and the

[1] Hopkins, E. S., *et al.*, *Soil Drifting in the Prairie Provinces*, Ottawa, 1937, p. 51.

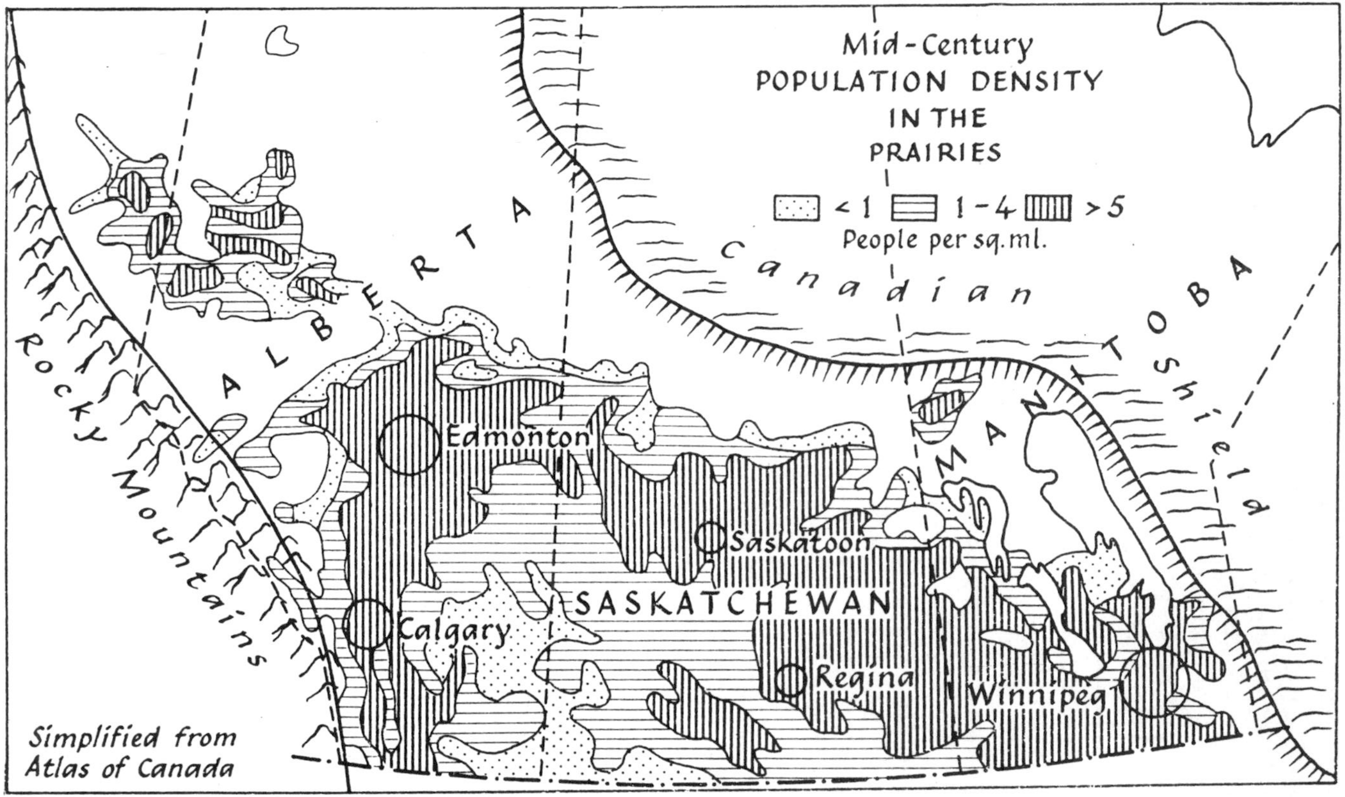

FIG. 103 The Population Zones of the Canadian Prairies. Compare with the soil zones. The densest populations are on the black and dark brown belts. Population falls off rapidly in the light brown and the grey wooded soils. (Scale, 1:11 m.)

'extensive' use of land, profitable crops of wheat could be raised. But it should be remembered that settlement occurred in wetter than normal years, and also when prices were high. Between 1911 and 1921 high prices resulted in a doubling of the crop acreage. Wheat came to provide the major portion of the farm income.

As prices declined in the middle 'twenties, it was difficult to get a profit from wheat. Yields were low. Only by using three or four sections of land and joining them together was it profitable for wheat farmers to maintain themselves (unless they were fortunate enough to own heavier, moister land than normal, or could tap irrigation waters). The average size of farm is over 650 acres. But extensive methods of farming—with large amounts of land and the use of machinery—mean fewer people on the land. So the population has gradually declined. That decline became an exodus during the Great Drought. In 1936 nearly two and a half million acres of farm land were abandoned, indicating that much unsuitable land had been taken up during the wetter than normal years.

Various studies of the proper use of land were started. In a detailed survey of the Sounding Creek area in Alberta, where the population had dropped from 10,535 in 1921 to 6,044 in 1936, it was found that 60 per cent of the district was sub-marginal for wheat production. Another 30 per cent was marginal—where wheat might succeed in good years and at good prices, but would be risky to produce at other times. Only 8 per cent was considered suitable for wheat farming. A wider survey showed that in the light brown soil zone as a whole 52 per cent of the land was marginal or sub-marginal for cultivation. Only 48 per cent was satisfactory for cultivation.[1] Consequently, the provincial governments encouraged a change-over from wheat farming (except in unusually favoured areas) to grazing, or a mixture of wheat farming and grazing. Under the Special Municipal Areas Act the province of Alberta—and later, Saskatchewan—sought powers to redistribute farms and to make a proper adjustment of farming methods to soil, drainage, and surface configuration.

The change-over has meant the abandonment of smaller farms and their amalgamation in larger ones. More of the land is left fallow and still more has gone back into pasture. The wheat acreage has fallen. Less than half the land is now under cultivation, and of this only 40 per cent is in wheat; 30 per cent is in fallow. (Compare with the dark brown soil zone.)

Ranching, which has always been important in the drought area, is on the increase. The rougher or drier parts have always been more suited to pasturing than cultivating. The hilly lands on the Alberta–Saskatchewan border, the Missouri Coteau, the Cypress hills, and the Sweet Grass hills are too broken for the extensive use of large-scale farm machinery, such as

[1] Waines, W. J., *Prairie Population Possibilities*, p. 11.

the wheat farmers demand. Cattle or sheep are raised. The cattle often stay outside the whole year. The mature cattle are sold off each fall. Lambs are sent to the St Lawrence lowlands to be fattened before being slaughtered. However, more of the ranchers are raising enough of their own winter fodder to feed the stock through the winter, fatten them off on the succulent summer pastures, and send them to market in first-class condition.

On the flatter areas a mixed type of agriculture is found, where field crops are grown on the heavier soils and the rest of the land is left to grazing. Irrigation is being taken up. It supplies high yields of alfalfa and other fodder crops, which are used to supplement the natural grazing, and to raise more stock per farm.

Irrigation was started as early as 1899 by the Mormons who trekked from Utah. They settled in the Lethbridge district, which is very dry. They were so successful that the Canadian Pacific Railway decided to develop an irrigation project on the Bow river. This was followed by a Canada Land project, also on the Bow. In 1906 the Canadian Pacific Railway extended their scheme eastward along the Bow. Here the annual rainfall was only 5 to 11 inches. The land was sold on contract at fifty dollars an acre, with water rates at $1.25. By 1921 there were 1,140 farms being irrigated under this scheme. However, abandonment took place in the middle 'twenties, and only 96,000 acres of a possible 400,000 acres were developed.

During the difficult 'thirties most irrigation schemes were finding it hard to meet the high cost of constructing and maintaining the works at rents which farmers were prepared to pay for the land. The annual interest charges, plus costs for repair and upkeep and for pumping the water into the flumes, were from two to five dollars per acre; yet few farmers were ready to pay this sum. Subsidies were required and eventually the Provincial and Dominion governments came to support the projects. For example, the Alberta government bought up land to sell at ten dollars an acre, with water at $1.75 an acre, and in this way attracted enough additional farmers to make irrigation worth while.

The chief problem of irrigation is economic, rather than geographical. The rivers flowing down from the eternal snows, or from the rainy foothills of the Rockies, can supply sufficient water for large-scale irrigation. Yet, at present, irrigated lands are not producing sufficient in excess of non-irrigated land to make extensive systems worth while. The systems that are best able to meet the high costs of construction are relatively limited ones, where the farmers use small plots to produce a very high yield of special crops, such as early vegetables, potatoes, sugar-beets, and so on. Alfalfa plots supply up to three harvests a season, and are quite profitable. The alfalfa has a good local market in the many ranches of the zone. The more successful schemes are on the Bow, St Mary, Oldman, and Belly rivers, especially at Lethbridge, Calgary, Taber, Vauxhall, Magrath, and Raymond. The South Saskatchewan scheme, the largest of the lot, will be able, when fully developed, to irrigate about half a million acres. In addition about 500 million kilowatt hours of electric power will be made available.

Bordering the brown soil belts is the **zone of black soils,** including the Park Belt and the Red river region. Climatically it lies between the drought and the frost, and is the most favoured zone in the Prairies. Annual rainfall is between 15 and 20 inches, with over 20 inches in the Edmonton and Red river districts. From two-thirds to three-quarters of this falls in the growing season, and is thus available for crop growth. Variability in the rainfall, though pronounced, is not as great as in the light brown soil zones. At Edmonton the range between the highest rainfall recorded (25·3 inches) and the lowest (13·8 inches) is only 65 per cent of the average. Compare this with Medicine Hat.

The growing season is from 110 to 150 days long, which is sufficient for wheat and fodder crops. However, the period free from frost, which is from as low as 90 days north of Edmonton to 110 at Winnipeg, varies quite considerably, and frost is sometimes a threat. It has compelled farms to rely on early maturing wheats, or to go in for mixed farming.

Ninety per cent of all the zone is occupied, of which three-fifths is improved. Only 23 per cent of the land is in natural pasture, as compared with 47 per cent in the light brown soil zone. The extensive grazing of cattle or sheep on the open range is not important. Nevertheless, the total number of cattle on the farms is much greater than in the brown-soil zones. That is because they are dairy or fat cattle being fed on hay and clover and fodder crops.

Most of the improved land is under field crops, 34 per cent in wheat, 17 per cent in oats, and 11 per cent in barley. (Contrast the low acreage of wheat and the high acreage in oats with the more arid soil zones.) Obviously, wheat is much less important, while crops grown for feed are more common. There are some wheat farms, but more often than not wheat is simply grown as a cash crop on a farm whose main profits come from cattle, dairy produce, or pigs.

Farming is, therefore, different. It is not extensive, but increasingly intensive. The farms are comparatively small, with an average area of 288 acres. But they are highly developed, producing high yields from a variety of crops. The value of the crops is increased by feeding them to cattle, pigs, and poultry. Some of the cattle are fattened for beef. In the Edmonton and Winnipeg plains they are kept for milk and butter. Large numbers of poultry are also kept.

The smaller size of farm and more intensive development permit a higher population density, with an average of 5–10 per sq. mile (see Fig. 103). Only

15 per cent of the area is considered sub-marginal, and the amount of abandoned soil during the Great Drought was four times less, proportionately, than in the brown-soil zones. Thus there seems to be greater security. The farmer's income is more stable. There has not been the need for as much government aid and direction. The main drawback is the lack of a large local market for dairy produce, and the dependence on the east or on foreign markets. The chief dairy districts are centred around Winnipeg, Brandon, Regina, Saskatoon, Edmonton, and Calgary.

North of the Park Belt is a **transition zone** of degraded black earths passing into the timber-grey soil zone. The soil has less organic matter, much less lime, and is more acid. It is suitable for hay, oats, legumes, and root crops. The land is difficult to clear, and must be carefully drained and limed, and supplied with nitrates and phosphates before satisfactory returns can be made. Over 50 per cent of the transition zone is sub-marginal, and 70 per cent of the timber-grey zone is.

Climate is another limiting factor. The growing season is from 90 to 120 days long, which is suitable for only a few early maturing types of wheat. Leafy plants like hay and clover grow quicker and are more suited to the region.

Farming is rather hazardous, and settlement has been slow. The best areas are where patches of black soil are found within the timber-grey zone, as in the Peace river district. The farms are family holdings, of a little over 250 acres. Seed alfalfa and seed grain are very profitable. A considerable part of a farmer's income may be in cutting wood out of the forest. Part-time trapping is also followed. The population over most of the region is less than two per square mile, and during the depression of the 'thirties there was severe abandonment of land in several sections (see Fig. 103).

The **forest reserves** of the Prairies are quite considerable. The forests sweep across the northern parts of all three provinces. Manitoba has over 90,000 sq. miles of which 30,000 are productive. This is more than the area of New Brunswick. It is usual to think of New Brunswick as a lumber and paper-making province. Yet potentially Manitoba has more forest wealth. The chief reason why it does not reckon to be a forest province is because the forest is relatively inaccessible. Forest cannot compete in attraction with agriculture. In New Brunswick the forest is much more accessible; there is a large market for its products; and it is more profitable than agriculture. The difference between the two provinces is not in the amount of forest they have, but in the proportion which is accessible to the market and in the relative importance of lumbering compared with other occupations.

The Manitoba forests clothe the northern and eastern shores of the Manitoba lakes, and stretch across the Shield towards Hudson Bay and

Lake of the Woods. The northern-lake district provides lumber for the busy mills of The Pas. The forests of Lake Winnipeg are easily and cheaply exploited by water. The logs are rafted to mills, and the lumber is often towed up the Red towards Winnipeg. The Manitoba escarpment is also heavily wooded and Swan river, between the Porcupine and Duck mountains, is another important lumbering centre.

The forests of Saskatchewan, though larger in area than those of Manitoba, are still farther away from the settled areas. The lakes of the Churchill basin are so far north as to be of little value for rafting purposes. Most of the northern forest is used as a huge conserve for game, where white and Indian trappers make their living by hunting and fishing. However, the Cumberland district provides some lumber, much of which is floated down to The Pas. Meadow Lake in the Beaver basin, and Prince Albert on the edge of the forest, are other important centres.

Alberta has a large forest area, including the foothills of the Rockies, the northern-lake district, and the Athabaska and Peace river basins. However, little of it has been developed. Enough is cut to meet the needs of the cities and farms for sawn timber, and the mines for pit props, but there is no extensive forest industry. Nevertheless, the potential is there, and developments in the north and west are promising.

Mineral wealth in the Prairies is considerable. Lying on the western margin of the Shield, Manitoba and Saskatchewan have important metal-mining areas. These will be considered, when the Canadian North is described. Lying on the eastern flanks of the Rockies, Alberta has a vast wealth in fuels, including coal, oil, and natural gas. Coal and oil are also found in southern Saskatchewan, and oil in south-west Manitoba on the edge of the Williston basin (see Chapter 2: also Fig. 72, Chapter 10).

In the west, the Tertiary and Cretaceous rocks have been bent into gentle basins and low upfolds. Here coal basins and oil fields have been preserved. Under Alberta is one of the largest coal fields in the world. Most of it is sub-bituminous, but parts are a near anthracite. The harder coal is in the Rocky foothill zone of Crow's Nest, Cascade and Mountain Park, near Jasper. The sub-bituminous or softer coal is found beneath the Alberta step at Nordeg, Drumheller, Edmonton, and Lethbridge. At Edmonton it is associated with natural gas. These mining districts produce about 40 per cent of Canada's coal. They could expand more but for the high cost of transportation to the chief coal-consuming areas of Ontario and Quebec. (It is cheaper in Central Canada to import near-by American coal than to pay the cost of transporting Alberta coal.) Relatively small amounts are sent to British Columbia. Most of the coal is used in the Prairies for domestic heating and city factories (Fig. 104).

Actually, there has been a decline in coal mining, because the market for

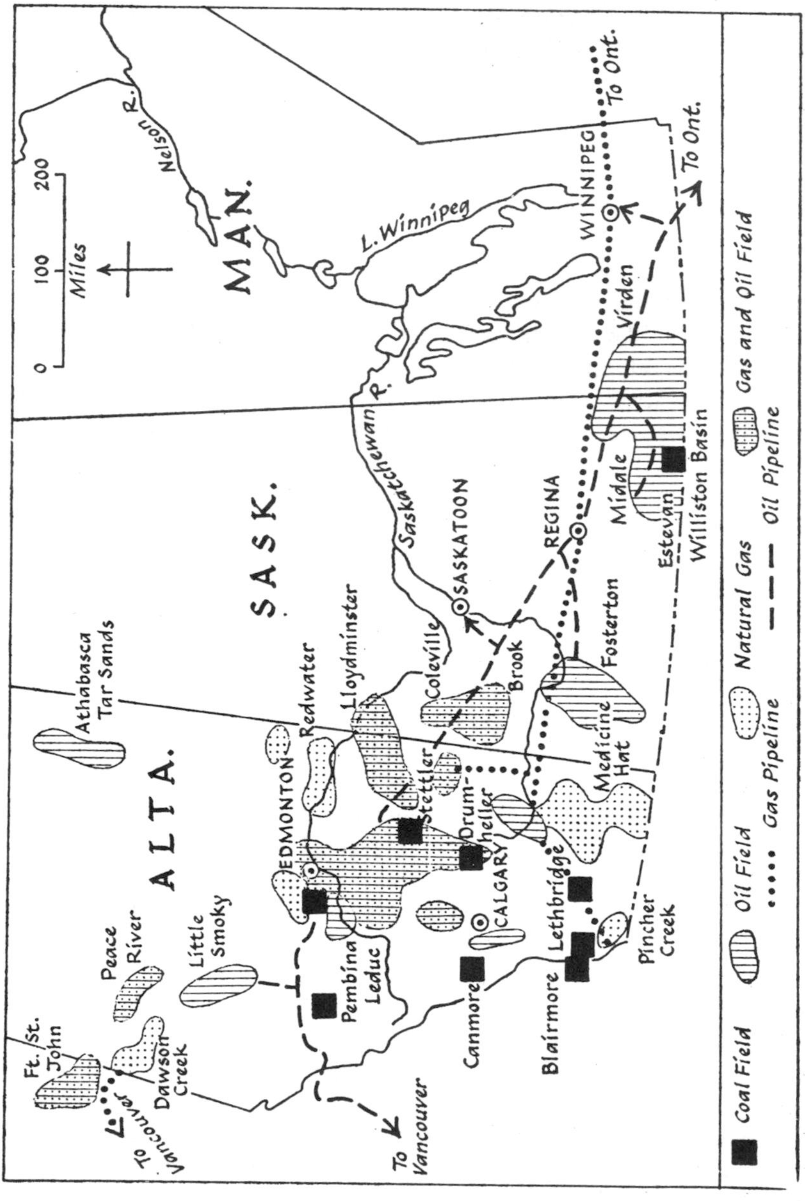

FIG. 104 The wealth of fuels in the Canadian Prairies.

fuel has swiftly changed over to oil. Most offices, institutions, and homes are now heated by oil; farm machines consume great quantities of oil; the railways have been converted to diesels; and cars and aeroplanes are using swiftly increasing amounts of petrol. The presence of large and readily workable oil fields in the Prairies has thus changed the whole picture of fuel consumption.

Mention has been made of the sub-surface corrugations of the region (Chapter Two) with their remarkable basins and buried reefs. Much exploration has still to be done, but by mid-century the proven reserves of oil, associated with these structures, were about four billion barrels. As in the case of coal, there are inner fields, close to the Rockies, and outer fields, trending north-west–south-east across the Prairies. The inner were the first to be discovered and developed. Between 1912 and 1914 oil was struck in the Turner valley, south of Calgary. This rich little field still produces petroleum but has long been surpassed. In the early 'twenties the Wainwright field, well to the east of Edmonton, was opened, but water made it difficult to develop. North of the Sweet Grass arch, the Taber and Conrad fields were next discovered, again along the inner zone, in the early 'forties and are still in operation. In 1947 a major area from Leduc to Pembina, in the inner zone, came into production; it has over a quarter of Prairie reserves. Meanwhile in the outer zone, the Vermilion–Lloydminster field was opened up. Here the oil, found in deeply buried sands, is partly emulsified with water, contains quite a lot of dirt, and has to be cleaned before use.[1] But it occurs in quantity. In the late 'fifties another oil-rich area was found in the Virginia and Swan hills to the north of Edmonton; it may have as much as a billion barrel reserve. Also in the late 'fifties, oil was struck in moderate quantity in south-east Saskatchewan, well in the outer zone, between Steelman and Midale. In south-west Manitoba, at Virden and Kirkella, a small but significant field occurs, on the edge of the Williston basin (see Fig. 104).

Natural gas is another fuel found in abundance in the Prairies. The first well was drilled near Medicine Hat in 1885 in search for water.[2] The Canadian Pacific Railway was being put through at the time. The gas became used for domestic and industrial purposes at Medicine Hat. Since then proven reserves of up to 300 trillion cubic feet have been discovered, and natural gas is now one of Canada's chief resources. The Bow Island field, opened in 1909, and the Foremost field, in 1916 (extended in 1943 to Pinhorn), made southern Alberta the richest producing region; however, in the 'thirties the Kinsella–Viking area of east-central Alberta saw the chief developments. This was widened, in the 'forties, by the Provost discoveries.

[1] Hume, G. S., 'The Interior Plains', in *Geology and Economic Minerals of Canada*, Economic Geology Series, 1, Canadian Geological Survey, Ottawa, 1947.

[2] Moore, E. S., *Canada's Mineral Resources*, Toronto, 1933, p. 208.

Gas is also developed in the Wainwright and Lloydminster oil fields. In the Kamask district near the Manitoba–Saskatchewan border a small field exists. Over 2,000 miles of gas-lines have been built in the Prairies, carrying the gas to the principal cities, while long gas and oil pipe-lines transport these valuable fuels to Ontario and Quebec, and also to western British Columbia. In this new way, therefore, the Prairies have once again proved themselves to be a vital link between East and West Canada.

SETTLEMENT TYPES

The settlement of the Prairies is essentially agricultural, or based mainly on agriculture, and, like its landscape, open and extensive. The pattern of roads and farms is like a mathematical grid. The direction of the roads and the lie of the farms do not follow the surface relief, except in rough country: they

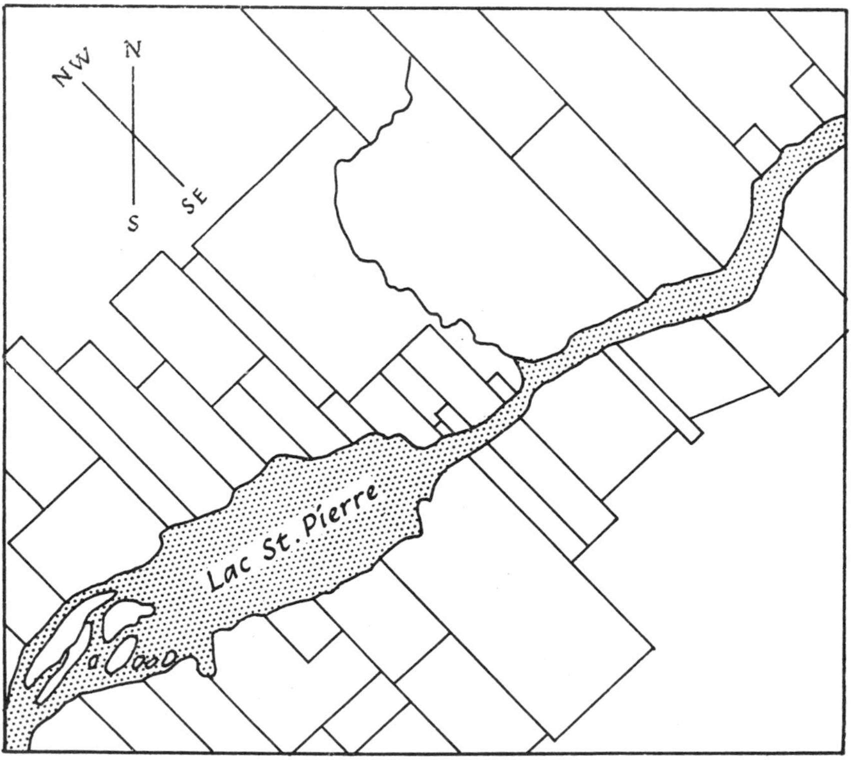

FIG. 105 The Land-division System of Quebec–the Seignories of the St Lawrence river. These were laid off from the river front and ran back at right angles to the main trend of the St Lawrence. Lots were narrow along the water front to give as many people as possible access to the great highway of the river. In compensation lots were very long from front to rear. (Scale, 1:0·75 m.)

follow the layout of the surveyor. Thus Prairie settlement differs markedly from the irregular type found in the Maritimes, or the riverine type found in Quebec, or even the grid type found in Ontario, where the grid system had been made irregular through the use of individual sections of river banks and lakeshores as the base of surveying.

Each pattern of settlement has responded to different historical and geographical factors. In the Maritimes, settlement tended to group round bays, into which rivers emptied. The roads followed the contours of the coasts or the direction of river gaps. They were therefore quite irregular, and the farms were spaced along them at irregular intervals, wherever there was cultivable land. There was a distinct tendency for farms to concentrate around villages which grew up at bridges or harbours. The land surface dominated the pattern.

This was also true in Quebec. The first settlers built their farms along the shores of the St Lawrence gulf or the banks of the St Lawrence river (Fig. 105). They laid off long, narrow lots from the waterfront into the interior. A river road connected all the farms together, like a thread of beads. As settlers moved farther inland, parallel roads were built. These again cut across narrow lots, which extended from either side of them. The farms were built on the roadfront, and in densely populated parts, gave the appearance of a street of houses. So there developed a linear concentration. Yet the lines of farms were not regular, but swung this way and that with the turn of the river, or with beach-ridges or lines of hills. Villages grew up, under the soaring spire of the parish church, wherever important 'rangs' crossed the 'chemins'.

In Ontario there was an attempt at a more regular type of settlement, and surveys were made and farms and roads located with reference to a definite plan (Fig. 106). Each county was divided into townships, which were more or less square or rectangular, and these were subdivided into concessions by survey-lines running parallel to a base-line. However, the settlers arrived at quite different points; some at Niagara, others at Kingston, the Bay of Quinte, the Windsor frontier, York (Toronto), Hamilton—and so on. Consequently, their surveys were made quite independently of each other, and were not co-ordinated. If the settlers arrived on the lakeshore, they would lay out a base-line along the immediate trend of the shore, survey parallel lines for the concessions, and then bound the settlement by township boundaries. But where the trend of the shore changed markedly, the base-line changed; the parallel concessions changed; and the roads took on a different angle. Thus the grid became irregular because it was done piecemeal, with each piece adjusting itself to a differently oriented base.

In the Prairies the grid became much more regular, because settlement occurred at a later time, when the Government had more say in directing colonization. Settlement also occurred in great waves, which enabled large

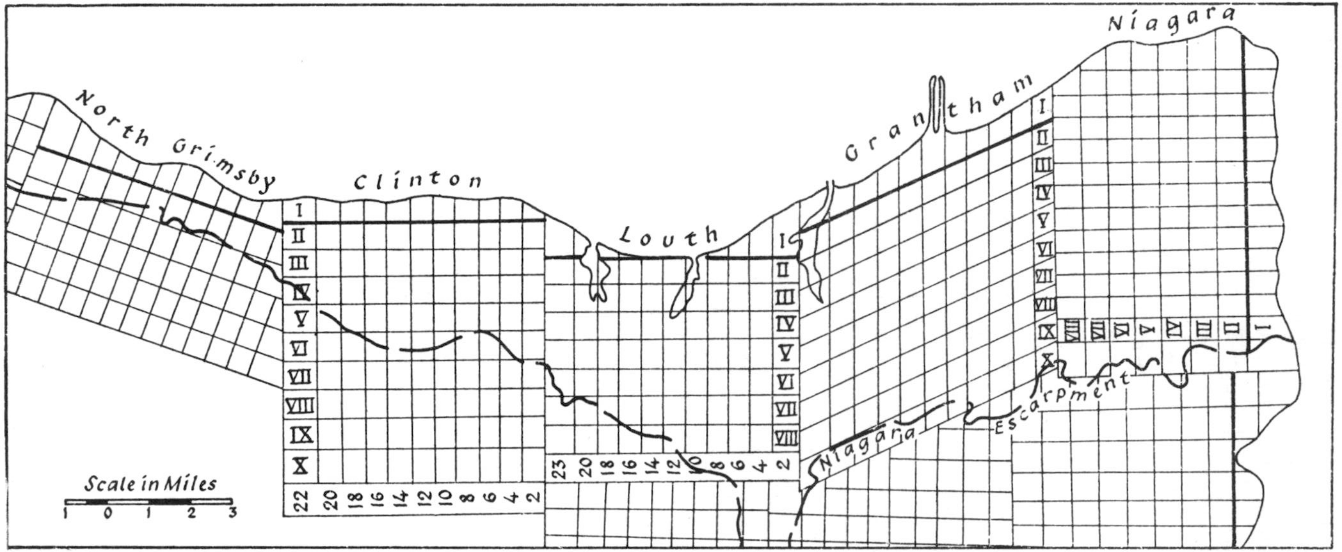

FIG. 106 The Land-division System of Ontario. Townships were laid out in a grid pattern based on base-lines individually adjusted so as to be parallel to different sectors of coast or river. Concession lines (I–X) ran parallel to the base and were cut at right angles by lot lines, shown in groups of two (2–22/24). The lines intersected each other at roughly half mile intervals. The system still obtains today.

areas to be opened up at one stage. Moreover, the land lent itself to a regular pattern, since so much of it was flat and open, and there were few relief barriers. The easiest way of developing it was to run mathematically surveyed lines across it, and then to follow with a grid of roads

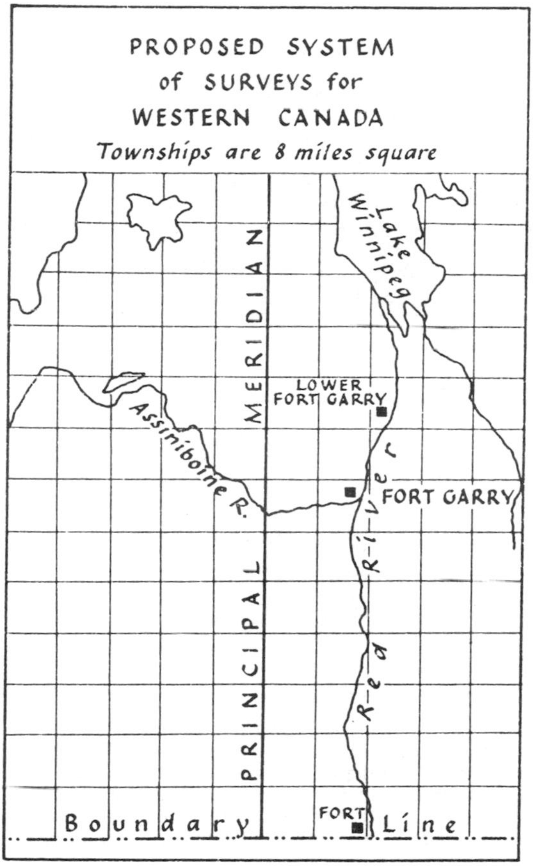

FIG. 107 The basis of the Western land-division system. This was a grid pattern based on parallels of latitude and meridians of longitude, and was thus much more regular than the older systems in the East.

and farms. In 1871 an order in council initiated 'a great and almost completely uniform land survey'.[1] Thereafter survey boundaries, instead of natural ones, became characteristic of the west. Where Nature failed to erect any well-marked frontiers, man was forced to create his own. The

[1] Kerr, D. G. G., *A Historical Atlas of Canada*, Toronto, 1961, p. 62, 'The Disposal of Prairie Lands'.

International Boundary followed a line of latitude (the 49th Parallel); the inter-provincial boundaries ran along lines of longitude. What more simple than to divide all the Prairie into similar lines, and make them the basis for settlement. Of course, where local relief features were important, then the grid was interrupted, but beyond this break, it continued unchanged (Fig. 107).

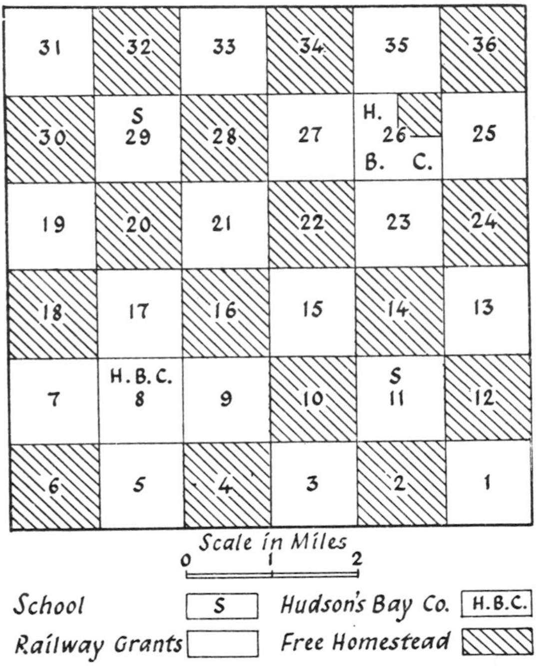

FIG. 108 A Western Township, set out in blocks of 640 acres each. Blocks were reserved for the support of schools, for the development of railways, and for the promotion of homesteadings. Since the land was taken over from the Hudson's Bay Company, some of it was reserved for its use by way of compensation.

The grid was divided into townships (not counties), six miles by six miles in extent, each with thirty-six sections. Each section was 1 sq. mile, or 640 acres. The sections were divided into half and quarter sections. Roads ran north and south between each section. East-to-west roads cut across these at intervals of two miles. The farms were spaced out fairly evenly along the roads (Fig. 108).

All this has come to affect the pattern of colonization. In the more densely populated sections (on the black earths, for example) many of the farms occupy a quarter section each; thus there are four of them spaced at the four sides of the square mile section. In the Park Belt 37 per cent of the farms are quarter section holdings. However, in the more sparsely populated sections, the farms may be half section, whole section, or combined-section holdings. In the Central Plains (on the brown soils), 27 per cent of the farms are whole-section holdings or larger. In the grazing districts of the semi-arid plains, farms are several sections each in size.

This sort of arrangement tends to isolate farms. Settlement is scattered, not concentrated. There are not many villages. Generally speaking, village life is lacking in the Prairie Provinces except where strong ethnic groups occur as will be seen. Most farms do not huddle around the edges of the village, but they are on their own, out in the country. A few villages have grown up at important cross-roads, especially if the railway station has come to form a 'node'. But actually they are like miniature towns; they are really commercial and servicing centres, rather than residential. Few farmers live in them. They do not house farm labourers to go out by day to surrounding farms. They are a collection of stores, offices, warehouses, with a station and elevator, and a few artisans and professional people. Their function is dominantly commercial rather than social or cultural (see Fig. 57, Chapter 8).

This fact makes the farmers very self-reliant. They use much machinery and home equipment to run their farms as independent units. Often farmers by-pass the local station or centre to use the large country towns or the cities. This is possible in a mechanized community, where most families have cars. Indeed, the dependence on the city has led to a strangely urbanized way of rural life. As Major Duncan Stuart writes:

> With wheat farming came a change in domestic life and economy. It became the custom to rely on the returns from the crops to provide not only all the food but the other necessaries of the family. The farmer's way of life became in essence that of a dweller in the city, who produces and sells his goods and buys everything with the profits of his industry. Some went further, and their wheat, their sole product, safely delivered to the elevator, they removed to the city for the six or seven months in which no grain farming work can be done. Thus we have 96 per cent of our farming population demanding as their right twelve months of a high standard of living, special roads, amusements, and every other concomitant of prosperity, on sixty days' work in the year! And so it came about that the farmer's menage, his wheat factory, consisted of his dwelling house and a stable for his horses and their fodder. Gardens, the household arts, spinning, weaving, even the homely knitting, curing of bacon and hams, 'preserves', butter making . . . became lost arts.[1]

[1] Stuart, D., *The Canadian Desert*, Toronto, 1938, p. 14.

Ethnic Problems

Though it is generally true that the rural pattern consists of evenly spaced, independent farm units (where mechanization has enabled farms to have direct contact with cities, and commercial agriculture has tended to make farmers adopt city ways), yet there are interesting differences which appear locally. These are most often due to 'ethnic' factors, rather than to physical ones.

Various people, in colonizing the Prairies, have tried to set up their own type of settlement. For example, the French brought their 'riverain' pattern of long lines of farms strung out parallel to the river, having narrow but deep lots running back from the banks. French farms are fairly near together, and form a rural street. Where a bridge crosses the river or a side road comes down to the bank the houses crowd together into a village. These villages are very picturesque, with the glistening spire of the parish church rising above the huddle of houses. Some stores, a bank, a school, workshops, and the lawyer's and doctor's office make up the other important buildings. Here village life is strong, and country arts, crafts, and pastimes flourish. In Manitoba there is a strong French influence throughout the area between the Red and Winnipeg rivers. St Boniface, across the river from Winnipeg, is a typical French town. Small groups of French are found in northern Manitoba and Saskatchewan. There are several French villages in the neighbourhood of Edmonton, while from Grande Prairie north to the Peace river many French colonists have settled. They form part of the great *French Belt*, in the northern forest, stretching from the Rockies, across the Prairies and northern Ontario into Quebec and the Maritimes. Throughout this belt French culture has concentrated itself in the compact, unified village, crowned with the twin roofs of church and school (see Fig. 57).

Other groups with a village tradition have also developed village communities in the Prairies. Although, as Dawson has pointed out,[1] 'the basis of the Canadian land settlement policy was the conditional grant of free land to bona fide single male agriculturists and heads of families', the wish of the Doukhobor would-be immigrants to settle in homogeneous groups, where they could practise their traditional form of Christian communism, was granted. It was agreed that whole blocks of homestead lands should be given to these religious refugees from southern Russia, group by village group.

> An arrangement was made between the government and the C.P.R. by which the latter exchanged its holdings [in the area in which it was proposed to settle the Doukhobors] for an equal number elsewhere. This

[1] Dawson, C. A., *Group Settlement, Ethnic Communities in Western Canada*, Toronto, 1936, pp. 7, 10.

> change enabled the Doukhobors to settle in compact communities rather than on alternate homestead sections. They started off with villages similar to those occupied by peasants in Russia. From twelve to twenty dwellings, one or two storeys high, were arranged in regular lines on either side of a broad street. Each house had its own grounds, trees, and a garden. One or two large barns, which served the whole village, were built back of the row of houses near a creek. The villages were spaced from two to four miles apart and located so as to give ready access to the surrounding farm land.[1]

Changes in their way of life have led many Doukhobors to accept the prevailing pattern of settlement and their villages are not as compact today as formerly. Nevertheless, they have preserved the strong co-operative and social spirit which village life fostered.

South of Winnipeg lies the Mennonite West Reserve, where German Mennonites have settled, bringing with them their old Teutonic love of village life. Before coming to Canada they had lived in the Russian steppes, and their migration to the Manitoba steppe gave them a 'home from home'. They were so successful that they spread into Saskatchewan, where they formed the Rosthern Mennonite colony, and also moved in small numbers to Alberta. When they arrived they divided the land into village areas, with from twenty to thirty families in each. The villages were built in the centre of the section, and consisted of two parallel rows of houses, very like the old 'Strassendorf' village types of Germany. The surrounding fields were divided into strips, and each family was given a number of strips which were scattered among the different fields. The village became the centre of every aspect of life; it was where the farmers lived, worshipped, had their recreation, and brought up their children. It was the centre of local government, transportation, and business. It therefore developed a neighbourly way of life which kept the people together and enabled them to solve their problems in common (Fig. 109).

The Mormons are also a village people. They migrated to Canada after 1887 and founded several towns and villages in south-west Alberta. From these settlements as centres they worked the surrounding country. It is interesting to note that by 1920 many of them were seeking individual farm sections, like the majority of the population. However, the village tradition is still strong. At Orton, for example,

> the various settlers first established their residence on the farms, instead of in a central village as is the Mormon custom. But they later decided that they would set aside an area for a village site and move their homes.

[1] Ibid., pp. 11–15.

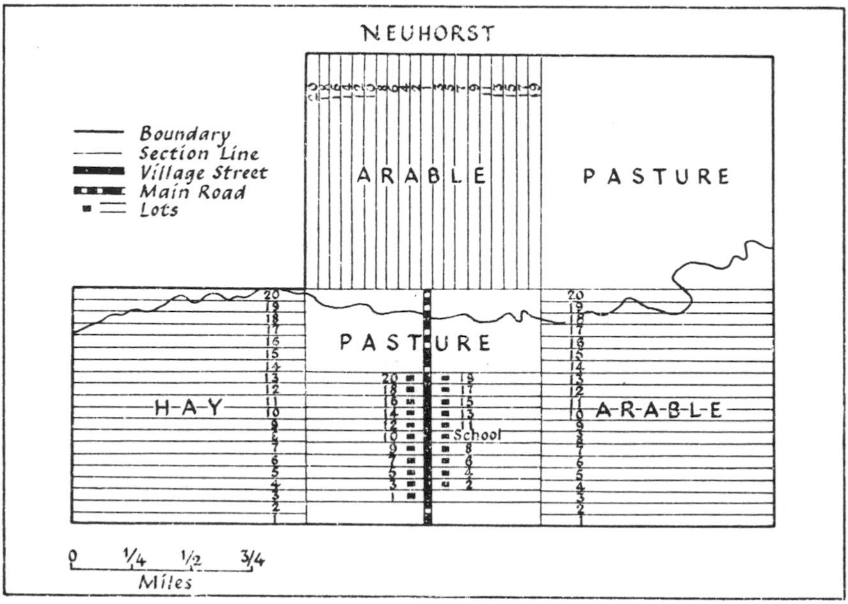

FIG. 109 Land System of a Mennonite Colony in the Canadian Prairies. (From Warkentin.) Many semi-feudal communities from central and eastern Europe migrated en bloc to Canada, during the late nineteenth and early twentieth centuries, especially to the Prairies, and there set up old-world agricultural villages, often with the old three-field system of working the land. Individuals held narrow lots of land scattered through the three fields. Although farm holdings are now being consolidated, the highly nucleated form of village often persists.

Then later some of those who moved their homes into the village, returned to their farms. At the present time there are eight homes on the village site and five individual farms. Opinion is divided as to the relative merits of living in the village or on the land.[1]

In Saskatchewan the German Catholics have two large colonies at St Peter's and St Joseph's. They came from America after 1900. In America they had been scattered in different States, and many of them had lost their sense of belonging to a separate ethnic group. Some of them wished to band together, and so they moved into the Prairies, where they were given large blocks of cheap land, especially to enable them to live in group communities. It is claimed that their migrations were due to the urge '*to change from a condition of scattered settlements in the United States* to a homogeneous colony of their own kind in Saskatchewan'.[2] Thus Canadian policy, which developed so differently from that in America, came to attract American settlement north of the border.

[1] Dawson, C. A., op. cit., p. 214. [2] Ibid., p. 278.

Indeed, most of the foreign-born immigrants into Canada feel the need to live near members of their own race, nationality, religion, or culture. They like to set up colonies of their own, rather than mix freely with the general population. This is quite understandable. By doing so they keep up the relationships and friendships which bound them together in the old country. They do not feel the new country is quite so strange. They can work with people who speak their own language and have their own faith. They can maintain their old habits of living with comparatively few changes. They are able to help each other in adjusting to the new environment. In this way they find root in the land of their adoption.

Nevertheless, it is impossible to keep to themselves. The necessity arises of accommodating themselves to other ethnic groups, and especially to the dominant Anglo-Canadian group. Public highways and railroads built through their colonies bring the outside world into the heart of their towns and villages. They must do business with people of other languages and faiths. They send their wheat to Canadian elevators, buy their supplies from Canadian stores, meet Canadian brokers and salesmen, insurance agents and bankers, and have to follow Canadian policies concerning tariffs and exports. They must copy Canadian business methods, and methods of production —or else they would suffer in competition.

This may demand changes in their way of farming, such as the amalgamation of strip-lots into consolidated farms; the adoption of cash farming in place of subsistence farming; the development of farms in individual units for individual profit; the use of mechanization to replace family labour, and so on.

Frequently, this invites a break away from the village or colony. If the village system is backward, compared with Canadian farming in general, then the more forward immigrant comes to the point where, for his own sake, he must leave the community and farm on his own. Or else the local village does not offer as many advantages as some near-by commercial centre, and he gives up using the local stores and banks to 'go into town'. Even if he stays in the village it is only to try to modernize it, and bring in stores, offices, and other agencies from outside.

When the womenfolk see their men working with tractors and using trucks, they want equivalent benefits for their homes. They start to Canadianize the house. They may add a veranda to it and have ornately carved gables attached, so that the outside appearance is Canadian. Then, if they can afford it, they buy electric ranges, refrigerators, and washers. This brings them into touch with Canadian salesmen and shopkeepers. They try to Canadianize themselves in other ways—buy Canadian-style dresses, read Canadian home magazines.

It is the children, however, who soon change things. For when they come of school age they go to a State-directed public school, where their course of studies is the same, no matter what their race or creed. Consequently, they see their own way of life in the light of the whole Canadian tradition, and give themselves up to larger loyalties. As they proceed through high school or college they take summer jobs, where they compete with Canadian youth. In seeking independent positions, outside the village or town, they realize that, by accepting Canadian ways, they have a better chance. Indeed, many of them leave the ethnic community because they believe there is more opportunity outside. Often they marry girls or boys outside the community, and in doing so try to bring up the third generation the Canadian way.

Many other influences act upon them. They may join a Canadian church, or political party, and in this way absorb the culture of the country. They read Canadian papers and listen to the national radio, until their ideas become those of the people as a whole. A great number joined the Canadian Services, and fought and suffered for the land of their adoption. Thus in the supreme way they identified themselves with Canada.

But it is important to realize that, although they came to be assimilated with the prevailing tradition, they contributed much as well. Assimilation is never a one-way process. The foreign-born greatly strengthened the multi-cultural aspect of Canadian life. Although village life was weakened, the neighbourliness born of community existence continued to survive, and influenced the Canadian outlook. New types of food and dress were introduced, together with new sports and business practices, new crops and ways of farming, new faiths and ideas of education. Already these things have influenced Canadian art, architecture, music and literature. In every way the 'New Canadians' have made the nation richer by their coming.

Population

The ethnic problem is by no means confined to the Prairies. It is a Canadian problem, found in every province, in every town. However, it is greater in the Prairies, because of the greater number of New Canadians. The Prairies have only been settled in a large way during the last fifty years. The colonists who came to Canada in that time found most of eastern Canada already occupied; therefore, they streamed out west, along with many Canadians and Americans. They formed a proportionately greater part of the western population than of the eastern. Thus while in Prince Edward Island they form only 1·6 per cent of the population, and in Quebec only 5·5 per cent, in Manitoba they represent 43·3 per cent, in Alberta 44·5 per cent, and in Saskatchewan 50·7 per cent of the population.

In the east, the immigrants have gone mainly to the cities. There they form separate ethnic quarters. But they are so far outnumbered by the native-born population that they are assimilated fairly rapidly. In the west, the immigrants were given large reserves of land or grouped themselves into large rural *blocs*. Here they lived in comparative separation. Therefore assimilation was slower, and many 'foreign' forms of settlement and ways of life continued, and still continue. However, the tendency over several generations is to abandon or modify the village settlement in favour of the 'native' grid system, and for the foreign-born and native populations to mingle and become indistinguishable.

The ethnic problem in the west has been increased by the **rapid rate of population growth.** There have been eight periods of population growth in the west. The first, between 1811 and 1871, was a stage of slow, hard pioneer development. It did barely more than open up the Red river valley. Then between 1876 and 1882 there was a rapid expansion, from eastern Canada and the United States, following the railway. However, depression struck in 1883, and from then until 1895 immigration was slow. It consisted largely of homesteaders, who took up land for a mere subsistence. Between 1896 and 1913 a tremendous influx took place, especially of European immigrants. Railways were built. Foreign markets were opened up. Wheat farming and ranching on an extensive, commercial scale became very successful. The First World War and the post-war slump tended to hold back settlement. Moreover, Canada had become very largely industrialized, and many immigrants preferred to settle in the cities rather than on farms. The sixth period of growth was again quite spectacular. Between 1926 and 1929 prices were very high. They attracted thousands into the Prairies. But the depression of 1930 checked the rush and the population began to show a slight decline. It also showed a marked drift into the cities. After the Second World War a new great wave of immigration flooded the Prairies, moving mainly into the cities, attracted by the boom in agricultural and petro-chemical industries.

This story of change indicates how big a part economic and social factors have in settlement. Thrice high prices and cheap transportation have led to rapid expansion; and twice this expansion has been checked by serious depressions. The commercialization of life in recent decades has made immigrants dissatisfied with homesteading, and led them increasingly into the cities. (This drift to the cities is actually drawing many westerners to the east and reversing the traditional westward march of the frontier. The new Canadian frontier is now along the St Lawrence seaway. In the hey-day of agricultural expansion, 1900 to 1920, the west had the greatest share of the nation's population increase. But in the large industrial boom of the late 'thirties and the Second World War, the east has benefited the most.)

The drift away from the rural areas into the cities has been aggravated by the rapid commercialization and mechanization of farming. Farmers have gone over almost completely to a cash basis. Almost everything they grow is for sale. This means more roads and railways, warehouses, and elevators, packing plants, mills and creameries, bankers, insurance agents and brokers. These are all urban services. Thus an expanding agriculture has called for the expanding city. In return the cities have helped the farmer to mechanize his production, and to grow more for less labour. Not all the farmers' children are needed on the farm. Having few, if any, village openings, they make for the city. More than half the population of Manitoba lives in the cities.

The extent of urbanization is different in the different provinces. In Manitoba it amounts to 60 per cent; in Saskatchewan, to 37 per cent; and in Alberta, to 51 per cent. This difference is explained by the different sort of production characterizing the three provinces.

Product	*Manitoba*	*Saskatchewan*	*Alberta*
	%	%	%
Agricultural	20	59	26
Mining	4	7·5	25
Hydro	4	2	2
Manufacturing	39	11	20

Manitoba has the most evenly balanced economy. The value of its factories, mines, and power plants is about the same as that of its farms. These activities centre in towns such as Winnipeg and Brandon.

Winnipeg, with a total population of about 500,000 if we include St Boniface and the suburbs, is the largest city between Toronto and Vancouver. It dominates the life not only of Manitoba but of the Prairies. Lying in the most fertile part of the Red river valley, just south of the Manitoba lakes, it is the point where all routes across or around the Shield meet. The routes then fan out from Winnipeg across the whole Prairies. The railways and roads converge on the river junction of the Red and Assiniboine rivers, and make a star-like city, with the rivers forming three main points, and the eastern and western railway lines the other two points. The land is flat and enables the city to expand in broad avenues and extensive suburbs. Large railway sidings, with wheat elevators, warehouses, and packing plants are found on the outer edge. There is a large business and shopping area in the centre. In between are the chief residential areas. New suburbs are spreading east and west of the rivers (Fig. 110).

The arrangement of the place is roughly that of a number of concentric zones around the central nucleus. Indeed, Winnipeg shows the 'ideal' concentric arrangement of most cities built on an open plain.[1] It is dominated by a central shopping and business circle, with a zone of apartments,

[1] Weir, T., 'Land Use and Population Characteristics of Central Winnipeg', *Geographical Bulletin,* no. 9, 1956, p. 6.

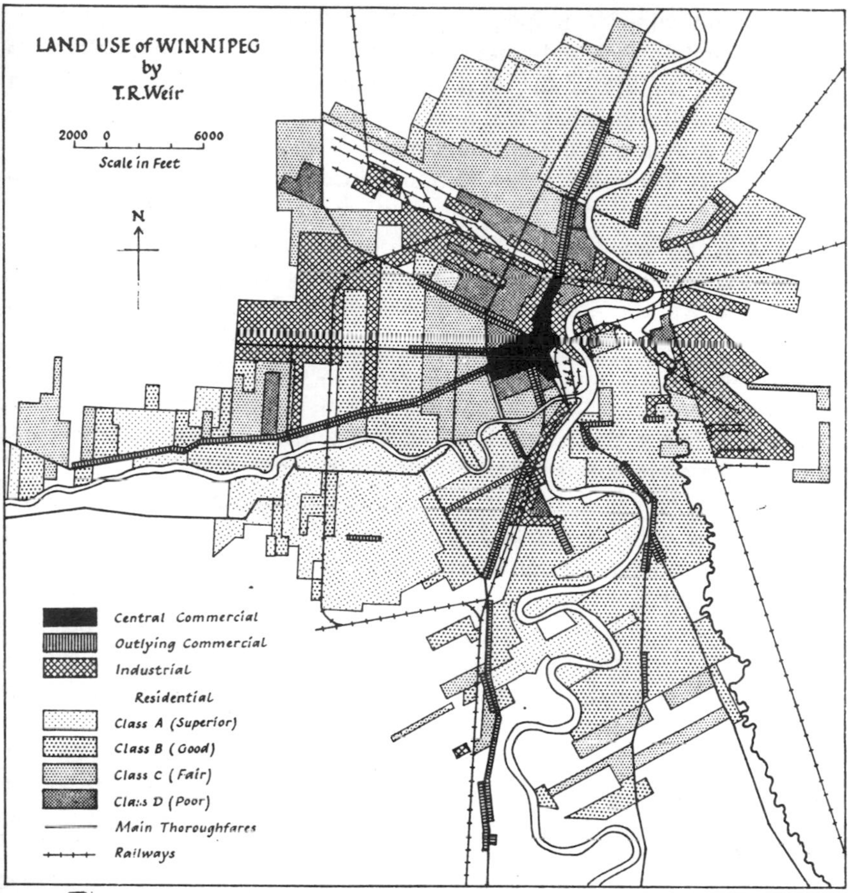

FIG. 110 Land Use in Winnipeg, showing the great concentration on the terrace just below the confluence of the Red and Assiniboine rivers, and the star-like shape of the central and outlying commercial areas. Radiating outwards are Winnipeg's strategic roads and railways, with housing areas in between them.

rooming houses, and duplexes round it. This passes to an interrupted zone of railway sidings, industries, and warehouses, surrounded by workers' homes. Finally there is a partially developed zone of suburban surveys on the outskirts, with institutions like the university, and with country and golf clubs.

Winnipeg is very cosmopolitan, with many ethnic groups who have contributed a great deal to its interest by their different traditions of architecture, clothing, and food. They have also played a prominent part in enriching the life of this outstanding cultural centre, by their contributions in literature, art, and, above all, music. St Boniface is strongly French in character, and within Winnipeg there are small *blocs* of European groups, who still maintain their old-country habits, even while they are helping to forge the new culture of the west. The university takes a large share in fusing these different elements together, and in giving inspiration and direction to the cultural life of the province.

Winnipeg is chiefly a transportation centre and a financial and commercial focus. Thirty-two per cent of its wage earners are in 'service' occupations, servicing industry, trade, and the farmers round about. Twenty-four per cent are traders, selling goods to a wide market throughout the province. Another 15 per cent are engaged in wholesale and transportation occupations. Only some 15 per cent are employed in manufacturing. Thus manufacturing is not very important. The costs of manufacturing are very great. Winnipeg is far from all coal, oil, gas, and metal mines. The chief advantage it has is the handling of huge quantities of raw materials. Its industries therefore consist of transforming the agricultural raw materials into consumer goods. It has large slaughtering and meat packing plants, flour and feed mills, butter and cheese factories, and bread and baking concerns. It also has important clothing workshops and printing and bookbinding works.

Winnipeg is a well-balanced city, with a balance between different occupations and different ethnic groups. This is one reason why it plays such a dominant role in all the Prairies. As a railway hub, business focus, and cultural centre, it is the capital of the west (Fig. 111).

The density of settlement in the Red and Assiniboine plains is so high that in spite of the large concentration of population in Winnipeg (with about one out of every two people in the province!) there are still enough people to group themselves into other towns. Chief of these are Portage-la-Prairie, guarding the strip of plain between the Manitoba escarpment and Lake Manitoba; and Brandon, at the centre of the great Assiniboine gap through the Manitoba scarp. They are railway towns, with small but flourishing agricultural industries. Brandon is also an important shopping centre for western Manitoba, and is the site of the well-known Brandon University.

Saskatchewan is much less urbanized than Manitoba, and yet it has the same sort of highly commercialized agriculture that centres in cities. There are two large and wealthy plains in the province, that of the Qu'Appelle basin, with its centre at Regina, and that of the Saskatchewan Forks, centred on Saskatoon. Here population is relatively dense. Railways and roads come together. Secondary towns have sprung up, such as Moose Jaw, commanding the gaps through the Coteau, and Battleford and Prince Albert, commanding the pioneer fringe on the north.

Regina, with a population of about 120,000, is the largest city in the province and forms its capital. It lies on a flat, elongated plain (once the

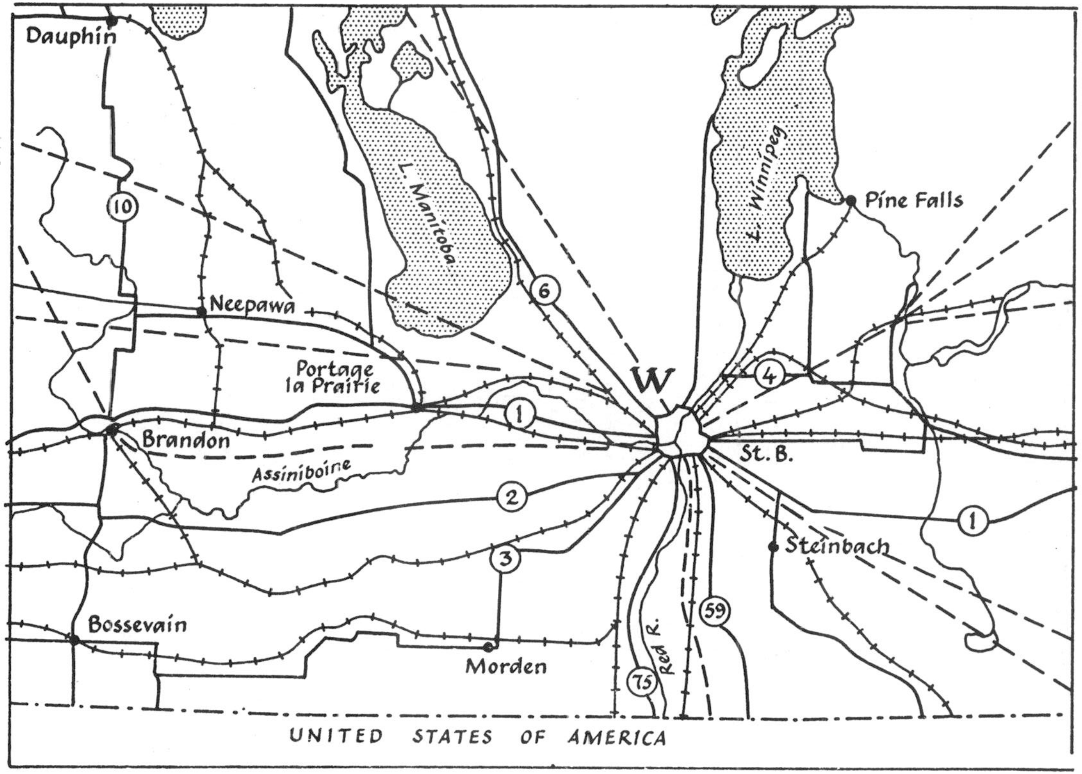

FIG. 111 Winnipeg—the Hub of the Prairies. On the edge of the Shield, in the rich Red river valley, in the narrow gap between Lake Winnipeg and the United States border, and with the whole of the Prairies widening to the West, the city of Winnipeg occupies one of the most strategic sites in Canada. All the chief railways, roads, and flight lines of the Prairie Provinces meet here. No wonder Manitoba is referred to as the 'Keystone Province', at the centre of the whole Canadian arch. Road No. 1 is the Trans-Canada Highway. Other roads are provincial highways. Airways shown by broken lines. (Scale, 1:2·5 m.)

floor of a large glacial lake) between the higher and less fertile land of the Coteau to the west and the Beaver hills and Moose mountain to the east. The Qu'Appelle waters the northern part of the plain, the Souris, the south. The soils are fertile chestnut soils, and make one of the best wheat areas in North America. Regina is at the centre of this area, on the main Canadian Pacific east–west line. Railways and roads also pass through it along the front of the Côteau, from Edmonton to Chicago. The greater part of the population is employed in servicing occupations, transportation, and trade. Only 9 per cent are engaged in manufacturing. The chief industries are oil refining, meat packing, flour-milling, and the assembly of ready-made automobile parts. A big steel mill, using scrap metal, is a noted addition. Regina is the headquarters of the Royal Canadian Mounted Police, who played such an important part in keeping law and order while the Prairies were being settled. From Regina they could contact all parts of the Prairies with equal ease. The beautiful Legislative Buildings of the province crown this city of spacious streets and residential suburbs.

Saskatoon, with a population of about 100,000, is the educational centre of the province, containing the fine campus of the University of Saskatchewan. It is also a busy railway junction where west–east and north–south lines come together in the middle Saskatchewan plain. The area is watered by the North and South Saskatchewan rivers, and has rich wheat and also mixed farms. There is a large Canadian government wheat elevator, for storing wheat.

Moose Jaw, with an expanding population, is the most active manufacturing centre of the province. It commands the ranching as well as the wheat areas of the south. Large Canadian Pacific Railway shops, a foundry, cold storage plants, stockyards, packing plants, a creamery, and a vast grain-storage elevator are the chief industries.

Alberta is rather more urbanized than Saskatchewan. Mining and transportation are very important, in addition to agriculture. Alberta lies on the largest coal and oil fields of Canada. Coal mining occurs near Lethbridge, Drumheller, and Camrose; oil and gas are found just south of Calgary, and west, north, and east of Edmonton. Some of these towns, like Lethbridge, Calgary, and Edmonton, are also important transportation centres, commanding the passes across the Rockies.

Calgary and Edmonton are the chief cities. **Calgary,** with a population of over 320,000, lies in the valley of the Bow river, east of Kicking Horse pass. North–south rails cross the main east–west line. The city is built on high river terraces above the deeply cut river valley. Railways converge at a busy industrial suburb east of the river; low, long bridges span the river; roads rise to the long, high terrace to the west where the skyscraper hotels, offices, and shops are lined together. The city spreads beyond this to western industrial areas and to residential suburbs with the University. Route terminals have large warehouses, which do a big wholesale trade. The central shops have a widespread retail trade, especially in the tourist season when thousands of visitors throng the central streets. The 'Calgary Stampede' is an annual event, when Indians and cowboys gather together to re-enact old times. It attracts thousands of tourists. Manufacturing is represented principally by saw mills, flour mills, packing plants, oil refineries, locomotive shops, and brick and cement works. Natural gas is largely used as a fuel, but Alberta coal and oil are also available.

Edmonton, with a population of over 380,000, has boomed very rapidly during and since the Second World War. It is the gateway to the north (especially the Mackenzie). Not only does it command the most northerly of the railway passes across the Rockies, and so the Prince Rupert outlet to the sea, but it is also the base for the Peace river development, and more recently for the Alaska and Mackenzie highways. These roads have opened up possibilities of vast new developments in the Yukon and the Mackenzie basins which will almost certainly centre on Edmonton. Thus a wide fan of routes spreads west and east, south and north from the city, making it the commercial capital of the province. It is also the administrative capital, and the seat of the provincial university. It has also been made the headquarters of the Western Air Command, as an indication of its strategic importance, guarding the northern approaches to Canada.

The city grew out of two settlements: Strathcona, built by the Canadian Pacific Railway, and Edmonton, by what is now the Canadian National Railway. At first the city tended to spread east, to make use of the low flats by the river for warehouses and industries. But the recurrent danger of flooding of the Saskatchewan river, as it became swollen with spring melt-waters or summer rains, prevented the use of the flats, and forced the city to expand west. The heavy industries are situated out from the centre along railway sidings. They consist of meat packing, lumbering, and large creameries. Recently large new oil refineries and a smelter have been developed. However, manufacturing accounts for only 14 per cent of the population. Transportation accounts for nearly as many. The city is still largely a commercial centre, acting as the outfitting, shopping, and business base for the mining, lumbering, ranching, mixed-farming, and pioneer communities in its hinterland.

CONCLUSION

Compared with eastern Canada, the Prairies are essentially agricultural. They have been settled mainly by farmers, and farming is still the basis of their prosperity. This settlement is closely controlled by relief, climate, and, above all, the soil belts. Yet agricultural prosperity depends on railways, mechanization, and city services; and farm and city are closely linked together. The cities are chiefly commercial and distribution centres. There is little heavy industry. What manufacturing goes on is mostly concerned with processing agricultural raw materials. Agriculture is not quite as limited as it used to be; more varieties of farming appear. At the same time, mining and forest activities are becoming more important. This has led to a more balanced population, not so rural as before, but with many urban occupations. The population is very mixed, since settlement was late and rapid. Many Continental Europeans were attracted to the region, as well as English- and French-speaking Canadians. This rapid and large-scale mixing of people with very different background naturally produced pressing ethnic problems, but it has also enriched Canadian life and bids fair to create a distinctive Prairie culture.

CHAPTER FOURTEEN

Southern British Columbia

British Columbia is Canada's third largest province, with an area of 359,279 sq. miles, yet its population of about 1,800,000 people is less than that of Greater Montreal. The last province to be extensively settled, its growth has been rather limited. That growth has been concentrated in the southern part of the province, from Kamloops south, and there is an appreciable difference between the more varied and balanced economy of this southern settled arc and the northern sparsely occupied area still largely engaged in primary and pioneer production.

The reason for this difference is partly geographical. There is nowhere much low, flat, and fertile land suited for large-scale settlement, but most of what there is occurs in the south. The greater part of the province is mountainous. Its boundaries are the Great Divide in the east and the coast of rocky fjords in the west. As a result, settlement is closely controlled by relief.

THE PHYSICAL ENVIRONMENT

Structure and Relief

The structure of the province has resulted from a long history of mountain building. This has already been outlined, but should be stressed. It produced five distinct physiographic divisions, which have had a great deal to do with occupation, transportation, and settlement in the section. They are: (i) the Islands and Coast Mountains; (ii) the Interior Upland; (iii) the Selkirk block-and-trench region; (iv) the Rocky mountains; and (v) the Transmontane high plains.

The Coast Mountains stretch for 1,000 miles from Alaska into America. They are about 100 miles wide, with an average height of 5,000 feet. However, many peaks rise to 10,000 feet, and Mt Waddington, 13,260 feet, is the highest mountain in British Columbia. The Coast Ranges were intruded by giant batholiths of igneous rocks, in whose cracks rich veins of ore have gathered. The ranges reappear off the coast in a string of islands, of which the Queen Charlotte Isles and Vancouver Island are the most important. The mountains have been heavily eroded by ice and are rugged. The lower parts of the glaciated valleys have been drowned by the sea, and turned into fjords. The rivers have been rejuvenated, and cut deeply into their valleys, leaving high terraces on either bank. There is little settlement except at the Fraser delta, and on the coastal plain of Vancouver Island. Few roadways cross the ranges, except up the lower Fraser and the Skeena.

The Interior Upland is a rough plateau, made up of sheets of lava, ridges of folded rock, and intrusive domes. It has an average level of between 3,000 and 4,000 feet. Although most of its summits are flat and sweeping, there is quite strong relief, since the valleys have been glaciated and are deep and wide. Rejuvenated rivers have deepened them further. Glacial and river deposits abound, often forming marked kame and alluvial terraces. Former glacial lakes have left a few quite extensive plains. However, these flats are in the 'rain shadow' of the Coast Ranges, and therefore suffer from drought. Settlement is sparse.

The Columbia Mountains consist of great intrusives, rich in ore deposits. They have been faulted into a block-and-trench structure, where the more resistant blocks tower above long, narrow trenches. The rivers follow the trenches and cut through the blocks, making a typical rectilineal pattern. The Rocky Mountain Trench, between the Purcell and Rocky Ranges, is followed by the upper Peace, Fraser, Columbia and Kootenay rivers. The Purcell Trench contains Lake Kootenay; the Selkirk Trench, the Arrow Lakes; and the Okanagan Trench, Lake Okanagan. Since these trenches continue across the International Boundary into America, and are, moreover, linked into a single natural system by the Columbia river, it is impossible to separate the natural regions of British Columbia from those of Washington, U.S.A.

It is no wonder the area was jointly settled by British and Americans and was long in dispute between them. However, with the drawing of the boundary across the natural grain of the country, efforts were made to join the trenches one to the other, laterally, by the use of east–west tributaries; and with great difficulty, yet with considerable success, east–west routes were built. The first of these was the Dewdney trail, carrying the furs and gold of the Selkirks out to Vancouver so that they would not go south to the United States. Later, the Canadian Pacific Railway built a tortuous track binding the Canadian portions of the trenches together. Superbly, the trans-Canada Highway has done the same.

The Rocky mountains rise abruptly from the Rocky Mountain Trench, as they do from the Prairies, in a sort of giant block. They have a chain of summits between 11,000 and 13,000 feet, including Mt Assiniboine (11,870), Mt Columbia (12,294), Mt Alberta (11,874), and Mt Robson (12,972). The passes through them are 3,700 to 5,400 feet high. The mountains consist of folded and uplifted sedimentaries, with a wide range of forms. One is struck by the number of high peaks (Assiniboine, Robson) that have virtually flat strata; this indicates the great amount of uplift. Most of the rocks are without important mineral bodies, but Cretaceous rocks contain small yet valuable coal fields. The Rocky block in the south forms the divide between the Fraser and Columbia rivers to the west, and the North and South Saskatchewan rivers to the east. However, in the north, the Peace and Liard rivers rise on the west of the Rockies, and have cut through the mountains in deep passes. Ice-sheets covered the Rockies, and formed huge cirques and wide U-shaped valleys. Small ice-fields and glaciers still exist in the higher reaches.

The Transmontane region is a part of the high plain, east of the Rockies, on to which northern British Columbia abuts. It is a strongly dissected plain, with hummocky moraines at the foot of the mountains and small fans of outwash at the valley openings.

These various structures influence very closely the climatic regions, the forests and agriculture, mining, transportation and settlement of the province.

Climate

The Cordilleras lie athwart the Pacific Westerlies. Air masses generate a continual succession of cyclones from the broad Pacific. Winds come on shore laden with clouds. Striking the mountain front, they are forced to rise and in doing so, cool rapidly. The water vapour swiftly condenses into rain, that falls on the mountain slopes. British Columbia is the rainiest province in Canada.

The distribution of rainfall runs in belts, parallel to the mountains (Fig. 112). The heaviest rainfall is on the windward, or western, slopes of the mountains. The leeward slopes are dry by comparison. The heaviest rain occurs along the west coast of Vancouver Island. Here the annual rainfall may be as high as 200 inches. The eastern coast of the island is comparatively sheltered, with an average of 30 inches. Winds at a higher level are still moist, and so the mainland coast has a rainfall of about 60 inches. As the winds are forced over the Coast Ranges, the rainfall increases to over 100 inches. The rain falls chiefly in the autumn and the winter. The cyclones are more numerous then, and there is a sharp contrast between the warm Pacific waters and the cold, wintry mountains.

East of the Coast Ranges the winds descend and therefore can carry their moisture in vapour form. Over the valleys, little rain falls. These interior valleys are in a rain shadow and are quite dry, especially the deeper ones between the Coast Ranges and the Selkirks. However, where local mountains force the winds to rise, as they pass over the uplands between the basins, or the Selkirks, the rainfall increases. The Okanagan with only 10 inches of rain has quite a desert appearance, where it is not irrigated.

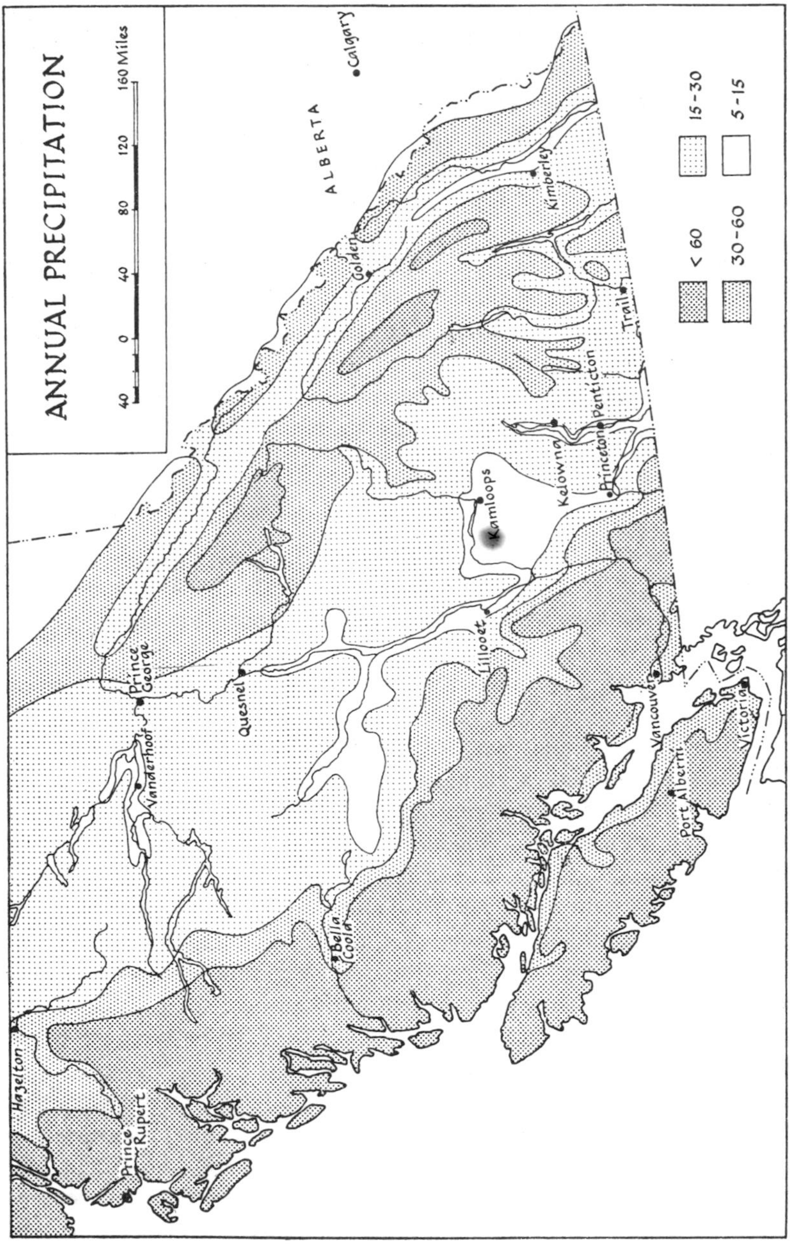

FIG. 112 The Rainfall Zones of British Columbia. Running in N.W.–S.E. patterns, they parallel the mountain belts. The Province has the widest range in Canada, from rain-forest conditions on the coast, to cactus desert in the interior.

The central Fraser and Thompson valleys, the Arrow Lake and Kootenay trenches also have low rainfalls, of from 10 to 15 inches. North of Quesnel, however, winds sweep in using the Skeena Saddle in the Coast Mountains and rainfall increases to between 15 and 20 inches. On the Selkirks it is between 20 and 40 inches. Much of the rain in the interior is thunderstorm rain; where the valleys become heated to a great degree, the air suddenly ascends, large thunderclouds pile up, and the heat is relieved by claps of thunder and sheets of rain.

The Pacific winds finally reach the Rockies and once again are forced to rise. However, by this time they do not have as much moisture as when they struck the coast, so that the rainfall is not very high — about 10 inches. East of the Rockies, the rainfall drops again to the rain-shadow area of the semi-arid prairies.

The temperature also varies with the relief. The Coast Ranges divide off a West Maritime climate, with comparatively equable temperatures, from an intermontane climate, with a fairly high range of temperature. All along the coast the winters are mild and the summers cool. This is due to the effect of the sea. The sea keeps warm in the winter and the temperatures are higher on the coast than in the interior for any latitude. The Kuro Siwo Drift from the south-west Pacific, although it does not reach the coast, helps to warm the winds that blow over the coast. At the same time, the Coast Ranges keep out the cold continental airs that tend to spread over the Interior Uplands. The January temperature at Victoria is around 40° F., or well above freezing.

In summer the sea heats up much more slowly than the land, and this, along with the upwelling of cool coastal currents, keeps temperatures low. The average July temperature in Victoria is about 60° F. This is rather cool for crops. However, many people like the equable climate, and go to Victoria or Vancouver for that reason. Their gardens are lovely, even in the winter.

The interior valleys and uplands are very different. Here the climate is definitely more extreme, with hotter summers and colder winters. The region scarcely feels the effects of the sea; during the summer the valleys become excessively hot at times, through local heating beneath cloudless skies; in the winter, cold polar air moves down from the mountains and from the polar continental air mass to the east. Freezing temperatures occur. The range of temperature between summer and winter is as high as 70°. Since summer temperatures are critical for crops they may be used to divide the interior into three regions: (*a*) the mountain ranges, with averages less than 57° F.; (*b*) the intermediate 'plateau' levels, 60°; and (*c*) the southern valleys, over 65°. These are important temperatures. Where they fall below 60° crops are not very safe. If they are above 65°, good crops may be expected.

Combining rainfall and temperature together, *there are three chief climatic regions in southern British Columbia.* They are: (1) the West Maritime, mild, moist climate of the western coast and islands; (2) the Alpine, cold, wet climate of the Coast Ranges, the higher parts of the Selkirks, and the Rockies; and (3) the semi-continental, warm, semi-arid climate of the southern interior valleys.

Vegetation

Relief and climate influence vegetation. Along the wet, mild west coast are dense forests of evergreen coniferous trees. They have an ample supply of water, and can grow most of the year round. They consist chiefly of the mighty Douglas fir and the red cedar, giant trees generally over a hundred feet, which yield magnificent lumber. The fir is cut, sawn into timber, dressed, and exported to Britain by way of the Panama, or shipped by train to eastern Canada.

Douglas firs also grow in the rainy climate of the Selkirks and the western slopes of the Canadian Rockies. Here they are mixed with the tall, slim lodgepole pine and the white pine. These forests too are very useful for lumbering.

Most of the Rockies are under a spruce-fir evergreen forest, mixed with lodgepole pine. This forest spreads northwards over the Interior Uplands, where the spruce-fir association is very dense. It is the forest of a short growing season with moderate rainfall.

South from the middle Fraser and Thompson, the rainfall slackens considerably, until in the Okanagan a desert flora is found. The higher slopes of the mountains are covered with a rather open forest of Douglas fir and yellow pine. On the lower slopes the forest gives way to open range country, covered with short grasses. Finally, in the valley flats, or low terraces, the rainfall can barely support a grass vegetation, and sage brush and other drought-loving desert plants dot the pale yellow, dusty ground.

Soils

The soils of southern British Columbia are closely related to vegetation and relief. They show a remarkable range from desert-brown through chestnut soils, in the drier valleys and terrace lands, to forest-brown soils on the wetter temperate slopes, to podsolic soils and podsols in the higher alpine areas. In the central valleys there is a marked gradation from mineral soils by the rivers, or organic soils in the silty deltas at the heads of lakes, through brown soils with sage brush and bunch grass on the lower, very dry terraces, to dark brown soils with range grass and ponderosa pine on upper terraces or lower slopes, to black soils under tall grass and pine, with aspen

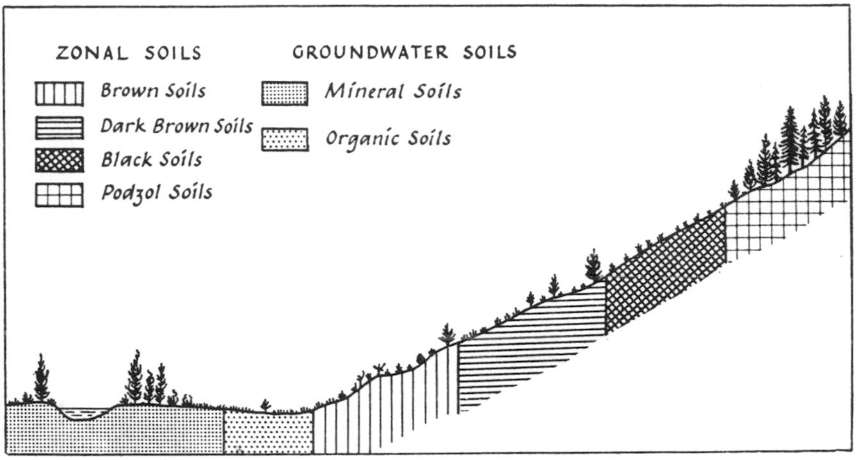

FIG. 113 Soils, vegetation, and altitude in British Columbia, a typical transect from the Okanagan valley. (From Kelly and Spilsburg.)

poplar, on the intermediate slopes, and eventually to podsols under lodgepole pine and fir on the tops of the ridges[1] (Fig. 113).

THE HUMAN RESPONSE—PRIMARY PRODUCTION

Forestry

Its upland-to-mountainous nature helps to make British Columbia a forest region. This is true not only because these uplands are wet and cool and thus well suited to trees, but also because they are steep, rocky, and inaccessible and thus ill-suited to agriculture. Farming offers little competition to forestry in the 'Mountain Province' (Fig. 114).

The richness and variety of forests in British Columbia have thus become the basis of a thriving forest industry in the province, and account for 15 per cent by value of the total production of British Columbia. Thus, lumbering is even more important than mining (6 per cent) and is more than three times as productive as agriculture (4 per cent).

The west coast forest is the most valuable. There dense stands of Douglas fir, western hemlock, and western cedar provide some of the best timber for construction purposes in the world. These trees grow to a height of from 100 to 200 feet, with diameters of 3 to 8 feet. The trunks are very straight, and free of lower branches or knots. The trees can be easily dressed, or the lumber cut to great lengths and breadths. The wood is extremely

[1] Spilsbury, R. H., and Tisdale, W., 'Soil-Plant Relationships and Vertical Zonation in S. Interior British Columbia', *Scientific Agriculture*, 1944, **24**, pp. 395–436.

strong. The cedar wood has a natural oiliness that makes it watertight and free from fungus growths and rot. It is used for pleasure boats, roofing shingles, piles for quays, and posts. The hemlock makes nice wood for the interior of houses. The Douglas fir is used for docks, railway sleepers, and all construction purposes requiring a very tough, durable wood.

The Sitka spruce, of Queen Charlotte Isles, is also useful lumber. It grows very straight for about a hundred feet and is easily cut, and gives a lot of good wood per tree. It is quite light compared with Douglas fir, and so is easily handled, dressed, and sawn. Much of it is pulped, and turned into paper.

The coastal forests are at present the most fully developed, because they are the most accessible. The trees are cut by machinery as much as possible, and then hauled out by tractor. The branches are trimmed off, and the logs are put in a boom and drawn along the coast to lumbering towns. The eastern United States is the chief market, having replaced Britain. Lumber is also shipped to Japan and the southern Dominions.

The Rocky Mountain spruce forms the next most important forest reserve. It grows in the Interior Upland and on the slopes of the Rockies. It is not as tall, and the wood is not as tough, as coastal timber. Nor does it withstand weathering. Therefore, it cannot match the west coast trees for construction purposes. However, it is light, and easily worked, and is suitable for boxes and the interior woodwork of houses. The forest is cut close to the railways, but north of the Prince Rupert line little lumbering occurs.

The yellow pine on the slopes of the dry, southern valleys is locally important. It is not a good construction timber, because it is so easily attacked by the weather, rot, and fungus. But it is quite suitable for packaging the fruit grown in the Okanagan and other southern areas.

The production of newsprint is only beginning in British Columbia, although there are suitable trees. However, they do not tempt the investor until the more profitable stands of tall timber have been cut. Nevertheless, pulp is now made from the wood chips and sawdust of the lumber mills, and north of Vancouver, on the coast, are several pulp and paper works, using the abundance of cheap power generated at the heads of mighty fjords. Ocean Falls is a good example.

The Government has shown concern recently over the very rapid cutting of the available forests. During the Second World War demand was tremendous, and companies cut seed trees, undeveloped trees, and ungraded trees indiscriminately. This may have been justified by the war emergency. But it is known that 'only about half the land at present being logged in British Columbia is properly regenerating itself'. Therefore, conservation practices, and even reforestation, are being resorted to, so as to regain forest land for the lumber industry.

Agriculture

Comparatively little of British Columbia is fit for agriculture, but what is fit produces good crops. The province has little lowland. Many of the valleys are profoundly eroded, and difficult to use. The climate north of Prince George or the Peace river has too short and variable a growing season. In many places forestry will always be more important than agriculture, even where it is possible to replace the trees with crops. The agricultural areas are often isolated, and people are cut off from each other and from the cities. Thus farming has advanced much less than lumbering or mining. Nevertheless, there are good local markets in the lumbering and mining towns and in rail and harbour settlements; and British Columbia has already produced more than it needs of apples, plums, pears, cherries, and peaches, leaving a surplus for export.

Altogether, about $4\frac{1}{2}$ million acres of land are occupied by farming. This compares with about 127 million acres in the Prairie Provinces, and 20 million acres in Ontario. British Columbia cannot pretend to be an important farming province. Actually, only 700,000 acres or so are improved. The rest is still largely bush or natural pasture. There are such wide regional differences, with specialization in ranching, dairy farming, fruit and vegetables, that it is impossible to give any general impression. But on the average mixed farm, only about a fifth of the land would be improved, as compared with over a half in Ontario. Farming in British Columbia, except for the irrigated areas, is still carried on very largely on a hay-pasture basis. The production of grain is not important, with 3·3 acres of oats, and 2·5 acres of wheat per farm. Hay (about 8 acres per farm), oats, and spring wheat are the chief crops, supporting dairy and mixed farms. The number of livestock is also small compared with the Prairies or the east. Aside from ranches, about nine cows are carried per farm, as contrasted to twelve for Alberta and thirteen for Ontario. The problem of marketing dairy products outside the province discourages developing a surplus production.

The farming divides itself into distinct types which characterize distinct regions (see Fig. 114). The *Interior Plateau*, especially between Quesnel, Lillooet, and Kamloops, provides most of the ranching land of the province. In the northern basins of the Chilcotin, middle Fraser, and Quesnel rivers, summer temperatures are rather cool, rainfall is moderate, crops are at a discount contrasted with hay and natural pasture, and most of the farms consist of large cattle or sheep runs. The Cariboo plateau is outstanding as a ranching district. In the North Thompson valley cattle and sheep are also common, but poultry are popular as an additional source of revenue, and potatoes are widely grown.

In the ranching country the farms are large, but the cultivated area is small. Many ranchers do not raise any winter forage, but trust to the

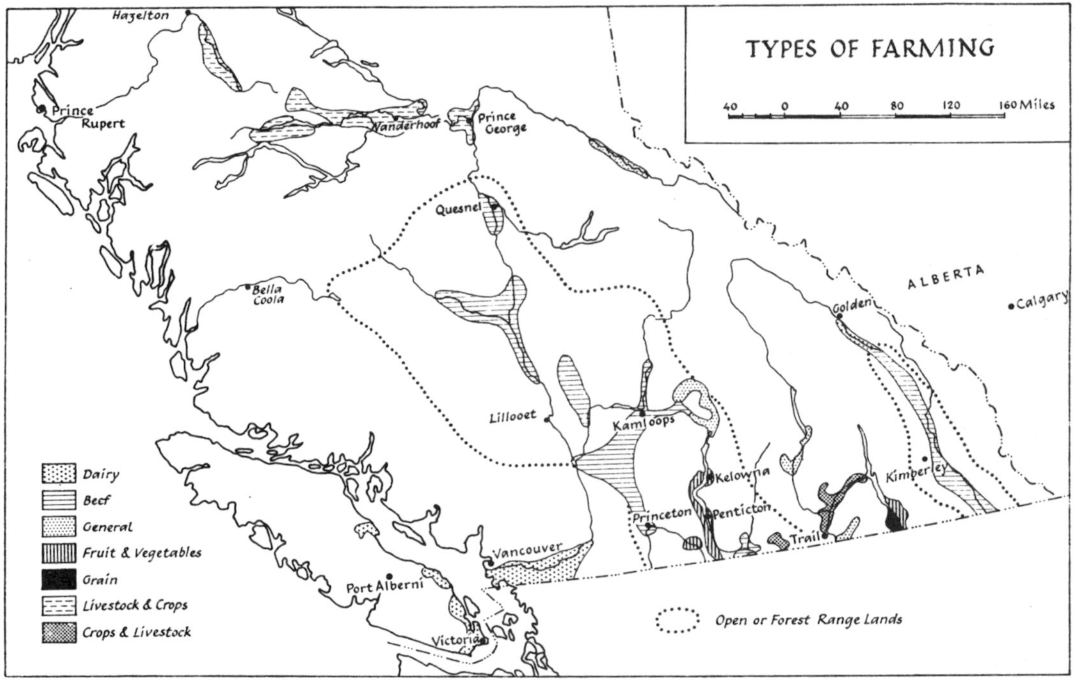

FIG. 114 Types of farming in southern British Columbia. Strong relief has resulted in fragments of farm areas, separated from each other by massive mountain blocks. Dairying at the coast, fruit raising in the warm southern interior, and cattle ranching in the cool northern interior are the main activities.

natural range. It is reckoned that 16 acres of natural pasture and timberland are needed to feed a grown steer. The cowboys drive the cattle over the whole range, so that they do not over-graze one portion and neglect another. In the summer they are herded up into the higher timbered slopes; and in the fall, come down to winter on the lower, grass-covered parks. Unfortunately, the areas of winter grazing, where there is no necessity to feed bales of hay to the cattle, although highly sought after, are highly restricted.[1] Long drives, involving the practice of transhumance, may be needed to come by it. The practice is increasing, however, of producing alfalfa to make up the scanty winter fare. Creeks are dammed, and valley flats irrigated and planted to the crop. This produces better and more saleable beef (Fig. 115).

South of Kamloops there is a more varied landscape, ranging from high mountain to low valley flat. The higher slopes have a podsolized soil. This passes into a grey-brown forest soil, where the yellow pines occur. The forest gives way to drier, grassy slopes, with fertile black earth soils. These change to the brown soils of the valley terraces and flats. Consequently; varied agriculture is found with cattle and sheep raised on the hill-sides, good wheat farms on the bottomland soil; and market garden and fruit farms on the irrigated terraces. This zoning of relief, soil, and farm type is found with little change in the Okanagan, Kettle river, Arrow Lakes, Lake Kootenay, and Kootenay river depressions. Sometimes the emphasis is on livestock, where irrigation farming is not possible; sometimes it is on wheat, where the soils are heavy; at other times on fruit, where the land is easily irrigated. Armstrong, like Kamloops, has cropping on riverside flats and ranching above; Salmon Arm goes in for dairying and orchards; the Okanagan concentrates on orchards and small fruits; Kettle river on dairy and fruits; the Arrow Lake area on fruit; lower Kootenay at Creston on wheat and fruit, the upper Kootenay on cattle, and so on. The pattern changes locally to fit local conditions to a remarkable degree.

The fruit areas are an interesting response to the environment. In a climate with only 10 to 15 inches of rain a year, the former must either go in for extensive sheep ranches, and possibly wheat production by means of dry-farming, or intensive cultivation based on irrigation. Very often the choice will depend on how easy it is to irrigate. In British Columbia it is relatively easy. There are high snow-clad mountains that feed perennial streams which flow down into broad, warm valleys. By damming the side streams, and running flumes from them it is possible to distribute the water quickly over a wide area, without the expense of major irrigation works. Moreover, the streams fall across terraces that line the main valleys, and these

[1] Weir, T., 'Ranching in the Interior Plateau of British Columbia', *Geographical Bulletin*, no. 3, 1953, pp. 15–19.

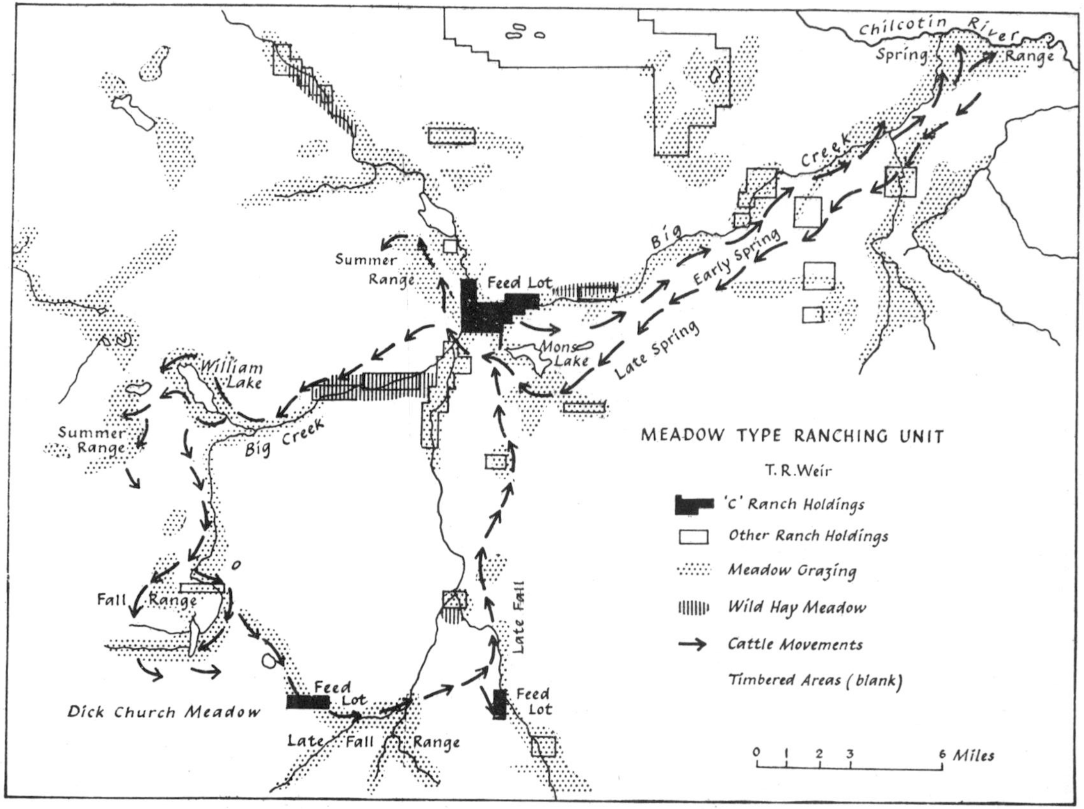

FIG. 115 Ranching in British Columbia. Here transhumance is typical, with the movement of men and cattle in spring and summer. However, women and children, old people, and business and professional families continue to live in the valley settlements.

make admirable sites for orchards. The terraces are flat enough to allow the orchards to be irrigated, and yet high enough to provide a natural frost drainage. The cold air spreading across them does not settle but is drained away to the bottom of the main valley.

Actually, danger from frost is not unduly great. In the northern Okanagan there are over 120 days free of frost; in the south up to 165 days. This is scarcely less favourable than Ontario, and is quite adequate. It is partly due to the shelter from very cold air masses given by the mountains, and partly to the influence of the lakes. In most of the long trench-like valleys there are narrow lakes such as Shuswap, Okanagan, the Arrow Lakes, and Lake Kootenay. These lakes keep the heat of the summer after the land has begun to cool off in the fall, and thus they retard fall frosts.

The soil of the fruit areas is often developed from sandy river-fans or gravelly kame terraces, and warms up rapidly in the spring, quickening spring growth. When the buds are out, and summer arrives, the weather is lovely and sunny. The lack of rain and cloud gives a high amount of sunshine during the growing season. As a result, the fruit matures with a beautiful colour.

The chief irrigated areas are around Vernon, the centre of the apple trade; Kelowna, Peachland, and Penticton on Lake Okanagan, in the middle of the peach belt; Oliver and Osoyoos, south of Lake Okanagan, famous for apricots and canteloupes; the Arrow lake mixed-fruit area, from Nakusp to Needles; and the southern terraces of Lake Kootenay, around Creston—noted for cherries and hard fruits. Altogether about a quarter of a million acres have been irrigated (see Fig. 114).

The problems of irrigation are very considerable, and the early hit-or-miss methods often caused hardships. The province runs the South Okanagan project and the municipalities of Penticton and Summerland have their own schemes. The Provincial government has also provided assistance to a number of private schemes, while various co-operative enterprises have tackled the problem successfully. Individuals by themselves have little chance, and their small and isolated systems are being taken over by municipalities. In the first place, an exhaustive survey has to be made of all the water resources of a region; an analysis of the nature of the water supply must be carried out; and an estimate has to be reached of its carrying capacity, especially in the driest year. The water has to be carefully controlled by dams and flumes so as to waste as little as feasible. Finally, it must be distributed as equally as possible among the different users. These conditions make some form of direction or at least co-operation necessary.

Over and above this, there is the problem of marketing the irrigated product. Here again the individual has little chance himself. He is very remote from his markets. The nearest one, Vancouver, is over 250 miles away. The Prairies are a good market (because their severe winters make it uneconomic to grow fruit), but they are also far away. Still farther are eastern U.S.A. and Britain. It would be too much to expect of each grower to study the trends in prices in these different areas, to advertise his goods, and to pack and ship them, so as to get the best price. But if he joins a co-operative, trades through a large company, or receives help from Government bureaux, then he can bargain effectively, and has the benefit of Government market surveys and other valuable advice. In this way he saves glutting markets, or seeing his fruit rot before it can be sold. Most growers have now come to copy the California producers, and have consolidated their bargaining power behind various unified growers' organizations. Farmers are learning the value of acting together to share the irrigation waters, to strive to overcome their isolation, and to aid each other in getting a market, and there are several active co-operatives functioning. These are important developments, and are vividly represented in the landscape by the offices, wheat elevators, packing plants, and warehouses of various companies and co-operatives.

The dairy areas are found around the large cities of Victoria, Vancouver and New Westminster, which present an ever-growing demand for milk, cream, butter and cheese. Here the climate, with its moist cool summers and mild, wet winters is ideally suited to meadows, hay, and oats. With the long frost-free period of 200–240 days, it sponsors the prolonged outdoor grazing and maintenance of cattle. The urban market also demands eggs, vegetables, and fruit. Consequently, in the great delta of the Fraser, and on the plains of south-east Vancouver Island, there are very productive dairy farms, market gardens, poultry runs, potato farms, and apple and small-fruit orchards. Nanaimo, and Courtenay are northern extensions of this mixed type of highly commercialized agriculture (see Fig. 114).

Fisheries

British Columbia has some of the wealthiest fishing grounds to be found. The long, indented coastline attracts fish to spawn, and provides many harbours. There is a mixture of warm and cold currents off the coast, suited to fishing. Though off-shore banks do not occur, there are groups of islands such as Vancouver and Queen Charlotte from which deep-water fish may be caught. The local demand for fish is not large and therefore most of the catch can be exported.

The chief industry is the salmon fishing. British Columbia forms part of the world's largest salmon fishery. Every fall, salmon swim from the sea up the numerous long fjords of the coast looking for freshwater pools or lakes in which to spawn. Large rivers like the Fraser, Bella Coola, Dean, Skeena, and Nass offer them ideal spawning grounds, not to mention many smaller rivers. The fact that these rivers have tributaries which tumble from glacial-lake basins is a further attraction. The fish seek out sheltered spawning grounds in headwater lakes or shallows along the upper river stretches, and there deposit millions of eggs. After the eggs hatch out, the young salmon remain in the lakes and deep-river pools for about a year, and then they swim out to sea. Sockeye salmon stay in the sea four years, until they are grown up, when they return to the river or lake where they were hatched, to lay their eggs. Pink salmon have a two-year cycle. So another catch of fish is born.

The fisherman try to catch these large, mature fish on the way up to their spawning grounds, because the fish are then in perfect condition. They take out small boats just beyond the mouth of the river, or at strategic points along its lower stretches, and drop a long 'gill' net, which has lead weights to drag it down. Cork floaters keep the top of the net at the surface. Thus the net forms a deep wall, against which the fish swim. There they are caught by their gills, and are so entangled that they cannot swim on, or wriggle back. The net is then drawn into the boat and the fish picked out.

Another method is to use the purse seine, or draw-purse net. This net is anchored at one end to a stationary boat. When a school of salmon approaches, a motor-boat hauls out the other end, circling right around the swarming mass of fish. Then a draw rope is pulled, which closes the net, just like a purse. The fish are trapped and hauled into the boat.

Other methods are also used, such as beach nets, strung across shallow beaches, or trap nets on the sides of the fjords and river mouths, and also fishing with hook and line.

Most of the rivers and lakes are far from large cities, and therefore the fish must be packed before they are transported to market, or sent abroad. Some fishermen dry out their catch; some put it down in ice. But most of them carry it to a local cannery, situated at the mouth of the salmon run. Packers often work with a fleet of fishermen, and travel with them wherever the catch is good. They collect the fish from the fishing vessels and take them to the shore canneries, particularly at Vancouver or Prince Rupert.

British Columbia exports over two-thirds of the annual salmon catch to countries such as Britain and France and the British Dominions, where there is a great demand for Canadian salmon.

The province is also noted for the halibut it catches. The halibut fisheries are out in the deep water off the coast. They are caught by trolling long lines, having small lines attached to them with baited hooks. The fish is brought to Prince Rupert, packed in ice, and sent to eastern Canada.

Herring are also caught in considerable numbers during the fall and winter when they come inshore to spawn. They are a valuable source of oil, fish-manure, and fish-cake (which is sold as cattle feed).

From the outer isles, like Queen Charlotte Islands, Canadian fishermen used to go on whaling and sealing expeditions. These hunts carried the fishing-boats as far as the Pribilof Islands, and helped to establish fishing settlements.

Thus, several types of fishing have emerged, associated with aspects of west coast relief; the salmon in the long fjords and river mouths; herring in the inner passages and fjords of the inshore; halibut in the deeper seas between the inner and outer isles; and whales and seals in the farther waters, beyond the outer isles.

Minerals

Another major resource in British Columbia lies in its wealth of metals. The intensely folded mountains, and the large intrusions of igneous rocks, make the Cordilleras a very notable mining region. Large deposits of copper, gold, silver, lead, and zinc are being worked, and also small but important deposits of iron, mercury, tungsten, molybdenum, and arsenic. Mining is a very important part of the life of British Columbia. The province is by far the largest producer of lead, zinc, antimony, cadmium, tin, and tungsten in Canada, and the second largest of silver.

The Rocky mountains have coal and oil fields on their eastern flank, though these fall in Alberta rather than British Columbia. However, small fields are found in the south-east and in the upper Peace, Finlay, and Liard river areas. The Crow's Nest field, in the south-east, contains more than half the reserves of the province. The coal is a good bituminous type, which produces quite good coke. It is therefore valuable for smelters. The Rockies proper are not rich in metals. This is because, apart from the waterless area, they are poor in igneous rocks. The Rockies are chiefly sedimentary and they have been lifted up by faulting as much as by folding, so that there are few igneous intrusions. Natural gas on their flanks forms a valuable resource in the Fort St John region.

The Interior Ranges, like Purcell, Selkirk, and Cariboo ranges, contain a great number of igneous rocks, many of which have been intruded into the folds of the ranges, and have since been exposed by erosion. The rocks in the folds were cracked by the heat and pressure of the igneous masses and the metals have filled up the cracks in rich lodes. Three batholiths, at the heart of the Cariboo range, the Selkirks, and the Purcell mountains are especially rich. The deep trenches between the mountains have often exposed the ores on their sides, and made them easy to mine and accessible to roads and railways.

In 1890 important gold deposits were discovered at Rossland, and were mined extensively until 1917. Gold was also worked at near-by Hedley and Sheep Creek (Salmo), in highly metamorphosed rocks in contact with igneous intrusions. Hedley-Mascot continued to produce until recently, and during the First World War was Canada's largest yielder of gold. Gold and silver are still being refined at near-by Trail. The region is best known for its silver, lead, zinc, and tungsten mines. The Slocan district was early opened up for its silver-lead deposits, worked by tunnels driven into the sides of the mountains. Sandon has been famous for its zinc-lead production. In the Nelson district a well-known tungsten mine is located, yielding that valuable alloy which is so widely used in manufacturing steel. The greatest mine in the region is at Kimberley. It is called the Sullivan mine, after its discoverer Pat Sullivan, who prospected it in 1892. It is Canada's largest producer of lead, and the chief provincial source of zinc and silver. Both tin and iron have also been extracted from the ore in recent years, and a large iron foundry has been built, the products of which are sent to steel mills to be developed at Vancouver and Regina. The ores are smelted down at Trail.

The Cariboo mountains saw a veritable gold-rush, and at one time were Canada's chief source of gold. The whole area has been heavily glaciated, and rich, though small, deposits of placer gold were found in fluvio-glacial gravel deposits at Barkerville. Lode ore is still being mined at Wells.

The Coast Mountains, including those of Vancouver Island, are also rich in ores. They are intruded by some of the largest batholiths in the world (Fig. 116). The igneous masses at the core of the mountain folds have developed huge ore bodies. These are chiefly gold, silver, and copper deposits with some tungsten and arsenic. Two large mining areas have grown up in the southern sector of the mountains at Britannia, on the coast, and at Bralorne, inland. The Britannia batholith is famous for its large copper deposits. The ore was discovered on the side of Howe sound in 1898. Copper, silver, and gold are produced. The Bralorne district produces about a quarter of British Columbia's gold. Silver and tungsten are also important. The gold lies in veins of quartz cutting across a stock-like body of diorite and granite. Gold mined at Zeballos, on the side of Vancouver Island, helped to attract settlement, although the area is now worked for iron.

A small, yet significant, iron field occurs on nearby Texada Island. At present, most of the production goes to Japan. Vancouver Island also possesses small coal deposits, running through the Cretaceous lowland of Nanaimo, a downwarped area on the edge of volcanic rocks. The coal began to be mined as early as 1860, and for seventy years helped to support the growth of Nanaimo and Comox. Imported oil is now more important.

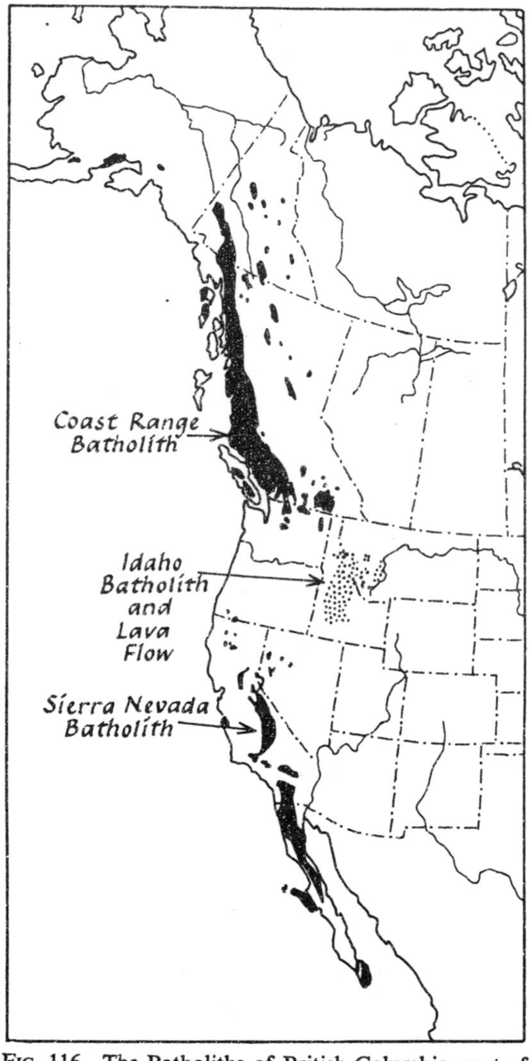

FIG. 116 The Batholiths of British Columbia, part of the Pacific belt of volcanic intrusions which is also a belt of mineral wealth. (Scale, 1:40 m.)

THE HUMAN RESPONSE—TRANSPORTATION AND SETTLEMENT

British Columbia's great natural resources and the way they have been developed have given rise to many mining and lumber camps, agricultural market towns, river and seaboard ports, and industrial cities. These in their turn have sponsored, and come vitally to depend upon, a complex though efficient system of routeways. Here again, all these developments have been closely controlled by local geography in the wider context of Canadian history.

Routeways

In a mountainous country, relief dominates transportation. The roads follow river valleys and passes. Railways can sometimes pierce through mountains by the use of tunnels, but they, too, must choose the line of least resistance. Even if this is the longest way round, it is the cheapest way of getting from place to place. British Columbia thus differs from most of the other provinces, by having a very irregular net of routes. The greatest contrast is with the Prairies where the routes generally follow the grid system, with as little respect for local relief as possible. The very approaches to British Columbia, the Rocky passes, and Pacific sounds show the importance of relief.

Since the rivers were not very navigable, being interrupted by gorges and rapids, they did not themselves play a great part, although their valleys were of crucial importance. British Columbia depended on the railways for development. The railways were vital in linking up the Pacific province with the rest of the Dominion. Mining, lumbering, agriculture, and business could only go ahead when the railway came.

The Canadian Pacific was the first line to be built; it reached the coast in 1886. It enters the province from Calgary by way of the Kicking Horse pass, 5,339 feet high. It then passes through the difficult block-and-trench country of the Selkirks. It does so by a winding course, down the Columbia, through the Connaught tunnel to Revelstoke, then by way of the Shuswap depression to Kamloops. There it follows the Thompson river to Lytton, when it runs alongside the Fraser to Vancouver. A spur of the Canadian Pacific Railway, called the Kettle River Line, leaves the main line at Hope, and takes a still more winding path through the Cascades to Princeton, down the upper Okanagan river. It serves a rich fruit-growing area at Penticton and then, passing through a ranching district, with irrigated alfalfa fields, makes its devious way to the rich mining districts of Rossland, Trail, Nelson, Kootenay, and Cranbrook (near the famous Sullivan Mine) until it taps the coal-mining area of Fernie. It links up with the Lethbridge–Regina line on the Prairies, by way of the Crow's Nest pass.

In 1904 the Grand Trunk Railway, now the Canadian National Railway, proposed to create a northern route, in competition with the Canadian Pacific Railway. The railway runs from Edmonton to the Yellowhead pass; thence it is carried along the great trench of the upper Fraser until Prince George is reached. There it enters the Interior Upland and, still following the upper Fraser, strikes the Bulkley valley, and so reaches the Skeena at Hazelton. Thereafter it follows the Skeena to Prince Rupert on the coast.

A spur line was built from west of Yellowhead pass southwards along the North Thompson river to join Kamloops. It is continued into Vancouver.

Another line, the Pacific Great Eastern, started from North Vancouver. and built *inland* from Howe sound, over to Seton Lake, and the town of Lillooet, in the Fraser valley. It aimed north, but could not take the direct route of the Fraser, since the river cuts a profound gorge in its middle sector. Therefore, it swung east to Lac la Hache, and then returned to the Fraser, above the gorge, and continued to Quesnel, after which it ran through plateau country to Prince George.

The roads of the province are few as yet, but they supplement the railways, and are doing much to open up new areas. The oldest road is the Cariboo Trail, running inland from Vancouver by means of the Fraser and Thompson to Kamloops, then north past Lac la Hache to the Fraser again and Quesnel. There it runs east to the gold-mining area of Barkerville, in the Cariboo mountains. It was later carried to Prince George.

An old west–east road was the Dewdney Trail, which left the Thompson at Spence's Bridge, and then wandered south over mountain and across valley to Penticton in the Okanagan. Another branch was built east to Trail on the Columbia, and thence to Kootenay and the Kimberley–Fernie mining district. Recently, part of this route has been revived by the Transcontinental Highway, which crosses the Rockies by Roger's pass, runs through the mining areas of Fernie, Nelson, and Trail, extends just north of the International Border to the rich fruit-growing areas of the Okanagan valley, and then makes for the still more productive Fraser delta, and Vancouver. Another major road enters the province by way of Vermilion pass and extends up the Columbia and down the Kootenay to Kimberley and Trail. Farther north, the road from Lake Louise passes over the Kicking Horse pass to Golden. Thence it ran around the 'big bend' of the Columbia, but now strikes directly across difficult mountain country to Revelstoke, and so to Kamloops.

A good road runs up the east coast of Vancouver Island from Victoria to Kelsey Bay. However, steamship routes are really more important in the waters between Vancouver Island and Vancouver, and most west-coast points keep in touch with each other and Vancouver by boat. Recently, air routes have linked Vancouver Island and Queen Charlotte Island with Vancouver.

Two very important air routes cross the province. One is the Transcontinental route from Vancouver to Montreal; and the other is the polar flight to Edmonton and thence north to Greenland and east to Norway. Air connexions are also made north-west to Alaska and Japan, and southwards to California and Mexico. Vancouver has, indeed, become a major air junction.

Settlement

No settlement in British Columbia can escape the dominating influence of relief. Nevertheless, the *types* of settlement, and their distribution, also show the work of other factors, such as the presence of natural resources, the ease of communications, the degree of development, and the nature of occupation.

Broadly speaking, there are five areas of settlement in British Columbia. They represent five geographical regions. In the north are the pioneer regions of Fort St John and of Prince George. In the central Interior Uplands is the Quesnel–Kamloops region. In the southern block-and-trench area are the Kootenay-Columbia-Okanagan settlements. Finally there are the coastal settlements, with a marked concentration on Vancouver. The last four groups belong to the southern settled section and will be treated here.

The Quesnel–Kamloops region is quite favourably situated, at almost the centre of the province. To the east are the Cariboo mountains, with gold; to the south, the plateau with large ranches; and to the west, the Coast Ranges, with the Bralorne and Pioneer gold mines. The long low ridges are covered with forest, which is a mixture of the northern spruce and fir, with yellow pine and some Douglas fir. It sponsors quite a lively timber trade. The climate is sub-humid, with a moderately warm summer. It is suited to natural pasture, hay, and feed grains. In the Chilcotin basin are many large ranches, while cattle and sheep are typical of the Thompson and middle Fraser valleys. This combination of mining, lumbering, and ranching gives variety to the settlements and has stimulated railway and road construction.

The region is served by the main Canadian Pacific Railway line from Calgary and the main Canadian National Railway line from Edmonton to Vancouver. The Pacific Great Eastern Railway provides a north–south axis. Quesnel is a supply and distributing centre for the surrounding mines and ranches. The railway runs south and crosses the Fraser at Lillooet, another supply centre for ranches in the vicinity. The Cariboo Trail leaves the railway route and turns south-east to Ashcroft, one of the earliest towns in the district. The forests thin out. The rainfall drops below 15 inches. Sage brush begins to mantle the slopes with its dusty, dull-green colouring. Small clusters of cactus appear. Indian horses and range cattle abound. One has reached the arid interior.

Kamloops lies at the heart of this district. It has become the chief town in the Thompson valley. It began as a fort and trading post set up by American fur-trading interests. A British post arose opposite to the American one, in the period of the joint occupation of Oregon. After the boundary was fixed, Kamloops became a Hudson's Bay trading post for the Indians, and then an outfitting centre for gold-rush prospectors. The quiet waters of the middle Thompson saw the arrival of the steamboat, but this was replaced by the railways. The Canadian National Railway line from the North Thompson and the Canadian Pacific Railway along the South Thompson converged on the town. These enabled cattle to be taken out without the long, difficult, and costly treks of earlier days, and Kamloops became the capital of the cattle empire. Subsequently, irrigation turned the lower terraces into strips of vivid green, raising not only alfalfa and hay for winter feed, but special crops like hops. Large turkey farms are a recent innovation, taking advantage of the dry and sunny weather. Kamloops is mainly a commercial centre, and marks the transition between the extensive agriculture to the north and the intensive type to the south. It is well laid out on a striking series of kame terraces above the junction of the two branches of the Thompson river. Fur-trading post, centre for gold prospecting, railway camp, and ranching town, it is a complete cross-section of life and development in the interior.

The block-and-trench structure farther south, in the complex Columbia mountains, has created the most varied region in the province. Forested heights contrast with arid bottom lands. Numerous lakes add beauty to the scene. The ranges are shot with mineral wealth; the valleys are intensively cultivated for fruit and vegetables. Intermediate uplands are grazed by cattle or cut over for their lumber. Next to the Vancouver–Victoria region this is the most productive and populous part of the province.

Lumber towns are found in the pine forests of the Rocky, Purcell, and Selkirk slopes. The older ones, like Golden in the Rocky Mountain Trench, are the ghosts of their former selves; the newer ones, like Cranbrook and Nelson, are still booming. Decline and expansion show all the characteristics we have already studied in Ontario. Rich gold, silver, lead, zinc, and copper mines, sunk into the Nelson batholith, also helped the growth of settlements. Fruit farms have sprung up, and the fruit is packed for export at the stations. Other notable towns are Kimberley, where lead and zinc are extracted, and Trail, where they are smelted. **Trail** is strategically situated so that it can serve the Rossland, Slocan, Nelson, and Kimberley mining areas. It is on a spur of the Canadian Pacific Railway by the Columbia river. The smelter is situated on a broad flat terrace, above which the little town rises towards the steep valley sides.

Typical agricultural towns are Salmon Arm, Vernon, Kelowna, and Penticton, in the Shuswap–Okanagan trench. They are situated on well-marked kame or lacustrine terraces, surrounded by orchards, with canneries and co-operative packing houses, basket factories and cold-storage plants. Nakusp and Needles are smaller examples on the Arrow Lakes. Revelstoke is a market town and distributing centre at the north of the Selkirk trench; Kaslo has a similar function in the middle of the Purcell trench.

The west coast settlements are more important than the rest put together. They include the towns of the Fraser delta, known as the Lower Mainland, and those of the eastern lowlands of Vancouver Island. More than half the total population of the province is settled in the Greater Vancouver area. This is an astonishing concentration. It means that the southern section of British Columbia is really Vancouver, writ large. The region of the city has grown wider and wider until the region at large has come to centre itself in the city. The metropolis has consumed the region which gave it birth (Fig. 117).

It is difficult to say whether growth stems from the metropolis, or from the district itself. Urbanization has developed to an extraordinary extent. It is a much bigger thing than the urban part of the population, although this, accounting for 73 per cent of the total, is certainly big enough. So much of the large-scale mechanized, commercialized expansion of mining, lumbering, ranching, and irrigation farming is centred in the city. Moreover, settlements in the 'country' are becoming more and more urbanized, and are simply small replicas of the city out in the 'country'. City standards are everywhere copied and in demand, and 'country' residents require urban-type business, recreational and social services. If smaller centres do not offer these, or do not provide them on an adequate scale, demands are made on the larger centres; much business is done on the telephone with Vancouver, a lot of shopping is carried on through mail-order houses in Vancouver, the Vancouver newspapers and radio programmes are the ones normally referred to, degrees are obtained by summer-school attendance in Vancouver, and trips to masonic, service club, church, or other conventions at the metropolis are regularly made from a very wide area. The lack of a truly rural life, related to the weakness of agriculture, has of course helped all this. The urban outlook has been free to grow and this mental environment, as much as anything else, has been responsible for the rise of the metropolis.

Thus it is in the **Victoria–Vancouver district** that the great wealth of the province, and its population, have come to be concentrated. **Victoria** (155,000) is the chief port and railway terminal of Vancouver Island, and the capital of the province, chosen when the colony's contacts were rather westward by sea than eastward by land. Most of its people are civil servants, business or professional men, and their families. Many have taken up residence in Victoria to retire. It is essentially a residential city, with beautiful homes and gardens, tennis and golf clubs, schools and churches. It is dominated by the lovely Provincial Legislative Buildings, and is also the site of Victoria University. Its port is at the head of an inner bay, set in an outer one. Not far west is the naval base of Esquimalt, with a large dry dock and with naval yards.

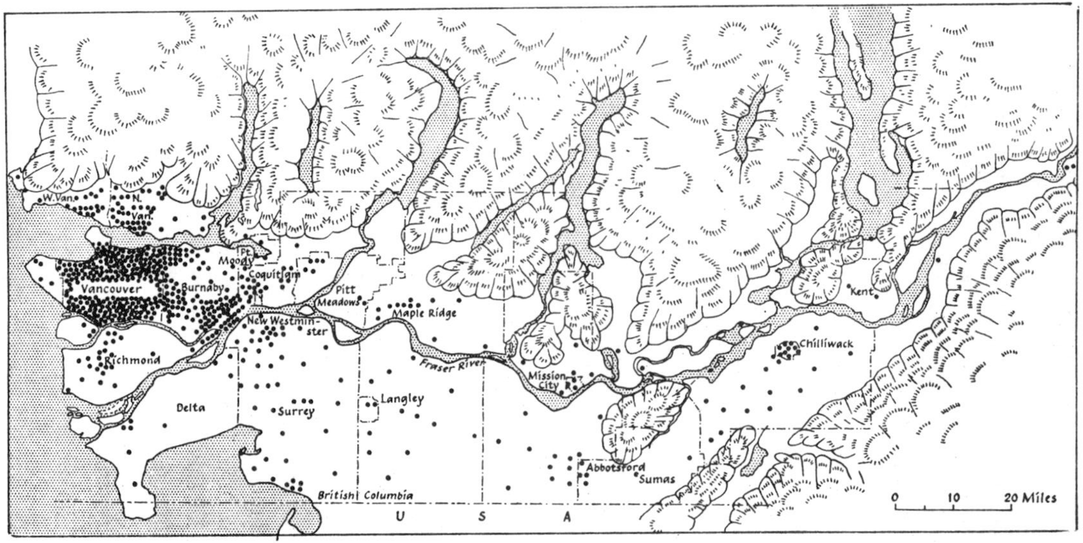

FIG. 117 The Fraser delta—heart of British Columbia. So favourable is this region, commanding sea approaches and mountain passes, and with a wealth of water power, forested slopes, and agriculturally productive alluvial flats around it, that it has concentrated about half of the population of the entire Province within this area. (From Lower Mainland and Regional Planning Board.)

Vancouver (850,000) is one of several cities and towns at the mouths of the Fraser. The river has built a wide delta, about 1,500 sq. miles in extent. This is the most fertile area in the province and is densely settled. The dense rural population supplies the large urban demand for milk, vegetables and fruits, and is one reason for the rapid growth of Vancouver. The city has spread to such an extent that it practically touches New Westminster to the south, and North Vancouver across Burrard Inlet. We may consider the three

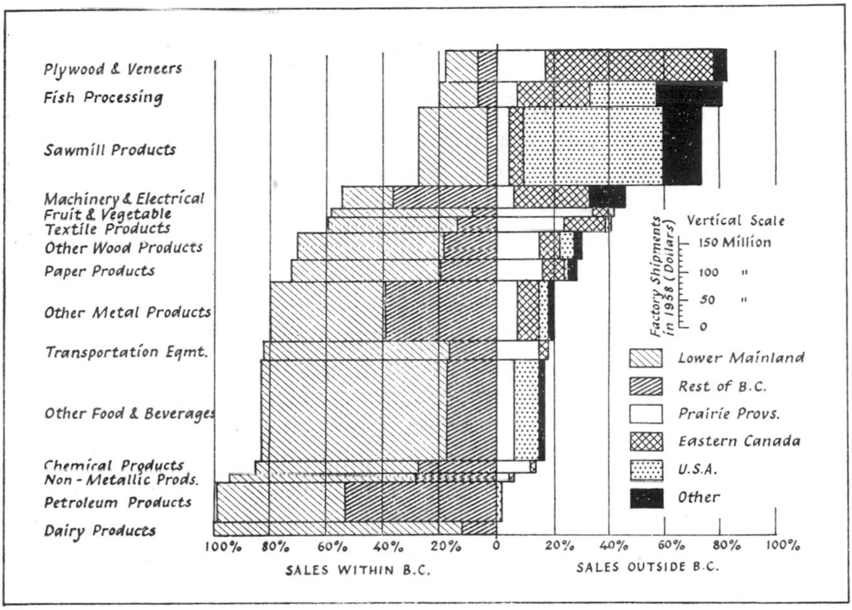

FIG. 118 The trade of the Greater Vancouver Area—what it manufactures and where it sells. (From 'Industry in the Lower Mainland', the Lower Mainland Reg. Pl. Bd.)

settlements as one. New Westminster was settled first, on a main channel of the Fraser river in 1857. In 1884 the advantages of Burrard Inlet, just north of the Fraser delta—close to the river, yet on a sheltered, long sea inlet—were recognized, and the Canadian Pacific Railway made Vancouver its chief terminal. In 1887 the first through passenger train arrived.

The early wealth of the district was obtained from lumbering. Even although the forest was cleared away, it continued to be worked from Vancouver. The lumber industry expanded north and into the interior, but Vancouver still remained the assembly point for shipping sawn lumber overseas or sending it by train to eastern Canada (Fig. 118). The next boom, between 1905 and the First World War, followed the export of large quantities of wheat from the Prairies. Hides and meat were also exported. About the same time salmon fishing developed in the many inlets of Georgia Strait, and canning the salmon became a major Vancouver industry. By 1912 the population had reached the 100,000 mark.

The city flourished because of the increasing trade between Canada and Japan, Hong Kong, and the Far East. These areas needed timber and could import surplus wheat. After the Panama Canal was opened, large shipments of timber and fish were sent to eastern U.S.A. and Britain. Vancouver also developed a big import trade from the Far East and Oceania, including the import of tea, coffee, spices, palm oil, coco-nut, sugar, silk, and tin. It began to process many of these products. Large sugar refining, soap-making, and oil extracting plants were set up.

As the city grew, local needs had to be met, and many industries developed for the local market; pulp and paper for the newspaper and publishing industry; the making of furniture and office equipment from fine local woods; creameries, fruit, and vegetable canneries, using the produce of the rich dairy farms and market gardens of the Fraser delta; bread-making and packing meat.

Finally, during and after the Second World War, new, large-scale manufacturing was introduced, including engineering and petro-chemical industries. The piping of oil and gas from the Transmontane section of British Columbia and from Alberta has greatly helped industrial expansion.

However, commercial interests are as important as manufacturing ones. Vancouver is still a great wholesale and retail centre, with a large business section. It is also a major tourist centre, with horse-racing, car-racing, golf, water sports, and beaches, together with the music and drama of the annual Vancouver Festival. It is the site of an important fair, known as the Pacific Exhibition.

The population of the city itself is now over 400,000. With New Westminster, Burnaby, Richmond, and North and West Vancouver, the population is nearly 900,000 or half that for the province. In other words, one out of every two people in British Columbia live in Greater Vancouver! This is a higher concentration than in Montreal or Toronto. Fortunately, the local site is ideal for the expansion of the city in all its different functions (Fig. 119).

The city straddles a two-pronged peninsula between the North Fraser outlet and Burrard Inlet; and gives way, between these two waterways, to a small inlet, known as False Creek. Burrard Inlet is narrow at its mouth, where Stanley Park juts out, and allows a bridge to be carried to North Vancouver. Eastwards the inlet opens out into a wide and long harbour, crossed at its upper end by another large bridge. On the south shore of the inlet are the crowded trans-Oceanic quays, with the railway terminal of the Canadian Pacific Railway. Only a narrow isthmus separates this from False

40. Wheat and mixed (wheat, forage, and stock) farms in fertile, open Saskatchewan plains. Note the wind-breaks, the many machine sheds, the large barns, and the rows of wheat-storage bins. The fields are very big, and are ploughed and harvested by machines.

The Settled Prairies, Canada

41. Winnipeg, at the confluence of the Assiniboine and Red rivers. Near the riverside railway yards is the Ft Garry Hotel, in the foreground rises the Provincial Capitol, and behind is the business centre with skyscrapers where Portage and Main Streets come together.

42. Southern B.C.—fruit farming on irrigated terraces of South Thompson River, near Kamloops.

43. Southern B.C.—Trail is a great smelting centre for lead, zinc and copper of the mineral-rich mountains around.

44. Southern B.C.—Vancouver, the metropolis of the Canadian west. The business section faces Burrard Inlet in the background. A multi-lane flyover expressway system carries traffic across the industrial area of False Creek.

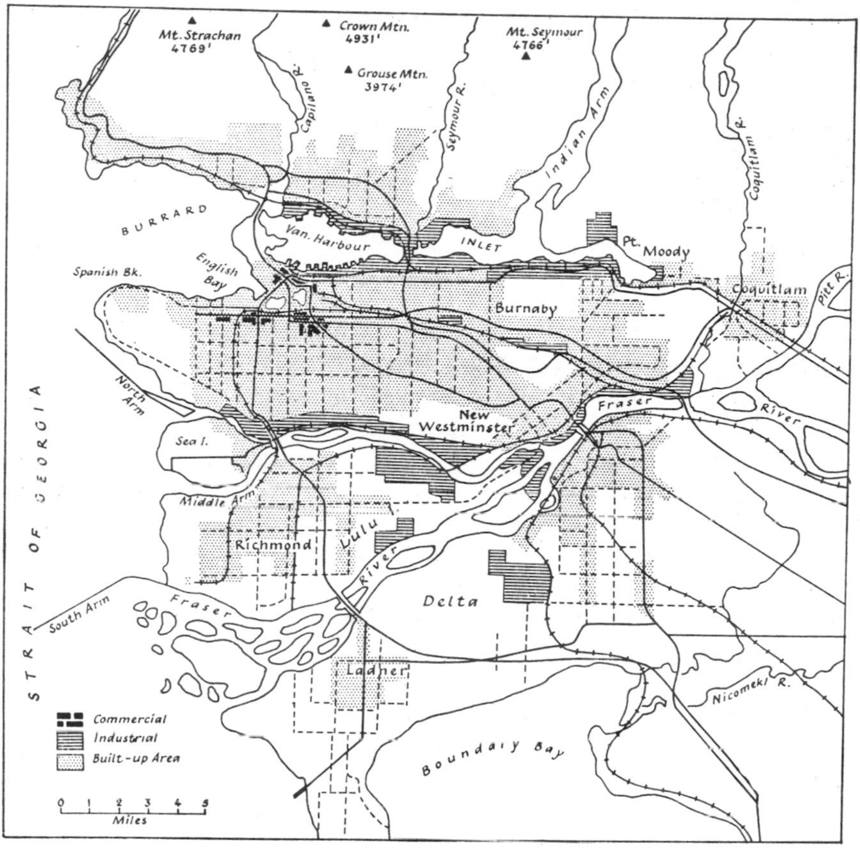

FIG. 119 The growth and structure of Greater Vancouver. This great city developed as Canada's chief western port, commanding an outlet from mountain and prairie to the vast world of the Pacific. It avoided the silt of the Fraser delta itself, and grew up on a peninsula between the Fraser and Burrard Inlet. The Fraser delta gives it flat land for spreading industry and population, and market gardens and dairies for a supply of fresh food. The Burrard Inlet offers deep and sheltered water and a long waterfront for its expanding harbour. In between, False Creek houses railway terminals, saw mills, and high-density housing. Access to fisheries, and forest slopes, and to water-power has given Greater Vancouver canning, lumber and pulp and paper industries. In addition are flour mills at the wheat terminals from the Prairies, sugar refineries based on Caribbean and Fijian imports, and oil-refining plants using Alberta oil.

Creek, with the Canadian National Railway terminals and quays. Between the two inlets is the business and shopping section with its towering offices and hotels. The factory area is mainly around False Creek, where there is plenty of low land available. Large lumber and construction yards rim the creek. Then the land rises to a broad-backed ridge on the broader isthmus between False Creek and the Fraser. Tier on tier of housing, from working-class duplexes by the creek to single-family bungalows on the ridge, mark out this southern part of the town. A new shopping and business section has grown up on the approach to the southern ridge, ending in a high-class residential suburb. The ridge extends out to sea in Point Grey, commanded by the spacious campus of the University of British Columbia. This, along with the Simon Fraser university, has played a major role in making the city an important social and cultural centre, as well as a busy commercial and industrial settlement.

SUMMARY

Because British Columbia is so young, and remote from eastern Canada, and so mountainous, it is not densely settled. Forestry, mining, and fishing are the typical occupations, using the rich Douglas fir and other forests, the gold, lead, zinc, and copper mines, and the salmon runs, for which the province is famous. Agriculture is rather limited. Commerce and industry are booming, and will have a great future as Canada expands its trade with the Far East. These various developments are closely related to the relief, which controls the distribution of natural resources and dominates the settlement and routes of the province.

Varied in relief and resource, the province is also varied in occupation and population. Although one of the most British of the sections of Canada, it possesses a significant number of French, and thus shares in a practical way in the great bi-cultural experiment which differentiates Canada from the United States. Chinese played an important part in opening up the mining areas; East Indians in developing the ports; Japanese in establishing the fishing and market garden industries. Since the Second World War many continental Europeans have migrated to the seaboard cities, where they are active in the retail and hotel businesses and in new types of manufacturing. Yet out of all this variety a real sense of unity has developed which sets its stamp on the region.

CHAPTER FIFTEEN

The Canadian North

North of each of the settled sections of Canada lies Canada's huge northland, a region that touches every other region, grows from each of the regions, and gives unity to them all. It is, in a sense, the Canadian matrix, helping to bind the individual sections into a vital and viable whole. It is the most distinctive thing about Canada, making Canada clearly different from the United States or Mexico. It is, in fact, the Canadian heartland, from which so many of the elements of life that are characteristically Canadian have sprung, and to which Canadians constantly return for inspiration and strength. Consequently, Canadians sing their country as 'The true north strong and free', strong in its rugged and rocky relief, strong in the severity and starkness of its climate, strong in the turbulence and power of its rivers, strong in its wealth of minerals and fuels: and at the same time free, free in the immensities of its horizons, free in the emptiness of its landscapes, free in all the potential that is there to be developed; free in the history that geography has yet to make.

It is the fact that this vast area is still to be exploited that makes it so significant. As Patrick Anderson has put it in his poem on Canada:

> Who are you—they ask?
> And she [Canada] replies: I am the wind that wants a flag
> I am the mirror of your picture
> Until you make me the marvel of your life.
> Yes, I am one and none . . .
> America's attic, an empty room,
> A something possible, a chance. . . .

America's attic, the northland long remained neglected and forgotten. But now that the lower rooms have been taken up and filled, the attic is coming into its own. Men are moving up there. They are beginning to discover what a lot it has to offer and how, if developed, it may top the development of the whole continent (Fig. 120).

The more readily accessible parts began to be opened up in the early twentieth century. These embrace Labrador, and New Quebec, New Ontario, the northern sector of the Prairies, northern British Columbia, and

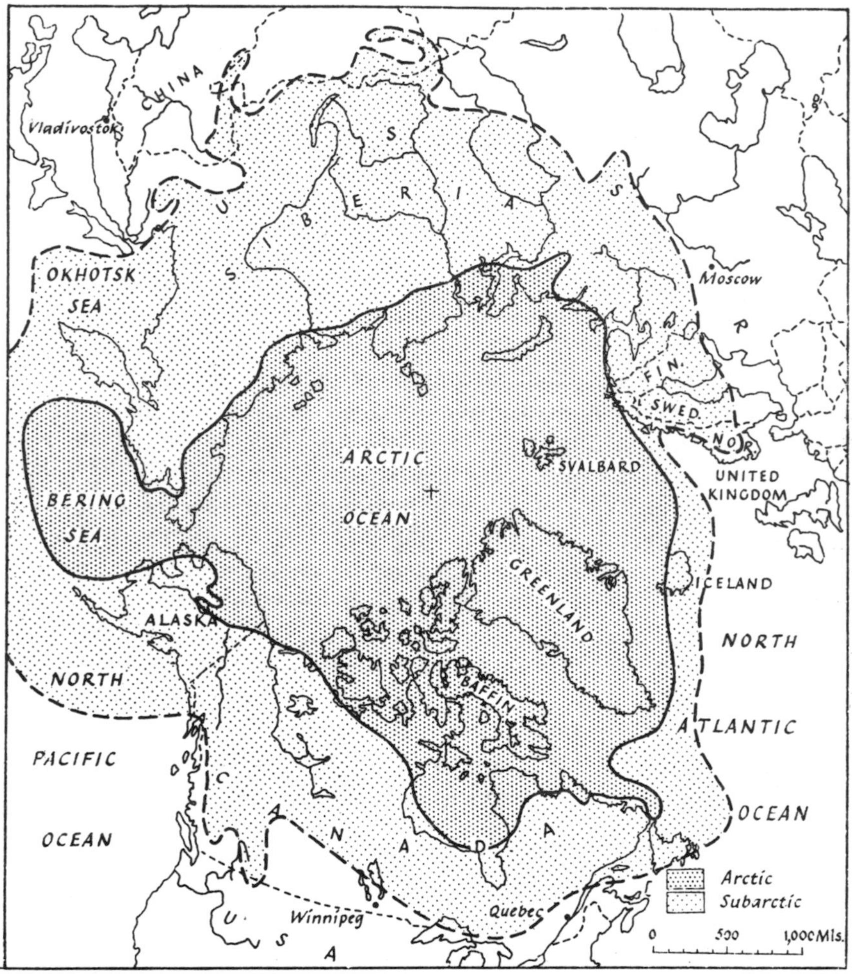

FIG. 120 The Canadian North is part of a great 'ring of emptiness' around the Arctic Ocean which is now offering all the northern countries in it new and substantial chances for development. The limits of the Arctic and Sub-arctic are here taken from the American Geographical Society's publication on the Polar Regions.

the Yukon. Together they form the 'inner north'. In recent decades, the remoter parts have been entered, including upper Labrador and Ungava, the Mackenzie district, and the Arctic archipelago. These constitute the 'outer north'. Both are alike in that they share the northness of great, grey, glaciated, rocky uplands; of moraine-ponded lakes and lake-filled basins; of thin, pale, leached, acid, and half-frozen soils; and of the aseptic cold of long, snowy, bitter yet brilliant winters. A great difference occurs, however, in that the 'inner north' is covered with forest and has agriculturally usable land, whereas the 'outer north' sees the woodland thin out and die and pass into the tundras and barren lands of the Canadian arctic.

CONDITIONS OF SETTLEMENT

Various factors have led to the opening up of the north. These include social pressures, economic interests, and strategic considerations.

Social pressures have come partly from the growth of Canada itself and partly from world growth. Psychological forces arise with growth that spur a nation on to still further growth. Slogans such as 'The nineteenth century may have been America's, but *the twentieth century belongs to Canada*', stir people and urge them on to expand. The mentality of expansion tips the scale so that, even if it may not be immediately profitable to enter the north and develop it, the risk is taken, on the assumption that the venture will ultimately succeed and bring in its returns. Thus growth begets growth. A country which can expand by nearly 30 per cent in a decade, as Canada has just done, becomes buoyant and optimistic and venturesome. And this psychology of expansion is carried into the business world as into every phase of existence.

Consider the record. In 1901 Canada's population was 5,371,315; by 1931 it had grown to 10,376,786. It did not increase very much over the 'thirties and in 1941 it stood at 11,506,655. But in 1951 it was as high as 14,009,000, and by 1961 had passed the 18 million mark. Notc the strong upward trend in post-war years. Here is a very sizeable increase. Part of it is due to the accession of Newfoundland to the union. Most of it results from optimism in Canada and abroad about Canada's future.

By the end of the century it has been calculated that the population will be at least 35 millions if not 40 millions. This is nearly as great as the present population of France, or of the population of England within the United Kingdom. So Canada should soon rival either of its mother countries in population, a fact of far-reaching consequence. It is a fact which colours all its thinking.

In a speech in January 1952 the then Prime Minister gave it as his considered opinion that 'by the end of the century there are apt to be no less than 35 million Canadians'.[1] He went on to say that beyond the achievement of peace and security there was nothing more important than the development and conservation of the country's resources and the acceleration of its productivity.

To a certain extent the upsurge in population, a part of which forced its way into the northland, was a world, as well as a Canadian, phenomenon.

[1] St Laurent, L., Annual Meeting, Canadian Federation of Agriculture, Montreal, 22 January 1952.

Population pressure produced land hunger and land hunger in the Old World led people to look with envy and expectation to the empty spaces of the New World. This factor was important in the settling of parts of the 'inner north', until the 'thirties, but has not been significant since, possibly because the surplus population is now streaming into the cities.

However, the world growth of population has demanded foodstuffs and so incited Canada to maintain such agricultural expansion as it had made. Population growth has been extraordinary. In 1931 the world's population was estimated at 2,013,000,000; in 1961 it was 3,218,000,000, or an increase of 1,205 millions. This works out at an annual increase of 40·17 millions. In other words, every year sees an addition of two Canadas to the world's numbers.

> According to a projection by the United Nations Population Division, world population will probably be between 3,395 million and 3,990 million in 1980. Can the production of food be increased sufficiently to keep pace? Two-thirds of the world's people already subsist on a diet which is inadequate both in quantity and quality. If simple adequacy were to be achieved overnight, the total increase of available food would have to be of the order of 25 per cent. If it were to be achieved by 1980, it would require, on a world basis, an annual increase of 2·25 per cent in food production. Of the world's main regions only North America shows an average annual increase in food production exceeding 2 per cent. Over the last fifteen years Europe achieved less than 1 per cent, and the Far East no more than 0·04 per cent increase of food production each year. The average for the world almost certainly was under 1 per cent.[1]

The Canadian North offers a great deal of as yet unused land suitable for cropping or grazing, and has thus a distinct opportunity, should economic conditions be propitious—or, for social reasons, be made to be so—to combat the food shortage. Although one should not exaggerate the possibilities which Canada has to offer, since the hardships entailed in developing them are considerable and the risks imposed by climate are severe, nevertheless the country still does have wide areas of reasonably good land ready for settlement (Fig. 121). Dr. E. S. Archibald of the Federal Department of Agriculture indicates that 'there are about 130,000,000 acres of land in Canada still available for cultivation. In addition there may be nearly as much land which, while not suitable for cultivation, may be used in grazing.'[2] This would suggest a probable total of about 260,000,000 acres.

---

[1] 'World Population and Resources', *Report of Political and Economic Planning*, London, 1955, pp. xvii, 29.

[2] Archibald, E. S., 'Cropping systems as an aid to sustained production', *Transactions of the United Nations Scientific Conference*, Lake Success, 1949, **4**.

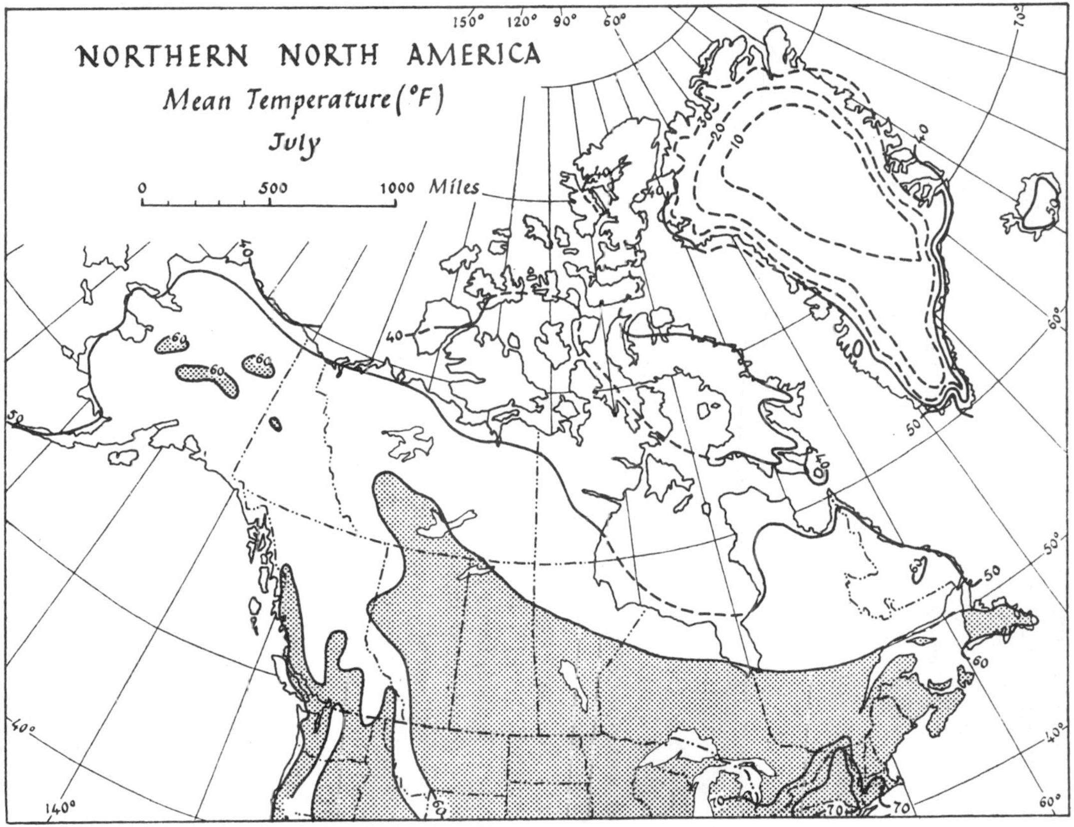

FIG. 121 Northern Frontiers of Development. Where relief, drainage, and soil are suitable, agriculture can be developed up to the 60° July isotherm, and lumbering up to the 50° isotherm. Note the great loop of warmth down the Mackenzie.

However, opinions vary as to what is 'agricultural' land. For example, the estimates above include 1,200,000 acres in the North West Territory and Yukon. But Trevor Lloyd, avers that 'There are believed to be a quarter of a million acres of arable land available in the Yukon, and five times that amount in the Mackenzie Valley'.[1] making a total of 1,500,000. A Provincian breakdown in terms of acres still available for occupancy would show: the Atlantic Provinces, 2,850,000; Quebec, 14,500,000; Ontario, 12,000,000; the Prairie Provinces, 84,500,000; and British Columbia, 5,400,000.

Immediately after the Second World War there was quite a strong 'back-to-the-land' movement; many veterans took up new land, as did a number of immigrants from Europe. The Prairies increased their acreage by 3,723,676 acres, and British Columbia by 668,704 acres. But a large part of this increase was within the pre-war settled area, albeit on the northern edge, and was due to drainage, taking in marginal land, irrigation, and farm consolidation.

The fact is, whatever pressure on land may have been generated by population growth, it has not led to the expected growth of the farm frontier. Indeed, many farmers have abandoned their land, selling it out to city or recreational interests. The type of farming that used to go with frontier settlement—done on a family basis—is dying out; large-scale commercial farming is more interested in making a better use of already settled land, near the market. Thus there is no great incentive to farm the north. Farmers, or would-be farmers, may be able to get a better living by mining, or on construction and transportation jobs. Nevertheless, farms along northern highways like Alaska, Mackenzie, and Chibougamau, and around mining centres like Pine Point (Great Slave Lake) do provide a valuable local service. Meanwhile, the potential for further development is there.

Economic interests may not at present warrant a wider, indeed a full-scale, onslaught on Canada's empty if usable agricultural lands, but they are sufficiently powerful to sponsor the exploitation of other unused resources, particularly northern mineral deposits, northern forests, and northern power potential. These are the real 'drawing cards' of the north, as Kirk Stone has long insisted.[2] Fortunately, Canada has more of these than it can consume, and therefore possesses a large surplus for development and trade. Actually,

---

[1] Lloyd, T., 'Future Colonization of Northern Canada', in *Canadian Population and Northern Colonization*, ed. Bladeu, Ottawa, 1961, p. 153.

[2] Stone, K. H., 'Human Geographic Research in the N. American Northern Lands', *Arctic*, 7, nos. 3 and 4, pp. 211–12. '. . . some research has been improperly limited by the idea that new settlement in northern N. America will be based on agriculture. We need the . . . denial of the assumption that future population will be rooted permanently only through agriculture.'

Canada depends less on its own population for a market than most countries. Where the United States consumes about 90 per cent of its own national product, and exports less than 10 per cent, Canada uses up only about 70 per cent and exports 30 per cent abroad. Indeed, in many instances it does more than that. Thus it exports 73 per cent of its wood products, 70 per cent of its metal production, 65 per cent of its wheat, and 42 per cent of its fish. Obviously, it depends to an unusual degree on foreign markets and world conditions.

This is seen in the fact that although Canada is a small nation it ranks fifth amongst the traders of the world, after the United States, the United Kingdom, Germany, and France. It buys and sells more than Russia, Italy, Japan, or India; countries that have many times more people.

Canada has developed its extensive foreign trade in order to have an outlet for its own tremendous energy and productivity and to keep up its high standard of living. Canadians can well be proud of their standard of living: more Canadians own their own homes, have their own cars, possess telephones and radios, electric stoves and refrigerators than any equivalent number of British people. More Canadians send their children to university than any equivalent number of British do. These are crude measurements, it is true, but they do mean something in security, comfort, and well-being.

The trade of Canada has had a better chance in the last decade or so than ever before, because the world has come to demand the sort of products which Canada owns, and which it owns in abundance. The increased industrialization of the world needs vastly more metals. Canada has either a leading or a major world role in the production of nickel, aluminium, copper, lead and zinc, platinum, uranium and gold. It has huge iron deposits which are now rapidly being developed. Industry and the growth of industrial cities also use more wood and wood products than ever before. The Canadian wood-products industry is now the leading one in the world.

Fuel is another important need of industry. Canada long relied on importing coal from the U.S.A. and Britain, and buying oil from the U.S.A. and Venezuela. It may still have to bring in coal, but its oil imports have been drastically cut as the western oil fields have opened up. It is obvious that they are making Canada independent of foreign sources. Further, they have already come to produce a margin for export. Canada has one of the truly large oil and natural gas reservoirs of the world.

For a long time Canada traded its raw materials and food with Britain and bought British goods in return. There was relatively little opportunity to do an extensive trade in its nearest market, the United States, because the United States produced most of the goods that Canada wished to export. But things have changed. Canada has gained an opening into the United States market. For the United States no longer has an abundance of all the things Canada produces. In fact, it is either short, or coming to the end, of much of its wood and many of its metals. It must import from abroad. It is also importing Canadian foodstuffs in spite of its own large production of foods, because it feeds so well. It has also come to draw on Canadian fuel as its own oil reserves are lowered.

American consumption of its own resources has always been tremendous, as was Britain's in the nineteenth century, as has been that of every great industrial nation. Britain very soon had to exploit her colonies and other countries because she began to exhaust her iron, copper, lead, tin, timber, agricultural land, and so on. America had a much larger reserve to begin with and could go on a longer time, supplying itself with its own needs. But large though it is, it has gone through many of its readily available commodities.

As Renner writes: 'After a mere 150 years of national existence, some 85 per cent of our useful wild game is gone, 80 per cent of our timber has been cut, 67 per cent of our petroleum reserves, 65 per cent of our lead and zinc, 51 per cent of our copper, 40 per cent of our iron ore, and 35 per cent of our anthracite have been used.'[1] Since then, reserves have dwindled further.

Meantime, United States demand for these and other products has jumped forward. The Paley report estimated that in the post-war boom the United States requirements for minerals and fuels would be doubled. The report makes the startling conclusion that 'the U.S.A. is outgrowing its present usable domestic base'.[2] It has begun to consume more than it can produce, instead of having a surplus, as it has hitherto had.

It is inevitable, therefore, that the United States should look abroad; and it is inevitable that it should look to Canada, its nearest neighbour. In the Canadian North there are still locked up many of the reserves which, if they could be fed to North American industry, would strengthen the whole western world; would in fact make the North Atlantic community really secure and sound.

Some of these resources like power and forests and soil can go on being used, if proper conservation procedures are followed, so that Canada may indefinitely contribute to western prosperity. Some are, of course, expendable. But here, too, conservation will greatly extend their use. In any event, Canadian supplies are so large that they should last for a very long time—at least until new techniques render us all less dependent on such materials.

Consequently it looks as though the present boom were not merely a boom, as most people understand that word, a sudden rise which would in due course spend itself, but might well be the beginning of a new stage of

[1] Renner, G. T., *Conservation of National Resources*, New York, 1942, p. 17.

[2] Paley, W. S., *et al.*, Report of the President's Materials Policy Commission, U.S. Government Printing Office, Washington, 1952, **2**, *The Outlook for Key Commodities*.

growth, which should continue; the new pioneer zone proving as successful in its way as the older one (Fig. 122).

Under the stimulus of newly roused economic interest the post-war development of forestry and mining in the northland has been considerable: most of it in the 'inner north', but an increasing amount in the 'outer north' as well.

The north is one of the world's main sources of lumber and pulpwood. Over a million and a half square miles of softwood exist, from Queen Charlotte Isles to the Isle of Newfoundland. Although most of this is difficult of access, it is steadily being penetrated, and lumbering and logging are pushing well into the north. Again, this is attributable to the world shortage of wood products which has provided the new incentive for expansion. Northward expansion has been assisted by depletion in some areas in the south and their replacement by rock barrens on hilly areas, or by farming in alluvial valley terraces.

New lumbering areas are being developed chiefly in the interior valleys of northern British Columbia and in the forest fringe of the Prairies. Worthy of mention are the developments round Williams Lake, and in the upper Skeena, British Columbia, in the Swan hills of Alberta, in the Cumberland House–Doré region of Saskatchewan, and in the Moose Lake–Wabowden areas of Manitoba. In Ontario expansion is proceeding down the Abitibi. But at the same time there is much reforestation of the denuded slopes of the Oak Ridge and Horseshoe moraines, where the new forests are doing much to halt erosion. The annual rate of reforestation is now about 60,000,000 trees. In Quebec there are some 350,000 sq. miles of forest in the northland, waiting to be developed; an area equivalent to Britain and France together. This is being attacked all along the northern fringe of the Gulf, in the Lake St John area, around Chibougamau, north of Senneterre. Quebec alone produces about a quarter of the world's supply of newsprint, the mainstay of the province's pulpwood industry.[1] In the east, the chief new lumbering area is in the northern part of the island of Newfoundland.

Once again the location of these advances is partly linked with the new roads opened up for mineral developments and with the markets which the northern mines are supplying. In the latter case, it is interesting to note that the rapidly developing mining region of Lake Athabasca is getting much of its wood from the forests of the lower Peace river.

Important as is the expansion in commercial lumbering, it is dwarfed by that in the extraction of fuels and metals. Growth in mining has continued at the rate of between 8 and 11 per cent per annum, or over twice the national product. Demand from abroad has remained high and the Canadian industry has been very competitive. About 60 per cent of the production

[1] *The Economy of Quebec*, Economic Research Corporation, Montreal, 1960, p. 91.

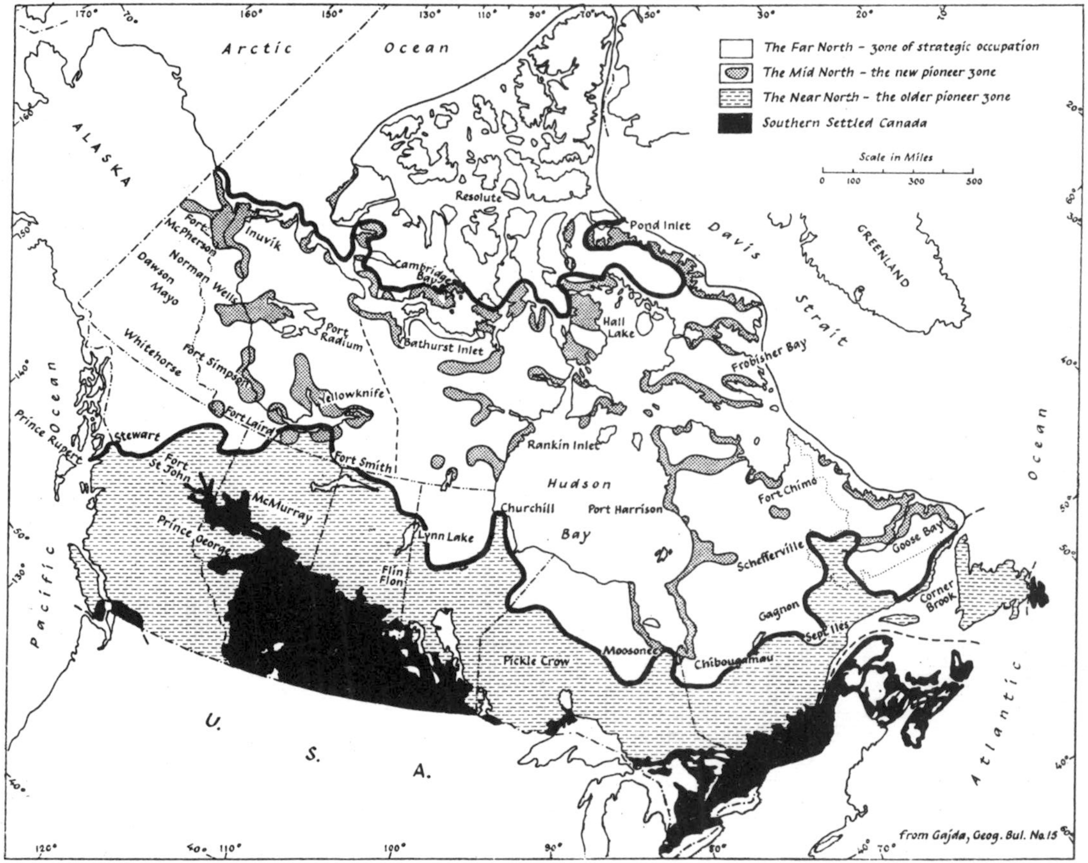

FIG. 122 Zones of Northern Development. From well-developed and evenly settled areas in the south, there occur three zones:

1, the Near North, of long ribbons of settlement, with pioneer agriculture supporting lumbering and mining, along isolated roads and railways;

2, the Mid North, consisting of pockets of settlement, mainly at mines, but also at lumber camps and fur-trading posts;

3, the Far North, with a few scattered military settlements, and little or no economic activity. (Modified from Gajda.)

is for the foreign market. Eighty per cent of this goes to the U.S.A., and the rest to Britain, W. Europe, and Japan. Of Canada's total exports, 32 per cent come from her mines. At the beginning of the Second World War the mining industry of Canada produced $500 million worth; in 1951 it had leapt to over $1,000 million and in 1965 it was about 3½ billion. Again, since the value of the dollar itself has shrunk, this is not an absolute measure. Yet when we look at the physical volume, the growth is still very remarkable. Taking the 1945–9 average as 100, the physical volume of output had risen to about 150 by 1951 and topped 330 in 1965.[1]

To a geographer the pattern of development due to mining is most significant because it has begun to fill up the Shield and invade the Appalachians and the Cordilleras in such a way as to turn these one-time barriers into bridges in Canadian development.

Professor Trotter once wrote about the barrier of the Appalachians in Canadian history;[2] but when those Appalachians began to be mined in the Eastern Townships, the Gaspé, and New Brunswick, they created a community of interests between the areas they had formerly divided. The continuation and acceleration of this trend should play a great part in cementing the flanking regions together. Thus the development at Bathurst, N.B., may eventually use the hydro-electric power brought from the Manicouagan river, P.Q., under the St Lawrence estuary to Gaspé. This would help to make Quebec and the Maritimes dependent on each other in yet another way.

Dr E. L. Bruce pointed out[3] that the Canadian Shield which was once thought of as a barrier, separating eastern from western Canada, was swiftly becoming a link joining them together. The mining communities of the north draw most of their construction timber, their flour, and meat from British Columbia and the Prairies, and most of their dairy goods and fruit, their clothing and, above all, their machinery from Ontario, Quebec, and the Maritimes. Thus they act as a powerful force to draw the economies of west and east together. The same could be said of the mines of the Cordilleras, that draw upon goods from the coast and from the prairies, helping to unite those strongly separated areas.

Consequently, as the mining industry grows it should act as one of the most powerful unifying forces of the country. Moreover, since that growth is mostly in the north, it pulls Canada towards the north; it gives the north a vital role in making Canada a distinct entity. In the Shield, Canada has something to all intents and purposes its own. And as the Shield changes

---

[1] *Canada Year Book*, Ottawa, 1966, p. 547.

[2] Trotter, R. G., *The Appalachian Barrier in Canadian History*, Canadian Historical Association, Report of Annual Meeting, May 1939, University of Toronto Press, Toronto.

[3] Bruce, E. L., 'The Canadian Shield and Its Geographic Effects', *The Geographical Journal*, 1939, xciii, p. 238.

from being a negative area in Canadian life, to becoming a very positive one, it may well be regarded as the Canadian heartland, giving Canada its true significance as a separate country. Since the bulk of this heartland lies to the north, its pull upon the nation will help to balance that pull to the south which has been apparent in its history heretofore.

The fact is, as long as development was mainly in terms of homesteading or raising cash crops for export, the south was bound to be envied and to exert a great pull because of its wide lowlands, rich soil, and warm climate. It is no wonder that most European emigrants in the earlier days made for the United States. There the central plains, deep in fertile soils, form the core of the country. Indeed, the contrast between the United States, with soil at its heart, and Canada, with rock at its heart, was, as we have seen, not too encouraging for the northern country. It undoubtedly was one of the reasons, if not the main reason, why the United States filled up much more than Canada.

But when development became possible in terms of water-power, lumbering and mining, instead of farming, the Shield and the marginal mountains began to play such an important part in the Canadian economy, that finally the United States started to look to Canada; the wheel had come fully round. Consequently it is Canada that is now to be envied. Having been slow to develop up to the present has given it a chance to advance more rapidly, now that its resources have become so opportune.

The great growth in the mining industry has been, or will be, mainly in the north-western and north-eastern sections of the Canadian Shield; from Moak Lake and Lynn Lake, Manitoba, through to Great Bear Lake, N.W.T., on the one hand, and from Gagnonville to Diana Bay, P.Q., on the other. In the north-western section the principal developments or potential developments are nickel and copper at Moak Lake, Mystery Lake, and Lynn Lake in northern Manitoba, and at Ferguson Lake, west of Rankin Inlet, in the District of Keewatin; lead and zinc at Pine Point, just west of the edge of the Shield on Great Slave Lake; gold at Yellowknife, north of Great Slave Lake; and uranium at Uranium City and Beaverlodge, Lake Athabasca. Large deposits of iron ore have recently been discovered in Baffin Island and on the borders of the Yukon Territory and Mackenzie district. Doubtless these will be turned to, as more southerly sources are exhausted. Meanwhile, the main iron prospects are in Labrador, mostly at Gagnonville, Wabush, and Schefferville at the southern end of the Labrador trough where they are being actively developed, and at Leaf Lake, Ungava Bay.

Also important are the mines and potential mining areas in the northern Cordilleras. Lead and silver in the Mayo Landing–Keno Hill area of the Yukon (extraction has been expanded since the war), and at Torbrit, B.C., are valuable additions, together with nickel and copper near Kluane,

Yukon; copper at Grandue, B.C., north of Stewart, asbestos at McDame, B.C., and Clinton Creek, Y.T., and tungsten at New Hazelton, B.C.

Most of these mines are sufficiently far north to experience sub-Arctic and even Arctic conditions, including permafrost, extremely low winter temperatures, a long winter, difficulty of access at break-up and freeze-up, lack of a local food supply, and the difficulty of laying in water and sewage at the camp-sites. The health and morale of the workers are other typical problems to be considered. The mines have to supply many services, pay high wages, stockpile machinery and spare parts, and also stockpile the ore that is mined, and these things make costs very high. They can only operate, therefore, in a high-price market. At present, world demand has sent prices up to where it is economical to write down the hazards of the north, and this is why Canadian mining is able to look to the north for the first time, on a reasonably big scale and with reasonable prospects.

Oil-bearing structures are not widespread in the north, since most of the region consists of igneous or highly metamorphic rocks. However, along the edge of the Rocky and Mackenzie mountains, in Mackenzie district, in the less disturbed sedimentaries of the Yukon plateau, and in West Hudson Bay, oil and gas reserves have been shown to exist. Indeed, oil has been produced at Norman Wells since the 'twenties, and meets the needs of mining towns in the Mackenzie basin. In 1959, oil was struck in the Yukon at Chance No. 1 Well, 325 miles west of Norman Wells. Permits for oil exploration in the Innuitias cover over 40 million acres. Natural gas in the far north may amount to 70 trillion cubic feet.

Strategic considerations are also important in the opening of the north. In fact, they are the chief factors in the 'high' north. Here neither social nor economic interests have had a chance to operate. The great discomfort of living in the far north, with its long and bitter winters, and the high cost of access, and of transporting men and supplies, made the remoter parts of the Canadian Arctic an undeveloped and largely uninhabited region, until the compelling needs of defence led to the establishment of air bases and other strategic outposts (see Fig. 122).

Here is a new situation. For a long time, the balance of world power was held by Europe, and Canada was on the margin of world affairs. If it had any part to play it was to support Britain across the Atlantic, or to help America in the defence of the eastern and western approaches to the continent. 'The north was not considered. Even as late as 1940, a noted writer on Canadian defence ignored the Arctic. Today that would be inconceivable.'[1]

This is so because today the course of world power has definitely been

[1] Watson, J. W., 'Canada: Power Vacuum or Pivot Area?', in *New Compass of the World*, ed. Weigert, Stefansson, and Harrison, New York, 1949, p. 40.

shifting to the north. The critical area in world politics would seem no longer to be the Mediterranean, but rather the Arctic, together with the North Pacific and North Atlantic (Fig. 123). As long as the Middle East was the pivot of world strategy, between the continental and the maritime powers who clashed for its control, Canada did not have much influence. But today

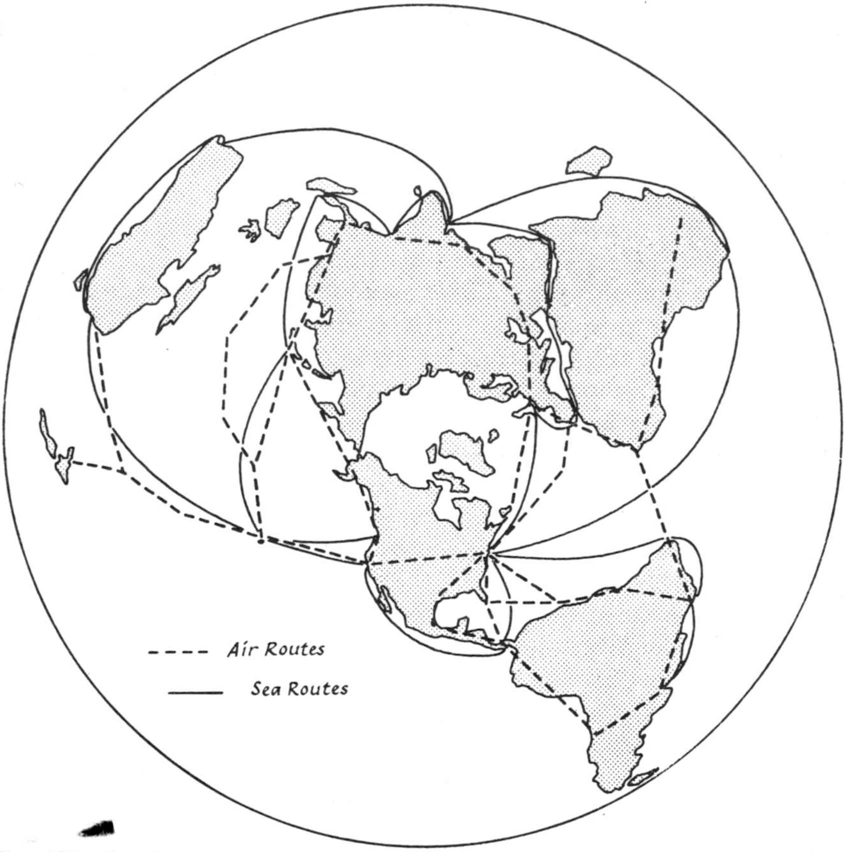

FIG. 123 Canada in a world dominated by the North. Canada's frontier on the Arctic North Atlantic, and North Pacific is greater than that of any other power.

Canada itself may well be regarded as in the centre of things, since the balance of world power now swings between the United States to the south of it and the Soviet Union to the north.

This is a new occurrence in Canadian geography. It thrusts the country into the forefront of the world situation. The groupings of America (with its possessions in Alaska and the North Pacific), of Britain, and of Russia around the north, together with Western Europe, China, and the Japanese Islands, have created a new arrangement of powers with a new meaning for

Canada. Most of these powers look in upon the oceans to which Canada looks out; they face Canada across the Arctic, the North Atlantic, and the North Pacific. It is a significant fact that in these three areas, which are possibly the three most important strategic areas of the world, no nation has a greater frontage than Canada. It alone has a large frontage on each of the geographically strategic oceans of the world. Its Atlantic frontage is as great as that of any other Atlantic power; it marches with the Soviet Union along the whole Arctic front; and it possesses a key position, between continental America and Alaska, and opposite China, on the North Pacific front.

Not only are the northern sea-lanes important, but also northern air-routes. The polar routes form the shortest and swiftest connexions between North America and Europe, including Russia, and also between North America and Asia, including Siberia. Canada recognized this towards the end of the Second World War, when it centred one of its two principal air commands at Edmonton, the gateway to the north. This was in answer to American criticism about the weakness of the Arctic frontier. In 1947 the Chief of the U.S. Air Force wrote: 'Through the Arctic every industrialized country is within reach of our "strategic air". America is similarly exposed. We are, in fact, *wide open at the top*!' He urged a complete reorientation of North American defence towards the north, claiming that 'Whoever controls the Arctic air-lanes controls the world today.'[1] Canada suddenly awoke to the fact that it had one of the most strategic frontiers in the world—but had done nothing about it.

This was soon remedied. Large new bases were built at Whitehorse, Edmonton, Churchill, and Frobisher Bay, along the edge of the 'inner north', with lesser, yet crucial, bases much farther north in the Canadian archipelago, notably at Resolute (Cornwallis Island), Mould Bay (Prince Patrick Island), Isachsen (Elef Ringnes Island), and Eureka and Alert (on Ellesmere Island). Between, and connecting these, lie the posts of the D.E.W. (Early Warning) line, with their powerful radio and radar stations. These many defence sites have thus carried settlement into the remotest parts of Canada, drawing the country ever deeper and involving it more and more in the north, its most distinctive region (Fig. 124).

Northern Developments and Regions of Settlement

The main developments in the north have taken place in several distinct sub-regions which include: (i) north-east Laurentia (Labrador, Newfoundland, and Ungava, P.Q.); (ii) central Laurentia (north-west Quebec and North Ontario); and (iii) the Canadian North-west (Northern Prairies and Mackenzie, Northern British Columbia, and Yukon Territory).

[1] Spaatz, C., 'Northern Rampart', *Herald Tribune*, New York, 27 October 1946.

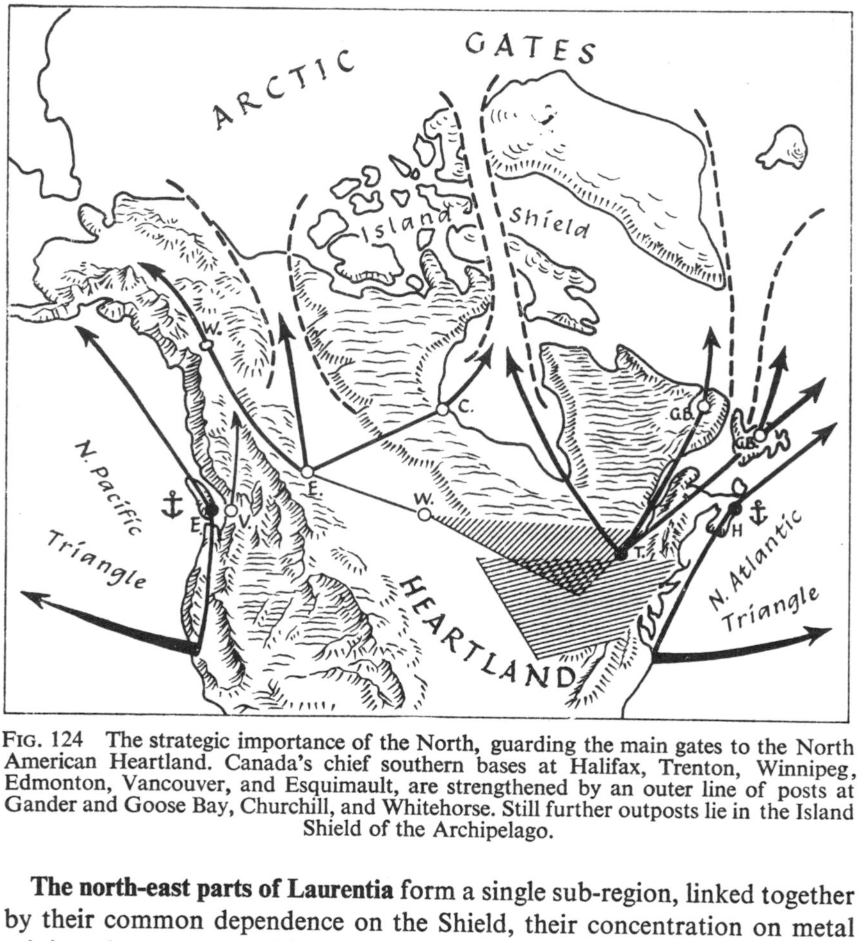

FIG. 124 The strategic importance of the North, guarding the main gates to the North American Heartland. Canada's chief southern bases at Halifax, Trenton, Winnipeg, Edmonton, Vancouver, and Esquimault, are strengthened by an outer line of posts at Gander and Goose Bay, Churchill, and Whitehorse. Still further outposts lie in the Island Shield of the Archipelago.

The north-east parts of Laurentia form a single sub-region, linked together by their common dependence on the Shield, their concentration on metal mining, the sameness of their problems—especially mining and transporting material through the long, cold, dark winter—their joint use of transportation out to Atlantic or seaway ports, and, not least, the mixture of French and British with the predominance of French personnel, but of Anglo-American capital.

Labrador and Ungava—the northern extensions of the provinces of Newfoundland and Quebec—were known to have significant quantities of iron and other minerals as early as 1893.[1] But the mineral zone lies well inland, in the upper Hamilton basin in Labrador, and in the Kaniapiskau–Koksoak basins in Ungava, and consequently nothing was done with the latent wealth until at length the more accessible ores in the Lake Superior district were

[1] Low, A. P., 'Report on Explorations in the Labrador Peninsula',1892–95, *Geol. Surv. Canada, Annual Rept.*, 1897, **viii**, pt. L.

partly exhausted or became costly to extract. At this stage, the cost of getting into Labrador-Ungava, high though it was, grew competitive.

The mineral zone is a major feature in a continent marked by large-scale occurrences. It forms a huge trough, composed of sedimentary and volcanic rocks, running for over 500 miles, from the Hamilton river in Labrador to the shores of Ungava Bay. Just before the Second World War serious exploration began, and six large deposits of iron ore were found on either side of the Newfoundland–Quebec border in the vicinity of Lake Petitsikapau. The war stopped further activity, yet the aftermath of the war, when American iron reserves had become sadly depleted, led to very rapid prospecting. By 1949 it was shown that there were about 400 million tons of high-grade ore, averaging 55 per cent iron, which could be worked by the open-pit method from unusual concentrations in fairly soft sedimentary rocks, and which could be shipped out by a direct and down-grade route to the Gulf of St Lawrence.[1] Altogether it is thought that about 2,000 million tons of ore lie in the trough, taking into account occurrences in the lower Koksoak, Leaf, and Payne basins, Ungava[2] (Fig. 125).

The main difficulty has lain in getting at the ore. Access by Ungava Bay was rendered very dubious by the long period during which harbours were frozen over. Landfast ice around the shore begins to form in November every year. Pack-ice drifts into the bay in December and fills the area from Cape Chidley to Cape Hopes Advance. This remains in Ungava Bay until the following August. Actually, the melting of ice at the river mouths, from George river to Payne Bay, does break up the shore-ice as early as July, but the vast mass of ice remaining in the centre of the bay well into the height of summer, makes shipping difficult if not dangerous. Not until this ice disintegrates and drifts out in late August into Hudson Strait and thence to the Labrador Sea, can shipping safely negotiate the Ungava region.[3]

Consequently, the longer overland route to the iron trough had to be developed. A railway was built from the little fishing village of Sept Iles—now a thriving port of nearly 20,000—over the scarp-like edge of the faulted Shield, across extremely rugged terrain, deeply eaten into by rejuvenated sharply entrenched rivers, a distance of 360 miles to the Knob Lake iron field. Here the town of Schefferville soon grew up, a major outpost in the wilderness. The making of the port, the building of the railway, and the installation of near-by hydro-electric dams and works, were all major operations, but with American backing they were soon completed, and in 1954 the production of ore started, and over 2 million tons of ore were

[1] Durrell, W. H., 'Labrador Iron Ore and the St Lawrence Seaway', *Eng. & Min. Jour.*, 1950, **151**, no. 5, p. 92.

[2] Campbell, T. C., 'Quebec-Labrador Ore', *Iron Age*, 1950 **166**, no. 9, p. 71.

[3] Drinnan, R. H., and Prior, L., 'Physical Characteristics of the Ungava Bay Area', *Geog. Bul.*, 1955, no. 7, pp. 32–36.

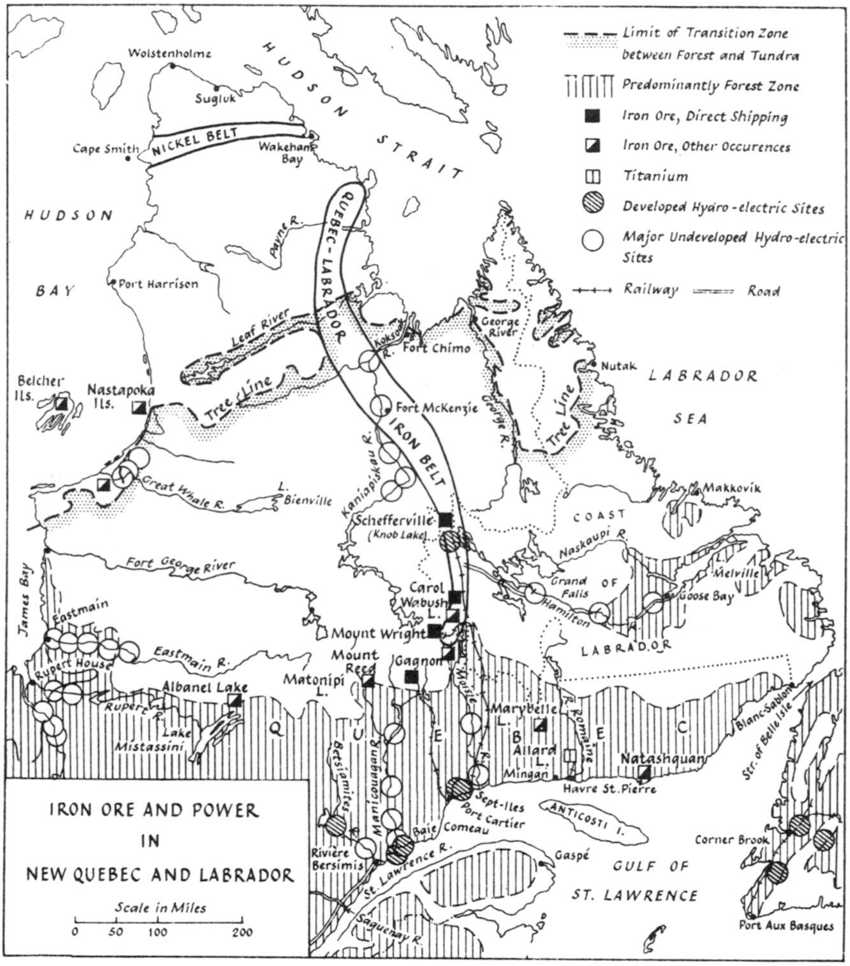

FIG. 125 Iron Ore and Power in New Quebec and Labrador—the development of the Canadian Northeast. (Courtesy, Bank of Nova Scotia Review.) Forest and water-power resources along the southern edge, and mining in the north, make this one of the richer areas of prospective growth, in spite of the lack of agriculturally usable land.

shipped out to the iron-hungry cities of the St Lawrence and Great Lakes lowland. The enlargement of the St Lawrence seaway made transportation costs remarkably low, enabling the ore to be sent to Hamilton, Cleveland, and beyond. Today over 20 million tons a year, including ore from Wabush, are being shipped out, and this will increase as Mesabi reserves decline.

Additional iron-ore deposits have been found farther south and west, in the so-called Grenville zone of the Shield, in the area lying between Mt Reed and Mt Wright. Big masses of specular hematite occur, containing about 35 per cent iron, the reserves of which have been put at over 750 million tons. Again, a new railway has had to be built from a new port, Cartier, across very rugged terrain to a new town, Gagnonville, in the heart of the iron district, while large new hydro-electric installations have had to be developed. From 10 to 12 million tons a year are being produced. In the meantime, yet a third set of ore docks were constructed at Havre St Pierre, for yet a third railway into a small but highly productive area, rich in ilmenite, at Allard Lake. Here 150 million tons are being worked, containing 40 per cent iron, and 35 per cent titanium dioxide. The titanium is a valuable metal used for hardening steel. The ore is shipped to Sorel, where it is smelted in a large electric smelter. The refined metal is then sent partly to Montreal and partly to New Jersey.

These developments have had a big effect in opening up the country. Lumbering has sprung up to provide mines and mining camps with much-needed building material. Hydro-electric developments are going on apace. Roads and airports are providing other means for business to exploit the many opportunities. Co-operation between Quebec and Labrador in making scope for all these projects is bringing these two provinces—long at odds on the question of the Labrador boundary—closer together. (The railway to Schefferville starts in Quebec, passes through Labrador, and then terminates in Quebec. The iron fields in Quebec will owe their major development to power at Grand Falls, on the Hamilton river, in Labrador.)

Central Laurentia, made up of western Quebec and northern Ontario, has also been quickened by new developments. Here the structure and scenery are more varied. The hard ice-scoured Shield dips below sedimentaries in the Lac St Jean–Saguenay area, and also in the Lake Temiskaming area, where towns and villages appear in clearings of the forest. Further depressions are formed by the little and great Clay Belts and by the Port Arthur plain. Across the crystalline rocks the Canadian National and Pacific Railways thread a slender beadwork of mining and lumbering towns. The St Maurice river, the upper Ottawa, the Abitibi, and the Nipigon make wide basins, into which lumbering companies have pushed, dotting the region with busy little camps. Elsewhere, the forest remains unbroken, and there are vast areas empty of permanent settlement. Hydro-electric power is an important feature (Fig. 126).

In western Quebec the chief areas of development are the Lac St Jean and the Temiskaming basins. *The Lac St Jean–Saguenay district* is a depression lying between lines of faults, with sedimentary rocks partially covered by marine clays. The western fault zone is followed by a remarkable escarpment. Glaciation has deepened the basin, and formed the profound gorge of the Saguenay. Glacial-lake terraces border the basin and valley. This district, sheltered by the scarp, with temperatures modified by the lake,

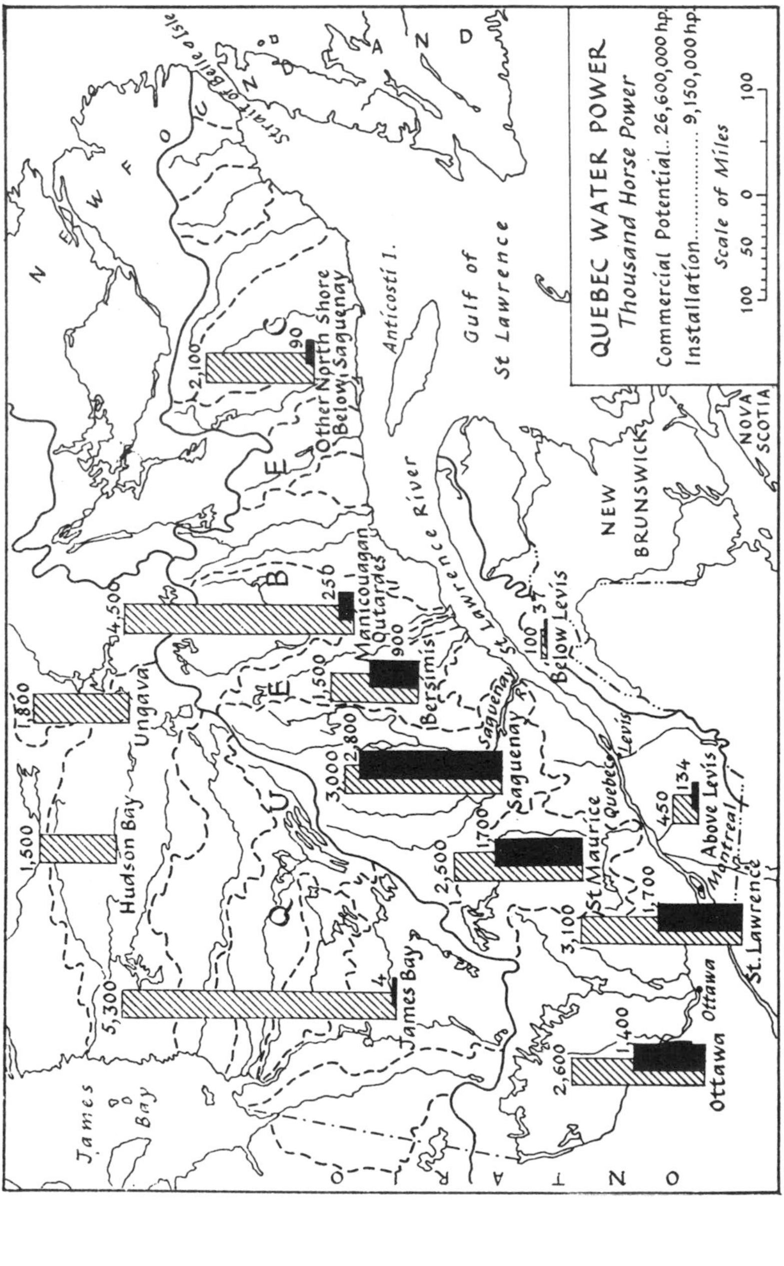

FIG. 126 The Power Resources of Quebec. (From McGuire.) Hydro-electric power is in many ways the basis of the economic penetration of Laurentia. In this Quebec is particularly rich.

having easy access to the St Lawrence by the river, and with cultivable marine terraces, offers the basis for many agricultural villages, as well as lumber towns. The farmers produce hay, oats, and potatoes, which are well suited to the cool, short summers. Dairy products are raised for the local market, together with hogs and sheep. Much of the farming is still of the pioneer sort, in which people raise enough meat, milk, and vegetables for themselves, but depend on lumbering, trapping, or acting as guides, to supplement their livelihood. The town of Roberval is a market and transportation centre for the lake district and has rail connexions with Quebec. Lumber mills occur at power plants at Bolbeau, Kenogami, Jonquière, Chicoutimi, and Port Alfred. Tadoussac, at the mouth of the river, is a port for the region and also for the lower gulf. It is an important lumber town.

At Arvida, the Aluminum Company of Canada has a large centre. There is no raw material in the vicinity, yet the factory is well placed, since the making of aluminium requires the bringing together of several different ores, which have to be smelted in electrical furnaces that require an immense and regular supply of electricity. Since the raw materials come from abroad Arvida is strategically located, on the lower gulf, at one of the outermost parts of Canada. It is easily accessible from the cryolite mines of Greenland, the bauxite of British Guiana, and the fluorspar of southern France. At the same time, it is easily accessible to the rest of Canada by way of the St Lawrence–Great Lakes waterway. The power resources of the Saguenay district are very considerable and offer cheap electricity with which to smelt the ores, and manufacture the aluminium ingots. Arvida is now the largest centre for the making of aluminium in North America[1] (Fig. 127).

In western Quebec lies the Temiskaming–Abitibi basin. When the ice melted from it, at the close of the Ice Age, the melt-waters filled the basin with the giant Lake Ojibway, the ancestor of Lakes Abitibi and Temiskaming. This left thick beds of sediments which form fertile terraces, interrupted here and there by bosses of ancient rock. The rockier and steeper slopes are densely wooded, while the lake-floor clays supply fairly fertile soils for agriculture. At Kipawa the International Paper has a large plant; the Abitibi Power and Paper Company has important interests at Abitibi; and lumbering is also carried on at Amos, La Reine, and Taschereau. Mining has, however, become the main development. Great gold and copper deposits occur at Rouyn and Noranda and these two towns have expanded rapidly. Recently, copper-gold finds as far north as Chibougamau have led to a great extension of the mining region. Altogether, some forty mines are in operation, producing gold, silver, copper, lead, zinc, and lithium. Indeed, the area bids fair to be 'the most important producer of metals in the province, and about

[1] Goodwin, W., 'Outlook for Aluminum', *Focus*, January 1961, **xi**, no. 5, p. 3.

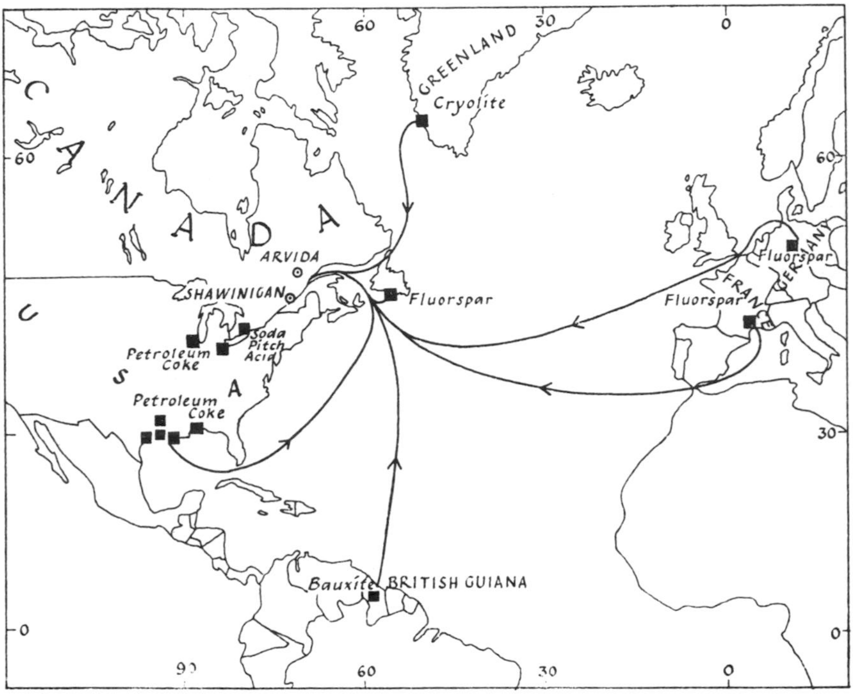

FIG. 127 The Aluminium Industry in Quebec–Arvida and Shawinigan. Large quantities of cheap power at the edge of the Canadian Shield, together with tidewater access to raw materials gathered from round the North Atlantic, and closeness to the great industrial markets of Canada and north-east America, make this an ideal site.

400 companies have staked claims or are exploring for deposits'. New railways and roads from St Felicien, near Lake St John, and from Barraute and Beattyville, in the Abitibi district, are rapidly making Chibougamau the capital of the new frontier. Lumbering and pioneer farming are moving north to help supply the greatly increased local market.

In northern Ontario occurs a widening extension of the Temiskaming metal belt. Here again mining has been the key to development. Mining has made it worth while building railways; has demanded hydro-electric developments; has used construction timber and firewood in great quantities; and has provided a market for farming. Therefore, the north is dependent in many ways on its mines, and each mining town is the centre of a wide sphere of activity.

Actually, it was in the building of the transcontinental railways that many of the mineral-rich areas were found. They were at once exploited, so that they could offer business to the railways and help to pay for the hundreds of miles of track through otherwise unsettled areas. Mining towns and lumber camps gave enough traffic to the railways to make them pay, and so did much to assist in linking up the eastern and western parts of Canada into one country.

Between 1865 and 1886 the various branches of the Canadian Pacific had been built from Montreal and Toronto through Ottawa and North Bay to Sudbury, Nipigon, Fort William, Kenora, and Winnipeg, spanning the province. They followed the lowlands of the Ottawa–Mattawa and the Simcoe–Muskoka Lakes to the Nipissing depression, and thence climbed the Height of Land and followed it to White river. Thereafter the track followed the north shore of Lake Superior to Fort William, whence it again took to a height of land to Kenora. Sudbury and Copper Cliff were the main mines discovered along this route and developed by it. Sudbury was opened in 1883. It is the world's largest deposit of nickel (Fig. 128). Also associated with it are copper, lead and zinc, gold, silver and platinum. The near-by Frood mine, opened in 1925, is Canada's largest producer of copper, and the world's leading source of platinum.

Twenty years later the Temiskaming and Northern Ontario Railway was being built, and the engineers accidentally discovered silver at Cobalt. Thus a new, fantastically rich mining area was developed. Cobalt has ceased to be important for silver, but still raises the valuable cobalt ore that gives it its name. The railway was pushed north to Cochrane, and prospectors soon discovered Porcupine (1909) and Kirkland Lake (1911), the largest gold fields in North America.

In 1913 what is now the Canadian National Transcontinental line was built from Quebec, across the flat height of land in Quebec province, through the low Temiskaming–Abitibi depression, over the Great Clay Belt, to the north shore of Lake Nipigon, whence it follows fairly high land to Sioux Lookout and Winnipeg. The Rouyn–Noranda mines of Quebec were developed by it, and also the Geraldton and Little Long Lac gold areas in Ontario. Today, the Red Lake area, north of Sioux Lookout, is opening up, with the use of short air routes from the railway bases.

As we have seen, the discovery of these mines has often been accidental. It was due in part to the way in which the railways struck for the heights of land, where there were fewer obstacles to overcome. But these heights are often composed of those very granitic intrusions, which, as we have seen, are most likely to contain 'fissure' minerals. Where the combination of easy routeway and mineral-rich intrusion occurs, there is an ideal site for a mine.

However, power is also necessary. It is fortunate that in a land so rich in minerals there should be so much hydro-electricity available. Three extensive transmission systems have been set up to make use of the vast volume of high head of water in northern Ontario. In the east there is the Abitibi system, radiating from the power works at Abitibi Canyon. This plant, the

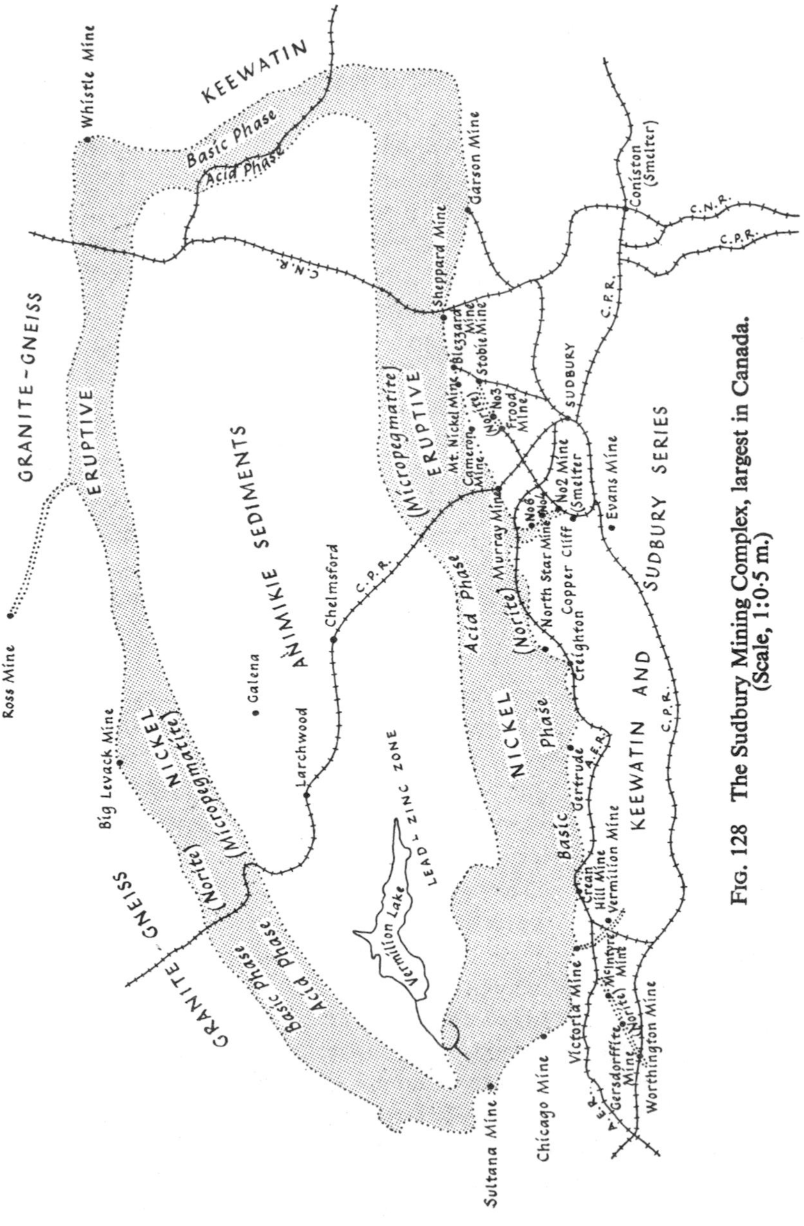

FIG. 128 The Sudbury Mining Complex, largest in Canada. (Scale, 1:0·5 m.)

second largest in the province, has an installed capacity of 330,000 horse-power. Transmission lines serve the eastern group of mines as far south as Sudbury. Local stations in between supply 60 cycle power to small mills, mines, and towns. Farther west the Thunder Bay system, with its generating station on the Nipigon river, has a capacity of 125,000 horse-power. It supplies the Long Lac–Fort William area. In the north-west, generating stations at Ear Falls (English river) and Pat Rapids (Albany river), which are connected by a transmission line, supply power to the mines of that part of the province. In addition to these larger systems, there are a number of privately owned power stations on the Abitibi, Mattagami, Spanish, St Mary's, Montreal, Seine, and Winnipeg rivers (see Fig. 98, Chapter 12).

The extension of power is helping to maintain sites as refining or manufacturing centres, even after the local ores have been used up. However, the history of mining, like that of lumber, is marked by ghost towns. For example, Cobalt in its hey-day had 12,000 people, but now it is a much restricted centre, with only 2,200. The mining towns also experience all the problems of 'boom' settlements, such as an excess male population; a haphazard urban growth with no logical pattern; the lack of social institutions to supply a normal social development; a very mixed population; the growth of ethnic blocks where the people of one nationality tend to congregate; low home standards and the presence of shanty-town quarters; a very mobile population in which there is little sense of neighbourhood responsibility. As a result, mining towns have a hard task to develop a balanced, stable society, and a well-planned settlement. Nevertheless, as the boom settles down to a more steady progress, these problems can be faced and overcome. This is especially so where the mining town discovers new interests, engaging in lumbering, the manufacture of various goods, and the marketing of farm produce. In this way it becomes the hub of a busy and varied region, and plays a fully representative economic and social role.

The rise or fall of towns has been very rapid in Ontario because the whole mining industry has developed rapidly. In 1891, when the Ontario Bureau of Mines was formed, it calculated the total production at about $10 millions. In 1941, only fifty years later, this had increased to nearly $270 millions. In that year Ontario's output was 48 per cent of the Canadian total. Today, although its percentage of Canadian output has fallen to 40, its total production has climbed to over $1,500 millions. The chief products are nickel, nearly 250 millions; gold, 100 millions; copper, 100 millions; zinc, 15 millions; and silver, 12 millions of dollars worth. At the height of the uranium boom, Ontario produced over $200 millions of that valuable ore a year.

This rapid increase in production shows the values of the human factor. Early in Canadian history that swashbuckling French-Canadian leader d'Iberville passed through Cobalt and Porcupine and was told of their mineral wealth. But it must have seemed an impossible task to extract the ore and get it out of the forest to Montreal. So he went on, more interested in the fur trade than in metals. Furs were accessible and could easily be transported. It was not until railways were built that metals became accessible. The rise of the mining industry had to await more and cheaper railways, improved methods of ore treatment, lowered costs, and a decrease in the productivity of the older mining areas of the world. Thus transportation, engineering, economic and historical factors, along with geography, all enter into Ontario's mining boom.

Four distinct subdivisions can be made out in northern Ontario, separated from each other by largely unoccupied land. These are the Sudbury–Sault (Soo) district, the Haileybury–Hearst district, the Superior–Nipigon district, and the Rainy River–Red Lake district.

The Sudbury–Sault area was the first to be developed. It includes the nickel-copper-platinum mines of the Sudbury region, the mining and lumbering of the Sault, Blind river, North Bay and Haliburton areas, and the farming of the glacial-lake clays around Huron and Nipissing lakes. The development of the whole district is centred in the towns, particularly in North Bay, Sudbury, and Sault Ste Marie. North Bay is the gateway to northern Ontario. It lies in the glacial channel between Georgian Bay and the Ottawa river which was used by Champlain and the fur traders, and collects the roads and railways from Toronto and from Ottawa before they fan out over the Shield. It is chiefly a distribution centre, and transportation occupies 25 per cent of its working population. It is also a market town, tourist centre, and manufacturing place, and thus has built up a variety of interests that keeps it well balanced and vigorous in growth. **Sudbury** (120,000) is also a route centre, where the railway from the Ottawa valley meets that from Toronto. There is a small area of farm land on lacustrine plains around, and the city is an important northern market for agriculture. But its chief wealth is in mining. In a piece of bare land where almost all vegetation has been destroyed by the acrid fumes of the mine, underneath the enormous smoke stacks of the International Nickel Company, the town is sprawled, with row on row of narrow wooden houses, opening on to the busy and pretentious shopping district. There is a great mixture of nationalities. One out of every five was born abroad, and even the Canadian-born spring from different stocks. The French are prominent, and there are French newspapers and radio programmes. However, there is less segregation than usual because the people all work in one or other of two large companies. The University has Anglican and Catholic support. Sudbury does not have much variety. Its wealth lies in 12 nickel mines. Fortunately, nickel has many uses and there is ample demand for it throughout the world.

Sault Ste Marie is very different. It is a canal town, on the grain, iron, coal, and lumber routes of the Upper Great Lakes. The Soo canals carry the largest tonnage of any in the world. They enable ships to by-pass the rapids between Lake Superior and Lake Huron. In addition, Sault Ste Marie is an important road and railway terminal, connecting Canada and the U.S.A. Indeed, before the trans-Canada Highway was finally completed, many people motored to the west from eastern Canada via Sault Ste Marie and the American Mid-West. Numbers of emigrants use the terminal to enter America. Thus the little city has many raw materials and an ample labour market to draw upon. The chief works are the Algoma Iron and Steel Corporation, using the flow of iron to the east and of coal to the west. Wood and paper products are also important. Over 40 per cent of the working population are engaged in manufacturing (Fig. 129).

The Haileybury–Hearst district is very large, and includes the chief mining, lumbering, and farming areas of the north. The main mining area is on the height of land between the Temiskaming and Abitibi basins; farming and lumbering are carried on in the glacial plains surrounding the lakes or along the river valleys. Railways provide adequate transportation; there is the Northern Ontario line through Haileybury in the south, and the Trans-continental through Hearst in the north. They meet at Cochrane.

Once again the economic life is closely bound up with the mill towns and mines. Hearst, Kapuskasing, Cochrane, and Iroquois Falls are the chief northern settlements and are engaged mostly in lumbering. Kapuskasing is beautifully laid out, in straight business streets and curved residential crescents, and has a fine community centre. It is an example of what a well-planned pioneer effort can create in contrast to the haphazard growth of most boom towns.

Along the height of land are the busy gold-mining towns of Timmins and Porcupine, while to the south are the gold, silver and iron mines of Kirkland Lake, Gowganda, Haileybury, and Cobalt. Timmins is interesting because though it originally grew up very rapidly as a shack-town mining settlement, after the fire of 1911 a new town site was laid out, and planned in such a way that the residential areas were segregated from the business and mining ones. Here, too, about one in five of the population was born abroad, and even the Canadian-born are very mixed, with many French Canadians. Nevertheless, by a planned development these people have learned to work and live together without forming separate *blocs*. The town has manufacturing plants. There are ten times the number of men employed compared with women, and the population is still 'male and middle aged', with few women and children or old people. This is typical of the urban patterns of the north. Timmins has been revitalized by copper-zinc discoveries.

The Superior–Nipigon district is the third area of development in northern

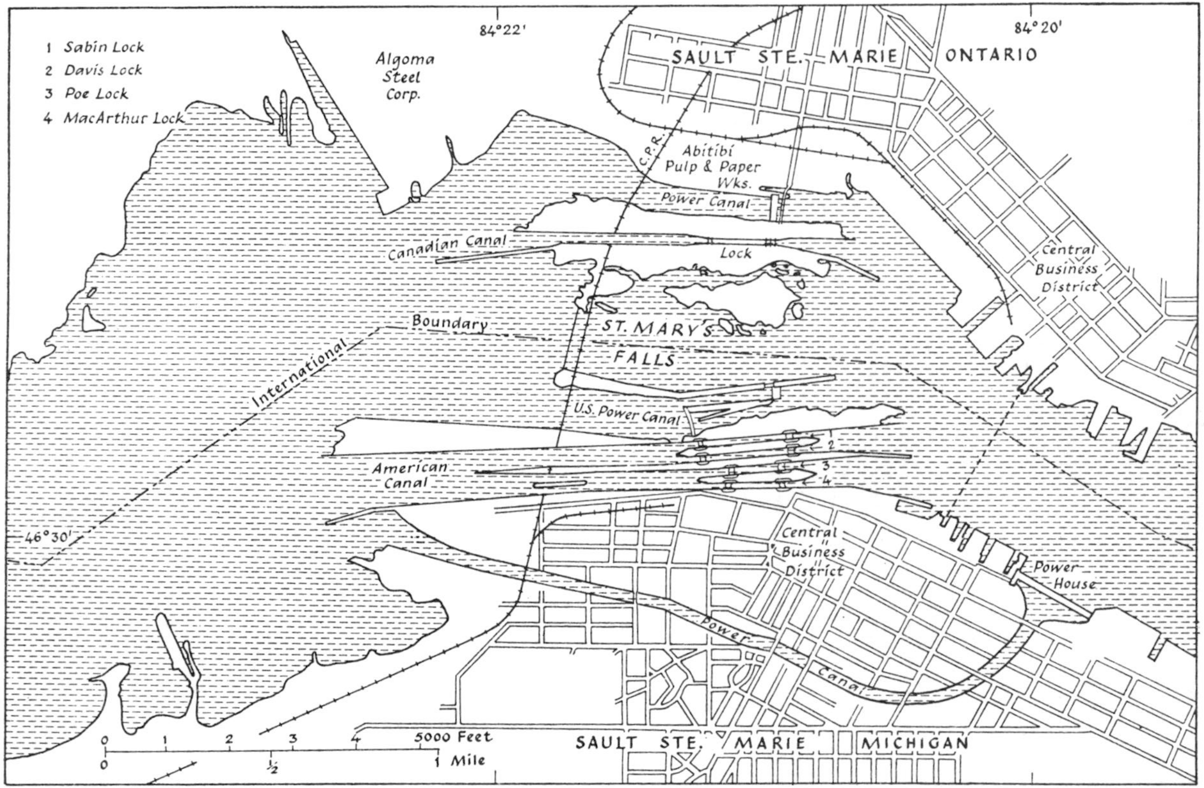

FIG. 129 The Soo canals. These carry more freight than the Suez and Panama canals put together. They have attracted to them busy industrial and commercial towns, producing steel and wood-pulp and paper.

Ontario. It is large and has loosely scattered settlements. There are four mining areas at Michipicoten (iron) in the east, Atikokan and Steep Rock (iron) in the west, Manitouwadge (zinc, lead, copper), and Long Lac (gold) in the north. The Long Lac district is not very important compared with Timmins, but its gold mines have helped to open the north. The iron workings of Michipicoten and Atikokan were nearly abandoned before the war because of high costs of extraction compared with American costs. However, during the war the New Helen mine was opened at Michipicoten, with an annual production of 700,000 tons of ore, and the Steep Rock mine was developed near Atikokan. Reserves of iron are large, but the difficulty of securing them is great. At Steep Rock a whole lake had to be drained away to expose the ore and mine it. The high grade of ore made this quite profitable, and Steep Rock has become a major source of iron. Manitouwadge is now booming.

Lake Nipigon and the north shore of Lake Superior are important lumbering districts. Some of the falls have been used to generate electricity and a thriving pulp and paper industry has grown up at Nipigon and at the twin cities of Fort William and Port Arthur.

However, the twin cities owe their prosperity not to the Shield so much as to the Prairies and the Great Lakes–St Lawrence waterway. They lie on the shores of Thunder Bay, and thus offer sheltered waters at the head of the longest water-route in Canada. At the same time, they are not far from the Prairies. Consequently, they act as the gateway for the intake of goods from the east (coal, oil, sugar, fruit, agricultural machinery, manufactured goods), and for the export of Prairie products from the west. **Fort William** is somewhat larger than Port Arthur and has more industrial plants, largely because it is the chief railway terminal. Both cities (together over 100,000) have enormous elevators and flour mills, coal yards, oil depots, and warehouses. They are also busy pulp and paper centres. Transportation and distribution employ more of the working population (33 per cent) than manufacturing (15 per cent). Like most harbours and railway terminals there is a very mixed population and one of every three people was born abroad.

The Rainy Lake–Red Lake district forms the fourth area of northern development in Ontario. It is the least populous, and the population is very scattered. Fort Francis is the centre of farming, lumbering, and the tourist trade on the Rainy river; Kenora is the largest town, and is an important railway station at the head of Lake of the Woods. It is a lumbering and market centre and tourist town. Red Lake is a new gold-mining area, served from the railway station of Sioux Lookout. Many of the camps are well to the north of the railway, and are being developed by air and tractor transport.

The Canadian North-west, embracing the northern fringe of the Prairies and British Columbia, together with the Mackenzie district and Yukon Territory, forms another great area of northern development. This region is quite different from the ones already described in that it embraces Shield, Interior Lowland, and young Fold mountains. It thus offers a wider range of structure, land form and soil, with a greater variety of resources. Indeed, apart from its relative inaccessibility, it suggests more scope for exploitation and settlement than any other sector of the northland. Along its eastern edge, overlapping the Shield, are rich concentrations of metal, and sites for power. On the western edge, which takes in the Cordilleras, are large deposits of oil and natural gas, and important though scattered bodies of metal. Here occur extensive forests as well. In between is a great lowland which, even though it is the Arctic margin of microthermal climate, affords many opportunities; it is the main axis of transportation, has fuel and mineral wealth, possesses the chief unused forests, and holds out distinct, though limited, agricultural responsibilities. It is the main corridor into the north and may well, as Griffith Taylor prognosticated, play the same role for the pioneers of the northland as the St Lawrence did for the settlement of the south.[1]

The region has been developed first as a gradual extension of, and then as a rather sudden break-away from, the northern fringe of the Prairies and British Columbia. Its description must therefore begin with that northern line of settlement from Le Pas, through Prince Albert, to Lac la Biche, Grande Prairie, and Fort St John east of the Rockies, and Prince George, Vanderhoof, Hazelton, and Prince Rupert to the west, which form, as it were, the jumping-off ground for northern development. This is a line just on the edge of the agricultural belt, and represents a transition between settled and pioneer conditions (Fig. 130).

The Northern Prairies are growing rapidly. Le Pas is an isolated centre, with new agricultural settlements developing near by in the drained marshes of the Carrot river plain, with a number of lumber camps making an attack on the mixed birch-poplar-spruce forest of the district, and with railways and roads striking to north-east and north to the very active mining centres of Moak Lake and Lynn Lake, already mentioned, and also to that northern outport of the Prairies and staging-base of the archipelago, Churchill on Hudson Bay. Thus it is a strategic centre of considerable importance for the pioneer fringe.[2]

Prince Albert is at the head of a great prong of agricultural settlement in the little 'mesopotamia' where the North and South Saskatchewan rivers come together. An active market town, with large elevators, oil depots, and machine yards, it is the road centre for pioneer roads leading through the

---

[1] Taylor, G., 'A Mackenzie Domesday', in *The New North-West*, ed. Dawson, C. A., Toronto, 1947, p. 39.

[2] Sim, V. W., 'The Pas, Manitoba', *Geog. Bul.*, 1956, no. 8, p. 20.

45. Pioneer farming in the Talkeetna valley, Alaska. A homestead family stands in front of their newly built loghouse and barn. Hay will feed their stock during winter.

The Northland

46. Mining is the chief activity in the North. Here at Thompson, Man., nickel is being taken out of the mineral-rich rocks of the Canadian Shield. Lumber and hydro-electricity are also abundant.

The American North and North-east—from New England to the Head of the Lakes

47. Superior, at the head of the Gt Lakes, sends wheat and iron from its vast elevators and ore piers to feed the people and factories of the American manufacturing belt.

48. The New England upland opens out into fertile, though restricted, valleys like the Connecticut. Here intensive farming is practised—in this case the raising of tobacco. (Note the long tobacco barns.)

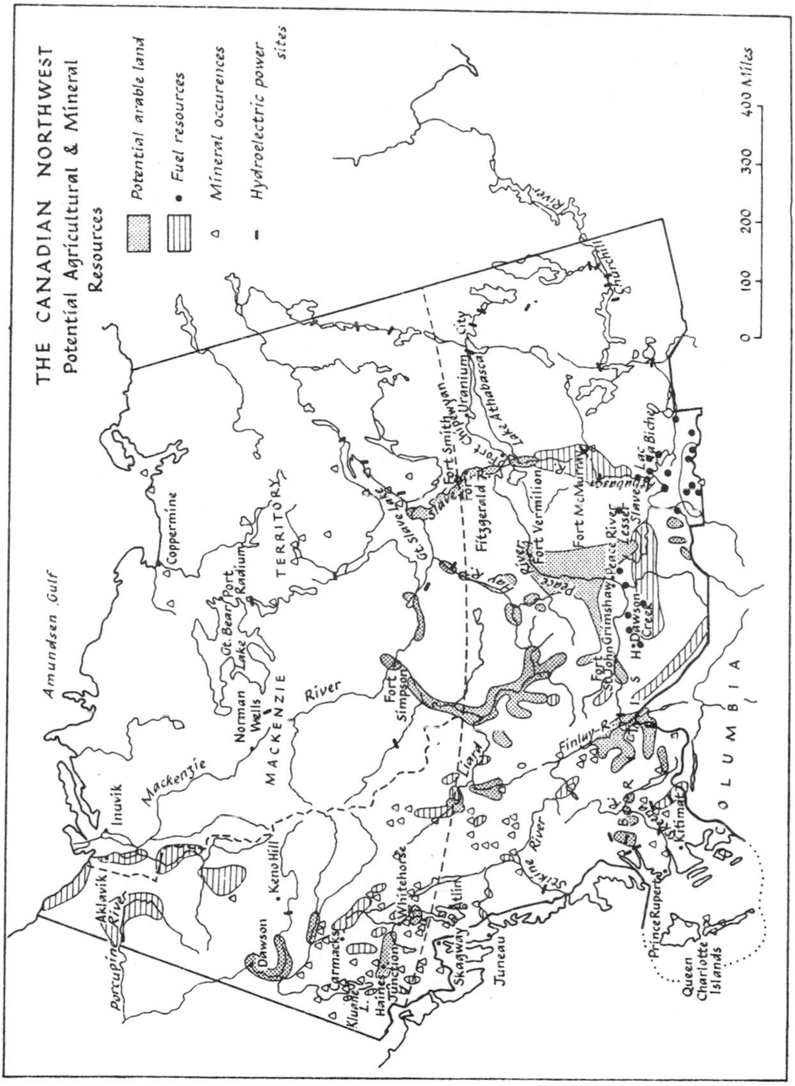

FIG. 130 The agricultural and fuel potential of the Canadian Northwest, in relation to power sites and mining prospects. The not inconsiderable though isolated ribbons and pockets of usable soil promise a permanent basis for settlement expanding beyond Skeena, Peace, and Athabasca.

R

'French Belt' to Lac la Rouge and Ile à la Crosse. Here lumbering is active, together with trapping, and tourism. The Bonnyville–Lac la Biche pioneer zone is on the fringe of agricultural possibilities, with a mean July temperature of 60° F.—usually taken as the northern limit of successful commercial production. 'Crops frequently suffer frost damage in the spring and autumn.' The population increased up until 1941, but then saw a decline.

> Such a drop by no means indicates a lack of success in the pioneer venture. It should not be read to indicate a deterioration in conditions, rather, it reflects an improvement. For it is the result of better organization of land, with a growing tendency to consolidate farms. When the first rush of settlers came in, the land was eagerly divided up and then became subdivided. As a result some of the holdings were too small.
>
> In an area such as this the margin of risk is considerable. The variability in the growing season, in the onset of frosts, and in the distribution of rainfall is marked. One of the best ways of overcoming this is to have an extra field or two. *Safety is bought with space.* Consequently, small holdings have in many instances been given up and have been absorbed in larger ones.[1]

Much the same may be said of the *Lesser Slave Lake district* around High Prairie and Grimshaw, and of the *Peace River country*. Farming has had marked opportunities in the dark brown and fertile parkland soils, and in the better timber-grey soils, but at the same time has had to adapt itself to severe limitations, notably to a cool summer with July averages of 60°–61° F. and killing frosts in the autumn coming as early as the third week in July. Yet this combination of challenge and reward has made agriculture very adaptive; the more generalized wheat farming that characterized the early pioneer wave (1906–14) has given way to a concentration on barley and oats grown in support of stock farming, or else to a specialization in seed oats, seed hay, and seed alfalfa. These last do particularly well because the region is still free from many of the weeds and pests with which crops are damaged farther south.

Although the French are still an important element in the population of the Lesser Slave and upper Peace river basins, they share the region with many British, Scandinavians, Poles and Ukrainians, and also with many Americans that found here a fresh frontier when their own pioneer areas had become filled up. This highly diversified kind of settlement is typical.[2]

---

[1] Baker, W. M., 'A Reconnaissance Survey of the Saddle Lake District, Alberta', *Geog. Bul.*, 1954, no. 5, pp. 19–20.

[2] Merrill, G. C., 'Human Geography of the Lesser Slave Lake Area'. *Geog., Bul.*, 1953, no. 3, pp. 41–47.

However, although members of different stocks do tend to reside next to or near each other, there are no significant 'bloc' communities. Farmsteads are scattered and apart.

> Agricultural land has been parcelled out in square lots (quarter sections) of 160 acres each. Even if all the contiguous quarter sections were occupied, as very often they are not, settlers would be placed at least one-half mile apart. When additional quarters are acquired, distances between neighbours increase. This individual mode of settlement has continued to prevail throughout the Peace river region. While here and there neighbouring homes may lie close together, distances are, in general, noticeably great.[1]

It must be remembered that this habit of establishing relatively isolated farmsteads was initiated in the motor-car era. As more cars became used and better roads were made actual isolation disappeared. The motor-car was significant in another way—it helped the rise of the central town, over against the local village which, more often than not, was simply a 'whistle stop' station on a railway line, or a service centre at a crossing of roads. Consequently, a few places forged ahead—Grande Prairie, Peace River, Dawson Creek—and the rest became static or even declined. Grande Prairie is the unacknowledged 'capital' of the Peace River country, and is the regional headquarters for banks and insurance companies, and of provincial government agencies.

The growth of these regional foci has helped to stimulate the areas for which they are the centres, and a more varied economy has developed. Lumbering is now as important as farming in many parts, while the extraction of oil and natural gas, at Sturgeon L. (Alta) and Boundary L. (B.C.), in the upper Peace, is expanding. The natural gas is piped to Vancouver and Seattle, but is also used locally. Indeed, the cheapness and availability of local oil and gas are major factors in the economic expansion of the region.

The Peace River country has long sought an outlet to Vancouver as well as to Edmonton. This was provided shortly after the Second World War when the Hart Highway was built, branching off the Alaska Highway at Dawson Creek. This route makes use of the broad pass through the Rockies opened up by the Pine river, and then of a portion of the Rocky Mountain Trench.

Northern British Columbia is developing rapidly. Here lies **Prince George**, a major centre of northern development. It is an important road junction, with the Hart, Skeena, and Cariboo Highways all coming together, and also a main railway connexion, where the Canadian National Railway

[1] Dawson, C. A., *The Settlement of the Peace River Country*, Toronto, 1934 p. 26.

to Prince Rupert is joined by the Prince George and Eastern Railway that winds its way south to Squamish and Vancouver. The town is also a thriving agricultural and lumbering centre, lying at the heart of a wide plain—formerly the bed of a large glacial lake—yet close by forested uplands. It has now reached Dawson's final stage in pioneer development, that of acting as an integrating centre for communities which were at one time largely isolated and self-contained.

Pioneering is still going on in the Stuart, Nechako, and Bulkley basins to the north, west, and north-west. Here the bush of small spruce, aspen, and birch is being actively cut into—or, rather, bulldozed back, the brushwood heaped into long piles and burned, the ash scattered over the virgin soil, and new farms, raising oats, barley and hay, sheep and store cattle, are everywhere springing up. However, the region is marginal and, as in the case of the Peace River country, has had to prove especially adaptive to meet the problems of frost, soil improvement, and access to market. Particularly difficult to bear has been the combination of frost and depression. Checks in expansion have occurred, but while these had unhappy results for some individuals, they proved useful to most, in that they brought down land speculation, weeded out wasteful and incompetent uses of land, and forced the freight rates to more reasonable levels. These checks also led to a more diversified economy and the development of forestry, fishing, and mining wherever possible. Molybdenum in particular is important (Endako).

The spectacular feat of reversing the drainage of the Nechako, and of drawing off water from its dammed-up lakes down a great tunnel cut through the Coast Range, enabled a large amount of hydro-electric power to be developed at the coast, which is used, in the main, by the great aluminium smelter at Kitimat—second only to Arvida on the continent (Fig. 131). North of this, at Hazelton, copper, lead, and zinc mining is active. **Prince Rupert** (12,500) is the main port of the north. In addition to being an active wholesale and trading community, it is a major fishing centre, canning the salmon caught in the Skeena and in neighbouring fjords, and also freezing and packing halibut, taken from north of the Queen Charlotte Isles. Its striking position at the mouth of the Skeena, which makes a deep, low-level cut through the Coast Range, and opposite Dixon Entrance, a wide break in the fringe of off-shore islands, has helped it to make considerable progress. However, its limited hinterland has not allowed it to have anything like the success of Vancouver and as the larger port has forged ahead, Prince Rupert has had to be content with a comparatively modest role.

The Canadian North-west offers much promise. Here, beyond the long line of pioneer settlements between the Shield (Le Pas) and the Pacific Coast (Prince Rupert and Kitimat), all of which have by now consolidated their positions and taken on the aspects of more stable communities, lie far-flung

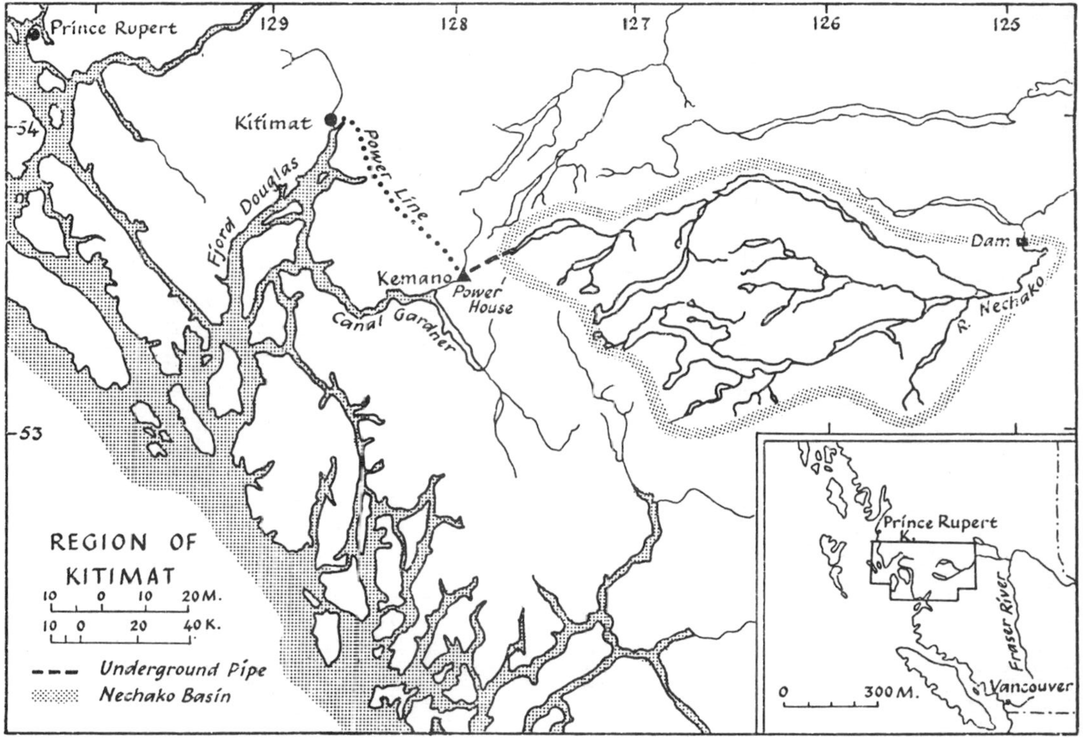

FIG. 131 Expansion North—Kitimat. Here at the head of a fjord, and therefore accessible by sea to distant raw materials and markets, and close to the vast water resources of the Rockies (made greater by damming back and reversing the Nechako drainage), Kitimat has become one of the world's leading producers of aluminium.

outposts of development. These are generally beyond railhead and are in the main too remote for the economic transportation of farm produce or lumber, although not too distant for the export of furs and precious metals. They are, therefore, chiefly fur-trading posts or mining centres. Today 'the fur industry is declining and fluctuating prices for pelts make it a precarious one. It is now but the third "industry" of the Territories, for in recent years it has averaged in value only about $750,000—about 7 to 8 per cent of the Canadian total.'[1] Currently, the emphasis on northern strategy has turned a number of earlier trading posts into air bases, or led to the establishment of quite new sites.

These northern outposts are served by river, road, and airway. The Mackenzie waterway is still important as an avenue of trade, although it suffers disabilities: it is frozen from November to May (even when the river thaws, Great Slave Lake is often blocked by ice); it is interrupted by impassable rapids, at Fort Fitzgerald, where a portage has been made necessary, and by swift water in the section known as the Palisades; and it has a most unequal régime, flowing deep and strong in early summer, but falling to a surprisingly low level, revealing sand banks and mud shoals, in the fall. None the less, river-steamers and tugs pushing great barges in front of them still carry most of the heavy supplies in and out of northern communities by this route. Later, the building of the Mackenzie Highway from Grimshaw to Great Slave Lake, cutting out the Fitzgerald rapids, came to offer serious competition. This road, together with a winter extension to Yellowknife, is now the chief artery of trade to at any rate the upper Mackenzie district. The Alaska Highway from Dawson Creek, in the Peace River country, across the Rockies, into the Yukon plateau, and eventually into Alaska, has done much to open up the Yukon. The railway to Pine Point is important.

There are at present two principal areas of development—the first in the Great Slave Lake area, and the other in the upper Yukon. These developments are centred in Yellowknife and Whitehorse.

The Great Slave Lake area has much to offer. As the relic of a once much larger glacial lake it lies in a basin fringed with clay flats, old sandy deltas, stranded gravel beaches, and well-drained sandy-loam terraces. The Slave and Hay rivers tributary to it, though deeply entrenched, have alluvial terraces that have good woods and wooded soils. Though frozen for eight months, the soils thaw out during the summer, and where climatic conditions are suitable, can be made quite productive. At present, there are very few farms, but farming at Keg river and Fort Vermilion, at the approaches to the area, is making good progress. Here there are 542,000[2] acres of black

---

[1] Nicholson, N. L., 'The North-west Territories, Geographical Aspects', *Can. Geog. Jour.*, **lx**, no. 1 (January 1960), p. 21.

[2] *The North Pacific Planning Project*, *Canada's New North-west*, Ottawa, 1948, pp. 43–44.

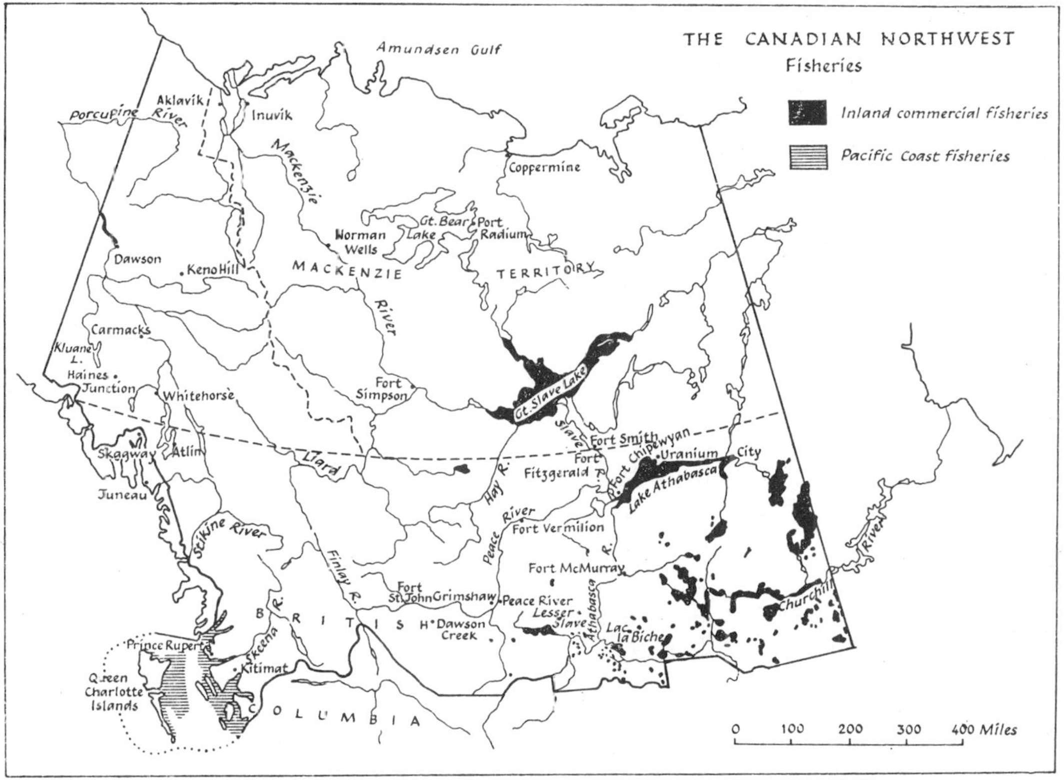

FIG. 132 Sea and Lake Fisheries of the Canadian North-west—an increasingly important resource drawing men into the North.

park or good grey-timber soils, while along the lower Hay and the south shore of the lake are another 200,000 acres that could be cultivated.[1] Here moreover is the longest growing season in the Mackenzie district, with 92 days free of frost (Fort Resolution),[2] where growth is stimulated by over 2,000 hours of summer light (cf. about 1,800 in Ontario), and by summer rains. The main drawbacks are the variability of the growing season and the lack of an accessible market. The frost-free season has been cut as short as 28 days (1912).

A local market is growing as other resources are being developed and commercial fishing settlements, lumber camps, and mines spring up. The fishery in Great Slave Lake, based on Hay river, is quite important, producing about 6 million pounds of whitefish a year. Caught in the short summer season, the fish are packed fresh between ice and sent in great refrigerator trucks down the Mackenzie Highway to the railhead at Grimshaw. Domestic consumption takes about 1 million pounds; the rest is exported (Fig. 132).

Lumber camps on the south shore of the lake, and along the Slave and Hay terraces, have local significance, providing sawn timber for the transportation and mining towns that are mushrooming in the area. Mining is, however, the most important occupation (Fig. 133). The structures of the Athabasca and Great Slave Lake enclaves in the edge of the Shield have already been referred to. The Yellowknife sub-province has some of the oldest formations of the Shield and is rich in gold, along lines of contact between igneous and metamorphic rocks. It opens out into the East Arm, a dominantly sedimentary belt, in which occurrences of copper, lead, and zinc are significant. New mines have been opened at nearby Tundra and Discovery. The Talston mountains to the south and the Athabasca plateau south of that have important uranium finds, some of which are worked (Uranium City). Yellowknife is the main urban centre and 'has become one of Canada's great gold camps despite transportation costs and a difficult period (economically speaking) for operators of gold mines'.[3] It has acted as the integrative force in making a distinct region out of the area.

Nickel, cobalt (East Arm) and lead and zinc (Pine Point, south shore) also exist in quantity. The lead ore is crushed and the concentrate shipped out by train to a smelter near Edmonton. This is a major project.

All these developments have helped to increase the population and economic viability of the Mackenzie District appreciably to the extent that it now has an Elective Council.

[1] Dickson, W., 'Northern Agriculture', in *The New North-West*, Toronto, 1947, p. 166.

[2] Robinson, J. L., 'Land Use Possibilities in Mackenzie District, N.W.T.', *Can. Geog. Jour.*, July 1945.

[3] Lang, A. H., and Douglas, R. J. W., 'Minerals and Fuels', in *The Canadian Northwest: Its Potentialities*, Toronto, 1959, p. 47.

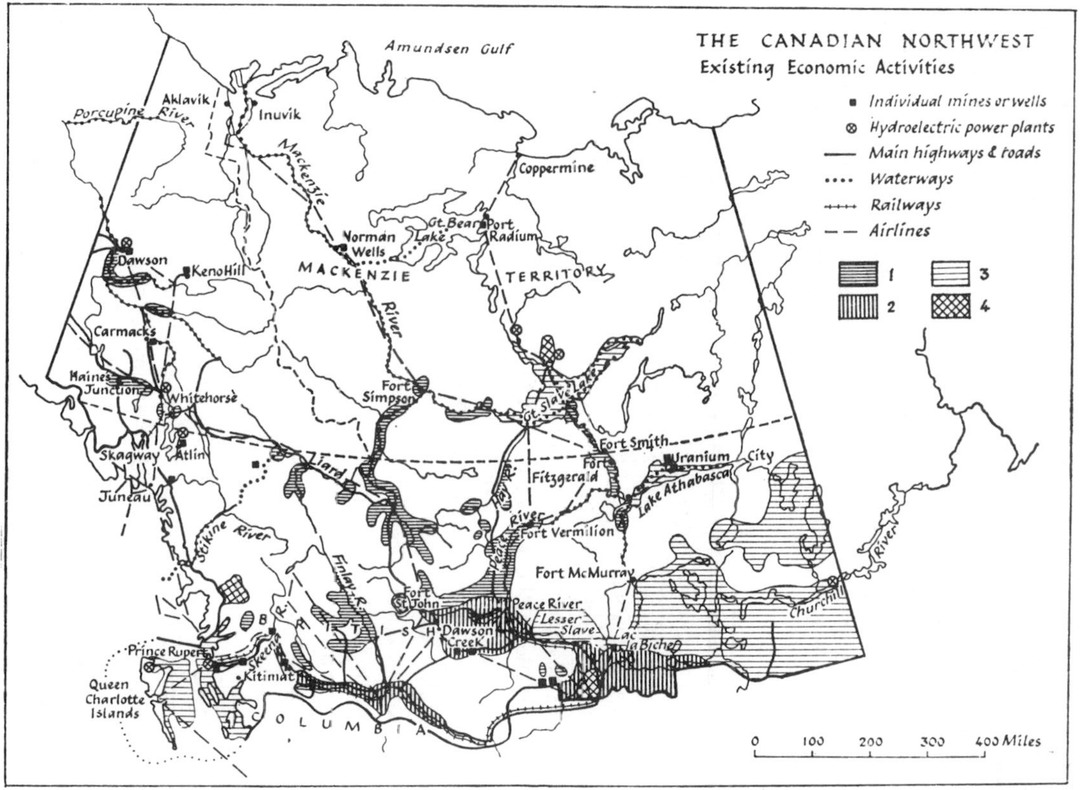

FIG. 133 Transportation, Key to the Canadian Northwest, together with areas of economic activity stimulated by the opening and development of routeways. The Inner Passage to Skagway, the use of the Yukon and of the Mackenzie waterways, the building of the railways to the Athabasca and Peace, and the construction of the Alaska and Mackenzie highways have opened up distinct areas of commercial development, which form the base for further expansion. A new railway has now been built to Pine Point, on Gt Slave Lake.

Key:
1, Potential agriculture; 2, Existing pioneer farming; 3, Fishing; 4, Mining areas, minerals and fuels.

The Upper Yukon forms a second area of active exploitation and settlement in Canada's North-west. It consists of a low plateau of from 2,000 to 4,000 feet in height. Most of the rocks are sedimentary and have a north-west–south-east trend. They have been mildly folded, and contain small basins of coal, and several oil-bearing formations. The soils on the plateau are mostly an acidic podsol, fit only for the rather thin forest of spruce. Terrace alluvium, however, is cultivable. Most of the rivers have well-marked upper and lower terraces, and offer about 250,000 acres of land suitable for agriculture.[1] But the coolness of summer and the shortness of the growing season, 60 to 75 days free of frost, make agriculture a hazard;[2] there are only forty farms, although there are many market gardens. The climate is more suited to forests, and on the northern aspects of the hills and river valleys woods of white spruce, aspen, Alaska white birch, and black poplar are found. About 2,000 sq. miles of merchantable timber exists, enough to supply local towns, but not enough to support a lumber industry. Several lumber camps are found near Whitehorse. Southern aspects tend to be bare of trees and carry grass and bushes, thus breaking up the forest area.

Mining is the chief occupation. The famous Klondike gold rush of 1897–8 opened up the region. The boom lasted till 1900, when $2 millions of gold were produced. Output still continues, although on a smaller scale. It consists mainly of working over the placer gravels already sifted and, by the use of powerful dredges and hydraulic screening, finding gold in areas thought to be too lean for 'panning'. Placer gold was also raised at Mayo, but here rich lodes were found in the near-by hills, and from 1916 on placer mining was replaced by hard-rock mining, and gold, silver, lead, and zinc have been produced in quantity. Silver is now Yukon's chief export.

Coal, oil, and natural gas also occur in the Yukon. There are significant coal deposits along the Big Salmon and Porcupine rivers. Mining has long taken place at Carmacks, the coal being used in the main by the river boats plying between Whitehorse and Dawson. Oil and gas are produced not far from Whitehorse and oil-bearing structures are being rapidly explored.

All this development has depended on transportation (see Fig. 133). Two main routes are used, the long waterway from Vancouver by the 'inner passage' to Skagway, followed by a railway to Whitehorse, and the Alaska Highway from Dawson Creek (B.C.) to Whitehorse. The convergence of these two major routes from Vancouver and Edmonton at Whitehorse has made this the most progressive centre in the Territory, and the capital was accordingly moved to it from Dawson. An important airport and a large

---

[1] Archibald, E. S., 'Agricultural Lands in the Canadian North-west', *Can. Geog. Jour.*, July 1944, **29**, no. 1, pp. 40–51.

[2] Robinson, J. L., 'Agriculture and Forests of Yukon Territory', *Can. Geog. Jour.*, August 1945.

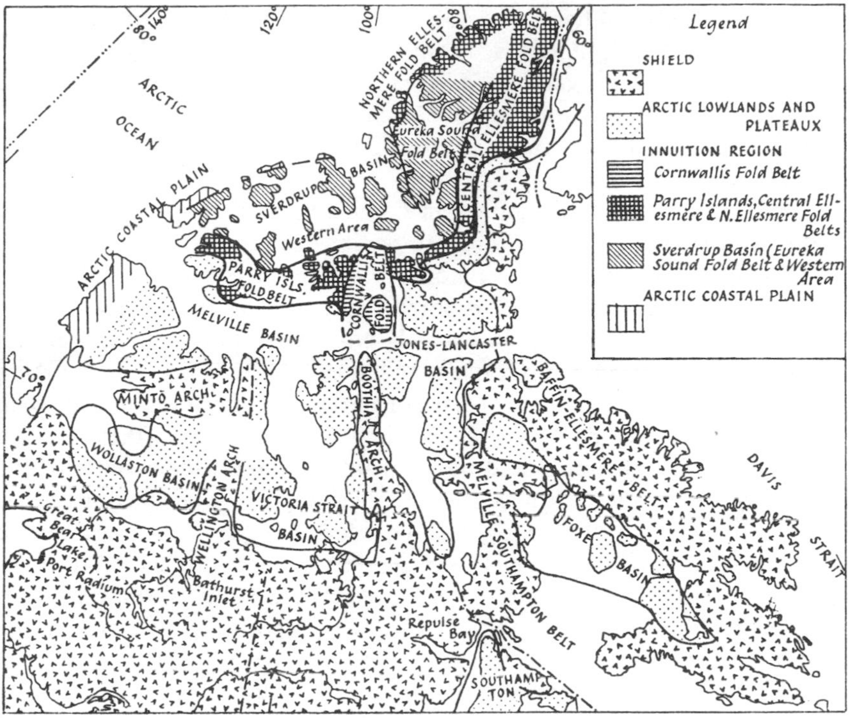

FIG. 134 The Structure of the Far North. (From Fortier.) Note the great belt of folding from the Parry Isles to Ellesmere. This is known as the Innuitian system. (Scale, 1:25 m.)

military and air-force base have added to its importance. From Whitehorse boats ply the river north to Dawson, while 'development' roads run north to Carmacks and Mayo. Thus Whitehorse has become the 'hub of the Yukon', and has helped greatly to knit the diverse region together into a growing unity.

The rest of the northland—the Porcupine, the lower Mackenzie, Hudson Bay, Foxe basin, and the Canadian archipelago—is still largely undeveloped and remains a fur-trapping and trading area. However, strategic reasons have, as has been noted, led to the rise of military settlements. They have also quickened scientific surveys until today we have a fairly good picture of the structure of the region and of its potential for development (Fig. 134).

CONCLUSION

Obviously, then, the Canadian north, though still empty and quiet, is waking up and being developed. It is coming into its own, and promises much for the future. This sense of promise, pervading the whole area, is giving it the feeling of being a region of its own, with its own problems and opportunities. The optimism is, however, level-headed, and the difficulties and limitations of the region are fully realized. But it is the pressing forward, the living for the future, that is now so characteristic.

As the Gordon Report states, trying to sum it up:

> There is widespread recognition in Canada that the northern reaches of the country, including the northern sections of the Provinces as well as the Yukon and North-west Territories, constitute a new economic frontier. Northern Canada today and tomorrow may be what the West was in the earlier part of our history. It not only offers attractions to those seeking adventure and fortune but it has seen industry become interested in these areas as a long-term source of basic materials. Major developments such as the Kitimat plant of the Aluminium Company in northern British Columbia, the new pulp and paper plants in the northern parts of the Prairie region, and the heavy investment leading to the production of iron ore in Ungava and Labrador, to note a few examples, are precursors of similar events in the future. The increasing demands for the products of Canada's forests and mines or for special hydro-power resources will probably lead to major developments, as transportation and other basic investments are made throughout the northern parts of the country. The exact form these developments will take, and the time which will elapse in each instance, will be largely determined by the interplay of the forces of supply and demand. The next few decades, however, will transform much of this northern area of Canada.[1]

---

[1] Royal Commission on Canada's Economic Prospects, Final Report, Ottawa, 1957, pp. 413–14.

CHAPTER SIXTEEN

The United States: the Country

The area of North America that became the United States long remained isolated—remote from the Bering Straits crossing out of Asia, and also from the northern and southern island arcs used by Ericson and Columbus sailing out of Europe. It therefore stayed backward, but its empty spaces and undeveloped resources eventually beckoned the European, and especially those who sought out newness. '*He is an American, who, leaving behind him all his ancient prejudices and manners, receives new ones from the new mode of life he has embraced.*'[1] An area of strong contrasts—of massive mountains and broad plains, of rainy coasts and dry interiors, of cold uplands and hot lowlands—it has offered a real challenge. Provocative, it appealed to '*men who appeared to have been allured by the very difficulties which discouraged others. They were hardy, enterprising men, fond of chance, and familiar with fatigue.*'[2] Diverse, yet centred in an immense and fertile basin, the area attracted at once strong individualism and independence and yet an overriding sense of interdcpendence and unity. So great was the division that at one time the country became half one thing, and half another—'half slave, and half free'. Yet integration was so real, that union prevailed. '*Physically speaking, we [America] cannot separate. We cannot remove our respective sections from each other.*'[3] United, the area found itself possessed of the most productive soils, the largest deposits of fuel and ore, the most comfortable yet most stimulating climates, and the most ramified system of river-routes on the continent. America became the new name for opportunity.

> '*Strong, ample, fair, enduring, capable, rich,*
> *The course of Time and nations . . . all converged in thee.*'[4]

The character of America is thus a blend of human and physical factors of psychology and physiography. The European who was willing to cut his ties with Europe and commit his destiny to North America, became an American, as Crèvecoeur put it, by being received in the broad lap of his

---

[1] Crèvecoeur, St J., *Letters from an American Farmer*, 1782.
[2] Hall, Hames, *Letters from the West*, 1828.
[3] Lincoln, Abraham, First Inaugural Speech, 1861.
[4] Whitman, Walt, 'America', in *Sands at Seventy*, 1881.

new Alma Mater. Here physical geography played a great role, and physical regions tended to work their way out in historical and economic divisions.

PHYSIOGRAPHY AND HISTORY

An important aspect of the physical environment consisted of marked changes in slope made by river valleys, plateau scarps, and mountains. Thus in successive westward drifts of the American people, natural boundary lines were met that served to mark, and to affect the characteristics of, the frontier. These were: the 'Fall Line', the Allegheny mountains, the Mississippi, the middle Missouri below the Missouri Coteau, the front of the High Plains, and the Rocky mountains. The Fall Line marked the seventeenth-century frontier; the Missouri that of the second quarter; the High Plains and the Rockies, the end-of-the-century frontier (Fig. 135).

'The Atlantic coast plain, with its drowned estuaries, allowed settlements to be grouped in enclosed sea-basins which carried vessels by protected waterways as far as possible into the land.'[1] Hence the living at the bay-heads. The broadening of the coast plain in the south invited that territorial expansion 'which early in the eighteenth century led the settlers to hammer at the gates of the mountain wall'.[2] Meantime, as long as settlements were bound to the coast, they were bounded by the Fall Line—the outer limit of the Piedmont plateau and the first interruption to river navigation. Once this was overcome by portage, or later by canal, settlement could advance over the Piedmont until it came to the Appalachian barrier. Semple makes a great deal of the Appalachians in early American history. The Appalachian barrier helped to consolidate British settlement. It narrowed the British horizon and 'shut out the great beyond; it took away the temptation to wide expansion which was defeating the aims of the Spanish and the French, and transformed the hunter into the farmer, the gentleman adventurer into the tobacco-grower'.[3] Eventually, however, the barrier was pierced through gaps in the Blue Ridge leading to the Great Valley. This line was most important. Whereas

> in the tidewater and Piedmont regions, the general movement of the population was north-west along the course of the drainage streams at right-angles to the coast, within the mountains, population advanced down the longitudinal valleys, along a north-east–south-west line, parallel with the trend of the Appalachian system, and it swept along in its tide all the little streams of outbound settlers who crossed the Blue Ridge. The

[1] Semple, E. C., *American History and its Geographic Conditions*, New York, 1933 edn., p. 46.

[2] Ibid., p. 52.

[3] Ibid., p. 67.

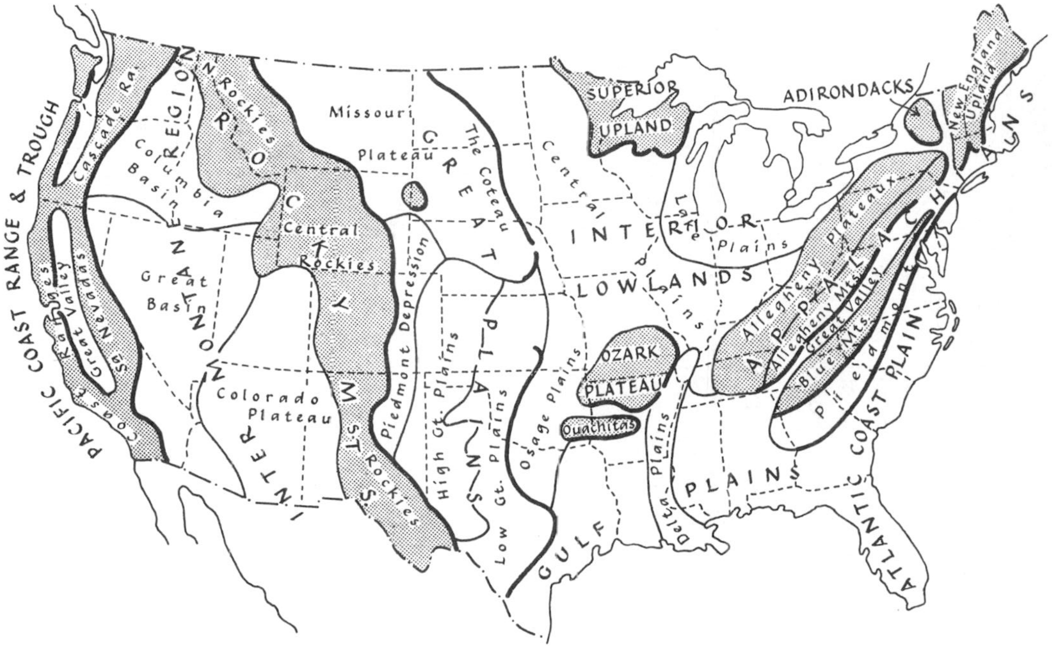

FIG. 135 The Major Physiographic Regions of the United States, showing principal barriers to the east–west advance of settlement. Since the main drive was latitudinal, man subordinated the longitudinal trend of the country to his own ends, stressing passes and tributaries that led west, till America reached from coast to coast. The main barriers are shown in darker lines and include the Piedmont edge, the Blue Ridge, the Allegheny Front, the Ozark and Superior uplands, the Coteau or Break of the Plains, the Rockies, the Cascades, and the Coast Ranges. (Scale, 1:35 m.)

consequence was that while the tidewater regions of the colonies kept each its distinctive character, born of distinct old-world sources and diverse environments, the backwoods population of the mountains, from the Wyoming Valley to the Yadkin, showed a wide mingling of ethnic elements—Dutch, German, Huguenot French, Scotch-Irish, and English —which obliterated the distinctive types of the coast, while the prevailing similarity of their geographic environment operated to produce the new type of the backwoods—the democratic element of the frontier.[1]

Finally, when the great trek across the Appalachians took place, the grouping of the mountain gaps and the way they debouched on the interior basins of the Tennessee and the Ohio, 'favored the expansion of the middle colonies. Their long line of western frontier was a chord subtending the rude arc formed by the Tennessee and Ohio rivers. The headwaters of these streams opened many gateways to the transmontane lands.'[2] Between the transmontane basins was the Cumberland plateau, 'a region condemned by its geographical conditions to isolation, poverty, and a retarded civilization'.[3] Settlers headed for the Nashville basin, the limestone depressions of Kentucky, and, above all, the alluvial terraces of the Tennessee and Ohio rivers.

If this emphasis on physiographic regions seems suspect because made by a geographer, one has only to appeal to the historians. Turner harks upon the influence of the West, and particularly on the effect of the interior lowlands, in all their immensity. The men of the Mississippi valley, he claimed, compelled the men of the coast to think in American instead of European terms. Yet, notwithstanding the way it fostered nationalism, the West sponsored sectionalism. This grew out of the discovery of new regions in the march across the continent. It was seen in the new democracy of the Allegheny front, in the local loyalties engendered within the Cumberland plateau and the interior 'highlands', in the special opportunities of the Ohio, in the peculiar problems of the Mississippi, and, above all, in the clash between the new north-west and the new south-west, a clash that eventually split the country. As recent a writer as Billington tells the story of western expansion mainly in terms of the physiographic regions that captured or repelled activity, routes, settlement, and population.

Held back for some time by the Indians in the Old North-west and by the Spanish in West Florida, the Americans found new freedom with new successes in the war of 1812–14. They were then able to move out from the Allegheny plateau, cross the Ohio, and enter the Great Lakes plain: at the same time, pushing down the Alabama, they reached the Gulf Coast plain.

[1] Semple, *American History and its Geographic Conditions*, p. 71.
[2] Ibid., p. 82. [3] Ibid., p. 82.

'The north-west seemed an agricultural haven to farmers from the hilly east.'[1] Here pioneers met for the first time that great and commanding feature, the Central Lowlands which, forming the heart of the continent, gave to America a very distinct advantage over Canada and Mexico. The oak-covered moraines, the 'oak-openings' or little prairies on the old glacial beaches, deltas and dunelands, and the rich alluvial terraces of rivers rejuvenated since glacial times, offered attractive sites for lumber camps, and for farm villages and homesteads. The heavily wooded and well-watered hills of the Shelbyville, Bloomington, Kalamazoo, and Defiance moraines were favoured for sites. The lacustrine flats of glacial lakes Chicago, Maumee, Whittlesey, and Warren were difficult to clear at first, having a good deal of swamp-oak forest, mixed with shagbark hickory and cedar, but when cleared and drained were widely used. The 'American Bottom' along the middle Mississippi was especially attractive, and drew many settlers.

So rapid and broad was the advance into the west that it led to large quantities of relatively cheap grain going on to the market. Eastern farmers found it difficult to compete. In New England many of them gave up crop farming and turned to sheep raising; in New York, to the fattening of beef and to dairy farming. Small general farms were bought up and amalgamated into larger beef or sheep farms, and thousands of smallholders streamed west, pushing beyond the Great Lakes to the Mississippi itself. At the same time, many southerners were driven west, either by the impoverishment of the soils in the east or by the lack of room in the rather restricted basins of Kentucky and Tennessee. Again, many of these were smallholders who found it profitable to sell out to big plantations, and break new ground out west.

The exhaustion of south-eastern soils went on rapidly on more marginal sites, until to many farmers there seemed to be only one solution: 'trade the butchered lands of the east for the virgin fields of the west. Thousands of farmers who reached that conclusion swelled the population of the Gulf Plains.'[2] The sweep of these southern plains across the Mississippi, with the continuation into Texas of the series of low scarps and intervening vales found in Alabama, invited farmers to take up land in what was once Mexican territory, but soon became American. Scarp and vale provided 'timber and prairie interspersed in convenient proportions', the black soils of the prairies offered 'land of exhaustless fertility'; while a 'well-nigh perfect climate for eight months of the year, with the unpleasant heat of the remaining four tempered by the steady breeze from the Gulf'—all beckoned men like Austin to cross the border and pioneer in the region.[3]

---

[1] Billington, R. A., *Westward Expansion*, New York, 2nd edn., 1960, p. 292.
[2] Ibid., p. 318.
[3] Barker, E. C., *Life of Stephen F. Austin*, Nashville, 1925.

Both in the south and the north, settlers were then faced with some very real barriers; these were the 'break of the plains', including long escarpments such as the Balcones escarpment and the Missouri Coteau, and a combination of a drier climate with sand hills or badlands. Settlement pushed up the Red, Arkansas, and lower Missouri river, on rich alluvial terraces, but then paused at the edge of the Great Plain. Explorers like Pike and Palliser had reported dry and difficult terrain ahead. Pike wrote: 'I saw in my route tracts of many leagues where the wind had thrown up the sand in all the fanciful forms of the ocean's rolling waves, and on which not a speck of vegetable matter existed.' It was suggested that farmers should 'limit their extent in the west to the borders of the Missouri and Mississippi, and leave the prairies incapable of cultivation to the wandering and uncivilized aborigines of the country'.[1]

However, the reports of other explorers, notably of Dr John Floyd, on the Oregon Country, west of the Rockies, which described that region as having good range land in its interior basins, and forests and perennial meadows along its wet coastal trench, drew settlers right across the Great Plains, through passes in the mountains, to the Columbia basin and the Pacific coast. The discovery at mid-century of gold in the gravel beds of rivers flowing into the Great Valley of California started a still greater rush to the west. It was followed by ranchers and farmers who saw the more permanent value of this great intermontane depression.

The physiography of the Cordilleras began to play its part in the history of the nation. The near approach of the Platte and Snake rivers to each other and their connexion by the soon-to-be-famous South Pass enabled the Oregon and California trails to be established. Similarly the comparative nearness of the upper Rio Grande, the Colorado, and the Gila rivers allowed routes to be built from Santa Fé by the Colorado to San Gabriel and by the Gila to San Diego, California. The great trench between the Sierra Nevada and the Coast ranges was early described as being 'remarkable for uniting the advantages of a good soil, temperate climate, a happy mixture of level and elevated ground, and vicinity to the sea'[2] and soon drew most of the settlers journeying to the far west. In the meantime, the sheer isolation of the basins between the Cascade and Rocky ranges, and particularly of the Great Basin, had gathered in its settlers—those who 'sought the most isolated, inhospitable spot on all the continent where they could worship God as they chose'. So the Mormons came to their 'desert Zion' in Utah, and began that pioneer experiment in irrigation which was to revolutionize the colonization of the arid interior.

---

[1] Morris, R. C., 'The Notion of a Great American Desert East of the Rockies', *Mississippi Valley Hist. Rev.*, September 1926, **xiii**.

[2] Shaler, W., quoted in Billington, *Westward Expansion*, p. 563.

Eventually the 'unfamiliar environment of the Great Plains', without the forests, the humid soils, the springs, the ever-flowing rivers that characterized the east, became occupied. First the ranchers moved in. After the Civil War a great northward trek of cattlemen from Texas took place. Cattle were the natural replacement for buffalo, and grazing the best use of the vast and almost unbroken grassland that swept from Texas to Canada. But as the pressure on land became greater, as the homesteader found it impossible to procure more free land, or cheap land, east of the Coteau, farming began to spread over the plains; the homesteader vied with the rancher for the region, and ultimately by the assistance of the wire fence instead of a wooden one, of the windmill instead of the hand-pump, and of machines for the mass sowing and harvesting of the crops, the man behind the plough took over and the cowboy went up to the hills. These developments depended a great deal on mechanical aids and so came later in time (1880–1905), when the industrial revolution in the east had set in.

Thus we see that from their short but eventful history of exploration and exploitation, Americans came to recognize several major landform regions. Their early occupation of the **Coast Plain** made them aware of its value. To the north, Canada was without one—from narrow and broken raised beaches the shore rose abruptly to Laurentian or Appalachian uplands. To the south, Mexico had only a very attenuated coastal lowland, backed by very lofty and rather inaccessible mountains. The presence of a long and wide Coast Plain, reaching from New England to Texas, thus helped to single out the United States and give it a distinct advantage. Soon the morainic ridges of Long Island, the wolds and vales of the mid-Atlantic area, the sandy reefs and swampy lagoons of the south-east, backed by marine terraces rising one above the other, the limestone plain of Florida, the belted lowlands of Alabama and Texas with their wooded scarps and dark-soiled prairies, and the alluvial plains of the lower Mississippi were all used for their different worth to give a very varied agriculture and a wide net of settlements.

Then the **Piedmont** was developed, with its upland soils, thickly branched dendritic pattern of streams, its peneplaned flats and deep, sharp valleys. Thereafter the whole of **the Appalachian mountain system** was penetrated; first of all in New England, where beyond the low eastern upland, carved into ample bays, or interrupted by long glaciated valleys, rose the Berkshire and Taconic hills or, farther north, the quite lofty White and Green mountains. South of the Hudson, the threefold system of the Blue Ridge, the Great Valley and the Ridge-and-Valley section, and the Allegheny–Cumberland plateau, was laboriously explored and developed. The southward drift of people along the beautiful and fertile plain of the widely meandering Shenandoah and the Coosa, turned west after the Revolution, and the great westward push occurred across the Cumberland plateau into the interior basins of Tennessee and Kentucky, with their fertile, grassy hollows rimmed by rock knobs or by plateau 'barrens'.

After the war of 1812–14 there was another great westward surge which discovered the broad **Central Plains**, reaching from the Great Lakes down the Ohio and Mississippi to the Ozarks. The fact that these were much more extensively developed than in Canada—where they were represented mainly in the Red River valley and the Lower Great Lakes lowland—again made something distinctive out of the United States; a distinction still more in evidence when the United States was compared with Mexico, without a central lowland at all. Most of the settlers seemed to prefer the heavier and more familiar soils of the drift plains north of the Ohio to the drift-free plains to the south. The Mississippi bottoms were especially favoured.

The next great region to be discovered, the **Great Plains**, including the **High Plains**, was slow to be developed; partly because of physiographic hazards like the Dakota Badlands, the Sand Hills of Nebraska, and the Stripped Plains of western Texas, but mainly because of climatic hazards like drought and duststorms. Consequently the westward push went through the region to the green and lovely land of the Willamette valley and Puget Sound in Oregon, and to the pleasant and fertile fans and terraces fringing the Great Valley of California. **The Cordilleran system** was rapidly opened up as miners found gold, silver, and copper along the flanks of the Sierra Nevada, as sheep ranchers discovered the value of the Dome-and-Park district of the American Rockies, and cattle ranchers the great rangelands in the intermontane basins, between the Rockies and the Cascade–Nevadan ranges. Irrigation enabled farmers to occupy parts of the Great Basin, and, above all, made a garden of the California valley, between the Nevadan and Coast ranges.

The way in which the Cordilleras reached their climax in the United States, being far broader and having a more ramified structure than in Canada or Mexico, once again helped to make America different. In particular the fact that its elongated western depressions—the Great Valley of California and the Willamette valley and Puget Sound lowland—had not been drowned by the sea as they were in Canada (the Inner Passage to Alaska) and in Mexico (the Gulf of California) was of the greatest advantage to the United States, and enabled its Pacific areas to become much more populous and fully developed than those of Mexico and Canada.

Finally, the demand for cheap meat and wheat led to the fresh and full occupation of the **Great Plains**, while at the same time the need for iron to support the growing industries of the east produced a rash of mining towns along the Iron Ranges of the **Superior Upland**—America's small but valuable portion of the Canadian Shield.

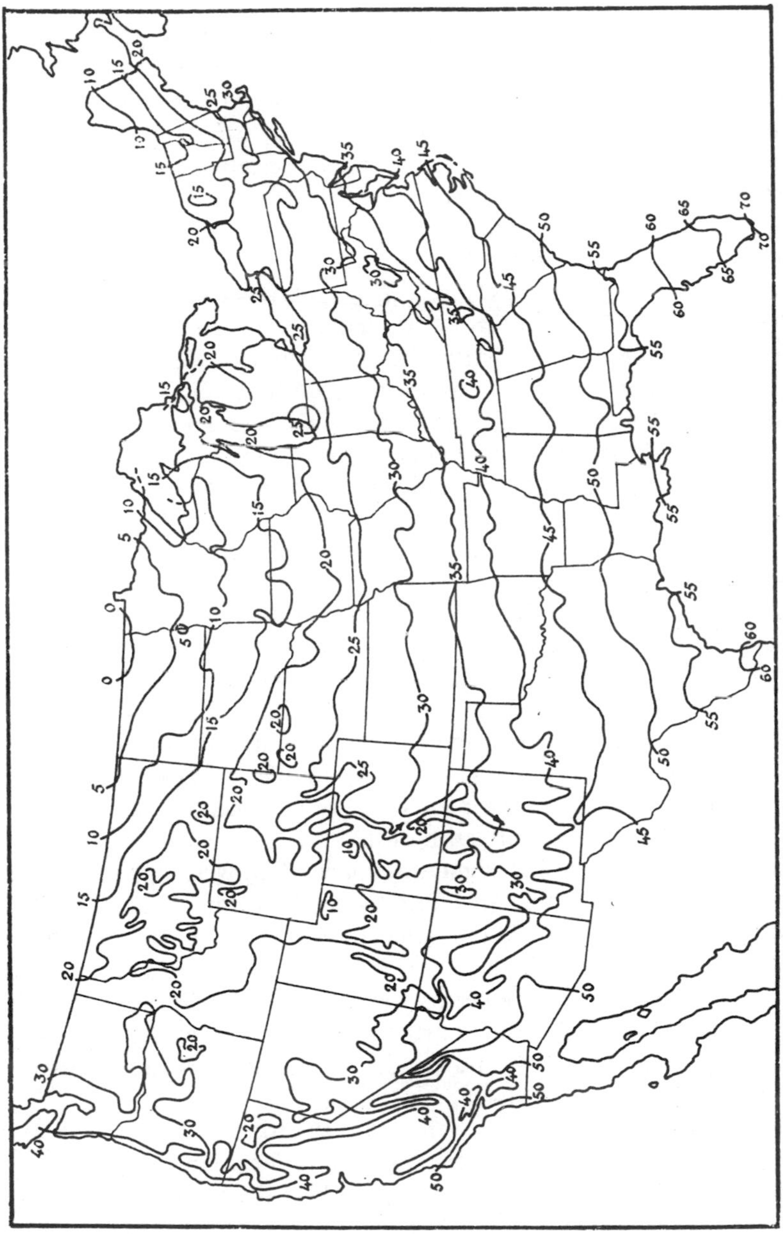

FIG. 136 The Distribution of Temperature: Average January Temperature (° F). Relatively little of the United States has sub-zero weather, making it distinct from Canada. (Scale, 1:32 m.)

CLIMATIC SUITABILITY OF AMERICA

Important though landforms were, however, they were by no means the only controls, and sometimes not even the main controls, of migration, settlement, and development. The climates, the natural vegetation, and the soils of the United States also played their part.

The climates of the United States, not unlike certain aspects of its relief, tended to single it out from Canada and Mexico, and give the nation a distinctive basis for development. They were found to be, in the main, more suitable for settlement. There is not the huge proportion of Arctic and sub-Arctic climates to be found in Canada (Fig. 136). It is true these are present in Alaska, but they are absent from the main part of the country, except on its higher mountain-tops. Similarly, there is not the wide extent of tropical desert or of tropical forest such as occurs in Mexico. The so-called Great American Desert is mainly semi-arid steppe land; there is relatively little true desert (Fig. 137). The swamps and gum forests of Florida and Louisiana are likewise comparatively restricted compared with the tropical forests of the rainer coasts of southern Mexico.

But America's attractiveness does not lie only in the avoidance of cold-and-keen climates, of cool-and-raw, hot-dry, and hot-wet régimes; rather, it lies in the presence of temperate humid climates which are alike comfortable and stimulating, especially for European immigrants used to not dissimilar weather across the Atlantic. Like Europe, America is swept by polar and tropical air masses, and experiences the stimulating changes in temperature, humidity, and air-movement that are typical of temperate cyclones. It has thus something very positive to offer, and has to that extent proved more attractive to the people of western, central, and southern Europe than areas to north or south of it.

When the Norsemen first sighted Canada they were appalled by its bleakness as well as its stoniness. Labrador was forbidding indeed, as it still is. Compared with Norway, in the same latitude, it is severe in the extreme. Thus Hebron has a mean January temperature of −5·9° F. compared with 34° F. for Bergen, Norway. Whereas the waters of the Gulf Stream bring warm temperatures to the most northern parts of Norway, a cold Arctic current bathes Labrador. It was no wonder, then, that the Norsemen gave up any attempt at settling in Canada.

Similarly, the southern coasts were not very attractive to the Spaniards. They were fringed with fever-ridden swamps and dense jungles. The Spanish settlers came from Mediterranean Europe, where the summers are dry and sunny; they found a country in the West Indies and the gulf coast of Mexico with hot, rainy summers and warm, wet winters. At Vera Cruz, where Cortez landed, the annual rainfall is 69 inches, which is twice the average

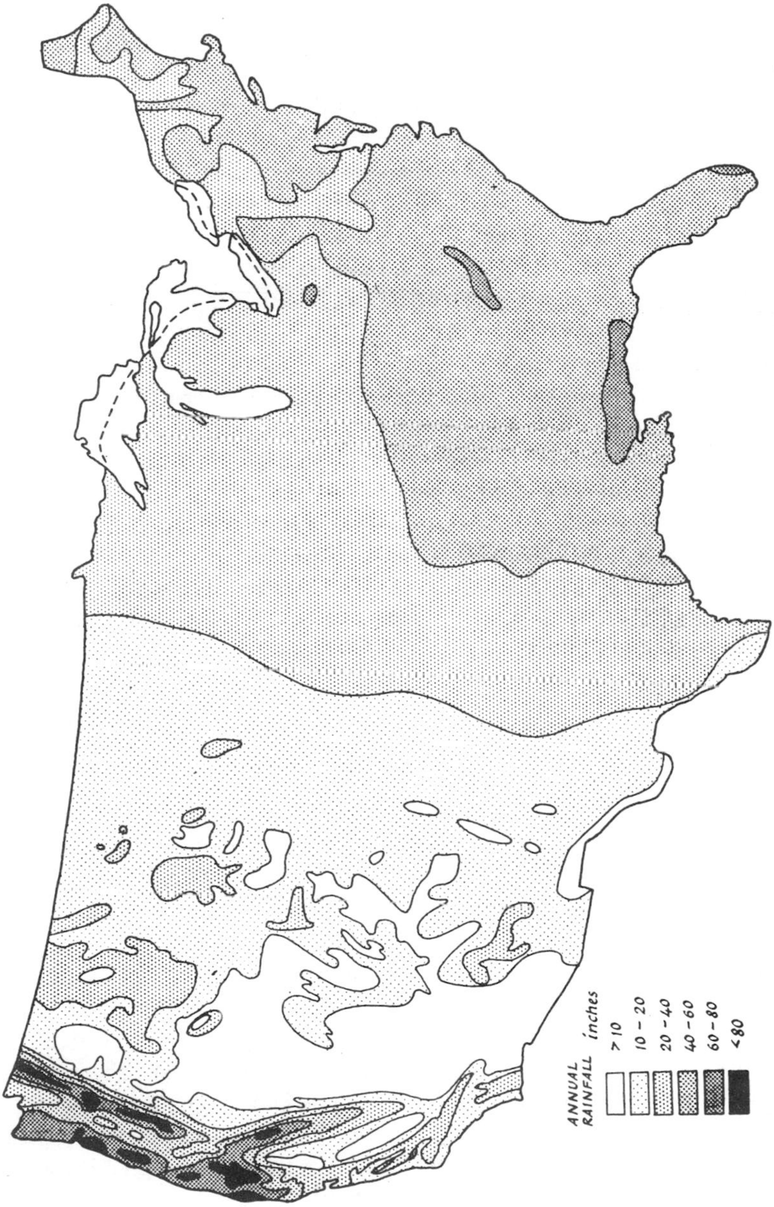

137 Annual Average Precipitation in the United States. There is relatively much less arid land in the United States than in Mexico, another distinctive feature of its climate. (Scale, 1:30 m.)

for Spain. He looked across a sandy shore, choked with swamp, up to steeply rising hills, clad in dense tropical forest. It was not until the Spaniards climbed the plateau and came to the Mexican basin that they found a suitable climate to live in. Yet, going northwards along the plateau trails, they soon struck arid desert.

By contrast, when the British, Dutch, and Swedes settled in New England and Virginia, New York, and Delaware they found land where the winter, though severe, had its mild spells when warm waves of air from the south were drawn into passing cyclones, and where the summer though hot and humid had its heat spells broken by returning cold fronts. Even although the seasonal contrasts were stronger than in west Europe this was the weather that, by and large, the European was used to. As Sauer has pointed out, it allowed him to carry on his way of life with relatively little change, he could wear the same clothes, build the same houses, grow the same crops, and raise the same animals. 'It would be impossible to cross an ocean anywhere else and find as little as unfamiliar in nature on the opposite side. In all the lands of earlier [U.S.] colonization, from Massachusetts Bay south to Virginia, flora and fauna were closely related to those in the European homeland and indicated to the settlers that they were still under familiar skies and seasons.'[1] In other words, most Europeans found in the United States—or at least its eastern half, a veritable 'home from home', and they took to it, and thrived in it. As Daniel Denton, an early settler reported, 'The climate hath such an affinity with that of England that it breeds ordinarily no alteration to those, who remove thither.'[2]

CLIMATIC DIVERSITY OF AMERICA

However, the climates of the United States are not merely the mirror image of Europe. The country is dominated to a greater extent by continental air masses, particularly the polar one, but also a tropical one. The Westerlies have a more limited reach; they are blocked off, at the surface, by the western Cordilleras: they do not have inviting basins such as the North Sea, the Baltic, and the Mediterranean to draw them deep into the continent. The Mediterranean type of climate, which has an immense sweep in Europe, is quite restricted in the United States. On the other hand, the China type of climate, found so widely in the south-eastern states, is absent from Europe. On the whole, the United States is marked by greater and sharper contrasts than Europe; there are more, and more challenging, differences.

In the north there is the contrast between the New England and the

[1] Sauer, C. O., 'The Settlement of the Humid East', in *Climate and Man*, U.S. Dept. of Agric., Yearbook of Agric., Washington, 1941, p. 159.

[2] Quoted by Camer, C., *The Hudson*, New York, 1939, p. 61.

Pacific north-west; both these humid areas afford a further contrast with the American prairies and northern Great Plains. In the south there are the differences between Florida and California; and between the humid, forested plains of the Mississippi and the dry, sparsely covered rangeland of Texas and the south-west. Above all, there is the division between north and south. These strong differences form an important element in the life of the United States.

New England has a rather severe, stormy, raw, and restrictive climate for the United States, with long, blustery and snowy winters, and short, sharp springs. Yet it has surprisingly warm summers in its valleys, and long, mellow, golden 'falls'. Winter is strong enough to strip many of the trees, turn most of the land white, compel farmers to keep their stock cooped up inside large protective barns and yards, require the laying in of both farm and household provender to spin the rich harvests out to the lean spring, and to demand storm doors and windows and central heating in homes and factories. Seasons create a strong rhythmic swing in clothing, between winter tweeds and summer cottons; in food, between warmth-giving chowders, stews and roasts, and refreshing salads; and in sports, between ice-hockey, curling, skating, and ski-ing in winter, and golf and tennis, canoeing and swimming in summer.

This winter-dominated, yet summer-sweet, strongly rhythmic climate nursed Puritan New England into being, its rigours being accepted both as a discipline and a challenge. Yet as the temper of the time changed, men found too little wealth in it to compensate for the rugged relief and glaciated soils, and they turned to the more productive and clement conditions farther west. Once the drift had begun, the harshness of the New England climate accelerated it, helping to drive more and more farmers west—or into the cities.

The Pacific north-west benefited by this. It is a much greener land with a distinctly longer growing season, with slower springs and more lingering summers. It affords a real contrast with the north-east. Though equally as stormy, it is less wintry—except upon its mountains, which are higher and more massive. Mildness is the characteristic thing, with short-lived snows on the seaboard plains, a comparatively verdant land, even in January and February, cows out to pasture most of the year, and golf courses and playing-fields in perennial use. Mildness, however, is bought with greyness, and there are few of the absolutely scintillating days of frost-sharp beauty found in New England winters, or the richly coloured, clear, serene spells of a New England 'Indian Summer'. The skies are cloudy or rainy for three-quarters of the year. This very wetness, nevertheless, attracted those who sought wealth from the trees and the leas—lumbermen, ranchers, sheep-raisers, and dairy farmers.

The interior plains of the north are more like the north-east than the north-west, but have a régime of their own. Seasonality reaches a maximum between the Great Lakes and the Rockies. Here are keen, bitter, windy winters, with the lowest temperatures in the United States—except for Alaska, and the high mountains—and short, hot, active summers. The year is really like two worlds, and one could hardly think the winter scene of tightly shut, double-doored houses, of fur-coated, fur-booted, and often fur-hatted people, of cities kept going only by heated trains and buses, and the even more heated shops, offices and factories, and, above all, the silent, inactive, empty fields, that this world was the same one as the summer-time landscape of tree-shaded, open-windowed, draught-ridden homes, of unconventionally dressed people in flowered cotton dresses, T-shirts and jeans, of fan-loud buildings, and of fields waving with grain and crawling and crowded with machines, or loud with the lowing of cattle.

Yet this very contrast between summer and winter has its attractions. It provides that rest from heat enjoyed by cool climates together with that escape from winter relished in tropical areas which, in a sense, makes the best of both worlds. It tends to be, therefore, a stimulating and invigorating climate. It has often been sought out by people from northern-central or eastern-central Europe, and probably played its part in making the region from Indiana through Minnesota to the Dakotas and Montana one of the chief homes of Swedish, German, Polish, and Ukranian settlement. These people, themselves used to a strongly seasonal climate, with a good taste of winter, but with more than a smell of hot humid summers, have taken well to the marked seasonality of the northern central states.

Indeed, looking at the United States as a whole, seasonality is an important trait. It therefore makes out a strong case for using Carl Troll's classification of climate which stresses seasonality, since so many areas differ not according to their annual means or ranges but to contrasting seasonal patterns. There is, for example, no very great difference between the annual means in southern California and northern Florida, if allowance is made for the California current and the nearness of the Sierras. Southern California has winters of from 45° F. to 55° F., northern Florida, of 53° F. to 57° F.; the former experiences summer temperatures of 70° F. to 95° F. (usually over 80° away from the coast), and the latter of about 80° F. Both are temperate in winter and tropical in summer. Yet how very different their winters and summers are!

In California winter is the rainy season of the year, with not infrequent storms, cloudiness, a rapid shift in winds, and quite sudden changes in temperature. The average winter precipitation is about 13 inches, which is over twenty-six times the average summer figure of just under 0·5 inch! In all but the drier interior basins winter is a green world, with changeful skies, the ground is carpeted with grass, many flowers and shrubs are still active, while evergreen trees abound to give colour where deciduous trees shed their leaves. But things are very different in the summer. Left in its natural state, the land is bare and brown, with most of the grass turned yellow and dry, with the soil quivering with heat between clumps of bushes or stunted, scattered trees, and with burning skies of cloudless unending blue. Of course, irrigation has made a great difference, and most of the valleys are actually a vivid emerald, and hum with all kinds of farm machinery. No longer do people move up into the hills, driving their cattle or their sheep before them. Activity is intense. Nevertheless, it takes place under different skies and makes for a different landscape.

The Florida year is not so sharply differentiated. In both winter and summer rain and sun succeed each other, the land is green, many broad-leaved evergreens and conifers retain their foliage in winter, summer growth is extremely active and strong, and the round of work and play has a more even tenor. The summers are particularly thick and lush, with skies that can be both black with storm and brilliant with sun, cloud-choked, yet pierced with light, turbulent and changeful. The land is clothed by a dense forest (where spared) of palm, cypress, southern pine, and live oak, together with many flowering shrubs, creepers, ferns, and tall, coarse-leaved grasses. The problem here has not been to stimulate growth, but to thin it out, or control it. Consequently, although the region vies with California in the production of nuts and citrus fruits, and vegetables of all kinds, although it, too, is a great centre for outdoor sports and the holiday trade, yet it presents a different and distinctive scene, season for season, compared with its west-coast rival.

The South-Central and South-western parts of America offer still more marked differences and distinctions between each other. The Mississippi is alive with the march and counter-march of air masses and the trooping of storms from the Gulf of Mexico to the Great Lakes, and is thus one of the liveliest and most vital parts of the country, whereas the western plateaux stand in relative isolation, removed from the major and most active weather centres of the continent, dominated by their own rather restricted continental air cells. The upper and middle Mississippi are swept by storms moving along the front of the polar continental system as it advances down to the Ozarks in winter and retreats to the Laurentian Shield in summer. These areas are also troubled by lee-storms, fed in part by Pacific maritime air drifting over the Cordilleras and generating lows from Colorado to Albert that then swing east over the central plains of America. The whole Mississippi basin is flooded in spring and summer by tropical maritime air advancing on a wide front from the Gulf of Mexico deep into the heart of the continent.

The air is thus stirred at all seasons; winter snows pass through a period of unequal spring showers to heavy thunderstorm rain in early summer, which passes in turn to late summer hurricanes and the rain of autumn cyclones. A rich summer-green forest, interspersed with openings thick with humid prairie, became the natural vegetation, although much of this has now been replaced by the production of cotton, tobacco, corn, and winter wheat. The summer appearance of the land is extraordinarily opulent, with huge slowly sailing piles of cumulus cloud from between which the sun pours down on clumps of broad-crowned, heavy-leafed trees, on tall verdant pastures in which cows seem to float, belly-deep, and on fields shoulder high with luxuriant crops. Yet there is the winter's rest when, except in the deltaic lowlands, trees drop their leaves, the corn becomes dry and sere, and activity dies down on the land or changes from production and garnering to cleaning up and preparation. The seasonal rhythm is not by any means as pronounced as in the northern Missouri and Red river plains, but it is important and gives the people a needed change.

The relative isolation of the south-west from the main air streams of the continent makes it a fairly stable and uniform area, dominated by dry cool winters, with cold air settling down from the mountains, and hot arid summers whose occasional convection storms, though violent, are short-lived. The prevailing aridity is accompanied by intense light, an extraordinarily transparent, crystal-clear atmosphere, burning blue skies by day, and nights of an incredible depth and brilliance. Evaporation is everywhere high, and there is a pronounced lack of water, except where great rivers, rising in snow-clad peaks, flow across the area. The vegetation cover is, therefore, thin and trees and grasses are often stunted or brittle and spinous. Much bare ground is in evidence, and the land has a 'lean and hungry look', except where fed with water in irrigation schemes. It is a poor cousin of the Mississippi, with thin soils, sparse fields and patchy woodlands. Few towns and even fewer villages occur and roads and railways are far apart.

North and South. Strong as are the contrasts between the eastern and western seaboards of the United States, and between these again and the interior plains, they cannot match the pronounced differences between north and south. These differences occur everywhere, but are most marked east of the Rockies. Here is a fundamental division of the country; a division between regions gripped by winter or swayed by summer, between those with a short growing season into which the utmost activity is crammed, and ones with an all-but perennial season of growth, where activity can be more even and varied.

The north has to content itself with a few agricultural products which it raises in great quantities through high yields obtained by the most intensive efforts. This has helped to make it, under an economic system where advantages are capitalized and exploited, highly specialized and commercialized. The challenge of winter, as Herbertson showed in connexion with northern Europe, has led to thrift and foresight and the accumulation in one year of enough to last over to and prepare for the next. The raising of such a supply tended to produce surpluses for export and so for profit and investment. Much of this gain went to prime business and industry, and helped to lay the foundations for the industrial supremacy of the north. Yet the challenge of winter had a more direct influence on industry, because it presented largely unprofitable time which could only be capitalized, in many cases, by turning from the field to the workshop. More and more energy went into tool-making and weaving and other traditionally off-season activities, until these became the main enterprises. Then winter-born uses of time became year-round occupations, and manufacturing and trade forged ahead.

The summer-rich south, on the other hand, found most of its time involved in the development and use of that land which gave it so much for so much of the year. The exploitation of long, hot summers and of mild and often open winters permitted a much wider range of crops, and stimulated a more varied range of activities. After the summer crops of tobacco, or cotton, or corn were lifted, there were winter crops to be put in, such as wheat, pulses, or vegetables. Two or even three croppings a year kept field and farmer busy. The land changed in appearance with winter but did not cease to produce, as in so much of the north. In the all-but tropical parts it remained surprisingly active, and often made its chief profit from the winter and early spring vegetables so greatly needed in the winter-bound north.

The concentration on the land may well have kept the south back in the industrial race, but the very advantages that made it agriculturally so rich have now come to support industrial development. A long, or even year-round, open season means that the south is free from the need of fall stock-piling of fuels and raw materials, and can avoid the winter 'traffic snarls' and work 'lay-offs' and absenteeism that cost the northern states so much. (For although winter did help to stimulate industry in the north, it also fronted northern industry with a high annual charge.) Meanwhile the varied agriculture has presented southern industry with a wide range of raw materials.

It is obvious, then, that climate, like structure and relief, offered a considerable set of opportunities and limitations to the immigrants who came to create and settle in the United States. The different conditions were recognized as of the utmost capital value and were seized upon and made the most of by the American settlers; and, indeed, this fact helped them as much as anything to develop their highly capitalistic, specialized, diversified, productive, and dynamic way of life.

CLIMATE AND SETTLEMENT—SOME MAJOR EFFECTS

Climatic differences, then, have come to have an important influence on American development and settlement. In particular the difference between warm and cool temperate climates along the Coast Plain (and indeed east of the Mississippi), the great variability of climate in the Great Plains, and the attractiveness of the climates of California and Florida, grew to be most significant.

The cultural differences between New England and Virginia have already been described; they probably caused the main divide between north and south. But they were reinforced by those climatic differences which allowed the homesteader in the northern States to concentrate on food and fodder crops and the planter in the southern States to make money from industrial and service crops. 'Tobacco dominated the upper South and cotton the deep South.'[1] The fact too that climate, soil, and terrain together made farming more difficult in the north, or at any rate in New England, meant that agriculture was never the chief interest of the colonists. New England forged ahead by industry and trade, thus widening the gap between itself and a basically rural south. The much longer growing season in the south, and temperatures that offered a much wider range of crops, tempted the southern colonists to put their faith in agriculture and make it the mainstay of their economy. Thus climate permitted the differences already inherent in the divergent social systems to become entrenched, and played its part in dividing the nation into its first great 'culture areas', the Northern and Southern sections.

Another outstanding example of climatic influence may be found in the late development of the Great Plains. Although Americans were poised to settle this vast region in the 1820s—the Kansa, Osage, and Choctaw Indians surrendered their reserves in Kansas, Oklahoma, and Arkansas in 1825—it was not really until the 1870s that settlers moved in to occupy and develop it. In the intervening years they had tended in the main to move *through* it to Oregon and California. This delay was due to the difficulty the eastern farmer, used to a forest environment, experienced when he came face to face with a grassland one.

> No longer could the pioneer employ the techniques learned by generations of his fore-fathers. He knew how to subdue the [forest] wilderness—by girdling trees, planting his crop of corn, building his log cabin, and clearing the land year by year; but in most of the Trans-Mississippi West, forests were absent. He even knew how to conquer the [humid] prairie—by breaking the sod, planting an 'ax-crop' of corn, and hauling in lumber

[1] Sauer, C. O., 'The Settlement of the Humid East', in *Climate and Man*, p. 163.

needed for his home; but in the interminable plains these lessons of the past no longer applied. He knew how to manage a small farm, but beyond the Father of Waters he discovered that sub-humid climates required an extensive rather than intensive agriculture. . . . Nowhere could pioneers find materials and living conditions with which they were familiar. There was no lumber for homes, barns, or split-rail fences. There was no water save the muddy gruel in occasional rivers. There were no belts of trees to save them from the baking sun of summer or raging winter blizzards. And worst of all there was in all the province seldom enough rainfall. The frontiersman, to succeed in that sub-humid region, had to devise new methods.[1]

All this was a great challenge, a challenge met by dry-farming, irrigation and conservation, and also by mechanization and great improvements in organization.

In more recent years, as Ullman[2] has shown, the climatic attraction of California and Florida has been counted one of the chief amenities of these areas, and has led a great many people to take up residence there. As a result, California is now the most rapidly developing State in the Union. And as industry becomes more 'foot-loose', it is likely to locate in areas of maximum amenity and will increasingly move to the sunny, healthy, comfortable parts of the country, other things being equal. This is undoubtedly one factor in the rise of the 'new' South, and the growth there of cities and industry.

THE FORESTS OF AMERICA

The forests of America have also had a great effect upon settlement, along with climate and relief. They are found mainly in the eastern, north-western, and northern areas. The Eastern Forest is chiefly deciduous. It covers a region of low relief with thick soils and a long growing season. Before being cut into, it was the densest and most continuous of America's forests. The Western Forest has grown up in a very mountainous region, where altitude and slope are all-important: consequently the forest is much more uneven and more interrupted. The Northern Forest has to adapt itself to a short growing season and is therefore chiefly evergreen (Fig. 138).

The Eastern Forests

The Eastern Forest covers the Atlantic and Gulf Coast Plains, the Appalachian mountains and plateaux, and the humid portions of the Interior Lowlands. Roughly, it stretches from the Mississippi east and from the St Lawrence south. Here the relief is low. The few high peaks in the

[1] Billington, R. A., *Westward Expansion*, pp. 405, 690.

[2] Ullman, E. L., 'Amenities as a Factor in Regional Growth', *Geog. Rev.*, **xliv**, 1, 1954, pp. 119–32.

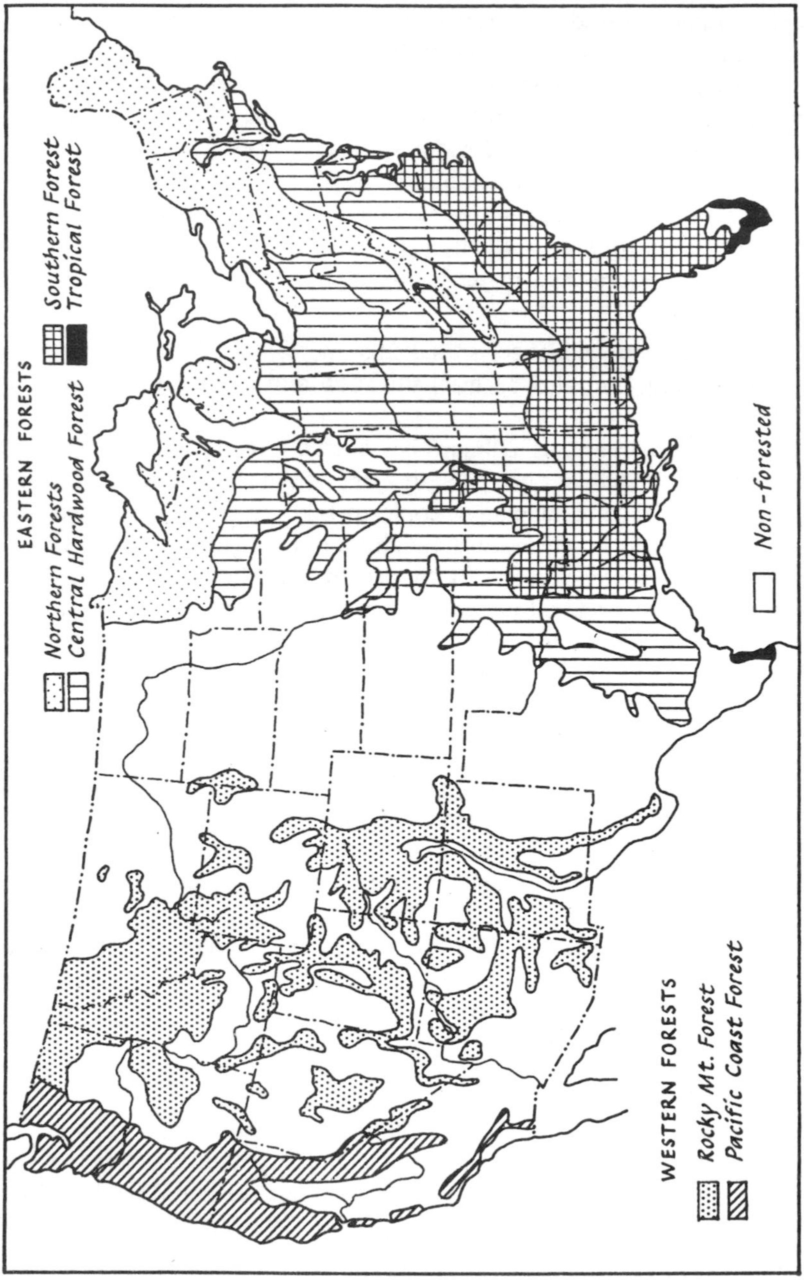

FIG. 138 The Forest Regions of the United States. (Scale, 1:26 m.)

Appalachians are not enough to form a barrier to winds, there are large gaps through the mountains, and wide plains around their flanks. Rainfall is plentiful and spreads far inland. It is fairly constant as a result of the constant conflicts of polar continental air from Canada and tropical gulf air from the Caribbean. Rainy winds from the west, south, and east converge, especially during spring, summer, and fall, just when the growing trees need them most. Moreover, since the warm air masses predominate, there is a long frost-free season of from over 300 days in the south to 150 days in the north.

The plentiful supply of rain during a long growing season has assisted the weathering and soil-forming processes. The Eastern Forest has therefore developed in zones of fairly deep, fertile soils. These are a yellow-red colour in the south, and grey-brown in the north. They help to account for the density of the forest, and for the preponderance of hardwoods, which require good soil, considerable humidity, and a long, open season.

Though all the trees of the Eastern Forest require the same rainfall, they have different requirements of heat. Consequently they can be divided into five belts, which run roughly west and east, except in the vicinity of the Appalachian highlands.

The Mangrove Thickets form the most southerly belt, and are found in southern Florida. They grow in hot, humid conditions where the July temperature approximates 85°. They are part of the Tropical Forest of the West Indies and the humid plains of Mexico. They produce a very dense jungle, with exuberant leafage and thick interlacing branches. The ground is often flooded by water and the black waters, together with the gloom that pervades the depths of the thickets, give the mangrove swamps a sombre appearance. On drier ground flourish palms and palmetto bush. Here Indians long found a refuge against white man; and indeed, the area today is still very sparsely settled.

The Southern Pineries form a second zone, where southern varieties of pine, such as the loblolly, longleaf, and slash pines, are the main vegetation. Loblolly pines grow on the richer, heavier soils; longleaf and slash pines on the poorer, sandier soils. In addition there are sub-tropical trees like the magnolia and live oak, and the forest changes rapidly with changing soil conditions. These pineries were early described by Washington as a 'land of sand and pine barrens and very few inhabitants'. They were avoided by settlers seeking heavier soils for corn and cotton crops, and were literally treated as 'barrens'. As we have seen, they formed a barrier of great historic significance between Coast Plain and Piedmont.

The Mid-Atlantic Oak Forest is the third zone, and is the largest hardwood area in America. On the southern flanks of the Appalachians, where the rainfall is high (50 to 70 inches) and the growing season long (6 to 8 months), the oak is mixed with chestnut and yellow poplar. The western part of the oak region, in Ohio, Indiana, Missouri, and Oklahoma, has a mixture of hickory, with walnut, ash, elm, and box elder. On sandier soils throughout the oak belt, there are many pines, especially along the Atlantic coast plain. The oak forest gave rise to a deep soil much appreciated by settlers, and although the forest was difficult to clear, it was chosen time and again by the early migrants pushing west.

The Northern Hardwood Forest is the fourth major division of the Eastern Forest region. It is made up of a mixture of beech and maple trees, with birch and hemlock, and covers the upper St Lawrence and southern Great Lakes, together with the plains of New England and the Maritimes, in an area of 140 to 160 days without frost. It forms the chief cover for the grey-brown soils. It was prized because of these soils, also because it indicated humid conditions, and because it provided excellent lumber for making farm implements.

The fifth subdivision consists of the Highland Spruce-Fir Forest which grows on the summits of the Appalachians, covers the Adirondacks and the highland areas in northern New England. The growing season is as short as 120 days. The forest is, therefore, a quick-growing, evergreen, softwood type, made up of black spruce and balsam fir in most localities, with red spruce on better drained sites. There was little attempt at clearing this forest for settlement, but it was prized as a source of furs, and later of softwood for pulp and paper making.

The Western Forests

The Western Forests of North America stretch from California to Alaska along the Pacific coast, and from Colorado to Alberta along the Rocky mountains. Farther north they merge into the great Northern Forest of Alaska and Canada. Southward, they extend into the Alpine forests of Mexico.

The relief of the region is high and rugged. In the United States, the Coast Ranges, the Cascades and Nevadas, and the Rocky mountains form a triple barrier, concentrating forest growth along north–south lines. The lowlands between are too dry for forest, and present huge gaps of grassland or desert scrub. The forest follows the pattern of relief.

The location of the Western Forest in relation to the various air masses brings the northern parts under both winter and summer rain: a central zone receives rain in winter, but is dry in summer; and the southern districts are dry all the year round. The rainy winds are chiefly from the west, so that the western slopes are the wettest; but in summer in the Rockies, the eastern slopes do receive some rain from the onrush of the gulf airs.

The growing season is comparatively short: in the north it is shortened by winter cold; in the south it is shortened by drought. Therefore, the trees that do best are the quick-growing, evergreen coniferous types. There are few deciduous types—which is a major contrast with the Eastern Forests. The soils of the region, mainly grey-brown and leached grey, are rather thin and poorly developed.

Broadly speaking, the Western Forest can be divided into *five parts*. These are not distributed in latitudinal belts, as in the east, but in belts which conform to rainfall and relief.

In the southern arid area the trees are small and sparsely distributed. Patches of grass or heath divide one clump of trees from another. The vegetation cover is really too open to be called forest. It is referred to, instead, as woodland. In the south-west, on the hills around Los Angeles, this woodland consists of 'chaparral' or scrub-oak, a broad-leaved evergreen wood that is stunted and thin. It passes upward on the higher ridges into yellow pine, and downward into sagebrush. It has to thrive in a winter which is semi-arid, and an arid summer. The rainfall is less than 20 inches a year. This is low in a hot climate, with high evaporation. Consequently the trees are small, with widely spreading roots, squat, thick-barked trunks, and leathery leaves, which reduce transpiration to a minimum and suffer very little from evaporation. Dwarf oaks are mixed with thickets of Californian laurel, cypresses, the holly-leafed cherry, and many thorn bushes. The scrub has been useful for cattle and sheep ranchers, but is otherwise not valued.

In the southern Rockies and the mountains of Arizona and New Mexico another type of woodland occurs, called *piñon scrub*. On the lower, drier slopes the piñon is mixed with desert sagebrush; farther up, junipers become more plentiful. On higher slopes there is a mixture of yellow pine and Douglas fir. The piñon is a small pine which is interesting because it bears tiny cones that carry edible seeds. The Indians liked to gather these, and every fall they made excursions into the piñon wood, pitched camp, and collected the seeds. These forests, too, were welcomed for spring and fall shelter, and for summer grazing, by western ranchers.

The Western Forest region is really noted, however, for its giant pines and firs. These form the timberlands as distinct from the woodlands. There are three types of timberland: the interior yellow pine and Douglas fir zone; the coastal cedar and hemlock zone; and the alpine spruce-fir timbers.

The interior yellow pine and Douglas fir forest is found chiefly on sub-humid highlands in the north and central parts. The winters are wet, although the summers are semi-arid, and there is enough rain, together with melting snows, to provide for a fairly dense forest cover with large trees. The growing season is relatively short, and so most of the trees are quick-growing evergreen conifers. On the Coast Range of California and in the Sierra Nevadas, the yellow pine is associated with sugar pine. This is the largest pine in America, and often grows 250 feet in height, with a diameter at the base of from 10 to 15 feet. The sap has a sweet taste, although it is not much used. Where the rainfall slackens off on the east slopes of the Cascades, and on the rims of the interior basins, Douglas firs become more common. These forests were much sought after for timber for building ranch houses, corrals, and fences. When cut down they gave place to excellent range, so that ranchers quickly took over from lumber men. This belt makes up some of the best western ranching land.

The cedar and hemlock forest grows on rather wetter slopes, where the rainfall is over 30 inches. It is found in the northern Rockies, the northern Coast Ranges of Washington and Oregon, and the western slopes of the Cascades. The cedar is mixed with Douglas fir and western hemlock, but above 2,500 feet Douglas fir disappears, and the forest changes to red cedar and hemlock, with Amabilis fir. Above 3,000 feet, balsams are mixed with the hemlocks. On the Coast Ranges of California redwoods are found with Douglas fir and western hemlock, to produce one of the densest of all timber forests in the world. Here the cool summers with their heavy fog and rainy winters, together with the long growing season, are ideal for forest growth. This forest has been the great timber forest of the west, and at once attracted, and still attracts, lumber interests to it. Here is a major western resource.

On higher slopes still, in cool humid locations, the forest changes to a spruce-fir assocation. In the Rockies, Alpine fir and Engelmann spruce occupy the windy heights from 7,500 feet to about 11,500 feet. In the Cascades red fir and Alpine fir rise above the limits of the cedar and hemlock (4,500 feet) to cool, moist sites. In the southern Rockies increasing altitude and growing rainfall are marked in ascending belts of pine, fir, and spruce; the corkbark pine and Engelmann spruce being particularly common. These are regarded mainly as value for summer pasture and as an important source of conservation of water supply for rivers flowing down through the arid basins and plains of the west.

The Northern or Boreal Forest

Across central Alaska there stretches the vast extent of the Boreal Forest. This is part of one of the largest forest areas in the world, and offers the United States an important, though as yet scarcely accessible, reserve of pulping wood. It lies on the lower mountain slopes between the dry, interior plateaux, and the cold, windswept barrenlands of the higher or more northern parts. The mountains are swept by Pacific storm tracks, with sufficient spring and summer rains and winter snowfall for forest growth. The frost-free season, from 60 to 100 days, is just long enough for quick-growing softwoods like pine and spruce and for small hardwoods like birch.

The Boreal Forest differs from the Western and Eastern forests in that it has fewer species. Conditions for growth are hard and limited. The area has been heavily glaciated, with wide stretches of rock practically stripped of their soil, and still other stretches plastered with glacial clays or sands. The drainage is chaotic and there is much ill-drained land. The soils are young and thin, often waterlogged or else leached. They are pale grey in colour and are unadapted to a rich variety of vegetation. The trees do not grow to a great size. They are constantly endangered by the spread of muskeg and of swamp. Spruce and pine cling to the higher, better drained slopes, while tamarack, poplar, willow, and alder crowd the cold, wet depressions.

The northern fringe of the forest is very irregular. The trees are scattered in small groups, except along the margins of the rivers, and there are wide areas of bog, moss, and berry-bush in between. The balsam, poplar, and aspen are common, grading southward into balsam fir, white, black, and red spruces.

THE IMPORTANCE OF THE FORESTS

The great areas of forest which we have described are of first importance in North America. Indirectly, they help agriculture by preventing flood and soil erosion, though unfortunately so much forest has been cut away that the damage from flood and soil erosion is rapidly increasing. More directly, the forests are helpful in supplying a home to countless fur-bearing animals, game animals, and birds, which are hunted by man and provide him with a livelihood and recreation. Above all, the forest is the basis of the great timber and wood-pulp industries, the construction business, paper manufacturing, the making of rayon, the extraction of wood alcohol, and modern chemical industries. Since paper products are in greater demand than ever before, and are an indispensable part of modern industry, United States forests are a major industrial resource. The Pacific States produce some 47 per cent of the nation's lumber, followed by the south-east and south central States with 30·7 per cent. The Southern States, on the other hand, are the chief source of pulpwood, followed by the Pacific North-west. The United States is, however, short of pulpwood and imports a great deal from Canada. The development of Alaskan resources should help to reduce this somewhat, but those supplies are very remote from Chicago, Detroit, New York, and Philadelphia, the chief consumer centres.

THE GRASSLANDS OF AMERICA

The early settlers in the United States lived in the forest. It seemed endless, covering plains and climbing over mountains. Yet at length, the pioneers broke out of the world of trees into the great open spaces of the prairies. It was unlike anything that they had ever known. Vast herds of buffalo roamed across the grassy plains. The wealth of fur and skin was phenomenal. Soon the herds of buffalo were almost killed off. Then the white man turned to ploughing, and discovered a new wealth in corn and wheat, which opened up the continent. Now there is little natural grassland left, except in the semi-arid range country. Agriculture has replaced the natural vegetation. Even where the farms have some grass pasture along with the corn, oats, and winter wheat, the grasses may be cultivated ones, very different from the original kinds.

The native grasses form four types of cover, including Tall Grass, on the sub-humid prairies; Short Grass, on the semi-arid Great Plains; Mesquite Grass, on the still drier southern Mesas; and Bunch Grass, in the very dry basins of the Pacific borderlands.

Tall Grass Prairies

It was the Tall Grass prairies that the pioneers first came on, as they burst out of the forest. The grasses, almost as tall as a man, mixed with myriad flowering bushes, were beautiful beyond description. Along the sides of rivers they gave way to lines of trees and often, in areas of coarser soil, to clumps of woods. Indeed, the Tall Grass prairie has long been a battle-ground between the grasses and the forest. It lies in a transitional belt between the dense forests, with a rainfall of over 35 inches, and the sparser, shorter grasses to the west, where the rainfall is less than 15 to 17 inches. Though at first avoided, the humid prairies were subsequently taken up with eagerness, and have given place to some of the finest farming in the Corn Belt.

The blue-stem sod-grass, together with the tall Indian grass, form the great prairie of the Mississippi valley. The decay of the grasses each year has built up a fine humus and the soil is a rich black earth. Consequently, it is very good for agriculture, and most of the prairie has been ploughed up to form the heart of the Corn Belt. Farther west, where it is less humid, the grasses cannot grow so densely but assume the bunch habit of growth. The blue-stem bunch-grass prairie has been transformed into the chief Winter Wheat Belt. In the cooler regions to the north, the growing season is shorter, rainfall is as low as 18 inches, and the grasses change to quick-growing needle grass or the tall, slender wheat grass. Here too the soil is black and fertile. This is the prairie the settlers found moving north-west across the Red River valley, and they helped to turn it into the Spring Wheat Belt.

Short Grass Range

After the pioneers had ploughed up the Tall Grass prairie, there still remained a huge area, on the higher plains sweeping west to the Rocky foothills, which was covered with short grass. The settler was at last beyond trees, even beyond bushes, in the heart of the grass domain. The landscape seemed barer than ever, and flatter and wider. Nothing broke the vision for miles and miles unless it was a few straggling trees in the hollow of a watercourse. It is difficult to imagine the range country—with its large blue skies, clear and dazzling, its level reaches stretching out into the distance, amazingly green after the warm Chinook has melted the snows or the spring rains have swept up from the south. Then the flowers come out overnight to paint the plains with an incredible beauty, only to fade in the hot autumn weather into a tinder brown, until they are buried again beneath the snows.

The change from the Tall Grass type of landscape to the Short Grass one takes place along the edges of the Great Plains where the rainfall lessens, and drops below 17-to-15 inches. It is not enough to keep the soil moist, or to feed the deeper roots of the tall grass. Only those grasses flourish which can grow quickly enough to take immediate advantage of the rainfall, before the autumn drought arrives. The short, swiftly growing buffalo grass will grow in 40 days. This grass, along with grama, wire, and western-wheat grass, makes up most of the Short Grass range. They form good natural pasture, and are the basis for the cattle empire of the west.

The soils of the region are light brown to yellow and not too well suited to agriculture, but when the price of wheat is high, or when unusually wet years happen, farmers are tempted to plough up the range, and turn it into wheat farms. They have succeeded where they have adopted dry-farming and use of drought-resistant grains, but from time to time a really dry spell of years will come and many farmers are ruined. Irrigation, however, is at least a partial answer to their problems.

The Arid Grasslands and Desert

In the southern Great Plains the grasses merge into a poorer and thinner covering which is the doorstep to the desert. Here in the plateaux and mesas of Texas, New Mexico, Arizona, and Mexico proper, appears the grey-green, dusty Mesquite range. The land is shut off from the moist airs of the gulf. It is under the influence of the tropical Pacific air mass or the Cordillera highs, which produce dry winds. The rainfall is as low as 12 inches, and is valuable for only a short time. When the summer heat arrives, evaporation is excessive. Thus only the quickest growing grasses, or specially adapted plants like desert bushes, can thrive, and even then they are stunted and sparse. They spring up in clumps, leaving lots of bare ground between. The grasses, such as the curly mesquite, the black grama, and the tobosa, are mixed with scattered sagebrush and cactus.

In the interior basins and Pacific depressions rainfall is even more scarce, and the natural vegetation is a type of bunch grass. The Columbia basin, cut off from rains by the Cascades and the Rockies, is floored with a grey-green, scanty growth of bunch grass and balsam root. The Great Valley of California, also cut off from rains by lofty mountains, is very dry. In the spring there is a luxuriant growth of brome grass, wild oats, California needle grass and poa, intermingled with gaily flowering clovers and the crimson California poppy; but the grasses are short-lived, and die out in the hot, arid summer.

In the inmost basins and in the south-western deserts rain is so scanty that it does not even produce much bunch grass. Only specially adapted bushes and trees like the sagebrush and cactus can live in the aridity. They have long roots, thick bark, and small leaves, and thus are able to tap the subsoil moisture, and to resist evaporation to a maximum. They form a patchy vegetation of desert scrub. Sagebrush makes a background to thorn trees and cactus from Idaho to Mexico. Yuccas and agaves intermingle with creosote bush and acacias to produce one of the dreariest landscapes on the continent. This is still the land of the Indian, although ranching on a very extensive basis has moved in wherever mountains are near by with piñon or other woodland to supply summer range.

CLIMATE, VEGETATION, AND SOILS

In studying vegetation types, we have noticed the strong influence of climate. Both climate and vegetation control the formation of soil. Thus major climatic regions produce dominant vegetation and soil types. It has often been shown that people get used to a certain combination of climate, vegetation and soil, and finally become 'rooted' there. That is to say, they find out what crops suit the climate and soil, and then base their agriculture on those crops. Customs of eating and drinking, the materials used in clothes and shoes, come to typify the people, and form an important element in their life. When associated with other elements they help to produce regional cultures.

It would be almost impossible to think of the culture of the Greeks outside the setting of fig and olive orchards, vineyards, the cultivation of winter wheat and of pulses, the growing of flax, the herding of cattle and sheep, and the whole round of agriculture associated with the Mediterranean climate and the limey, red soils of their homeland. Similarly, western European culture became rooted and grounded in the deciduous forests and brown forest soils of the west maritime climate. When the French and the British landed in eastern North America, they met with rather similar grey-brown or light-grey soils and they were able to develop their old agriculture relatively unchanged, even when they took over the cultivation of Indian corn. It was partly due to the ease with which the customs of British life were transplanted in American soil that the British civilization was so well adapted to the New World.

When the British advanced south and west to new soil zones, such as the yellow-red earths and the black-earth prairie soils, they were no longer so successful in carrying with them their old ways of life. As a result, friction and conflict broke out. The climate and soil of the southern colonies were so different from the north that they prompted a different type of agriculture and a new way of life. This reinforced the social and economic differences between the plantation of the Southern States and the family farm of the Northern, between an aristocratic community which required slave labour to develop its large estates and a middle-class community that owned and operated its land. These contrasts reached a critical stage in the Civil War.

Then again, as settlers moved west, they left the land of small farms to take to the open range, and this change from humid grey-brown soils to semi-arid light brown soils led to a conflict between old traditions and new demands. 'The period of so-called lawlessness in the American plains was a period of such adjustment and conflict . . . when people moved from one soil to another.'

Climate, vegetation, and soil, therefore, have played a very important part in the colonization of North America and the development of such different ways of living as are found in Massachusetts or California, in the Corn Belt or the Cotton Belt.

CONCLUSION

From all this it will be evident that the United States does have a certain physical as well as historical distinctness in North America. Especially important is the wide development there of the Atlantic and Gulf Coast Plains, of the great Central Plains, and of the Pacific-margin intermontane depressions. Also significant is the great variety of climate and its suitability for settlement. The dominance of the warm summer phase of the cool temperate climate, the exclusive occurrence of the China and Mediterranean types of climate, and the great extension of the sub-humid to semi-arid steppe are especially typical. Although the physiographic regions are basic and in most cases are strengthened in their effects by associated climatic divisions, some of the main landform units, such as the Atlantic Coast Plain, the Mississippi lowlands, and the Pacific margin depressions have been divided by climate and exert their influence in different ways, mediated by different weather systems. Thus fairly simple, broad natural regions have come into being. These then became the stage for human development and, above all, for European colonization and exploitation.

CHAPTER SEVENTEEN

The United States: The Nation—Economic Regions

Important though the physiography and climate of the United States may have been, and are, their effects on the ultimate appearance of the landscape have been modified by man, having been increasingly mediated through technology and organization. The natural regions have nearly everywhere become subordinate to human ones, and the country has been given new life and meaning by the nation. Indeed, in a man-ridden, man-dominated world 'geographic regions only become articulate because of economic incidence and cultural conflict'[1] (Fig. 139).

The real geography of the United States is thus largely the geography of how Americans have used their physiography and climate and other resources. It is the geography of the great economic spheres (the agricultural, mining, and manufacturing regions), together with the social divisions (the rural and urban parts) of the country. The climatic distinctions between north and south along the Coast Plain, and the physiographic division between east and west running down the Appalachians were made matters of competition and conflict, or co-operation and integration by human ideals and policies. This was recognized at the very beginning by Washington, the father of the nation, who urged that 'every portion of our country' should find

> the most commanding motives for carefully guarding and preserving the union of the whole. The north, in an unrestrained intercourse with the south, finds in the productions of the latter great additional resources . . . and precious materials of manufacturing industry. The south, in the same intercourse, benefiting by the agency of the north, sees its agriculture grow and its commerce expand. . . . The east, in a like intercourse with the west, already finds, and in the progressive improvement of interior communications by land and water, will more and more find, a valuable vent for the commodities which it brings from abroad, or manufactures at home. The west derives from the east supplies requisite to its growth and comfort, and what is perhaps of still greater consequence, it must of necessity owe the secure enjoyment of indispensable *outlets* for its own

---

[1] Odum and Moore, *American Regionalism*, p. 35.

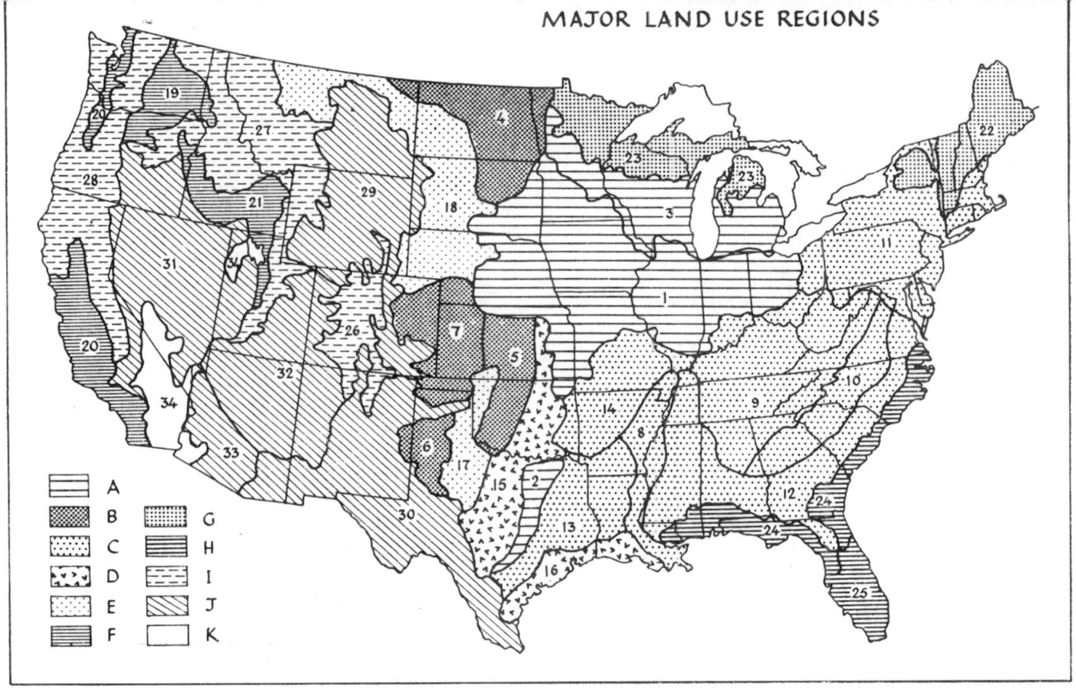

FIG. 139 Man's use of Nature's Resources in the United States. (U.S.D.A. Map.) A: Cropland-Pasture-Forest; 1, Central Plains Farm Belt; 2, Texas Black Prairie; 3, Lake States Farm Forest region. B: Cropland-Grazing; 4, Dakota Plains; 5, Oklahoma-Kansas Plains; 6, Llano Estacado; 7, Central High Plains. C: Forest-Cropland-Pasture; 8, Mississippi Delta; 9, South Appalachians and Plateaux; 10, Piedmont; 11, Mid-Atlantic region; 12, Upper Eastern Coastal Plains; 13, Gulf Southwest Upper Plains; 14, Ozarks. D: Grazing-Cropland-Woodland; 15, Texas Cross-timbers; 16, Gulf Lower Coast Prairies. E: Grazing-Cropland; 17, Texas Red-beds; 18, Northern High Plains. F: Grazing-Irrigated and Dry Cropland-Woodland; 19, Columbia Basin; 20, Pacific Depressions; 21, Snake River and Utah Basins. G: Forest-Pasture-Hay-land; 22, Northeastern Forest region; 23, Lake-States Cut-over region. H: Forest-Grazing-Cropland; 24, Atlantic and Gulf Coast Flatwoods; 25, Florida Everglades and Coasts. I: Forest-Grazing-Hay-land; 26, Southern Rockies; 27. Northern Rockies and Utah Mountains; 28, Sierras–Cascades. J: Grazing-Woodland-Irrigated Cropland: 29. Arid High Plains; 30, Rio Grande Plateaux; 31, Great Basin; 32, Colorado Plateaux; 33, Southern Arizona. K: Mostly unused; 34, American Desert. (1:37·5 m.)

productions to the weight, influence, and the future maritime strength of the Atlantic side of the union, directed by an indissoluble community of interest, as *one Nation*.[1]

It was in the making of that nation, then, that Americans came to make the geography of the United States. It was out of their newly aroused community of interest, it was from their genius for organization, that they discovered the links between the often very different natural regions, and drew them together into a remarkable unity. These two themes therefore dominate; the discovery and exploitation of difference—diversity: and the development of togetherness and integration—unity. *E Pluribus Unum.*

THE EVOLUTION OF SETTLEMENT

The work of modifying the natural regions, transforming them to sectional purposes, and uniting them in a national economy took a good deal of time. The colonists had to make many experiments to succeed. However, they were helped in all this by the Indians, who had cleared many openings in the forest and long tried out useful methods of farming. Indians taught the settlers how to tap maple trees for sugar, and how to clear the forest quickly by girdling trees. They showed them the way to plant native corn, together with beans and squash, in little mounds of earth between the trees. Thus the first pioneers were able to make a living without digging up tree stumps or ploughing the land, and without using draft animals. This allowed them to get a footing in the land and keep going until the forest could be completely cleared, and the soil ploughed and put under rotation.

The Settlement of the Eastern Forest

The main drawback in the Eastern Forest was the lack of suitable grasses and cereal crops. This was serious because western European husbandry depended on grass pastures to a great extent. However, pasture grasses were introduced from England and France with great success, and by the middle of the seventeenth century had begun to change farming on the American continent. The native Timothy, however, made an important hay crop. 'The cool New England climate was fully congenial to the introduced European grasses and to white clover, in contrast to that in the southern colonies.'[2] Of the introduced grains, oats were the most successful, standing up better than wheat to the humid climate, and making a better use of the rather acid soils. Thus a rotation of hay, oats, and corn was founded, as the basis for cattle and sheep farming, and later for dairying.

[1] Washington, George, Address to the People of the U.S.A. on his Retirement from the Presidency (The Farewell Address), 1796.

[2] Sauer, 'The Settlement of the Humid East', in *Climate and Man*, p. 164.

While New England replaced its forests of maple and beech with grasses, hay, and oats, and went in for meat production and dairying, the Mid-Atlantic States preferred a fuller rotation of corn, wheat, and oats along with clover and hay. They went in more for dairying. This was probably because of the Dutch and German settlers, who introduced better methods of rotation and new kinds of milking cows. They were also responsible for the Dutch barn that combined granary, byre and tool shed in one, and enabled herds to be 'wintered in'. Their fuller type of agriculture responded well to the warmer climate and deeper, more mature soils found in the oak-hickory forest. Potatoes were much in vogue with the Irish. Today, in addition to the older system, the production of canning crops, vegetables, and fruits have become popular.

The southern colonies, with their hotter climate and greater rainfall, replaced the forests of southern oak and pineries with rich plantations of tobacco, sugar-cane, rice, and cotton. Cotton, sweet potatoes, corn, and peanuts form the staples of present-day farming, along with tobacco. Upland or short-staple cotton was particularly useful, since it was able to colonize the poorer soils and use the shorter-growing season of the Piedmont and the northern fringe of the Cotton Belt.

Once the farmer had adapted himself to a certain rotation of crops at the coast he felt quite confident in trying out the same crops farther and farther inland because the climatic belts ran latitudinally and reached westward to the Mississippi without much change. The Alabama Black Belt allowed the cotton growers to move westward, south of the Appalachians, into terraces of the Mississippi delta. The gaps through the Appalachians allowed the tobacco growers of Virginia to move into West Virginia and Kentucky, whence they spread to Tennessee. Meantime, the Hudson–Mohawk and the St Lawrence gaps invited the westward extension of hay, oats, and dairying to the Great Lakes States and Ontario.

The Settlement of the Prairies

However, once the prairie soils and the grassland climates were struck, settlers met with a different set of circumstances. The lack of timber was serious. Consequently, the pioneers kept to river valleys, lined with trees. The first prairies to be struck were the humid ones in the Central Plains lying within the Eastern Forest.

> Particularly impressive was the Grand Prairie of central Illinois. No traveller failed to be impressed by the magnitude of that vast plain, stretching away as far as eye could see, and covered with a six-foot growth of grass that billowed gently in the wind or, in the spring, dazzled onlookers with its color-splashed carpet of wild flowers. Yet the prairie

country was shunned by the first settlers, whose frontier technique was adjusted to a wooded country.[1]

If the Tall Grass prairies were shunned, the Short Grass prairies of the Great Plains were much more so. Indeed, as has been pointed out, many settlers trekked right across this more arid zone to the Western Forest, where they set up homes in wooded surroundings in Oregon, rather than change their way of life. 'They sought the familiar and shunned adaptation to the grassland.'[2] This was the main reason why America expanded so rapidly into the Pacific, and entered the farther west before developing the Mid-West.

However, certain forces were at work which soon favoured prairie settlement. First, in eastern America and Canada, a large industrial population was growing, which needed cheap food. More land had to be taken in; the prairies offered free, available land. Secondly, railways crossed the Appalachians and began to fan out across the forested plains. Soon they reached the Mississippi. By 1860 the river was crossed in fifteen different places, opening up Missouri and Iowa, Kansas and Nebraska. Thirdly, certain inventions helped. The windmill-pump was invented in the early 'sixties and allowed farmers to get a permanent water supply on the semi-arid steppe away from the edges of the rivers. The invention of barbed-wire in the 'seventies, for fencing purposes, made relatively close settlement of the prairies possible.

Once the pioneers ploughed up the sod, they found an extremely fertile soil. It was easy to till. Large acreages could be cleared in a little time, and large-scale methods of farming easily adopted. Consequently, wheat production became very popular and there was a rapid advance throughout the Tall Grass prairies. Later, practical experience taught farmers that in the more humid areas corn did better than wheat: the corn was fed to cattle and swine and soon became the basis for a thriving hog industry. For a time Cincinnati was the hog-capital of the Mid-West; now it is Chicago. Wheat production moved farther west, where the climate was rather too arid for corn.

In the still drier soils of the Great Plains it was at first difficult to grow grains, and the Short Grass and Bunch Grass steppes were left as natural range to feed vast herds of cattle or flocks of sheep. These arid ranges formed the cattle empire of the 'eighties. Railways were pushed west to Denver and Cheyenne and helped to produce a great cattle boom. However, the ranges became crowded with stock, the pastures were over-grazed, and

---

[1] Billington, R. A., *Westward Expansion*, p. 294.

[2] Trewartha, G. T., 'Climate and Settlement of the Sub-humid Lands', in *Climate and Man*, p. 172.

soil erosion set in. At the same time, prices fell and many ranchers were ruined.

Then, in the 1890s, the climate became wetter. Wheat farmers were tempted to move on to the arid plains. They did so well that much of the range was bought out, ploughed up, and sowed to wheat. Unfortunately, a drastic drought followed which ruined thousands of farmers. Immigration stopped and there was actually an emigration of many of the settlers into the moister regions of the Pacific border. 'In some of the western Kansas townships, two-thirds of the farm population was forced to leave because of the drought. Many entire towns were completely abandoned.'[1] Nevertheless, their experiences were useful because they led to dry-farming methods and to irrigation. These methods allowed some grain farming to continue, along with ranching. On the whole, ranching forms the more reliable use of the land, and much farm land is now going back into range.

The Settlement of the Western Cordillera

The settlers who moved across the Rockies found very varied conditions in the semi-desert plateaux of Idaho and Utah, Nevada, Arizona, and Colorado. The rugged relief gave well-watered slopes next to arid basins. Timbered mountains provided lumber for building homes and corrals; there was open range of sagebrush and bunch grass for flocks; and snow-fed rivers could be used for irrigation. Farms were built at the mouths of canyons, where the mountain waters met the basin-plains, and it was possible to grow a few irrigated crops to eke out the scanty pasture. In 1847, Brigham Young diverted the waters of City Creek to irrigate the lands for his Mormon colony at Salt Lake. A compact settlement developed about the fan of irrigation ditches, surrounded by the desert range. The Mormons did much to establish irrigation farming. Nevertheless, irrigated crops only served to supplement the range, and the inland plateaux and basins still form the sheep empire of North America.

Irrigation farming is more important and more successful in the dry climate of the California valley. It was brought there by the Spaniards in the late eighteenth century. The irrigation was used largely for orchards and garden vegetables. Dry-farming methods were relied on for grains. Ranching was carried on in the open range. These three types of farming are still practised in California.

The Spaniards laid the foundations for the prosperity of California by introducing fruits from the Mediterranean. These were well suited to the region and the figs, olives, and grapes which the missionaries planted flourished in the Great Valley. Oranges and lemons were soon added, along

---

[1] Thornthwaite, C. W., 'Climate and Settlement in the Great Plains', in *Climate and Man*, p. 184.

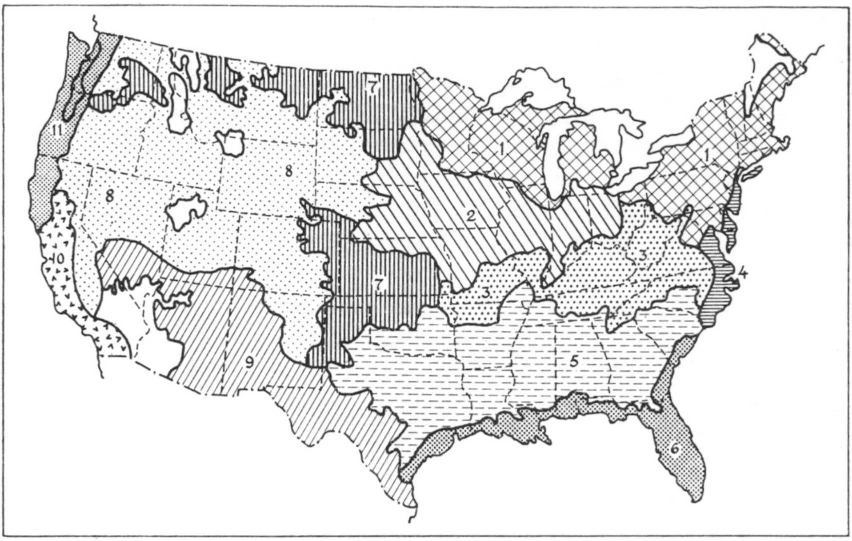

FIG. 140 Agricultural Zones in the United States. (From Baker and others.) 1, Dairy Belt; 2, Corn Belt; 3, Mixed Farming; 4, Mid-Atlantic Coast Truck Belt; 5, Cotton Belt; 6, S.E. Atlantic and Gulf Coast Truck Belt; 7, Wheat Belts; 8, Grazing with Irrigated Crops; 9, Extensive Grazing; 10, Irrigated Fruit and Truck Farming; 11, Dairy and Fruit Farming. (Scale, 1:45 m.)

with plums, peaches, and apricots. The rainless summers have made it possible to dry fruits out in the open and raisins, dried apricots, and prunes are exported in great quantities.

Today, dairy farming based on irrigated alfalfa and market gardening are rapidly expanding, to supply the large and growing cities of the region.

Thus we see that, as the pioneers moved steadily across the continent, they practised new kinds of agriculture and new crops to make use of the different climates, soils, and types of vegetation which they found. In this great story both history and geography have played their part, until today no continent has a more varied or progressive agriculture than North America. The north-eastern cool parts form a large Dairy Belt; the semi-arid plains give rise to the Wheat Belt; the humid interior plains to the Corn Belt; and the south-eastern warm regions to the Cotton Belt. Cattle and sheep ranching are found on the arid steppes of the Great Plains and interior basins. Irrigation farming, with the emphasis on fruit orchards, characterizes the Pacific borderlands (Fig. 140).

AGRICULTURAL REGIONS

The Dairy Belt

Dairying developed and has become concentrated in the north-eastern and northern-central areas. It has made use of the microthermal climate, with fairly warm summers and snowy winters, and a rainfall of over 30 inches. The grey-brown soils are well watered and deep, though rather acid. These conditions are ideal for red clover, Timothy hay, oats, winter wheat, silage corn, turnips, and potatoes; that is to say, for forage crops which can be used to feed dairy cattle. Since the largest cities of the United States are situated in the region (New York, Philadelphia, Boston, Detroit, and Chicago), there is a ready market for fresh milk, butter and cheese, and also for the poultry products and vegetables that are usually raised on the farms. Thus, as Russell Smith remarks, 'In this region earth, air, and history join to make the silo and the dairy barn the most conspicuous parts of the farm equipment.' Herds of Ayrshire, Holstein, or Jersey cattle are seen in the fields, and creameries or cheese factories glisten at the outskirts of towns and cities. The Europeans who settled this great area were the French from dairy-rich Normandy, many west-of-England people from the dairy districts of Cheddar or Cheshire, Dutch, and Germans who brought over their herds of Holstein and Friesian cattle, and Belgians and Swiss, famous for their cheese manufacture. They preserved these traditions and implanted them in a soil and climate that were not unfamiliar.

The Wheat Belt

Originally, the settlers in the east had also tried raising wheat as a cash-crop. Both winter and spring wheat were grown. After repeated failures, spring wheat was abandoned. Winter wheat was still planted, but it was no longer as important, because new settlers, moving farther west, found conditions much more suited to wheat production. They developed the Wheat Belt.

Wheat suffers several disadvantages in the humid areas of the east, which are not present farther west. The thawing and refreezing of the ground in the eastern winter often causes 'heaving'. The wet springs, with early rains and melting snows, may lead to waterlogging. The warm, cloudy summers, with temperatures between 70° and 80° F., foster crop diseases. The protein value of the grains is less in the moist climate of the east than in the drier, sunny climate of the west. The grain is soft, and does not make good bread. (However, it produces a useful 'pastry' flour and is, therefore, still worth growing in the populous east, where pastry consumption is high.)

The chief wheat regions are the northern Spring-Wheat Belt, and the southern Winter-Wheat Belt. The northern area reaches from Missouri northward to the Dakotas and the Canadian prairies: the southern region extends through parts of the southern Great Plains, from the Missouri river to the Arkansas. In the north, winters are too severe for winter wheat, and compel the farmer to choose the hardier, spring variety. The wheat finds an ideal site in the black earths and chestnut soils. Perhaps the chief limits to wheat production are rainfall; on the east it is limited by too much rainfall, on the west by too little. The best wheat is grown in an area with a rainfall of 15 to 30 inches. Very variable weather has led to a withdrawal of wheat farming in marginal areas in favour of ranching or irrigated farming.

The southern hard-wheat region is bounded on the east by 30 inches of rainfall, and on the west by 17 inches. Rather more rain is required because evaporation is higher. However, the wheat makes great use of the winter rains, and, as a winter variety, is able to ripen before the summer droughts threaten it. Sometimes, though, the hot, cloudless summers, with temperatures of over 80° F., may 'shrink' the grain, especially where a hot, dry wind is blowing. The southern wheat is associated with reddish chestnut and red-brown soils, which are well suited because they are rich in lime, and hold the water from winter rains and the spring thaws.

In the State of Washington, in the Big Bend of the Columbia, and on the upper Snake river plains, spring and winter varieties of hard wheat are grown on the semi-arid prairies at the foot of the mountains.

The Corn Belt

In the climate of the 'Oak-openings' and the Tall Grass plains, floored with prairie soil, the growing of corn early took over from wheat. This is actually not the home of corn, but with better soil and weather than the Eastern Forests or Mexican plateau, it has long outstripped them in production. Corn is suited to a warm temperate climate of moderate humidity. It needs a warm, moist soil, which is slightly acid and is rich in organic matter. The dark colour of the prairie soil makes it warm. It is moist with plenty of available water in the spring and early summer, when the corn shoots up most rapidly. Yet the leaching of the soil is not as great as in the rainier climates of the east, and the nitrates and phosphorus, needed so badly, are fairly near the surface and readily available.

The heart of the Corn Belt is Iowa, but the belt extends into the surrounding states, and east into Indiana and Ohio. This whole region has a warm summer of from 70° F. to 80° F. and a rainfall of from 25 to 45 inches a year. The seasonal weather is well suited to the crop. Corn starts germinating at 50° F. and needs a warm, moist spring. The Corn Belt lies in the path of the northward sweep of tropical gulf air, and it heats quickly once the polar continental air is driven back. Cyclones occur to supply abundant rain. Corn needs a temperature of 80° F. to flower, and therefore hot summers are ideal. These are typical of the interior plains, where the land warms up to an unusual degree for the latitude. During silking and tasselling, corn uses a maximum amount of water. This is provided by the deep soils which retain their moisture, and in part by the summer thunderstorm rains. No matter what the total rainfall is, if the summer rain is not sufficient, corn will fail. Corn needs a lot of sunshine to ripen. Cloudy weather is not suitable. But, as we have seen, the continental climate provides bright sunshine after the thunderclouds disappear.

These requirements keep the maximum production of corn to a zone between the Dairy Belt in the north (too cool in summer) and the Cotton Belt in the south (too hot and moist), and also east of the Wheat Belt (too dry). The yield is so high within the area that it adds up to more than the combined production of wheat, oats, barley, rye, buckwheat, and rice, making corn the most important crop in the continent. The corn is not used to any great extent for human food, but is mainly fed to cattle (in part from the west) and to hogs (raised locally). It has a high food value and oil content and readily fattens the animals, which are then slaughtered in Cincinnati, Kansas, Omaha, and Chicago and packed for sale. The corn is now mixed with other grain and fed as cake to stock which are penned in large feed lots. It is no longer economic to let animals fend for themselves in the fields.

The Cotton Belt

In the Southern States cotton is king. It was introduced from the West Indies by the British colonists and rapidly spread from Carolina to the Mississippi. In its natural home, cotton is a long-lived, tropical perennial. In the United States it is north of its real home. Therefore it is very sensitive to weather conditions. It likes heat, but will not stand great humidity. Yields decrease as rainfall increases. It does well where the frost-free season is longer than 200 days, where the mean July temperature is over 77° F., and the mean annual rainfall is less than 60 inches. These conditions are found on the southern Atlantic coastal plain and the Alabama plain, and also on the southern soils of the Piedmont, which together form the oldest parts of the Cotton Belt. Other production areas occur on the Mississippi levees, and the 'prairies' of the Texas coastal plain. Irrigated cotton is rapidly expanding in New Mexico and California.

Many of the cotton plantations seek the protection of the Appalachians and the Ozarks, so as to avoid the spring and autumn frosts of the continental interior. At the same time, they avoid the wetter parts of the Mississippi valley, where disease is rife. They also avoid the extreme coastal sites along the gulf and the Atlantic coastal plain because the summers are too wet. At this season the tropical Atlantic air mass sends hot, wet winds on to the south-eastern coasts to retard fruiting and favour the spread of the boll weevil. Cotton plantations do not normally extend very far west in Texas and Arkansas because the change between very hot days and cold nights favours the cotton aphid: moreover, sandstorms from the semi-arid steppe 'sand off' the seedlings in the spring, while hailstorms are sometimes destructive in the summer thunderstorms.

Cotton is preyed on by many pests and diseases, the worst of which is the boll weevil. Since the buds which develop after July are more subject to attack then those before, the tendency is to grow early maturing varieties, or to move plantations on to early maturing soils. For example, the lighter, sandy-loam soils are preferred to the loams, silt-loams, and clays because, although less fertile, they reduce the dangers that come with wet springs and summers, and they help the crops to mature more rapidly.

The United States' share of the world's cotton crop was once as high as 60 per cent. However, it has fallen to about 40 per cent because American farmers in the Cotton Belt have more and more taken to mixed farming. The rapid industrialization of the south has produced large cities which demand milk, butter, eggs, and meat, and therefore farmers can get good profits from livestock, dairy products, and vegetables, as well as cotton. Cotton is increasingly grown in rotation with other crops.

The Western Ranchlands

The more arid parts of the Great Plains and the dry Intermontane Basins provide natural range for cattle and sheep. The areas are too dry for much arable farming. Annual rainfall is less than 15 inches, except on the mountain slopes. The grasses grow in bunches, covering only 50 to 70 per cent of the ground. This enables their roots to spread out and draw soil moisture from the spaces in between. Rainfall is very variable, and during abnormally dry years the grasses wither and there is not enough feed for the herds. Therefore, irrigation is practised to raise additional forage crops, like alfalfa, as a protection against drought. Today, some 35 per cent of the cattle feed is raised by this means.

To help prevent the ranges from being overgrazed, the animals have to be driven from one area to another. In the spring, as the snow melts from the mountain sides, and the grasses begin to grow, the shepherd folds his tent, packs his burros, and drives the sheep up to the hills. He moves slowly until the little lambs grow stronger. Then they climb higher and higher to graze on the summer 'alps'. When the snows return, they move to winter pastures in the basins. In the south-west, where it is very dry, the sheep may travel more than 200 miles in their migrations from low to high slopes and back to the desert again. On the plains there is not the same opportunity for movement and irrigation crops of hay and alfalfa are used to augment the spare range of autumn and winter.

As a result of careful management of the range and of breeding animals suited to drought and heat, the arid parts of the continent are now playing an important role in feeding and clothing the people.

Fruit Farming

In the Eastern and Western Forests a natural use of the land, after clearing the trees, was to plant orchards. The Indians themselves cultivated fruit trees. The Europeans introduced scientific methods and new kinds of trees until fruit-farming became very important. Tropical, sub-tropical, and temperate fruits are now produced in abundance. Mangoes and pineapples are grown in southern Florida, but cannot flourish where there is danger of 'northers' blowing down from the edge of the polar continental air mass. The sub-tropical fruits can stand some sub-freezing weather without damage, but are sensitive to prolonged cold. Actually, oranges, grapefruit and lemon, avocados, olives and figs like some cool weather; they do not really flourish in wholly tropical conditions. The temperate fruits, such as peaches, cherries, plums, pears, and apples can withstand sub-zero weather, provided the summers are hot and moist enough.

Most of the fruit grown consists of sub-tropical or temperate varieties. Citrus fruits are the chief sub-tropical types and are produced both in semi-arid California and Texas, and in humid Florida. They can stand winter temperatures as low as 28° F., but only for short times. Where frosty weather is common the risk is too great. However, if they are planted on slopes, the frosted air drains down into hollows and the fruit escapes damage. Sometimes smudge-pots are lit and placed in rows between the trees to prevent frosting. The summer temperatures should range between 79° F. and 91° F. for the best results; as for example in the Californian valley.

The deciduous tree-fruits, belonging to temperate climates, are found in northern California, Oregon, and Washington, in the west; and the Appalachian States and parts of the Great Lakes lowland, in the east. All temperate fruits require a winter, but cannot all stand the same degree or duration of cold. If the trees are not sufficiently 'winterized', the buds do not open in the spring; on the other hand, the buds may be killed by severe winter cold. The trees do best when a slow spring gives way to a warm summer followed by a sunny fall. The fall should not be too open or else the stems are not hardened enough, when winter comes, to stand the low temperatures. When thoroughly 'hardened', apples, plums, and sour cherries will stand temperatures as low as −30° F.; pears and sweet cherries, −20° F.; peaches and apricots, −15° F.

In the west, the mountain slopes protect the crops from severe frosts; in the east, the Great Lakes and maritime influences moderate conditions. On the prairies and American Great Plains there are no ameliorating influences and the full shock of the polar continental cold waves is felt, with frequent cold snaps below these critical temperatures. Not much fruit is produced except in small, unusually favoured, localities.

As for summer temperatures, peaches and apricots require warm weather of between 70° F. and 80° F. to ripen, whereas apples can flourish at 65° F. to 70° F., and sour cherries at about 65° F. A minimum of 30 inches of rain is needed by all deciduous fruit, and this keeps them to the neighbourhood of lakes or coasts, or to mountain slopes. Irrigation is necessary in drier areas like the Columbia valley, Washington.

AGRICULTURE AND ECONOMICS

Agricultural regions are by no means only a response to physical factors like relief, climate, and soil. They are also a reflection of economic and of social conditions. As the author has shown elsewhere, agriculture tends to vary as the economic nearness to, or social distance from, great metropoli.[1] Close to populous industrial centres the cost of land is high, agriculture must compete with suburban expansion, the dispersion of industry, and the spread of recreational facilities; therefore it must be highly specialized and very intensive. It must compete with the city in social ways as well, offering good schools, churches, hospitals, and clubs to people who are sufficiently aware of city standards to want to match them. However, farther from the city, land values drop, agriculture has so much less to compete with (it may have to vie simply with forestry or mining), and it can afford to be more extensive and, in many cases, more generalized. Here it may be practised by people who wish to have less exacting, costly, and sophisticated standards than urban ones, and who choose a more generalized kind of farming, possibly linked with hunting or fishing 'on the side', so as to live 'the simple life'.

Von Thunen expressed these tendencies in his theory of concentric zones by which he suggested that agricultural differences separated themselves out in economic belts developing outwards from centres of population. Around these centres a zone of market gardening and poultry production tends to grow up. Beyond this is a zone of dairy farming. Farther out still is a zone of fodder production and the fattening of pigs and cattle for the meat market. Beyond this again may be a zone of extensive grain farming. Finally, on the economic outskirts, cattle and sheep ranching, and general subsistence farming will be found (Fig. 141).

There are certain parts of the United States for which this is very true. Going north from the Boston–New York region, for instance, one passes through truck and dairy farms, to farms fattening beef stock, to sheep farms, and finally to rather backward general farms that are a relic of pioneer days. Or again, south-west from Chicago, one journeys across a market-gardening and dairy-farming zone into the Corn Belt, fattening hogs and beef cattle, out to the great Wheat Belt of America and, beyond this, to the cattle

[1] Watson, J. W., *General Geography*, Toronto, 1957, p. 401.

ranches of the Rockies. Finally, eastward from Los Angeles, one can see a roughly zonal arrangement of dairy farms and orchards in an inner intensively used area, passing to wheat farms and cattle ranches in the remoter parts of southern California.

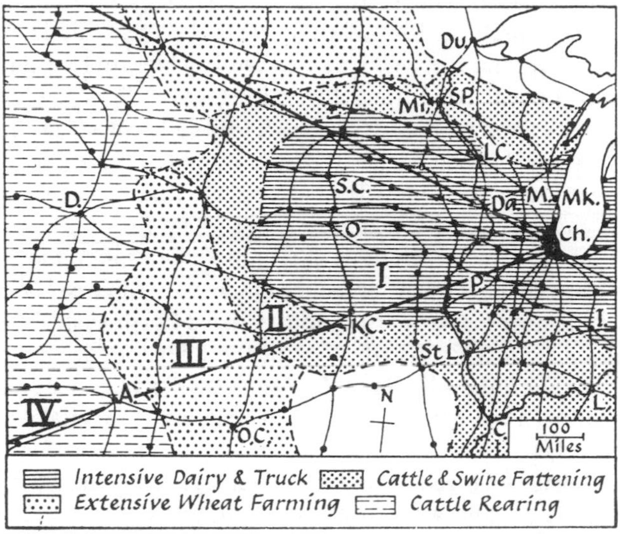

FIG. 141 Agriculture and Economics; a Price-belted Lowland. Von Thunen's Theory of Land-use Zonation suggested that zones of farming intensified in ratio to the economic distance from the regional centre. In the Mid-West, the main agricultural areas do tend to fall in belts in ratio to their price-distance from Chicago.

I, Truck and dairy farming which can afford the highest prices for land, crowd near to Chicago; II, then, on still high-priced land, come stock-fattening farms; III, beyond, on distinctly lower-priced land, are wheat farms; and, IV, most remote from Chicago, where competition for land is at its lowest, are the cattle and sheep ranches. Note that a measure of the increasing intensity of land use at the centre is the density of routes and settlements.

Moreover, quite apart from these city-centred zones, there has been a historical tendency for a zonal development, with the early generalized pioneer farming being displaced by more highly specialized and more intensive farms in the older settled parts; while grain farming and, above all, cattle and sheep ranching migrated out with the frontier.

Nevertheless, great though the influence of America's metropolitan centres may be, and important though the frontier may have proved, they have not yet made American farming simply a series of intermeshing concentric circles, based mainly on cost-distance from the industrial concentrations in the older settled parts of the land. In the main, the agricultural belts are a response to climate and soil, though undoubtedly modified by economic and historic forces. Truck farming is tied to sandy soils and a long growing season as much as to cities; the dairy belt extends well north of the manufacturing belt to make full use of a climate suited to hay, silage-corn and pasture. Tobacco and cotton farming seem more closely related to soils or the frost-free season than to the smoking public or to factory centres. The Corn Belt is based on Iowa, not so much because this is half-way on the value curve for land from Chicago to the Rockies, but because here are the optimum physical conditions for raising corn. It is true that wheat growing migrated from western New York to stabilize itself in the Dakotas, but this was at least as much because the humid climate of the east was never well suited to wheat production as because land was cheaper out west. (Land is still cheaper in the Great Basin, but wheat farming has not moved out there!) Finally, cattle ranching is a natural adaptation to the Short Grass prairie, and this accounts for its presence in the western Great Plains at least as much as its remoteness from the industrialized north-east. Fruit belts are highly localized, and their distribution in the Shenandoah valley, western New York, eastern Lake Michigan, in Georgia, Florida, and southern and central California, is in almost all cases a response to climate rather than distance to market.

Economics has changed the whole status of American farming, strengthening the big and weakening the small units. The number of farms has fallen from nearly 7 millions in 1935, at the height of the 'back-to-the-land' movement, to barely 3½ million in 1965. Today, 1,200 elite farms (or one thirteenth of one per cent of all producers) raise as much on their big consolidated units as 1,600,000 small-hold farmers! Of the remaining 1,800,000 middle-class farmers, less than one third provide profits comparable with good family businesses. As a result, farms are being amalgamated, and many farm families are leaving the land. But although depopulation occurs, the standard of farming is improving, and farm surpluses are bigger than ever.

Only where the pressure of population and the competition of industry have been unusually strong has an obviously economic arrangement been superimposed on, and come to displace, a climatic pattern. This is not to deny the importance of economics, however, in discovering, capitalizing, and exploiting the climatic pattern, for it was mainly, and in many cases only, through the forces of economic competition that the differences between climatic areas were appreciated and made use of.

CONCLUSION

From this general survey it is obvious that agriculture is closely related to geographical forces such as relief, climate, and soil. It is also a reflection of historical factors, including new traditions, inventions, breeds and seeds, and changes in economy and organization. Progress has been made largely by paying more careful heed to the limitations of nature and making the most of its opportunities. This is especially so in our modern economic system, where farmers have to specialize in the crops for which their region has a special aptitude. Thus the competitive and individualistic system, which is at the heart of the American way of life, has discovered the great opportunities in the natural environment. It has also greatly improved farming, though reducing the farm population.

FOREST WEALTH AND FOREST DISTRICTS

The forests of the United States are one of its principal economic assets. Forests cover about a third of the area of continental U.S.A.—i.e. 1,040,000 sq. miles out of 3,022,387. This is a very considerable proportion, particularly when it is remembered to what extent they have been cut down and replaced by agriculture.

Although the settler was interested in the land which he could clear and sow, and therefore may have seemed to treat the forest as a nuisance, he did so only on the soils best suited to agriculture, and he left a lot of the forest to remain and replenish itself as forest. Actually, wood products were vital, having in many instances to play the role in seventeenth- and eighteenth-century development that iron occupied in later time. The settlers from Europe were originally forest dwellers. As Gottman points out, they 'knew how to do away with trees and how to utilize them: timber was the prime raw material of western civilization. The search for bigger and better timber supplies was one of the driving motives for the development of North America.'[1]

The Eastern Forest predominates with 60 per cent of the total forested area, leaving 40 per cent for the Western Forest. Of the Eastern Forest, the northern mixed hardwoods make up 28·6 per cent of the area, the central hardwoods, 21·5 per cent, and the southern pineries and hardwoods, 49·9 per cent. Of all these, the south has the highest amount of commercial timber, with about 40 per cent of its forest area suited to sawing or pulping. About a third of the central hardwoods, and 35 per cent of the northern mixed forests, may be regarded as commercial, but only 23·9 per cent of the Western Forest—this mainly on account of its marginal nature in the intermontane basins and in the Pacific south-west.

The northern mixed hardwood-softwood forest replaces itself faster, is generally better managed, and has a higher ratio of growth to cut than elsewhere, although it is closely followed by the central hardwood forests.

[1] Gottmann, J., *Virginia at Mid-Century*, New York, 1955, p. 29.

Together they have a replenishment ratio about twice as high (1·86) as the national average (0·97). The south has also an above average ratio of growth to cut (1·22), but the west has seen, and still sees, a low degree of regrowth (0·5). Here 'drain exceeds growth by a wide margin, because of the virgin timber that is still being harvested'.[1]

Both the Federal and the State governments have large areas of national and State forests. Indeed the combined area under public control is now just about 30 per cent of the total. Much of this is under lease to contracting companies and is being cut out, but the contracts usually call for good forestry practices such as will allow the woods to replenish themselves and to do so with merchantable timber or pulpwood. Much, however, is maintained as range land, or simply as a means of conserving moisture and preventing soil erosion. By far the greater part of the forest wealth is in the hands of private owners, but most of these now practise forest management, to preserve their ability to go on using this resource.

MINING DISTRICTS

The Appalachians

Although the early settlers in the United States were disappointed at the apparent lack of mineral wealth, they soon came upon this as they moved west up the Lehigh and other valleys into the Appalachians, and as they crossed to the Allegheny plateau. That wealth mainly lay in fuels—in coal or oil. It had to wait the dawn of the industrial revolution to be used in any quantity, but when this tremendous technological advance occurred, the wealth of coal gave the United States a very real advantage. Iron was also found, though not in such large quantities, except in the south. The Appalachian mountains evolved in part during the great coal-forming periods of the Carboniferous Age, and have the richest coal fields in the world. Mountain building folded the coal beds, which were preserved on the sides or bottoms of the folds and so became readily available for mining. The coal fields were closely dependent on fold structures. In the Ridge and Valley area, where folding was intense, the coal was very strongly compressed and turned into 'hard' coal or anthracite, with a high carbon content. The Pennsylvania anthracite field is the chief example. In the Allegheny plateau the folding was more gentle; the coal was not compressed as much and it remained 'soft' or bituminous coal (Fig. 142).

In both the anthracite and bituminous fields the valleys cut deep into the coal formation, exposing the seams on their sides. The anthracite mines occur chiefly by the side of the Wyoming and Lehigh valleys; the bituminous

[1] Diller, O. D., 'Our Forest Resources', in Smith, G. H. (ed.), *Conservation of Natural Resources*, New York, 1950, p. 180.

seams are exposed in the Allegheny, Monongahela, New, and Big Sandy rivers. The anthracite seams are narrow and often broken by faults. They are difficult to work. Moreover, they extend to a great depth, and deep shafts have to be sunk with many side galleries. The bituminous seams are generally thicker. The famous Pittsburgh bed has an average thickness of 6 feet; it seldom goes down deeper than 400 feet below the surface; it is horizontal over wide areas and can easily be mined. The Pocahontas seam in West Virginia has similar qualities. The Connellsville coal makes an excellent coke,

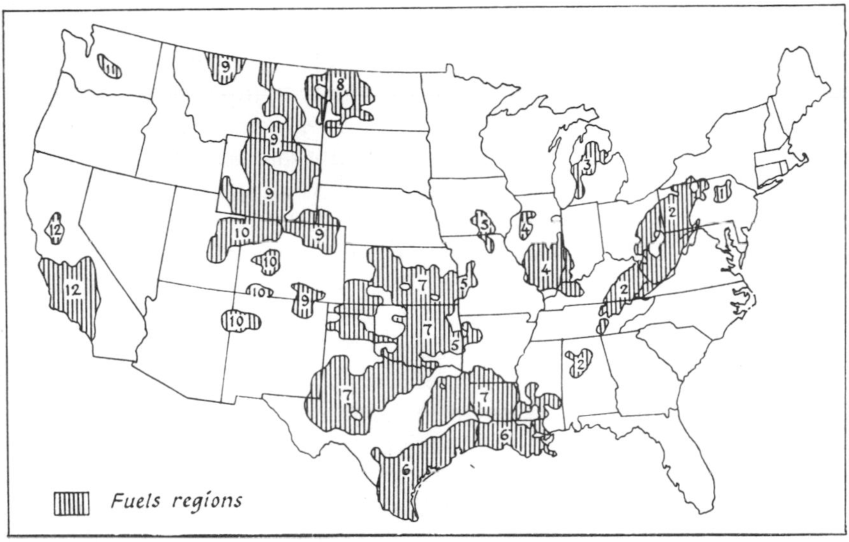

FIG. 142 Fuel Regions of the United States. (From E. W. Miller.)
1, Eastern Appalachian (Anthracite); 2, Western Appalachian (Coal and Oil); 3, Central Michigan (Coal and Oil); 4, Eastern Interior (Coal); 5, Western Interior (Coal); 6, Gulf Coast (Oil and Natural Gas); 7, Midcontinent (Oil and Natural Gas); 8, Williston Basin (Oil); 9, Northern Gt. Plains (Oil and Coal); 10, Colorado Plateau (Oil and Natural Gas); 11, Western Washington (Coal); 12, Southern California (Oil). (Scale, 1:45 m.)

widely used in steel production. In Alabama the bituminous coal field is dominated by the Pratt coking coal, a 4-foot seam which is easily mined.

The Appalachian coal fields have easy access to the coast or to the interior, thanks to the many gaps through the mountains. The anthracite can be hauled eastward through the Reading or Harrisburg gaps to Philadelphia and New York, or westward by the Susquehanna gap to Buffalo and the Great Lakes cities. The bituminous coal of the Pittsburgh district can be sent east by the Potomac to tidewater, or north by the Allegheny to the Great Lakes; the West Virginia soft coal goes west by the New river and the Ohio or east by the James river.

There is a great demand for Appalachian coal in New England and the

Mid-Atlantic States and in the Great Lakes States and Central Canada. These regions have little or no coal of their own, but need a great deal for their homes, cities and industries. The Appalachian coal is also on good water connexions to the mining districts of the Superior Upland and is central to the prosperous agricultural towns of the dairy, corn, and cotton belts.

In addition to coal the Appalachians are noted for oil and gas wells. The first oil wells in America were struck into oil-rich sands in Pennsylvania in 1859. These sandstones are of Carboniferous Age, and it is probable that the oil came from the former swamps, by means of slow distillation and seepage. Small pools of oil on the flanks of gentle folds reach from western New York to West Virginia and eastern Kentucky. Above the oil, natural gas is also trapped in the arched-up rocks. The pressure of the gas was quite enough at first to bring the oil to the top of the well: but so much natural gas has been drawn off for urban and industrial use that there is little pressure left and oil wells have to be pumped. The Appalachian field yields the highest quality oil in the United States, but it is nearing exhaustion, and only produces 2·3 per cent of the national total. Many of the wells are so near to exhaustion that they can be pumped only once a week, so as to allow time for the oil to seep from the sands back into the well.

Coal and Oil in the Interior

The Interior Lowlands are noted for their agricultural rather than their mineral wealth. Nevertheless, they possess gentle arch-like structures which have brought coal beds sufficiently near the surface to be worked. The structures have also trapped considerable pools of oil. The Interior coal fields are not as great as those of the Appalachians; they account for only 25 per cent of the U.S. total. However, the Interior oil districts yield 55 per cent of the national production (see Fig. 142).

The coal of the Interior Lowlands was formed during two periods when shallow seas invaded the continent. In the Central Plains they developed during the Carboniferous Age, and in the northern Great Plains during the Cretaceous Age. The central fields are divided into four basins, separated by low arches. The largest is the eastern central field, which lies on the flanks of the Cincinnati upfold, and extends from Kentucky, through Indiana to Illinois. It produces about 17 per cent of America's bituminous coal. The seams are two to seven feet thick and lie at such a shallow depth that it is possible to mine a considerable amount by stripping off the glacial till and sedimentaries above, and shovelling out the coal with mechanical scoops. Most of the mining is confined to the rim of the basin, where the coal is readily obtainable. The coal is not good for making coke, but serves well enough for raising steam, and was long used in railways, ships, and central-heating plants throughout the Mid-West. The Ohio, Wabash, and Illinois rivers flow through the basin, and offer cheap transportation to Cincinnati, St Louis, and Chicago. The field is thus assured of good markets which are relatively remote from the higher-grade, but more costly, coals of the Appalachians. However, it has suffered a steady set-back since the war, due to a switch-over to oil. The trains have now been dieselized and most buildings are heated by oil-fired systems.

The Western Central field lies in a broad, shallow basin west of the Mississippi, in Oklahoma, Kansas, north-west Missouri, and Iowa. Though the field covers a huge area, it does not produce much, largely because the coal is of a poor quality. Indeed, it can be generally stated that the quality of coal declines westward, until the Rocky mountains are reached. The coals of the Michigan basin and Texas fields are also of a poor-grade bituminous type and are only locally important.

The northern Great Plains are underlain by a coal field which is perhaps the largest in the world, and extends from Wyoming through Montana and the Dakotas to Saskatchewan and Alberta. Nevertheless, in spite of its enormous area, it is not very important. Most of the coal is a very impure bituminous type or an even softer lignite, that is still quite 'woody'. It is no good for coke and is a poor steam coal. It is mined and used locally, simply because the cost of hauling higher grade coals from west to east is too prohibitive. Farther towards the foothills the coal has been altered by the Rocky mountain folding movements and is a better quality, forming excellent steam coal. But unfortunately the local market is not great; population is sparse; there are few industries or large cities.

The Interior Lowlands are much more important as sources of oil than of coal. Large pools of oil lie on the slopes of the Rocky foothills in Wyoming. Truly enormous pools lie on the flanks of the Ozark Dome and the Ouachita folds. Fairly important reserves are found in the central basins, particularly along the side of the Cincinnati upfold. Thus we see that the structure of the rock rules the location and extent of the fields.

One of the largest of these oil fields is known as the Mid-Continental, yielding over 40 per cent of the U.S. total. It lies on the western flanks of the Ozark Dome and west of the Ouachita mountains. The most famous pool is that at Cushing, which has, however, long passed its maximum.

Farther north in the Central Plains lies the Illinois–Indiana field, centred in Peoria. It yields 5 per cent of the American production. It supplies fuel oil and natural gas to the Chicago and Detroit industrial areas. A small field around Lima also helps to feed the Lake Erie manufacturing zone. It lies on the western flank of the Cincinnati upfold.

South of the Ozark mountains is the Gulf field, on the shores of the Gulf of Mexico, producing about 30 per cent of the country's total. It is rather unique, since the oil is not found on the sides of upfolds, but around salt-domes. The pools are local, but numerous. They are under great pressure from gas and release the oil in remarkable gushes.

The various interior and coastal oil fields are situated near to industrial areas or to ports, and the oil can be easily transported or piped to the large refineries, whence the finished products are distributed to the consumer. The 'oil cities' in the petroleum-producing regions like Tulsa, Saco, Peoria, Lima, and Oil Town usually collect the crude oil, and separate out the lighter products, such as kerosene and gasolene, from the heavier. Then the different oils are carried or piped to huge refineries in the petroleum consuming districts, and there broken down to a wide variety of products, to suit the needs of different industries. The larger refining centres are Chicago, Toledo, and Buffalo in the Great Lakes areas, and Pittsburgh, Bayonne (New Jersey), and Philadelphia in the eastern areas.

However, it is important to note that oil does not draw industry to the oil fields as coal has done to the coal field. This is because oil pools become exhausted much quicker than coal seams; because oil is not quite as necessary to basic industries as coal (which not only supplies heat but also carbon for the manufacture of iron and steel); and because it is generally cheaper to transport the oil to a favoured industrial site than to move industry to oil. Coal is by no means as cheap to transport, unless near to water. Many industries have thus moved to the coal field.

(The main exception lies in the vicinity of the Great Lakes. These form a point of convergence for the down-flow of iron from the Superior Upland, and the up-flow of coal from West Pennsylvania and West Virginia. At points of convergence great iron- and steel-making centres such as Buffalo, Cleveland, Gary, and Duluth-Superior have emerged.)

The Iron of the Superior Upland

American industry long found it difficult and costly to get iron. Although many small amounts existed in the Appalachians and Adirondacks, no large field was found, with the exception of the Clinton ores, near Birmingham, Alabama.

In 1844, however, things began to be different. William Burt discovered outcroppings of iron south of Teal Lake near Marquette. In 1847 production got under way at the Jackson mine. Operations were at first confined to ores at or close to the surface, and the iron ore was shipped out to be smelted. A railway was built in 1857 down to the port at Marquette and this downgrade route enabled the ore to be sent out quite cheaply. Cheap transportation was also offered by Lake Superior and the Soo canal to centres of demand near Chicago, Cleveland, Buffalo, and then by the Welland canal to Hamilton. Although mining began at the surface, it has now reached a depth, at Negaunee, of over 3,000 feet (Fig. 143).

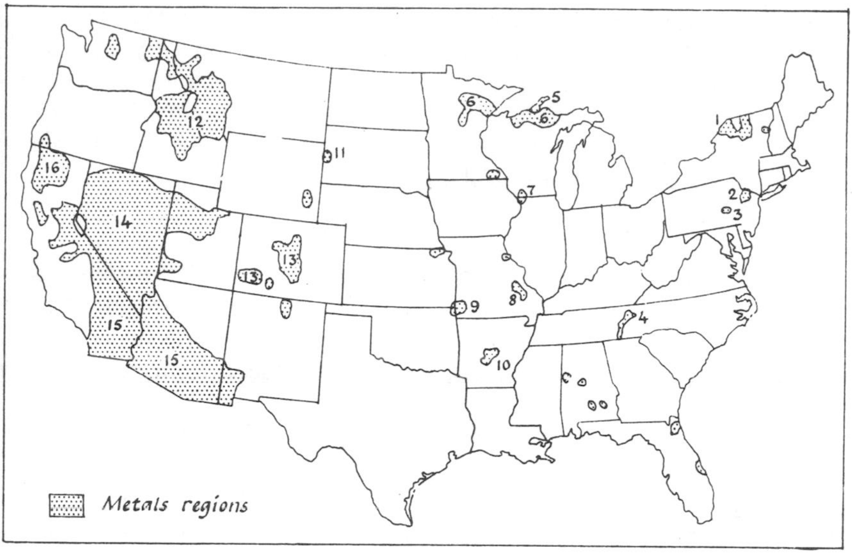

FIG. 143 Metalliferous Regions of the United States. (From E. W. Miller.) 1, Adirondacks (Iron); 2, Northern N. J. (Zinc); 3, Cornwall–Morgantown (Iron); 4, Great Smokies and S. Appalachian (Ferro-alloys); 5, Keweenaw (Iron and Copper); 6, S. and W. Superior (Iron); 7, S. and W. Wisconsin (Lead); 8, South-east Missouri (Lead); 9, Tri-state (Zinc–lead); 10, Central Arkansas (Bauxite); 11, Black Hills (Gold); 12, N. Rockies (Copper, Various); 13, C. Rockies (Ferro–alloys); 14, N. Gt. Basin (Copper); 15, S. Gt. Basin (Silver, Copper); 16, California (Gold). (Scale, 1:45 m.)

Soon all the major iron ranges were discovered, lying around the western end of Lake Superior. These low rocky heights contain large sheets or pockets of haematite or red oxide of iron. The ore has an iron content of from 52 to 65 per cent and there is not much waste. There are said to be about 70,000 million tons still left for use, although the greater part of this is low-grade ore which has no commercial value at present. But what remains as commercial ore is still tremendous and produces four-fifths of the iron in the United States. In the Vermilion, Mesabi, and Cuyuna iron ranges the iron is at the surface, and easily mined by stripping. In the Penokee, Marquette, and Menominee fields it occurs in large pockets in the rock, and has to be mined by shaft.

Of all these the Mesabi field is easily the most important, accounting for half America's production. It has a huge mass of ore, often 200 feet thick, which lies in great sheets near to the surface. It is covered with only a thin layer of slate, which can easily be broken, or of till. Steam shovels can scoop away most of this overburden and then bite out the iron in immense open-pit mines. At Hibbing lies the largest single mine in the world; its workings have cut down tier below tier to a depth of 350 feet. There are over seventy miles of railroad track inside the mine carrying the ore to the surface. The ore does not have a great distance to go to Duluth at the head of the lakes and can then be moved cheaply over a very wide area. The main limitation to mining lies in the climate which freezes up the ore on the tiers of the pits and dumps a heavy fall of snow in the mine craters. Work slows down for three or four months in the winter, except where ore is being taken out by shafts.

The Western Cordilleras

The Cordilleras are among the richest areas in minerals and metals within the United States. They have basins with coal and oil, which are absent from the Shield. At the same time, they have huge mountain cores intruded with igneous rock, with many metals, which are absent from the Interior Lowlands (see Figs. 142 and 143).

How do they compare with the Appalachians? They are much richer in metals, but rather poorer in coal. It is highly probable that more of their coal would be mined if it were as cheap to market as Appalachian coal. Similarly their iron fields are too far away from the iron-consuming districts to allow extensive development. Therefore, the tendency has been to concentrate on the costlier metals, like gold, silver, and copper, which can pay their way to market, or on products like oil which are cheap enough to transport. Nevertheless, wherever coal or the base metals are found near railway passes or ocean ports, they have been developed.

We have already seen that the gold rushes to California, British Columbia, and the Yukon did much to open up the west. Gold is still important. The geology of the mountains offers ideal conditions. Veins of gold streak the rocks of coastal Alaska and upper California. Some of the veins have been weathered and the gold has been washed out and carried down by the rivers. It settled in 'placer' deposits by river banks, lakes, or the sea-shore. Thus mining is of two sorts: blasting out the gold veins, often after tunnelling to them down shafts, and sluicing and panning the placer deposits. Nome, Alaska, is the largest centre of beach-placer workings.

However, most of the gold mined in the United States comes from California, which produces 30 per cent of the total, and South Dakota, with 24 per cent. Colorado is the third largest producing district, with 14 per cent. The gold in California lies in the upper Sacramento valley, where gold and quartz veins radiate through rocks in contact with intrusions. The gold has been washed out in many places into river gravels. It was mined at first by simple panning methods as the individual prospector went in with his pick, shovel, pan, and burro. Scooping out the river gravels, he screened them in his pan. The gold would sink to the bottom, being heavier than the sands and gravel. Removing the waste, he picked out bits of gold and took them in leather bags to the nearest bank. However, today giant hydraulic water jets are played on the placer deposits and whole banks are washed away at once down into sluices. There the gold is mechanically screened. The South Dakota gold field is related to the large granite intrusions of the Black hills, an 'outlier' of the Rockies. The Home-stake gold mine is the largest in the U.S.A.

The Cordilleras are also rich in copper, silver, and lead and to a lesser extent in zinc. They produce 85 per cent of the silver and lead, and 30 per cent of the zinc. The mines lie in a great belt; namely, the inner and outer Rocky zones in Idaho, Montana, Utah, Arizona, Colorado, and New Mexico, where the fold and fault structures, intruded by granitic domes, sheets of lava, or other volcanic material, have proved ideal for metal formations. Although the Rockies produce only a third of the American zinc, it is of a higher quality than the average. Most American lead and zinc ores are of such a low grade (5 per cent as compared with 13 per cent for Canada) that it is doubtful whether they could be mined were it not for the protection of a high tariff. American copper is both plentiful and of a high grade. Michigan was long the chief producing centre; but the Cordilleran deposits are much larger, and Arizona, Utah, and Montana are the outstanding centres. At Anaconda the shafts have gone down 3,500 feet, and over 1,000 miles of passages have been dug from them into the richly veined rock. Iron mining is much less important in the Cordilleras than in the Shield or Appalachian regions. The deposits are found along the foothills of the Rockies in Wyoming, or in the interior basins of Utah; but the production is small—about 1 million tons a year. The ore is used for making pig iron for local industries, or as flux in smelting copper and other metals.

The Cordilleras are also rather poor in coal. Nevertheless, the coal is usually a high-grade bituminous type of anthracite, and is valuable. Small but excellent deposits of anthracite coal occur in the Puget Sound region of Washington State. Bituminous coals in the Willamette valley of Oregon and the lower Californian valley are of local importance. Larger fields exist in the basins of the Rocky foothills in Montana, Wyoming, and Colorado, but most of the coal is of a poor-grade bituminous type. It is also too remote from the large industrial cities to compete with the central and eastern mining areas. However, it remains as a huge source of latent power, which new techniques and new demands may some day release.

The chief sources of power in the Cordilleras are oil and hydro-electricity. In the Californian valley is a broad downfold where large pools of oil have collected under minor arches in the rocks. The California oil fields began to be developed on a large scale in 1900, and now are the third largest on the continent after the Central and Southern ones, yielding 15 per cent of the U.S. production. The Rocky mountain field in Wyoming yields 1½ per cent.

MANUFACTURING IN THE UNITED STATES

The great natural wealth in fuels and metals possessed by the United States, and the remarkable wealth of agricultural and forest products, have together helped the American nation to build up what is without doubt the greatest industrial and commercial machine in the world, a machine that has brought them enormous prosperity and the world's highest standard of living. Actually there are a whole group of factors responsible for this development.

Opportunities for Industry

The United States has unusual opportunities. These include: (i) Its position between Western Europe and Eastern Asia which puts it in touch with the two greatest markets in the world. It is also close to the rapidly expanding markets of Latin America, and not far removed from promising markets in Africa and Oceania. (ii) Its relief, which allows easy movements of goods into or out of the continent. The narrow isthmus of the Panama Canal has given it command of Atlantic and Pacific trade. The Gulf of Mexico, backing on to the plains of the Mississippi, opens up the southern half of the continent: the Hudson estuary, cutting through the Appalachians, serves the eastern and central parts; the Golden Gate and Puget Sound pierce the Pacific borderland, and favour the west. The wide extent of lowland in the heart of the continent makes communication easy and offers room for settlement. (iii) The United States has comfortable and stimulating climates, ideal for health and energy. It has been found that the best climate for man is one of moderate variation around a mean of 60° F. The ideal climate, claims Sir David Brunt, would seem to be one in which the mean temperature of the hottest month of the year does not exceed 75° F., while the mean temperature of the coldest month does not fall so low that it becomes unduly costly to raise the indoor temperature to 60° F.[1] Actually, a range between 75° F. and 42° F. is most suitable. Such climates are found in most parts of the United States. Temperature is by no means the only consideration, however; humidity, pressure, air movement, and precipitation are also significant. In fact, one of the most significant things is the constant bombardment of man by successive changes in the grouping of all these things together—a common feature of the weather of the United States, which is dominated by frequent polar-front storms, along many tracks (see Chapter Three). Their constant passage has helped to keep conditions stimulating. (iv) U.S. supplies of industrial power and of raw materials are unusually plentiful. America has developed about two-fifths of the power used for manufacturing in the world. This comes from the large reserves of coal and oil locked up in its rocks; and from the water-power and hydro-

[1] Brunt, D., 'Climate, Weather and Man', *Endeavour*, 3, no. 2, pp. 87–97.

electricity stored in its many lakes and large rivers. In addition it is the world's chief source of valuable metals such as uranium, silver (66 per cent), zinc (53 per cent), lead (48 per cent), and copper (40 per cent). It mines nearly a third of the world's iron and a quarter of its gold. The agricultural raw materials are also considerable. North America raises over two-fifths of the world's cotton, nearly one-third of the wheat, and one-fifth of the pork products. It is an important producer of all but the tropical crops. (v) The population of the country, about 200 million people, is sufficient to provide a large home market, and to produce a surplus for overseas trade. This population has been characterized by venturesome individuals from Europe and Asia, who love freedom and believe in their own worth and are inventive and industrious. Education is well advanced and there is a large body of skill on which industry can draw. (vi) Through generations of well-based and productive agriculture and of widespread commerce America has developed a reserve of capital, extensive investments, and many far-flung trade connexions.

Localization of Industry

Such advantages, though shared in to some extent by the whole country, are not evenly distributed. On the contrary, they are highly localized. Although the Superior Upland produces vast quantities of iron, it sees relatively little manufacturing, because there is no coal or oil; the climate is severe; the people few, and they are remote from markets. Similarly, although the western Cordilleras yield gold, silver, and copper, orchard fruits, wheat, and sheep, yet the population is so thin and patchy, and transportation so dear, that manufacturing is very limited. The Southern States are rich in agriculture, but poor in metals and coal, and therefore they too have not had the conditions which up till now have sponsored industry. However, the northern-central and north-eastern areas have a concentration of geographical advantages which, together with their historical heritage—essentially one of investment and trade—has given them the lead in industrial affairs. In this large region more than three-quarters of the people live in cities, over two-fifths engage in manufacturing and another fifth in commerce. Here is one of the world's major industrial areas.

The region lies between the Shield and the Appalachians and between the ocean gateways and the continental heartland. Therefore it commands mines and fuel, and interior and foreign markets. It has become, without question, the power centre of the continent, straddling the largest coal fields, with the greatest amount of hydro-electricity yet developed and close to the largest supplies of oil. It is also Ameria's, transportation centre, controlling the main inlets and outlets across the Appalachians and linking the continent with Europe, the largest market in the world. It is, at the same time, the population centre with the greatest number of producers and consumers and the widest variety of skills. It has become the nation's financial centre, where the historic leadership of the east in economic matters was won and the present control of capital is vested. The region is, over and above, an important agricultural producer and in close touch with the agriculture of the cotton, corn, and wheat belts to the south and west. It can therefore count on sufficient cheap food to feed its huge city populations, and has a

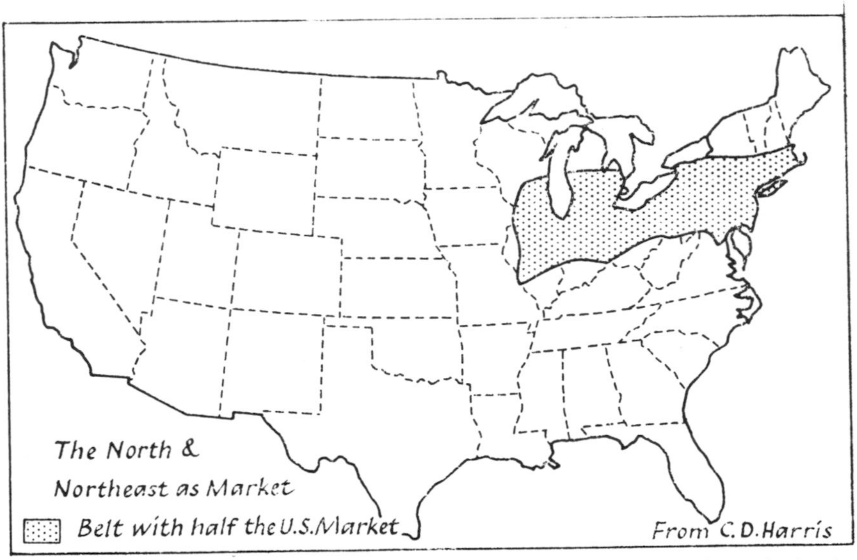

FIG. 144 The Concentration of Buying Power in North-eastern U.S.A., a factor in the rise and concentration of industry. (Scale, 1:45 m.)

near-by agricultural market. It also has considerable mineral wealth, with the largest iron fields in the United States and considerable copper. It possesses quite large salt deposits and has a good supply of building materials. With many supplies, it also has many demands, and is America's chief market (Fig. 144).

The American Manufacturing Belt

For these and other reasons manufacturing has become concentrated in the north-eastern and northern-central parts of the United States, roughly within the triangle marked by Boston, Massachusetts, and Baltimore, Maryland, on the east, and Chicago, Illinois, on the west.

Historical Development

The geographical advantages of the area, great though they may have been, were only brought into play by long historical processes. They were quite unknown to the Indians, who never learned the value of coal or iron, or discovered the use of machinery. Not until Europeans arrived who had had a long training in the arts of manufacturing, trading, and transportation was the wealth of the region realized and developed. Thus, as Isaiah Bowman says: 'The natural environment is always a different thing to different groups.' Its resources are always present, but their use depends on the knowledge and skill that particular people may have or the aims they hold in life. To a simple hunting and gardening people, like the Neutral Indians, Niagara Falls was but an object of wonder; to the industrialized American it became a vast source of power for manufacturing. The Falls have always had a *potential* value as power, but power was actually *developed* only by the white man. In other words, geography is conditioned by history.

The first areas to develop were **New England and the Mid-Atlantic States.** Here sites for manufacturing could be found on tidewater, available to direct sea-borne trade with other colonies and with the motherland (an important consideration when land travel was difficult or impossible). Many of these sites were at waterfalls, where the rivers, flowing across the Piedmont and New England upland, plunged down to the coastal plain, providing cheap and ample water-power for the early mills. Some sites were also on rivers that provided interior connexions to the opening markets of the West.

With the demand for steam-driven machinery, instead of water-power mills, a search for coal began. In the early nineteenth century the **Mid-Appalachian States** started to compete with the tidewater settlements for industrial supremacy. They afforded much greater sources of power in the anthracite and bituminous coal fields at their disposal. They also had local supplies of iron, for the founding of an iron and steel industry (the coking coals were excellent for smelting the ore). They were at the very gateways to the rapidly expanding interior markets. The enormous call on iron for railways, bridges, fences, and agricultural machinery soon exhausted local sources, but the Appalachians were close enough to the Great Lakes to be able to pay the cost of transporting the Lake Superior iron ores to the coal fields. They paid this cost largely by exporting their coal to the Upper Lakes.

However, the Appalachians have had this serious drawback, that they are very rugged. Their deep, narrow, rejuvenated valleys do not allow enough room for industrial expansion. Plants cannot spread. The population must either crowd into terribly congested cities or live farther away from the plants, in suburbs up the valleys. Therefore, as the Mid-West opened up, in the latter half of the nineteenth century, more room was found for industrial expansion west of the mountains.

Thus the **Southern Lakes (Erie–Michigan) plain** began to flourish as a manufacturing district. It had the advantage of lying almost exactly half-way between the Appalachian coal and the Lake Superior iron. It was also between the ocean gates and the continental heartland. It dominated the transcontinental routes, as these were developed. Then, too, it was near to power and metal reserves, especially in the Superior Upland, and lay at the opening to immense agricultural belts in the Interior Lowlands. These offered very real prospects.

Broadly speaking, then, the manufacturing belt of America grew to include (*a*) the coastal districts of New England and the Mid-Atlantic; (*b*) the river gap districts of the Appalachians; and (*c*) the lowlands of the Great Lakes. We can call these the Sea Gate, Bridge, and Heartland regions. They are served by 'feeder' regions to north and south. The main axis of the manufacturing belt runs from New York through Detroit to Chicago. It is crossed by another major axis running from Boston to Washington. The main axis, or Lower Lake line, is fed by Central Canada (mines and forests) and the Central States (oil and agriculture). The axis of the Atlantic coast is fed by Atlanto-European connexions in the north and Caribbean-Latin American ones in the south. Since both lines cross at New York, it has become the largest city and chief industrial and financial centre of the whole belt (Fig. 145).

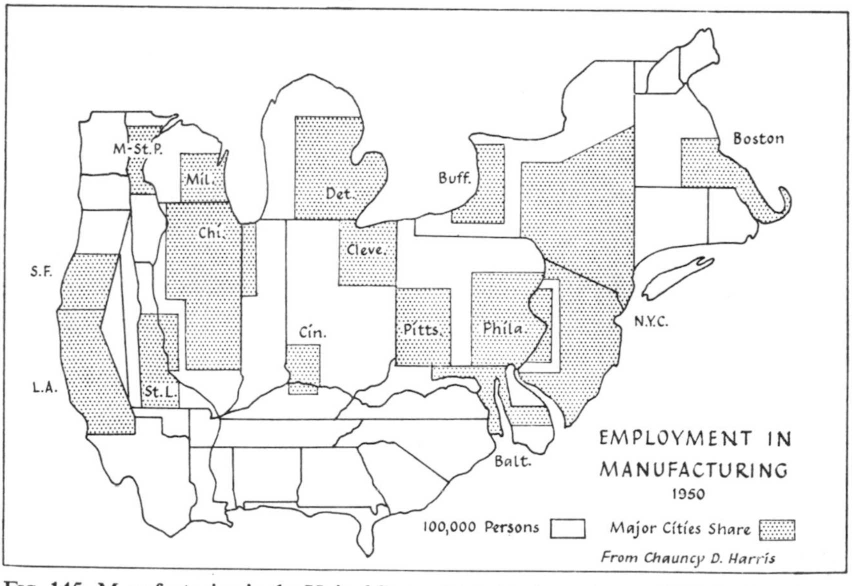

FIG. 145 Manufacturing in the United States. Note the importance of (A) the North-east and Great Lakes, and (B) the chief metropolitan cities. The Manufacturing Belt, from Boston to Chicago, dominates the American industrial scene; compare it with the south and west. Size of State is shown as proportional to State's share of U.S. manufacturing labour force.

The Sea Gate Industrial Region

The chief sea gates into America are those of New York, Philadelphia, and Baltimore, along the inlet coast of the middle Atlantic. Others are Montreal and New Orleans on the gulf coasts. The gulfs actually appear to reach farther inland, west of the Appalachians, than the inlets; but the inlets go back to short gaps, and open the most direct routes to the interior markets.

The sea-gate region is typified by a great diversity of industry, both heavy and light, but with a preponderance of the latter. It depends on raw materials, which are cheap to assemble, many of which are drawn over sea from distant places. It tends to exploit those raw materials which, after they have been transformed into consumer goods, bring a high profit and thus pay the cost of their transportation. The demand on fuels is considerable, but much is made of hydro-electricity developed in the Appalachians. Oil can be imported in quantity from Venezuela and Texas. The dense, polyglot population is counted on to provide plentiful labour and many skills. Therefore, industries either rely on mass production, using cheap labour, or a limited production of high-quality goods, requiring skilled manufacture. The large local market in the giant cities of New York, Philadelphia, and Boston—larger than all the population of Canada—provides a safe investment, and there are still larger markets inland or overseas. The region specializes in processing American raw materials before they are shipped overseas, or foreign raw materials before they are redistributed in America.

In the New York industrial area there live about 14 million people. They have prospered because New York is the best harbour on the Atlantic coast and therefore the focus of sea routes. At the same time, it commands the most direct gap into the interior (Hudson–Mohawk) and is a focus of land routes. It handles over half the nation's commerce. The harbour includes the estuaries of four rivers and has a direct waterfrontage of 771 miles. It is connected by the Erie Canal with the Great Lakes. It is so busy during daylight hours that an average of one ship enters and one ship leaves every 10 minutes. Their goods are carried inland by twelve railroads and by the famous new New York Thruway (U.S. 90).

It is only natural that industries should spring up to make use of these facilities and connexions. But they have relatively little flat land to expand over. Consequently, they do not concentrate on heavy products like iron and steel, which require a lot of space and also a great deal of coal, oil, and electricity. Their most space-consuming industry is the petroleum one, based on refining the oil brought overseas by tankers or piped to the coast from the interior. The refining of sugar sent from the Indies is also important, as is the packing of coffee. The area specializes in making silk, rayon, and nylon goods and ready-to-wear clothing. It manufactures rubber goods and high-quality metal products. It is the country's chief chemical centre. Industries to feed its vast population, like flour-making, meat packing, and the canning of vegetables and fruit, are also important. All this varied effort could only be justified by the large interior and foreign markets, by the many skills of a very heterogeneous community, and by great capital reserves.

Two sub-regions extend from New York—one north-eastward to New England and the other south-west into Pennsylvania and Delaware. The New England district revolves around Boston, which is the nearest large port to Europe, is always free of ice, and has fairly good connexions with the interior. The chief industries are shoe-making, cotton and woollen mills, hardware and machinery, and small metal wares. These are ideal for the area because they consume little fuel, they depend on assembling imported raw materials at little cost, they utilize highly skilled employees, and serve a wide national and international market. Boston's overseas connexions are closer to Europe and Africa than those of New York, partly because of the historic Great Triangle trade with Liverpool, West Africa, and the West Indies. Cotton from the Southern States and Egypt, wool from England, South Africa and Australia, leather from England and Morocco, cocoa from West Africa, sugar, molasses, and rum from the West Indies are outstanding imports.

The south-western sub-region is centred in Philadelphia, which is situated at tidewater between two famous estuaries, the Delaware and Schuylkill, near to the Schuylkill falls on good connexions with the interior. It has a large lowland for industries to expand on and is close to the Appalachian coal fields and to the iron deposits of northern New Jersey and southern Pennsylvania. Its climate is more equable than that of Boston, it has more power resources, and better rail connexions—therefore it has forged ahead as an industrial centre. In addition to the cottons and leather goods, where it competes with Boston, or the silk goods, oil and sugar refineries, where it competes with New York, it has heavier industries, such as the manufacture of iron and steel, of locomotives, railway equipment, steel tools, and large ocean-going ships. It is the nation's largest ship-building centre. Again, these industries depend on the refining, processing or handling of raw materials imported from distant countries or exported from the interior. They exploit the dense population, many skills, and considerable capital reserves so typical of the sea-gate area. They have built up a great industrial complex sometimes called the Ruhr of America.

The Bridge Region

Between the coast and the interior lies the Bridge region, composed of the Hudson–Mohawk valley, the Lower Great Lakes, and the Pittsburgh districts. These all command the Appalachian crossings and are on or near to the Appalachian coal and oil fields. The Hudson–Mohawk valley occupies the only water-level route from New York to the Great Lakes. It is used by America's chief canal, the Erie Barge Canal, some of its leading railway systems—the New York Central Railroad, Michigan Central Railroad, and Erie Railroad—and its main transcontinental highways, U.S. 20 and U.S. 90. It is therefore well located for access to internal or external markets, and the assembly of raw materials. It also has large power supplies from waterfalls like Niagara Falls, Genesee Falls, and the International Rapids; and near-by fuel reserves in the Appalachian coal and oil fields. It can count on an abundant labour market, because it lies on the chief immigration route into the continent.

It has become one of the most highly urbanized areas in America. The cities tend to specialize on a few products each, those in the east, near cotton and wool imports, on textiles; those in the west, near iron and steel centres, on metal goods. Cohoes, Troy, and Utica specialize in knitwear and clothing, particularly in shirts; Schenectady, Syracuse, and Albany in electrical appliances, rolling stock, foundry products, and auto accessories. Rochester, once a famous flour centre, is now noted for precision instruments and clothing establishments.

The Lower Lakes district, stretching west from Rochester to Toledo, is still more important. It is at a zone of transhipment of Pennsylvania coal to lake boats and of Lake Superior iron to railheads. It is close to the vast wood and metal reserves of the Canadian Shield. It forms an apex of concentration of raw materials from the American Mid-West and the Canadian prairies. It is a channel of dispersal of goods made in the east, or of imported raw materials. It shares the power of Niagara Falls and is near to the Appalachian and Eastern Interior coal and oil fields.

To make use of these advantages it has developed: (i) important iron and steel mills and iron-using industries, such as automobile factories, at Buffalo, Lackawana, Erie, Cleveland, and Toledo, making the most of the coal-iron trade; (ii) flour-milling and meat packing, using the products of the west, as, for example, at Buffalo; (iii) other industries, using imports from the east such as rubber goods at Akron; and (iv) electro-chemical goods around Niagara Falls.

The Pittsburgh district is the fuel centre of the Bridge region. It straddles the greatest coal field in the world, and at the same time is not too distant from tidewater and lakeshore ports. Power and raw materials are most accessible and therefore costs of production are relatively low. The local supplies of iron are now finished, and the oil is nearly exhausted, but iron and limestone flux are easily imported from Lake Erie ports, and oil piped in from the interior fields. Consequently, Pittsburgh has maintained its position as the continent's outstanding metallurgical centre. It produces basic iron and steel products, together with machine tools, machine parts, machinery, electrical appliances, and auto parts. It supplies the steel for the machine industries from Cincinnati to Albany and also many of the machine parts. This wide distribution is made possible with the aid of the Ohio, Allegheny, and Monongahela rivers and the railways that follow them.

The Heartland Region

Though the Bridge region, as its name implies, can serve both east and west, it is displaced at the coast or at the interior by regions which specialize in coastal or continental contacts. The Heartland region, stretching from Detroit to Chicago, has grown in importance with the opening up of the Mid-West and the farther west. It is strategically placed between the metal-rich Shield, the coal-rich Appalachians, and the oil-rich plains. It also commands the great transcontinental routes across the plains through Rocky passes to the Pacific. It is at the very heart of the agricultural wealth of America.

The great need of the Interior Lowlands, the Shield to the north, and the Cordilleras to the west is steel. It is required primarily for railways and rolling stock, where thousands of miles of railroad have been laid across the continent. The vast potential of the country, to north and west, has been tapped largely through the railway. Transportation has transformed the continent. Highways and airways have also developed, and the automobile and aeroplane industries require great amounts of steel and other metals. Timber and pulp mills in the Canadian Shield and the many mines there, and in the Cordilleras, also demand a lot of steel machinery. Above all, the millions of farmers in the American Mid-West have depended on steel to develop the land. As agriculture has become more mechanized, the need for tractors, multiple-disc ploughs, harrows, binders, and combines has given rise to large plants making agricultural machinery. Windmills, water-pumps, gas and oil wells, fences, steel barns, all make additional demands. Finally, the packing of the meat and the canning of other farm products have used more and more metal.

Consequently, heavy, large-scale industries predominate, making iron and steel, machinery tools, rolling stock, automobiles, aeroplanes, lake ships, agricultural implements, and mining equipment. These are focused on two centres—Detroit and Chicago.

The Detroit district is the true gateway to the interior, and has specialized in transportation and agricultural machinery. At Ford's steel is made locally; much more can be obtained quite cheaply from the Lake Erie or Lake Michigan mills. The steel bars and plates are made into highly valuable cars, aeroplanes, and agricultural machines for export to the west or the east. Detroit is the automobile centre of America and forms the 'hub' for several rings of cities which produce car parts and accessories, auto bodies, radios, seats, seat-covers, rubber tyres and parts, auto glass, pumps, air-brakes, and so on. An outer ring of larger cities, like Flint and Lansing, makes carriages, diesel engines, hoists, etc. The aeroplane industry has recently been established to use the skilled labour, trained in making high-grade machines.

The Chicago district has grown where east–west railways cross north–south waterways. It has joined the gaps in the Appalachians with those in the central and northern Rockies around the salient of the Shield and its lakes. Thus it has become a focus for the forest and metal products of the north, the agricultural products of the west and south, and the trans-continental exchange of goods and passengers from Atlantic to Pacific. It owes its importance to its position rather than to fuel or metal resources. It has no such resources. Nevertheless, iron can be sent more cheaply from northern Lake Michigan and from Lake Superior than to Cleveland or Pittsburgh; and coal from West Virginia and from the Western Interior field is not too costly to transport. There is a large supply of oil from the Indiana and Illinois fields and from the Mid-Continental field, farther south. Above all, there is plenty of level land on the margins of the lake on to which large-scale industry can expand. There is also a large population to count on for industrial production and consumption.

Therefore, South Chicago and Gary have established 'the best balanced primary metallurgical district in North America'. The huge iron and steel plants provide the metal for the machine industries of Chicago and Milwaukee. They have several advantages over Pittsburgh. They can import iron ore and limestone flux more cheaply; they are much nearer the large steel-using markets of the interior; they have more space for expansion; they are nearer sources of fuel oil; and they have much larger supplies of water.

There are some 15,000 factories in the Chicago district. The large-scale industries include iron and steel, foundry products, machine tools, agricultural machinery, refrigerators, electrical machinery, aeroplanes, rolling stock, automobiles, oil refining, and meat packing. Notice how these use the various advantages of the location, already mentioned.

SUMMARY

It will be seen that man's use of the land has created certain great economic regions in the United States. Perhaps at their broadest these divisions may be considered in terms of: (i) an industrialized north-eastern and northern-central area, where the landscape is dominated by cities, factories, harbours, railway yards, a dense network of roads, rural depopulation, and the concentration of people in great metropolitan centres. (ii) A commercialized cropping area, in the humid central plains, the more humid parts of the Great Plains, in the Gulf plains, and the south-eastern part of the Atlantic coastal plains. Here agriculture dominates, and the landscape is one of dairy farms in the north, farms raising corn and fattening pigs and cattle in the centre, tobacco and cotton farms in the main part of the south, and fruit and truck farms along the southernmost coastal fringe. Town life is important but mainly as it serves and expresses agricultural interests, although some mining, oil refining, and industrial cities are outstanding exceptions. (iii) An area based chiefly on cattle and sheep ranching, on the drier parts of the Great Plains, and in the western mountains and intermontane basin. Here cropping is mainly subsidiary to ranching and, though highly valuable, is limited in extent, being based chiefly on irrigation. In this sub-region mining is extremely important and may in some instances be the principal source of revenue. It gives rise to notable but rather isolated cities. (iv) A far western area of very heterogeneous uses of land, between the Cascade–Nevadan ranges and the Pacific, where ranching, intensive commercial crop farming, mining, and industry all prevail and are important, with primary production being more significant in the Pacific North-west, and industry and urbanization in California.

Increasingly, great urban centres like New York, Chicago, and Los Angeles are creating new regions which transgress the older ones, uniting parts of them into new organizations of land and life.

CHAPTER EIGHTEEN

The United States: The Nation—Social and General Regions

Although the economic regions of the United States have a fairly close relationship to the physical ones, the social regions are rather more independent, arising less from the 'suggestions of the environment' and more from the aims and ambitions of men, their customs and creeds. Economic regions do not of course necessarily obey the dictates of relief and climate. Men chose to concentrate on tobacco and cotton in the South as much because of the need for cash crops, giving quick returns, as because of climate. Had the objectives of the southern colonists been different, had settlement been by way of small-scale homesteading rather than large-scale plantation farming, corn, winter wheat, and cattle might have been major products. Corn was the staple of such agriculture as was practised by the Indians before the white man came. Similarly, the general farming of the North only passed over to dairying with the rise of northern industry; the Dairy Belt was as much an outcome of urbanization as of climate.

SOCIAL IDEALS AND GEOGRAPHICAL RESULTS

Behind the choices that directed economic enterprise were the social customs and drives of the people. It was southern squirearchy that took to plantation farming, and, developing tobacco and cotton plantations, based on slave labour, then pushed that economy as far as the climate would bear, thus creating a characteristically southern landscape over quite different pieces of terrain. There had been a hunting frontier, a ranching frontier, and a homesteading frontier in the South, lying up-country from the plantations. But these soon became secondary elements in the scene, and, as people concentrated on cotton, grew to be quite subordinate. Not until the rise of a new South, in the late nineteenth century, when the South tried to benefit by northern experience, did corn, small grains, and cattle come back, and a more balanced economy emerge.

Social forces were also powerful in the North, for it was the northern choice of individual operation-and-ownership that led to the rise and proliferation of the small unit of production. Since this unit had to support the major needs of the family owning and operating it, to produce meat, breadstuffs, vegetables, and wool, it at first gave rise to general farming: corn, wheat, and oats were grown, clover and hay were raised, cattle and sheep were kept, and a very different kind of landscape was created from that of today. In time, individualistic treatment of land led to competition, specialization, and segregation; and dairy, fruit, corn, wheat, and ranching belts emerged. Throughout this process, social selection was at work. The competition between homesteader and rancher, between ploughland and range, was at least as important in the final distribution of wheat or meat production in the Great Plains as any particular isohyet. More important still, the competition between the free and the slave made all the difference in the trans-Mississippi west, and the fact that the 'free half' won out turned this into a white domain—a fact which has had the greatest significance in the visible landscape and especially in the geography of institutions and settlements.

In the case of the Great Plains the social factor did probably more than anything else to give its residents a feeling of their own—indeed, of being on their own.

> The region is distinctive [says Kraenzel] because it has been an exploited hinterland and remains so today. In self defence, the residents have developed a set of attitudes and behaviour patterns best described as minority conduct. These psychological and social aspects are . . . too deeply rooted for rational action. This minority status means that the Plains residents are on the prod. They fight at the drop of a hat. It means that they cannot now act to protect themselves against exploitation by others. Schisms between groups are too great. The residents have [themselves come] to live as minorities. They live in island-like communities separated from each other in many ways and for many reasons.[1]

Frustration at treatment from without led to frustration within that kept development and settlement fragmented, though a common environment might have been expected to produce a common way, if not a united front.

Even where physical factors *are* prominent *they have often come into prominence only through social ones.* Thus the wonderful climate of California meant relatively little to the primitive seed-gatherers of the Pacific South-west, before the white man came. Even to the Spaniards it meant little beyond pleasant mission gardens. It was not until widespread irrigation, commercialized agriculture, rapid transportation to market, modern packaging and refrigeration transit, large-scale advertising, and a ramified business organization all materialized, that the Californian climate came into its own. Indeed, it was not until the United States evolved such

[1] Kraenzel, C. F., *The Great Plains in Transition*, Norman, 1955, pp. vii, 228.

a high standard of living that people had it in mind to enjoy the climate for its own sake that the area really became prominent. This new mental attitude of living where it is most enjoyable has done as much as anything to make California the most rapidly growing part of the United States today. The climate has always been there, but it has only been 'maximized' through this new psychology. (See Chapter 16, p. 511.)

One of the best expressions of social and psychological factors, as also of economic and physical ones, is population (Fig. 146). People avoid difficult and marginal areas—unless of course they are refugees—and concentrate on what they deem to be favourable regions. Some prefer the bustle, excitement, competition, and opportunity of industrialized districts and by gathering there swell such districts in strength and intensity. Some like the rural life, stay on the farms, and help to evolve great agricultural belts. Some like to do their own work, and enjoy those regions where the family farm and the family business are honoured. Some like to have others do at least the more menial work for them. Many of these used to own slaves, and so kept to those areas where slavery was accepted; today they still like to have black labour serve them, and remain in the South. Some are chronic home-movers and are drawn to newly developing areas, or areas of unusual expansion, thus helping them to expand still more rapidly. Population is, then, a measure of the potentialities in the environment and a mirror of man's power to adapt it to his needs and aims.

THE POPULATION OF THE UNITED STATES

One of the essential and most typical things about America has been its attraction for the adventurous or hard-pressed and harried individuals from Europe, or other parts of the Americas, or remoter regions of the earth. As a result it has become, in Bailey's words, 'the half-brother of the world', with representatives from almost every land. Remarkable as this may be, it is even more remarkable that all these people should somehow or other have been fused into one. Yet that is what has happened, as Zangwill claimed in his play, *The Melting Pot*:

> America is God's Crucible, the great Melting-Pot,
> Where all the races . . . are melting and reforming.

This was true to a certain extent even when the United States was a British colony; French Huguenots, Dutch, and Germans were important elements among the new-comers. But after the country became a Republic, and when it secured vast areas of relatively empty land, crying out to be used, it drew people in altogether greater numbers. Moreover, the American

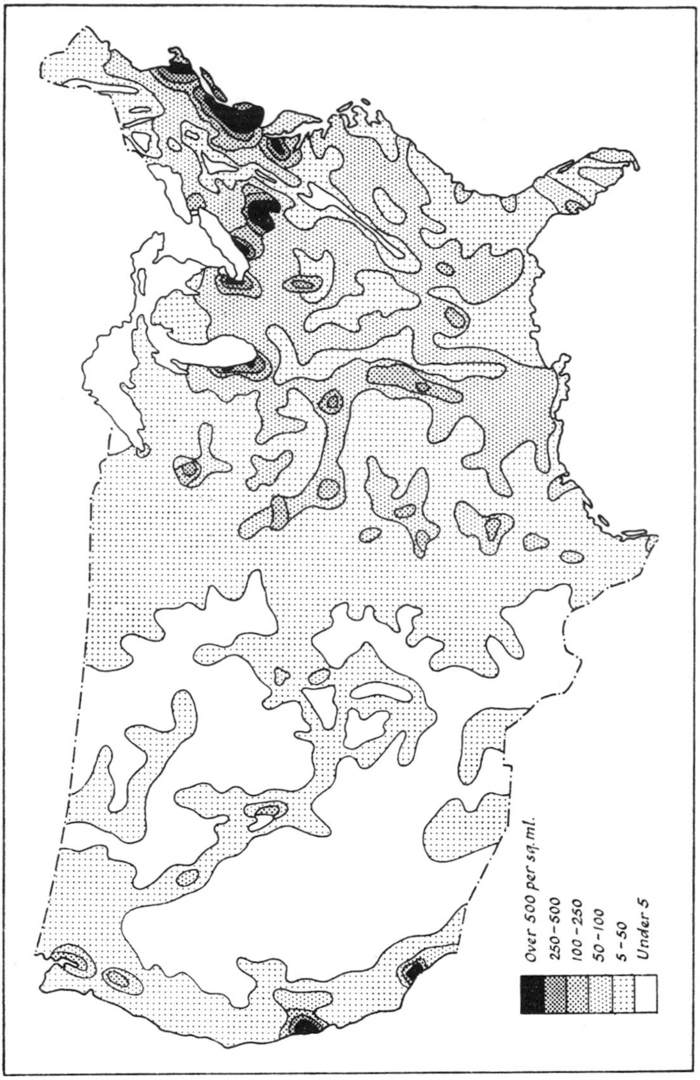

FIG. 146 The Distribution of Population in the United States, the clearest reflection of how man has used the advantages and has had to respect the limits of the environment. (Scale, 1:35 m.)

policy with regard to the land 'amounted to a social and economic revolution. The middle class (who came to power in the War of Independence) proceeded to eliminate various features of the feudal system existing in the colonies. Quit rents, entail, and primogeniture were abolished, and within a few years . . . the disestablishment of religion had been effected in all the states.'[1] Free land to be freely used, became an immense incentive; and the tide of population swept in.

Historical Progress—Population Growth

When the first census was taken in 1790, there were 3,929,214 in the young nation. Independence, political and economic, attracted a great influx within the next twenty years. The war of 1812–14 slowed immigration down: war-torn Europe did not want to exchange its problems for war-rife America. But the stabilization of the Canada–U.S. boundary at least as far as Lake of the Woods (1818), and agreements with Spain about the U.S.–America border, on the Sabine (1819), allowed a very rapid expansion, and by 1830 the population was growing at the astonishing rate of 3·5 per cent per annum, until it reached no less than 12,800,000. America was already one of the principal powers, judged by population (Fig. 147).

Europe meanwhile drifted towards famine and revolution, which struck in the 'forties. The failure of the potato crop in Ireland during 1845 was disastrous. The Irish peasants were already

> the worst housed, the worst fed, and the worst clothed of any in Europe. They live in mud cabins littered upon straw; their food consists of dry potatoes, of which they are often obliged to stint themselves to one spare meal. Sometimes a herring or a little milk afford them variety, but sometimes also they are driven to seaweed and wild herbs. Those were the ordinary circumstances of Ireland, and to such a state of affairs famine was now added with all its attendant horrors, pestilence and death. In the southern and western parts of the country, the population was decimated; 10,000 persons had died in the Union of Skibbereen, which numbered 100,000.[2]

Conditions were bad, too, in England and in 1846 the Government repealed the Corn Law and permitted the flow of cheap food into the country, unrestricted by high duties. This helped matters, and England escaped the revolutions of 1848 that swept Italy and Germany; 1848 was the year of the discovery of gold on the American river in California. This fortuitous

[1] Faulkner, H. U., *Economic History of the United States*, New York, 1937, p. 49.

[2] Green, J. R., *A Short History of the English People*, Everyman Edn., London, 1915, p. 812, quoting Disraeli.

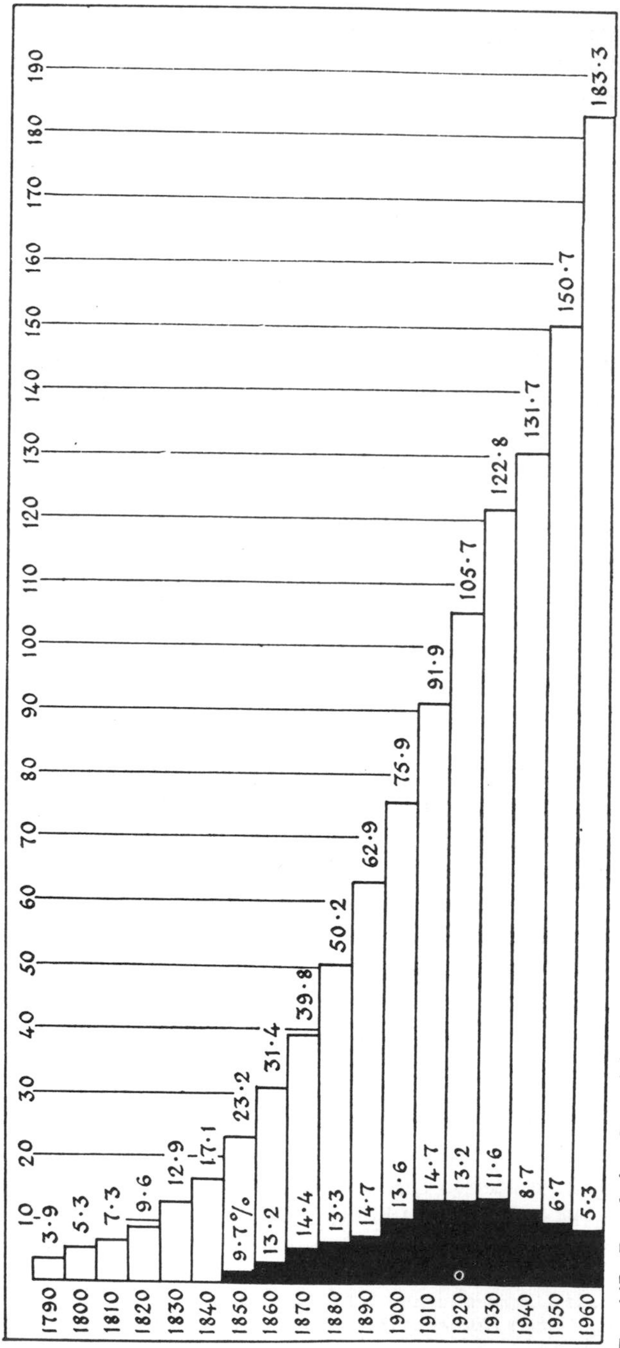

FIG. 147 Population Growth in the United States, in millions of people per decade. The proportion shaded in black represents the percentage of foreign-born Americans.

discovery, occurring at such a critical time, led thousands to journey to America's Far West. At the same time, American farmers in the Mississippi lowlands had a golden opportunity in supplying cheap grain to Europe. People flocked to the United States. Growth continued at more than 3 per cent per annum till the Civil War, at which time there were over 35 millions in the land.

That first of total wars again held back development and put off many prospective immigrants; nevertheless, when peace had been firmly established, the lure of the west became as strong as ever, particularly with the opening up of the Great Plains to the homesteader. Moreover, railways were now ('60s to '80s) pushing out west, and these offered land grants and special rates for immigrants, and at the same time provided outlets for pioneer production. They drew millions to the new frontier. Not only did population grow by the addition of streams of foreigners; it actively reproduced itself. Big families were an asset in starting up farms, and the birth-rate was high.

By the 1890s most of the empty land had been taken up, and immigration slackened off; yet population increase was still quite high—at the rate of 2·6 per cent per annum. Land may no longer have been the great attraction it was—the choicest parts had gone; the less accessible or the marginal land had now to be faced—yet industry was growing, and the great cities of the east proved as strong a magnet as the prairies of the west. This industrialization quickened noticeably in the new century, especially during the First World War when America became the 'arsenal for democracy'. Consequently the demand for people was high, and the rate of natural increase kept up. The war years led to a marked break in immigration, and growth slowed down to a rate of about 1·5 per cent per annum. But the boom of the 'twenties saw another rush, both to city and farm, and the population passed the 100,000,000 mark. America was now one of the giant nations of the world. Unfortunately, prosperity was short-lived. The Great Depression came, followed by the Great Drought. Factories were closed by the thousand; farms abandoned by the scores of thousands. A serious check occurred. Nevertheless, the impetus to growth was there. The momentum of the past bore America forward, and although its growth sunk to an all-time low of 1·45 per cent per annum, this was well above that in Europe, which had declined to about 0·4.

The Second World War again saw a tremendous resurgence. Once more America proved to be the arsenal of the West. It poured out arms to Britain and Russia. But more, it poured out food as well. The farm area, and farm production, expanded very considerably. Under the excitements and tensions of the war many young people married and started a family. The successful transition to peace-with-plenty kept up the high birth-rate

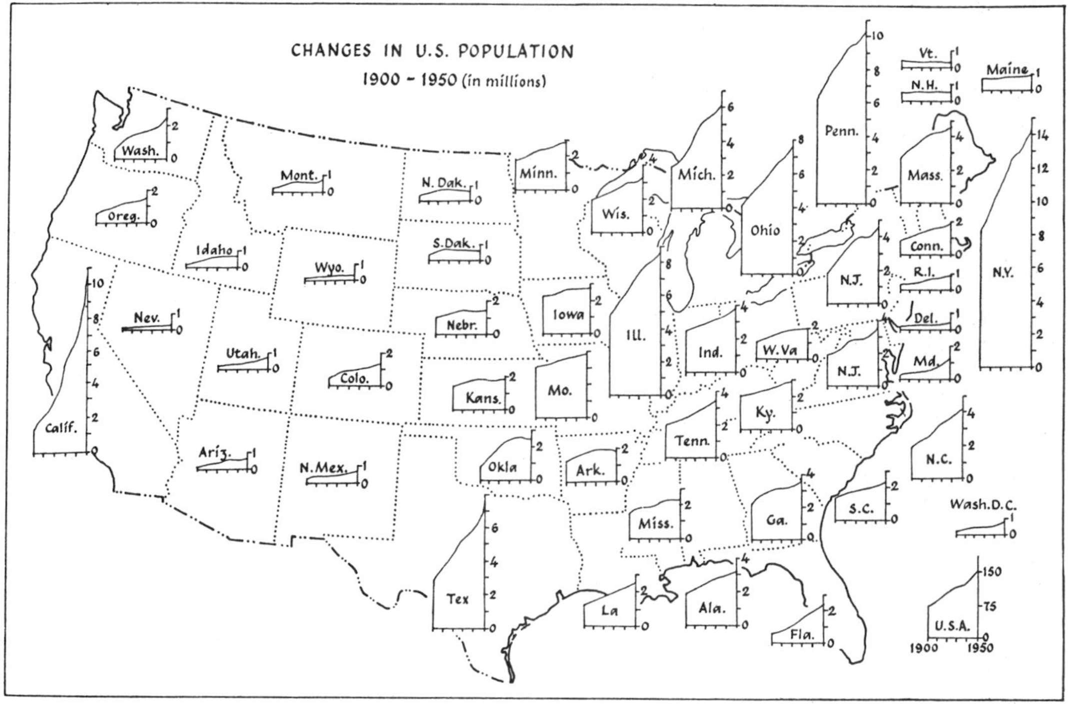

FIG. 148 Fifty years of change in the Population of the United States. (From Geddes.) Note the very rapid growth of California and Texas, and the continued growth of the North-east and Lake States.

and also invited many Europeans, sick of warfare and its results, to cast their lot in with the New World. Between 1945 and 1960 the population leaped forward by nearly 40 million, until today it stands at about 200 million and is increasing at the rate of about 1·85 per cent per annum, or nearly 4 million a year. The areas with today's greatest growth are the Mid-Atlantic and Great Lake States, together with California (Fig. 148).

ETHNIC COMPOSITION

As a result of this continued and rapid rise, built up to a considerable extent by immigration, there are now over 35 million Americans who were either themselves born abroad (12 million), or one or both of whose parents came from abroad (23 million). Of these, 15 per cent migrated from the British Isles, 14 per cent from Germany, and 13 per cent from Italy. Over 8 per cent came from Poland, 7·5 per cent from what is now Russia (but may have been East Poland and the Baltic republics, together with Ukraine), and 7 per cent from Scandinavia. The Danube lands also sent about 7 per cent.

While most of the migrants came from Europe, it should be noted that many moved from other parts of the Americas, even from such tolerably well-off areas as Canada. This shows how strong indeed the pull of the United States has been. Canadians account for most of these, with nearly 3 million or over 9 per cent of the total foreign-born or native-born of foreign parents; Mexicans amount to 4 per cent. Thus in spite of the way in which America grew at the expense of these countries, many of their citizens preferred to live in America and crossed the border. The movement is still going on. Not a few West Indians, Central and South Americans also come to live in the United States. A few Asians likewise come, although the day of considerable migrations of Chinese and Japanese to work on building the railroads, in digging the mines, and in developing irrigation has now largely gone. Nevertheless, the Chinese laundrymen and restaurant keepers are ubiquitous, having spread throughout the States.

Today, the United States is growing so rapidly through natural increase that it does not need immigration. However, it still maintains its long tradition of offering itself as a refuge to the afflicted of the world. But it now no longer follows the 'open-door' policy of taking in all-comers; instead it has adopted a quota system, at any rate for would-be immigrants

from countries other than those of the Western Hemisphere. Until 1920 there was only a qualitative limitation on immigration. [The United States was still anxious to take people with professional training and mechanical skills, and those with the capital and experience to farm, develop mines, and so on.] The 1921 Act (Immigration and Nationality) placed the first numerical ceiling upon immigration. Each country's quota was to be 3 per cent of the number of people born in that country who were residing in the United States as reported by the 1910 census. The 1952 Act based the quota on a flat one-sixth of 1 per cent of the (related foreign) population in the 1920 census, totalling 155,000 a year.[1]

By far the greater part of the foreign born now come to take up jobs in the North-east and Northern-central States, especially in the Mid-Atlantic States and those States bordering on the Great Lakes. New England also takes a good number of these eastern settlers, though not nearly as many as it used to, in proportion to the total. In fact, New England's place has now been ousted by the Pacific Coast States, especially California. This now forms a major objective in immigration to the United States. The Southern, Mid-West Agricultural, and the Mountain States do not draw many immigrants, while the East South-central States have the least drawing power.

Ethnic problems in the United States have been considerable. Many are still unsettled, although conflict between European groups has been overcome, albeit not without a good deal of friction. As has been pointed out, 'The overwhelming majority of all contemporary Americans have had ancestors who were members of minority groups in America.' This has helped to breed tolerance and accommodation and to make 'America Divided' into a united America.[2] However, a major divide long separated white from black, although this is being overcome.

The negro in America, brought in to help the development of the country, has come to form one of its main problems. In whatever way that problem is solved, the fact remains that the American population will always have a distinct negro strain in it, and that this is one of the most distinctive things about the geography of the United States (Fig. 149). This helps to distinguish that country from both Mexico and Canada. These neighbouring countries never did rely on negro slaves to any great extent; the Spaniards enslaved the Indians, the French and British in Canada largely did without slave labour. Both these countries early abolished slavery. Mexico actually tried to forbid Americans, who wanted to settle within Texas, bringing in slaves. America, by continuing to use slaves right up to the Civil War, thus made itself different from the other North American nations. This is a most important factor in distinguishing one region from another on the continent. Until recently it created features in the visible landscape not found in Canada or Mexico—different public conveniences for whites and blacks, separate negro schools, and whole negro quarters in city after city. Anti-segregation laws are, of course, making an impact, especially in towns, but the *relics of the*

[1] *Statistical Abstract of the United States*, U.S. Department of Commerce.
[2] Rose, A. and C., *America Divided*, New York, 1948, p. 65.

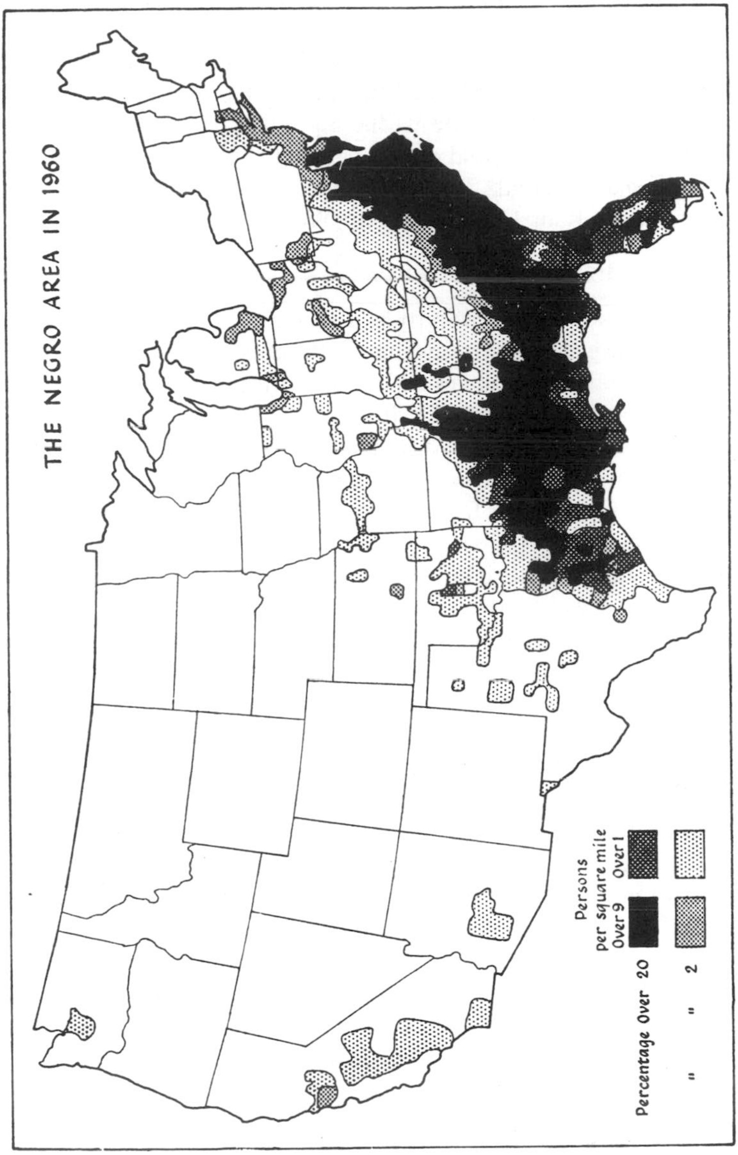

FIG. 149 **The Negro** in the United States. Still centred in the Southern States, considerable numbers have moved to the Mid-Atlantic States, to the industrial cities of Ohio and the Great Lakes, and to the Pacific South-west. (Scale, 1:28 m.)

geography of segregation still segregate out America in North American geography. By the same token, the geography of integration will mark out the United States in world geography: this is something few multi-coloured peoples have achieved.

There are today nearly 20 million negroes in the United States, mainly in the South. During the First World War they replaced immigrants into the North, and continued to migrate to the big industrial cities. With ten per cent of the population they hold eleven per cent of the industrial jobs. They are no longer mainly rural. There are over 6 million in the U.S. manufacturing belt, and about 1½ million in the West.

CHANGES IN POPULATION STRUCTURE

American population is thus seen to be a very varied and dynamic thing. It has played a great part in the geography of the country as a whole—and will continue to do so. For it changes as it grows. Indeed, even in the last three or four generations it has changed. It was once very male and mobile, but is now becoming more feminine and stay-at-home. The age of the frontier was the age of the frontiers*man*. In his theory of the development of American democracy Turner frequently appealed to the persistent leavening of frontier callings, and to the maleness of the west. These facts made America more simple, forthright, free-living, and equal-minded. The frontier was more than a forward moving area, promising individuals a better chance to improve themselves than they could find elsewhere; it was a great transmutation, making different people of those who sought it. 'Frontiering' was a process through which the customs and institutions imported from the Old World were transformed by adaptation to the New. Men had to revert to the primitive; they had to be *men*—to rely on themselves, rethink their ideas, and make new customs in line with their new and simpler needs. The hunter, the trader, the axe-man, the boatman, the hog-driver, the circuit-rider, the cowboy, the gunman—these were the makers of America. The frontiersman found a life which meant a continuous application of adaptability, self-reliance, inventiveness, and 'drive'. Hence the American 'drive' today—an outcome of its former maleness; though this 'drive' now characterizes women and children, as well as men. Thus the frontier, though it has passed away—together with most of the male callings with which it was associated—has left its stamp on American character, having created

> that coarseness and strength, combined with acuteness and inquisitiveness; that practical inventive turn of mind, quick to find expedients; that masterful grasp of material things, lacking in the artistic perhaps but powerful to effect great ends; that dominant individualism, working for good and evil; and above all that buoyancy and exuberance, which come with freedom.

The maleness of American society persisted right down to the Second World War; then, what with combat losses, and with the subsequent restriction in immigration, the males lost their dominant position. In 1950, for the first time, there were more women than men. Today there are 100 women for 96 men. However, women are ahead in only two groups of States, New England and the Southern Atlantic seaboard States. These are the oldest areas of settlement. They have lost many of their men either to New York, which lies between them and draws off so many of the younger executives, professional men, and skilled artisans, or to the west, which was very largely built up by eastern emigration. The areas where men still form the majority consist of the Mid-Atlantic and Great Lakes States (where transportation and heavy industry demand male labour), in the agricultural States of the Ohio, the Mississippi and the Gulf plains, in the ranching and mining communities of the western Great Plains and Mountain States, and in the rapidly expanding, speculative, polyglot farms, mines, lumber camps, and cities of the Pacific Coast States.

The mobility of population has always tended to go along with maleness, and has been another outstanding feature of the United States. Washington Irving early wrote of 'the shifting throng that forms the population of most of our country places'.[1] This was partly because of the empty frontier, which kept on calling the young man to 'Go West, and grow with the country'. But it was partly an outcome of the American mind. Many went West, not to settle down, but to find adventure, or to make a fortune. 'The typical frontiersman', one American affirms, 'was a land speculator first and a farmer afterwards. His chief interest was to pick a likely looking spot and there squat with a minimum amount of farming until the land increased in value sufficiently for him to sell out at a profit.'[2] Then he would move on, and repeat the process elsewhere.

Today, the American repeats the process in the suburb. He shrewdly judges the venue of a new push from the crowded city centre towards the countryside, builds a small home on a large lot, then subdivides the lot for new-comers, finally sells out his bungalow at a big profit, and builds himself a better home in a better suburb. Working-class families speculate on the properties left behind, and flit from inner zones passing into shops and offices to outer zones vacated for the suburbs. Three out of five families move at least once; one out of four move yet again, or perhaps again.[3] 'Mobility of population within the nation has been one of the privileges of our people.'[4]

---

[1] Irving, W., *The Legend of Sleepy Hollow*, 1810.
[2] Faulkner, *Economic History of the United States*, p. 89.
[3] Lynd, R. S., and Lynd, H. M., *Middletown*, New York, 1929, p. 109.
[4] Brunner, E. S., and Kolb, J. H., *Rural Social Trends*, New York, 1933, p. 1.

American people are people on the march. Movement has never ceased. Up to 1870 men went mainly to the west, and at that time two-fifths of all the people living west of the Mississippi had come from the east. This fell to about one-third in 1890, and to about a quarter in 1910. From then on, the tide slackened. 'The economic opportunity of eastern industrialism plus the end of free land, checked the tide.' There then occurred, 'the other great population movement within the nation, that from farm to city. This trend began as early as the 1870s in New England and was a national phenomenon from 1910 on.'[1] Since 1920 nearly half a million people a year have moved out of farm or village into the city. The drift is still mainly to the West.

Notwithstanding this, the pace of movement has slowed down considerably—not as many Americans are moving as often as they used to do, and more of them are confining their movements to within their home region, county, or town. Today nearly 75 per cent reside in the State in which they were born. This is a new and a significant change, although it should not be made to obscure the restlessness and drive which induce people to alter their jobs or move from home to home, locally.

URBANIZATION

Local drifts from country to town are particularly meaningful since they point up the growing importance of the town for its area, everywhere (Fig. 150). The result of this is that *America has changed from a rural to an urban nation.* In 1800, 93·9 per cent of the total population was rural, and the rural rate of growth was about 34 per cent per decade. Today, the rural population has declined to 30 per cent, and its rate of growth has fallen to 3·4 per cent. The great opportunities are now in the cities, and America is committed to an industrialized way of life. Even agriculture is becoming industrialized, at least in so far as it is going in for mass production based on highly mechanized and commercialized procedures. The tractor is now replacing the farm hand, and more and more food is grown by fewer and fewer people. More and more land is brought into production on fewer and fewer farms. Small farms are being amalgamated into large ones, many of which are operated by managers for big city corporations, such as milling concerns, packing houses, or 'groceterias'.

A major reason for these changes is the cost of labour. From the beginning the United States has been a high-cost area, and has traded land for labour. Jefferson early remarked that while in Europe 'the object is to make the most of the land, labour being abundant: here it is to make the most of our labour, land being abundant'. To make the most of its labour America has gone in for trade and industry, and concentrated its work force in the

[1] Brunner, E. S., and Kolb, J. H., *Rural Social Trends*, pp. 2, 8.

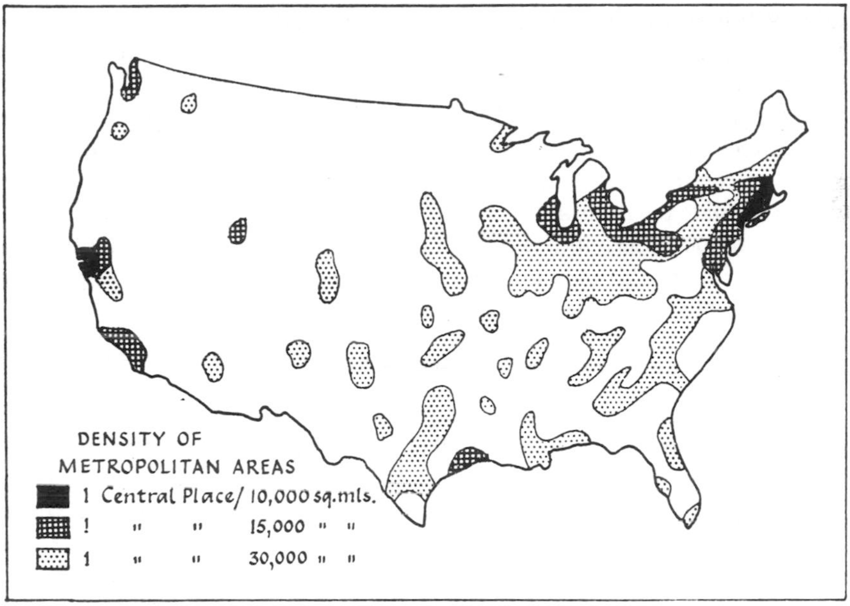

FIG. 150 Major Regions of Metropolitan Development in the United States, showing the greatest concentration between (a) Washington–New York–Boston. (b) Buffalo–Pittsburgh–Detroit–Chicago. (c) San Francisco–Los Angeles. (d) Puget Sound. (e) South central Texas. (Scale, 1:50 m.)

cities. The most highly urbanized parts are the Mid-Atlantic States (4:1), New England (3:1), the Pacific Coast States (3:1), and the East North-central States (2·5:1). The only two areas that remain predominantly rural are the South Atlantic and the East South-central States. This unequal distribution of city and farm folk has greatly affected the over-all density of population, which is at a maximum in the Mid-Atlantic States (300 per sq. mile) and New England (150 per sq. mile). The East North-central States also have a fairly high density (125) compared with that for the country as a whole (50).

Urbanization has proceeded so fast and so far that many cities have become veritable metropoli for their areas. The nation recognized this by setting up metropolitan areas, for which special census data are abstracted. During the first half of this century the number of Standard Metropolitan Areas with a population of over 1 million has increased threefold, and these metropolitan areas have become increasingly the focus of economic and social development for the nation. Today over three-fifths of the total population of the United States lives in some 150 metropolitan areas—an astonishing concentration for a country of such vast proportions. During the Second World War this concentration was remarkable, and between 1940 and 1960 it accounted for nine-tenths of the total U.S. growth in population! The average rate of growth for the metropolitan areas is today about half as much again as that for the nation as a whole. Thus in the age of the new geography—that of *megalopolis*—America has rapidly become simply the spheres of influence of New York, Los Angeles, and Chicago. These immense conurbations which have concentrated into their built-up area and immediate environs about 15, 8, and 7 millions of peoples respectively, have economic, social, and cultural effects that not only dominate contiguous regions but reach throughout the nation. Indeed, as Bogue says, 'a gigantic reshuffling of the people has occurred'.[1]

SUMMARY

The population of the United States has grown actively from the beginning, and is one of the phenomena of modern times. At the start of the nineteenth century 'people seriously thought it would take between 500 and 2,000 years to settle and develop the country'.[2] Instead, it took barely a hundred years. In this period it has seen ten times the growth of Canada, and six times the growth of Mexico; thus it has risen head and shoulders above its neighbours. This is something distinctive about the United States—due in part to the fact that it has at the heart of the country the heartland of the continent, but due also to its outlook, and, above all, its sense of manifest destiny.

The population which in 1790 had its centre just *east* of Baltimore and had barely reached the Allegheny front had, by 1820, centred itself *west* of the mountains, in West Virginia, with great streams pushing westward up the Mohawk and Lower Great Lakes, down the Ohio and Tennessee, and around the southern end of the Appalachians. In the main this early pattern was the pattern of coasts and rivers, but since some of the rivers were tortuous and deeply entrenched, roads were often used, built on the broad interfluves. In the 1830s the rivers on the west side of the Mississippi carried the population to the break-of-the-plains. Then, as we have seen, population channelled itself along the Oregon, California, and Santa Fé trails to cross the Great Plains and mountains and reach the Pacific. Here it ceased its westward drift and moved up and down the longitudinal depressions. In the 1850s–1880s occurred the great age of railway building and the population was drawn out along the railway lines to spill over the western plains and intermontane basins. Growing accretions of people took place at railway and road junctions or at the crossings of railway and river. The population centre moved west into Ohio and in 1880 rested just west of Cincinnati. The immense growth of industry between 1890 and 1920 led to the intensification of population in the North-east and East North-central States, and the

[1] Bogue, D. J., *The Population of the United States*, Glencoe, Ill., 1959, p. 54.
[2] *U.S.A., its Geography and Growth*, U.S. Information Service, London, 1955, p. 22.

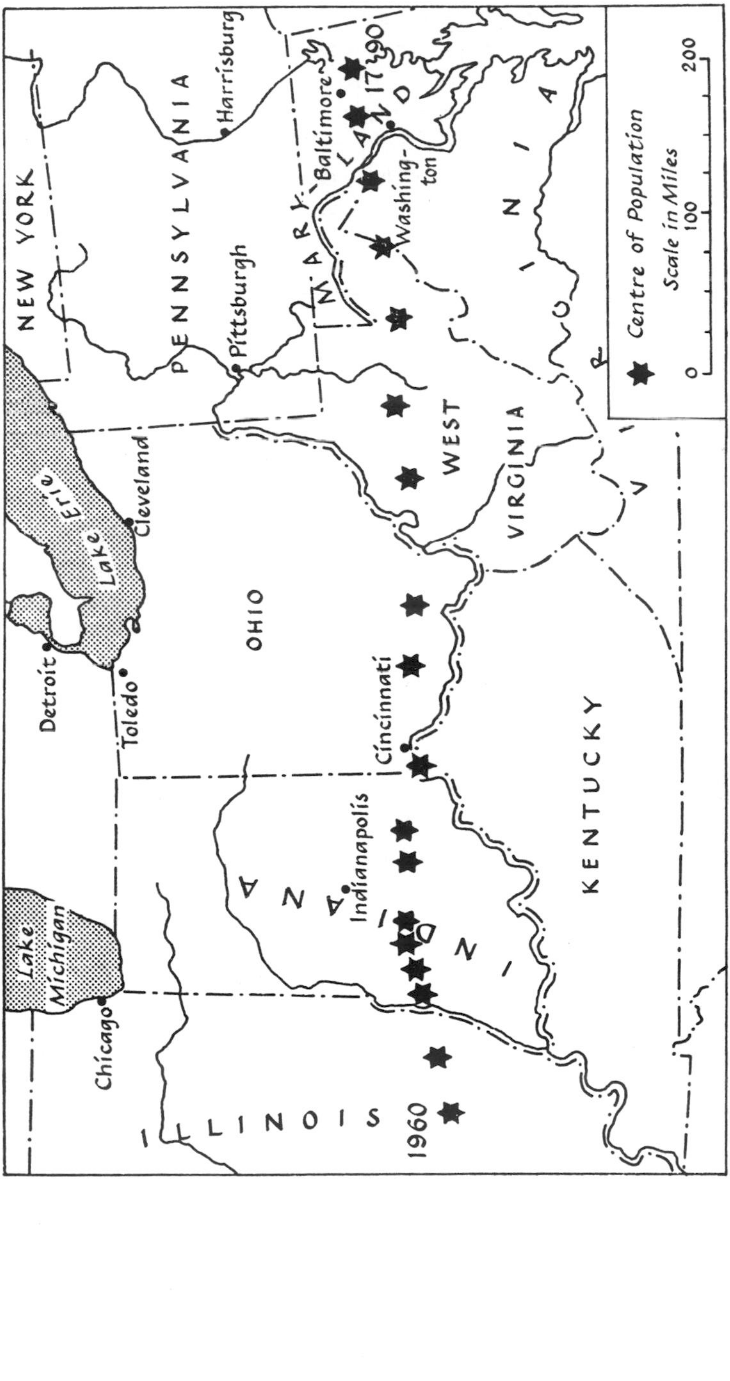

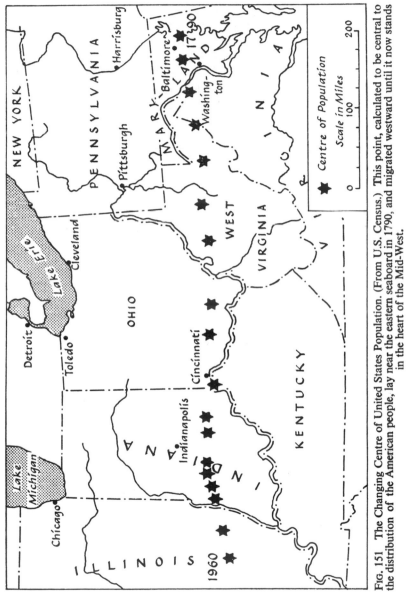

FIG. 151 The Changing Centre of United States Population. (From U.S. Census.) This point, calculated to be central to the distribution of the American people, lay near the eastern seaboard in 1790, and migrated westward until it now stands in the heart of the Mid-West.

population centre did not migrate very far, but came to rest in Indiana. Today it occurs in southern Illinois (Fig. 151). Increasingly, population has grown by concentration on the more favoured areas. The Great Depression followed by the Great Drought actually drove many people from the more marginal lands and led to a further concentration in the optimum areas. The greatest gathering together and accumulation of people took place in the cities, and from 1940 onward concentrated particularly on the metropolitan areas. The principal areas of contemporary expansion lie along three extraordinary strips of the running-together of giant cities: (i) between Boston and Baltimore (centred in New York); (ii) between Milwaukee and Michigan City (centred in Chicago); and (iii) between Santa Barbara and San Diego (centred in Los Angeles).

Social Regions of the United States

As a consequence of all this, certain distinct social regions have emerged in the United States. These include: (i) New England; (ii) the Mid-Atlantic and Great Lakes States; (iii) the South-east and East South-central States; (iv) the West South-central States; (v) the West North-central States; (vi) the Great Plains and Mountain States; and (vii) the Pacific Coast States.

New England is characterized by very old and complex communities, with high densities along the coast and even moderately high densities up the interior valleys, with a very heterogeneous population, including a large number of foreign-born, particularly French-Canadian and Irish, with a great predominance of white and only a very small coloured minority, a fairly stable population, now more feminine than male, and one with a median age that is distinctly above that for the country as a whole.

The Mid-Atlantic and Great Lakes States also have well-established communities, depending nearly as much on industry and trade as New England but also on agriculture and transportation. They too have high to moderately high densities of population, of from three to ten times the national average, concentrated in a significantly large number of metropolitan centres. They have an even more mixed population than New England, with many more people of German, Italian, and Central European origin, with a large number of Anglo-Canadians, many Puerto-Ricans, and the highest proportion of negroes in the north. Perhaps because of this great influx of immigrants the population is more male than female, although not to a pronounced extent; it is also older than for the nation as a whole, though not as aged as in New England. Its outstanding feature is perhaps its high degree of urbanization (Fig. 152).

The South-east and East South-central States are, by contrast, still mainly rural. In fact, they are the only considerable areas in the United States that are more rural than urban. There is a distinct, though not great, emigration

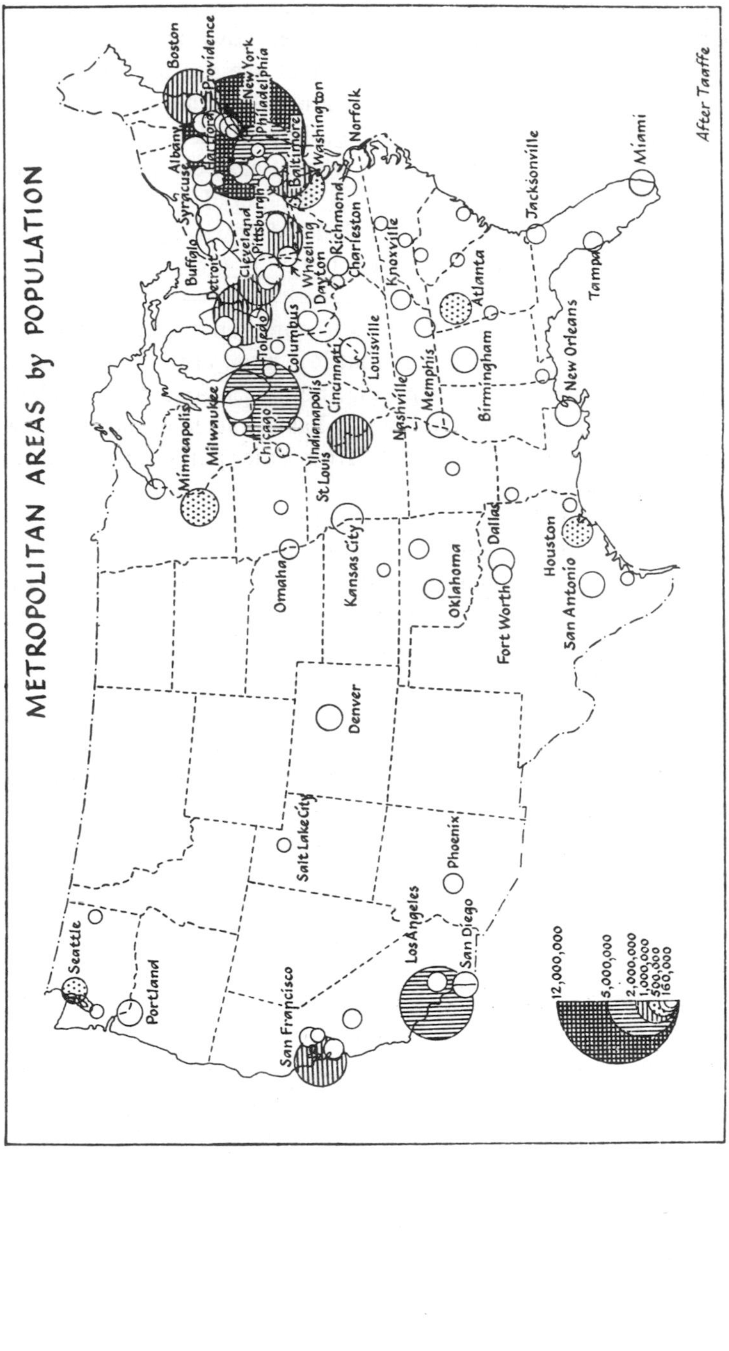

FIG. 152 The Concentration of Urbanization in the North-east and East North Central (Lakes) States. Most of the 'million' cities lie between Washington and St Louis, Boston and Minneapolis. The only great centres to the west are those at San Francisco and Los Angeles. (Scale, 1:35 m.)

from the area, mostly of young men, many of them negroes, and the population is slightly more female than male. This loss of native-born population has been going on at least since the Civil War, and though it has been more than balanced by natural increase, it has slowed down the over-all rate of increase which has been less than the national average until the late war years and the post-war boom in the South. There has been very little immigration to the area and the total foreign-born stock is negligible, except in Florida. Even there it is a twentieth of what it has become in the state of New York. The proportion of negroes in the population is higher than elsewhere, so that this forms the 'black belt' of America, with about one black for every three whites, rising to 1:1·5 in Georgia and 1:1·2 in Mississippi.

The Gulf South-west has many features in common with the South lying east of the Mississippi, yet it differs in that it is more urban than rural, and has an appreciably lower ratio of negroes, about 1: 5. Also, far from having seen an outward drift of the native-born, it has attracted an inward flow of other Americans into the region—mostly from other parts of the South, but increasingly from the North as well.

The agricultural Mid-West, comprising the more humid parts of the West North-central States, differs from the industrialized Mid-West (or East Central States) in having a distinctly lower population density (a fifth as dense). It shows only just over half the density of the nation as a whole. Similarly, its rate of increase is much less than (about half) that of its industrialized eastern counterpart. It also attracts far fewer foreign-born (about a quarter) and fewer negroes from the south (less than a quarter). But though mainly agricultural it is not mainly rural; on the contrary, it is becoming increasingly urbanized, and there are large towns in it devoted to manufacturing and trade.

The Western Great Plains and the Intermontane Basins have conditions of their own. These are not as clear as they might be because the Great Plains are divided; the sub-humid parts are typical of the West Central States, the high and more arid parts—of the Mountain States. Taking the arid area as one, it has the lowest density of population in the United States, with large farms or ranches supporting relatively few people. It also has the lowest percentage of the population engaged in industry (less than 1:10) and has very few metropolitan cities. It is easily the most masculine region in the United States, and is also one of the most youthful. It is mainly white, with very few negroes and is at the same time mainly native, made up of migrants from other parts of the States rather than from foreign-born. It has shown a strong gain from other regions and its population is fairly mobile.

The Pacific Coast States are the fastest growing in the United States today. This is both through a great influx of native-born Americans, and also through extensive immigration from abroad. After New York State, California has the highest percentage of foreign-born in the United States. There has also been a sharp increase in the negro population, mainly in the Pacific South-west, and there are more negroes here than in any other western region. Many of the incomers, of all races, are people about to retire, and so the age of the population is greater than for any other area except New England, and is distinctly higher than the national average. Most of these come to live in cities, and the Pacific South-west has a higher proportion of its people living in metropolitan areas than anywhere else except the Atlantic metropolitan belt. The population is very varied in its occupations, and there is a good deal of movement from job to job, reflected in movement from place to place. Few areas in the country are as mobile.

Although there are variations within each of the regions set forth, yet prevailing conditions are such as to mark them out as distinct social units. Nevertheless, in all regions a most striking characteristic is the increasing importance of the metropolitan areas. These are dominating the economic and cultural life of the nation to an ever larger extent.

Major Regions of the United States

A combination of physical, economic, and social factors has tended to create major areas of difference in the United States. Their development has changed and is changing and they do not admit of any finality; but this is not to deny them some degree of reality. In a general survey such as this book has attempted to make, only the *major* groupings need be considered. There are many lesser groupings, but these have been treated in more detailed works.

In the main, the groupings are based on social and economic factors, and this is especially true in the older areas of settlement where historic influences were so strong, and where they have been allowed to play an important part up until today. West of the Ohio, however, physical factors have had more say, and may be recognized to be basic to the economic regions evolved there.

The main divisions suggested are: (i) the industrialized North-east, Mid-Appalachian, and Great Lakes region; (ii) the 'South'; (iii) the agricultural Mid-West, where cropping is preponderant; (iv) the Western Great Plains, and Intermontane Basins, where aridity is a common physical condition and ranching, dry-farming, and irrigation form the corresponding adaptation; and (v) the great valleys of the Pacific States and the Pacific coast, where very strong structural control is reflected in both the variety and unity of land uses. The last two regions may be grouped together in many respects as the West (Fig. 153).

The Industrialized North-east and Eastern North-central part of the States straddles three great physiographic regions—the Atlantic Coast Plain, the

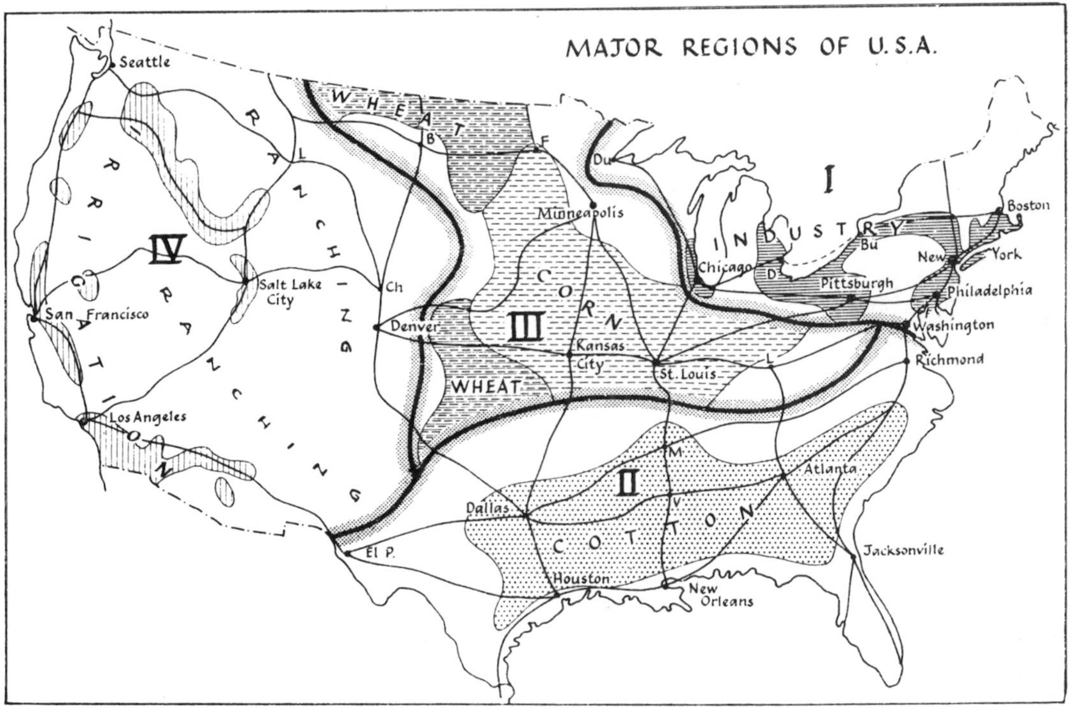

FIG. 153 Major Geographical Regions of the United States and some of the factors associated with them.

I, the North-east and Lakeshore region is linked with industry, trade, transportation, dairy farming, and high population density; II, the South by contrast is agricultural, rural, with a fairly open net of railways, few large towns, and a moderate to low population density but a high density of negroes; III, the Agricultural Mid-West is dominated by corn and wheat, large market towns, and a moderately dense population; IV, the West has contrasts between extensive ranching and intensive irrigation farming, and between wide areas of sparse settlement and a concentration of people at a few large cities. It is marked by a rapidly expanding population. (Scale, 1:35 m.)

Appalachians, and the Central Lowlands; it also embraces both the severe winter and the warm summer sub-types of the microthermal climate. Therefore, it does not have much physical unity. The Great Lakes afford it some unity in the west and the Mohawk–Hudson some in the east, but essentially it is a physically divided and fragmented area. Only because of human factors may it be considered to be a region. The historical traditions of New England and the Mid-Atlantic colonies fused into one in upper New York State and in the Great Lakes region, making for a population of independently owned and operated farms and businesses associated with an early and widespread development of town life. The great importance of the trans-Appalachian transportation systems—turnpike roads, canals, railways, and motor 'throughways'—from coastal parts like Boston, New York, New Jersey, Philadelphia, and Baltimore to the vast interior between Ohio, Great Lakes, and Mississippi also gave, and still gives, the area unity. Finally, the unparalleled growth and concentration of industry here, from New York to Chicago, and of an industry with a great many cross-connexions and ramifications within the region, has helped to produce a regional consciousness, expressed in a highly urbanized landscape having most of the giant cities of the United States.

The South likewise is no respecter of physiographic regions since, although no doubt principally based on the south-east Atlantic and the Gulf coastal plains, yet it strides across the southern Appalachians, parts of the Mississippi valley, the Ozark plateau, and a section of the High Plains. It does show a stronger accord with climatic types, since most of it lies in the humid warm temperate zone, yet it stretches south to the hot, wet monsoon and west into the semi-arid steppe. The South is not the South because of southern climate, or a distinctive relief characterizing the south-eastern part of the country; it is the South because of historical, economic, and above all social conditions that give it internal unity and yet mark it off from regions outside of it. The South is historically the region of plantation culture, linked at the outset with a New-World variant of the manorial system, but very soon run on the lines of large-scale exploitive enterprise. It remains to this day mainly rural and even where it is becoming industrialized its industries are very often agriculturally based. Much of its cropland is under industrial crops, which separates it out from most other agricultural regions in the United States. Above all, the South is the region where white is inextricably mixed with black, and where the negro population forms a high, though not a major, part of the whole. The negro problem has created a geography of segregation which is unique on the continent. The South is, of course, changing; it is becoming more industrialized and urbanized, more cosmopolitan and middle-class, but the old traits still remain, and they are still the operative, the distinguishing, traits.

The Agricultural Mid-West, unlike the last two regions, does have a strong basis in physical geography; it is the region of the lower Ohio, upper Mississippi, and lower Missouri basin; the basin that is bounded on the north by the low height of land between the Mississippi and the Great Lakes–St Lawrence drainage systems, on the east and south by the Appalachians and Ozarks, and on the south-west by scarps of the High and Staked Plains. Only in the west does it overleap physiographic bounds, in having extended beyond the Missouri Coteau; but it is closely associated with another physical boundary, that of the 17-inch isohyet. This area has a sub-humid to humid continental climate, where the conflict between Pc and Tg air is especially marked, and it was dominated in early days by humid prairies giving way to oak-chestnut-hickory forests along the rivers. These strong physical influences were paralleled by equally well-marked human traits; this was the zone *par excellence* of the homestead pioneer, of a mixture of New England and Southern white traditions, and of the dominance of river towns and then railway junctions in the organization of the area. Above all, this was and continues to be the main cropping region of the United States, including forage crops for dairy farming in the north, the extensive development of the spring and winter Wheat Belts, and the massive expansion of the Corn Belt. Its interests, outlook, and policy are still very much dominated by the needs, problems, and opportunities of the farm.

The western Great Plains and the Intermontane Basins are two separate physiographic regions, yet they do have their physical links and likenesses. They both grew out of the wearing down of the Rockies and associated ranges, and are connected to each other by the passes through the mountains; both have sections of highland and high plain. Their main similarity rests in the semi-arid nature of their climates and in the Short Grass prairie or sagebrush steppe that prevailed in the area before the white man intervened. True, the interior basins are drier than the high plains and have districts marked by true desert; but drought is the common problem and has given rise to common responses such as ranching, dry-farming, and irrigation. The general sparsity of population and openness of settlement, the maleness of western life, and the large scale on which farming, lumbering, and mining are carried out, the isolation of the people, their sense of independence, and yet the problem of their actual dependence on eastern markets and supplies, all tend to give a social unity to the area that sets it off from other parts of the United States.

The great valleys of the Pacific and the Pacific slope form another western region. With them may be included Alaska, which, though geographically separate, is economically and socially linked with the Pacific North-west. In this far western region there is a great variety of production, and that variety is concentrated and closely knit together. Mining and lumbering in the mountains, ranching and farming in the great valleys themselves, fishing in the rivers and off the coast, all make their separate contribution, yet all are integrated with each other. Routes and cities have played the main integrating role and are of greatest importance, and the dominance of Seattle, San Francisco, Los Angeles, and San Diego in their respective parts of the region has become an outstanding feature. The whole area, including Alaska, is one of the most rapidly growing parts of the United States and still attracts many migrants from the Mid-West and from the east, and also many immigrants from Europe. Their capital and skill are being exploited in the swift expansion of industry, especially in California. This, and the Atlantic metropolitan zone, are probably the two most dynamic regions in America today.

It may be argued that these suggested divisions of the United States are too inclusive and do an injustice to areas subsumed within them but which may have in fact an independent existence, and might well demand an independent treatment. New England, for example, is more than just a part of the industrialized north-east and north; it has strong cultural traditions rooted in the New England church, or college, or in the New England village, not to be found in the rest of the region. In the same way, the south-west has a degree of urbanization and industrialization and a range of occupation that might well set it off from the remainder of the South. The Great Plains should perhaps be regarded as a single separate region, and ought not to have been divided up and its divisions given over to eastern and western regions. (Such divisions do exist, but the two great parts singled out may be thought to be too closely related and too dependent on each other to be considered as really distinct. Perhaps the two sectors should be treated as parts of a zone in transition, linking east with west.) In the same way, possibly the two sectors of the Far West, namely, the Pacific North-west and South-west, do sufficiently differ from each other to be considered as separate regions. The Pacific North-west was influenced more by the practices of the Humid East than the South-west, which had already been modified and moulded by Spanish settlement and continued to owe a good deal to its Spanish heritage.

But of subdivision in geography there is no end. The writer has tried to restrict himself to the broader distinctions such as would strike an outsider who, having made a tour of the country, came home to try to put his impressions in order and who, to do so, would use the simpler, more striking, and more generalized categories.

Seen in this way, the United States, for all its sense of a pervasive unity, for all its belief in a national destiny, is a country with real and strong regional differences. Unity is great; some people would call it uniformity and regard this trait in American life as outstanding. 'Already', says

Siegfried, contrasting this growing uniformitarianism in United States culture with the continued diversification found, for example, in the Mediterranean, 'we see the machine supplanting the tool, mass production opposed to craftsmanship, the group or the gang taking the place of the individual worker, and collective organization replacing personal initiative. Ford seems to be confronting Ulysses, the patron of ingenuity and of *debrouillage*.'[1] But Ford does not oppose difference; rather, he capitalizes on it and, using the key ideas of inventive individuals, gives them to the masses, in free and open competition with the mass exploitation of other ideas. American unity does not rest on homogeneity, either innate or imposed, but on a variety the best features of which are incorporated into the nation as a whole. Thus regionalism does contribute in a very real way to Americanism; the American destiny has been in fact to make oneness out of division, in bringing to all the benefits of the few.

[1] Siegfried, A., *The Mediterranean*, London, 1948, p. 30.

CHAPTER NINETEEN

The United States: The Industrialized North and North-east Region

THE DEVELOPMENT OF THE REGION

In colonial times the north-eastern part of what became the United States differed considerably from the south-eastern. As we have seen, the earliest administrators and geographers clearly divided the north or east, as New England was known, from the south, which included Virginia, the Carolinas, and Georgia. In between lay the Middle region, which was thought to be transitional since it had elements of both the north and south within it.

Because it was transitional, the middle area contained parts that were not always treated as separate from the neighbouring regions. In particular, New York was sometimes put in the north, and Maryland in the south. The Middle region really came into its own with the expansion into the west. At that stage it was broadened out beyond Pennsylvania to include Ohio. It is true that the term Middle States in this wider sense did not last long. Soon the west became a separate division and included all the trans-Appalachian territories in it. The Middle region shrank to the area bordering the coast and became known as the Mid-Atlantic States.[1]

Nevertheless west and east remained intimately linked. Indeed, their relations grew closer with time. It was from New York, Philadelphia, and Baltimore that the early roads, in the late eighteenth and early nineteenth centuries, were built to the Ohio and the Old North-west; it was from these points that canals were attempted across the Appalachians in the 'twenties and 'thirties of the nineteenth century; and these were the seaboard termini of the first great railways to the trans-Appalachian West, in the mid-nineteenth century. New England was not to be left out, but vied with the

[1] Jensen, in listing the groupings of states made by geographers between Morse (1793) and McMurray and Tarr (1901), points out the changing ideas about the relationship of states to sections. Morse (1793) first included Maryland in the south, but in his seventh edition (1819) put it in the Middle Section. Malte-Brun (1827), Olney (1837), Fisher (1852), Swinton (1880), and McMurray and Tarr (1901) all include Maryland in the Middle States, as do Jones and Bryan (1924), Wright (1948), and Paterson (1960). However, Olney in his edition of 1851 puts Maryland in the Southern Section, and this is the practice of Miller and Parkins (1928), and Parkins (*The South*, 1938). The Middle States included parts of the Mid-West in Flint (1832), Tucker (1850), and Cruikshank (1867), but usually confined themselves to the Atlantic area, particularly after Appleton (1881) introduced the term Middle Atlantic States (see Jensen, p. 60) in place of the older and broader term, the Middle States or Section.

Mid-Atlantic States in road and railway building; and though it did this in a spirit of competition, yet that very fact tied it up with the Middle States. Consequently a three-way tie-up emerged of New England, the Mid-Atlantic, and Old North-west.

This linkage was not only based on transportation. It rested on migration as well. The people of the seaboard streamed west and became the pioneers who developed the interior. New England was particularly prominent in this movement, and its people played a major role in exploiting and settling up-state New York, Ohio, Michigan, Indiana, and Illinois. In fact, at the mid-nineteenth century, before the mass immigration of Europeans really began, the Old North-west was another New England, with a land settlement system, with towns, with educational and religious institutions, that were modelled on, or became an outgrowth of, New England. Many people from the Mid-Atlantic States also went into the Old North-west and there mingled with the New Englanders and gradually worked out a common life together. The triangle of New England, Mid-Atlantic States, and Old North-west was reinforced.

It was, however, with the rise of industry that this triangle took on the strength of a region in itself, uniting the two older areas east of the Appalachians with the newer area to the west. The industry which began at the seaboard, from Boston to Baltimore, pushed rapidly across the near-by gaps in the Appalachians, invaded the Lower Great Lakes region, and eventually spread to the Lake Michigan shores. Throughout, industrial growth was financed from New York, depended for much of its management and drew many skills from New England, and found expanding opportunities in the Ohio and Great Lakes area. Such an intricate network of relationships grew up that the three districts, though in some respects quite different from each other, became inescapably connected in their main issues. This had its results in the landscape, making the three districts part of one vast urbanized region, with great metropolitan centres joined to each other in a dense meshwork of roads, railways, air-routes, and power-transmission and telephone lines (Fig. 154).

Thus the puritanism of New England, the capitalism both of that area and of the Mid-Atlantic States, and the rugged individualism of the north-west frontier all played a part in creating a predominantly middle-class society, based on property, with factory and office as its chief symbols, and finding its principal expression in the city.

THE PHYSICAL ENVIRONMENT

The northern and north-eastern industrial region, having achieved a measure of unity, has been able to exploit to the full its considerable

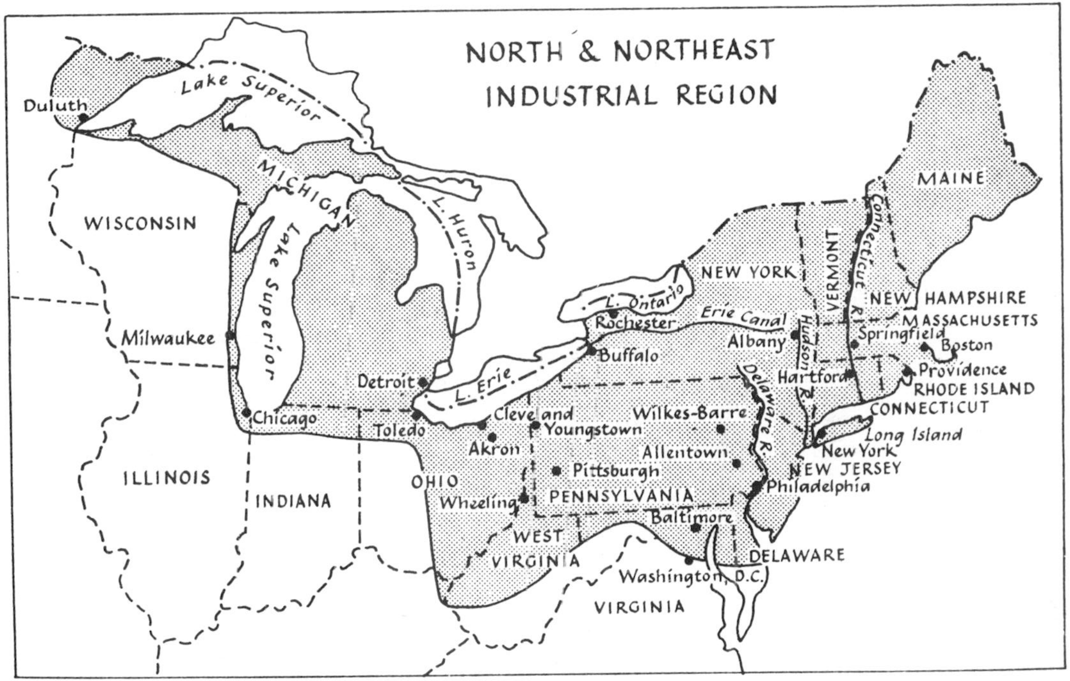

FIG. 154 The North and North-east Industrial–Urban Region of the United States is made up essentially of New England, the Mid-Atlantic and Upper Ohio States and the Lakeshore sectors of the Great Lakes States. It possesses great sources of coal and iron, rich agriculture, America's greatest concentration of canals, roads, and railways, and America's greatest ports and largest interior routeway junctions. (Scale, 1:16 m.)

diversity. It has a very diversified structure, providing not a few ore bodies, large fuel deposits, a considerable extent of upland for forestry and power development, and eastern and western plains which are well suited to agriculture. The whole is tied together by navigable rivers or routes using low mountain gaps, and which slope down to great lakes or arms of the sea, ideal for trade.

Four important structures here run together. They include the Atlantic Coastal Plain, the Appalachians, the Laurentian Shield, and the Interior Lowland. Undoubtedly it is this happy juxtaposition of such very different structures, each with its own suite of economic opportunities, that has had much to do with the rise of the region, and with its leadership in the affairs of the nation. (See Fig. 2, Chapter 1; Fig. 135, Chapter 16.)

The Atlantic Coastal Plain is represented in the region only by a small part, seen in Cape Cod, Nantucket, Long Island, and the New Jersey peninsula. Long Island is formed of two parallel end-moraines, making hummocky ridges, in the centre of which is a narrow, rather marshy depression. A broad outwash plain slopes to the sand-fringed shore. The New Jersey peninsula has a vale-and-wold surface, so typical of the middle Atlantic coast, with intensively cultivated truck-farming lowlands separated by pine barrens. A remarkable series of sandy spits and off-shore bars parallel the land. These are ideal recreational sites and are crowded with cottage colonies or hotel resorts, catering for the vast urban population near by. Martha's Vineyard, a middle-class 'family retreat', Coney Island, a working-man's pleasure beach, and Atlantic City, a 'convention' centre for all-comers, are typical.

The Coast Plain exists in a very fragmented state since most of it has been drowned. While this has meant a sad lack of arable land in an area generally short of it, drowning has also meant easy access to the sea for much of the region. Long estuaries and wide basins penetrate the land. Boston Bay, Narragansett basin, Long Island Sound, the estuary of the Hudson, and Delaware Bay have all provided excellent harbours and greatly aided that specialization on commerce for which the north-east has been famous.

The Appalachian system is very complex in this region. To the west is the coal-rich Allegheny plateau, where rivers have cut so deeply that the relief is quite rugged. It terminates in the bold Allegheny Front, which proved such a barrier to canal makers. This swings eastward into the broad-backed narrow-bottomed Catskills, terminating against the busy Hudson and Mohawk valleys. A wide, sinuous belt of narrow fold ridges and terraced valleys then gives way to the Great Valley, affording some good agricultural land. South of this in turn rise the old, highly metamorphosed ridges of the Reading Prong. A much-rumpled Piedmont plateau then extends eastward to the Fall line. East of the Hudson valley, the wooded Taconic, Green and White mountains rise and fall in parallel lines and then give way to the rather barren plateau of eastern New England. This plunges right into the sea, in a rocky or hillocky coast. Few plains of any consequence occur except the wide, long Triassic lowland of the Connecticut, and the expanse of Narragansett basin.

The northern part of the Appalachian system has been glaciated, with rounded ice-scraped summits and deep wide valleys. It is mantled with till-moraine. Many rock-cut lakes or moraine-dammed lakes occur, and at the sea there are examples of ice-deepened inlets and island-studded drumlin coasts. The glaciation has created many melt-water channels, with marshy bottoms, or well-drained fluvio-glacial terraces, especially on the plateau of western New York. Very different is the unglaciated deeply dissected plateau in South Pennsylvania.

The Laurentian Shield intrudes into the region in the Superior Upland and the Adirondacks, two widely separated ancient massifs. The former is a highly ridged and highly faulted area, with a series of low rugged ridges, in which the Vermilion, Mesabi, Cuyuna, Gogebic, Marquette, and Menominee iron fields occur, rising above a much eroded plateau. Many long flat summits testify to ancient peneplanation; they offer little impediment to mining and transportation. Faulting has let down the western end of Lake Superior, fringed by a narrow plain giving way abruptly to the Duluth and Superior fault scarps to north and south. These dominate town structure and railway layout. Another down-faulted lowland is that south of the Keweenaw peninsula, but it is squeezed out by the Huron mountains. There is very little land suited to cultivation. This is a country of isolated mines and lumber camps and miles of wilderness. The lake coast thrusts out in bold headlands or is mantled with wide, high dunes; it provides magnificent scenery and is a real tourist attraction.

The Adirondacks are another part of the Canadian Shield and carry the Frontenac axis into America. They are a series of granitic masses, worn down by long erosion into a plateau, and then cut by ice into rounded hills, deep lake-filled basins, and U-shaped valleys. A few monadnocks such as Mt Marcy lift themselves as high as 5,000 feet. The Adirondacks lie between the densely populated valleys of the Hudson–Champlain and the Hudson–Mohawk and are one of the chief playgrounds of the Northern States. They are also densely wooded and form a useful and continuing source both of softwood and hardwood lumber. They had an early importance as a supply of iron, but most of the iron is exhausted, and less than a million tons a year are now produced. However, the fact that the ore is of high quality (61 per cent), and near to centres of use, has kept up the demand.

The Interior Lowlands form the last of the four major physiographic units in the region. Structurally they consist very much of a series of broad down-sags between narrow up-swells (see Fig. 6, Chapter 1). Mention has already been made of the Cincinnati anticline separating the Erie basin from the basin of peninsular Michigan. Southward the La Salle anticline terminates the Lake Michigan depression, which is marked off on the west by the Wisconsin rise. The lowlands are made up of curved belts of limestone and shale dipping away from the Algoma and Superior uplands. A very conspicuous feature is the Niagara escarpment which, beginning as an eastward-facing cuesta in western New York, sweeps through peninsular Ontario and Manitoulin Island to reappear in the Thumb of Michigan and form a westward-facing cuesta overlooking Green Bay. Glaciation has profoundly affected the area. The ice deepened the shale depressions underlying the Lower Great Lakes and Lake Michigan, helped to create the Great Lakes as they now exist, festooned the lake plains with immense lobate moraines, and strewed the sides of the lakes with old raised beaches and stranded lacustrine flats. Of special significance in marking off the industrialized lakeshore plains from the more agricultural lowlands farther inland have been the Valparaiso moraine south of Chicago, the Lansing moraine south of Lansing and Saginaw, and the Fort Wayne moraine west and south of Detroit and Toledo. The glacial Lake Chicago and Maumee plains, once avoided by settlers because of their marshiness, have proved a boon to industry in Chicago, Gary, Detroit, Toledo, and Cleveland by reason of the broad expanse of lacustrine flats they offer for factory growth. Now drained and limed, they are also the basis for a much-needed dairy- and truck-farming industry. (See Fig. 164, page 626.)

Glaciation helped to link up the Great Lakes area with the Mid-Atlantic coast by providing melt-water connexions between Lake Warren—one of the forerunners of lakes Huron and Erie—the Finger Lakes, and the Susquehanna river. Later Huron and Erie formed the considerable body of water known as Lake Lundy, and this drained eastward by the Mohawk into the Hudson. Later still when Lake Iroquois lay in the Ontario basin its waters drained through the Mohawk to the Hudson. Thus nature itself supplied an intimate connexion between the northern central and the north-eastern parts of the continent, a natural linkage that Americans were to confirm, strengthen, and enlarge until it became the basis of a vast industrial empire reaching from New York to Duluth.

It is the rivers, and the use man has made of them, that give unity to the region. The two plains flanking the Appalachians are not as divided as might be supposed, but are joined together across the barrier of the mountains by the Lower Great Lakes–Susquehanna or Mohawk melt-water channels and the Hudson and Chesapeake estuaries. Of these the Hudson system is the most important, with the Mohawk and Champlain. It crosses the heart of the region from interior to coast, and flows from the edge of the Great Lakes plain, past the Adirondacks and the Allegheny plateau, down a part of the Great Valley, by the New England highlands. It is thus the epitome of the region. It compares favourably with St Lawrence and Mississippi as a route to the centre of the continent, and has become the chief axis for the commercial and industrial development of the nation.

Other important rivers through the Appalachians are the Delaware and the Susquehanna, which flow through the Pennsylvania anthracite field, and provide gaps for railways to the Lower Lakes and to the Pittsburgh iron and steel district. In New England the rivers parallel the mountains, and so do not offer the east–west gaps to Boston that the Hudson, Delaware, and Susquehanna do to New York, Philadelphia, and Baltimore. Nevertheless, they open up the interior to the coast and furnish water-power for industrial development.

The great routeway of the Hudson, the coal fields of western and eastern Pennsylvania, the iron deposits of Superior and of the Adirondacks, the water-power of New England, the harbour bays and estuaries of the coast, and the space for expansion and freedom of movement offered by the Great Lakes—these have been the special advantages of the north-eastern and northern central region, which enabled it to become so highly industrialized and urbanized. Historically, this region was nearest to England, and developed close commercial relations with her. It was settled by industrious, thrifty, and ambitious puritans, who were seeking the liberty to get on, as well as religious liberty, in their flight to the New World. The fact that they wanted to get on quickly led them to choose commerce and industry, rather than agriculture. (At the same time, agricultural land was limited; most of the region was glaciated plateau or rugged mountain, unfit for cultivation.)

However, the *climate* was, and is, well enough suited for farming, given accessible lowlands. Doubtless it was less attractive to the early immigrants who came from a land of mild winters and cool summers than to the farmers of today, brought up to accept its hot summers and severe winters. But the present-day farmer, having learned to overcome winter killing and to adjust to a somewhat limited frost-free season, has exploited to the full the hot, bright, rainy summers. Moreover, he has a large urban market at hand, giving him a high price for milk, eggs, butter, vegetables, and fruit. The New Jersey and Long Island Coastal Plains have a hot summer of over 72°F., suited to truck- and fruit-farming. The Triassic lowlands of Pennsylvania and New England are not quite so warm, but are fairly sheltered, have a long frost-free season (about 170 days), and are easily tilled. They have rich dairying, truck, and fruit farms. The interior valleys and the shores of the Southern Lakes (Ontario, Erie, Michigan) are also fairly sheltered and offer good frost drainage. They are famous fruit, dairying, and fatstock regions. Elsewhere, on the upper slopes of the valleys, and on the plateau levels, summers are too short and cool (60° F. to 65° F.) and the winters too severe (about four months under freezing) to permit of many crops. Hay and oats can readily be raised, however, and cattle, sheep, and horses bred.

The climate is suited to the growth of trees, and the region was once densely forested. There is ample rainfall (30 to 60 inches), thanks to the clash of polar continental, Atlantic, and tropical gulf air masses, and the

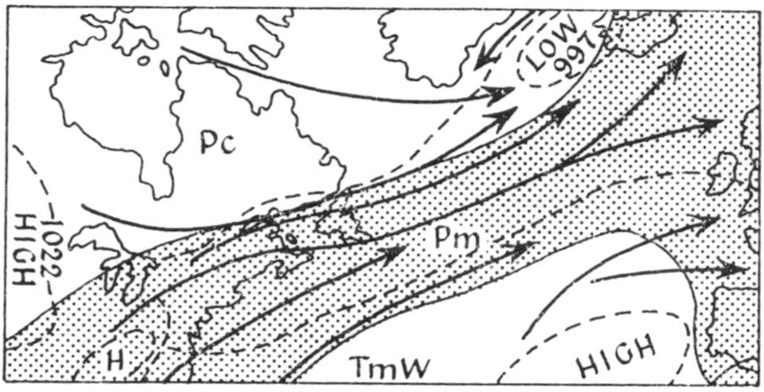

FIG. 155 Climatic Stimulus in the American North-east. In the Ohio, Great Lakes, Mohawk–Hudson, other Appalachian valleys and the Atlantic Coast Plain are concentrated most of the cyclonic storms that sweep across the United States.

resultant cyclones that sweep the area. In the Superior upland, the Adirondacks, and the higher Appalachians, where the growing season is short, a quick-growing forest of spruce and fir is found. Over the Allegheny plateau and New England plateau a mixed forest occurs of hemlock along with maple, beech, and birch. Up the larger valleys and spreading over the Piedmont is a forest of chestnut and oak, while on the sandy parts of both the Great Lakes and the seaboard plains there is an oak-pine cover. In the days of wooden sailing ships and wooden machines, these varied forests were of great use to the New Englanders, who became the chief boat-builders of the world. This launched them on their famous 'Great Triangle Trade', in which they carried molasses, rum, and sugar from the West Indies, together with cotton and tobacco from the Southern States, across the Atlantic to England; picked up English goods and sailed for America again; stopped on the way at West Africa to get a shipment of slaves; sold the slaves and manufactured goods in the West Indies and Southern States, and so completed their triangle. The westerly winds carried them swiftly to Britain; the trades took them to Africa and the Indies.

The climate has, perhaps, been less helpful to industry. The heavy winter snows add a great deal to the cost of economic activity—yards, railway sidings, and roads have to be cleared time and again; buildings have to be made with extra strong roofs to bear the weight of the snow; while in the time of thaw, ways must be found of quickly getting rid of a lot of surface water. The winter cold means that all buildings must be centrally heated and supplied with storm windows and storm doors, transports must be garaged and heated, and raw materials prevented from being frozen while in storage. On the Great Lakes the ports freeze over, and so enormous dumps of coal and iron ore, huge piles of lumber, and other heavy raw materials have to be stock-piled in the open-water season to last out the closed season.

However, in one respect climate is beneficial: it is healthy and stimulating and helps to prevent debility and fatigue. The concentration of storms in the Lower Great Lakes–Mohawk–South New England zone must be one of the greatest in the world and leads to a stimulating series of changes in temperature and humidity, making for human adaptability, alertness, vigour, and sutained work output (Fig. 155).

THE HUMAN RESPONSE

The North-east and eastern northern states have come to reveal many advantages for development and settlement. They command the approaches from the sea and the great riverways into the interior, together with a number of remarkable mountain gaps between. They also possess, or are near, great supplies of metals, fuels, forests, water-power, and agricultural plains. Under the American system, they forged ahead (Fig. 156).

The early colonists along the Atlantic coast, both in the north and in the south, were extraordinarily dependent on the sea. The southern colonists left this mainly in the hands of British merchantmen; but in the north, settlers soon began to exploit the sea, both for trading and fishing. To some extent this was because the land was rugged and more difficult to use than in the south. The presence of many harbours, the good supply of timber, and easily available water-power encouraged the New Englander to build his own fleets and launch out on the seas. Hence New England soon competed with Old England for the carrying trade, a competition which, suppressed as much as possible in colonial days, became most effective after Independence. American trade grew to be carried more and more in New England bottoms.

The New Englander soon discovered another profitable trade, *the carrying of fish* to Catholic countries in southern Europe and Latin America. This fish was a major local resource. The warm and cold currents off the coast mingling over large off-shore banks were an ideal environment for fish. Moreover, New England was very close to the Canadian banks and New England schooners soon became famous on the Newfoundland and Nova Scotia banks.

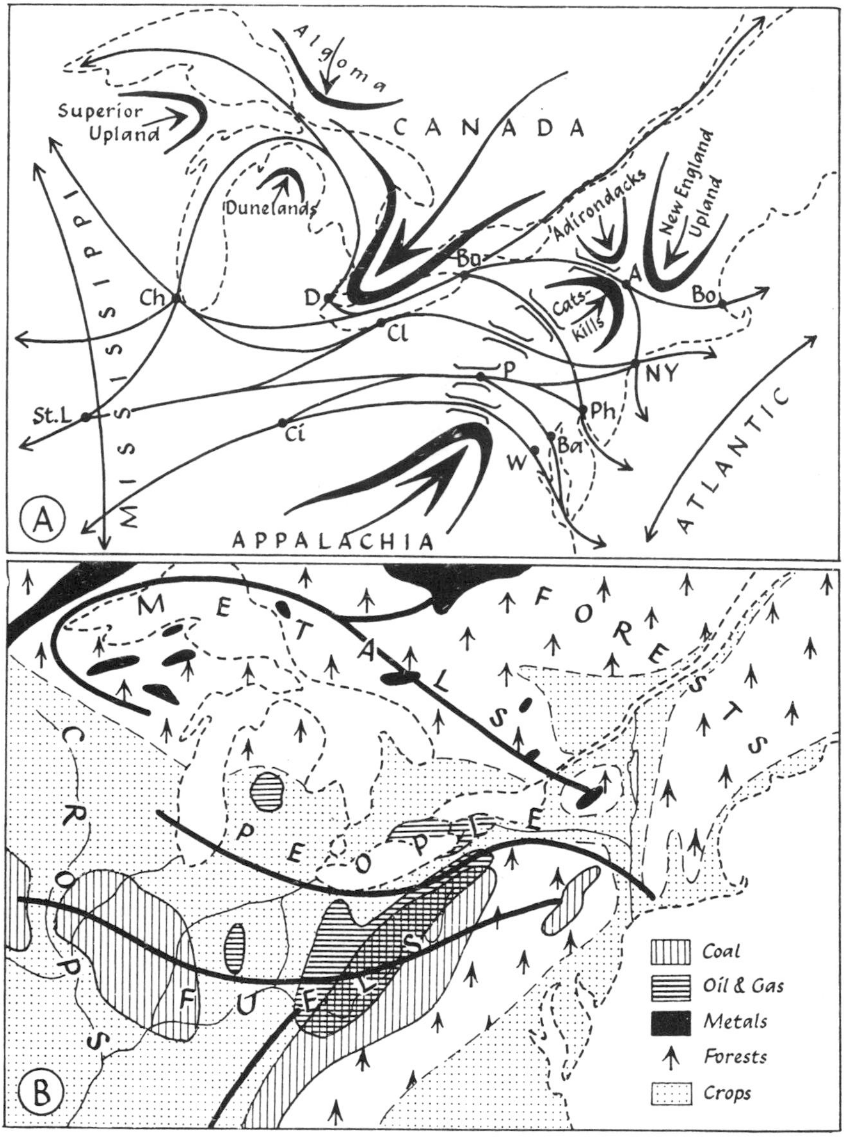

FIG. 156 The advantages of the North-east and Lakeshore States. These are quite outstanding and consist in (*a*) commanding oceanic and interior contacts and connecting routeways, and (*b*) commanding great supplies of natural resources and rich agricultural land. Between the thrust north of Appalachia and the thrust south of the Canadian Shield lies a belt of mountain gaps that draw together most of the chief railways and roads of America. These have become principal immigration routes and there is a wealth of population to make the most of the wealth of fuels and metals, forests, and water-power in the region.

Later, other resources were used. Flax was grown for its linen. Sheep farmers on the uplands supplied wool for woollen goods. Then cotton was bought from the southern planters and turned into textiles. New England became a milling centre. Its many streams, tumbling down from rugged uplands to the sea, had waterfalls and rapids which were eagerly turned into power to drive machinery. They still do so, though, wherever possible, the water-power has been converted into hydro-electricity, so as to maximize power potential and serve a wider area.

Parts of New York and Pennsylvania also had rivers plunging over falls near to tidewater, and here, where tributaries joined the Hudson and the Delaware, little milling towns grew up. Manufacturing spread up into central New York and up the Schuylkill and Lehigh valleys into eastern Pennsylvania where wool from the near-by farmers on the uplands and cotton from the not too distant planters were made into textiles. Saw-milling, associated with extensive hardwood forests, also became widespread, together with the milling of flour and brewing of beer.

The settlers of the North-east States in general thus became industrialists as well as traders. They developed a tradition of craftsmanship and of business-dealing which grew richer with the years. As a result, they created more and more industries. It was early found that iron existed in the New Jersey highlands and the Adirondacks. This was smelted by charcoal made from the woods. An iron industry emerged in New Jersey and New York. Next coal was discovered in the valleys of eastern Pennsylvania. It was hard, anthracite coal, rather difficult to mine. On the other hand, it was easy to transport because it lay in the Lehigh, Schuylkill, and Wyoming–Lackawanna valleys, which were reached from Philadelphia. The discovery of the western Pennsylvania coal field, which makes excellent coke, led to a second iron and steel centre in Pittsburgh. When local iron was used up, the Lake Superior iron was imported fairly cheaply up a short rail haul from Lake Erie.

The spread of industry inland, and the opening up of the American interior, meant a new development for the north-east. It not only continued to make ships, catch fish, manufacture textiles, and export American goods overseas; it began to make rails and railway engines, and to import more and more goods from overseas to feed the needs of the increasing population. This required many roads, canals, and railways. The Appalachian gaps allowed the coast to link up with the interior. The role of the North-eastern States began to take definite shape (see Fig. 156 (A)).

Several important roads were built: the first was from Fort Cumberland on the upper Potomac to the Forks of the Ohio by the Youghiogheny, a southern tributary of the Ohio. This was known as Braddock's road because it had been cut through the forest by British soldiers under Braddock's command. Farther north occurred Forbes' road, connecting the Juniata river in eastern Pennsylvania with Pittsburgh at the Ohio forks in Pennsylvania west. Later this was modified and became the famous Pittsburgh Pike. Then there was the revivification of the Mohawk trail in New York, from Albany to Buffalo, making use of the Hudson–Mohawk gap. This was known, from Utica west, as the Genesee Road. Boston was not to be left out in this drive to the west. A difficult but workable wagon road was built through the various ridges of New England to connect Boston and the middle Connecticut settlements with Albany. This was the Mohawk turnpike. A link was made with it from Hartford on the lower Connecticut known as the Greenwood Road. All these roads did a great deal to involve New England, New York, Pennsylvania, and Maryland with the opening of the west (see Fig. 49, Chapter 7).

Canals became the next vehicle of western expansion. The Erie canal was built from New York to Buffalo, and carried great quantities of goods into and from the interior. The Philadelphia–Pittsburgh canal was not so successful, since it did not have the advantage of a sea-level route like the Hudson–Mohawk to follow. It began at Reading on the Schuylkill; crossed to Harrisburg on the Susquehanna; and followed the Juniata to Hollidaysburg. Here a portage railway carried goods over the Allegheny front to Johnstown, where the goods were transhipped on to canal boats that used the Conemaugh to the Allegheny river and so to Pittsburgh—a most involved route. Baltimore challenged the more northern centres with its even more difficult Baltimore–Chesapeake–Ohio canal, although it relied mainly on the Cumberland–Wheeling road, known as the National turnpike (see Fig. 50, Chapter 7).

The mid-Atlantic cities really began to boom with the advent of the railway. From New York there ran the New York Central Railroad, a line that was built up out of the amalgamation of smaller lines, via the Hudson–Mohawk to Albany, Syracuse, Rochester, and Niagara Falls. There it crossed into Canada, to follow the shortest route to Detroit. Also from New York was built the Erie Railroad, using the lower Hudson, then turning west at Piedmont, to strike to the upper Delaware and upper Susquehanna, eventually crossing the Appalachians to reach Lake Erie at Dunkirk. Later extensions were made to New Jersey in the east and Buffalo in the west.

Philadelphia became the terminal for two famous lines: the Lehigh valley, following the Lehigh, Susquehanna, and Finger Lakes to Buffalo; and the Pennsylvania Railroad, using the Juniata and Conemaugh gaps to cross to Pittsburgh. From Baltimore, the Baltimore and Ohio Railroad, the oldest of the trans-Appalachian rail crossings (1842–53), ran up the Potomac and down the right fork of the Monongahela to Pittsburgh.

Boston shared in the rail boom by building the Boston and Albany Railroad that crossed the New England mountains to Albany, and thence used the Mohawk valley to strike west (see Fig. 51, Chapter 7).

The railways strengthened the harbour towns and the inland junctions; they concentrated activity on Boston, New York, Philadelphia, and Baltimore on the coast; and upon Syracuse, Buffalo, Pittsburgh, and Cleveland in the Interior Lowlands. The coastal towns, in addition to the older industries they had evolved, began new industries by processing the wheat, meat, and leather that poured through them from the Mid-West, and also packing and refining the coffee, cocoa and sugar that poured into them from overseas. This rich two-way trade gave them a greater variety of industries.

The interior towns were concerned chiefly with iron and steel goods for the vast internal market, but also made coke and refined oil from the interior, and ground western wheat for their own use and for export.

As industrialism grew it could not keep to these larger centres. The railways attracted it up the gaps between coast and interior. The coal fields supported many additional factories. The old water-mill sites were revived by hydro-electricity. These smaller centres often developed as satellites around the bigger ones, making parts of goods assembled in the bigger cities, or making machines used there, or shoes, clothes, furnishings, and food products consumed there. Soon the north and mid-Atlantic seaboard, the mid-Appalachian valleys, and the Lower Lakes plain became known for the wide variety of high-quality goods they turned out. This trend helped them to compete favourably with the new industries opening up in the Ohio valley, and later in the southern Appalachians.

The canal era and the railway boom drew out the eastern industrial zone farther and farther into the west, and soon helped to develop industry around the western end of Lake Erie, in the Saginaw Bay district, in the lower Michigan peninsula, and along the south and south-west shores of Lake Michigan. By the 1840s the Pennsylvania system of canals converging on Pittsburgh had been extended north-west past Youngstown to Cleveland, on Lake Erie. Meanwhile canals from Toledo were built west to Fort Wayne and Lafayette, and somewhat later the Soo canal was cut to open up navigation into Lake Superior. The old Chicago and Territorial roads, built west from Detroit in the early 'thirties south-west to Chicago or west to Kalamazoo, were paralleled by railways; the Michigan Central strung together the main lower Michigan towns to debouch on Lake Michigan in 1849 at New Buffalo—later it was extended west to Chicago and also east across South Ontario to Buffalo; while the Michigan Southern ran from Detroit to Toledo and then struck west for South Bend, La Porte, and Chicago, in 1851. Meanwhile the New York Central, Erie, Pennsylvania, and Baltimore and Ohio railroads were all carried across Ohio and Indiana to converge on Chicago, thus prising the Ohio valley loose from its erstwhile dependence on, and outlet to, the south.

The westward extension of transportation through Cleveland, Toledo, and Detroit to Chicago soon led to a whole belt of towns and the rise of new industries. Most of these, to begin with, were based either on transportation—boat-building and carriage making—or on processing the farm goods produced on the lake plains—flour-milling, meat packing, and brewing. After the 'fifties, when the Soo allowed through iron from the Superior Upland, iron and steel making and the manufacture of railway rolling stock and agricultural machinery became important.

This growth required people, and the western territories were flooded with people from the east. At first most of these came from New England because conditions there first led to a serious surplus of the rural population. This was due in the main to the 'sheep craze' that swept the region between 1825 and 1840. The mounting demand for wool in the textile mills encouraged farmers to adopt the Saxony Merino sheep, a good wool-bearer and one suited to the severe climate. As a consequence 'farmer after farmer turned his cultivated fields into pasture lands'. Younger sons and hired hands were not needed to the same extent. Small homesteads were amalgamated into large sheep runs, and the 'little' farmer had to move out. Many drifted into the cities, but many others went west to upper New York, Ohio, Michigan, and northern Indiana and Illinois.

Meanwhile, in the Mid-Atlantic States agriculture was suffering a decline of another character, having begun to feel the competition of cheap grains, hogs, and cattle being raised on the shores of the Lower Great Lakes or in the Ohio valley. Wheat and corn from these interior regions were sent east down the Erie canal in the late 1820s and throughout the 1830s, growing in volume with every year. When railways were built in the 1840s the competition between railroad and canal reduced the freight rates to such an extent that a bushel of wheat could be sent from Chicago to New York for 25 cents. By the mid-'forties over a million and a half bushels a year were coming into the Mohawk–Hudson valley to be shipped to New York and other seaboard points. This flood of cheap food lowered prices so considerably that many farmers in New York, New Jersey, and eastern Pennsylvania, and also in southern New England, could no longer operate their circumscribed and highly mortgaged farms at a profit, and so they sold out and went west. By 1850 there were 518,000 people from the Mid-Atlantic States and 172,000 from New England who had migrated to the Old North-west. This amounted to about one in five of all the inhabitants of that region. Thus it may be seen how very much the upper Ohio and southern Great Lakes area had come to depend upon, indeed had grown out of, the Atlantic north-east. Today these areas are very closely integrated indeed (Fig. 157).

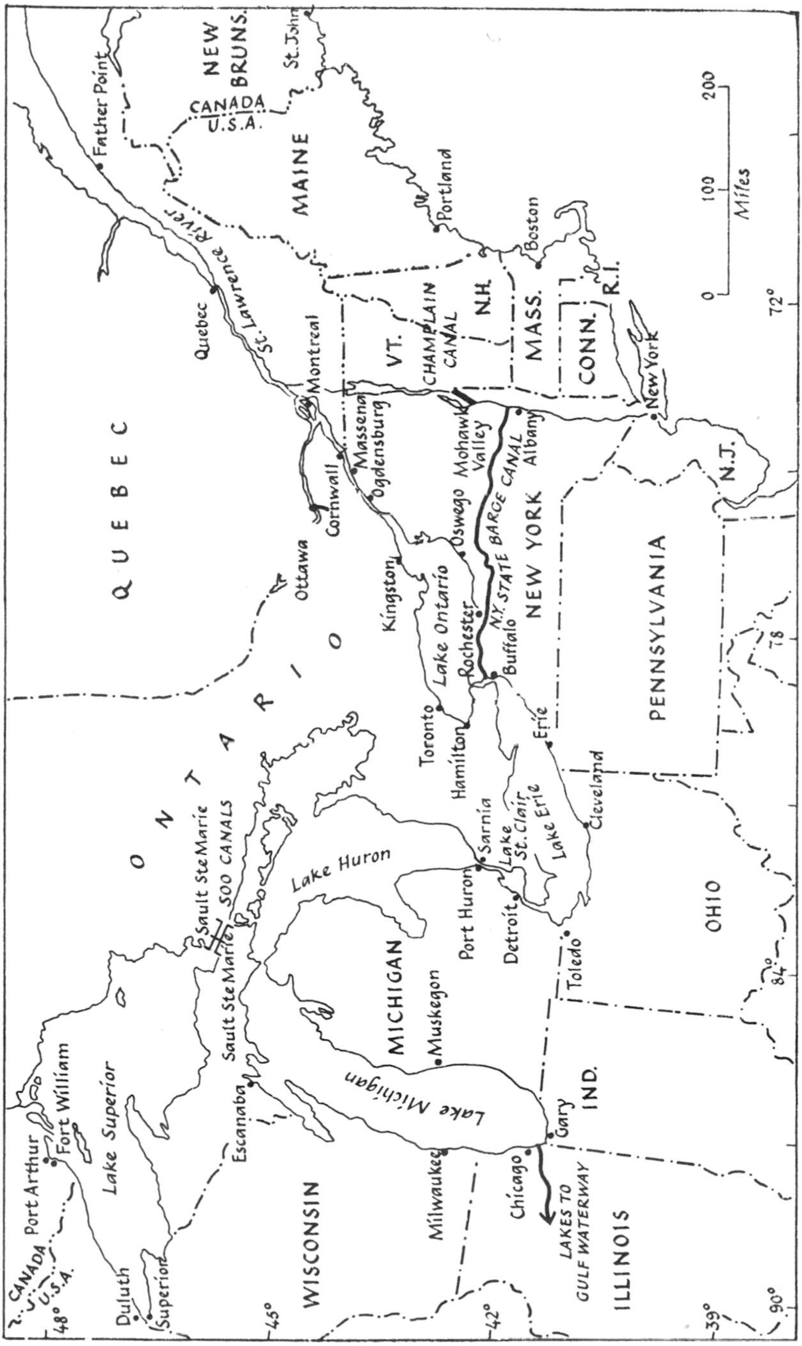

FIG. 157 The Integration of the New England, Mid-Atlantic, and Great Lakes States of the United States along the line of the Hudson–Mohawk and Lower Great Lakes.

LOCAL CHARACTERISTICS OF THE REGION

The north-east (New England and Mid-Atlantic States) and the east north-centre (upper Ohio and the Great Lakes shore), while having much in common, including an integrated relief, an unusual concentration of cyclonic storms, a unique meshwork of roads, canals and railways, interconnected businesses and industries, and many people of similar origin, nevertheless have their differences, such as enrich and strengthen the life of the whole region. These will be briefly outlined.

The north-east sub-region is made up of an outer coast section and an inner mountain section.

The North and North-east—the Coast Section

This is partly a drowned *plateau* in the north, or a drowned *plain* in the south and east. Drowning is the chief characteristic, and it has resulted in bringing ocean waters up to or within the very plateau, up long estuaries (Chesapeake, Delaware, Hudson), and within wide bays (Narragansett, Boston, Casco). Thus it has made great ports possible, often with good connexions running into the interior. Drowning has also flooded the end-moraines along the coast, and turned them into a series of islands (Long Island, Nantucket). The many drowned inlets and off-shore islands helped to create a seafaring tradition which has expanded into great naval and commercial traditions.

The plateau area of the coast section, including the Piedmont and the edge of the New England plateau, has, in common, plentiful sources of water-power. The rivers flowing over it from the wet interior highlands have speed and volume, and plunge over a series of falls down to the coastal plain, or to the sea (the Potomac Falls, Schuylkill, Woonsocket, Fall river, Lowell, Lawrence). This was the first impetus to manufacturing.

The plateau is rocky though scarcely rugged: a sea of gentle swells. Its general appearance has been well described by Davis. The inequality of the surface would be quite moderate, with long, low, even sky-lines, 'were it not for the few mountains that rise above it and the many valleys that sink below it. The slightly rolling high-level surface of one hill after another approaches the plane of the circular sky-line. It requires but little imagination to recognize in the successive hill-tops the dissected remnants of a once even and continuous surface.'[1] The northern part of the plateau is glaciated and has coarse, heavy, stony, and acid soils, a cloudy summer and severe winter, which inhibit agriculture, but favour forestry. Unfortunately much of the woodland is poor quality second growth. The Piedmont is not glaciated and

[1] Davis, W. M., 'The Physical Geography of Southern New England', in *The Physiography of the United States*, New York, 1896, pp. 269–71.

is rather better drained. It has fairly mature grey-brown to yellow-red soils on its broader interfluves and carries good dairies. Where the Triassic lowlands are let down in the plateau, as in Pennsylvania, New Jersey, and Connecticut, a warmer climate and more fertile, sandy-loam soils invite special crops, like tobacco, hard-fruit orchards, truck-farming, and dairying. Intense cultivation of these small areas helps to supply the large urban markets of Baltimore, Philadelphia, New York, Hartford, and Springfield with milk and vegetables.

The Connecticut is the most important of these highly productive enclaves. Compared with the rough, wooded, rather empty, declining areas of the plateau around, it may well appear to be

> a little exotic. There is a suggestion of the south in the broad, open meadows, the reddish soils, the tobacco and onion fields; and of Europe in the vineyards and the bronzed foreign women and children at work on the land. The bold green slopes and dark cliffs of the trap ridges add a touch of wildness. Immense cheese-cloth tents spread over the tobacco fields and the great wooden sheds in which the tobacco is stored bear witness to a costly and intensive type of farming different from anything found on the New England uplands. But the manufacturing cities with their tall factory chimneys and endless streets lined with small workers' houses are typical enough of industrial New England.[1]

Water-power has been used where the river has been impeded, particularly by the trap ridges, and small textile and paper-making towns, like Holyoke and Greenfield, early sprang up. The main cities, Springfield, Hartford, and New Haven, developed as route junctions, markets, and trading centres, and have continued to grow as the foci of very varied engineering industries, insurance businesses, and publishing. At New Haven is one of America's oldest and most renowned universities—Yale.

Much of the plateau, both in the Mid-Atlantic and in New England States, has been hit by rural depopulation, the abandonment of farm land, the destruction of the good forest and its replacement by scrub and even barrens, as erosion has got to work. Indeed the European visitor is astonished at how run-down and deserted the land can look, often next door to populous and flourishing communities.

Thus Toynbee remarks:

> I was once travelling in a rural part of Connecticut when I came across a deserted village—a not uncommon spectacle in those parts, as I was told, yet a spectacle which is none the less surprising and disconcerting. For

[1] Wright, J. K., 'Regions and Landscapes of New England', in *New England's Prospect*, New York, 1933, p. 36.

> some two centuries, perhaps, Town Hill—such was its name—had stood with its plank-built Georgian church in the middle of the village green, its cottages, its orchards and its cornfields. The church still stood, preserved as an ancient monument; but the houses had vanished, the fruit trees had gone wild, and the cornfields had faded away.[1]

This is typical—except where townsmen are buying up the derelict farms to turn them into summer homes.

The plains area of the coast section of the north-east does not have much room for agriculture to develop. It is very narrow, so that agriculture never was extensive. Now it has to vie with cities or citified uses of land, like riding schools, flying clubs, golf courses, and holiday resorts. The plain varies a good deal. It has a northern glaciated section and a southern unglaciated one. The glaciated part is made up of swarms of drumlins and spreads of ground moraine from Boston north, and portions of end-moraines left above sea in Long Island, Martha's Vineyard, and Nantucket. From these have been developed wave-built features like Cape Cod and the barrier beaches along the south New England shore. The islands, spits and lagoons have long been bases for the inshore fisheries. They are frequently cultivated, except where cottage colonies have been established when they are used for recreational purposes. The frost-free season (160 to 180 days) and the light, warm sandy soil yield many special crops such as potatoes, asparagus, and tomatoes. Poultry farms are also popular. The produce helps support the dense populations of Boston, and New York. Off Long Island's southern shore are long spits enclosing quiet bays, noted for their pleasure beach 'colonies' and yachting resorts.

The southern unglaciated part of the coastal plain consists of the outer vale-and-wold plain of New Jersey and Delaware; and the inner Triassic lowland of New Jersey. Both are highly fertile, with hot summers (over 70° F.) and a long growing season (over 200 days), and are under fruit and market gardens. The magnificent line of spits and sand reefs off the coast is famous for its seaside resorts like Atlantic City, Ocean City, Surf City, and Long Branch.

The coast section of the north-east centres round the nuclei of Boston, Philadelphia, New York, and Baltimore. Here indeed is the most extensive urbanized strip in North America, and one of the greatest industrial-financial complexes in the world (Fig. 158). From Portsmouth south to Plymouth Bay occur town upon town in the lower Merrimack valley and Boston basin; then from New Bedford, on Buzzard's Bay, to Narragansett, on the bay of that name, there is found another ring of cities; while from New

[1] Toynbee, A. J., *A Study of History* (Abridged Edition, ed. Somervell, D. C.), London, 1960, p. 84.

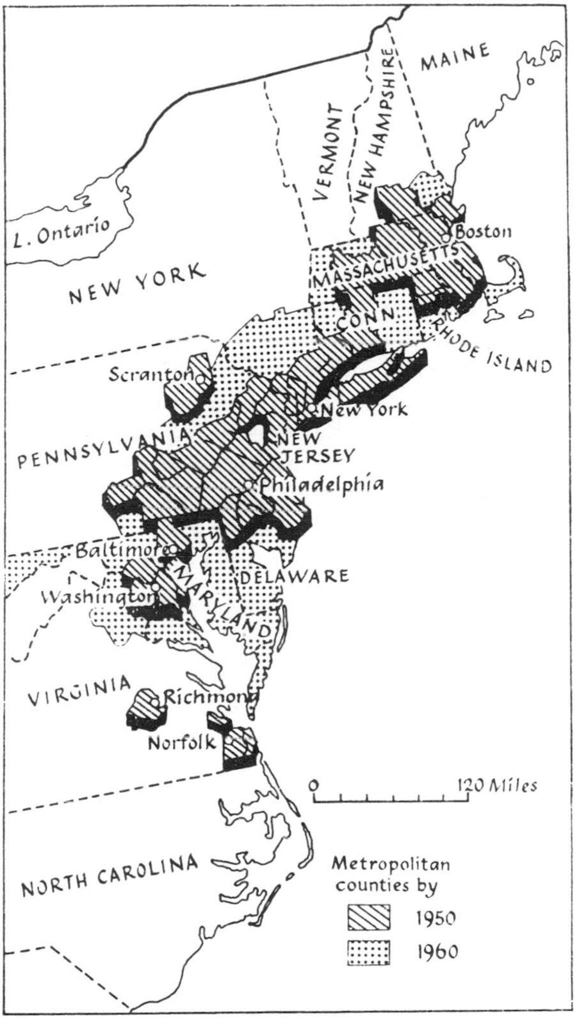

FIG. 158 The American Megalopolis—the Urbanization of the North-east. (From Gottmann.) The shaded zone in the above shows the core area of American Megalopolis, with all its major cities. The zone in dots is the metropolitan shadow area. (See Gottmann, *Megalopolis*, fig. 3.)

Haven to New York 'towns stand so close together, their suburbs merge into one another, making an almost continuous built-up area'.[1] Opposite New York another virtually unbroken sprawl of buildings, yards, sidings, wharves, roads, and circum-urban wastes may be found from Paterson to Perth

[1] Wright, *New England's Prospect*, p. 24.

Amboy. A short break then occurs—but one filled with multi-tracked railways and multiple-lane highways and festoon upon festoon of high-tension power lines—until the Delaware is reached. Here the Ruhr of America provides a smoking mass of factory-packed cities from Trenton past Philadelphia to Wilmington. Finally there is the wide urban splurge around Baltimore almost running into the expanding suburbs or dormitory satellites of Washington.

In this relatively short distance is concentrated about three-fifths of America's industrial and commercial power, a concentration only to be matched elsewhere by that taking place in the London basin, in Britain, and around Tokyo and Osaka Bays, in Japan. Altogether over 33 million live in the area, in a narrow strip of cities scarcely 450 miles long. There are forty-two cities, in all, of over 50,000, including five of over 1 million, two over a half million, seven over a quarter million, twelve of over 100,000, and sixteen between 50,000 and 100,000. In this great galaxy three centres stand out: the Boston area with over $2\frac{3}{4}$ million, Philadelphia and vicinity with 5 million, and the New York–north-eastern New Jersey district with over 15 million people. To this huge urban sprawl Gottmann has given the name, the American Megalopolis.

Boston (2,860,000), Massachusetts, lies at the head of Boston Bay, one of the larger re-entrants in the East New England coast. The bay goes back to a distinct basin, marked by a rim of low rounded heights known in part as the Blue Hills. The relatively soft Carboniferous rocks were eroded into a low plain, sloping gently down to the Charles river and the head of the bay. Glaciation plastered the basin with an uneven spread of ground moraine whose hummocky surface includes many marshes and small lakes as well as wooded knolls. A small swarm of drumlins characterizes the lower part of the basin, rising in humpbacked heights to about 200 feet above the general level; many of these form peninsulas and islands in Boston Harbour. They originally carried a broad-crowned forest of oak and maple, lifting their lighter greens above the darker hues of hemlock and cedar in the hollows. Except for a few lacustrine flats around shrunken glacial lakes, and marine benches near the bay, there is little good agricultural land. Much of the basin is poor second-growth woodland or derelict land waiting to be taken up for building. One is struck by the absence of extensive market gardens or dairy pastures. Speculative wastes are rampant.

Boston itself grew up on a low, blunt 'neck' or peninsula between the drowned lower part of the Charles river and the inner waters of the bay (Fig. 159). There are four drowned inlets in the vicinity and the rather tortuous waterfront, well sheltered from the notorious east winds off the Atlantic, affords many miles of quays. The old church of 1630 and the Town House were built at a central crossways, where King Street, up from the harbour,

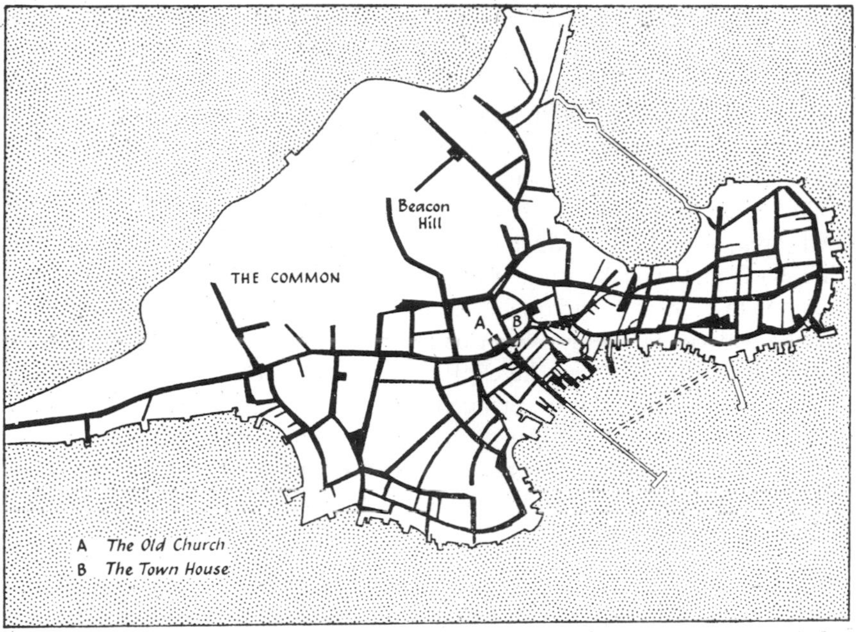

FIG. 159 Old Boston—the Street Pattern in 1722. (From Bonner's Map.) A, the Old Church and B, the Town House, were at the centre, with the Port below and the Commons and Beacon Hill above. Its crooked and narrow streets, clinging to the contours of the land, and its extensive common, are still features redolent of Colonial America. Relief was used to express and to protect status from the wealthy homes near Beacon Hill to the tenements of the bay side, and status divisions are still strong, especially as between old Anglo-Saxon sections and Irish, French-Canadian, and Italian areas.

crossed Cornhill, the axis of the peninsula. Today State House and City Hall are still at the town centre. This, with its great green flanked by public buildings, together with an active shopping district spreading out to rather narrow winding roads following the contour of the peninsula, is very European, as is the abundant use of brown stone and red brick for offices and dwellings. The old harbour and the main railway station were developed on flatter land to the south. Bunker Hill to the north, across the river, tended to hold back development and west of it the pleasant residential town of Cambridge grew up, with Harvard University and, later, the Massachusetts' Institute of Technology. A northern harbour and station were developed on the nose of the Boston peninsula, and road and railway bridges were built across the river, allowing swift urban and industrial expansion to Somerville, Medford, and Malden on the sides of the Mystic Creek and its arms. At the same time there was a southern spread to the drumlin-dominated height of Brookline, whence the town divided, streaming out along the Boylston highway to Worcester, and the Blue Hills towards Narragansett Bay. Eventually town sprawl linked up Boston with Quincy and Weymouth, on Quincy Bay, and extended the built-up area to the foot of the low scarp between Waltham and Lynn that forms the north rim of the basin. A series of multi-lane trunk highways then radiate out to connect the inner group of towns in Greater Boston to an outer circle on the lower Merrimack, the Worcester basin, the Blackstone valley (Woonsocket), and the Brockton plain.

This great outward spread is something new, with the result that the outer town area, with its individual homes in large tree-shaded lots, looks very different from the packed inner town, with its tall narrow houses, sometimes built so close on such narrow lots that there is no room for driveways and garages between the homes. But this is typical. As Manners points out, 'the twentieth century has seen the explosion of the American Metropolis. The essentially vertical city of the last century, compact and intensive in its land use, has been surrounded by a horizontal, land-devouring suburbia.'[1]

As a result, the whole countryside is changing. One consequence is of special interest. Former farm villages, which had been declining for eighty years or more, have become

> important residential satellites of the larger industrial and commercial cities. Drive where you will between urban centers located ten, twenty, or thirty miles apart and you will generally see one or more of the old communities undergoing a new phase of residential growth. So pronounced has been the change and so close are the centers, that in between Boston and the Merrimack valley Cities—Lawrence, Lowell, Haverhill, Amesbury and Newburyport—there is now almost continual residential occupation of roadside lands. The countryside has virtually become an urban appendage.[2]

Boston's position on the sea, rather than its connexions with the hinterland, has accounted for this phenomenal growth, although its role as a service centre for other eastern New England towns is of increasing significance. As the nearest large American port to Europe, it long handled the European trade. However, it does not have a through gap to the interior, like New York, and it lost its importance to that better-situated port. Boston has good connexions with the Merrimack and south shore cities, and thus with the 'fall towns'. It has also easy contact with the middle Connecticut. A ring of textile towns such as Lowell, Fall River, and New Bedford (cottons), and Lawrence, Providence, and Woonsocket (woollens) look to Boston for services and trade. An outer ring of metal-working and

[1] Manners, G., 'Decentralization in Metropolitan Boston', *Geography*, November 1960, xlv, p. 276.

[2] Thompson, J. H., and Higbee, E. C., *New England Excursion*, I.G.U. XVIIth International Geographical Congress, Washington, 1952, p. 46.

engineering centres also looks to Boston. This includes Manchester, New Haven, Bridgeport, and Springfield. Boston and its near-by satellites Lynn and Haverhill form the centre of the nation's shoe and leather industry. Boston also has textiles and metal (machinery) industries; ready-to-wear clothing; coffee and cocoa factories; and luxury industries, such as jewellery and watches. It thus depends on easy access to overseas markets and raw materials; on highly skilled craftsmen; on the production of high-value goods that can be made by electricity and do not require large amounts of coal; and on populous surrounds, with many interrelated industries which it can serve.

The Boston, Narragansett, and lower Connecticut areas had the great advantage of an early start in the industrial race. Lowell claims to be America's oldest industrial city. Early beginnings are both an asset and an embarrassment; they give a region a lead, provide industrial momentum, and build up a great pool of skills. But they may mean the dead hand of tradition and a lot of obsolescent buildings and equipment. Momentum carried New England forward into the 'twenties of this century, but with the Great Depression, outmoded buildings and practices became a drag and the textile industry, in particular, suffered. New England lagged behind the newer industrial areas of the Mid-West and even the South. However, its accumulated know-how and skill came to its rescue and, by changing over to textile engineering, the making of precision instruments, quality paper, and high-value goods in general, it was able to maintain its historic position. Today, many other regions—the Mid-Atlantic, the Mid- and the South-Appalachians, and the Lower Great Lakes industrial cities—are having to make the same kind of reappraisal and adaptation. 'New England leads the nation in this process of transition. New England's economic prosperity is inextricably linked with industry's ability to adopt new techniques and products. In many of the region's industries the dominant reason for success is the ability to do something better than competitors elsewhere.'[1] Geography does not now afford many advantages; human wisdom, initiative, and skill are the things that largely count today.

The evidence that they do count lies in Boston's continued expansion and particularly in *the way* in which it is expanding as a centre of science, education, and culture, of new methods of business organization, experiments in new technology, and, above all, ever renewed efforts at basic thinking and research. The freshness, strength, and keenness of the Boston mind—which no doubt made Appleton remark, 'A Boston man is the east wind made flesh'—is now as important as the accessibility, openness, and wealth of its waters.

[1] Ellis, G. H., 'Goals for New England', in Bright, A. A., and Ellis, G. H., *The Economic State of New England*, New Haven, 1954, p. 698.

In this Boston has undoubtedly been helped, as have most of the leading industrial cities of America, by the many different kinds of people it has attracted, with their various traditions and skills, each competing and conflicting with the other, yet each learning from the other and contributing something to the whole. After the Revolution, Boston attracted many Irish from southern Ireland, and these still play a prominent part. Then the city became the Mecca of French-Canadians who drifted down through Maine from their homes in neighbouring Quebec and New Brunswick. Later many Italians and Ukrainians flocked to the city, willing to compete with native-born Americans for the rather low wage industries (clothing, textiles, boot and shoes) of the city and its vicinity. A third of the population is foreign born.[1]

New blood has brought new ideas and Boston is now in the throes of urban revolution. The 52-storey Prudential tower on Commonwealth Avenue vies with the State House. The expanded business core is matched by an enlarged Government Centre. An apartments area at the Charles River Park, in the West end, and neighbourhood redevelopment in the South end, have improved housing. The uses of the waterfront have been rationalized, and the whole has been given fast and freer traffic circulation by the Central Artery and the extension of the Massachusetts Turnpike. New industries have sprung up along the great ring routes, and the Universities have expanded into high-rise blocks near the city centre.

Philadelphia (4,985,000), at the opposite end of the Atlantic metropolitan zone from Boston, has now become America's fourth greatest metropolitan city, with nearly five million people in its immediate district. From the first it attracted settlement, partly because of the great popularity of Penn's liberal policies—which stood out in strong contrast to Boston's exclusiveness—and partly because of its geographical site and setting. It has still followed the policy of attracting all types of people from many lands, and has a very polyglot population. English are still important—and rows and rows of red brick houses remind one of nothing so much as the streets of industrial Lancashire—but Huguenots, Irish, and in more recent times, Poles and Ukrainians, have added to the industrial strength and social wealth of the city.

Each in their different way helped to see the value of, and to develop, the local site. That site 'was selected for settlement in 1682 to meet William Penn's injunction to find a place that was "high, dry, and healthy" (an important factor on a coast marked by swamps) and where ships might load "without boating or lightering". Here the sweep of the Delaware

[1] Thompson and Higbee, *New England*, p. 140.

around a bend throws its currents against the western bank and makes for deep water on the side with the continent at its back.'[1] Although not at the head of navigation, which lies upstream at Trenton, it was nevertheless at a strategic site, where the Schuylkill joined the Delaware, thus giving the town the command of two valleys. A long, well-drained peninsula extended between the two rivers where they ran parallel to each other. This allowed a well-laid out, geometrically designed town to be established, with its short east–west axis, where the rivers came closest, providing Market Street and Town Square, and its long north–south axis, following the interfluve, giving the city the room for expansion it soon came to need up Broad Street and the Old York road. The City Hall grew up at the main road-meetings, where Penn's statue now overlooks the recently widened Penn Centre. Independence Hall, built on the main street, farther east, now faces a newly constructed Mall on one side and the National Historic Park on the other. It is an eloquent reminder of the fact that the First Continental Congress was held in Philadelphia in 1774, and that, between 1790 and 1800, the city was the capital of the United States.

It was chosen as such largely because it was so central, lying about halfway between Richmond, Virginia, and Boston, Massachusetts. But the choice partly rested in the fact that it was 'the largest and busiest city in all the colonies'.[2] This was due, in no small measure, to other aspects of the local site. The broad deep waters of the Delaware to east and south of the town centre offered scope for quays, warehouses, and the early narrow tall factories; the marshy tract at the mouth of the Schuylkill was excavated for a naval yard and became the Navy dock area. Philadelphia itself was on the coastal plain, but just behind it lay the sharp step-up of the Piedmont, where the Schuylkill, the Wissachikon, Poquessing, Neshaminny, and other local tributaries, tumbled across the 'fall line' to provide power for eighteenth-century industries. Where the tributaries fell down to the Delaware plain they tended to build out meander flats. These were marshy and were at first avoided, but became good sites for the flat, broad-based, space-using factories of the twentieth century. Thus the town had the physical facilities for every stage of expansion, and though it lost out to New York as a trading centre, mainly because it lay 101 miles up-river from the sea, it continued to rival it as an industrial centre and, in this capacity, far outstripped Boston. Indeed, as the focus of the lower Delaware, the Schuylkill, and the Lehigh industrial complex, which is increasingly concentrating on large-scale, heavy industry, Philadelphia is the heart of an area that is often called the 'Ruhr of America' (Fig. 160).

[1] Klimm, L. E., 'The Philadelphia District', in *Industrial Cities Excursion, Guide Book*, I.G.U. XVIIth International Geographical Congress.

[2] Wilder, H. B., Ludlum, R. P., and Brown, H. M., *This Is America's Story*, Boston. 1954, p. 96.

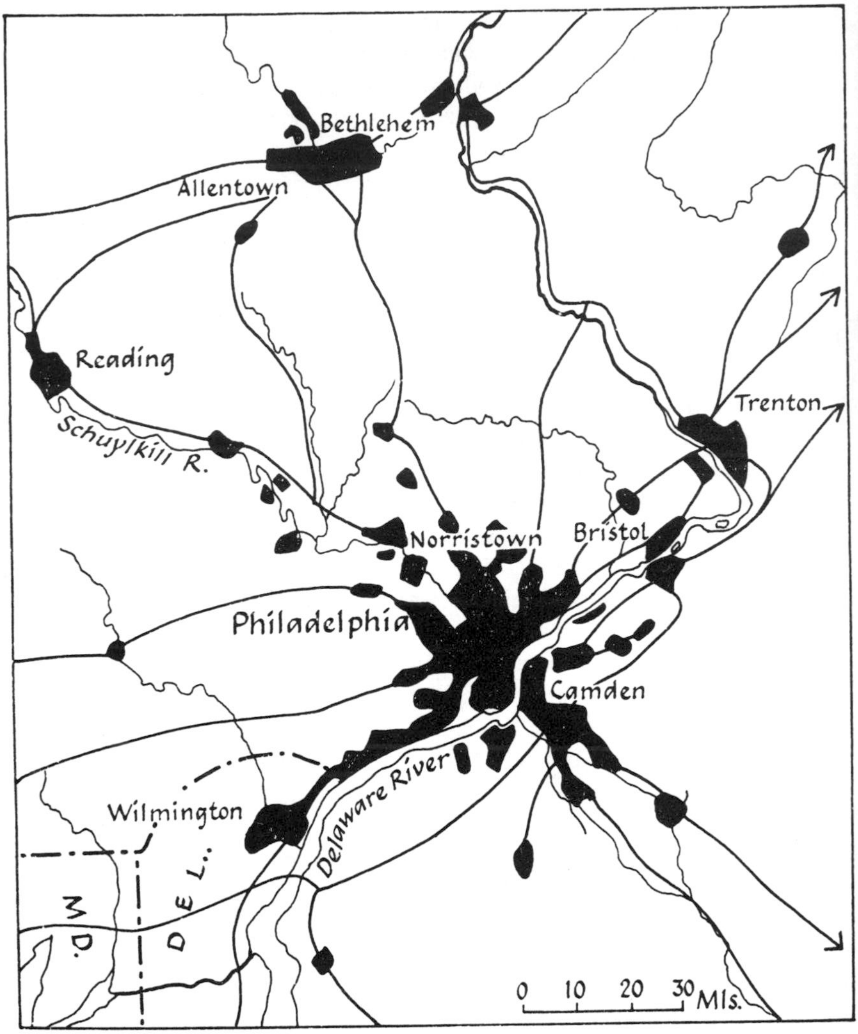

FIG. 160 The Philadelphia Industrial Complex—the Ruhr of America. At tidewater, with good canal connexions between the coastal rivers, near to passes in the mountains, at Fall Line water-power, close to the coal fields of eastern Pennsylvania, and with access to imported iron from Newfoundland, Cuba, and Venezuela, Philadelphia has developed great iron and steel, ship-building, railway engineering works, other engineering and refining and chemical plants in association with a whole ring of industrial cities. At the same time it has maintained its commercial and cultural activities and influences.

The Mid-Atlantic States cradled the first governments of the United States at New York and Philadelphia. Subsequently, Washington was chosen capital since it was on the border between North and South

49. Independence Hall, Philadelphia, housed the Constitutional Convention of 1787, and is one of America's chief shrines.

50. Washington, on the Potomac, is laid out as a spectacular city with great avenues radiating out from the U.S. Capitol.

51. Pittsburgh, at the confluence of the Allegheny and Monongahela Rivers with the Ohio. Here is the famous Golden Triangle, one of the wealthiest pieces of real estate in America, which the people of Pittsburgh have recently remodelled and beautified.

The American North and Northeast—the 'bridge' and 'heartland' regions, as typified by Pittsburgh, dominating the trans-Allegheny routes, and Chicago, commanding the lakeshore plain

52. Chicago grew up where the Chicago river enters L. Michigan. The river became canalized, linking the Gt Lakes with the Mississippi. This canal carries an enormous amount of traffic, but its operation holds up road traffic in the very heart, or loop, of the city. Today the Calumet Canal is being used to bypass the central Chicago area, which is becoming a second New York.

Philadelphia was farther from Europe than both New York and Boston; this was an initial handicap. But it lay nearer the interior, controlled several Appalachian gaps, had water-power sources at hand, and more especially sources of coal. It became more essentially industrialized, and today has 37 per cent of its people engaged in manufacturing—well over the national average. Colonial industries were woollens and leather tanning, paper-making, printing, and sugar refining, which have been kept up, thanks to imports of overseas supplies. It has gone over to the production of rayons on a large scale, and to the making of railway rolling stock, motor-cars, ships and electrical machines. These take advantage of its position as a great railway terminal and harbour, and also of its nearness to the eastern Pennsylvania coal field. Huge oil refineries have been established below the city, while iron and steel production has developed across the river at Woodbury, and upstream at Morrisville.[1] These reflect the ease with which it can import oil from Venezuela and Texas, and iron from Newfoundland and Labrador.

Philadelphia, like Boston, has developed in association with outer rings of thriving industrial settlements. These are Bethlehem and Allentown (iron and steel), Hazelton (machinery), Trenton (ceramics and locomotive parts), Chester (automobile assembly and ship-building), and Wilmington (once flour-milling and textiles, now largely chemicals—du Pont). Camden, which lies on the opposite shore of the Delaware from Philadelphia, is now part of the large city. It is noted for its canning and soup-making factories, using the vegetables and fruits of the rich truck-farming area in the New Jersey vales. Over 50 per cent of industrial workers in Philadelphia now work outside it. But though there has been industrial flight, new commercial and institutional pressures have occurred at the city centre, actively being redeveloped.

New York and vicinity (15,300,000) form the chief settlement of Atlantic America. Here the coast swings in from Cape Cod and Cape Hatteras to the Hudson estuary and the most direct route into the interior (Fig. 161). Although Verrazano discovered New York Bay in 1524, during the course of an exploration trip for Francis I of France, nothing was made of it until Henry Hudson sailed up the river inlet, realized something of its promise, and set up a trading post at the foot of Manhattan Island, on behalf of the Dutch. Christiaensen and Block came to trade for furs in 1611 and the Dutch West Indies Company built a fort on Manhattan point and began to develop the region. In 1626 Peter Minuit bought the whole island from the Indians, and the Dutch soon created a thriving colony. This divided the

[1] 'The United States Steel Corporation's Fairless plant is the largest single integrated iron and steel mill. It was begun in 1949 to serve the eastern market and to use iron ore imported via the Delaware River. It has an ingot capacity greater than that of Japan, or Australia, or India, or Sweden. The plant area covers 3,800 acres.' Klimm, *The Philadelphia District*, p. 37.

English colonies to north and south and, as we have seen, threatened British expansion in New England. In 1664 the British captured the Dutch settlement and changed its name from New Amsterdam to New York, in honour of the Duke of York. The city once more became Dutch in 1673–4, but then returned to the British under whom it remained until 1783, when it passed to

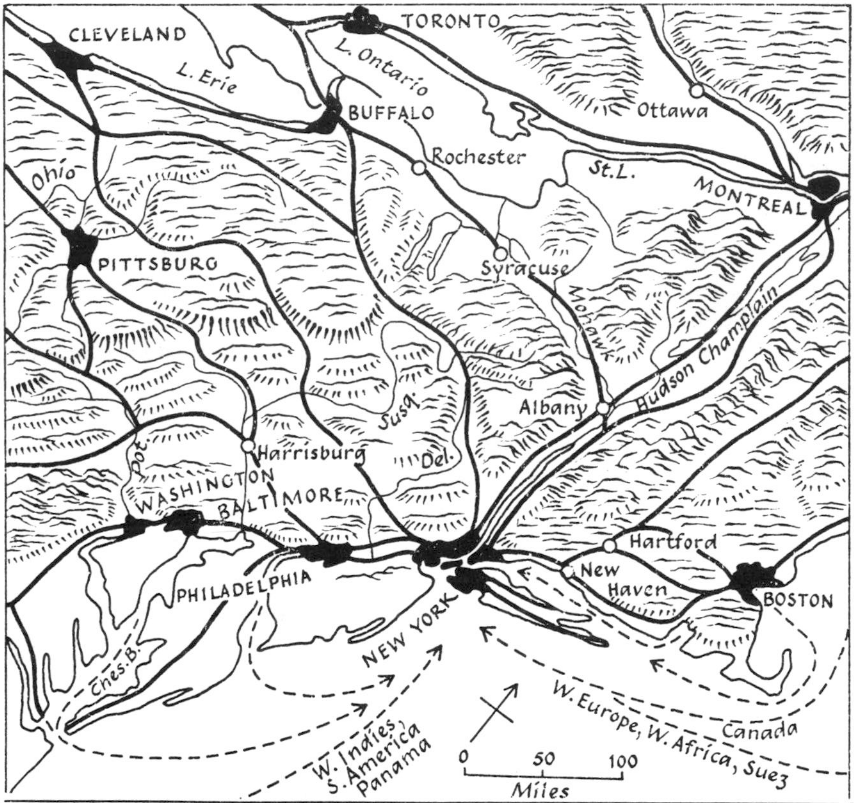

FIG. 161 New York as Focus, uniting New England, the Mid-Atlantic States, and the Lower Great Lakes, and commanding trans-Atlantic and trans-Appalachian connexions. No other site has such a setting. It is small wonder that New York does about half the trade of the nation.

the Americans. These early struggles pointed up its great strategic value as the link both between the northern and the southern colonies and also between the Atlantic and the interior. This is still one of its key roles.

The town grew up at a remarkable meeting-place of waters in upper New York Bay. Here the Hudson, with its distributary the Harlem river, joins the continuation of Long Island Sound in what became known as the East river, and is joined by the Hackensack and Passaic rivers through the waters of Newark Bay. Long Island and Staten Island come close together to provide an easily fortifiable narrows, and north of this lies Manhattan Island, at the very centre of the mesh of navigable waterways that have 'made' New York.

In this locale

> there is as much water as land in sight. From the beginning, the waterways were the important unifying factor and provided a means of transportation that made a metropolis possible. They served the numerous settlements that sprang up on Manhattan, on Long Island, up the Hudson, in New York State and Connecticut (and the neck of New Jersey). The waterways gave New York the fastest and most comprehensive transit to be had at the time by any colony.[1]

The early town was thus oriented to water. The high humped back of Manhattan, with commanding rocky elevations like Murray Hill and Morningside Heights, was neglected for the narrow marine bench beneath. Here, from Battery point eastward along Pearl Street the early business houses were constructed. The East river saw the main expansion, partly because the flats were distinctly wider than those along the Hudson, where precipitous shores were soon met with, and partly because there was virtually no floating ice such as sometimes drifted down the Hudson during the winter and in the spring thaw from its winter-frozen tributaries in the mountains. To add to the accessible waterfront the Dutch cut a canal in the nose of Manhattan. This was later filled in and became Broad Street, which passed north into the common or 'The Fields'—now a park dominated by the City Hall. The town was enclosed by a stockade, later replaced by Wall Street. The waterfront was then extended, shored-up and filled in, and was followed by Front and Water Streets. The junction of Water and Wall was long the centre of business in New York. Gradually, as more room for quays and warehouses was needed on the flats, businesses migrated west up Wall Street to its junction with Broadway; in the meantime many shops had moved from Pearl to Broadway. The city wisely bought up most of Manhattan and also a large part of the Brooklyn waterfront on the opposite shore of the East river; this gave it considerable control over its development. In 1811 a street plan was drawn up which, although Henry James later derided it as a series of 'pettyfogging parallelograms', had the advantage of simplicity and subsequently allowed for rapid transit up the great south-north avenues northwards to Bronx, Westchester and New England, and across the short west–east streets to Queens County and Brooklyn on Long Island and eventually to Jersey City and Newark in New Jersey (Fig. 162).

Warehousing, shopping, and business stuck very much to the southern

---

[1] Rodgers, C., and Rankin, R. B., *New York, The World's Capital City*, New York, 1948, p. 7.

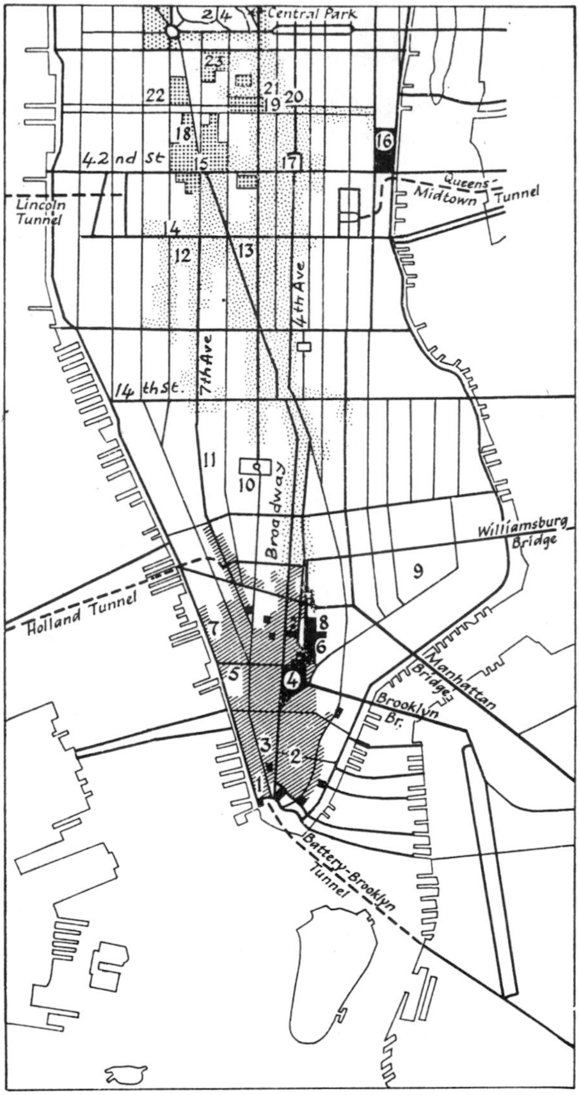

FIG. 162 Downtown New York. Here competition for land is at a maximum, and has helped to produce a growing segregation of economic activity and social institutions into distinct and distinctive urban areas. These include the administration (black) and financial (ruled) districts of the point of Manhattan, together with the retail (light dots) and the entertainment and cultural quarters (heavy dots) of Mid Manhattan. Points of interest are: 1, Cunard Building; 2, Wall Street, N.Y. Stock Exchange; 3, American Stock Exchange; 4, N.Y. City Hall; 5, Washington Mkt.; 6, U.S. Court House; 7, Fruit Mkt.; 8, Chinatown; 9, Lower East Side; 10, Washington Square; 11, Greenwich Village; 12, Pennsylvania Stn.; 13, Empire State Bldg.; 14, Macy's; 15, Times Sq.; 16, U.N.O. Bldg.; 17, Grand Central Stn.; 18, Warner's; 19, Saks; 20, St Patrick's Cathedral; 21, Rockefeller Centre; 22, Madison Sq. Gdns.; 23, Carnegie Hall; 24, Central Park. (Scale, 1:80 th.)

tip of Manhattan to be near the waterfront, and the northern avenues like Fifth Avenue and Park Avenue, now thronged with large departmental stores, offices, and hotels, were residential into the nineteenth century. The port was extended to the west side of Manhattan and here the passenger boats that arrived with the steamship age were able to unload within a few hundred yards of the heart of the city, an advantage very few other cities of similar size possess. Consequently, business has stayed in lower Manhattan. This has meant an enormous pressure on space. Eventually in the twentieth century relief was sought from that pressure in the building of great skyscrapers. The city, unable to expand outward, soared upward, until its tallest buildings exceeded a thousand feet, towering three times or more over the spires of Trinity, St Paul's, and St Patrick's that once topped the New York sky-line. Today these churches are mainly conspicuous for the astonishing maintenance of quiet graveyards in the midst of the thronging city.

Railways added to the problem of overcrowding. Most of the transcontinental railways wanted terminals in New York or its vicinity, but only two, the New York Central and the Pennsylvania Railroad, have been able to secure stations within Manhattan itself. The New York Central follows the Hudson down from Albany, comes in down the west side, and swings over to Grand Central Station on 42nd Street. (The terminal migrated from 14th Street in lower town back up to mid-town as town pressures increased.) A large group of hotels and big departmental stores grew up in the vicinity and spread north along Fourth Avenue and Park Avenue. Similarly when the Pennsylvania Station was built, Macy's, Gimbels, and Saks came in along near-by Fifth Avenue, with another group of large hotels. Broadway then changed from a shopping to an entertainments centre, becoming the 'Great White Way' of America. These developments extended the massive buildings of the lower town right up to Central Park. Beyond this, however, New York is still mainly residential, sinking down on the east side to working-class tenements, found notably in Harlem, and on the west, rising to heights crowned by Columbia University, Riverside Church, and upper-class apartments and residential hotels. Other railway terminals including those of the Erie, and Lehigh valley, are in Jersey City, opposite New York, or on Staten Island (Baltimore and Ohio), south of Manhattan. Most of these have connexions with Manhattan either by ferries or by the Lincoln and Holland tunnels under the Hudson and the Bayonne Bridge out of Staten Island. The presence of most of the terminals west of Manhattan has meant that heavy industry has tended to grow up in Jersey City, Newark, and associated settlements, leaving Manhattan to concentrate on business and finance—although there is a very active and large clothing industry on the island (see Fig. 162).

The need for industrial space has led to the spread of industry all along the East river, and along the Brooklyn shore of New York Bay. The big Bush terminal in south-west Brooklyn has greatly extended the harbour area. It is flanked by big Army and Navy bases, which also contribute much to the activity of the district. But expansion has created a problem of integration. This is partly a political matter—the grouping together of separate municipalities, Bronx, Queens, Brooklyn, Richmond, and Manhattan into the metropolis of New York—but partly a physical question of the actual linkage of all these units. Here tunnels, bridges, and expressways have been of prime importance. Jersey City and beyond it Newark and Elizabeth, from which the New Jersey turnpike and the Pulaski skyway converge, are linked by the Holland tunnel and short streets across Downtown Manhattan with either the Brooklyn tunnel or bridge with Brooklyn: similarly, Hoboken, Union City, and West New York are linked by the Lincoln tunnel with Midtown Manhattan and, across the Queens–Midtown tunnel, with Queens. The Henry Hudson Parkway up the west side of Manhattan leads to the Washington Bridge, Englewood and Paterson (by the Passaic expressway), or to the Hudson Bridge across the Harlem river to Yonkers and Westchester; the great eastside expressway, the Roosevelt Boulevard, swings over the Triborough Bridge to link up north with the Bronx and east with Queens. A remarkable Belt Parkway joins all the outer burghs together and ties them in with the inner expressways converging on Manhattan. Thus, in an extraordinary fashion, man has triumphed over the very fragmented relief of the area to make a real unity. Results are at least twofold: more people can get out of New York faster to more suburbs than in any other large city, with the possible exception of Los Angeles, and more motorists can converge upon the heart of Manhattan to make for a greater concentration of business there than ever! These motorways have been connected with the great airports of La Guardia, created out of the marshes of Flushing Bay on the East river; Idlewild, built up from mudflats and beaches around Jamaica Bay (Long Island); and Newark, developed from the huge extent of marsh around Newark Bay—a marsh which, together with the Hackensack marshes to the north, still looks astonishingly empty next to such densely built-up cities. These airports now handle between 30 and 35 million passenger-flights a year from abroad.

New York, then, has made a notable use of its site, at each stage of development, until today it is swiftly fulfilling the prophecy made in the early 'twenties that the New York region would include 'the Atlantic Highlands and Princeton; the lovely Jersey hills back of Morristown and Tuxedo; the incomparable Hudson as far as Newburgh; the Westchester lakes and ridges to Bridgeport and beyond, and all of Long Island'.[1]

[1] Adams, T., *Planning the New York Region*, New York, 1927, p. 33.

Undoubtedly, this has been due to its situation which has given it a better chance than Boston to trade in the Southern Colonies, the Caribbean, and South America, and a better chance than Philadelphia to trade with New England, Canada, and Europe. Above all, New York is situated on the shortest and easiest route into the continent. It is no wonder then that New York does nearly half the total import and export trade of the nation—an extraordinary concentration! It has become all this with few of the advantages usually associated with industrial and commercial centres. It does not lie on a coal field, nor is it near iron or other metals. However, it can obtain coal from near-by Pennsylvania, import oil from the Caribbean, and obtain scrap iron from the neighbouring states and the interior, so that fuel and metals can be assembled fairly cheaply. They are used in many machine shops and small foundries.

The chief industries are those carried on in relatively small workshops, depending on highly skilled labour, making goods that are readily sold throughout the nation. About a quarter of its workforce is engaged in making men's and women's clothing, for New York is the fashion centre of the New World. Other clothing goods like furs, silk goods, and millinery are next in importance, together with a wide variety of luxury goods, such as cosmetics and jewellery. Printing and publishing is a major New York industry. Food products are important to supply its huge population.

Yet New York is more than famous workshops and warehouses. It is also a great cultural centre, with eleven universities, the American museum of Natural History, two famous cathedrals—St John's and St Patrick's—and the head offices of a great number of foundations and scientific and other learned societies. Not far away are the Army and Navy training schools. New York art galleries, symphony orchestras, and theatres are the foremost in the country. Recently New York has become the home of the United Nations Organization.

Back of all this is its unique geographical situation. That situation has enabled it to develop in two supremely important ways: first, as the chief centre of attraction of European immigration; second, as the main centre of dispersion of American financial control. The Statue of Liberty and Wall Street are the two outstanding symbols of New York, the one inviting ambitious, adventurous, freedom-seeking migrants from every country, of every race, creed, and culture; the other organizing financial assistance and stimulating foreign investment in virtually all parts of the globe. These give it the people and the power to be such a great cultural, industrial, and commercial centre.

New York is, in this respect, the epitome of America. It has Americans from every quarter of the country living there, with an especially large influx of American negroes from the south. There is no negro settlement or section of a settlement in the south as large as Harlem. New York has also made Americans out of immigrants from every quarter of the earth; important are the Irish, who poured in after the Great Famine; European Jews, Italians and, latterly, scores of thousands of Puerto Ricans. All this has had its impact.

'The push of population change finds New York surrounded by ever-burgeoning satellite suburbs whose weight the City must shoulder by providing the jobs, educational facilities, transportation conveniences, and recreational outlets that a great metropolis must offer to city-dweller and suburbanite alike. The massive outward movement of the middle class, spurred by good roads and increased living standards, has been countered by a huge in-migration of lower-income families—many of them Negroes or Puerto Ricans, whose upward mobility has been thwarted. The net result of these changes has been the creation of mounting demands to encourage the retention of the middle class by providing higher quality urban amenities, and to develop massive welfare, and educational programs to help those who have been trapped by social barriers in our era of affluence. Physically, our expansion has created a vast network of new and complex problems: traffic congestion, parking dilemmas, airport location, jet noises, commuter line-snarls, and air pollution. New development has created new cities which must be provided with all the improvements we have come to expect in a modern metropolis. Here too the march of progress often serves as a dramatic contrast to the obsolescence, the blight and the lack of adequate facilities that still persist.' It is within this dynamic context that the bold attempt is being made to fashion an orderly plan for the development of the whole metropolitan area.[1]

Baltimore (1,900,000) is described by Parkins as the first city of the south, by Wright as the principal 'commercial and distributing center for most of the eastern south',[2] and by White and Foscue as one of the Atlantic's principal gateways to the interior; it obviously is transitional in position and status. In early days it was mainly of the South. 'It has commercial traffic lines that reached to all parts of Maryland, down the Great Valley even to the valley of eastern Tennessee.' But with the building of the Baltimore and Ohio railway it began to serve the Old North-west as well as, and then to a greater extent than, the south. The necessity to make the most of its northern connexions led it to extend the Baltimore and Ohio to New York, where it has a terminal on Staten Island. Nearness to Pennsylvania coal and to Cuban and Newfoundland iron then prompted it to expand as a great iron and steel centre, with the huge steel plant at Sparrows Point, the largest on tidewater. The rise of other industries like copper smelting, machinery, aeroplanes, oil

[1] New York City, City Planning Commission Report, 1966, p. 3.
[2] Wright, A. J., *United States and Canada*, New York, 1948, p. 142.

refining, chemicals, textiles, canning, and meat packing have now made it more like a northern industrial town than a southern commercial centre, a likeness that springs to the eye in row on row of terraced brick houses which again, what with their whitened door-steps, white sills, and white brick-work over door and window, seem identical with their Lancashire counterparts in the slums of industrial England. This industrialism has linked Baltimore firmly with the north-east. As Gottmann points out, a map of counties along the Atlantic shore dominated by a metropolitan economy shows a metropolitan belt 'the continuity [of which] is clearly established from Washington's metropolitan area to that of Hartford, Connecticut'.[1]

Washington (2,400,000) is also transitional between North and South. Its choice as a capital, instead of either New York (1784–90) or Philadelphia (1790–1800), was undoubtedly made as a concession to the South. 'Washington and other Virginians proposed to connect the Potomac and Ohio rivers by a canal, and to make that route the main highway to the west. They wanted to locate the national capital on this route and planned to develop it not merely as the seat of government but as the industrial and commercial center of the nation.'[2]

But while the city grew up on the very verge of the South, it too, like Baltimore, got caught up more and more into the mesh of roads, railways, telegraph lines, and urban-industrial development typical of the North, and is now without doubt a part of the Atlantic megalopolis, stretching from the Potomac to the Merrimack.

This transitional position actually makes it ideal as a capital in that it shares the interests and problems of the two main sections of the nation. From the beginning it was planned to do this; its site at the head of navigation on the Potomac just below the Potomac falls helped it unite Coast Plain and Appalachian Piedmont, and be the linch-pin in the chain of Fall Line cities from Rhode Island to Alabama.

The city is a magnificent example of a planned capital, bearing the marks of that French inspiration which made it the Paris of the New World. From the tidal basin on the Potomac, above the harbour, there run the broad, straight east–west thoroughfares of Independence and Constitution Avenues with the beautiful tree-lined Mall between, where the towering white Capitol building dominates the centre. In front of this is the great sweep of park to the Washington Monument and the Lincoln Memorial. Northward lies the White House, at the convergence of a number of great avenues coming in like the spokes of a wheel to bind the periphery to the hub. Beautiful circles and squares keep the city open, and provide vistas of urban façades and sky-lines without equal in North America. Washington University, Georgetown

[1] Gottmann, J., *Virginia at Mid-Century*, New York, 1955, p. 472.
[2] Rodgers and Rankin, New York, p. 66.

University, Washington Cathedral, and Howard University form an inner ring of famous institutions, with an outer ring of American University, Trinity College, and the University of Maryland. Fine art galleries and museums add to the cultural attraction of the city. But the most striking buildings are the great government offices, done in white marble, set in lovely grounds, and faced with Roman colonnades. Washington's main function is administrative, and by far the greater part of its population consists of civil servants. It is, however, a great road junction and major airport and has important rail connexions, and transportation is one of its more significant aspects. All this has enabled it to be America's outstanding tourist centre, and over four million tourists visit it every season.

The North and North-east—The Mountain Region

Although the coastal plain dominates the north-east, and has concentrated upon it the bulk of the population with the largest urbanized area on the continent, the neighbouring uplands are also important, being great sources of coal and hydro-electricity, a major timber reserve, and a much-needed playground for the people.

The East North-central States touch, and the North-eastern States straddle, the Appalachians. This great structure, so influential in history as well as in the economy, here consists of two ridged, broad-backed plateaux flanking a central series of highlands and valleys. On the east is the New England plateau, rising to the White and Green mountains, and overlooking the Hudson–Champlain lowland. On the west is the Catskill–Allegheny plateau, overlooking the Mohawk–Hudson and the great Appalachian valley.

The New England upland is made up of a series of folded and metamorphosed rocks which have been partially planed down by very long erosion, and then attacked by ice and newly rejuvenated rivers. It is a rough, uninviting region, with a severe climate, having long snowy winters (four months below freezing), rather infertile, poorly drained soils, and a heavy coniferous forest. The area is difficult to clear, stony, hard to till, and a test of sheer human endurance. Many settlers have abandoned their farms, and the region is being swiftly depopulated. New settlers, who do not know the situation, buy up land—it is an area of foreign-born, ethnic groups; but they, in turn, drift away, to seek better things in the city or farther west. Over large areas nothing better than subsistence farming may be attempted. However, the larger valleys like the upper Connecticut, the upper Merrimack, the Kennebec, and Penobscot have better soils, and a relatively long frost-free season (120 to 160 days). They carry dairy herds, as well as general farms.

The region still has considerable value for lumber. Most of northern

Maine and of the White and Green mountains are heavily forested with spruce and pine, which are cut and floated down or carried by truck to small lumbering towns. The rivers supply water and hydro-electric power. It is recognized now that much of this land should never have been cut over for farming; forestry is its best use and there has been a great revival of interest in New England's forest resources. This is as it should be. 'More than three-fourths of the land area of New England is forested. Although the region contains only 2·1 per cent of the nation's land area, it has 6·7 per cent of the commercial forest area in the United States. Maine and New Hampshire, with 84·5 per cent and 83·9 per cent of their land in forests, rank well above any other State in the country.'[1] Forest industries give direct employment to 10 per cent of the New England workforce. Unfortunately much of the cut-over forest has not replaced itself with good timber and New England has less than half the national replacement average. The knowledge of better forest-management practices, the amalgamation of a great number of small forest properties, the wider use of less favoured trees and of forest by-products and wood waste, and the burning of oil or gas instead of wood for household fuel are, however, bringing about a marked improvement.

The main problem is the small owner-operator. Ninety-five per cent of the forest is privately owned, much of it in the hands of small owners who just do not want to be bothered with their woodlands. 'Such owners can get sufficient from their property, in many cases, by renting it out for hunting and fishing. Not a few are city men who have bought the land for the sake of finding a refuge in the woods. The forest as a frontier may have passed, but the forest as a frontier symbol lives deep in the heart of almost every American.'[2]

Consequently, probably the greatest industry associated with the forest today is not milling, or pulping, but tourism. This lovely area of rolling hills, enclosing hundreds of beautiful lakes, with its fine fishing rivers and forests full of game, is becoming one of the chief attractions for the people of Boston, New York, and Montreal. Thousands of people have their summer lake-side cabins or their winter ski huts on the mountains to which they go for inspiration. The American love of the wilderness has been an abiding characteristic ever since it was so beautifully expressed in Thoreau's writings.

The Allegheny plateau, by contrast, is a much more bustling and productive area. Most of it escaped glaciation. Its valleys are deep, sheltered and warm, and the soils are a yellowy silty, or sandy loam, developed from the underlying sandstone. These warm up in the spring. They are relatively easy

[1] Kelly, R. S., and Bright, A. A., 'The Forests of New England', in Ellis and Bright, *The Economic State of New England*, p. 25.

[2] cf. Nevins, A., ed. Cooper, J. Fenimore, *The Leatherstocking Saga*, Kingsport, 1955. Note the Preface, where Nevins stresses the impact of the forest, as Cooper treated it, on American thought, and especially on boyhood imagination.

to work, although they require considerable liming. Parts of the plateau are so deeply dissected that the farms are inaccessible and backward. But where the Allegheny and Susquehanna flow through, good routes are provided to large urban markets. Dairying is the general practice.

The lowlands within the mountain sub-region are better developed, except for the Ridge and Valley sector of the Appalachian valley, which again is rather inaccessible. It is under general farming. But the Great Valley, the Hudson, and the Mohawk are well farmed, chiefly producing milk, butter, and eggs for the coastal cities. The Ontario-and-Erie lowland, across which the Allegheny plateau looks in the north, is exceptionally favoured. It is sheltered by the plateau in the south, and for a part of its length by the Niagara Scarp, and feels the beneficial effects of the lakes to the north. The frost-free season is about 170 to 180 days long, the summers are warm, between 68°F. and 71°F., July average, and the soil well drained, sloping down a series of old lake beaches. Consequently, fruit and market gardening are very much in evidence. The Finger Lakes and the western New York peninsula are well known for their grapes and wines; the Rochester plain for its peaches.

Far more important than its agriculture, however, are the mineral resources and routeways of the mountain sub-region. In the valley sections in East Pennsylvania is the largest anthracite field in production in the world, while on the western slopes of the Allegheny plateau is one of the best coking-coal fields. These are the basis for the prosperity of Philadelphia and Pittsburgh respectively. In addition there are small oil pools in western Pennsylvania and a large natural gas field.

The rich fuels of western Pennsylvania are made available to all of the North-eastern States and also to the Northern-central States through the river routes, and the railways that follow them. Running through the centre of the district is the Allegheny (which has a low divide connecting it to Lake Erie), and the western tributaries of the Susquehanna.

Pittsburgh (2,750,000) has become the outstanding centre of the region and is one of the leading metropolitan areas in the nation. Here the Allegheny is joined by the Monongahela and the Youghiogheny rivers, which flow through the coal field, and make a low divide with the Potomac. Out of Pittsburgh the Ohio flows south-west. Thus the city is in the centre of riverways leading to the Great Lakes, the Central Lowlands, and the mid-Atlantic ports. (These rivers today carry loads of coal and iron which form a greater tonnage than the traffic of the Suez or Panama canals.) It was at the meeting-place of the three main rivers, in what is called today 'The Golden Triangle' (because it is one of the most valuable pieces of real estate in North America), that the city grew up (Fig. 163).

Its evolution is very dependent on the local site. Here three things were

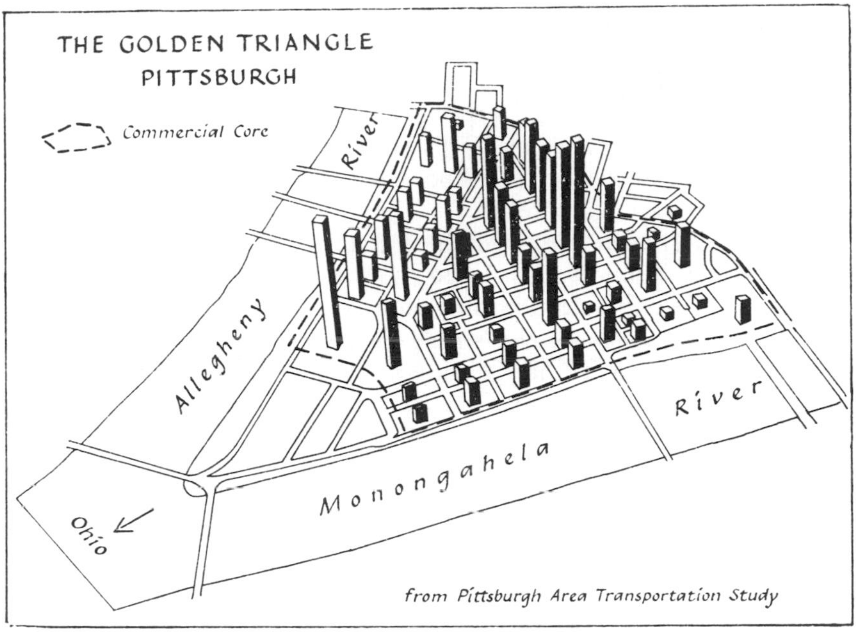

FIG. 163 The Golden Triangle—Pittsburgh, one of America's most-valued sites. Here at the meeting of the Allegheny, Monongahela, and Ohio rivers the busy city grew up. A fort at the point of land later became squeezed out by bridge-approaches, railways, and roads; and the point of the triangle was a tangle of routes. Today this has been cleared away for planned road approaches (bringing expressways into the heart of the city) together with a civic centre and park. Behind these soar the great skyscrapers of the commercial core.

important—'the formation of the Carboniferous coal seams, uplift of the Allegheny Plateau, and glacial and post-glacial river development'. These things were 'unrelated events in the geological and physiographic history of western Pennsylvania'. But the white man put them together and in 'combination they provide the initial resource-basis for the industrial greatness of the Pittsburgh District'.[1] Rich coal seams emerged between layers of sedimentation in the jungle-choked swamp that once covered the area. As the Appalachians rose to the south, rivers from its edge and also from the Shield, not far to the north, formed huge deltas in the shallow seas that overlay the continent in this vicinity. Eventually, uplift led to the draining away of the sea and the preservation of the coal deposits along its margin. The fact that the uplifted plateau was subject to gentle folding kept the coal seams relatively close to the surface, especially on the crests and sides of simple anticlines, but did not expose the seams to the strong erosion characteristic of the Ridge

[1] Nystrom, J. W., Schmidt, O., Howe, G., Netting, G., 'Pittsburgh', in Mayer and Philbrick, *Industrial Cities Excursion*, p. 84.

and Valley section to the east. The rivers ate in deeply to the elevated surface. In glacial times their entrenched meanders became filled with melt-water deposits. When the ice retreated, further uplift of the land led to renewed erosion which cut well-marked terraces in the glacial sands and gravels. The newly strengthened rivers often abandoned pre-existing meanders, whose stranded beds, 200 feet or more above the present bottomlands, offered welcome scope for urban spread.

The Golden Triangle itself is made up of towering skyscrapers and great multiple stores. Multi-level road and railway bridges connect it with the three main valleys up which Pittsburgh has expanded. Sweeping road-bends and a complex pattern of city streets then carry the population to the terraces and eventually to the plateau tops, crowned by residential suburbs. Some of the valley bottoms and lower terraces still carry houses, although most lower sites have been pre-empted by industry. Such strips of houses as do exist—very narrow, a door and a window wide, but long and high—have become blackened by smoke and eaten into by the acid-laden winds, and form virtual slums. Here, as on Pittsburgh's South Side, 'dwell many people of foreign origin—Serbian, Hungarian, Polish, Lithuanian and Irish'.[1] For Pittsburgh is extraordinarily cosmopolitan. From the beginning it has been a crossroads, both from east to west and north to south, a gateway leading to wider horizons. An interesting sidelight on this is that in its university it has special classrooms dedicated to different nationalities in the city, as a symbol of 'the values for which Pittsburgh is a center. For Pittsburgh is still a crossroads for those things which mean most in our world today; friendliness, the courage to go ahead, good will, and happiness.' The classrooms are representative of the following Pittsburgh groups: Swedish, German, Scottish, Russian, Chinese, Czechoslovak, English, French, Greek, Hungarian, Italian, Lithuanian, Norwegian, Polish, Rumanian, Yugoslav, Syrian, and Lebanese.[2]

These people have poured into the city, attracted by the good employment, but not put off by the arduous nature of the jobs. They crowd together on the flats or on the lower slopes so as to be near their work. Space is at a tremendous premium as is seen, amongst other things, by the building of a skyscraper for the university. There are sharp breaks between the different levels of the town, marked by steep wooded slopes, and then the bottoms are reached, thronged with great steel works, coal and iron yards, coal-generated electricity stations, road and rail terminals, and river wharves. Although Pittsburgh is still the chief steel-making centre in the United States, with more than 20 million tons of steel-making capacity (about equal to that of the whole of Great Britain, and just over a fifth that of all of

---

[1] Nystrom, *et al.*, op. cit., p. 88.
[2] *University of Pittsburgh Handbook*, University Press.

America), it affords very little room for expansion. Fourteen major plants are squeezed into the low, long, narrow Monongahela and Ohio valleys, and factories simply do not have the room for new extensions, let alone for completely new modern horizontal layouts. For this reason Pittsburgh is slowing down in its growth, giving way to places like the Gary and Philadelphia districts where flat open plains are available for modern plant development.

Local iron ore and the huge coal deposits started the production of iron and steel at Pittsburgh. Eastern sources of iron have now been used up, but it is possible to obtain iron fairly cheaply from the Lake Superior region by the long water route of the Great Lakes and the short rail haul from Lake Erie. The coal going west out of Pittsburgh pays for the iron returning east to the city.

Not only does Pittsburgh have local resources and good routes, but it is strategically placed to send its products east to the coast or west to the interior. This has been, and remains, one of its greatest assets. Along with Buffalo it forms the main link between the eastern and western sectors of the American manufacturing belt. Based on transport, it has provided the means for the extension of the great transportation routes. Half of its products by value are iron or steel, mostly in the form of plates and rods that can be used in making rolling stock, etc. It also makes locomotives and cars, a great deal of electrical and mining equipment, and has become a major centre for oil refining. Like other 'metropolitan' areas, Pittsburgh is associated with lesser cities, which it serves, or which contribute to its prosperity. About 80 per cent of the industrial work force is employed in centres outside the metropolitan area. This has led to rapid and widespread suburbanization, and made the whole landscape around very citified.

The North and North-east—The Interior Lowlands

The highlands and uplands of the north-east contact the interior lowlands of the north in western New York, at the terminus of the Hudson–Mohawk route. Here the land widens out to the plains of Lake Ontario and Lake Erie. A series of beach ridges left by former glacial lakes (Warren, Iroquois) provide fertile, well-drained soils, suitable for intensive cultivation. The mild climate, moderated by the presence of the lakes, is well adapted to fruit- and truck-farming.

The Niagara and Onondaga escarpments run through the peninsulas of western New York. Niagara Falls plunge over the Niagara escarpment. Many other falls exist and they were early used for milling flour, sawing lumber, and running woollen mills. For example, Rochester, on the Genesse Falls, early became a milling centre and is still important for the flour it makes.

Water-power has now been transformed into electricity, in which this area is particularly rich. Rochester is now the centre of electrically operated 'precision' machines, and light manufacturing, including men's clothing. It is the home of the great Kodak firm of camera makers. Niagara Falls is noted for its electro-chemical plant, and Tonawanda for electro-metallurgical works.

Buffalo (1,560,000) is the centre of this western lake-front region. It is the point of transhipment of goods imported via the Hudson–Mohawk for distribution in the interior, or for interior products carried down the Great Lakes and intended for export. Buffalo is on the coal route from Pittsburgh. Oil is found in near-by Pennsylvania, and there are local gas fields. It thus has raw materials and fuels, and cheap transportation. Its industries include large flour mills, and timber and paper concerns making use of the Great Lakes trade in wheat and wood; and also metal works, shipyards, railway yards and foundries, and automobile plants. Large chemical industries using Niagara Falls power have been established. To west and east are the steel centres of Lackawanna and Tonawanda.

Connecting Buffalo (and the interior) with New York (and the coast) and forming an axis to the whole north-east and eastern central region is the Erie canal and Mohawk valley zone. It has very restricted areas for agriculture, but is well suited to industry, with its excellent location, good routes, and nearness to electricity, coal, and oil. Through it flow goods from west and east. It is the chief corridor of American immigration. Thus it has become highly industrialized—concentrating on metal goods, chemicals, and textiles. Syracuse is the chief city, with large foundries and machine shops, agricultural machinery plants, and big chemical (salt and soda) works.

When the Mohawk axis is extended to the west it meets the Lakeshore plain of Lake Erie which is carried west, without any break, to the shore plain of Lake Michigan. This, the route of the old Lakeshore railway, and of the Michigan Southern and the Michigan Central railroads, forms the great western wing of the industrialized and urbanized region of the north and north-east of the U.S.A.

There must be doubt, at the present stage of development, whether to include it, as the writer has done, with the rest of the manufacturing belt, most of which lies in the east, or to treat it as a part of the Mid-West to which, physically and historically, it belongs. True, a part of it, the Ohio plain, was traditionally grouped with New York and Pennsylvania, as Middle America; but with the vast expansion of the west this view of it was given up. The Middle region really broke in two, and came to comprise either the Mid-Atlantic States or the Mid-West.

The Mid-West cannot really be thought of apart from the Lakeshore plain; it runs from the Ohio up to the Great Lakes and then swings west across the Mississippi to the Missouri, the break-of-the-plains and even beyond. It helps to feed raw materials, fuel, food, and people to the great cities of the Lakeshore plain such as Cleveland, Toledo, Detroit, Gary, Chicago, and Milwaukee. They in their turn supply it with the railways, motor-cars, agricultural machines, and other needed goods without which the Mid-West could not thrive.

Nevertheless, in terms of landscape and life, this string of cities and the highly citified land between them does seem more akin to the Mohawk, Hudson, and the Atlantic metropolitan region than to the rest of the Mid-West which is so strongly agricultural. And this will probably prove to be more true and not less so in the generations to come—unless of course the increase of industrialization widens out the manufacturing belt to include all the Mid-Western States as well as the Mid-Atlantic and the New England States.

Obviously this is debatable. The Census does separate the Lakeshore region from the north-east (New England and Mid-Atlantic States), treating the two as different entities, but then it also separates off the east north-central (or Lakeshore) States from the west north-central ones forming the bulk of the Mid-West. To some extent this is understandable because the Census is dealing with groups of states; its regions are groups-of-states regions. This being so, it has to lump in all the agricultural parts, and in doing this achieves averages of population density and occupational structure that do make the east north-central area distinct from the north-eastern one.

Had it taken out the manufacturing area (and those areas devoted mainly to forestry and mining which might be considered to be intimately connected with the manufacturing belt—providing it with fuel and industrial raw materials), then it would have found a zone with conditions very like those prevailing in West Pennsylvania, northern New York, and New England, but different from those in the Wisconsin–Ohio dairy region, the Iowa–Indiana Corn Belt, or the wheat areas in North Dakota and in Nebraska. Consequently, the writer here proposes to treat the Cleveland–Detroit–Chicago strip as part of the northern and north-eastern industrial region, regarding it as a western counterpart, albeit not as yet so fully developed, of the Boston–New York–Philadelphia string found in the east. However, certain aspects of it will also be included in a description of the Mid-West.

The Lakeshore plain is given remarkable physical unity by the history of development of the Great Lakes, leaving stranded to the south of the present shore a series of great lacustrine flats intimately connected with each other by old melt-water channels. From western New York these lacustrine flats link up the glacial terraces of the Finger lakes with the Lake Warren shore-line, south of Lake Erie. This shore-line passes west to the Lake Whittlesey and Lake Maumee shores and the great flat south-west of Toledo. Both those lakes had wide extensions west of Detroit up what is now the Lake St Clair region. Lake Warren broadened out more than the earlier ones into Lake Saginaw, and from this the waters passed by the channel of the Grand to Lake Chicago. This spread as far north as Green Bay and left its old beaches and beach platforms behind both Chicago and Milwaukee. Thus all the way from Syracuse to Milwaukee is a unique flowing-together of lines and levels which has been a major factor in linking these cities and intervening sites in a triple band of water, road, and rail connexions, and also in

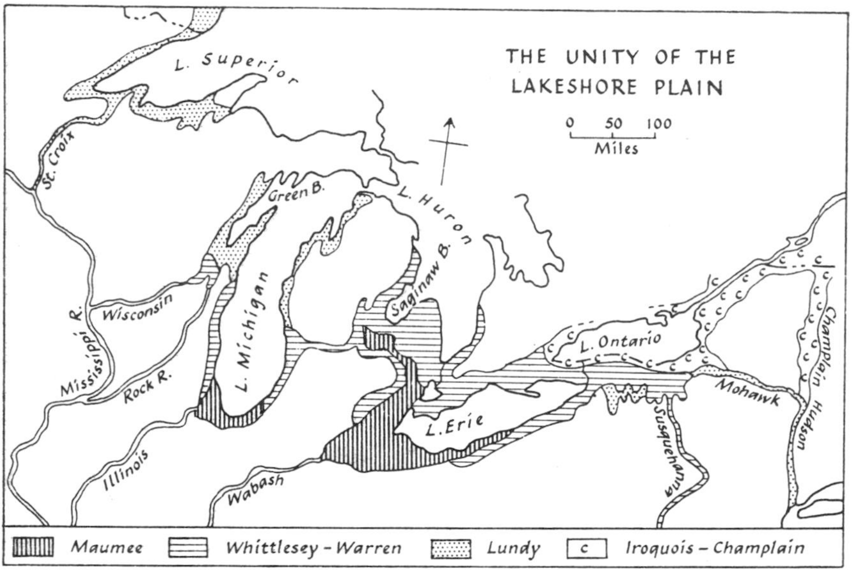

FIG. 164 The unity of the Lakeshore plain, a legacy of the Ice Age. This unity is based on former glacial lakes, many of which overlapped their earlier counterparts, and also on glacial melt-water channels. Such physical bonds have done much to link up the shore-line terraces of the Great Lakes.

giving them similar kinds of opportunities for factory expansion and urban growth (Fig. 164).

Not only is this string of local sites very favourable; the general setting is as well. Conditions for industry could hardly be more ideal. There is a large market to serve; a highly productive and varied agriculture from which to draw raw materials; huge quantities of iron in the north-west and coal in the south and south-east; excellent waterways to transport bulky goods like iron, coal, wheat, corn, on the Ohio–Mississippi and the Great Lakes systems; a dense network of railways and highways built, without interruptions, across the flat plain; a large and industrious immigrant population; a stimulating and healthy climate; and a 'go-ahead' tradition. The region now produces more than a third of the United States manufactures.

Industry developed where canals and lakes connected with each other, as at Buffalo, Cleveland, Toledo and Detroit, and then where railways debouched on lakes, as at Chicago. There were centres off the lakeshore, but it was the lake ports, on a very cheap transportation route, having close connexions with the North-east States by the Mohawk valley, lying between the chief iron and coal fields of the continent, and possessing ample land for expansion, that forged ahead. They now dominate the industrial picture. They extend the New York-to-Buffalo axis, through Cleveland and Detroit, to Chicago; making it the main axis of the American manufacturing belt.

The Lake cities, from Milwaukee to Erie, produce 75 per cent of the agricultural implements, 70 per cent of the motor vehicles, and 40 per cent of the iron and steel of the United States. These figures reflect the highly mechanized farming, lumbering, and mining of the region; the wide spaces, laced with automobile roads; and the need for steel rails, bridges, quays, warehouses, and machines of all kinds, in a market stretching between the Appalachians and the Rockies.

Cleveland (2,080,000) was one of the first steel centres in the region. It is the point on the iron-coal trade route of the Great Lakes where coal goes upstream and iron comes down. It gets coal cheaper than Chicago and iron cheaper than Pittsburgh. It has a fine local site where the Cuyahoga makes a quiet estuary between spreading deltaic flats. There is a large outer harbour on the lakes, protected by a long L-shaped mole, where goods are transhipped. An inner harbour, on the sandy flats by the river mouth, is the site for the chief industries. There has been ample room for the city to expand southward, over old glacial-lake terraces. Various steel-using industries have grown up. Cleveland is the second machine-tool city of the United States; it has a large automobile industry; it makes electro-metallurgical equipment; and has large oil refineries. The oil is pumped from Indiana, Illinois, and even Oklahoma.

Detroit and the Detroit district (4,200,000) is still more busy. It is the hub of the automobile industry, able to assemble steel parts from Chicago or Cleveland, to turn them into motors and then to distribute the cars and trucks either west to the Pacific or east to the Atlantic. The position is ideal, about half-way on the Great Lakes, with the markets of Central and of North-eastern America about equally available. Detroit is the centre of two outer rings of satellite towns, all manufacturing cars, car parts, car furnishings, or car accessories. Altogether, about 790,000 people are directly employed in the production of motor vehicles; and the value of their product is higher than that of any other major industry. Detroit manufactures machine tools, radios, refrigerators, marine engines, and aeroplanes as well as cars.

This remarkable development has been due very largely to a few outstanding individuals like Ford and Olds. But while people stress their genius mainly in terms of inventiveness and organization, that genius expressed itself, too, in the choice of an ideal industrial location. Detroit, which was a small French trading post and fort from 1701 to 1760, and then a British outpost until 1796 (used to rally Indians on the British side), really began to grow with the opening of the American West. When lake steamers appeared on Lake Erie in 1818 and the Erie Canal was completed in 1825, linking Lake Erie with the Mohawk–Hudson route, the town exploded into life. Amongst other things it began to build boats and marine engines, and so developed a flair for engineering that was most important.

The canal had a direct effect upon Detroit. It deflected

> the immigrant stream from the Ohio Valley to the Great Lakes. Passengers from the east, on reaching Buffalo, sought passage on lake steamers, particularly when a packet line opened regular service between Buffalo and Detroit. Deck passage cost only about $3.00, allowing a traveller to secure fairly comfortable transportation from Massachusetts to Michigan for less than $10.00. Detroit felt the impact from 1831 as lake steamers deposited the first immigrants at its docks. 'Almost every building that can be made to answer to a shelter is occupied and filled', the local newspaper reported that summer. More were hastily thrown together, and the sleepy little frontier village rapidly emerged as a new metropolis. By 1836 it boasted 10,000 inhabitants, a theatre, a museum, a public garden, schools, churches, a library, a lyceum, a historical society, a ladies' seminary, a water and sewage system, and street lights of such efficiency that—if the city's newspaper can be believed—only a few more were needed to produce total darkness.[1]

But Detroit was not the end; it was a new beginning. From it the Chicago and Territorial roads fanned out to the west. These were coach roads. Detroit built the coaches. And that old tradition, with the skills that went with it, was one of the factors in the rise of the motor-car business, started in 1899.

Detroit grew up at the narrowest point of the strait (d'étroit) between Lake Erie and Lake St Clair, clear of the low islands dividing the channel above and below. While its early significance lay in the short crossing from Canada, its later growth depended on the deeper water on the downstream side of the bend which it commanded, and the broad plain behind. A good harbour and a spacious railway and road junction, it offered the framework for relatively easy and unimpeded industrial growth. From the city hall,

[1] Billington, *Westward Expansion*, pp. 302–4.

which lies between the two lakeshore railway and shipping terminals, 'grand' avenues radiate out cutting across a central rectilinear arrangement of streets. Although this does provide a number of open spaces at the intersection of oblique and lateral streets, it has added to the concentration at the centre and produced very heavy pressures on space from which the city has only been able to find relief by soaring up in a set of skyscrapers. Part of the shipping has been removed from the central waterfront so as to ease the situation and the area affected has been turned into an attractive civic centre. The huge Ford plant is on the formerly unused, rather marshy flats of the River Rouge that flows through the west part of the city. The factory employs over 90,000 men. The great Dodge plant used to be on the outskirts of the city, in the north-east, but now the city has swept around it. The Hudson and Chrysler plants are at the northern end of the strait, where it broadens out and is flanked by very low, extensive flats. Detroit is thus rather unusual in that it has no definite factory district.

> The population of Detroit is highly cosmopolitan. During the twentieth century the city has been the gathering ground for many of the European people who have migrated to the United States. One quarter of the city's population is foreign born, and almost another third of its people are children of foreign or mixed foreign-and-native parentage. Newcomers have tended to settle by nationality groups,[1]

so that there is very much a mosaic of foreign communities. Detroit has also attracted a large negro element, making up two-fifths of the population.

Toledo (547,000) is the largest of the satellite cities associated with Detroit. It has the largest harbour on the Great Lakes, where the Maumee river flows into Lake Erie. It is a most important coaling port, exporting coal from Ohio, West Virginia, and Kentucky. At the same time, it manufactures steel, automobiles, auto accessories, and railway equipment. Toledo was an early canal port, connecting the Great Lakes with the Ohio, and a rail staging point for Chicago. The territory to the west of it, particularly in the low area at the head of the Maumee and the Wabash that once carried vast amounts of glacial melt-water, tended to be swampy, and was long avoided. The Black Swamp of north-east Indiana got a black name until after the canals were driven through when it was realized that most of it was not in fact swamp, and that, with adequate drainage, it could be made quite fertile.

In the meantime, however, settlement had spread north-westward into Michigan, swinging round first to Saginaw Bay, in the 1830s, and then to the Grand river in the 'forties. The town of **Grand Rapids** (400,000) grew up at the barrier of that name where an 18-foot fall in the river gave substantial

---

[1] Kohn, C. F., 'Detroit', in Mayer and Philbrick, *Industrial Cities Excursion*, p. 69.

amounts of power for saw mills and grist mills. The countryside throughout this middle part of Michigan is made up of moraine after moraine and has been and still is heavily wooded, with a mixed hardwood and softwood forest. Grand Rapids soon became a centre for lumber products, including ready-made house parts such as doors, window frames, and tongued-and-grooved clapboard. Then it branched out into furniture-making in general and now supplies automobile parts. Westward, at the end of the road, the port of Grand Haven was developed to ship goods out to Lake Michigan industrial towns, which were vast consumers of lumber.

Most of the Michigan peninsula, with a few exceptions such as on the old 'prairie rondes' of the Kalamazoo valley, and the lacustrine flats of Saginaw Bay, is rough morainic land best suited to lumbering. North of Saginaw, the sides of the whole peninsula are marked by wide belts of high dunes, whipped up from the old glacial beaches by the strong northerly winds sucked into the rear of passing cyclones. These are virtually useless for agriculture and were denominated 'barrens' by the early settlers. But what were barrens to homesteaders were wealth to lumbermen, since great pine forests had everywhere colonized the dunes. The lumber boom did much to colonize North Michigan.

> Lumbermen swarmed into the country during the latter half of the nineteenth century, attracted by some of the finest pine forests in North America. From Tawas City where the first saw mill was built in 1854, north to Alpena, about 12,000,000,000 board feet of timber were cut between 1866 and 1896. Each spring the Au Sable, the Thunder Bay, and other rivers of the region were filled with logs being driven to the saw mills. To the lake ports lumber boats came in the summer to carry the lumber away to help build the nation.[1]

In particular the lumber helped build up the cities of the American manufacturing belt, characterized as they are by millions of wooden (frame) houses and other buildings.

The best pine is now gone and today the Michigan dunelands along the lakeshore are noted principally for their cottage colonies, State camping parks, and holiday resorts which annually attract hundreds of thousands from the industrial belt of South Michigan.

Lumbering was succeeded by mining. There are several important mining regions which contribute greatly to the manufacturing zone to the south, and indeed to industrial cities from Chicago to Cleveland. Between Saginaw Bay and the Kalamazoo valley is the coal field at the heart of the Michigan basin: although the coal is not suited for metallurgical coke, it is used for

[1] Historical Society plaque at Tawas beach.

many other purposes, especially for making steam in steam-generated electrical-power stations. The power is widely used from Detroit to Grand Bend. Michigan is also very important as a main supply centre for limestone flux used in iron manufacture. (To make 1 ton of pig iron, 0·4 ton of limestone flux, 0·9 ton of coke, and 1·7 tons of iron ore are required.) Much of the northern rim of the structural basin that forms the Michigan peninsula is limestone, and at Rockport and Rogers City this stone is particularly suited for iron smelting. This small region supplies 27 per cent of the limestone flux devoured by America's huge iron and steel industry.

More important still are the mines of Minnesota, already described, where the ores from the great iron ranges of the Superior upland are extracted and shipped out from the big iron ports, such as Duluth-Superior, Marquette, and Escanaba.

Although the flow of iron from at least the northern ports has been through the Soo Canal into Lake Huron and so is rather more accessible to Detroit than Chicago, and although the calcite rock from Rogers City is certainly nearer to the former, and although good coking coal from West Pennsylvania and West Virginia is still nearer, nevertheless Detroit did not become the great iron and steel centre of the west. The Chicago region did, instead. Obviously, then, it was not so much nearness to iron, limestone, and coal that counted, as nearness to the huge opening market of the western-central lowlands of America. Chicago, not Detroit, was the real gateway to the opening up of the west, as it later became the hub of western progress. It therefore concentrated the basic industries needed by the west at the south-west end of Lake Michigan and, from them, developed a whole host of subsidiary industries, supplying consumer goods to the population between the Great Lakes and the Mississippi basins.

Chicago and the Chicago district (7,100,000) is, then, the unquestioned centre of the central States, and mainly for that reason has become the western spearhead of the American manufacturing region. Heavy industry is most important—iron and steel, transportation, agricultural machinery—but industries based on agricultural products are very valuable. Chicago has also many commercial and other interests. All combined, these have made it the largest city in the central United States.

It grew up as an Indian and then later Pioneer portage station on the low portage from the Chicago river, Lake Michigan and the north, to the Illinois river, the Mississippi and the south. Here water routes and land trails had long met, where the Great Lakes make their deepest thrust into the most fertile plain in the world. Later, Lake Michigan compelled all north, north-west, west, or east-going railways to loop round its end, making Chicago the focus of the railway era. These railroads converge from the Appalachian gaps and the Rocky passes. They bring to Chicago the products of mines and lumber camps from the Superior upland; wheat and cattle from the western plains; corn and hogs from the central plains; and oil and coal from the south and east. Chicago is thus the centre for the agriculture and mining of all the Central Lowlands and bordering regions. It also has a unique opportunity to distribute goods to the farms and mines.

Chicago is fortunate in its local site. To the east lies Lake Michigan, a boundless source of water for the water-avid industries of the shore. To the west, north, and south there stretches the flat, low, open plain which was once the beach platform and part of the bottom of glacial Lake Chicago. This gives complete ease of access of roads and railways, with virtually no slopes to climb, and only creeks to bridge; it provides very level land for the layout of plants, particularly of the horizontal integrated low-built factories of today, and also for the growth of commercial and residential areas; and, above all, it offers room for expansion, and so is ideal for the space-consuming steel mills, stock yards, oil refineries, and other industries, as it is for the sprawling suburbs eating back farther and farther into the country-side. The plain also affords good agricultural land—in the spaces left for agriculture, and dairy and truck farms in the neighbourhood help to supply Chicago's huge demand for milk, butter, eggs, and fresh vegetables (Fig. 165).

The town grew up on the south bank of the estuary of the Chicago river, in the lee of Fort Dearborn. The river provided a suitable harbour for early shipping. At the same time, it led back, over the glacial lake plain, to a low gap in the Valparaiso moraine used by the Chicago portage and roads west. The river soon divides into a north and a south fork, and it has been on the peninsula between the south fork (on the west), the estuary (on the north), and the lake (on the east) that downtown Chicago has developed.

This peninsula became more and more crowded as, first, the docks of the harbour pushed back up the estuary; next, the railway terminals came in along the lakeshore; and finally industry started to grow up the forks of the river. Chicago grew into a crowded city, in spite of the roominess of the surrounding plain. As a result, building became more and more dense and at the so-called 'Loop', where public transportation from all parts came in and then went out again, a close-packed area of massive skyscraper offices, shops, and hotels has emerged. Here lake-front streets, flanked by magnificent department stores, cross riverside ones, lined with great business offices and markets: this junction is without doubt one of the busiest in the world. Very high land values have led to a maximum use of space. Only one per cent of Chicago's area, the central business district represents 14 per cent of the work force. Over 1 million people make the trip into the city centre daily. Altogether, Chicago business accounts for 55,000 concerns, employing nearly $\frac{3}{4}$ million workers, or 40 per cent of the city's jobs.[1]

[1] Chicago, Basic Policies for the City Comprehensive Plan, 1965, p. 36.

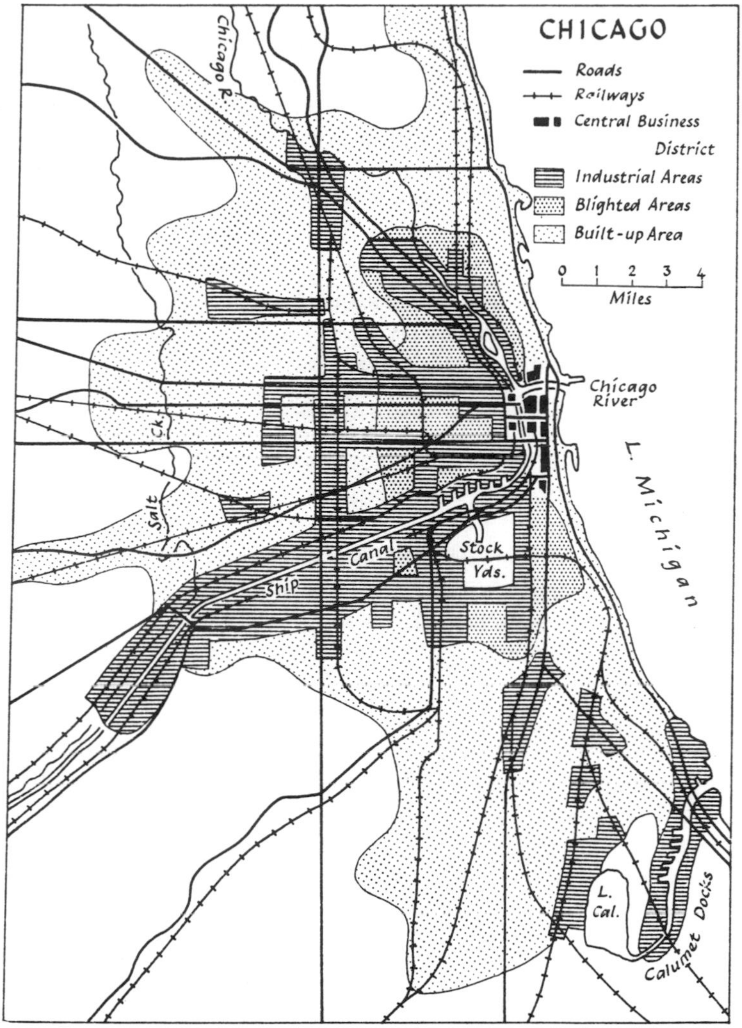

FIG. 165 The pattern of Chicago evolves from the sweep of the lakeshore and the two arms of bifurcated Chicago river. However, easy access over an open plain led to highly competitive rail and road development, and this competition itself has been a main factor in the build of the city. It has produced a great concentration of business and industry at the centre, which has in turn blighted much of the older residential parts of the city.

People have been squeezed out of the downtown area, which showed mid-century decreases of up to 18 per cent, compared with increases in population of 35 per cent ten miles or more from the city hub.

The excessive crowding of business at the centre has been aided by the way in which main roads and railways converge upon it. Although there is a rectangular street pattern, which as Mayer points out was 'based on the rectangular township and range system of land survey used throughout the Middle West', so that 'the entire urban framework was surveyed at once and in advance',[1] folk did not keep to the grid-iron pattern but ran roads across the grid, especially along the lakeshore front and down the south-west and north-west arms of the Chicago river: these came in like the spokes of a wheel to make the Loop a veritable hub for a great arc of developments. Railways made matters worse, by trying to run their lines to great terminals next to the central business district itself.

Chicago has overcome the downtown problem only at great cost. It has more or less abandoned its once thriving and valuable docks. The Navy Yard is still there, but the port facilities have been removed from the lower river to Calumet Harbour, to the south, which is now the main terminal for the Great Lakes or the St Lawrence seaway traffic. 'On the verge of a transformation from being the major inland port of the North American continent to becoming a major world port,'[1] it can no longer rely on the use of the narrow estuary of the Chicago river as a harbour. The old harbour has been replaced, on the outer pier, by the University of Illinois, and up the river by two-tiered roads such as Wacker Drive and 'bird-cage' multi-level parking buildings, to help the traffic through the city centre. A number of the railway stations have been put underground, and huge parking lots or great buildings erected above them. Thus above the Chicago and North-western Railway station has been built the monumental Merchandise Mart of Chicago, with no less than 63,000,000 sq. feet of floor space, devoted mainly to advertisers' showrooms, and wholesalers' stock and order rooms. The Illinois Central and the Michigan Central Railway stations and sidings occupy about seven miles of the original lake front. Part of the latter has been built over, mainly by the immense Prudential skyscraper but also by parking facilities. In the same way Chicago Union station has been largely built over by the lofty offices and extensive plant of the *Chicago Daily News.* Space has also been provided by extending out the shore; and east of the railway tracks a large area has been filled in, over a four-mile stretch, which is used in part for huge parking lots, and in part for lovely lakeside parks, graced by fine public buildings.

The old industrial areas above the forks are still much in evidence with their huge gasometers and tall old-style mills, but they are no longer actively

[1] Mayer, H. M., *The Port of Chicago and the St Lawrence Seaway*, Chicago, 1957, p. 1.

growing into the city centre; pressure has been relieved by the development of new industrial areas on the outskirts and, more particularly, in the Calumet district. Here are the main iron and steel plants and modern space-consuming industries, making railway rolling stock, lake steamers, machines, and chemicals. Here are immense railway freight yards, timber yards, oil depots, and grain elevators. The Chicago Ship Canal has also been an area of industrial development. In the east, fairly near the commercial core, are the canal docks; the Chicago Produce Terminal lies to the west —the great market for fruits and vegetables; and the Union Stock Yards spread their immense grid of pens to the south. Many canning and meat-packing plants have developed in the neighbourhood, while south-west is the tremendous factory of the International Harvester Company and other agricultural machinery plants.

Between the industrial areas along the north and south forks, by the canal, at the Calumet district, and in the central business district is the main mass of working-class homes in Chicago. These are chiefly tall tenements and triplexes, tightly packed together. Close to the commercial sections, they have been blighted by commercial invasion and give rise to a zone in deterioration marked by red-light districts and vice areas (see 'Blighted Areas' in Fig. 165). A veritable shatter belt has arisen, between expanding industrial and business areas, which has some of the most unstable social conditions in America. These slum-ridden areas stand out in marked contrast to Chicago's 'Gold Coast', the lakeshore residential districts with their magnificent luxury apartments and private hotels surrounded by private gardens and overlooking lakeshore parks. This close juxtaposition of the Gold Coast and the Slum is very typical of the rapidly expanding industrial cities of the American manufacturing belt, where groups at very different economic levels have segregated themselves out, yet lie cheek by jowl in their competition for the amenities of downtown life.

Also typical is the way in which minority groups segregate out, usually in terms of newness of arrival into the community. Chicago's Near West side (between the old industrial zone of the river, and the marts and yards of the canal, together with several freight terminals) is a good example.

> Immigrant groups, differing radically in culture and economic status, have moved out along axial lines (through this area—as through the Near South, and Near North sides), displacing other groups, who in turn have continued this outward trend. The Near West side was settled first by the Bohemians (Czechs), but when the Jews began to crowd into the area after the Chicago fire the original occupants, accustomed to spacious surroundings, forsook the region for more desirable quarters. With the egress of the Czechs went also the Irish, who had occupied a portion of

the area. But the Jewish residents had hardly become firmly entrenched in their new homes when the Italian invasion came. Between 1910 and 1918 more than half of the Jewish population, their security and status threatened by the ingress of a people with a different cultural background (South European—Catholic) and a lower standard of living, moved to other parts of the city. The influx of hordes of Negroes into the area proved an added stimulus to the Jewish exodus. A considerable portion of the area that was once in the heart of the ghetto has become the Black Belt of Chicago.[1] Today there are nearly a million negroes in the metropolitan region. They make up over a quarter of the city proper.

This outward push of older by newer in-comers, paralleled by an outward move of upper-class native-born people, has led to an ever wider growth of the urban area, with an astonishing proliferation of suburbs and satellite towns—a growth accelerated and widened by the addition of new industrial estates all around the urban fringe. Chicago has thus declined in itself but expanded as the centre of ring upon far ring of satellite cities. Indeed, a whole urban-industrial complex has here been built up, reaching from Michigan City in the south-east to Milwaukee in the north-west.

CONCLUSION

The East North-central and North-eastern States of the United States are the most dynamic and developed parts of an extremely dynamic and highly developed country. Though only about a fifth of the total area, they are responsible for three-quarters of the industry and two-thirds of the business. This represents an extraordinary lead over the rest of the nation. It is due in part to early social conditions concentrating trade and finance in New England and the Mid-Atlantic States, and in part to geographical advantages such as a highly indented coast leading back through the Hudson–Mohawk gap to the Great Lakes, along with unusually large deposits of coal and iron and other resources.

Primary production and the rural way of life began to be displaced towards the end of last century and have now been far surpassed by trade and industry, by services of various kinds and by the greatest development of city life, and especially of great city life, in the continent. The enormous range of industry and the almost unbounded opportunity it has offered has led to prolonged and continuing immigration into the region of European capitalists, managers, foremen, workmen, artisans, and professional people

[1] Gist, N. P., and Halbert, L. A., *Urban Society*, New York, 1946, pp. 185, 190.

of all nationalities. A very cosmopolitan society has emerged, made still more varied by the mass migration of negroes from the south.

This multifarious, polyglot, competitive, creative, free, progressive population has grown to such power that it has the highest standard of living in the country, measured particularly by the mass enjoyment of urban amenities and has set the standard for the nation in business and industry, education, religion, and culture, starting most of the great movements and carrying them to fruition. This is the true heartland, the core, the pivot area of the country: indeed, it is one of the most influential regions in the world, with effects reaching far beyond the United States.

CHAPTER TWENTY

The American Mid-West

The American Mid-West lies between the Appalachians and the High Plains, between the Canadian Shield and the Ozark plateau. This region is the heartland of the country. It stretches from the deciduous forests of the east to the semi-arid grasslands of the west; from the sub-tropical climate of the middle Mississippi to the cool-temperate one of the Superior Upland. Its vast area, flat extent, varied climate, and fertile soils have made it the chief agricultural region of the United States. At the same time its central location, good natural communications, and abundance of fuels have given it great commercial and industrial opportunities. This combination of agricultural and industrial riches has made it a chief goal of migration, and the population is very mixed. From the days of Horace Greeley's *Go West, Young Man*, it has drawn people from New England, the Mid-Atlantic and the Southern States. They have co-operated together in developing a new identity—that of the Mid-westerner. European immigrants have also streamed into the region from every part of Europe. It is America's chief melting-pot.

Consequently there has been established a reputation of being free from tradition, of doing new things in a new way, and, if possible, in a bigger and better way. The bigness of the region, its sweeping horizons, the long rivers, the striding railways, the tireless roads, have all produced a sense of the limitless, a belief in the ultimate, which is characteristic of the Mid-West. From the Civil War on, it has been the region of opportunity, of big undertakings, of large-scale farming, and large-scale industry. Furthermore, everything in the region is so well integrated—drawn together by river and rail, by the balance of agriculture and manufacturing, that people recognize a common interest in each other. This has helped to develop 'regional consciousness', the feeling that here is a region less trammelled than the east, freer than the south, and at the same time more mature and settled than the farther west (see Fig. 153, Chapter 18, Major Regions of the U.S.A.).

THE PHYSICAL ENVIRONMENT

The outstanding physical elements of the region are its central location, great size, remarkable openness, integrated drainage, a climate of bold dontrasts, and fertile soils: dominance, magnitude, freeness, unity, challenge, productivity—the main elements of America. As Garland has pointed out, 'The interior of no other continent possesses a combination of natural resources so favourable to human utilization as North America.'[1] Latin America has the great plain of the Amazon at its centre, but the plain is scarcely used because of its hot debilitating climate; in the same way Africa has the jungles of the Congo at its core. The heart of Australia is a desert, and of Asia a whole series of deserts separated by knots of high mountains. Only Europe has anything at all approaching a usable central plain, yet the Great North Plain of Europe is really not central, but, decidedly excentric, favours the eastern part of the continent. America alone has a wide, well-watered, undivided, stimulating, and lucrative lowland at its very heart.

The relief of the Mid-West is made up essentially of the Central Lowland, together with bordering plateaux or high plains. The Central Lowland is floored for the most part by palaeozoic strata sloping gently away from the Shield and the Appalachians. These are not entirely flat, for they swell up into broad anticlines, like the Cincinnati anticline, with shallow basins on their flanks. These structures are responsible for the huge oil and coal fields which are tapped and developed on the flanks of the anticlines or around the edges of the basins. Westward, the lowland rises to the Great Plains, consisting chiefly of mesozoic rocks, which extend in a series of fairly flat but elevated strata, often capped by resistant scarp-forming beds. The Great Plains are distinctly higher than the Central Lowlands, and are sometimes spoken of as the Missouri plateau. The Missouri–Mississippi–Ohio network of rivers helps to give the two sub-regions an essential unity.

The Central Lowlands slope northward to the Shield and southward to the Ozarks. The Canadian Shield extends into the United States around western Lake Superior. It is a low, glaciated plateau, rich in forests, water, copper, and iron. The Ozarks are also forested and have deposits of lead and bauxite. Mainly a plateau, they rise to a moderately high ridge in the Boston mountains.

The main feature of the Central Lowland is its division into a glaciated and an unglaciated section. The northern half is glaciated with the exception of the Wisconsin drift-free area (a dissected plateau with caps of limestone making spectacular features above sandstone slopes). The drift area extends as far as the Ohio, dominating surface relief. It does, however, have minor differences. The youthful Wisconsin drift covers the Great Lakes region with a thick uneven mantle of boulder clay, and has left behind well-marked moraines. Specially important features are the flat lake-bottom terraces formed by different glacial Great Lakes at the different levels of their development. These levels are edged by sandy or gravelly beaches. The drift area west of the Superior upland has similar well-marked moraines, and

[1] Garland, J. H. (ed.), *The North American Mid-West*, New York, 1955, p. 3.

encloses glacial-lake plains such as those of Minnesota and Agassiz. The older drift areas lying farther south do not have as thick a glacial mantle, and they are flatter, with lower ridges. They are without any large glacial-lake plains or beach features. The glacial mantle wears very thin, west of the Mississippi, where dissected till plains occur (see Fig. 3, Chapter 1).

In the extreme south, along the Ohio, and in the Osage plains, are areas beyond the reach of the ice, where river erosion has created dissected sandstone and limestone plains. These merge into the Gulf coastal plain in the middle Mississippi, under alluvial deposits of a wide meander belt.

The differences between unglaciated and glaciated lowlands, and between old and recent glacial till-plains, are the chief surface features of the Central Lowlands, and give them considerable variety. Much greater variety is provided by local differences in climate, soil, and natural vegetation.

The climate of the region, taken as a whole, is an Interior warm humid type, with hot summers, but cold winters. It is essentially a continental climate, distinct from the maritime types of the North-eastern and Southern States. It is a climate of extremes. In the winter it comes under the sweeping influence of the polar continental air mass, when great waves of cold air spread southward from the Shield to the Ozarks. Temperatures fall below freezing. The weather is stimulating and generally bright and dry, although snow storms do occur, especially with the sweep of depressions developed in the lee of the Rockies (Fig. 166). With spring, the Gulf air mass moves north, in swift advance after the retreating polar airs. Conflicts rage between the two air masses. Lows are numerous. Cyclonic rain falls over wide areas. In early summer the Gulf air is predominant. The land heats up. Heavy thunder-shower rains occur, interspersed with cyclones. By late summer the humidity falls. There is clear, sunny weather. Then the polar airs advance once more. Squalls fly. They soon change to flurries of snow as winter approaches.

Thus throughout most of the plains the rainiest month is in early summer. Late summers are sunny and fine. However, precipitation occurs in all seasons; and the annual rainfall (15 to 50 inches) is that of a sub-humid to humid climate. The wetter parts are to the east, in the Mississippi–Ohio–Great Lakes area, since the lows tend to converge on the Ohio and Lower Great Lakes, as they move eastward across the continent. The western parts, particularly on the Great Plains, can be invaded by drought.

The frost-free season varies considerably. In the areas bordering on the Ozarks and Appalachians it is 200 days. From the middle Missouri valley to the southern parts of the Great Lakes it is 175 days; while in the north-west it is less than 150 days. The Mississippi–Ohio–Great Lakes are more favoured than the western high plains. However, it is fortunate that in these western regions there is a higher proportion of early summer rain, which makes the short growing season a very active one.

53. Strip-farming in the Spring Wheat belt in Montana. The immensity of the flat, open prairie has been brought under cultivation, with strips of wheat and strips of fallow to help conserve moisture and prevent wind erosion.

The Agricultural Midwest

54. The Corn belt has big farms, set in trees, with square fields of corn, rotated with small grains and hay. Rows of corn storage bins are being loaded with mechanical syphon. A great deal of machinery is needed on these highly commercialized farms.

The American West—Ranching and Irrigation

55. Ranching is the main use of much of the short-grass prairie of the high plains and intermont basins of the west. Many ranches now find a more lucrative return from the oil found beneath the surface.

56. An irrigation scheme near Weslaco in the Rio Grande valley, Texas, has turned poor grazing land into rich orchard land, raising citrus fruit. Alfalfa is also raised for near-by ranches.

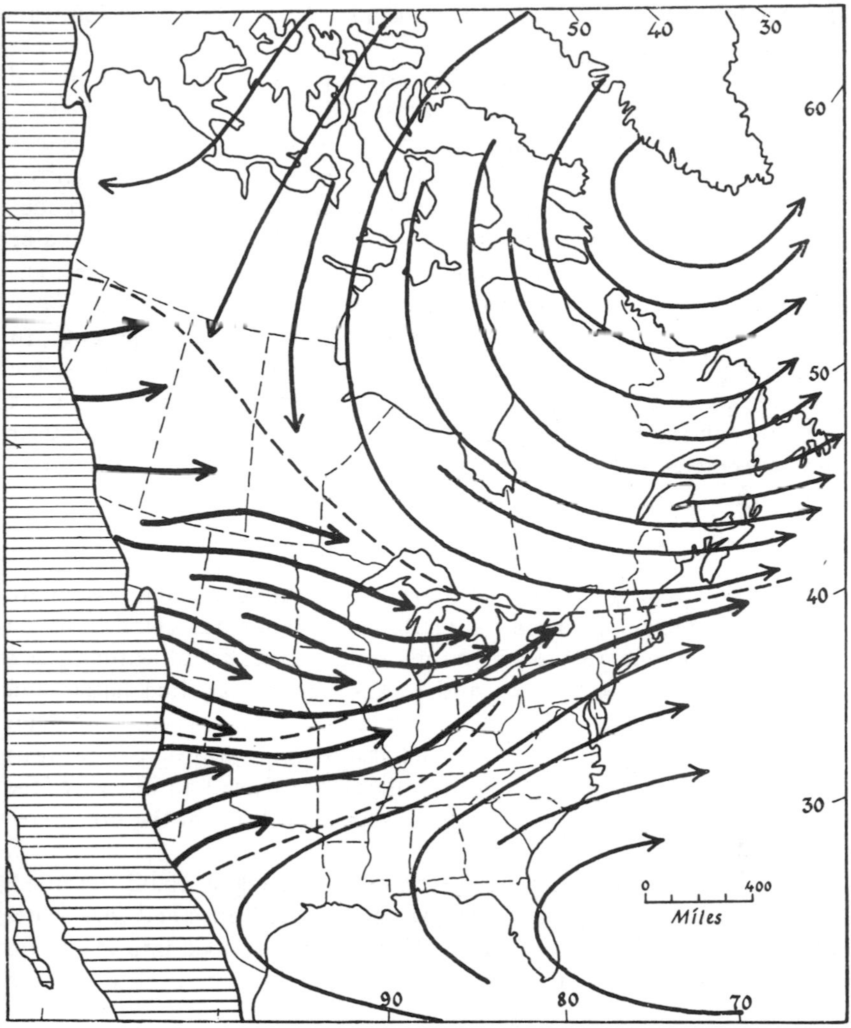

FIG. 166 Mid-West Climate: the Chief Streams of Air. The region is a zone of conflict between Polar continental air streams out of the north, lee depressions sweeping east from the Rockies, and Tropical maritime streams of air from the south. (After Borchert.)

Thus, broadly speaking, there is an east–west division in rainfall and a north-east to south-west division in temperature. In the south-west the Osage plains have a sub-humid, long growing season; in the south-east the middle Mississippi–Ohio plains have a humid, long growing season; in the western prairies of Kansas and the Dakotas there is a sub-humid climate with a medium to a short growing season; while in the sector between, from the lower Missouri to the Great Lakes, is a moderately humid region with a moderately long growing season.

There is the same south–north and east–west division in soils, only the soil regions are rather more diverse, because differences in parent matter, drainage, and vegetation are also taken into account. There is a general progression from warm red-yellow earths in the south to cool podsolized soils in the north, and from humid grey-brown earths in the east to sub-humid black earths and even semi-arid brown soils in the west. A major difference is between the rather thin soils of the unglaciated areas as compared with the deeper ones on the drift plains. Vegetation shows the same change from a warmth-loving oak-chestnut-hickory forest in the south, to a beech-maple-birch forest in the cooler north. Still farther north on the Superior Upland is a spruce-pine forest. The vegetation changes also from the humid oak and beech forests of the east to the central prairies, with their mat of tall grasses, and the edge of the western prairies, where the Short Grass range begins.

THE HUMAN RESPONSE

The Mid-West proved tremendously attractive to Americans once they were free to move into it and begin its development. It was sufficiently like the east with its cyclonic weather, its humid soils, and its broad-leaved forests to give a sense of the familiar and to allow many acquired habits and techniques to be maintained; on the other hand, it was sufficiently different, with its huge rivers, broad prairies, and vast horizons to inspire new ideas and awaken again the pioneer spirit with all the drive and initiative, the inventiveness, freedom, and individuality that had brought the first Europeans to the country's shores.

Four things had to be done, however, before the region could be settled. The Indians had to be pacified, or driven out. Territories and then states had to be set up. The land had to be surveyed and divided into townships and lots. And roads, canals, and later railways had to be pushed through the forests, over the rivers, and across the prairies.

The Indians proved a very real problem. They were more aware of the white man's aims, more suspicious of his practices, more disillusioned about his agreements, and better armed against his incursions than the Indians had been who had met the original settlers on the Atlantic shore. The only thing they had not learned from the bitter lessons of the past was greater unity among themselves. The Americans soon realized this and by a masterly application of the old imperial art of 'Divide and Rule', they ultimately got the upper hand, and harried the tribes one by one across the Mississippi and into the deserts and mountains.

The main Indian barriers to white settlement were in the Old North-west, across the Ohio, and between it and Lake Erie; and in the south, around the southern flank of the Appalachians, between those mountains and the border of Spanish Florida. The Indians in the Mohawk valley did not prove to be a great difficulty. Most of them had remained loyal to the British and had been given a substantial reservation in the Grand River basin of Ontario after their unsuccessful attempt to hold the Americans back during the American Revolution. Only a remnant was left in their original home, and with these a treaty was soon made. However, powerful tribes lay farther west in the plains of Lake Erie and of the Maumee, Miami, Wabash, and Illinois rivers: these included the Chippewa, Ottawans, Delaware, Wyandot, Miami, and the Shawnee. They straddled the main route from the Hudson–Mohawk, and also from the Ohio to the Great Lakes, and thus denied the Lakeshore plain and some of the best bottomlands of the Ohio and Mississippi tributaries to pioneer development. They themselves remained either ignorant of or indifferent to the rich possibilities of such fertile tracts, but the pioneers, having long struggled with the Catskill and Allegheny plateaux, looked with envy on those lands about which doughty frontiersmen had brought back such glowing reports.

It was the age-old struggle, and one that the British were facing in Canada, in Africa, in Australia, and other parts: should forward-looking pioneers be held up, should civilization be impeded, because backward tribes refused to or could not develop the great potential in the lands they possessed but which they used in such a primitive way? Doubtless the tribesmen had the rights of prior possession; but who had the prior right to development: the native who kept only a handful of people alive at a very low standard of living in an extensive and wasteful economy, or the white man who could find a livelihood for millions—including the Indians—at a much higher standard of living by the most intensive, economic, and gainful occupation of the land? The settler assumed that there was only the one answer, and pushed on into Indian territory and started to cut down the forest, kill off the game, till the soil, raise crops, feed herds of cattle and flocks of sheep, erect mills and foundries, establish towns, and set up an organized and responsible government.

The United States proposed to secure the lands more obviously suitable for agriculture by a treaty of peace with the Indians.[1] A Committee on Indian Affairs was set up which was given the task among other things of 'establishing a boundary line of property for separating and dividing the settlements of the citizens from the Indian villages and hunting grounds, thereby extinguishing as far as possible all occasion for future animosities, disquiet, and contention'.[2] The boundary proposed was from the lower

---

[1] U.S.A., Papers of the Continental Congress, clxxxvi, p. 151.
[2] U.S., Com. on Indian Affairs, *Jour. Continental Congress*, xxv, p. 686.

Ohio river up the Great Miami and thence across to the Maumee and so down to the head of Lake Erie—giving the Americans everything between the Ohio and the Lower Great Lakes. In 1785 the Chippewa, Ottawans, Delaware, and Wyandot were induced at Fort McIntosh to surrender all their hunting lands east of the proposed line, except for one or two small reserves around their more settled communities. The Shawnee, however, refused to recognize the Fort McIntosh treaty. So did the settlers! Before any final settlement with the Indians could be made, restless, aggressive, and adventuresome frontiersmen and squatters, mostly from Kentucky and Virginia, slipped across the then frontier of the Ohio to stake out so-called 'tomahawk claims' in the best lands of the north-west. The government,

> alarmed lest this invasion arouse native resentment, instructed Colonel Josiah Harmar, who commanded the federal troops on the north-west frontier, to drive them out [i.e. the American illegal settlers] by any means necessary. This was done in the spring of 1785, but the commander of the force brought back discouraging news. He found several thousand 'banditti whose actions are a disgrace to human nature' squatting on the [Indian part of the] federal domain, well organized, with their own elected governor, and 'firm in the belief that every American had an undoubted right to pass into every vacant country, and there to form their constitution'.[1]

It would have been political suicide for a government whose chief officers had but recently drenched the continent in blood and shaken the civilized world in the sacred name of liberty, to have restrained the liberty of their subjects to do a little blood-letting amongst a handful of savages in the remoteness of the wilderness! War was declared on the recalcitrant tribes, especially as the Iroquois had renounced their treaties, and small bands of Indians were making counter-raids against the colonists. General Clark was sent with two well-armed levies north from Kentucky into Miami territory on the Wabash and into the lands of the Shawnee across the Great Miami. Unfortunately, the militiamen mutinied after a long and unsuccessful march, and the expedition ended in ignominy. The Indians then repudiated the Fort McIntosh treaty, and maintained that the Ohio should be the frontier between the two peoples. In the meantime, however, the government had sent its surveyors out beyond the Ohio to mark off the public land for sale to settlers. Strong action was called for. The Indian commissioners were urged to make separate bargains with the weaker tribes 'at different times and places and to discourage every coalition'.[2] But though this did help to

[1] Billington, *Westward Expansion*, p. 210.
[2] U.S.A., *Jour. Continental Congress*, **xxvi**, p. 152.

divide and confuse some Indians, it only made the stronger nations more resentful. In 1790 General Harmar was sent against them, but suffered a humiliating defeat. Next year General St Clair was beaten still worse. 'Out of his two thousand, fifty came back uninjured.'[1] A really determined effort was then made under General Wayne which at length crushed the Indians in the north-west and, by the Treaty of Greenville, made in 1795, secured most of the Ohio country for white settlement. The area left to the Indians was the great Black Swamp of the Maumee, on the ill-drained flats of old glacial-lake Maumee, south-west of Toledo, land which the whites did not want, and did not look at for another generation.

The period was also a difficult one for pioneers in the south. Here the very broad mass of the Appalachians so separated them off from the east that they had very little protection, and were completely exposed to the machinations of the Spaniards and the hostility of the Indians. It is difficult for us today to understand just how isolated they were, but Spain realized this and played on it, especially when the pioneers became irritated by the slowness of Congress to support them against the Indians.

> When the war [of American Independence] closed, there were half a million settlers on the frontier, with the majority in the south. Although these communities were off-shoots of the older states, there was little if any sense of loyalty, either to the states or to Congress. The frontier was like a great floating island, temporarily moored alongside the United States, but free to cut loose and form new connections provided there was any advantage in doing so. Geographic and economic conditions explain this lack of close union between the older and newer sections. Because of the difficulties of transportation, it was easier for the farmers, even in western Pennsylvania, to send their produce to the east by way of the Ohio and Mississippi rivers to New Orleans (and then by sea to Philadelphia and New York), than directly across country. The people in Kentucky and Tennessee were even more completely dependent on the Mississippi. To make a living they had to sell goods, but these could only go in one direction. The pioneers needed the right of 'deposit' at the mouth of the river [in New Orleans, in Spanish America]; that is, the right to store goods there, without payment of duty, until shipping could be secured.
>
> In 1786, Spain closed the river to the pioneers, and denied the right of deposit. The purpose in doing this was to impress upon the minds of the frontiersmen how completely dependent they were upon the good will of Spain, and to emphasize the powerlessness of Congress to furnish any assistance. By this means in time the south-west might turn to Spain for

[1] Harlow, *The Growth of the United States*, p. 249.

> protection, and the United States would be pushed back to the Alleghenies, where Spain thought it should have been kept in 1783.
>
> At the same time, Spanish agents encouraged the Indians to make life so miserable for the settlers that, out of sheer desperation, they would finally turn to Spain for relief![1]

The Indians responded with a will and made it extremely difficult for the pioneers to advance. For fifty years they had been giving up here one part and there another of their domains to the English; now the Americans were threatening them. Tempers rose on both sides. Georgia was so incensed at what it took to be the pusillanimous attitude of Congress over acquiring Indian land—the government 'had promised that title to Indian lands should be extinguished as soon as it could be accomplished peacefully and on reasonable terms'[2]—it was almost ready to declare war on the United States so that it could have a war with the Indians, and drive them out. Treaties were forced on weaker tribes in western Georgia, Alabama, and Tennessee, but the pioneers out-ran the treaty makers, took the law into their own hands, and moved into Indian lands.

Congress simply had to support its settlers. Not to have done so would not merely have humiliated them before the Indians, but might have driven them into the arms of the Spaniards. In 1790 a great deal of pressure was put on the Creeks, and a land treaty signed with them. But the land thus gained only whetted the appetite of the settlers for more. It seems to be an axiom of political geography, as Ratzel claimed, that eating, far from satisfying hunger, begets it! The settlers were insatiable. Jackson, the hero of the south-west, crushed a revolt of the Creeks in 1813 on the Tombigbee and urged that the Indians be removed beyond the Mississippi. In 1817 he put this proposition to the Cherokee, promising them free transportation and supplies, but they elected to remain.

As the industrial revolution quickened its pace in England and the demand for American cotton began to rise, American cotton-growers started to demand the rich black 'prairies' to the west of them for the expansion of their plantations. These highly fertile soils were in the possession of the Choctaws and Creeks, who were making relatively little use of them. A clash of interests was inevitable. The cotton-growers would only be satisfied when the Indians were thrown back over the Mississippi; the Indians felt the time had come to stand firm for their homes.

'A more aggressive policy was needed and Monroe publicly endorsed removal [across the Mississippi] as a means of protecting red men from the evils of white civilization.' The Creeks finally agreed to go but the Cherokee

---

[1] Harlow, *The Growth of the United States*, p. 218.
[2] Clark, D. E., *The West in American History*, New York, 1937, p. 235.

held on. They were no nomads of the forest, but an agricultural folk who owned 22,000 cattle, 2,000 spinning wheels, 31 grist mills, 10 saw mills, 8 cotton gins, and 18 schools among their 15,000 people. Yet they were ordered to go. Although they appealed to the Supreme Court against the decision of Congress (the Removal Bill of 1830, authorizing the president to transfer any eastern tribe west of the Mississippi if it were in the national interest), the decision was allowed to stand. The new President, Jackson, had been put in by the frontiersmen and he put the frontier first. Indian power was broken and one by one the tribes were bullied or bribed into journeying west. The Alabama, Tennessee, and Kentucky plains or basins were free for white expansion.

Yet the story was not done. While white men were making the position of the Indian quite unbearable in the Old South-west, pioneers moved into new Indian areas in the farther North-west. The knowledge that there were rich lodes of lead in the hills of the Wisconsin drift-free area led to a swift northward push of miners and traders, followed by lumbermen and homesteaders. These quickly and rudely took over land in the territory of the Winnebago Indians. The Indians at once put forward their complaints. When these proved ineffectual they took matters into their own hands and killed several of the more isolated settlers. The Winnebago War was the result, in which the Indians were defeated, in 1827, and most of their land expropriated.

Five years later it was the turn of the Sauk and the Fox. Representatives of those tribes, 'said to have been intoxicated at the time', had signed a treaty at St Louis, ceding their lands between the Illinois and the Wisconsin rivers, but 'retaining the right to occupy the land until such time as the government decided to make it available for settlement'.[1] Again white pioneers moved much faster than their government and in 1830 'settlers without any legal right began to encroach on the Sauk and Fox lands along the Rock river, occupying their cornfields and plowing up their burying grounds. Black Hawk, their chief, made frequent protests to no effect. In the summer of 1831 he became more threatening and destroyed some of the fields and houses of the settlers. Thereupon there arose a great outcry and urgent demand for protection.'[1] The Black Hawk war followed, where again the Indians were defeated, gave up their lands, and promised to move west, only here they had to surrender a wide strip of land on the west bank of the Mississippi as well as on the east.

By 1840 it looked as though a new Indian frontier had been set up and acknowledged, running from Green Bay to the upper Mississippi and then down to the middle Missouri, the western Arkansas, and the border of Texas. East of this line 12,400 Indians had been given permission to stay in

[1] Ibid., pp. 231–2.

small, scattered native reserves, 40,000 were under agreement to migrate to the west, and 51,000 had already migrated. The power of the Indian was broken. Even as they moved, they knew that their new homes would again be invaded and that again they would be pushed out and on: as indeed happened. Pressure was eased only when the desert itself was reached!

State-making had, meantime, become an urgent issue in the Mid-West. The pioneers were civilized people used to municipal, county, and state government. They set up farms and mills, established towns, began to trade with each other, built churches, schools, and colleges. All these things required legal title to land, legal protection of transactions, legal recognition of powers: they demanded a formal system of government. Yet the federal government could scarcely give small handfuls of people the rights and privileges of the well-established states of the east. A compromise was made by which the public domain was divided into federal 'territories', and then, as these, or parts of them, became filled with people, they could be turned into 'states'.

But next the question arose as to how to divide the land into states. General Washington wanted what he called 'compact' states, based as much as possible on natural frontiers, which would make for an orderly movement of the frontier by the cell-like growth of one settled area along with or out of another. He was opposed to large, loosely organized, and sparsely settled areas becoming states. Sparse settlement, he pointed out, would allow for 'simultaneous attempts at settlement throughout the territory, to the detriment of law, good government, and the effective extension of federal aid'. In particular he wanted 'a realistic association of state-making with Indian cessions'.[1] Thus by the main weight of compactly settled areas America could wear down, deflect, or nullify Indian resistance and prevent that awkward interpenetration of white and red that was leading to such frustration on the part of the settlers and resentment on the Indians' part. It was for this reason Washington suggested a simple division of the north-west into a compact area south of Lake Erie and east of the Maumee–Great Miami which could well be handled by white development, and advised the use of these rivers as forming obvious, clearly understood boundaries.

However, the tide of immigration was rolling out over the west on a huge front, it had many salients and it was thinly spread. There were too many gateways through which it might spill, and too many channels down which it could flow, to be gathered together in compact forms of expansion. This lay in the very geography of the plain. It was a plain; it was open; it was undivided. Into it the whole land sloped from the Catskills to the Cumberland plateau; and down that great slope ran the Genesee and the Cuyahoga,

[1] Pattison, W. D., *American Rectangular Land Survey System, 1784–1800*, Chicago, 1957, p. 30.

the Sandusky and the Maumee, the Allegheny and the Ohio, the Kanawha and Kentucky, the Cumberland and the Tennessee, the Tombigbee, Warrier and Alabama, and all the other rivers between Lake Erie and the Gulf of Mexico, which were sluices for the white advance.

The geography of the east may well have been the geography of compactness; the geography of the west was the geography of amplitude—of the immense and beckoning and open plain.

Mid-West geography also made the idea of natural boundaries difficult to apply. There were no such boundaries, unless between drift-free and drift-covered terrain, or an oak-walnut as against an oak-maple forest, or yellow-red soils as distinct from grey-brown ones. But these differences were too gradual or too inconspicuous to act as state frontiers! Moreover, it would have been less defensible to have states confined to natural regions—with all their eggs in one basket, as it were, than to have them straddle several regions, where, though they might not be fitly bounded, they could at least benefit from a variety of conditions. The only conspicuous features on the plain were the rivers. But even if the major ones could be used, because their very size did in effect make them lines of division (although they were also highways of trade), the lesser ones were quite unsuitable; they too often formed the very axis round which a state was built, e.g. Kentucky, Tennessee, Illinois, Wisconsin.

Consequently, Jefferson's ideas began to be favoured, of artificial boundaries enclosing geometrical areas which, by being equally squared off, would on a plain as uniform as it was, provide for each state a more or less equal distribution of resources, and ensure a chance at equal wealth. The idea responded better to the environment; it was a clearer expression of the geography. Jefferson realized that for the west a western pattern had to be evolved. The vast plain stretched before him like a drawing-board; it called out to be squared off; and he was architect enough to enjoy this freedom. As a result he drew up plans that became basic to Mid-West development. His ordinance for the government of western territories, 1784, allowed for: (i) free adult males in any part of a federal territory to meet and form a temporary government, provided they adopted the laws of any one of the original states; (ii) establishment of a permanent government when the population rose to over 20,000 free inhabitants, but under a governor with the power of veto; (iii) the right to statehood when the population topped 60,000 adult free settlers.

The ordinance laid out the method of defining states. This should be:

> '(i) by parallels of latitude so that each State shall comprehend from north to south two degrees of latitude, and (ii) by meridians of longitude, one of which shall pass through the lowest point of the rapids of the Ohio, and

> the other through the western cape of the mouth of the Great Kanawha; but the territory eastward of this last meridian, between the Ohio, Lake Erie and Pennsylvania shall be one State whatsoever may be its comprehension of latitude.[1]

Thus allowing for the one exception of Ohio State, all the other western states were to be defined strictly by latitude and longitude.

However, this extremely regular layout—the draughtman's use of the drawing-board of the great interior plains—was not followed; it was not given a chance. Settlement had gone ahead of the state-maker and made its own mark. A compromise was struck between the two notions of state building. In general, lines of longitude and latitude were used, but they were often chosen to start off from pre-existing settlements on the major rivers, and so sections of river courses were included as parts of the state boundaries. Thus the Ohio, because of its historic importance as a frontier, remained a boundary, dividing off a northern central tier of states (Ohio, Indiana, Illinois) from a middle tier, Virginia (later West Virginia), Kentucky, and Tennessee. In the same way the Mississippi came to be used to divide off an eastern from a western-central group of states. None the less, most of the boundary-making in almost all the states followed parallels or meridians, to give a distinctly chequer-board effect to the west (Fig. 167).

Land division was even more geometrical. This was a distinct departure, since both in the south and in New England land divisions constantly reflected local variations in the trend of shores and rivers. Reference has already been made to the conflict between the southern 'warrant' system of individual and indiscriminate locations of land divisions, and the more methodical New England practice of regular surveys on a township basis drawn up prior to settlement. This was clearly brought out when the proposals for the west were being aired.

> It has been the custom of the Southern States [wrote Howell, a New Englander] to issue warrants from a land office. The person taking a warrant has to look for unlocated lands to cover with his warrant, of which he makes a return. In this way the good land is looked out and seized on first, and land of little value and of all shapes left in the hands of the public. In the Eastern [New England] States, as you all know, the custom has been to sell a township by bounds, or certain lots taken flush, good and bad together, and to pass out settlement in compact columns [of lots].[2]

Actually, the New England system, though more regular than the Southern one, was far from rigid. The tendency was for 'compact columns

[1] U.S.A., *Jour. Continental Congress*, xxvi, pp. 275–6.

[2] Quoted in Staples, W. R., *Rhode Island in the Continental Congress*, Providence, 1870, pp. 480–1

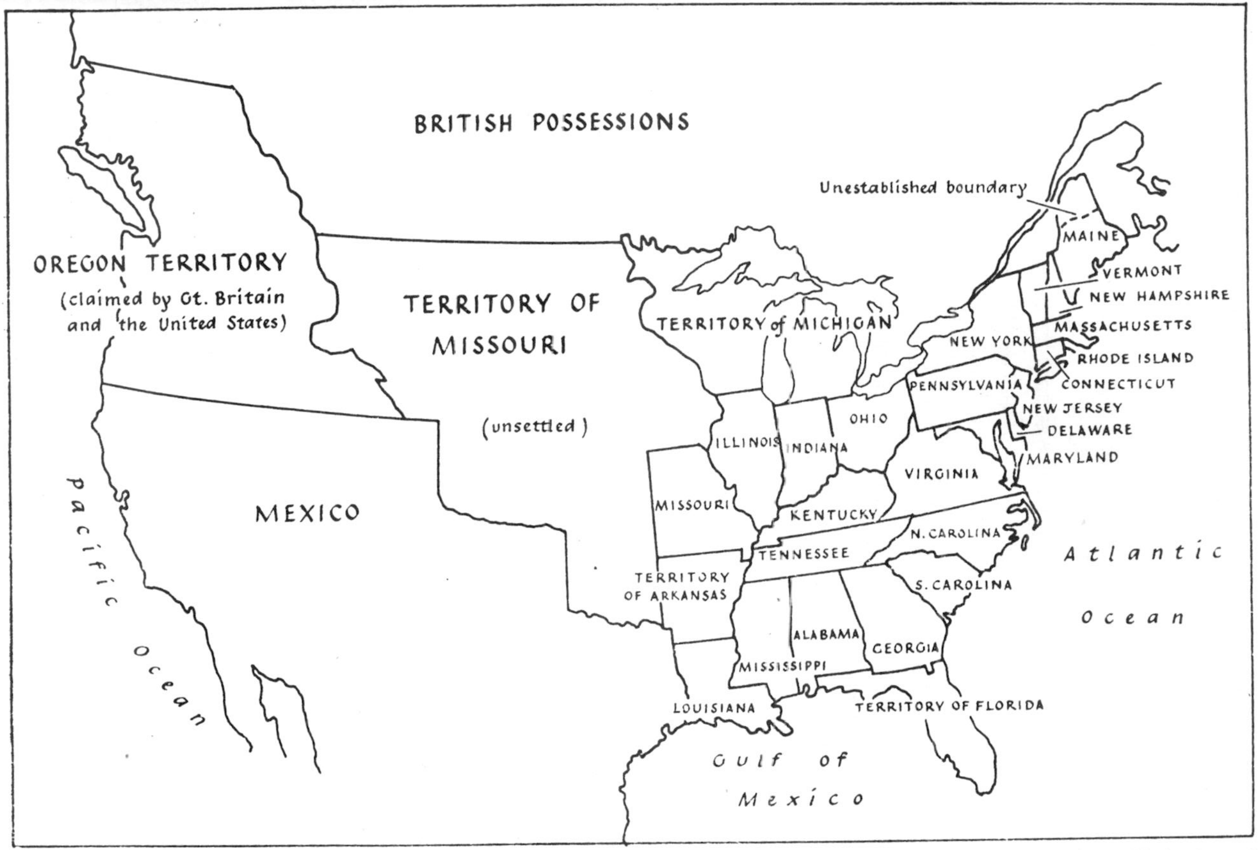

FIG. 167 State-making in the Mid-West, the creation of States and Territories up to 1829. Note the use of parallels of latitude and lines of longitude coupled with natural features such as great lakes, the chief rivers, and major divides. (Scale, 1:35 m.)

of lots' within groups of townships to be laid off from a whole series of separate base-lines, as these were conveniently drawn along a major trend of coast or length of river. *Within* these groups everything was regular enough; but *between* groups there were many offsets, gores, and other irregularities.

The west wanted a system that would be simpler to operate than both the earlier ones, and yet one which would, at the same time, have some of the merits of each of them. The system was simpler because it was completely regular, being based on: (i) the use of square blocks of lots divided into square sections and square subsections; (ii) definition by latitudes and by locally adjustable meridians (such as would avoid the convergence of geographic meridians and maintain the squareness of the blocks of lots). The land division lines thus always crossed each other at right-angles, and the rectilinear grid that resulted was carried right across the west.

The system did include good points from the earlier ones. Like that in New England it rested on manageable blocks of lots which were the equivalent of townships. More important still, it was based on the prior survey of the land, before land could be taken up. Yet it acknowledged the usefulness of Southern practice in that it permitted individuals to obtain land by warrant, provided the lot they chose fitted into the grid scheme once the grid advanced to the selected area; and it allowed surveyors to start surveying sections of the grid wherever the land was most in demand. Ultimately, however, such surveys had to tie in with the national system. It also permitted the southern 'county' unit to prevail, where desired, which was larger than the township.

In 1785 the so-called 'Geographer's Line' or base-line of the new system was surveyed. This ran from the point where the west boundary of Pennsylvania cut the Ohio, due west along a parallel of latitude. From this a number of equally spaced north–south lines, or 'ranges' were run, to intersect with the Ohio river. In this way the **Seven Ranges** of public land were laid out, and settlers were able to move in and take up land (see Fig. 47).

Taking up land was also carefully regulated. Originally, to effect a compromise between New England and Southern settlers, the townships were to be taken up alternately, one divided into sections for individual purchase and use, and one to be bought *in toto* and settled by a group. In actual fact, however,

> townships were no longer thought of as holding forth an inducement for neighborhoods . . . to confederate for the purpose of purchasing and settling together, and purchase by sections was no longer fought for as a means of approximating that freedom of choice which characterized indiscriminate locations. Townships were simply tracts or parcels of land

> expected to prove attractive to speculators either as wholes or in quarters. Sale by section was looked upon as a means of bringing land closer to the financial reach of actual settlers.[1]

Large land companies soon bought up great groups of townships and sections to dispose of in whatever way they could.

When it came down to it, very few settlers went out in groups and took up a whole township together. Group settlement, in fact, became frowned on because it was thought to militate against the free mingling and mixing of people of different origins and cultures which the American policy of 'the melting-pot' aimed to promote. As Kohn points out, 'the pattern of rural settlement in the Mid-West has remained, almost exclusively, one of a linear arrangement of dispersed farmsteads, the uniformity of which is undoubtedly an important factor in the unity of the region, despite variations in agricultural activities and physical conditions. The rural village, as it is known outside the United States, is for the most part absent.'[2] In the huge area of the Ohio, Mississippi, and Missouri plains Kohn mentions about a dozen 'Christian-socialist' group settlements, seven villages set up by the Amana pietistic society, five Hutterite communities, with farms in common and families living in sections of a common dormitory, and two or three score 'co-operative' groupments founded under the New Deal as 'rural-industrial' settlements. Township colonization, then, has not been at all significant in the west compared with the highly individualistic taking up of land which has been the general rule.

Transportation vitally affected the degree to which land was taken up and developed. Although land was the settler's chief interest, transportation was his chief need. He had to be able to get the produce of his farm to market. The pioneer was no peasant. He had not given up commercialized farming in the east, however successful, to sink himself in mere subsistence farming in the west. Even the peasant from Europe soon began to raise crops and stock for cash. This was nineteenth- and not seventeenth-century pioneering. Money was needed to maintain a standard of living on the western farm which would not fall short of its eastern counterpart. Lawyers and merchants had to be paid for, and churches, schools, and colleges maintained, on a par with the east. This could only be done by having outlets for trade.

The extraordinary difficulty of the trans-Appalachian roads, compared with the ease of river transport, threw the west upon the bosom of the Great Lakes, or into the arms of the Mississippi. Water transportation was all-important (Fig. 168). Yet before the advent of steam it was very slow. Flat-boats or 'arks'—rafts with a rim—were used for down-stream trade to take

[1] Pattison, *American Rectangular Land Survey*, p. 195.

[2] Kohn, C. F., 'Settlement Forms and Patterns', in Garland, *The North American Mid-west*, pp. 28–29.

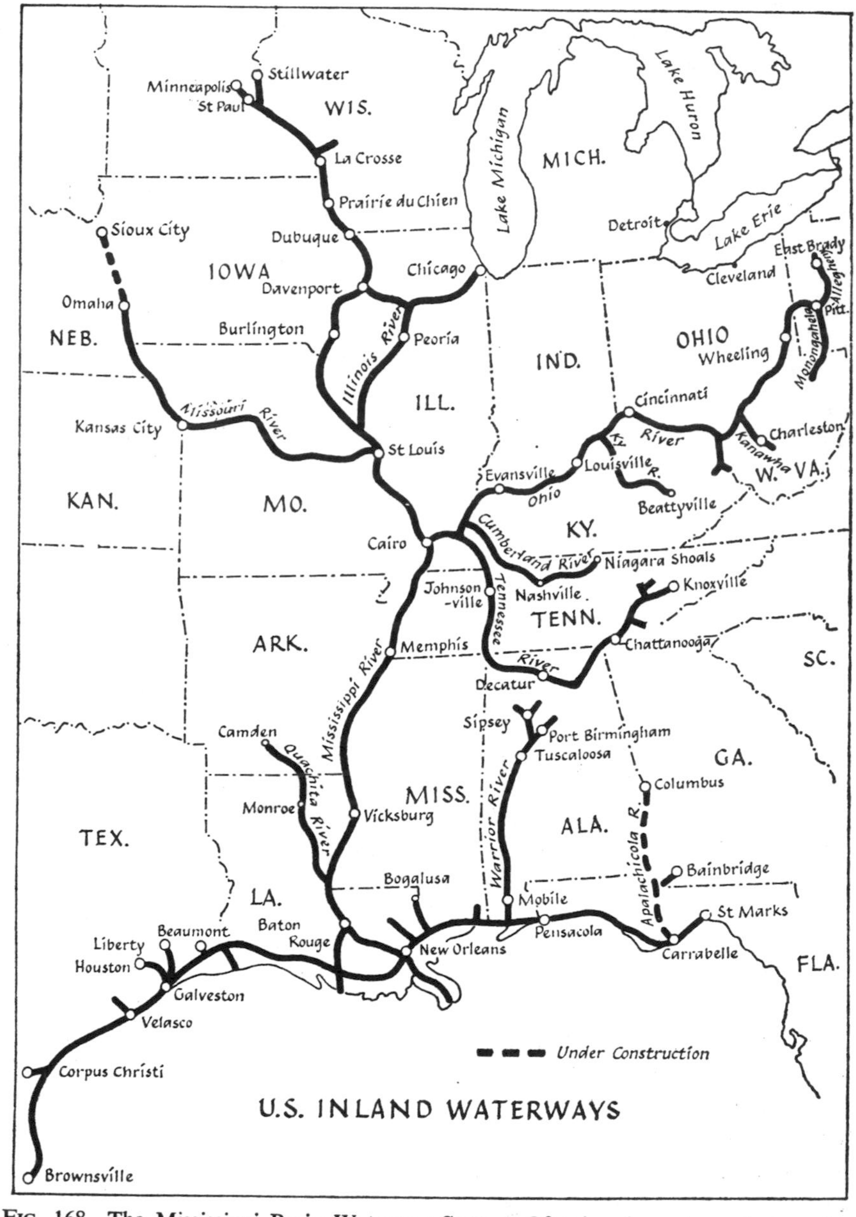

FIG. 168 The Mississippi Basin Waterway System. Of prime importance before the advent of railways and motor-roads, the system is still very valuable for the movement of bulk goods, and it supplies the Mid-West with cheap, if slow, transportation. (Scale, 1:15 m.)

farm produce down river to New Orleans, where it was put on boats for the Atlantic ports. The arks were then dismantled and sold for lumber and the boatmen returned overland up the Natchez Trace. The up-stream trade was much more difficult. Important machines, home utensils, chinaware, cloth, etc., were sent up in keel boats usually propelled by poling. A running-board was built on each side of the boat down which the crew walked pushing against long poles set in the river bottom. It took about three months to make the trip up the winding and strongly flowing Mississippi and Ohio from New Orleans to Cincinnati. The boatmen were a tough lot and contributed to the rough-and-ready, aggressive, plain, and outspoken character of the west. The boast of Mike Fink was not untypical of the region and age when he claimed: 'I can out-run, out-jump, throw down, drag out, and lick any man in the country. I'm a Salt river roarer, I love the wimmen, and I'm chock full of fight.'

There was one great disadvantage about the river trade. All the farm produce tended to arrive at much the same time in New Orleans, creating a buyer's not a seller's market, and as a result disappointing prices were often received. This was changed only when the Erie canal allowed the Great Lakes–Mohawk–Hudson route to compete with the Ohio–Mississippi one, or when distinctly better roads were built, able to take heavily laden wagons.

The success of the Erie canal widened the use of water transportation. However, by the time *most* of the canals were built, steamship navigation on the Mississippi and its tributaries had greatly quickened traffic and brought down the relative price of goods. Freight rates between Cincinnati and New Orleans fell from nine cents a pound to less than one half cent! Competition between the Mississippi and the Great Lakes was therefore keen: a competition that helped the west enormously in bringing more and more people and goods into the region, reducing freight rates for western produce on the way to market, and offering a freer choice of markets.

Many attempts at deflecting the Ohio trade north were made by the building of canals connecting the river with Lake Erie. These included, to begin with: the Ohio canal (1833) from Portsmouth on the Ohio river to Cleveland on the lake, following the Scioto, Muskingum, and Cuyahoga rivers; the Miami canal (1845), between Cincinnati and Toledo, following the Miami and Maumee rivers; and the Wabash canal (1836–54) connecting Evansville to Lafayette on the Wabash, and this, through Fort Wayne, with the Maumee and Toledo. These canals greatly helped the development of farming and lumbering in the older North-west. Whereas local prices for corn at Indianapolis were usually around 20 cents a bushel at this time, the price in the more populous Ohio and Lake Erie cities was three times as high; farmers on the polypotamic plain between Mississippi, Ohio, and Erie could thus make a substantially higher income off the usual quarter section farm if they could sell their grain in Cincinnati, Pittsburgh, Cleveland, or Buffalo—particularly Buffalo because it was on the shortest route to New York. In 1833 the Welland canal in Canada helped the northern pull still further, as American wheat sent down the St Lawrence and milled into flour at Montreal or Quebec could get into the English market which was closed to direct export from New York. Finally, the Chicago canal (1836–48), linking up the south fork of the Chicago river with the Illinois, provided direct access from the Mississippi to the Great Lakes. (This canal today has a volume of traffic of over 15 million tons a year and is second only to the Erie canal in importance.)

These canals played a most important role in helping to bind Ohio, Indiana, and Illinois to the north and east (and especially to New York), and in loosening their ties with the south and New Orleans. Thus canals had their part in the growing division of the United States into the two vast and opposing sections of the north and south.

Most of them were scarcely completed, however, when they lost much of their usefulness to the railways. Canals and rivers suffered a major drawback—they were roundabout and slow. They lay across the vast east–west stream of migration; railways paralleled that stream and therefore came, more and more, to channelize it. This fact made the railways, not the waterways, the axis of the modern development of America. The new geography created by the railways was in line with the geography of mass immigration from Europe, through the eastern ports, ever farther and farther west, across the central plains, over gaps in the mountains to the Pacific. To a marked degree the history of American development became the geography of its railways.

The New York Central railway pushed west by buying up the Lakeshore railway along the southern shore of Lake Erie, and absorbing the Michigan Southern from the head of Lake Erie to the foot of Lake Michigan and so to Chicago. This linkage of Chicago, Toledo, Cleveland, Buffalo, Syracuse, Albany, and New York was a major factor in helping this string of cities to become the industrial axis of America. The continuation of other lines from New York, Philadelphia, and Baltimore gave pre-eminence to the Northern-central States in the development of the Mid-West. The South lagged sadly behind. This was partly because the South went at the task in a very piecemeal way, building railroads essentially to connect up and supplement waterways, but mainly because Southern capital was almost all used up in buying land and slaves in a tremendous westward push of the cotton plantation economy. The very unequal development of railways was of great significance during the Civil War, when the South found it difficult to move men and material from east to west, and to manœuvre against the great flanking attacks of the North, supported by a surprisingly dense meshwork of railroads (see Fig. 51, Chapter 7).

The Baltimore and Ohio railway pushed out a great westward-reaching tentacle from Cumberland on the Potomac to Wheeling on the Ohio. It then more or less followed the route of the National Road to Columbus, after which it swept south by Cincinnati to St Louis. Here it could tap the lower Missouri as well as the middle Mississippi trade. Originally the railway did not attempt the long bridges necessary over the wide and often flooded rivers it had to 'cross', but used ferries, so that, by 1857, when the line was completed the railway trip from Baltimore to St Louis involved 'changing cars five times, crossing rivers twice on ferries, and making two short trips on steam boats'![1] None the less the route was a great improvement on the earlier road or river ways, and helped to make St Louis one of the great jumping-off points for the trip to Oregon or California. The Baltimore and Ohio also bought up a line from Pittsburgh to Chicago.

The Pennsylvania Railroad was quick to offer competition. It built or bought up railways extending west from Pittsburgh first to Cleveland (1853) and west along the Lakeshore route to Chicago, and second from Pittsburgh to Fort Wayne and Chicago. The latter route had a branch to Columbus and Indianapolis and thence west by Terre Haute to St Louis on the Mississippi (1853). The Erie railroad also pushed west from its terminal at Dunkirk, where the line from Jersey City reached Lake Erie (1851), along the Lakeshore route to Toledo (1853), and thence to Chicago. Thus the Mid-West between Buffalo, Detroit, and Chicago, on the north and between Pittsburgh, Indianapolis, and St Louis in the centre, was tied into the north-eastern trading area and taken still farther from the South.

The South tried to meet this challenge by building railroads west from Richmond, Charleston, and Savannah. From Richmond, Virginia, a railway was projected across the Blue Ridge into and down the Great Valley to Knoxville and Chattanooga; from Charleston, the so-called Georgia railroad was driven north-west through Atlanta to Chattanooga and then west, using part of the Tennessee valley to strike across to Memphis on the Mississippi—a spur line from this went up to Nashville; while from Savannah the Macon and Western railway pushed west through Macon to Atlanta, or from Macon to Montgomery, and then, cutting across all the southward flowing rivers, to Vicksburg on the Mississippi. Long sections of these railroads were built in the boom between 1848 and 1850, but certain difficult yet critical sections were not finished until the Civil War, or after.

The predominance of the North in railway building was obvious, and drew much of the Mid-West into the sphere of the Mid-Atlantic States (see Fig. 51, Chapter 7). This movement was, however, helped by other economic

[1] Clark, *The West in American History*, p. 301.

considerations. Those States and New England offered a much better market—because they had a much greater need—for Mid-West products than the Southern States. In the north-east, industrialization had become so advanced that the rural population was being attracted into the cities, and the production of wheat, corn, and meat on a local basis was not nearly enough to fulfil the demand. The South, by contrast, was in the main self-sufficing, since, although the cotton plantations often had to buy in food, there was enough food produced locally by the 'yeomen farmers' who still played an active role in the south. For example, although the average American consumption in the mid-'fifties was four bushels of wheat and twenty-five bushels of corn per head per year, New England produced only 0·4 bushel of wheat and 3·7 of corn. For the South the figures were 2·47 and 30·83. For the west they were 7·52 and 44·14.

> Hence New England had to import 3·6 bushels of wheat and 21·30 bushels of corn *per capita* per year, while the south needed only 1·53 bushels of wheat and had an excess of 5·83 bushels of corn. The west, on the other hand, must sell 3·25 bushels of wheat and 19·14 bushels of corn for each of its inhabitants. Obviously its best market was not in the south (which produced most of the food it needed), but in the north-east where the demand far exceeded the supply.[1]

AGRICULTURE AND SETTLEMENT

With this great demand building up, immigrants to the Mid-West turned eagerly to farming as their best means of securing the money to build homes, support schools and churches, and evolve a settled life. Incentives existed to make them find out what best could be grown and how best to grow it. To begin with, in the Ohio country, they tried to carry on their old ways and were fairly successful. But as they came to the open prairie things were not so easy. They had come to a different environment. Large areas were without enough timber to build houses, barns, and fences. Timber had to be saved and not wasted. Some pioneers felt so strange in the wide prairie that they avoided it and kept to the river bottomlands.

Nevertheless, once the prairie was conquered it offered very rich soils and a favourable climate, which was warm and moist. Both in the formerly forested and in the prairie regions conditions were good, and cattle farming, grain farming, raising of corn, and the fattening of pigs were tried in quick succession. Most of the land was too fruitful to be left to cattle range; and in much of the area the climate was rather too hot and moist in summer for wheat; and so more and more corn was grown, more hogs were raised, and the heart of the Mid-West became America's famous Corn Belt. However,

[1] Billington, *Westward Expansion*, p. 399.

the rest of the region had its own offerings. Winter wheat continued in the rougher and drier south-west plains; and spring wheat production did very well in the Red river valley, with its cooler and shorter growing season. Thus several farming zones evolved, in close association with vegetation, soil, and climate. These included: spring wheat farming in the cooler north-west; hay, oats, and dairying in the cool, humid Great Lakes region, with its grey-brown soils; corn-feed and hog farming in the central prairie, with rich forest or prairie soils, heavy rains in early summer, followed by a sunny autumn; and winter wheat in the drier south-west. A rather special district was the Michigan Fruit Belt, on the east side of Lake Michigan. The west winds blowing across Lake Michigan are made warmer and wetter, and delay autumn frosts, giving a long growing season for grapes, peaches, pears, and apples. Thus the basis of Mid-western wealth became its varied agriculture (Fig. 169).

Spring wheat. In the north-west, spring wheat is the wealth of North Dakota, and parts of South Dakota, Minnesota, and Montana. Here the climate is suited to quick-growing crops. It has too cold a winter for winter wheat. The summers are not long enough or hot enough for the best varieties of corn. But the short growing season, spring and early summer rains, and bright sunny autumns are ideal for spring-sown wheat, barley, oats, and rye. Wheat is the chief crop, because it fetches the highest price; but most farmers, after experiencing the dangers of growing wheat year upon year, now rotate their fields with other grains. The Spring Wheat Belt might equally well be called the Barley Belt, or Rye Belt, since more of these crops are grown there than anywhere else in the United States. The black earth soils of the Red river and the brown soils of the upper Missouri are very productive; the flatness of the land encourages large-scale mechanized production; the farms are large; and since the population is small there is a big surplus for export to other parts of America, and also overseas. Increasingly, farmers are turning to mixed farming, because it is better for the soils, and is more secure. Quantities of flax are grown, chiefly for the oil crushed out of the seeds. Some of the fields are sown to hay, and are pastured to beef cattle. These are sold, when still young, to be fattened in the Corn Belt. Dairying is important locally, to serve city markets. Thus farmers are avoiding the dangers of soil exhaustion and soil erosion, which are characteristic of a one-crop system, and though wheat still dominates —every town has its elevator—prosperity is more widely based.

The area is not without its problems. Periodic blizzards of great intensity sweep across it, causing some loss of life among sheep and cattle. Most mixed farms now have cattle barns, like farms in the east, in which to winter stock; but many only have the old horse barns where they simply shelter the younger or weaker beasts. (Going over from wheat to mixed farming, that is,

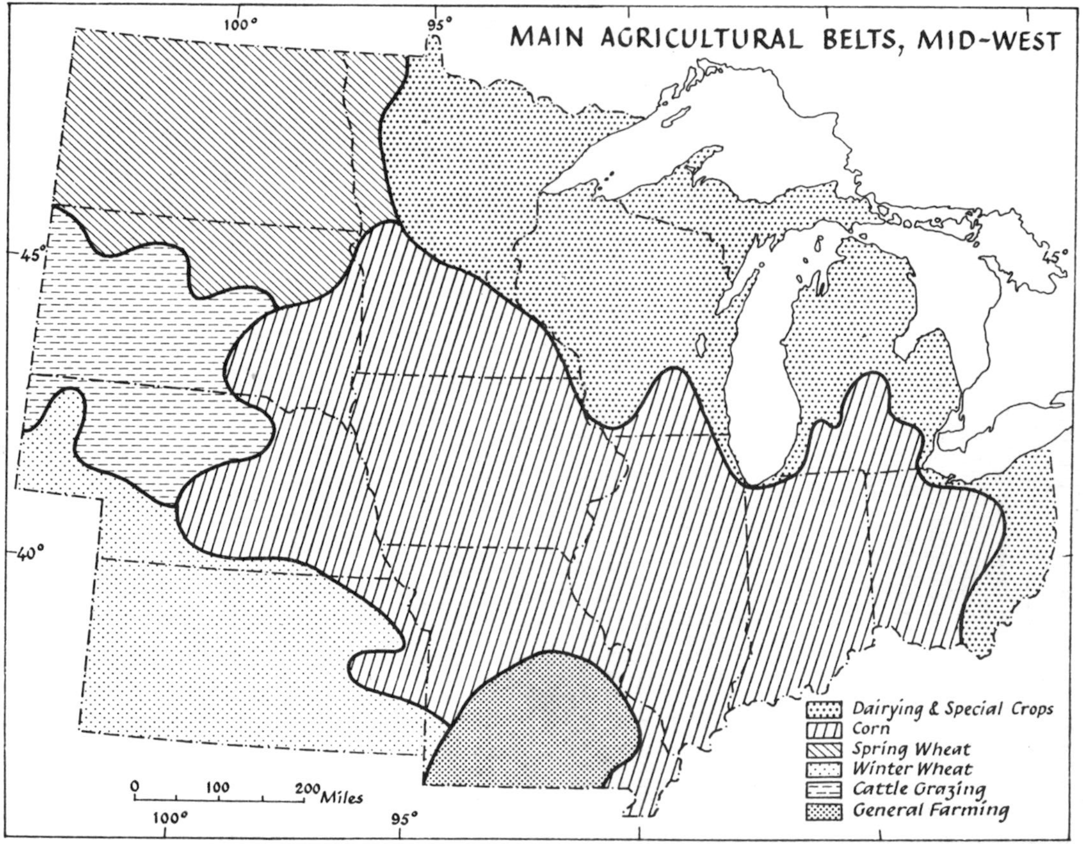

FIG. 169 The Chief Agricultural Regions in the Mid-West Group of States. The Corn Belt is the dominant feature, although it should be remembered that wheat is almost everywhere grown as a subsidiary crop outside the Wheat Belts themselves.

from an essentially summer-based economy to one based on the all-year use of the land, has surprisingly not been followed everywhere by the winterizing of the farm, with buildings, shelter belts, feeding yards, and sunning-out spaces specially constructed and laid out to meet winter hazards.)

More destructive are periodic summer droughts. These can usually be survived if they only last for a season; but if they continue over several years they can bring ruin in their trail. This is especially true on the Great Plains, above the Coteau. Here special methods have been adopted to meet the situation, including dry-farming, forestation, water conservation, and irrigation.

Dry-farming was practised and publicized by H. W. Campbell of South Dakota in the late 'eighties of last century, and since then has spread widely throughout the drier parts of the Spring Wheat Belt—indeed, it has been the prime factor in the extension of that belt over the northern part of the Great Plains. Ross's experiments in Canada also helped. He showed that by spring ploughing of land ploughed year after year only five bushels return could be got for every one bushel sown; but by fall ploughing fields left fallow for two consecutive years, a return of no less than twenty-eight bushels for every bushel sown was obtained. These results concentrated attention on the *method of cropping* the land. Later, interest was roused in breeding drought-resistant grains, and in the *types of crops*.

Practices to be encouraged were shallow ploughing, late ploughing, early seeding, thin seeding, and quick harvesting, also the staged or 'staggered' ploughing and seeding of land, the resting of land from cropping, and the rotation of wheat with other crops. Fallowing and rotation were particularly important.

Summer fallow helps to store plant food and moisture by letting the soil rest for one year in two or three, by putting it, in the early summer rains, in such a condition that it will absorb the rain but keep it at the surface. Ploughing in June or early July helps to open the soil to the moisture. Summer tillage keeps the weeds down, prevents loss of water by transpiration, and turns the weeds into green manure for later cropping. Summer tillage also stops the soil from baking and cracking and losing soil moisture by evaporation from the cracks. Often the fallow is ridged with a 'lister' in the fall, which helps to catch and hold the snow in the winter (to provide melt-water in the spring) and also checks soil blowing.

Fallowing is still widespread and the brown of the summer-fallow fields may be seen quartering the gold of the wheat, or the pale yellow of the stubble, in most parts of the semi-arid plain; but the practice is not as common as it used to be. Instead, intertilled crops, in a crop rotation that keeps all the land productive, are more popular. Corn and potatoes are often grown in this fashion; they are then disked into the ground in the fall, in preparation for the sowing of the wheat in the spring. While 'summer tillage without crop has given the highest average yields of any method, yet on account of its high cost due to extra labor and alternate year cropping, it has not always been the most profitable practice. Disked corn ground has given consistently high yields and this, together with the low cost of preparation (no further plowing, and no cultivating needed), has resulted in its showing the highest average profit.'[1] Often forage crops, especially oats and alfalfa, are grown in rotation, and this has been much encouraged as then the manure from the cattle, to which the crops are fed, goes back on to the land to help fertilize it.

The types of crops are being experimented with constantly to breed new drought-resistant varieties. Hard red wheat predominates, mainly of the Kubanka and Marquis breeds. Durum wheat is actually much more able to withstand drought, but it is a macaroni not a bread wheat, and so only grown in the more arid parts of east Montana and west Dakota. Hannchen, a two-row barley, is quite widely used in place of the more common six-row barley, while Smyrna, a short-stemmed kind, untroubled by wind spoilage, is highly recommended in Montana. Emmer wheat used to be grown for horse feed, but now that horses have virtually gone, it has shown a marked decline. It has been found important to go in for non-shattering varieties of grain, since, as Bracken has indicated, heavy winds at harvest-time can shatter or 'shell' the seed head. Kubanka hardly ever shatters. Cattle are becoming more popular, and western rye grass and brome grass have been found to make the best dry-farming pastures. Alfalfa is also popular, but is more commonly grown under irrigation; only the hardiest varieties, such as 'Grimm', can take the bitter winters, if sown in the fall.

By these and other means farming has colonized all but the really marginal or true range lands on the Great Plains and extended the Wheat Belt well beyond the confines of the Central Plain. Everywhere, across these wide north-western plains, one sees these great farms, with the homes spaced miles apart up long lanes leading off the straight dusty highways. Many homes are low one-and-a-half storey bungalows, built to reduce the shock of the winds which are such a feature. They are often sheltered by a wind belt of evergreens or thick-leaved balm-of-gilead poplars. The farmstead is close by and consists of a number of great machine sheds and rows and rows of granaries—the older ones, small oblong wooden structures painted red, trimmed with white; the more modern types, round, glistening aluminium bins. Often isolated granaries mark the farther fields, and great rows of king-sized bins now flank the so-called 'villages' as well as the traditional elevators. Few barns hit the eye; many cattle are left out in winter, especially where there is some bush on the farm.

[1] U.S. Department of Agriculture Bulletin no. 214, p. 43, Sect. 7, 11.

The Dairy Belt makes a great contrast to all this. One notices right away how green the land is; there is no brown fallow, and not a great deal of golden cropland or yellow stubble—but much more hay and pasture. Barns, which are inconspicuous in the wheat-growing west, here dominate the scene, towering above the other buildings, including the house. They are usually double affairs, with an immense loft above for storing dried hay and thrashed oats, and with a big byre beneath to house the dairy herd throughout the winter. These barns have earth ramps going up to them, on which tractors can pull up the loads of hay. They also have a big concrete silo at one end, with a silage lifter, to take the green corn or clover stored as green food for the winter. Thus winter dominates. This is seen in the steep roofs of the barn and of the house, and in the storm windows and doors with which the house is fitted, in the winterized garages, and in the ubiquitous snow-plough in the farm-yard. Your dairy farmer's house is large and often rather pretentious, set up on a basement half out of the ground (usually built of the glacial boulders taken from the field). It is entered up a flight of steps across a veranda and then rises at least two storeys with an attic above, or three full storeys high. The rooms are large, the ceilings high, and the windows tall, often with a Gothic arch. The façade is decorated with highly carved wooden eaves and lintels, and, if of frame, is well painted. Where made of brick it frequently has a white-brick trim along the edges worked into red-brick facing. There is always a well-kept front lawn, often shaded with great maples or chestnut trees. Settlement is closer and villages are larger. The glistening chimney of the creamery replaces the tower of the elevator at the centre of the country towns (see Fig. 169).

The land around is gently rolling, and partially wooded. Many poorly drained spots interrupt the fertile fields. Large-scale mechanized farming is not as practicable. The soils are podsolized, grey-brown earths. They are rather acid and not well suited to wheat. The long, severe winters are unkind to wheat, as well, causing a good deal of winter 'heaving'. The summers are too short for the heavier yields of table corn. They are wet summers, and are better suited to hay and silage crops. Grasses introduced from abroad have done very well, especially English hay, fescue, orchard and Canada blue grass. Red clovers thrive on the damp, slightly acid soil. Therefore farmers have gradually come to rely on grass pastures, hay, and silage crops as the basis of a thriving dairy trade. The large urban markets around the Great Lakes have encouraged this. Production is now enough for other parts of America, and for overseas. Wisconsin cheeses are particularly famous.

The Corn Belt forms the heart of the central plains, stretching from eastern Nebraska to Ohio (Fig. 170). It is said that corn reaches its highest yield where the average July temperature is 75°–77° F. and the average summer rainfall is about 11 inches. The Corn Belt lies between the July isotherms of

80° F. in the south and 70° F. in the north, and between the summer-rainfall isohyets of 8 inches and 14 inches. If one were to draw two lines between these isotherms and isohyets, representing 75° and 11 inches, they would form a cross at the very heart of the Corn Belt. Corn also thrives on the moist, deep prairie soils, which, though they have a high organic matter content, are not acid, but neutral. This suits corn very well.

However, though corn is the major crop, other crops are raised in the Corn Belt. In the spring the corn-belt farmer sows his oats or hay: then about May puts in his corn. The early summer weather, with its rainy nights and hot days, hastens crop development. Weeds also shoot up and have to be

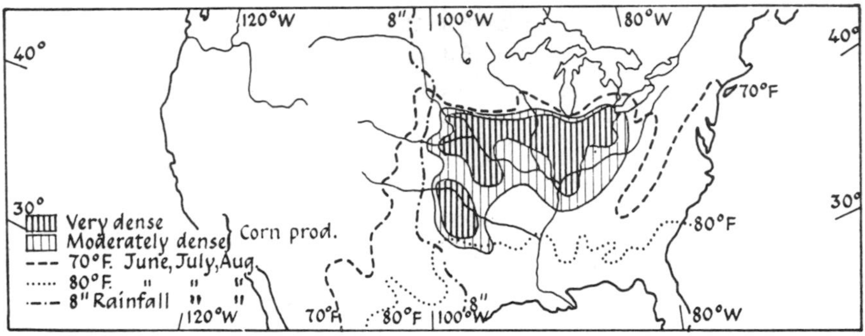

FIG. 170 The Corn Belt—Heart of the Mid-West. Although corn is grown much more widely, from southern Mexico to central Canada, it is concentrated in an area with summers between 70° and 80° F., and a summer rainfall of between 8 and 12 inches. The Corn Belt concentrates itself in optimum conditions where man makes the most of natural advantages.

cleared with a cultivator two or three times in May and June. Towards the end of June the hay is ripe and is harvested, dried, and put in the barn. In July the oat crop ripens, and shortly after it the fall-sown wheat is ready to cut. It is dried out and threshed in early August. Meantime the corn is filling out, and as the cobs grow long and fat, the tassels shrivel and die. By the end of August or early September the corn is ready to harvest. But generally it is left until the ears are dry. Then it is cut and the ears husked. This may go on throughout the fall into the early winter. Corn is not damaged once it is dry. Time is taken out to plough the fields for the winter wheat. Cattle and pigs are turned loose in feed lots where corn and concentrates are fed to them to fatten them quickly for market. Their manure is liquified and pumped out to the fields.

Thus the farmer rotates his land between corn, winter wheat, and pasture, keeping the soil in good heart. The wheat may be sold off as a cash crop, but the hay, oats, and corn are raised for fattening cattle and hogs. The cattle are often bought in from the western ranges when they are still young, but are also raised locally, fattened and sold to be slaughtered in near-by packing plants. The hogs are reared on the farm, fattened and sold to the packers. Nearly half the swine of the world are in the United States, and most of these are bred and fattened in the Corn Belt.

In this zone farming is becoming big business. It is heavily capitalized, the operations are organized as though done to time and motion studies, the latest scientific finds and mechanical devices are put to use, and the maximum cash value is sought off the land. This has tended to drive out the small farmer and has led to a widespread amalgamation of farms into bigger productive units. Many of these farms still handle their own buying and selling, but an increasing number are on contract work to specific milling companies or packing houses. Not a few are actually owned by the user-corporations and are simply their producing agents. Vertical integration is getting more and more common, in which the milling company will buy up farms, put in managers to run them, and take up the produce as a part of a chain of development from the field to the warehouse. Grocetarias are going even further and running their own farms so that they can control events from the field to the breakfast-table.

When this first came in during the 'thirties' the attitude to it was one of extreme disfavour. Brunner and Kolb used local examples to illustrate this:

> In one [a particular] corn-belt community a corporation was operating a unit of 2,400 acres, one tenth of its total holding within the corn-belt, made up of amalgamated fore-closed farms of between 160 and 320 acres. 'Each tract in the group is operated as a single field and is planted to a single crop in a rotation program. In the working of its present holdings, the Company employs 75 general purpose tractors, 19 combined harvesters-and-threshers, 15 two-row harvesters, 75 plows, 40 grain drills, and associated equipment. The machinery is transported over a hard surfaced road system by means of 10 motor trucks with trailers capable of handling three tractors to a load. Field machinery is entirely equipped with electric lighting system to permit twenty-four hour operation.' This company uses no livestock, has removed all fences, groves of trees, and often the buildings from the [former farm] holdings. It employs only unmarried men.[1]

It was found that such a 'farm' would buy in all its supplies not through the local merchants and dealers but from its own agents in the city.

As a result of all this, the small family farm (say of 160 acres, or a quarter section) is declining—it now makes up only one in three farms, while the bigger ones are getting bigger. This has meant considerable and widespread

[1] Brunner and Kolb, *Rural Social Trends*, p. 51.

rural depopulation, but on the other hand it has meant a far greater productive power and far more efficiency in production. Between 1935 and 1965, the number of farms was halved, but productivity nearly doubled. The Corn Belt is probably the most highly organized, best run, most economic, and highest yielding farm area of comparable size in the world.

This is seen in the landscape.

> The Corn Belt farmstead [writes Trewartha] is high grade, reflecting the general well-being and prosperity of the region it serves. It has a relatively large number of separate buildings. Two-storey, well painted houses, the majority of them with basements, are the rule. Barns are average or even small in size and many are of a type which does not indicate large hay-storage capacity. Unpainted barns are not numerous. In proportion of hog houses, machine sheds and corn cribs the Corn Belt ranks high.[1]

It is also noted for extensive pens where stock is fattened from feed brought in from the fields.

Winter wheat replaces corn in the less humid areas of the south-west plains in Nebraska, Kansas, and Oklahoma. These districts have rather too little summer rain to make corn the major crop. Corn is grown, but as a subsidiary crop. Most of the rain comes in the spring, which is more suitable for wheat. The winters are not as cold as in the northern Spring Belt, and consequently winter wheat is raised. This is a hard variety, because it ripens in a fairly dry and sunny summer. It has a high yield, and, grown on large farms, makes a big crop. Since the population is low, there is a considerable surplus for trade (see Fig. 169).

The southern Wheat Belt is similar to the northern one in many respects; it too has adopted dry-farming methods, with a good deal of summer fallow, or with intertilled crops grown in preparation for wheat. Yet it is significantly different in possessing few mixed farms and maintaining few cattle. This is mainly because there is a distinct mid-summer drought. Although the fall-sown winter wheat is able to ripen before this, perennial pasture grasses are not able to do so, and thus there is very poor summer pasture. Or at any rate the expectancy of summer pasture is so uncertain that relatively few farmers are prepared to keep much stock. Silage corn is also an uncertainty because of its need of mid-summer moisture. Field corn, grown in rotation to supplement wheat, is made up of earlier-maturing, drought-resistant types.

The greater danger of drought in the southern Wheat Belt has led to some local adaptations. There is no real ploughing done. The soil is not turned

[1] Trewartha, G. T., 'Some Regional Characteristics of American Farmlands', *Annals Assoc. American Geographers*, 1948, **38**, p. 220.

over, as this tends to dry it out, but is simply disturbed at the surface—enough to cut the weeds, prepare a surface tilth that keeps the moisture, and to form an adequate seed-bed. The duckfoot 'plow' is quite often used; it undercuts but does not turn over the stubble, thus allowing the stubble to remain on the soil surface as 'trash' which protects the soil against wind erosion and moisture loss. The Graham Hoeme 'plow' is also much in use; it thrusts a dozen shovels into the soil, cutting a 12-foot swath but only tears through the sub-surface, to cut weed roots and loosen the top soil. It hardly breaks the top of the soil. The rod weeder is also becoming popular; this is a 20-foot rod on small wheels which is let into the soil and then dragged along a few inches under the surface, rotating on its axis. It thus disturbs the roots of weeds and kills them, without greatly affecting the surface.

These machines require very large tractors to pull them, and southern wheat farms are largely rated on their tractor force.

> A one-tractor wheat farm generally has about 1,200 acres of crop land. Half of this is in fallow and half in crop and is handled on an alternate stripping and perhaps even contouring basis. Planning starts with summer fallow. Since the tractor travels at an effective speed of 4·5 miles per hour, it takes about twelve to fourteen days of fourteen hours each to do the summer fallowing on 610 acres. During the remainder of the summer, two or three weeding operations are performed. At ninety acres per day, this consumes fourteen to twenty-one days. By mid-summer, the crop seeded during the previous fall in the alternate fields is ready for harvest. The combine operation, at fifty-five acres per day, takes about twelve to fifteen days for the 610 acres of cropland. At the same time, the wheat has been hauled. Immediately following the combining, the alternate fallow land is ready to be seeded for next year. When the moisture is right, this fallowed land is disced and seeded. It takes about ten to twelve days to complete this operation.
>
> Except for machinery repair, hauling some farm-stored wheat, preparing seed for next year, and mending a few boundary fences, all the work is finished with these operations. Altogether, the dry-land wheat farmer cannot find more than one hundred days of work on the farm, unless he has livestock also and other cash crops. But these operations do not often mix efficiently with the wheat unit in the Great Plains.[1]

Often he spends the rest of the year in town, or puts in the winter in California.

The need for large farms with a lot of machinery, but the lack of large local corporations interested in taking over farms, has led to the rise of

---

[1] Kraenzel, *The Great Plains in Transition*, pp. 305–6.

many co-operatives in the southern Wheat Belt; these co-operative offices, storage bins, machine depots, and seed warehouses are quite a feature of the landscape, along with the ubiquitous wheat elevators.

The growing size of the farm and the increased mechanization of farming have together meant fewer people on the land. Consequently, rural depopulation is widespread. The year 1930 was one of maximum rural population: then the States of Nebraska, Kansas, and Oklahoma had 1,066,500 farm people, thirty years later they had barely 700,000. One result was that the rural counties could not keep up many of the rural schools and churches they had formerly supported, and the countryside became spotted with closed-up rural institutions. In 1942, Kansas had 30 per cent or more of its elementary school districts with closed schools.[1] Since then consolidation has amalgamated half as many again.

As farming changes across the Mid-West with climate and soil, settlement changes with farming. The relatively small farm and compact farmstead in the east, with its huge Dutch barn, gives way to a medium-sized farm, where a huddle of smaller buildings, pig pens, and corn cribs occur between the barn and the house; then in the south-west and the north-west are large wheat farms, with tractor and binder sheds, or former horse stables, and rows of shining bins or granaries, instead of pig pens and cattle byres. So each type of farming creates its own pattern of settlement. That pattern allows a fairly dense population in the east; but a much sparser population in the west.

The farmers sell most of their crops and livestock in cities where the grain is milled into flour, the corn crushed into oil and cattle-cake, the hogs and cattle slaughtered, packed, frozen, or canned. Then the products are sent to the huge industrial areas of the Great Lakes and North-eastern States, or exported overseas. Agriculture has expanded with the rise of the cities, mills and packing plants, and the building of railways and roads. The cities have also benefited. They have obtained cheap food, in large quantities, from the farms. They have found a huge market for agricultural machines, wire, nails, lumber goods, cement, artificial fertilizers, chemical sprays, automobiles, home equipment, and so on. This huge internal market helped many industries to become big enough to compete in foreign markets. Agriculture has aided industry and commerce.

Other industries have risen by using the mineral wealth of the region. The Wisconsin uplands and the Missouri hills continuing the Ozark massif have large deposits of lead. In the Illinois, Indiana, and Michigan basins south and east of Lake Michigan are large coal fields, on the slopes of the La Salle and Cincinnati anticlines. Ohio, West Virginia, and Kentucky on the eastern

[1] *Closed Schools in Kansas*, Kansas Legislative Council Pub. Bul. no. 113 (September 1942).

flank of the Cincinnati anticline also have important amounts of coal. Small oil fields are found in gentle upfolds, in Ohio, Indiana, and Illinois, and immense ones in Oklahoma.

INDUSTRY, COMMERCE, AND SETTLEMENT

The conditions for industry are favourable. There is a large demand for farm machines, lumber and mine equipment, transportation equipment, and road and house building material, as well as for consumer goods amongst farmers with above-average levels of income who are used to spending. Also, as we have seen, the region is rich in certain raw materials, especially farm products, but also wood, clay, limestone, iron, copper, lead and zinc, coal and oil. The Mississippi and Great Lakes waterways offer cheap if slow transportation for bulk commodities, and there is a dense network of railways and roads with low gradients on an unimpeded plain to provide fast and direct movement of goods and people. Finally, those people are very varied, for the Mid-West has been the great melting-pot of America, and from their varied backgrounds many ideas and skills have been made available.

There are, however, several problems. For one thing, the raw materials are very dispersed, and a great deal of outlay is needed to concentrate them for manufacturing. Likewise, the market is thinly spread over an immense area, and the cost of taking manufactured goods to people is high. Climate is sometimes a handicap. Throughout the northern part winters are bitter, if not long, and much money has to be spent on winterizing plants, clearing yards and roads of snow, and stock-piling raw materials before the lakes and rivers freeze up. In the west, water-supply may not be constant or large enough for industry, except on the largest rivers. The rivers themselves can be a hazard. Vast floods on the Mississippi, Missouri, and Ohio occasionally cause serious damage, and most river towns have to pay out a lot (partly taken in from increased corporation taxes) to protect themselves, their factories, and suburbs from the risk of flooding. The T.V.A. in the Tennessee has shown the way to reduce floods and to control and exploit the power of the rivers, but as yet similar valley authorities and development programmes have not taken over in other river basins. On the whole, however, advantages far outweigh disadvantages, and have made the Mid-West an important industrial region.

A marked feature of Mid-West industry is its very unequal development. There is an area to the north and north-east (the south shores of Lake Michigan to the south shore of Lake Erie) that is fairly evenly industrialized throughout; but outside of this, industry tends to gather in clusters around a few major centres, or to exist at widely scattered individual points. 'The seven states lying east of the Mississippi River reported 33·5 per cent of the national factory production, whereas the seven states lying west of the river reported only 5·5 per cent of the national total. Thus the industrial development is confined very largely to the eastern part of the area.'[1] Actually, it is confined to the north-eastern part. If we compare the distribution of income derived from manufacturing in the individual states with the U.S. average (22·1 per cent), we find that only five states are above this average—Michigan 39·5, Indiana 32·7, Ohio 32·5, Wisconsin 28·5, and Illinois 26·6. None of the other states have an industrial income as high as the national average, and cannot in fact be regarded as industrial.

But further, large parts of Wisconsin, Illinois, and Indiana, and about half of Ohio do not have an above average industrial income. The only continuous areas showing a higher average are the lake-plain of Lake Michigan from Green Bay to Muskegon; the lower Michigan peninsula and the north-eastern part of Indiana; the lake-plain of Lake Erie and the triangle between it and the upper Ohio basin. 'These areas, which are the most significant industrial developments of the Mid-West, contained about seven-eighths of the manufacturing of the entire region.'[2] In them, concentrations occur where the percentage of the income from industry is well over thirty. But 'it appears that when an area has [this kind of concentration] in manufacturing it has room for little or no economic activity not directly related to it'. Thus we may take it that the districts referred to are distinctly unusual in the Mid-West in that they have 'a unique capacity to create [truly] industrialized communities, a tendency to form a solid, continuous region, and a generally east–west elongation'.[3] They are, in fact, parts of the greater east–west zone of industry, the American Manufacturing Belt. They owe as much to the Mohawk–Hudson gap, the Erie canal, the massive railway systems originating from New York, Jersey City, Philadelphia, and Baltimore, to the banks of New York and the insurance businesses of New England, and the whole commercial and industrial genius of the East, as to the Mid-West, and all its opportunities. They are a prolongation of the East into the West and have an altogether wider significance than their local region. For that reason they have been treated as the western spearhead of the north-eastern section of the country.

Nevertheless, although they do stand out sharply from the rest of the Mid-West, they are physically a part of it, draw much from it, and contribute a lot to it. They must be included in the context of both great sections. Certainly Chicago is much more than an industrial city in a chain of industrial cities; it *is* the Mid-West, and dominates and pulls together the whole region.

---

[1] McCarty, H. H., 'Structure of Industry', in Garland, *The North American Mid-West* p. 54. [2] Ibid., p. 55. [3] Ibid., p. 61.

Chicago (7,100,000) has become the region's centre because it has helped to mediate the east to the west, and links the north with the south. The Erie canal, the Chicago Road, the New York Central, Pennsylvania, and Baltimore and Ohio railroads brought in the east; but from Chicago, the Great Northern, Northern Pacific, Union Pacific, Milwaukee, Santa Fé, and the Illinois Central railroads radiate out west or south to the Pacific and Gulf coasts. Even where other 'gate towns', like St Louis, were used to connect east and west, they soon perforce had to link themselves up with Chicago, and after that tended to be displaced by Chicago. Modern roads similarly turn into and go out of Chicago: the New York Thruway, joined by the Massachusetts Turnpike from Boston, and their continuation in the Interstate expressway 90; the Pennsylvania Turnpike, continued in the Ohio Turnpike, and Interstate expressway 80; U.S. Highway 40 from Baltimore and 50 from Washington, by way of Indianapolis; and U.S. Highway 41 from Atlanta, and 61 from New Orleans, in the south—all converge here; while similar great highways fan out to the west, including Interstate Highway 90 to Seattle; 80 to San Francisco; and U.S. 66 to Los Angeles. While these all no doubt contribute to Chicago as an industrial city, they help it to fulfil the far greater part of regional centre. 'The general radial pattern [of all routes] which centers on Chicago illustrates the role of that city as the major transportation center of the Mid-West'[1] (Fig. 171). Originally, this helped industry, although now it makes for industrial overcrowding. Industry declined by 18 per cent in the 'fifties to 'sixties, but trade expanded.

The tremendous development of railway and road terminals within Chicago, as well as its extraordinarily busy airports at O'Hare and Midway show a regional and, in fact, inter-regional significance out of all proportion to the demands of local manufacturing. They point up Chicago's great influence as a service centre, now its most important function.

> Chicago's railway traffic exceeds that of the next two most important American railway centres, St Louis and New York, combined. Converging on Chicago from all directions are 27 railroad routes of 20 line-haul carriers. The terminal facilities include six major passenger depots at the fringe of the central business district, 250 freight stations, and nearly 6,000 private sidings, together with a ring of major freight-classification yards on the periphery of the built-up urban area. Some of the latter, such as the central Clearing Yard, have capacities for more than 10,000 freight cars each. These classification yards are all interconnected by several systems of belt lines, classifying thousands of flat cars in one day.[2]

[1] Booth, A. W., 'Trade and Transportation', in Garland, *The North American Mid-West*, p. 84.

[2] Mayer, H. M., and Philbrick, A. K., 'Chicago', in Mayer and Philbrick, *Industrial Cities*, p. 41.

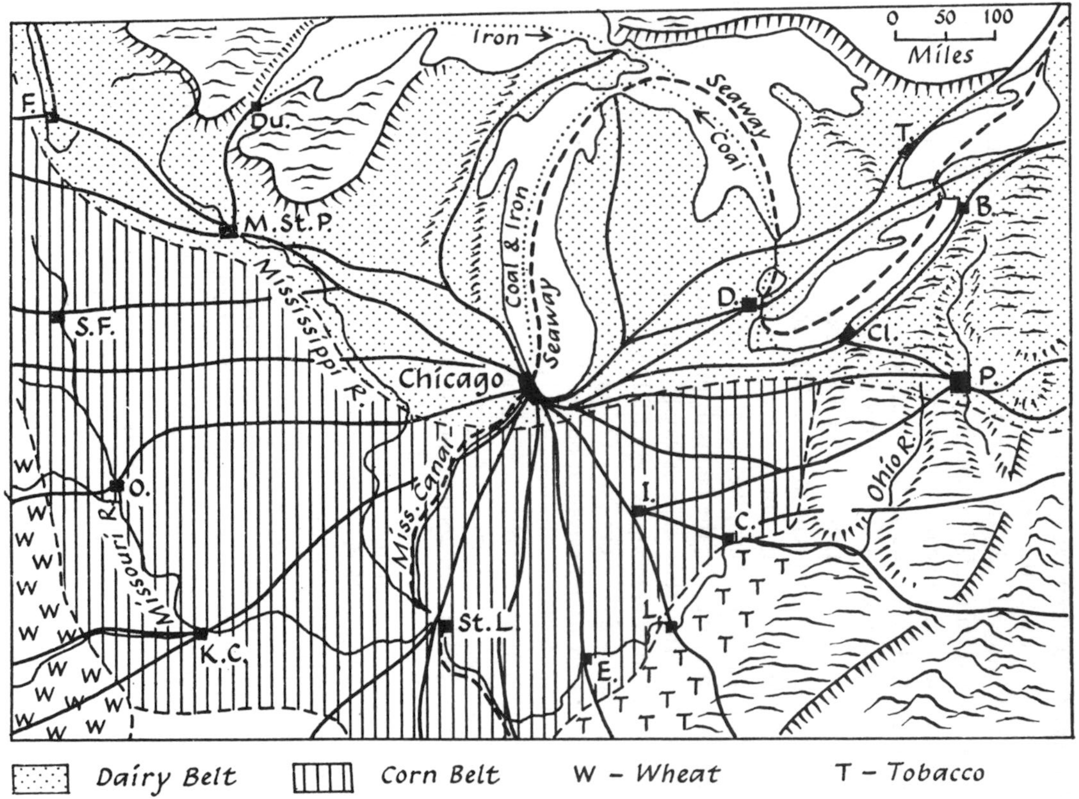

FIG. 171 Chicago—the Heart of America, linking up the industrial North-east with the agricultural Mid-West, and exploiting the iron of the Shield, the soils of the Interior Plains, and the waterways of the Great Lakes, the Ohio, and the Mississippi.

F., Fargo; S.F., Sioux Falls; O., Omaha; K.C., Kansas City; M.St.P., Minneapolis St Paul; Du., Duluth; St L., St Louis; E., Evansville; L., Louisville; C., Cincinnati; I., Indianapolis; D., Detroit; Cl., Cleveland; P., Pittsburgh; B., Buffalo; T., Toronto.

Through this vast network of routes Chicago collects hogs and fat cattle from throughout the Corn Belt, to be bought by meat-packing companies; store cattle and sheep from the rangelands of the west, to be auctioned off to the buyers that fatten stock; and both spring and winter wheat from the Wheat Belts, either for local millers or for transportation to eastern milling centres. Chicago's grain exchange sets prices for the whole Mid-West; similarly its fatstock auction controls, or leads the pace for, the trade in hogs and cattle in the main parts of the region. The Chicago Board of Trade influences other developments from the Ohio to the Missouri, and the Chicago Stock Exchange (Industrial Shares, Government and Municipal Bonds, etc.) is next only to that of New York.

The stock yards draw from a tremendous area, reaching almost to Denver in the west and Cincinnati in the east, in spite of competition from Kansas City, Omaha, Des Moines, and Cincinnati. The yards are over a mile long and half a mile wide. 'Contained within them are 13,000 pens; 35 miles of cattle alleys; 5 miles of hog alleys; 150 miles of railroad tracks; and a nine-storey office building. Nearly 50,000 cattle, 120,000 hogs, and 70,000 sheep have been received in a single day.'[1] In its hey-day it drew trade even from southern Texas, from which, in the cattle boom of the 'nineties, it would get over 700,000 head of cattle a year. This has now fallen because of competition from local centres; but Chicago's power to buy is still outstanding.

Chicago serves the Mid-West in many other ways; it is the main centre in this region for branch offices of U.S. Government bureaux; it has the chief western offices of many national businesses, foundations, educational, and church associations; it has the largest concentration of university students in the Mid-West, and the Graduate School of Chicago University not only draws key students from all the other Mid-western universities but attracts students from throughout the nation, and from abroad. Chicago is the great 'convention' city of the west, and its museums, art galleries, concert halls, and theatres have a far-reaching effect. So have its several newspapers, and Chicago is now rivalling Boston as the second most important publishing centre after New York. All these things give it a tremendous impact on its region. Indeed, in many ways the region is really becoming Chicago's sphere of influence.

Since the other industrialized parts of the north-eastern section of the Mid-West have been described, it remains simply to outline activity in the other centres. These do not lie in extensive and continuous belts of built-up industrial development; on the contrary, they form either small clusters of cities, usually centred in a large metropolis, or consist of isolated foci

[1] Mayer, H. M., and Philbrick, A. K., 'Chicago', in Mayer and Philbrick, *Industrial Cities*, pp. 50–51.

of trade and manufacture. The first to emerge were the river towns of the Ohio, Mississippi, and Missouri; some of these were enormously strengthened by the advent of railroad and highway. A second group comprises towns that came in essentially with the railway and grew as great railway junctions. All these centres owe their prosperity either to processing local agricultural products, mainly for export out of the region, or to making or assembling goods for the local market from materials or parts gathered together from the more basic industries in the north-east zone (Chicago–Pittsburgh) or from outside the region.

Ohio river towns, outside of the Pittsburgh–Wheeling complex (considered to be in the north-eastern sector of the nation), are principally Cincinnati and Louisville. **Cincinnati** (1,220,000) is the more important of these. It was once nicknamed 'Hogopolis' because of its huge hog-slaughtering and packing plants. Lying at the eastern edge of the Corn Belt, it was in a good position to buy hogs, slaughter them, and sell the pork products throughout the great market in the North-eastern States. It also bought wheat, grown as the second crop in parts of the Corn Belt, and milled it into flour for the eastern market. From Ohio grain it brewed some famous beers. These industries still flourish, but when the chief centre of Mid-western agriculture shifted from the Ohio to the Mississippi–Great Lakes, then Cincinnati was not as favourably located as St Louis, Minneapolis, Milwaukee, and Chicago. Therefore it has lost out to these centres as a meat-flour-beer (agricultural) manufacturer. Today it is using the animal and vegetable fats from the Corn Belt for its famous soap factory; but more important, it is relying on coal and iron from Pittsburgh to make agricultural machines, machine tools, and other steel products, which it can distribute westward throughout the Corn Belt, or south into the Cotton Belt. It is a major centre in the United States for high-quality machine tools.

Louisville (800,000) also owed its early industrial wealth to local agricultural products, and was one of the first large distilling centres, making whisky from corn. (Since the problem of transporting corn to the east was a very great one, it could be more profitably exported in the distilled form of 'bourbon'.) Louisville was at first dependent on water-power, lying on the bend of the river just below the Falls of the Ohio, but then, like most other Ohio river cities, it used coal from the Kentucky or West Virginia coal fields. Today it is tied in with the electric grid that gets much of its electricity from the hydro-electric developments of the Tennessee valley (T.V.A.). It uses electricity in many of its more modern industries such as the making of cigarettes, flour, and leather goods from local agricultural products and also electrical appliances. Near to the hardwood forests of the Cumberland plateau, it is also important for saw-milling, the veneer industry, and furniture.

Mississippi towns next grew up as trading and industrial centres, especially St Louis and Minneapolis-St Paul. **St Louis** (2,553,000) forms one of the most strategic centres in the Mid-West. Lying not far upstream from the Ohio, it is just downstream from the mouth of the Missouri; so it early received settlers moving down the Ohio to the Mississippi and then up the Mississippi to the Missouri. Founded as a French fort in 1765, it was no more than a trading post until the pioneer stream reached it in the early 1800s. 'Farmers came with a rush between 1815 and 1819; every day from thirty to fifty wagons loaded with homeseekers waited to cross the Mississippi at St Louis.' It became a great fitting-out centre, especially in the 'forties and 'fifties with the rush to Oregon and California. In the 1850s it was connected with Baltimore by railway, and its warehousing grew to still greater proportions. St Louis is still more important as a transportation junction, supply, and service station for the lower Mid-West than as a manufacturing centre. River traffic down the Missouri, Illinois, and Ohio, as well as up and down the Mississippi, still throngs its busy quays. Twenty-eight railways converge on it, bringing additional trade, and 'over two and a half million cars a year are handled annually by the Terminal Railroad Association of St Louis'.[1] All this is of greatest value to manufacturing, which is growing rapidly. Industries can use cheaply assembled coal, oil, and agricultural raw materials, brought together by river and rail. They have a large market, with good distribution facilities. In the heart of the Corn Belt the city is one of the largest meat-packing centres in the United States. It manufactures leather, and after Boston is the most important boot and shoe making city in the country. It also brews large quantities of beer, using grain from the southern Winter Wheat Belt and the southern part of the Corn Belt. The different industrial types are segregated within sharply defined localities related to the local environment.

Minneapolis-St Paul (1,650,000), known as the 'Twin Cities', have grown up on the Mississippi above and below the Falls of St Anthony. Minneapolis began as a saw-mill town, using the power of the falls for cutting lumber floated down from the thick forests of the upper river. However, as wheat farming grew in importance, Minneapolis—the largest power centre near the northern wheat district—turned to flour-milling, and is today one of the two chief flour-milling cities in the United States. St Paul flourished as a commercial town at the head of navigation on the river. Both centres have large foundries and machine shops, repair shops, lumber mills, and furniture factories. South St Paul has a major meat-packing business. Their functions have become much more than industrial, however, and they act as the metropolitan centre for Minnesota, the two Dakotas, and Montana.

[1] Thomas, L. F., *The Localization of Business Activities in Metropolitan St Louis*, Washington University Studies, New Ser. I, St Louis, pp. 1, 2.

The Missouri river has given birth to several large agricultural cities. Where the Kansas river joins it, stands the double settlement of **Kansas City** (1,200,000). Farther north is Omaha, not far from the confluence of the Platte and the Missouri. The railways from the east pass through these cities, using the western tributaries to strike across the Great Plains and enter the Rockies. With good rail and water connexions the cities are ideally placed for assembling and distributing goods. Kansas City, especially, still has a large wholesale and service function. Both centres are on the borders of the Corn Belt and the western livestock regions. Every year thousands of head of cattle and sheep are sent from the west to the Corn Belt to be fattened. They are sold in the huge auction markets of Kansas City and Omaha. Many of them are killed and their meat prepared in large packing plants to be sent throughout the country. Omaha is now one of America's largest packing centres. The cities are also near the Winter Wheat Belt, and have developed large flour mills and cereal factories. Kansas City is the principal U.S. market for winter wheat. **Sioux City** (108,000), at the confluence of the Big Sioux and the Missouri, also has large packing plants and grain mills. It has a big plant for repairing railway engines and rolling stock.

Railways have actually helped to make all these river towns. In addition they brought towns into being not on major river routes (although having water supplies, of course, from tributary streams).

There are several cities which have grown up chiefly as a result of railway building, having thus become important nodes for collecting raw materials, offering services, and in some places for Government administration. Columbus, Ohio, Indianapolis, Indiana, Springfield, Illinois, and Des Moines, Iowa, are important Corn Belt market towns. Grand Rapids and Lansing, Michigan, and Madison, Wisconsin, in the Dairy Belt; and Fargo, North Dakota, in the Spring Wheat Belt are other market towns. Some of these are the capitals of their states, though not being on the Great Lakes or the Mississippi waterways, they do not rank as large cities, with the exception of Columbus and Indianapolis. These have become very important as producers of agricultural and other machinery, using iron and steel forms and parts from the major steel-making industrial area to the north.

Columbus, Ohio (750,000), although founded as a small village where the Olentangy stream meets the Scioto river, showed little promise of its future until the National Road was built through it from Baltimore on the way to the Mississippi. The road was a great stimulus to westward migration, and improved services like the 'Great-Western Mail', but was too long for the use of bulk freight. Really extensive trade still had to wait for the railway age. The first railway lines were built along short distances to lake or river; to Sandusky (1848) and Cleveland in the north, and Cincinnati in the south (1847–52). Trade at once increased, but it was not until the Baltimore and

Ohio carried the line through from the coast, which was later continued to Indianapolis and St Louis, that prosperity was assured. Almost at the centre of the state, Columbus was chosen as its capital, and has a number of industries supporting administrative functions. Near to cheaply transported coal from South-east Ohio and West Virginia, and to iron and steel made in Cleveland and Pittsburgh, it has developed many metal-using industries, making various kinds of machinery. It is an important paper-making and printing centre, uses Ohio clays for ceramics, and leather from the cattle of the Corn Belt for leather goods.

Indianapolis (800,000) has a very similar history. Growing up as a small village on a fork of the White, itself a fork of the Wabash, it was largely by-passed, especially when the Wabash and Erie canal used the main stream to the west of it, connecting Evansville on the Ohio with Terre Haute and that with Fort Wayne and Toledo. Crawfordsville was even more important. But again when the railway came Indianapolis blossomed forth as a major junction with lines from Cincinnati and Madison converging on it from the Ohio; with connexions north through Lafayette to Chicago; and, above all, with east–west connexions with Baltimore and St Louis. There was also the link up through Crestline with Cleveland and the Mohawk–Hudson to New York or with Pittsburgh and the Delaware to Philadelphia. Indianapolis by 1855 was already a major railway junction. Near the eastern-interior coal field of Indiana–Illinois it has cheap fuel, either to be used directly or converted into electricity. Industries include automobile parts, airplane engines, and farm machinery. Indianapolis is the site of America's most famous motor-car racing track.

Farther west, beyond the Missouri, although the railways have not seen the rise of such large cities, they are probably even more important in the life of the community. They form great long belts of communication and activity, paralleled as they have come to be by modern highways, lines of telephone poles, high-tension cables striding from pylon to pylon, and, quite often, by strips of irrigation works developed on railway land. Railway stops came to form the main 'villages' or towns, and be the centre of merchandizing and farming. They, not the rivers, have grown to be the chief lines of flow.

Sutland and Yonland. They are in fact the main service zones of the west. For this reason Kraenzel has called them 'sutlands', the venue of the 'sutler' who

> historically was the supply agent of the army post before the day when the army maintained its own supply services. The sutland is the more densely settled, often string-like, area along the main avenues of transportation. It is the location of the main arteries for the wholesaling, business, industrial,

educational, health, governmental and social functions in the region, plus being the site of concentration of certain types of agricultural specialities.

Away from sutland are 'in-between' areas, generally without major transportation avenues and major public services and utilities. The towns are smaller with more limited services and facilities. There is a real problem in getting adequate finances and sufficient people to support the services. This area is the 'yonland' of the Great Plains—the area 'out-yonder', out from the sutland; the area without adequate services. The 'outback', as used for the Australian inland, comes nearest to the meaning of yonland. But the outback refers to a single large land mass. This is not the case in the Plains. Here the yonland represents smaller areas that are dispersed among the sutland belts.[1]

This useful suggestion well represents the striking differences between the great chords or thrusts or 'string-like' developments that penetrate and cut across the western drier parts of the Mid-West following the railways, and those emptier, quieter, less formative, and less well-peopled parts in between.

CONCLUSION

The American Mid-West is thus seen to be a broad, low plain, in the heart of the continent, divided into broad zones by climate and soil, associated with broad agricultural belts. Agriculture is the basis of wealth, but large deposits of iron, coal, and oil serve for industry. The great waterways of the Great Lakes and Missouri–Mississippi–Ohio systems help to draw the different parts of the region together. A dense network of railways does the same. The development of the region has become more and more commercialized and mechanized, and therefore tends to centre in the cities. The Mid-West is thus characterized by a 'rurban' civilization, where cities are intimately associated with, and exceptionally dependent on, the agriculture of the region, and the rural districts are centred in the cities, thanks to the highly commercialized agriculture. Thus the Mid-West contrasts with the essentially urban civilization of the North-eastern States, and the predominantly rural civilization of the Southern States. It has a distinction of its own.

---

[1] Kraenzel, C. F., 'Sutland and Yonland Communities in the Great Plains', *Rural Sociology*, December 1953.

CHAPTER TWENTY-ONE

The American West

The Western States of America are its youngest, boldest region. They are young historically, having been settled extensively only since the railways struck the mountain passes in the 1870s. They are also young geologically, with young mountains and young rivers. This has given them a striking scenery, where all the contrasts of mountain, plateau and plain, of canyon and fault-cliff coast are still violent, and have not been worn away, as in an eastern landscape. There are also the contrasts between hot, tropical climates and cool, alpine ones; between humid coasts clothed in majestic forest and arid interior basins, without any vegetation, glistening with the scales of alkali.

These contrasts are heightened by the fact that everything is at an extreme; here are the highest peaks in America, and the profoundest depressions, below sea-level; here are the most bleached and austere of deserts, and irrigated oases that blossom as the rose. Such extremes challenge human conquest. They challenge the miner to wrest gold out of mountains, in barren improbable places; they attract the venturesome, the missionary, the pioneer, the fortune-hunter. They have called forth the greatest feats of rail-road building, with lines laid across desert, and flung over mountains; they have built fabulous cities, thronging with all America.

But it is the new America. There is something so different about the west that it commands new methods, a new outlook, fresh initiative, and endeavour. People forget that they were southerners or easterners or plains-men; they become westerners. 'Here you find American optimism, enterprise and individual accomplishments at the maximum.' This optimism covers everything. People live for the future. They 'think big'. Like one of Tennessee Williams' characters, they have 'fallen in love with long distance'. It was because people could see over the long distance from the east, and see at the end of it a newness of life that would out-distance anything they had, that they came.

And they came in ever-increasing numbers, with the result that here the population has grown and is growing faster than anywhere else in the United States. Between 1910, when migration had got into its swing, and 1930, when it was slowed down by the Depression, the Pacific States increased 239 per cent compared with 49 per cent for New England. Even during the

Depression the west expanded with a growth between 1930 and 1940 of over 17 per cent as compared with 4·5 per cent for the north-east. In the war years there was a spectacular boom, and the Korean war that followed still kept the west to the fore. The Pacific Coast States expanded by no less than 48·8 per cent compared with the war-time average of 14·5 per cent for the U.S.A. In 1960 California became the most populous State in the Union with 18,084,000 people, compared with 17,975,000 for New York. Since then it has grown to equal Canada, with 20 millions. Yet in California there are some of the most sparsely settled districts in the country. It is no wonder that the west has been called 'the land of contrast' (see Fig. 153, Chapter 18, Major Regions of U.S.A.).

THE PHYSICAL ENVIRONMENT

Physically these contrasts embrace the immense stretches of the upper Great Plains, broken here and there by outliers of the mountains; the vast system of the Rockies, faulted and wall-like in the north, swelling to great domes and parks in the centre and bursting into ragged volcanic peaks in the south; the inlier of a more ancient structure in the Colorado plateau with, across from it, the Great Basin and the lesser basins and ranges, lying between the loftier lands; the step-up over fault on fault to the contorted rocks and snow-covered summits of the Nevadas—continued north in the Cascades; the profound depressions of the farthest west, partly drowned as in Puget Sound, but offering throughout the greater part of their length the most attractive of valleys for settlement and use; and finally, again in striking contrast, the volcanic knots and strings of fault-ridden and fold-twisted ridges of the Coast Range, plunging steeply into the Pacific.

Physical contrasts are strengthened by climate, with the striking differences between coast and interior, especially between the at-all-times wind-swept and rain-washed north-west coast and the perennially dry, but sunny interior and southern basins—between the ever-changing glooms and luminosities of maritime light and the burning blues and diamond-flashing whites of an interior clear as crystal. There is the difference between the summer-dry winter-wet climate of California and the wet-at-all seasons régime of the shores and west-facing mountains of western Oregon and Washington, and the difference too between the expected lack of rain in the interior plateaux and basins and the unpredictable and generally unexpected droughts of the Great Plains.

Climatic contrasts in association with relief are so great that often they give rise to sharp differences in vegetation and soils. There are few parts where, in the short space of a hundred miles, from basin-bottom to mountain-top, one may not traverse the whole range of types from cactus and sagebrush on desert brown soil through grass parks and open forest on good black earths to heavy mixed forests on podsolized grey-brown earths, and thence to high coniferous forest or alpine pastures on leached grey podsols, such as it would take thousands of miles to see, journeying from Colorado to Canada. This fact is the key to the extraordinary compaction of varied uses of land to be found in parts of the west from the Colorado Piedmont at Denver to the Great valley of California behind San Francisco, or from the Imperial valley in the south to the Okanagan valley in the north. Rarely does one find in other parts of America such very different uses of land coming so near together; they can often be seen in one panorama. This is not to say, however, that there are not long stretches of sameness: there are, and here is yet another contrast. There are areas, usually along the north south sweep of plain or mountain slope or crest-line, where the landscape scarcely changes for hundreds of miles, and one is met with a sheer monotony of wide-open or of shut-in horizons, of ocean-billowing grass, or the darkness of forest like the shadow of endless cloud.

THE HUMAN RESPONSE

A conditioning factor of almost everything in the West is the speed at which it has been developed. The region is scarcely more than a hundred years old. Historians of its growth have in many cases lived through much of that growth; their histories almost take the form of reportage. Looking back, Parkman writes:

> I remember that, as we rode by the foot of Pike's Peak, when for a fortnight we met no face of man, my companion remarked, in a tone anything but complacent, that a time would doubtless come when these plains would be a grazing-country, the buffalo give place to the tame cattle, farm houses be scattered along the watercourse, and wolves, bears, and Indians be numbered among things that were. We condoled with each other on so melancholy a prospect, but we little thought what the future had in store. We knew that there was more or less gold in the seams of those untrodden mountains; but we did not foresee that it would build whole cities in the waste and plant hotels and gambling houses among the haunts of the grizzly bear. We knew that a few fanatical outcasts were groping their way across the plains to seek asylum from persecution; but we did not imagine that the polygamous hordes of Mormon would rear a swarming Jerusalem in the bosom of solitude itself. We knew that more and more, year after year, the trains of emigrant wagons would creep in slow procession towards barbarous Oregon or wild and distant California, but we did not dream how Commerce and Gold would breed nations along the Pacific, the disenchanting screech of the locomotive break the

> spell of weird mysterious mountains, woman's rights invade the fastness of the Arapahoes, and despairing savagery, assailed in front and rear, veil its scalp-locks and features before triumphant commonplace. We were no prophets to foresee all this.[1]

Yet Parkman and his friend came to see it in fact, and to see more. In their own lifetime the West passed through the fur-trading boom and the gold boom, the cattle boom and the lumber boom, the homesteading boom and the wheat boom. Thereafter it was to go through the oil boom and the boom in fruit, the boom in films and the real-estate boom, and now it is in the best-ever boom, persuading Americans of all walks of life and from all quarters of the land that this is the best-ever place in which to live—or at the very least in which to retire. And so on it goes, with astounding energy, and astonishing speed.

This has partly been because of lessons learned from the experiences in crossing the Appalachians and conquering the Mid-West. Great political, social, and economic freedoms had been discovered that permitted swift, bold answers to the problems of the Far West. A spirit had been generated that subordinated geography to history, or rather made the geography of the west appear to be the means of climaxing the history of the east.

The big problem of the Indians had been met and, if not solved, at any rate dealt with; State-making was a known technique; the compromises had been worked out between the New England and Southern systems of land survey and disposal; and the acceptable means of administering local affairs in rural counties and townships and in municipal areas had been agreed on.

Above all, the expansion to the West had brought social and economic freedom. It had allowed people to escape from the village, particularly the New England village, and get out and live by themselves. In the same way it had helped them to escape from the plantation system. Even the regulated disposal of land in townships or sections, suited to the relatively dense settlement in the humid Mid-West plains, was departed from where necessity arose, and the great ranches were able to take up whole blocks of land. Thus an open disseminated form of settlement based on the wide scatter of individual farms was typical from the outset; fitted into the grid-iron scheme of sections where possible, but able to meet the strong dictates of exceptional people or circumstances as these arose. The West, then, benefited from that liberalization of land laws which more and more acknowledged, as Benton claimed, 'that the public lands belong to the People and not to the Government'.[2]

It benefited too from a freer attitude to education and religion. The

[1] Parkman, F., *The Oregon Trail*, New York, 1849, Preface to 4th edn.
[2] *U.S. Register of Debates*, XIXth Congress, 1st Session I, p. 727.

courses in the schools and colleges were broadened, particularly by being applied to practical problems. Education was thus more immediate, and more immediately beneficial. Religious freedom also allowed dissentient groups, who felt that 'the crust of custom was holding down the leaven of the spirit' in the more conventional forms of worship in the east, to found their own sects and develop their own ideas in the west. 'The widest variety of conditions are found. Emotional sects flourish, giving rise to a high birth-rate and death-rate among the churches.'[1] This helped in the starting of many new communities, most of which continued even if the original purpose for which they came together disappeared.

The West likewise offered a more democratic way that attracted people to it, and enabled them to appraise their new environment in the manner they chose—rash, realistic, idealistic, individualistic, co-operative—without interference from 'the dead hand of the past'. As Turner indicates, 'All the western states entered the Union with manhood suffrage, and accepted the doctrine of the rule of the majority rather than of property.'[2] There was land wealth, but no landed aristocracy. Caste and class meant little if anything. Men were free to make their own way by their own merit. As a result, there was a flight from tenancy, and its replacement, wherever possible, by land ownership: this was greatly strengthened by the chance at virtually free land.

The Far West likewise gained from the battle which the Mid-West had fought for the growth of domestic industry, the development of a home market, protection from foreign competition, and all that was involved in 'The American System'. Miners, lumbermen, cattle ranchers, wheat farmers, and would-be industrialists could go ahead, confident that they would be protected from the competition of Canadian lumber and wheat, or Mexican silver and cattle, or European or (later on) Asiatic manufactured goods.

Above all, the people moving to the Far West were caught up in that great sense of 'manifest destiny' which had first been expressed in the crossing of the Mississippi. In Congressional debates on the desirability of occupying the Oregon country, Floyd tried to indicate the significance of the march to the Pacific, not only in terms of the China trade, the whale fisheries, fur trading, and agricultural land, but of the rounding out of the nation. Baylies supported him, urging America 'to anticipate the grandeur that awaited her'.[3] The West responded by trying to live up to, fulfil, or provide that grandeur.

For many westerners this was a compelling motive, more important than land hunger or even the hunger for a new chance. As Ghent says, land

[1] Sims, *Elements of Rural Sociology*; cf. *The Rural Church, A Regional View*, p. 585.
[2] Turner, *The Rise of the New West*, p. 175.
[3] *U.S. Register of Debates*, XVIIIth Congress, 2nd Session, I, p. 37.

hunger has been greatly overstressed. 'Many of those who made the journey already had good, productive land, which in their eagerness to go they sold or even *abandoned.*' No, the China trade, whales, otters, free land—these were not the sum of things. 'Patriotism had its share, for with many the dominant motive was the eager desire to thwart the purposes of England in disputing the possession of what was firmly believed to be American territory.'[1] Yet it went even beyond this. Keeping out England was negative; the positive factor was a bursting confidence in America that carried the nation to the Pacific and that there set up the most dynamic society ever seen upon its shores.

And it was this dynamism that pushed the trails, and drove the roads, and thrust the railways over the Great Plains, across the Rockies and the Cascades, down at length to the fertile valleys beside the Pacific coast; this dynamism that made the great cattle kings, and lumber kings, and wheat kings, and oil kings, and the kings of the cinema; this dynamism that is transforming the landscape today with vast, new, throbbing cities; as it is this dynamism that has carried the West out upon the ocean itself, up to Alaska, and across to Hawaii, and to the far corners of the Pacific realm, linking the New World once again with the Old, and fulfilling at last that long quest for Cipangu and Cathay that first involved the Old World with the New.

THE CHIEF REGIONS OF THE WEST

Most of the West is a clear enough region, from the Rockies to the sea. There is some doubt on its eastern margin. Does this extend to the physiographic break, known as the 'break-of-the-plains', separating the Great Plains from the Central Lowlands, or simply to the more arid part of the Great Plains not yet overrun by, and subordinated to, the agricultural Mid-West? It can well be argued that the real break between Mid-West and West is a climatic one, and not where the Missouri plateau ends.

This is about the only instance where physiography does not dominate the West. Elsewhere, to the sea, relief is a compelling factor. Therefore, within the region as a whole, fairly clear-cut sub-regions are easily identified. This is important, and distinctive. Unlike the situation east of the Missouri, where low relief and old-established settlement have allowed cultural geography to dominate, here physical geography comes into its own, at least in delimiting *major* sub-regions. The west is moulded by mountains, They set the trends of the relief. High plains slope away from them. Plateaux are bounded by them. Deep trenches follow them. Rainfall, rivers, vegetation, agriculture, people fall into line with them. They are inescapable, and

[1] Ghent, W. J., *The Early Far West*, New York, 1936, p. 314.

mark out four chief regions: the Great Plains; the Rocky mountains; the Intermontane basins or plateaux; and the Pacific borderlands.

The Great Plains

Because of their distinctly lower and more open relief and also because of the way in which they were settled, the Great Plains form the least clear and 'western' of the regions of the West. They are essentially a transitional region between Mid-West and Far West.

> In the minds of most Americans [writes McCarty] a distinct difference exists between the Mid-West and the West. The Mid-West is . . . corn, hogs, fat cattle, hot summers, cold winters, rich soil, luxurious vegetation, monotonously smooth surfaces. But the West means 'magnificent' distances, sparse population, grass, stock ranges, sagebrush, wheat, water shortages . . . irrigation.

He goes on to say, 'Certainly there are marked differences between the Mid-West and West, but where the boundary between them lies, is a question.' Then he indicates that there is no *one* boundary, but a whole series of boundaries, running in a broad zone up and down the tier of states known as the Great Plains. This would seem to suggest that the Great Plains do not form a region in themselves, but constitute a sort of no-man's-land between the greater regions on either side. Transition, McCarty claims, is their identifying characteristic. They 'should not be thought of as a region in any other sense'.[1] They lie along an abnormal belt between normally dry lands to the west, and normally wet ones to the east (Fig. 172).

It is this debatability about the Great Plains area that forms its chief problem. Unfortunately, many easterners did not realize there was or could be a debate, and so they swarmed over it and began to develop it as though it were part of the Mid-western plains. The result was ruin when, all of a sudden, the dry west advanced against them, carried itself to the Missouri, and destroyed their fond illusions.

The United States is learning better. A recent official publication begins the description of this area as follows:

> 'From the 98th meridian west to the Rockies there is a stretch of territory whose history is filled with more tragedy and whose future is pregnant with greater promise than any other equal expanse within the confines of the Western Hemisphere.' This is how a member of the U.S. Department of Agriculture described the Great Plains in 1911. He might be speaking today: the tragedy has continued, and the promise is not yet fulfilled.[2]

[1] McCarty, H. H., 'The Upper Missouri Valley', in Garland, *The North American Mid-West*, p. 229.

[2] U.S. Information Service, *U.S.A., Its Geography and Growth*, London, 1955, p. 81.

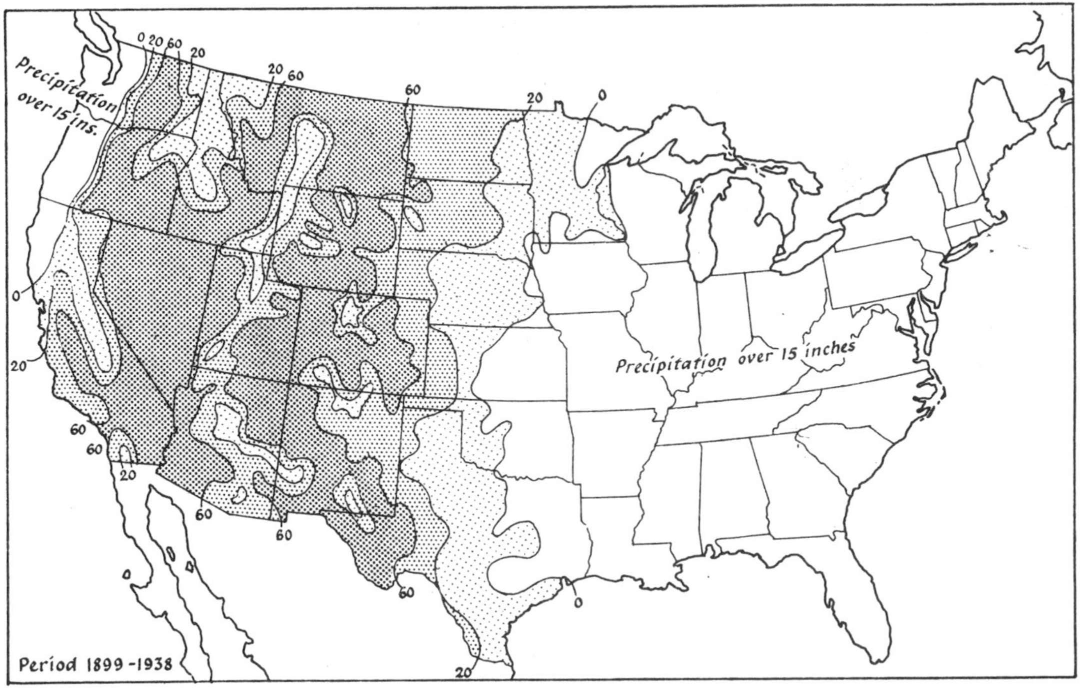

Fig. 172 The transitional position of the Great Plains between areas to the west where 60 per cent of the years can count on drought, and those to the east, where 80–90 per cent of the years are normally wet. (Map shows percentage of years between 1899 and 1938 with less than 15 inches of rainfall. From *Climate and Man*, U.S. Dept. of Agric.) (Scale, 1:35 m.)

Both tragedy and promise will be described later in this chapter. The present point is that tragedy and promise together, in the same region, do seem to suggest a very 'mixed-up' character.

This is precisely the subject of Kraenzel's study, *The Great Plains in Transition*. Although he argues that the Great Plains do form a region—mainly because they did form one once, before the farmers came from the east, and could form one yet, if only farmer and stockman could get together and work a truly flexible adjustment to changes in the environment—nevertheless (he is forced to admit) in their present state they are torn in two, and have become a zone in transition. Kraenzel recognizes

> a basic cleavage between the eastern and western portions of the Plains, a split of interest and function that has made it difficult for the two series of states [the more humid, farmer-dominated ones, and the more arid, rancher-led ones] to function co-operatively in the same region for their mutual interest. The eastern tier of states affiliate themselves with their eastern neighbours; the western tier with the west.[1]

This is mainly because the Plains area cannot exist on its own, and for itself. It is a hinterland, either for eastern or for western flour and meat packing, and other, interests. Consequently,

> Plains people look to other areas of the nation for their markets and for the refined and processed goods and services they consume. Because of this, the residents on the eastern edge of the plains have their attention drawn to the Mid-West, while those on the western edge look towards the Pacific Coast. The Plains people are, therefore, unable to act in a united fashion.[2]

As a result the area has been split into a number of minority groups, the wheat farmers, the ranchers, and the cotton planters—and several others, which vie with each other, trying to get support from the Mid-West, the West, or the South for their particular needs and programmes when they put these up to Congress. 'To accomplish these ends the wheat farmers have resorted to building a strong "we group" feeling among themselves. Since ranchers of the Plains have not participated [in their plans for the area] they have become identified as the "out-group"; the "coat-tail" riders; and even as "enemies" in the opinion of the dry-land farmers.' The tragedy of the 'thirties and the prosperity of the 'forties educated the farmers to the need for, and in the benefits of, co-operation. They have done a great deal to promote co-operatives. 'And they feel grieved because their fellow plainsmen, the stockmen, have not exercised a similar initiative.'[3] These and many

[1] Kraenzel, *The Great Plains in Transition*, p. 173.
[2] Ibid., p. 212. [3] Ibid., p. 257.

things provide evidence of a region which is divided or transitional in character.

As far as the regional geographer is concerned this dilemma can be resolved only by considering the Great Plains in the context of both Mid-West and West. The wheat-growing areas have already been described in the treatment of the agricultural Mid-West. One could therefore confine oneself to the 'rump' of the area, the ranching-mining zone, in a description of the West. Nevertheless, because of its unity as a physiographic region, its past unity under the ranching economy, and its potential unity as an area of the growing and real interdependence of ranching and farming, it will here be outlined as one, although the emphasis will be on its western affiliation.

The Plains Environment

The western boundary of the region is quite clear. It is the Rocky Mountain front. But the eastern margin is indefinite. In the north it runs along the Missouri Coteau, a well-marked escarpment that overlooks the Central Lowlands. In the south it ends abruptly at the Balcones escarpment of Texas. But in the centre no major physical feature marks its edge, although the Red and Smoky hills indicate somewhat of a break. Climate and vegetation are better boundaries.

The Great Plains are vast and flat, but are broken by many interesting features. The nearly horizontal beds of rocks which floor most of the region are lifted up into sharp hog-back ridges in front of the Rockies, and arched into great domes in the Bear's Paw, Montana, and Black hills, South Dakota, districts. The sedimentary rocks have been stripped off the tops of the domes, leaving hard, older rocks showing through as bold and rugged mountains. The Black hills are fairly rich in gold, but a main use of the uplands is for summer pasture for the ranches.

The slope of the plains is considerable, from over 5,000 feet in the west to about 1,500 feet in the east. Large eastward-flowing rivers occur. These have cut broad valleys into the plains, leaving high interfluvial areas standing up as mesas or buttes, fronted by escarpments—like Pine Ridge escarpment, Nebraska. Erosion in weaker rocks has produced the notorious Badlands of South Dakota. The sand hills of Nebraska are another unusual landscape, where for a long time sand has blown off shoals in the braided river courses during low water and has been heaped up in dunes on the broad interfluves. Sheets of loess also extend across the eastern-central edge of the plains.

The rivers are fed by snows and rains in the Rocky mountains, and begin their downward course in strength, bringing quantities of pebbles and sand with them. But as they flow across the semi-arid plains they lose volume. During the summer large rivers like the Arkansas, Canadian, and Platte dwindle down to a trickle. They drop their load of sand. It forms shoals and banks which cause the rivers to shift their beds, or run in divided streams. They are not suitable for navigation.

The climate of the Great Plains is semi-arid. The climatic break between the plains and the Central Lowlands is not sharp; but a zone of change begins to occur at the isohyet of 20 inches of annual rainfall in the south, and 15 inches in the north. Where the rainfall decreases below 17 inches in the south or 12 inches in the north, evaporation is so high that there is not enough rain left to support much vegetation. Trees are scarce. The natural vegetation is grassland. Medium length grasses, growing fairly close together, once carpeted the eastern plains; short grasses, in scattered bunches, covered the western, drier parts. The rainfall in the western margin is as low as 10 inches. Soils show a change from east to west following the rainfall. The soils of the moister, long grass region, are rich, dark brown to black; those of the drier, Short Grass prairies are chestnut to light brown soils.

A major characteristic of the climate is the way it changes. Rainfall is very variable. The average does not mean very much: the rainfall is hardly ever average; it is usually growing wetter than normal over a period of years, or getting abnormally dry. These wet and dry periods have played an important part in the history of settlement (Fig. 173).

The Settlement of the Plains

The Plains Indians no doubt experienced these dry and wet spells, but they were able to adjust to them by migrating from drier to wetter regions. They lived a wandering life, hunting the buffalo. They did not have a settled, agricultural existence.

Nor did the early frontiersmen. White hunters followed the herds of buffalo just like the Indians and moved where they moved. Even after the buffaloes disappeared life was not very different. Range cattle and sheep replaced the buffalo, and the cowboy rode the range herding the cattle up to hills and bluffs in the dry times, and then down to the plains when grass became green. Nevertheless, permanent settlements began to be made. Claims were staked to the land. Little towns appeared. Stage-coaches bumped along tracks across the prairie. In the late 1860s railways were built. The farmers moved in. The migratory habit of life came to an end. In the Homesteader Act the farmer had to live on his claim and cultivate the land for five years before he could have the title to it.

When the homesteaders arrived, between 1875 and 1880, the weather was wetter than normal. They thought that it would continue so. Many of them ploughed up land believing that rain actually followed the plough.[1] But the weather changed. A disastrous drought spread over the plains. Thousands

[1] Smith, H. N., 'Rain Follows the Plow; the Notion of Increased Rainfall for the *Great Plains, 1844–1880*', Huntington Lib. Q., **Vol. X**, No. 1, Feb. 1947.

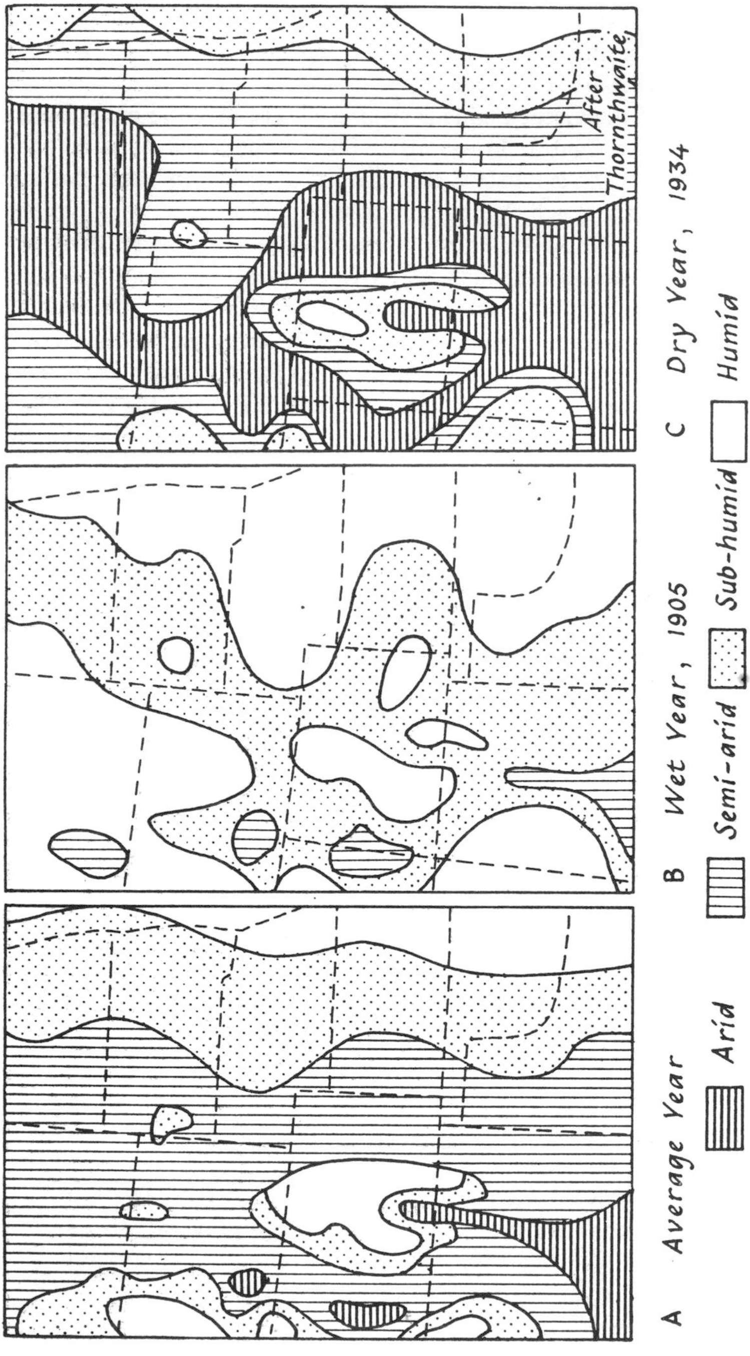

FIG. 173 The changefulness of climate in the Great Plains.

of farmers were ruined. Immigration was stopped. In fact, emigration out of the region began, many abandoned their homes, and scrambled back to the humid east (Fig. 174).

A similar story occurred in the 'twenties and 'thirties. After the First World War there was a depression in the cattle market. Many ranchers had to sell up their land. This was bought by land speculators at from \$2 to \$4 an acre. These speculators wanted to make money on the land, and so they went through the Central and Eastern States to persuade farmers to move out west. Now it happened that wheat prices began to rise and reached a dollar a bushel, which seemed high at that time. Therefore many farmers bought up land and sowed it to wheat and hoped to make a fortune. But they had big expenses to pay off. They bought the land from the speculators at \$30 to \$40 an acre. They had lots of equipment to purchase. The cost of machinery had gone up. The cost of labour was also high, and a lot of labour had to be hired during the harvest. A few got rich; but most of the farmers were only beginning to pay off their mortgages when the Great Drought struck in 1931.

Once again the farmers had been 'fooled' by the weather. When they settled in the plains in the 'twenties the weather was wetter than normal, but they mistook it for normal, or at least they hoped it would last long enough for them to make a fortune. It did not. The drought came. It followed a severe economic depression. The two calamities together ruined thousands of farmers. The purchasing power of the farmer dropped 42 per cent; mortgage indebtedness rose by over 50 per cent; local taxes nearly trebled—and the crop failed, and failed again! Nearly a quarter of all the farms were foreclosed in the more arid areas, and 'many of the foreclosure sales failed to net the mortgage'.[1] Thousands had to give up. Then schools and churches were closed. Whole communities disappeared. Their tragic story has been grimly recorded in the novel of the drought, *The Grapes of Wrath*.

> The last rains lifted the corn quickly and scattered weed colonies and grass along the sides of the roads. In May the sky grew pale and the clouds that had hung in high puffs for so long in the spring were dissipated. The sun flared down on the growing corn. The clouds appeared and went away, and in a while they did not try any more. The surface of the earth crusted, a thin hard crust. As the sharp sun struck day after day the leaves of the young corn became less stiff and erect; each leaf tilted downward. Then it was June and the sun shone more fiercely.
>
> A wind followed that softly clashed the drying corn. The wind increased. The dust from the roads fluffed up and spread out. Little by little the sky was darkened by the mixing dust. The sun shone redly and there was a

[1] Brunner and Kolb, *Rural Social Trends*, pp. 42, 300.

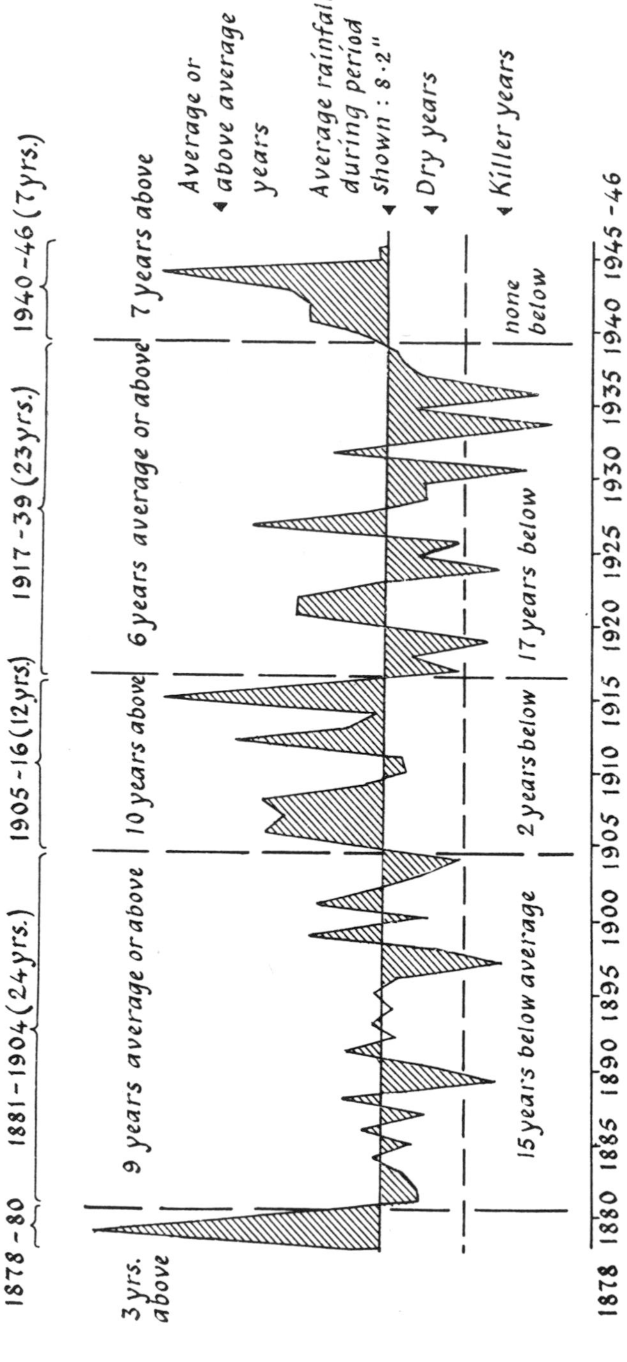

FIG. 174 Precipitation variability in the Great Plains (E. Montana), according to T. Lommasson.

> raw sting in the air. During the night the wind raced faster over the land, dug cunningly among the rootlets of the corn, and the corn fought the wind with its weakened leaves until the roots were freed by the prying winds and then each stalk settled wearily sideways towards the earth. The dawn came, but no day. In the grey sky a red sun appeared, a dim red circle that gave a little light, like dusk; and as that day advanced, the dusk slipped back toward darkness and whimpered over the fallen corn.
>
> The people came out of their houses and smelled the hot stinging air and covered their noses from it. Men stood by their fences and looked at the ruined corn. The men were silent and they did not move often. The women came out to stand beside their men—to feel whether this time the men would break.[1]

And many of them did break, and, ruined by the repeated duststorms and the long agony of the drought, seeing their women age and their children grow thin and pale, they left their farms and trekked west to California, or drifted back east, or ended up in Government relief camps.

This failure was obviously due to a lack of adjustment to geography, but that lack of adjustment, in its turn, was due to the unusually rapid history of development. The settlers had scarcely given themselves time to learn the peculiarities of the region. The result of the drought has now shown that not all the Great Plains are suited to cultivation. Much of the ploughed land should return to grass. The drier parts should be left to cattle or sheep ranches. Even in the more humid parts the production of corn and wheat will always be subject to climatic fluctuations.

The droughts have had some beneficial effects. After the drought of the 'nineties, farmers took up dry-farming methods. These methods aimed at conserving all the moisture there was, through maintaining a 'dust mulch' after every summer rain, and by leaving some of the land fallow. These techniques have already been described. They helped somewhat, but did not meet the problem in the worst areas of recurrent drought and erosion. Since the Great Drought, irrigation has been tried, and along rivers like the Pecos, Arkansas, Platte, Missouri, and Yellowstone there are important irrigation projects producing high yields of wheat, corn, sugar-beet, potatoes, and alfalfa. The alfalfa is sold to the ranches to supplement the rather scanty pastures of the high and drier plains. The irrigated farms are small, and there are many people per square mile. However, the increase of population in the irrigated areas has not made up for the decrease elsewhere. The abandonment of many farms, the consolidation of others into bigger farm units, the change back to ranching in the drier areas—have all decreased the rural population of the plains.

---

[1] Steinbeck, J., *The Grapes of Wrath*, Heinemann, London, 1939.

This has meant major changes in the settlement pattern. The farms themselves are few and farther away from each other. Many schools have had to be closed down, and the school districts greatly enlarged—the children being collected by bus and driven to and from school. Churches failed left and right. One survey showed that 53 per cent of the rural churches, established for barely fifty years, had closed by 1935, after five years of depression and drought.[1] Again the church districts have had to be enlarged, and there are now fewer church-centred hamlets. In many rural service-centres only the post office, village store, and gasolene station are left. In fact, such centres have declined greatly in number as the big farms have put up their own petrol pumps, and have bought 'deep freezes' and lockers for storing food obtained directly from the town. The churches have recognized this. 'There is so much centering of church forces in the towns that the church has been called "the church of the center".' It is no wonder that 'half of the rural communities and a fifth of the population are now without a church'.[2]

The result of this has been that wheat farming, when it becomes marginal on its drier edge, so thins out settlement and population that it is difficult to maintain the usual appurtenances and amenities of farm communities; nevertheless the attempt is made to do so—that is, to keep up roads, bridges, schools, churches, townships, and county offices and officials as though this were all a part of the farm civilization of the east, from which the farmers came and to which they cling. A point arrives, however, where they cannot do this, and for the sake of the lack of amenities if not the lack of rainfall they give it up. Rangeland takes over.

Ranching has thus come to dominate the marginal as well as the really drier parts of the Great Plains. Men have slowly recognized that too much land has been put under the plough and that a great deal of the marginal country should be returned to natural pasture. Actually, the really rough land has always been left to the rancher, even where it fell within the subhumid climatic belt. Thus the Dakota badlands, even east of the farm front, have remained ranching country. They could hardly have been used in any other way—unless left to the Indians. Similarly the sand hills of Nebraska, fringing the Platte, those of eastern Colorado, between the Platte and the Republican rivers, and those in Kansas, along parts of the Arkansas, have remained stockmen's territory, sometimes well to the east of the wheat frontier. Consequently, the Spring and Winter Wheat Belts are separated by a vast bulge eastwards of western range.

From the beginning, stock areas came to differ from the farmer's realm. Here culture played a very real role. A great number of the ranchers were

[1] Hollingshead, A. B., 'The Life Cycle of Nebraska Rural Churches', *Rural Sociology*, June 1937.

[2] Belknap, H. O., *The Church of the Changing Frontier*, p. 109.

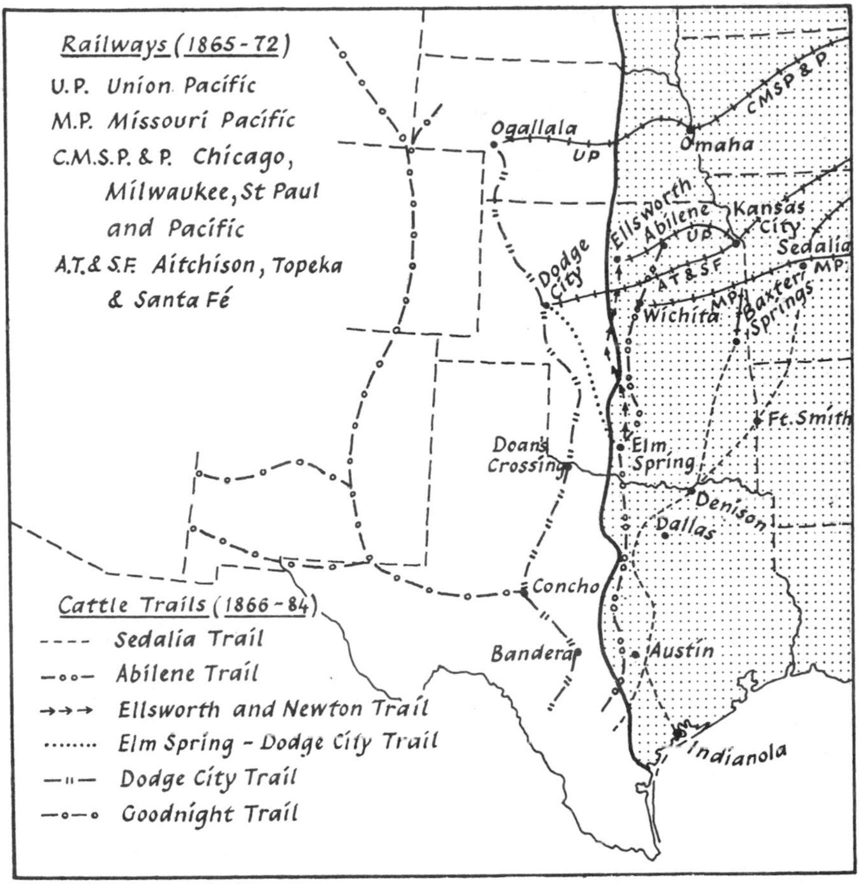

FIG. 175 Ranching on the Great Plains, 1866–84, the critical period of struggle between trail and railway, cattle-men and homesteaders. The stippled area represents the humid plains; cropland soon took this over, forcing the ranchers to the semi-arid west. Their trade, however, continued to be with the eastern sector, whose cities dominated the cattle business. (Scale, 1:8 m.)

Southerners, not Mid-Westerners, far less Easterners. They had come up from Texas after the Civil War and they organized the parts of the range they took over, even as far as western Montana, along *their* lines. In 1866, for instance, Nelson Story drove a herd of cattle all the way from Dallas, Texas, to Gallatin, Montana. Everywhere Texans were on the move (Fig. 175). Thornthwaite describes their historic migration.

At the end of the Civil War the Great Plains were chiefly waste land occupied by roving herds of buffalo and scattered nomadic Indians. [This was *less* than a hundred years ago, when the Victorian era was in full swing in England.] The few existing settlements were trading posts that had developed as a result of the Gold Rush. These found cattle-raising profitable as a side line and furnished the nuclei for the subsequent development of the cattle industry. To the south lay Texas, with a culture organized around cattle raising and a land system well adapted to the requirements of that culture and to the peculiarities of the semi-arid climate. The Civil War had brought about a cattle shortage in the north but had left Texas fairly overflowing. The resulting price differential was so great that vast numbers [nearly six million before 1885] were driven over the trails to the railroads [west from Kansas City and from Omaha] to the northern and eastern markets. Actual and prospective profits from the cattle drives caused a phenomenal extension of ranching over the entire Great Plains area.[1]

Even if cattle-men thereafter had to retreat in front of the wheat farmers advancing from the east, they kept the less accessible, less readily tillable, and drier parts of the plains to themselves; and do so to this day. These are the western parts, parts which are continuous with the range lands of the Rockies and of the Intermontane basins. Consequently they knit together the western half of the Great Plains with the rest of the West, making it firmly and clearly a segment of that region.

The life of the cattlemen was from the first admirably adapted to the plains, and in the light of the repeated sufferings of those homesteaders who tried to colonize the area, one cannot help but regret that the drier plains did not remain under the open range. (And in this light one also cannot but regret the attitude of the films in making the cattlemen the enemies of progress, and honouring the homesteader in tearing up the sod. In many cases the crime lay not in shooting the man behind the plough, but in driving the plough into the soil.) As Webb points out:

> If the cattleman led a life different from the easterner, it was because he had adapted himself to an environment that was also different. Cattle herding was a natural occupation which used the land in its natural state and altered it hardly at all. It was expansive, covering enormous areas of land. The population of the range was, therefore, a very sparse population . . . the human particles were far apart, and they oscillated over wide spaces. Men had to give up old methods and adopt new ones when they crossed the ninety-eighth meridian . . . only those who were willing to do this and do it rapidly would survive.[2]

---

[1] Thornthwaite, C. W., *Migration and Economic Opportunity*, Philadelphia, 1936, pp. 207–8.

[2] Webb, W. P., *The Great Plains*, New York, 1931, pp. 244–6.

In the main, those who came up via Texas were able to do so; those who pushed in from the humid Mid-West were not. This was evident, as much as anything, in land policy. Texas, when it was a Republic, adopted its own land policy for the plains, which it was able to maintain even after entering the Union. This took account of the space needed for ranching and of the rancher's oscillation between river and range, by allowing individuals, first, to take up much larger blocks of land—up to eight sections—than was the case in the humid Mid-West; and, second, to take this up in different ways, so that they could buy land along a stream for winter and spring pasture and also up on a mesa or hill, often quite some distance away from the ranch, for summer and autumn grazing. Furthermore, they could lease land from the public domain for additional grazing, and leasing was always a major part of the ranching programme. Thus a Texan settler on the plains could buy over 5,000 acres for himself, and two or three times that amount as a family concern. The homesteader from the Mid-West, however, had to do with his 160 acres.

When the Texan passed north he was not given as much liberty; nevertheless by using the public domain to an even larger extent, and by buying up groups of sections in the names of dependent individuals—even his cowboys, he was able to manage. The clash came when the homesteader moved in, supported by the legislators framing the State laws on the lines of the humid Mid-West. A major clash of practice resulted. The eastern tier of states to which the wheat farmers spread 'followed the humid-area policy of getting all the land into the operators' hands'. This insistence upon the alienation of all public lands was part of Mid-Western—indeed, of Eastern—ideology: an ideology that profoundly altered the geography of the Great Plains. The ranchmen could not buy enough land, since larger units than the legal quarter-section or section, were difficult to get, if permitted at all; and in the eastern tier of states they could not lease grazing from the public domain. There was virtually no such thing.

Today, for example, North Dakota has only 5 per cent of its area in public lands—including only 520 acres in forest, but with no area denominated as grazing land. It is no wonder that the rancher has been squeezed out.

Fortunately for him, he had managed to preserve enough influence in the western tier of Great Plains states to be able to have the State and the Federal governments maintain a large share of the land as public domain. Montana, for example, the neighbour of North Dakota, has 37 per cent of its territory as public domain, including over 16 million acres of forest and about 6 million acres for public grazing. This, with the belated privilege of buying more land than was customarily allowed in the Mid-West, kept the rancher going, and enabled him to preserve his place in the region. In doing so, he has been helped by the southern practice, carried into this western tier of plains states, of using the county as the administrative unit, instead of the township (or the combination of township and county authorities) used in the eastern tier. Since these counties are very large, not many offices or officials have to be kept up. 'County-busters' did try to break up these larger units in favour of townships (which gave more people a say in affairs and put more offices in their way), but were only partially successful, and that only in the eastern counties. By and large, county government in the stockman's area has been better adapted to the sparse population and the difficulty of maintaining public institutions and services, than the more costly system in the plains of the farmer.

Thus, although the differences between the western and eastern parts of the plains are essentially geographical, going back to climate and soil, they have been very definitely exacerbated by cultural differences which have now become the immediate dividing factors. It is not surprising that, with these differences, there has been a good deal of friction between cattleman and wheat-farmer. Their needs, ambitions, practices, in fact cultures, are different. Consequently the plains have been split and do not operate at the present time as a cohesive unit.

In the western half, however, that is, within the cattleman's domain, there are signs that the two groups are getting together. Certainly, in a few areas, like the Colorado Piedmont, they have discovered a use for each other which is now helping to bring about the integration of grazing and crop agriculture. In this particular area, as Miss Beyer has shown, the land at the edges of the basin is rather too rugged for cropping; yet it is too dry for really profitable ranching. The ranchers have been leasing land from the public domain in the forested mountains, above. 'The typical pattern of western range use—summer pasture in the high alpine meadows and spring-to-fall grazing on the intermediate and drier public domain lands'[1] has been modified by the extensive irrigation of the wide river flats, and the provision of feed for the ranch from the surplus of the farm. In addition to the alfalfa hay which the farmers sell to the ranchers, there is a considerable amount of irrigated pasture, on which beasts can be wintered or fattened. But a good two-thirds of the valley land is for highly specialized cash crops on which the farmer mainly relies, such as fruit, vegetables, beans, corn, oats, and wheat.

The feed sold to ranchers has helped to increase and improve stock in the region and consequently 'more stock are sent to local farms for fattening'.[2] (It is interesting that although Denver, on the plains, has acted as the main market, 'smaller packing plants in the Mountain and Pacific states have sent commission agents into the region to make contracts with ranchers and

[1] Beyer, J. L., *The Integration of Grazing and Crop Agriculture*, Chicago, 1957, p. 4.
[2] Ibid., p. 14.

farmers'. Here is a definite instance of the western contact of the plains area.) Thus irrigated lands provide supplementary feed for the livestock grazed on the drier, rougher slopes (on which most of the ranches are located) and also on the forested slopes of the public domain, 'maximizing the use of the local grazing resource base'.[1] Some of the farmers own their own herds for breeding and selling, and only sell their surplus hay to the ranchers;

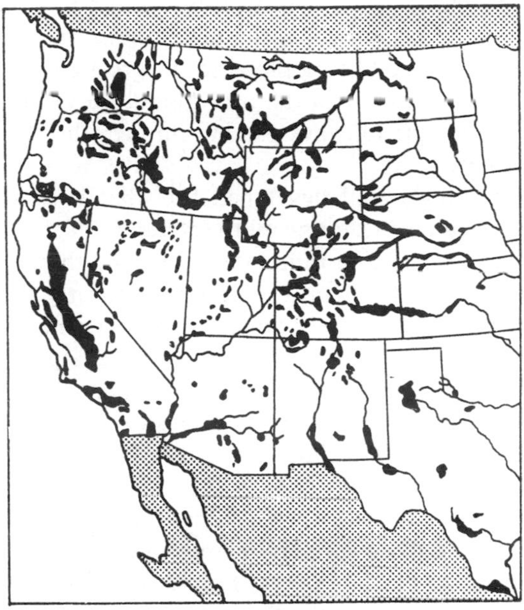

FIG. 176 Irrigation in Western United States, one of the great achievements of man in mastering his environment.

others, usually smaller operators, buy young cattle from the ranchers and fatten them on their farms. A few rent grazing, usually in the form of summer pasture, to ranchers who prefer to meet their summer grazing requirements in this way, or who may need this extra pasture over and above what they can rent in the forests.

Extensions of such practices are found in many parts of the upper Great Plains where the damming of the mountain-fed rivers has supplied an increasing basis for irrigation. Thus irrigation, while doubtless most useful for special crops, dairying, and the fattening of beef-cattle on valley farms, is having a growing impact on the ranches, and is helping to bring rancher and farmer together (Fig. 176).

[1] Ibid., pp. 61, 62, 73.

Mining is another occupation on the plains that tends to draw the area to the west, and give it kinship with the Mountain states on which it abuts. The mineral resources are quite large, including gold, coal, lignite, and oil. On the whole, however, they are more of a potential than an actual source of wealth. There is not the man-power to develop them; but even if there were, the high cost of mining and transporting them would be prohibitive. They are too far from the cities; and there is no large local market. They cannot compete favourably in the Central or Eastern market.

Nevertheless, on the eastern edge, the mid-continental oil field has been developed to the full; the oil being piped to the great consuming centres in the Mid-West, or to southern ports; and along the western edge coal is mined, at one time for the railways passing through the Rockies, but now for the western cities.

City life is surprisingly well developed for what is essentially a rural, sparsely populated region. Although all the states, both eastern and western tiers, with the exception of Colorado, are more rural than urban, this does not reflect either a richness of rural centres or a poverty of urban ones. It simply indicates that most of the people live on big ranches or big farms. 'The close observer', Hewes remarks, 'may note the larger farms . . . than farther east and an accompanying decrease in number and size of farms. The activity of the rural areas centers on the farmsteads.'[1] Nevertheless, many live in cities. The anomaly is explained by the lack of hamlets, villages, and small country towns. These have not declined so much as failed to grow in keeping with the growth of the city, which has now become the ranchman's or the farmer's main and regular service and social centre.

Most of the cities are on the eastern, humid edge; but a few of them are in the foothill trench, in front of the Rockies. The eastern ones are linked to the Central Lowland and are really satellites of Minneapolis, Omaha, Kansas City, and Dallas.

Wichita, Kansas (380,000), is the only large independent settlement. It is on the Arkansas valley, near to the Wichita oil field, and has refining plants and aeroplane factories. Its chief interests are marketing wheat and cattle, milling flour and packing meat.

Denver (1,100,000) is the main city of the western plains. It lies in a pre-cordilleran trough, which is well watered and has a favourable climate. It stands a mile high in altitude, and has a clean, crisp, healthy atmosphere. It is the focus for the western ranches, mines and tourist trade, and has large meat-packing plants, factories for making mining equipment, iron works, and leather, rubber, and luggage works. Its main function, however, is as a transportation, wholesaling, and administrative centre. Seven major

[1] Hewes, L., in Powers, W. E., and Logan, R. F., *Transcontinental Excursion Guide*, I.G.U. XVIIth International Geographical Congress, Washington, 1952, pp. 35, 37.

railway lines converge on it from Chicago, St Louis, and Memphis in the mid-west, from Fort Worth in the south-west, and from Los Angeles and Seattle on the Pacific coast. More important,

> it is now one of the biggest centres for transcontinental trucking; and main warehouse and repair facilities are maintained here by several of the large trucking concerns. The wholesaling and warehousing functions of the city have now expanded until they serve . . . the needs of at least six Rocky Mountain states. In general, Denver acts as a sub-distribution centre for Kansas City and Chicago, many of whose distribution functions it is rapidly assuming.[1]

Denver is also a regional centre for many departments of the Federal government. Indeed, a whole part of the city, known as the Denver Federal Center, is devoted to government activities, and here is 'the largest single concentration of government operations outside of Washington'. This has helped the city to become a major shopping, residential, and cultural attraction in the western plains.

Thus we see that the Great Plains are a varied region, which in the drier west are like the mining-and-ranching states of the Rockies, but in the east are like the farming states of the Central Lowland. Their sparseness of population, remoteness, and lack of industry are typically western features; yet much of their farming is orientated to the central plain. Their problems of a fluctuating climate with recurrent drought and widespread erosion, are largely their own and distinguish them from the more humid east and the more arid interior.

The Rocky Mountains

These mountains are long enough and broad enough to be considered a second major subdivision of the American west. Indeed they are so massive that at one time it was considered that they might well divide America in two, and prove an insuperable obstacle to national unity. Tracy, of New York, doubted the value of expanding beyond the Rockies and declared that 'nature has fixed limits for our nation; she has kindly introduced as our western barrier, mountains almost inaccessible, whose base she has skirted with irreclaimable deserts of sand'.[2] However, even as the debate went on, frontiersmen and traders were pushing into the Rockies, and beyond, to make it all-but-inevitably a part of America.

Here physical geography is pre-eminent. The Northern Rockies consist of high blocks of folded or uplifted sedimentaries, which have been faulted steeply producing a block-and-trench structure. Some of the blocks are

[1] Crain, C. N., in Powers and Logan, *Transcontinental Excursion*, pp. 41–42.
[2] Turner, *Rise of the New West*, p. 129.

tilted on one side, and slope more gently on the other. Some of the valleys have been covered with huge outpourings of lava, that form tablelands between the ridges. Farther south the country becomes more open. The Central Rockies form a dome-and-park terrain. Occasional domes have had their crests stripped from them and stand up, a rugged igneous core surrounded by infacing escarpments. South of the Wyoming basin rise the volcanic peaks of the jagged Southern Rockies, which pass through a belt of highlands into the Sierra Madre Oriental of Mexico.

The Rockies are fairly rich in metals and minerals. The hard granite cores that are exposed in the domes, the many igneous intrusions, the volcanic veins—all carry rich lodes of ore. The Northern Rockies produce about 10 per cent of the United States gold, and the Southern Rockies 14 per cent. In many parts, the land is barren, the way into the hills difficult, railways snake into the mines and have to bring the food and equipment for the miners from long distances; nevertheless, these obstacles are overcome and the gold is dug out. However, when the mines are exhausted, there is nothing to keep the people, and they melt away, leaving empty mine shafts and desolate buildings in swiftly decaying 'ghost' towns.

Sixty-nine per cent of the United States' silver is extracted in the Rocky Mountain states. Most of this is mined in the Northern Rockies, in Montana and Idaho, and the Central Rockies of Utah. Colorado is also quite important.

The Rockies also produce about 30 per cent of the copper of the country; 27 per cent of its lead; and 26 per cent of its zinc. Most of the production comes from the Northern and Central Rockies, which are thus seen to be one of the nation's chief sources of metal. In Wyoming, on the flanks of the Continental Divide, is an important iron field, while not far from it is a small coal-mining district. Coal occurs in many valleys in the Southern and Central Rockies, and on the eastern flanks of the Northern Rockies, but often it is of poor quality, and it is so remote and costly to transport that not much is mined. The total yield is not much more than 15 million tons a year. However, it serves a useful purpose for the metal-refining cities, and it assisted in the development of the railways of the region. In the Wyoming basin are fairly large pools of oil that have been tapped by wells. Here again the remoteness of the field has restricted production. There is not much oil in the Northern Rockies because of the extensive faulting, although to the east is the large Williston oil basin.

The Rockies have a wide climatic range, as would be expected of a region with such a range of altitude, and lying between 35° and 49° north. The high northern ridges are in the sweep of the rainy westerlies, and receive a lot of rainfall throughout the year. They are clothed with dense pine forest. The eastern slopes of the southern and central ranges receive rainfall in spring and summer from the humid Gulf airs, but their valleys and leeward slopes tend to be dry. The frostless season is from 150 to 180 days long in the southern valleys, where wheat, alfalfa, fruit, and vegetables are raised. In the northern valleys the length of the season, though shorter, 120 to 150 days, is still suitable for hay, oats, clover, and hard fruits. Rivers running down from snow-fields, or rain-swept peaks, have an abundant water supply, and are dammed up frequently for irrigation purposes.

The Rockies are an important source of timber and of grass. In the south the middle slopes are covered with juniper; in the centre with fine stands of lodgepole pine; and in the north with pine and larch. On all the higher slopes, as far as the forest extends, are spruces and fir. Above this are high alpine pastures, beautiful with flowers. Below, in the valleys, steppe vegetation is often found. In the 'parks' short grasses predominate. In the southern, drier valleys, mesquite grass and sagebrush are found. Ranchers make use of the lower pastures during the winter and drive their sheep or cattle through the timbers to the high alpine pastures in the summer. Hay and hardy small grains, grown in the valleys, supplement the winter feed. The Wyoming basin is one of the chief sheep-rearing districts in the country.

Settlement

There are no large towns in the Rockies, and the rural population is scanty. Valley farming is limited; sheep and cattle ranching are done on an extensive basis and do not support many people; lumbering camps are scattered and often migratory. The chief settlements are railway, mining, and tourist towns. The railways are very important. They hinge on the Rocky mountain passes. The *Union Pacific* was the first line to be built; it went through Laramie and Granger in the Wyoming basin to Salt Lake City. (This followed the historic Mormon trail.) The *Northern Pacific* uses the Yellowstone, upper Missouri, and Clark rivers to pass from Billings to Spokane via Livingstone and Helena. The *Denver and Rio Grande* uses the Royal Gorge of the Arkansas, and passes through Grand Junction. The *Santa Fé* uses the pass at the town of Santa Fé; while the *Southern Pacific* follows the Rio Grande and the Gila rivers crossing between them at El Paso.

The chief mining towns are Butte, Helena, and Anaconda in Montana, centres of the copper industry; Leadville and Salida, zinc and lead-mining centres in Colorado; and Cripple Creek, in that state, famous for its gold. Cœur d'Alene in Idaho is the focus of the silver-mining district.

The tourist trade is becoming yearly more important. The Rockies offer mountain scenery, glaciers, lakes and forests, clear sunny skies, and healthy air. Colorado Springs is the outstanding tourist centre, with lofty Pikes Peak (14,000 feet) and the Garden of the Gods near by, and also the spectacular Royal Gorge of the Arkansas. The three chief national parks are the Rocky

Mountain National Park, in Colorado; the Yellowstone Park in Wyoming; and Glacier National Park in Montana. Sun Valley, Idaho, is noted as a sports centre for summer and winter recreation. Employment of local men for trail making, the building of lodges, and as guides for hunting and fishing is significant.

The Rocky Mountain region has well-marked human traits. It is a man's country. The population is far more masculine than in any other area in the United States of the same size. It is also very mobile, families moving from one part of the region to another, or into or out of the region, in a recurrent restlessness. The people are very scattered and are probably more isolated from each other than in almost any other region. They enjoy few amenities. 'No section has so great a transient, "vagrant", and short-tenure ministry as this one. The church was one of the things the homesteader left behind when he came west. Nor has the church followed him as it ought. Hence absence of church has become a habit. The region is marked by under-churching . . . such as we meet in no other section of America.'[1] Social life in general is limited, except in the larger mines; even here it is limited in reach, if not in strength. It has not attracted many immigrants, and three-quarters of the population is 'old' American. It is also mostly white, with few negro colonies even in the mining cities. In the main, the region has appealed to the pioneering American, fond of his independence and willing, in the pursuit of it, to live in relative isolation and not infrequent hazard.

The Intermontane Plateaux

Between the Rockies and the Pacific highlands there is the large region of intermontane plateaux. Some of this is flat country, consisting of horizontal beds of sedimentaries; some is uneven tableland, made up of thick sheets of lava; some is mountainous, where faulting has produced a basin-and-range structure. Three large sub-regions occur. They are the Columbia plateau, the Great basin, and the Colorado plateau.

The Columbia plateau consists of lava tablelands, through which there thrust half-buried mountain peaks. It was originally an area of valleys and high ranges, but became fissured, and then inundated under flows of lava that poured up through the fissures. The lava filled valleys, buried lesser ranges, and lapped the higher peaks around with basalt. Thus it built up a plateau, which is at places 5,000 feet thick.

The lava surface cracked as it cooled and was swiftly attacked by weathering and stream erosion. The weathering has produced some very fertile soils. The stream erosion has developed deeper and deeper canyons, some of which, like the Snake River gorge, are very profound. The rivers are

[1] Sims, *Elements of Rural Sociology*, pp. 583–4.

youthful, and often plunge over waterfalls, like those of Shoshone (210 feet). River terraces line the valleys. They often make good farm land, or benches to carry railways and roads. The region was glaciated, and glacial troughs and melt-water channels are common. The most spectacular melt-water feature is the Grand Coulee, cut into the plateau when ice blocked the upper Columbia. This has been made into one of the largest power and irrigation projects in America.

No prominent mineral deposits are associated with the lava, and mining is not important in the Columbia plateau. The forest wealth is quite considerable. The slopes of the Cascades and the Rockies are covered with coniferous forests, which thin out around the margins of the plateau and then give way to grasses or scrub. But much of the forest forms summer grazing for cattle and sheep, and much is held in reserve for possible future development, when more readily accessible reserves are used up elsewhere. The chief wealth is in agriculture. This depends on climate, soil, and vegetation.

The climate of the plateau is very varied. Differences in rainfall and temperature are considerable. The Columbia–Snake river depression has a long growing season, of 150 to 200 days free from frost. Yet this is the most arid district, with under 10 inches a year. The wetter parts—the margin of the plateau and the Blue mountains—with 20 to 40 inches of rain a year have the shortest frost-free span of 80 to 120 days. In between are the most favoured areas, with a rainfall of 10 to 20 inches and a growing season with 120 to 165 days free of frost.

The soils vary considerably. Around the outer edges of the plateau and on the Blue mountains they are shallow and stony, not suited to cultivation. From the inner edges of the plateau down to the middle Columbia valley, three great crescent-shaped soil belts occur. These are the black earths on the cool, sub-humid plateau; the chestnut soils on the sub-humid to semi-arid plateau; and brown soils on the semi-arid inmost margin. Finally, in the plains of the middle Columbia valley are the arid grey desert soils. The humid but shallow stony soils are covered with forest; the black earth and chestnut soils have a natural vegetation of tall grasses and bushes; the brown soils have a short grass prairie, with sagebrush; and the desert soils are dotted with clumps of sagebrush or bunch grass.

The chief types of agriculture are stock-raising, wheat farming, and irrigation farming (Fig. 177). The southern, highland rim of the plateau, and the mountains to west and east are grazed over by cattle and sheep. The ranches are on the plateau edge. The animals are fed on the lower fields in the fall; then rounded into pens and fed on alfalfa and forage grain—generally bought from the irrigated farms; in the spring they are let out on to the pastures again; as these dry up during summer, which is a droughty season on the plateau, the

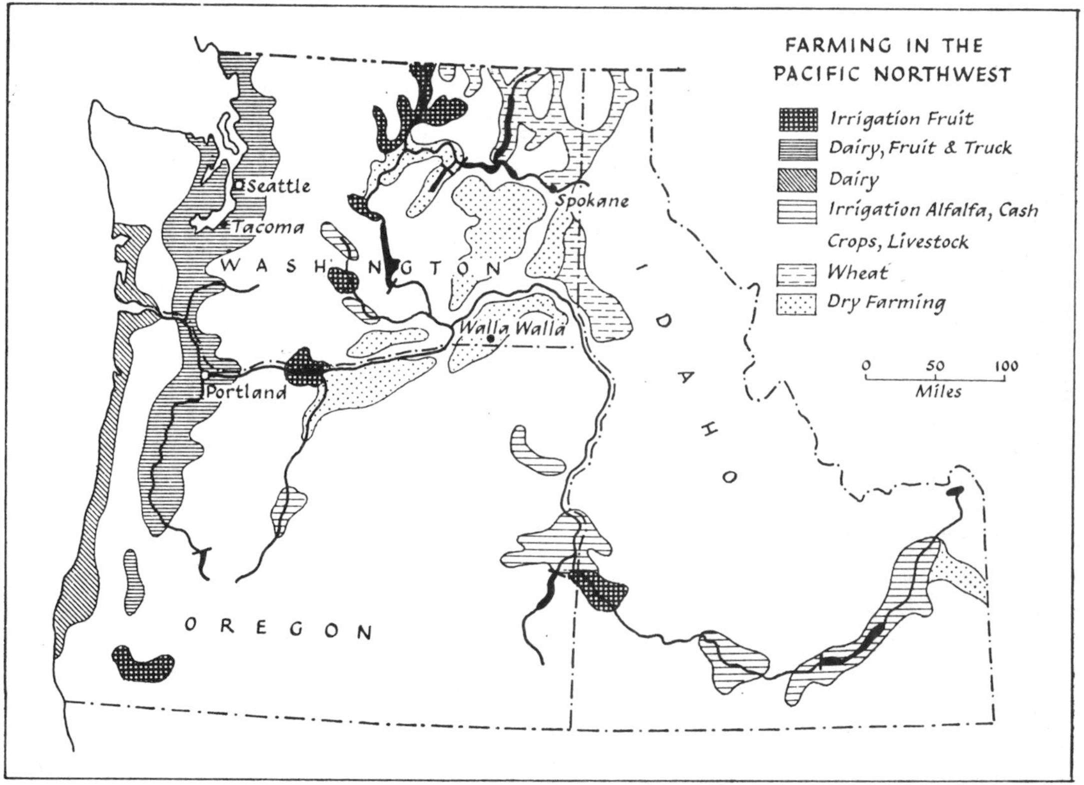

FIG. 177 Farming in the Columbia basin. Although very fragmented, the farm area is highly productive. The unshaded areas are given up to lumbering and grazing.

herdsmen drive the stock to the timbers and the higher mountain grazing. The sheep are sheared before they move to the alpine pastures and the fleece sold to the wool merchants. Sheep farming is specially noted in the Snake River valley, where irrigation provides winter forage.

The black earths and chestnut soil belts are ideal for wheat, rye, oats, and barley, and the Columbia plateau is the third most important wheat-producing area in the United States. Both winter and spring wheat are grown; the winters are not too cold for winter wheat. The rainfall is moderate (15 to 20 inches), but is ideal for small grains because it falls in the winter and the spring. The winter rains moisten the winter-sown crop, and get it started; the spring rains increase its growth, and also encourage the spring-sown wheat to flourish. The sunny summers ripen the crops, and produce a grain with high food-value. Where the rainfall is too scanty for yearly crops the farmers practise dry-farming. That is, they plough a field one year, leave it fallow for a season, and then plant the crop the following spring. When the field lies fallow, the farmer goes over it with a harrow, after every rainfall, to loosen up the soil and let the rain sink into the soil. This prevents it from evaporating away, and allows the soil to store the moisture.

In the interior is an almost desert part of the plateau. Indeed, as Brown points out, the Snake river plains were originally written off as desert, and the pioneers of the Oregon trail pushed on to the welcome sight of the Blue mountains, with their greater rainfall—'The prettiest place we have passed on the route'; continued past the mission station near Walla Walla; followed the Columbia 'over dusty plains "sufficient to appal the stoutest heart"';[1] until they reached their goal in the verdant valley of the Willamette, or the shores of Puget Sound. Today irrigation is transforming the land. The Columbia basin project, including the middle Columbia beneath the dam at Grand Coulee, will irrigate well over a million acres of arid soil, when completed, and will also supply huge quantities of hydro-electricity for use on farms and in cities. Here, and in the great Snake river irrigation scheme, an important crop is alfalfa, which is raised to supplement the scanty feeding of livestock. Idaho potatoes, sugar-beet, and vegetables are also produced in quantity. Increasing in importance are the irrigated apple orchards in the valleys round the basin. The Okanagan, Yakima, Wenatchee, and Hood river valleys have been made fertile oases by irrigation. These 'densely populated, irrigated sections with their numerous trading centres and intensively cultivated small farms present a striking contrast to adjoining dry-farming and stock-raising country where the population may be less than one person per square mile'.[2]

---

[1] Brown, *Historical Geography of the United States*, pp. 466–7.

[2] Freeman, O. W., 'Columbia Intermontane Province', in Freeman, O. W., and Martin, H. H. (eds.), *The Pacific North-west*, New York, 1954, p. 76.

The chief settlement in the basin is **Spokane** (279,000). It is on the Spokane river, an eastern tributary of the Columbia. It commands three important passes through the Northern Rockies, and, lying between the Columbia and Snake river valleys, is a focus for routes within the region. It acts as a collecting and distributing centre, and has large flour mills, packing plants, and lumber works. Cheap hydro-electric power is supplied from the river.

The Basin-and-Range Province. This structure forms the largest of the intermontane plateaux. It is actually a series of basins, lying between a number of north–south mountain ridges, of from 6,000 to 11,000 feet in height. The mountains are the edges of faulted, upturned crustal blocks. They have been savagely attacked by erosion, and their feet are covered by large fans of eroded material. 'Showers in this arid land are infrequent, but they are likely to be of torrential proportions when they do occur. Water, running in sheets down all the slopes, supplies vast quantities of detritus to the raging streams, which in turn use such material as abrasive tools for the further erosion of their gorges.'[1] The material is then carried out, and dropped, and is slowly filling up the basins. In the end the mountains will be worn down and the basin built up to form a more or less even plateau. At present striking contrasts occur, as between the depression of Death Valley, 280 feet below sea-level, and near-by Telescope Peak, 11,000 feet high.

During glacial times the region was flooded by large rivers, flowing down from the glaciers. Huge glacial lakes, such as Lake Bonneville and Lake Lahontan, formed. After the Ice Age the climate became drier; the rivers smaller; and the lakes shrank to their present size, leaving wide glacial-lake plains and old strand-lines around them. Great Salt Lake is only about one-tenth its original size. Since the area has become a region of internal drainage the freshwater lakes have turned salt. For thousands of years they have been receiving salts from the rivers, without a chance to sluice them away. Evaporation around the shrinking edges of the lakes has left beaches of gleaming white salts. Many rivers and small lakes are intermittent. They flow and fill up in the moist season, but disappear in the dry season. As the lakes dry out they leave alkaline encrustations on their beds. Such lakes are called *salinas* or *playas*. The chief basins within the province are the Great Basin, including the Great Salt Lake basin, the Carson Sink, and Death valley, together with Imperial valley, and the lower Colorado basin.

The climate is very dry. Around the edges of the region, on the flanks of the Cascades, Sierras, and Wasatch mountains the rainfall is about 20 inches. The north-western cooler part, known as the Great Sage Plains, has a rainfall of from 10 to 20 inches a year. The central part consists of very dry

[1] Logan, R. F., 'Major Landform Divisions of the South-western Interior', in Zierer, C. M. (ed.), *California and the South-west*, New York, 1956, p. 16.

desert basins, with less than 10 inches, although the ranges in between have up to 20 inches. In the south the rainfall is less than 10 inches, and at Yuma averages about 3 inches a year. These averages, however, as Leighly has shown, obscure nearly as much as they reveal. 'The means conceal large variations from year to year. Moreover, the arithmetic mean usually gives an over-estimate of the amount of precipitation to be expected: at most places there are more years with precipitation below the mean than above it.'[1] Droughts are long, broken by short sharp spells of rain. The southern area is a true desert, named in separate parts as the Mohave, Colorado, and Sonoran deserts. Most of the region has very little vegetation to cover it. The southern deserts are cactus country: sagebrush dominates the rest. Grasses clothe the plateau edges, and thin forests climb up to the crests of the ridges. The soils are poor in organic matter, and are often strongly alkaline; but, where irrigated, they can be made fairly productive.

Agriculture in the Great Basin is limited to range cattle and sheep, dry-farming and irrigation farming. Most of the land is livestock range. The ranches have to be very large to supply a living for even a medium-sized herd or flock. The animals change pastures with the season, moving up into the timbered ranges in summer, and returning to the basins in winter. The chief agricultural area is the Salt Lake oasis, which is watered by streams descending the lofty Wasatch mountains. Brigham Young led his Mormons to this centre, and they turned the desert into a rich and beautiful land through their extensive use of irrigation. This was one of the great feats of western colonization, and it did a lot to open up the intermontane plateaux to settlement. For it showed that people could 'hold on to the social, economic, and spiritual conditions, won for themselves through centuries of struggle, on the conquered desert, as well as they had in humid regions. That was the challenge to the pioneers of 1847—to build communities of modern, civilized people "under the ditch", comparable or superior to those in rainfall regions from which they came.'[2] Utah became the 'Cradle of American Irrigation' when on 23 July 1847 the Mormons broke ground, directed the waters of City Creek into irrigation channels, and planted out corn, potatoes and beans, buckwheat and turnip seed. Development is still going on, and three important Federal Irrigation Projects have recently been developed on the Bear river, at Ogden, and at Strawberry valley (Lake Utah). At the last, water from the Yampa valley is being diverted and integrated into the Strawberry reservoir scheme. The main crops raised are sugar-beet, potatoes, wheat, vegetables, and fruit. Many farmers also produce irrigated forage crops, which are fed to beef cattle or dairy cattle. The Wasatch and other ranges form sheep country. Here grazing is the mainstay, but the sheep

[1] Leighly, J., 'Weather and Climate', in Zierer, *California and the South-west*, p. 33.
[2] Widstoe, J. A., 'A Century of Irrigation', *Reclamation Era*, **xxxiii**, 1947, pp. 99–102.

herders supplement this with hay bought from the oases. They also sell lambs to be fattened in these near-by irrigated tracts.

A second important oasis centres in the Truckee–Carson irrigation project, on the western edge of the Great Basin. Irrigation is also working wonders in the Humboldt river valley, Salt river valley, and Imperial valley. The great Roosevelt dam on the Salt river, Hoover dam on the Colorado, and Imperial dam above Imperial valley have stored huge supplies of water to turn the American desert into an American Egypt. Date groves, 'early' vegetable farms, fruit orchards, and cotton plantations are characteristic. A lot of alfalfa is grown, and is trucked a considerable distance to the dairy farms of the Los Angeles area.

The chief settlements of the Great Basin are mining towns, or centres of irrigated oases. Mining made Nevada. The discovery of gold at Comstock in 1859 was followed in 1864 by the admission of the state into the Union. A great boom had taken place. But the gold industry has had its ups and downs. In 1877 the Comstock mines raised $36,000,000 dollars worth of ore out of the ground. Virginia City thrived. By 1900 it was a dying city. Other boom towns rose at Tonopah, Goldfield, and Bullfrog in the early twentieth century. They too have declined. There is nothing else to keep them going. Gold is still produced along with silver in the vicinity of Carson City. In the ranges of eastern Nevada are large deposits of copper, lead, and zinc. **Las Vegas** (150,000), in southern Nevada, near to the Boulder dam, is an important centre for lead and zinc production. Gaming and tourism are also important. The chief mining settlements, however, are in Utah, around Lake Utah at the edge of the Wasatch mountains.

The importance of Utah's mineral industries is suggested by the following:

> Utah ranks second in the United States in production of silver, copper and gold, and is among the first five states in lead and zinc. Of the nation's total production of these five non-ferrous metals, 23 per cent originate in Utah which places the state first in the total value of these metals. Within a 30-mile radius of Salt Lake City is to be found the greatest concentration of non-ferrous mining, milling, and smelting in the nation if not in the world.[1]

Here is Bingham, largest copper mine in the United States. Recently it mined 18,000,000 tons of ore in one year. The little town lies in Bingham Canyon, surrounded by terrace upon terrace of copper workings. These terraces have been made by the successive blasting and stripping of the sides of a copper mountain. Railways run along the terraces, carrying the ore to Garfield, on the edge of the Great Salt Lake. Here it is smelted, with the use

[1] Hawkes, H. B., 'Salt Lake City', in Powers and Logan, *Transcontinental Excursion*, p. 80.

of coal from Carbon County. The copper is then sent to the North-eastern States to be reworked and manufactured into copper goods. Iron County, in southern Utah, has large deposits of high-grade iron. Being fairly near coal, it has become the basis for an important steel industry, and the thriving centre of Geneva is an auspicious beginning. However, up to the present, the steel made in Utah is only about 1 per cent of the nation's total.

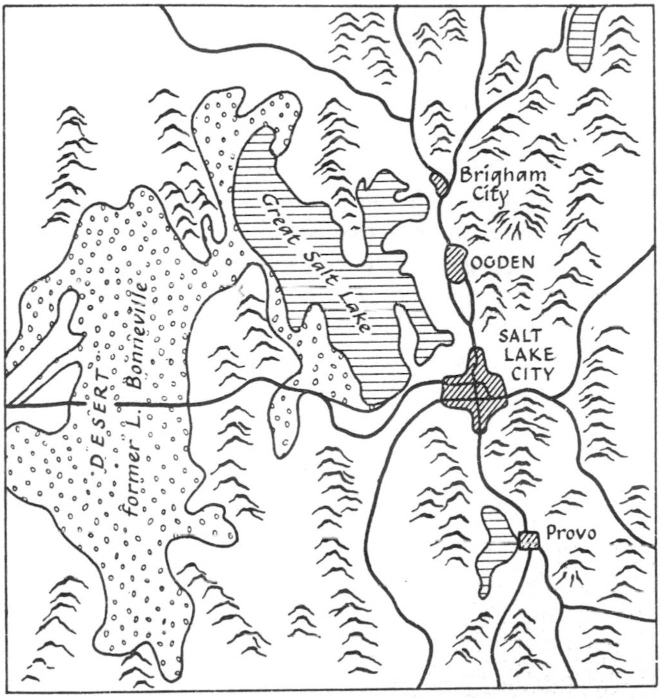

FIG. 178 Salt Lake City and Environs. Between the mountains and the desert, between mining and ranching, the city, based on irrigation farming and its command of natural routes, is an outstanding example of what man has achieved at great odds. (Scale, 1:3 m.)

There is not enough labour or local demand to sponsor really large metal industries (as distinct from mines) in the Intermontane States. Petroleum production along the axis of the Uinta basin, in Jensen and Roosevelt, is growing in importance and now supplies 97 per cent of Utah's needs.

The largest settlements are the agricultural towns in the irrigated oases. **Salt Lake City** (450,000) is outstanding (Fig. 178). Its site, as seen from the abrupt fault scarp of the towering Wasatch mountains, inspired Brigham Young to cry 'This is the place!' and to end the long Mormon migration there. It commands the entrance through the Rockies, known as South Pass, and is opposite the Truckee Pass, in the Sierras. It thus attracted settlers who streamed into the Great Basin from the east, or moved on to California, farther west, on the California trail. The early prosperity of the city owed much to the outfitting of these settlers and miners who went into the hills of Utah and Nevada. It is still the chief distributing centre for the Great Basin. Important factories have been built to make sugar, can fruit and vegetables, make butter and flour, and pack meat. **Ogden** (121,000), farther north, is in a garden area, and has large canneries. It is also the wheat mart and flour-milling centre of the oasis, with three huge elevators and two large flour mills. Meat packing is also important.

In western Nevada are Carson City and Reno. They are near to the gold mines of the Sierra Nevada and also to the large irrigation projects in Carson Sink. Reno guards the Truckee Pass, and was a gateway city on the California Trail. It is now on the Southern Pacific–Union Pacific transcontinental line. Near to the heart of the gold-mining district, it became a centre of relaxation and gaming. Even after gold declined it kept up these functions, and through its transcontinental connexions reached a nation-wide clientele. It is notoriously the 'divorce capital' of the western hemisphere.

Phoenix (850,000), the capital of Arizona, is on the edge of the Sonoran Desert where the great Roosevelt Lake has provided water for an expanding agricultural oasis. Both Phoenix and near-by **Tucson** (390,000) are important wintering places, attracting tourists from the Northern States. Yuma and Brawley are other growing oasis settlements, in the Salton Sea trough and lower Colorado.

The Colorado plateau. This great plateau really consists of a number of plateaux, dropping down from a high mass of land in central Utah, over a series of escarpments. The plateau is made of deep accumulations of nearly horizontal sedimentary rocks. Though one of the oldest and most stable areas of the continent, it has experienced considerable uplift and has been cut into profound canyons by the Colorado river. The most spectacular of those is the Grand Canyon, which is a mile deep, about fifteen miles wide, and two hundred miles long. It is one of the chief tourist attractions of the world. Another attraction lies in the clarity and colour of the landscape.

> Everywhere aridity prevails. The scanty soil and sparse vegetation permit the bedrock to show through. Sandstones, of drab shades in most parts of the world, here have a pristine whiteness, or are sometimes bright yellows and brilliant glowing crimsons. Still more striking are the variegated hues of the shales; interweaving of purple, blue, magenta, lavender, red, white, yellow, and chocolate have caused the name Painted Desert to be applied to the south-western part of the area.[1]

[1] Logan, R. F., 'Major Landform Divisions of the South-western Interior', in Zierer, *California and the South-west*, p. 24.

The plateau, rugged in itself, is surrounded by high and eroded mountains, including the Uintas to the north, the San Juans in the south-east, and the Mexican and Arizona highlands in the south-west.

Though dry, the region has rather less desert than the Great Basin. Much of the region has a rainfall of from 10 to 20 inches a year, and supports a thin to moderate covering of grasses. Higher parts of the plateau have quite dense stands of pine. These are an important timber reserve. Lumbering is carried on, under National Licence, in the forests of the Zuni mountains—a ragged dome thrusting through the generally horizontal beds of the plateau.

The rivers are so deeply entrenched in the plateau that it is difficult to use them for irrigation. Their valleys are too narrow for farms. The cost of getting their water up to the wider areas above is too great. It is true the Hopi Indians practise irrigation; but they use the little streams that descend the hills and escarpments. Their irrigation works are small, though efficient. Today, they help the Hopi to feed his flocks of sheep. The Navahoes, traditional enemies of the Hopi, have never taken kindly to farming. They were hunters, until the Spaniards introduced them to sheep. Now they are shepherds, moving about the Navaho desert around one watering place or another, driving their flocks before them. Their beautiful Navaho rugs are woven from the wool they produce.

White men moved into the area in the 'sixties. They found a country so rugged and inaccessible, so cut up by canyons and escarpments that they could build few railways across it. The Santa Fé follows the southern edge of the plateau; the Denver and Rio Grande, the northern edge. Later the Denver and Rio Grande put in a line via the Poncha Pass and the Gunnison river into central Colorado, but even so the railway net is very open. The lack of railways tended to hold back farming. However, sheep can be driven to the railhead. Gradually white settlers took up sheep ranching, in lands taken from the Indians. Today, sheep ranching is the chief occupation of the plateau. It is carried out on a very extensive basis, supporting few people for the amount of land occupied.

In the Arizona highlands, to the south of the plateau, is a very rich mining area, which produces 7 per cent of the United States gold, 17 per cent of its silver, and 37 per cent of its copper. Arizona now leads in U.S. copper production. The mines are scattered along an extended belt of ore-rich country at Bisbee, Jerome, Metcalfe, and Globe. Douglas is an important smelting centre. 'Life in these towns shows how man will live in almost inaccessible places to carry on mining. About the towns stretch arid mountains. All activities are connected with mining. Men, animals, food, clothing, and all equipment move in from other areas.' When mining fails, the settlements become ghost towns, and die. There is nothing else to keep them going.

The intermontane plateaux in general have been described as a 'stingy region', with relatively little to offer man. They are the most thinly populated and least developed areas in the United States. This lack of population is due primarily to a lack of cultivable land. In spite of immense efforts at increasing the cultivable area through irrigation, by far the greater part of the region remains grazing land or unusable desert. Lumber reserves are considerable, but they are less accessible than others in the United States, and so are not economic to develop on a large scale. Mineral resources are very great; but here again lack of population, inaccessibility, and the high costs of production and transportation hold back development. Precious metals, copper, lead, and zinc are mined extensively, but much coal and iron cannot be exploited, due to these handicaps. Nevertheless, man has made tremendous progress. He has also discovered a wealth of beauty in the region which makes it one of the chief tourist attractions and health resorts of the continent.

The Pacific Borderlands

The populous parts of the west are the Pacific Borderlands. These consist of a three-part landscape of Coast Range, Interior Valley, and High Sierras, connected and made into single regions by the river systems. In two places the lines of the Coast Ranges and inland Sierras knot together, in the Klamath mountains and the Los Angeles ridges, thus dividing the Borderlands into three sections. These are: (1) the north-western section, including Puget Sound and the Willamette valley; (2) a central section, made up of the Great Valley of California, and the coastal basins of San Francisco and Monterey; and (3) the Los Angeles basins, together with the Salton Sea trough (included in the Basin-and-Range province, but belonging to the Borderland as well).

The Coast Ranges rise from a very narrow continental shelf. They are young fold mountains, which have been heavily faulted, and from time to time are shaken by violent earthquake shocks. In the north they rise in the isolated group of Olympic mountains, nearly 8,000 feet in height, and then sweep along the Oregon shore in the form of a rugged plateau, humid and clothed with forest. In the centre they consist of a knot of volcanics in the rugged Klamaths, and a number of closely packed, parallel ranges, which are often divided by faulted troughs. Cliffs plunge down a faulted coast into the sea. The ranges run north-west–south-east, at a slight angle to the sea, and therefore form a promontory coast, with headlands at ridge ends and sweeping bays in between. The higher peaks are from 6,000 to 7,000 feet. In the south the Coast Range is made up of the small, short block-like ranges of the Los Angeles district, and then continues south as the arid spine of the California peninsula.

All along its length the sea has broken through great gaps and flooded back, drowning portions of the Interior Valley. This is what has happened at the San Juan de Fuca strait, and Georgia and Puget Sounds, and in the California gulf. Drowning has not flooded back quite so far in the Columbia estuary, San Francisco Bay, and San Pedro Channel (Los Angeles), but has been equally important. Large harbours have grown up within easy reach of the interior plains.

East of the Coast Range is the **Pacific Borderland Depression** that runs from Alaska to Mexico. In Washington and Oregon it is made up of the plain of Puget Sound and the Willamette valley. The Puget plain is varied by glacial hills, and gravel terraces, broad sandy deltas, and narrow, flat marine benches. It slopes up to a mass of bouldery deposits, which, according to Atwood, 'mark the terminal position of a lobe of the Cordilleran ice-sheet that formed in British Columbia and moved southward into what is now the state of Washington'.[1] South of this, down to the Columbia valley, are sheets of fluvio-glacial gravels, laid down by glacial melt-waters, and great spreads of outwash sand. Through these there thrust up small steep-sided basaltic hills. The Willamette valley is floored by rich alluvials, constantly being added to by a river that cannot carry all its load to the sea. It is fringed by a festoon of fans made by tributaries, and at its lower end joins the old delta of the Columbia. At its upper end the valley is terminated by the Klamath Knot. South of this is the Sacramento valley, which, together with the San Joaquin, forms the Great Valley of California. This major structural trough is marked out along its western sides by a series of deep faults. It is over 450 miles long and 50 miles wide. Its area of 21,000 sq. miles is little short of that of Belgium and Holland. Along the eastern edge are a number of large, well-watered fans. In the south are lakes of internal drainage. For the greater part, it consists of a vast alluvial plain, and is extraordinarily flat for much of its length.

The San Gabriel Knot, in the Los Angeles ranges, divides the Great Valley from the Pasadena plains and the Salton Sea trough.

The inner margin of the Borderlands is marked by the high **Sierra Nevadas and Cascade mountains.** The Sierras are young fold mountains, which have been intruded by igneous rocks (rich in minerals), and then faulted. They thus form a granite-centred block, lifted up and tilted. The eastern front has been faulted into several north–south trenches, with fault mountains between. The western slopes are broken by west–east faults, and are also scarred by deep river canyons. The higher peaks have been heavily glaciated, and tower in jagged majesty to the crowning summit of Mt Whitney (14,501 feet), highest mountain in continental United States. Many of the peaks and higher shoulders are of a similar altitude and are relics of the old

[1] Atwood, W. W., *The Physiographic Provinces of North America*, p. 463.

Sierra peneplain. The Cascade mountains form a much eroded long, narrow plateau, above which rise beautiful, snow-topped volcanoes, such as Mt Rainier (14,408 feet) and Mt Hood (11,255 feet). There are at least 120 volcanoes, of which Lassen peak was active as recently as 1914–15. Glaciation has produced deep valleys, which allow oceanic airs to penetrate eastward to the Columbia basin.

The climate of the Pacific Borderland varies with latitude, altitude, and sea aspect. North of the Klamath Knot the climate is mild and moist, an extension of the cool maritime climate of British Columbia. Southwards it becomes warm and dry, until in the Yuma district it is a hot desert. In each latitude there is the added change from valley climates to mountain ones and from coastal (equable) to interior (extreme) climates. Indeed relief dominates climate, as is particularly evident in the distribution of rainfall (Fig. 179).

In the north the weather is dominated by the polar Pacific air mass. This is humid and mild, but is constantly disturbed by travelling depressions which whirl in from the sea and pass into the mountains. It is fairly weak in summer, but is strong in winter. This helps to keep winter temperatures up, as warm waves of air are repeatedly sucked into the front of the moving depressions; but it makes the winter very wet. Temperatures of Aberdeen, for example, with a July average of 59° F. and a January one of 39° F., or of Seattle, with 63° F. and 39° F., provide a low annual range of only 20° to 24°. The climate is distinctly equable. The average rainfall is between 40 and 80 inches. However, both temperature and rainfall vary with aspect and altitude. Coastal towns have milder summers than interior ones, but longer growing seasons. The Coast Range has over 60 inches of rainfall; in the interior valley rainfall is as low as 30 inches; then it rises to over 60 inches on the Cascades.

In the mid-Pacific coast district the weather comes under the alternate influence of the mild, wet polar Pacific airs and the hot, dry, tropical Pacific airs. During winter the former extend their influence south of San Francisco and bring winter rains to the Great Valley of California. In the summer polar airs retreat before the drought associated with the tropical Pacific air mass. The climate is therefore more extreme than in the north with a greater range (as for example at Fresno) between winter (45° F. January) and summer (81° F., July). It is also drier on the average, with between 10 and 20 inches, most of which occurs in the winter. A 'Mediterranean' type of climate thus prevails.

In this mid-Pacific section the difference between coast and interior is much greater. The coast is rainy or cloudy most of the year—at least north of San Francisco, thanks to recurrent onshore winds, or widespread fog banks. The interior has virtually no rain in the summer and little in the

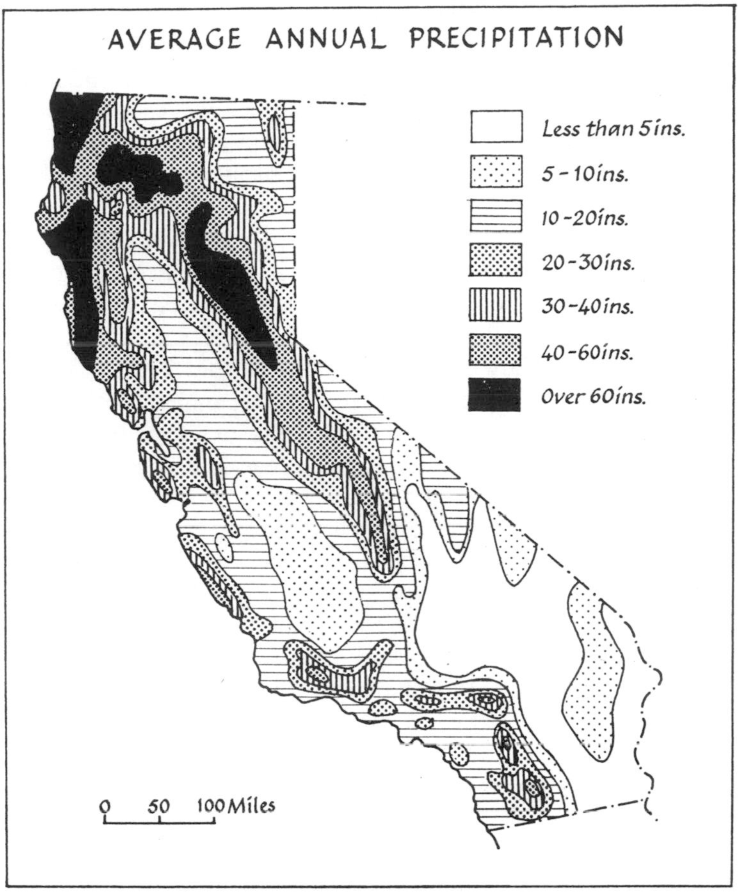

FIG. 179 Relief dominates climate in the Pacific South-west—rainfall patterns showing up the pattern of mountain and depression.

winter. Evaporation is high. Annual rainfall is as low as 10 inches. The rainfall increases again to over 40 inches on the Sierras.

In the south the tropical high is more or less constant, while dry air from the interior continental air mass spreads over the area. There is very little rain at any season. The hilly coast does receive some, due to onshore winds; but the Salton Sea trough is extremely dry. The highlands to the east, unlike the Cascades and the Sierras, are also dry. They form part of the Sonoran Desert.

Vegetation and soil vary with relief and climate and make an intricate pattern, often showing considerable differences in a small area. The north-west, with ample rain at all seasons, has a dense covering of Douglas fir, western cedar and western hemlock. The forests once clothed coastal upland, interior lowland, and interior highlands alike. They have largely been cleared from the Willamette valley and the Puget lowland, but still remain a principal source of wealth on the ranges. Some attempt has been made to clear them from the valleys in the Coast Range and to replace them by farms. But it is found that in this rough, humid district, forests do better than crops: consequently, they will probably be allowed to come back and become dominant.

South of the Klamath, vegetation changes. On the wet and foggy slopes of the Coast Range, facing the sea, are dense stands of tall and valuable redwoods. These slopes, too, are better suited to forests than to crops. On the east slopes of the Coast Range, and on the west face of the Sierras is a more open forest of yellow pine. The valleys in this forest belt can more easily be cleared, and may be used for pasture, or irrigated fruit crops. Around the Sacramento valley the forests thin out to a foothill zone of short grass prairie. This passes in turn to a semi-arid vegetation of bunch grass, in the rain-shadow area of the valley floor. Farther south in the San Joaquin valley, in the region of interior drainage, the short grass prairie disappears; bunch grass takes its place, and there are areas of desert.

South of San Francisco the Coast Range is clothed with a scrub-oak woodland of stunted and scattered chaparral. This sparse, open, and low woodland also grows on the Los Angeles ranges. But at the coast at Los Angeles, where it is very dry, chaparral gives way to bunch grass. In Imperial valley and the Yuma district is a very arid desert, with thorny cactus growth.

The soils of the northern Puget–Willamette lowlands are grey-brown or forest brown earths which have developed in the humid climate, under the dense forest. They are quite fertile. The soils of the California valley are drier, and consist of chernozems and brown steppe soils, which are very fertile, especially where irrigated. The soils of the Los Angeles lowlands are a brown steppe type. Farther south they change to true desert soils, which have to be irrigated to produce crops.

Human response to those conditions led to an early distinction between north-west and south-west. In the cooler, wetter, more heavily forested north-west, deeply invaded as it was by the sea, lived the fishing and hunting tribes with their large villages built of timber and bark, their long fishing and war canoes hewn out of trees or made with planks, and their great, elaborately carved totem poles. In the hotter, drier areas of the south-west, where vegetation was thin and game not very plentiful, were food gatherers and primitive hunters. The Spaniards coming into the south through a belt of arid territory had adapted themselves to the sweep of open range and the confinement of small irrigable valleys, and they carried ranching and mission horticulture to the head of the Great Valley. The British, moving out to the west, through forest or along forest-lined rivers, carried their fur trapping and trading into the otter-rich streams and beaver-loud ponds of the Oregon woods. Russian fur traders also moved down the forested coast towards the Pacific north-west. American pioneers likewise discovered and emphasized regional differences. Those moving north-west along the Oregon trail went in for general farming and lumbering; the ones who followed the California or the Santa Fé trail took up cattle and sheep ranching, fruit and wheat farming, or, above all, mining.

The California Borderland or Pacific South-west

One of the distinguishing things about the south-west is its Spanish past. Not that this was strong enough to become the mould for the American development, but it did at least influence that development, creating uses of land that the Americans adopted, and finding sites for settlement that became great American cities. As early as 1542—before Cartier discovered Quebec—Cabrillo had sailed into San Diego harbour. Subsequently, Spanish galleons returning from the Philippines made their first landfall north of San Francisco on their way down the coast to Acapulco, in Mexico. Drake's raid on this trade in 1579 made it more necessary than ever to use California. Later, the Russian advance southward, and the extension of their fur trade, led to new Spanish efforts at holding the region. In 1769 San Diego was occupied, and in the next year the first of the Franciscan missions was established there. In 1770 the first *presidio*, or centre of civil administration, was set up at Monterey, which became the early capital of the new colony. Here another mission was founded, on the banks of the near-by Carmel river. Meanwhile the great bay of San Francisco had been discovered (Fig. 180).

The coastal strip with its small fertile basins between protective hills close to ocean transport attracted the rapid spread of settlement, but at the same time efforts were made to press inland. In 1771 the missions of San Antonio de Padua, inland from Carmel, and of San Gabriel Arcangel, near present-day Pasadena, were set up. Luis Obispo, in 1772, San Francisco de Asis, and San Juan Capistrano in 1776 soon followed. Civic communities, or *puebloes*, were also founded, as for example at San José, in 1777, and Los Angeles, in 1781. 'The first California was, thus, that of the mission, the *presidio*, and the village. Irrigation ditches were dug, fields tilled and crops grown, vines and fruit trees planted. Horse herds and cattle herds gradually increased. In the villages a more industrious spirit developed, and the gardens and small fields were cultivated with earnestness if not with skill.'[1]

As this California was growing up, the United States came into being, and at once there began that great push to the west that was to carry America to

[1] Ghent, *The Early Far West*, p. 48.

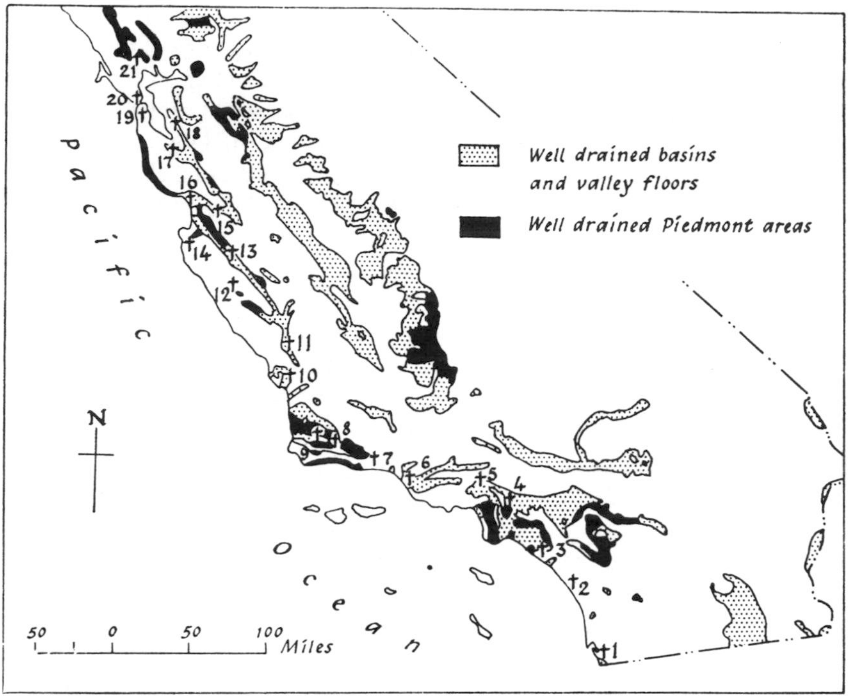

FIG. 180 The Pacific South-west—Early Settlement in California: the coastal missions in relation to site and soil. (From Gentilcore.) The missions were: 1, San Diego; 2, San Luis Rey; 3, San Juan Capistrano; 4, San Gabriel; 5, San Fernando Rey; 6, San Buena Ventura; 7, Santa Barbara; 8, Santa Inés; 9, La Purísima Concepción; 10, San Luis Obispo; 11, San Miguel; 12, San Antonio; 13, Nostra Señora de la Soledad; 14, San Carlos de Monterey; 15, San Juan Batista; 16, Santa Cruz; 17, Santa Clara; 18, San José; 19, San Francisco; 20, San Rafael; 21, San Francisco Solano de Sonoma.

the Pacific. Spanish developments were enough to attract traders by sea and settlers by land, yet not enough to restrain opportunists or keep out adventurers. 'Privateers, fitted out in Baltimore, and commissioned in Buenos Aires, swept Spanish commerce from the seas, and no longer could the supply ships come up from San Blas to California ports.'[1] Yankee shippers began to supply the goods instead and, although foreign ships continued to be excluded by law, they sold Boston goods in return for the leather—derived from the great ranches of the interior—which was to help Boston retain its leadership in making leather products. Yankee whalers also called at Monterey and San Francisco, using these as bases for the north Pacific whaling fields. As many as thirty whalers used San Francisco, and they bought in green vegetables and meat from the Californians in exchange for American goods.

[1] Ghent, *The Early Far West*, p. 170.

Meanwhile, the secularization of the missions and the parcelling out of the land in large tracts, attracted settlers from the interior. Many turned aside from the trek to Oregon so as to press into California. In 1826 Jedediah Smith had pioneered the path from Great Salt Lake down the Virgin to the Colorado and thence across to San Gabriel; in 1827 the Patties had blazed the Santa Fé trail farther south, using the Gila river, and arriving at San Diego; in 1830 Young found the Cajon Pass in the Sierras and blazed a route to be known as the Old Spanish trail from Santa Fé to the Colorado and thence to Los Angeles; in 1833 Walker went west from Great Salt Lake, struck the Humboldt river, and found the passes by Walker Lake, and also at the head of the Truckee river, which opened the California trail to San Francisco. American goods soon began to move westward along these routes, in return for which Californians exported horses and mules.

Some of the traders decided to stay and become settlers. One of the chief of these was Sutter, who arrived at Monterey in 1839, and secured a large grant of land on the banks of the American river, a tributary of the Sacramento. Here he built Fort Sutter and established a huge ranch. Sutter was loyal to the régime, in 1840 became a Mexican citizen, and in 1845 supported the governor, Micheltorena, against the rebel, Alvarado. Nevertheless, an increasing number of settlers became restive, felt that they could develop and govern the region better than the Mexicans, and began to talk of taking California over. Captain Shaler, one of the illicit traders of the coast, wrote: 'The conquest of this country would be absolutely nothing; it would fall without an effort to the most inconsiderable forces.' Tension mounted. The Spaniards and Latinized Indians grew apprehensive at the spread of American ranches and wheat fields. It was reputed that the Spanish governor was inciting the Indians to attack the American ranches and farmsteads. Meantime, war broke out in Texas between the United States and Mexico. This gave the American settlers their chance. Not waiting for Kearny, who was to lead an expedition to California as soon as he had overrun New Mexico, they revolted, captured Fort Sonoma from the Spaniards, June 1846, and ran up the flag of their own California Republic. When Frémont, at the head of his settler band, reached Monterey he found the American fleet in the harbour and the Stars and Stripes flying in the city square. The Spanish barrier to American occupation had been overrun; California became American.

At this time cattle raising was easily the most important activity in the region, followed by wheat farming, and then by the raising of fruits and vegetables. The missions, having been secularized, had lost a good deal of influence, but some of their sites were used. New sites, better suited to the needs of rancher and farmer, were developed, especially in the Great Valley, and hundreds of immigrants took up and settled the land.

Gold, however, not peace, was the thing that transformed California. In 1848 gold was discovered at Sutter's on the banks of the American river. At once, a rush of people occurred, anxious to 'get rich quick', and by the end of 1849 the population of California had risen, in an astonishing way, to over a hundred thousand people! Nothing like it had been seen before, and it did more than anything else to 'make' the American West. However, the great boom did not last long. Although between 1849 and 1853 production had soared to over $50,000,000 a year, by 1860 most of the readily available placer gold was used up. Then mining had to start the more difficult operation of blasting and digging the gold from the gold-rich veins of quartz that run through the rocks of the Sierras. More recently large steam dredges have revived placer mining. These dredges scoop up the sands and gravels from the beds of the rivers in huge amounts, and then screen the gold from the worthless matter. Thanks to these new methods, California still has an important place, having yielded only to Alaska, as a U.S. producer of gold, with 13 per cent of the nation's total.

Oil—or black gold—is now California's main mineral product. In the southern part of the state several rich pools of oil have been found. Production began as early as 1887, but progress was slow as there was relatively little demand for oil in the west, and it was too costly to transport to the east. However, with the growth of large cities, and the expansion of trucking and air services, the oil industry has grown. It also fuels the U.S. Pacific Fleet. The oil is especially valuable because of the lack of coal in the Pacific Borderland (the only field of any importance is in the Puget lowland; but its production is small). Including the Los Angeles oil field, California is the second largest oil-producing district in the country, yielding 12 per cent of the total. However, much of it is stagnant or on the decline.

Farming returned to its early importance, after the first gold boom had passed. Large cattle ranches divided the natural prairie of the foothills and the drier grazing land of the valley floor. Then wheat became important, especially with the use of dry-farming methods. Wheat soon replaced cattle on the better black soils. Finally, irrigation became common and today California is noted for its fruits, vineyards, rice fields, and cotton plantations. The rivers that flow from the high sierras bring down ample supplies of water; the frost-free span is from 240 to 280 days long; the summers are hot, bright, and dry; the winters are mild. These are ideal conditions for fruit or cotton farming. The rainless summer makes it easy to dry fruit out of doors—a very cheap process. California is the nation's chief citrus and grape-producing area. The Fruit Growers' Co-operative in California has done a lot to standardize production, pack and distribute the fruit, and advertise products throughout the world. Special fruit trains run direct to Chicago, New York, and Canada, to distribute the goods in the centre, east, and north, where citrus fruits are in great demand. Early vegetables are another important industry, supplying these urban markets (Fig. 181).

These different types of farming use different aspects of the Pacific south-west. In general, ranching is carried on in the relatively arid hills; fruit is raised on the river terraces and the many river fans, although much is also grown on the flats; wheat, rice, alfalfa, cotton, and vegetables are produced on the floorland of trough and basin. Fruit and vegetables account for nearly a third of the farm product. Deciduous fruits dominate in the cooler parts to the north, citrus fruits in the warmer and safer south. On the fans, citrus fruits are usually grown on the higher slopes, with the best frost drainage, and deciduous fruits and nuts on the lower slopes.

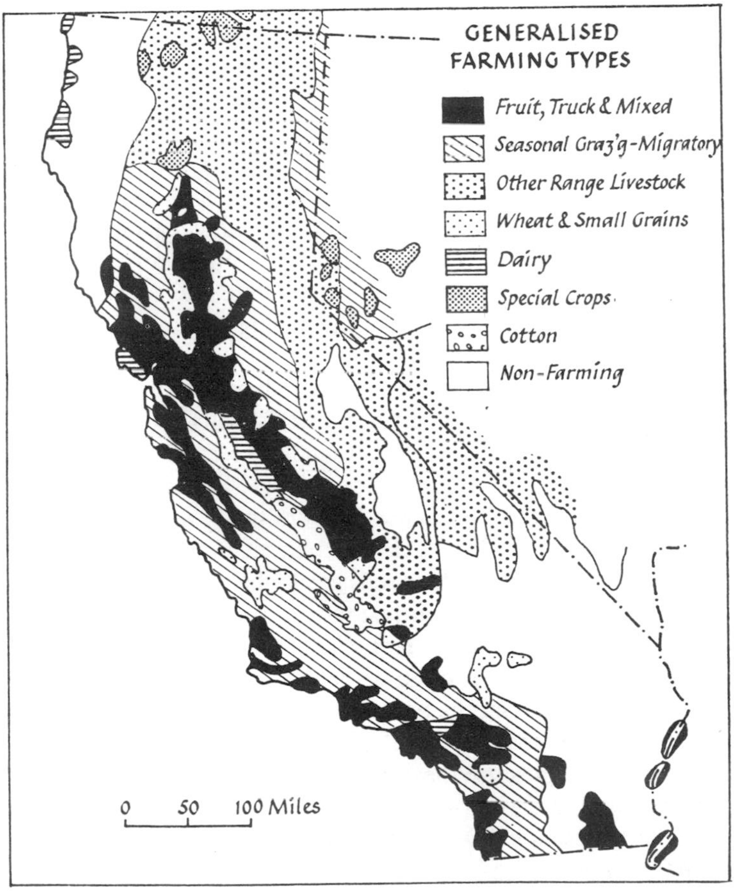

FIG. 181 Farming in the Pacific South-west; note the great concentration on fruit and truck crops in the Central valley, the San Francisco basin, and the Los Angeles plains. However, most of the area is under grazing, much of it quite seasonal.

There are five chief areas of production: the Sacramento valley, the San Joaquin valley, the San Francisco and mid-coast basins, the Los Angeles and south-coast basins, and the Imperial valley. In the Sacramento, ranching is still the main use of the Sierra slopes, as it was in Sutter's day. Winter wheat and barley are common on terraces stretching out from the east slopes of the Coast Range, much of the wheat being fed to poultry. Rice is an important crop under the natural flood-waters of the middle Sacramento. Deciduous fruits are widely grown on irrigated tracts in the lower parts of the valley. Citrus fruits are not often attempted, as they are subject to frost. Alfalfa has become the chief crop of the flatlands. It is sold to the ranchers in the hills for winter feed. In 'islands' in the Sacramento delta, between the distributaries, asparagus and sugar-beet are grown.

The San Joaquin valley, from Fresno down, goes in extensively for fruits and vegetables. It is claimed that half the raisins of the world are raised in the Fresno district, many of them being dried in the open in the hot, dry summers. Wine grapes are also popular, and Californian wines are now widely sold throughout the United States. Orange production is equally typical. The San Joaquin is drier than the Sacramento, and its western and southern sides, away from the great tributaries flowing out of the Sierras, are devoted to dry-farming. Wheat, barley, and forage crops form an almost continuous belt, the barley being used for brewing, the hay being trucked to dairy farms near Los Angeles. In southern irrigated sectors, the intensive cultivation of cotton is carried out.

The San Francisco basin is highly urbanized and there is not a great deal of farm land left. This is mostly given up to dairying, poultry keeping, and market gardening. In the small, all-but landlocked and sheltered valleys of the Coast Range, as for example at Santa Rosa, Healdsburg, and Napa to the north, or Santa Maria and Santa Barbara to the south, vineyards, hop-yards, orange and apple orchards, the production of prunes and walnuts, and the growth of flowers and flower seeds are highly specialized undertakings.

In the Los Angeles basin urbanization is again taking up more and more land. But on the urban fringe are many large dairies. They have only a little land, however—often just enough to let the cows out—and rely heavily upon imported fodder from the San Joaquin and Imperial valleys. The fans around the basin are most intensively developed. The rivers that water them do not flow all year, but since they seep into the loose sediments, they supply large underground reservoirs for the irrigation of many orange and lemon groves. These are usually developed on the upper middle slopes of the fans, above the frost hollows.

> The groves appear as artificial and un-natural in a rural region as the most complex industrial areas appear in an urban landscape. Here everything

> is ordered; in place of the thickets of native vegetation, the citrus groves are carefully planned to get the maximum number of trees into minimum space. Their welfare is watched, and they are fed, watered, protected against frost damage and tended so carefully that there is little about them to suggest . . . agriculture, to the visitor from the east.[1]

They are in fact the object of a highly organized, highly mechanized, modern kind of gardening.

The Imperial valley was once one of the driest areas in the south-west, much of it in a deep sun-baked depression, beneath sea-level. However, it is near to the Colorado river, and water was early taken to it from above Yuma. Today the All-American canal, along the International Border, carries the water across the trough. Date groves, canteloupe farms, and grapefruit orchards are common, with extensive acreages devoted to cotton. Alfalfa is also widely grown, although there are no local ranches. It is dried and sent by road or rail to Los Angeles, for the dairy farmers. The growing season is so long that truck and hay farmers can raise several different crops a year from the same fields.

Irrigation has been the making of the Pacific south-west (Fig. 182). Much of this has been done by trapping the snow-fed rivers coming down from the High Sierras. A very bold attempt has been made, in the Central Valley Project, to supplement and integrate these supplies, on the widest possible scale. The upper Sacramento has been dammed at Shasta, where the reservoir can store over 400 million acre-feet of water. This huge supply has enabled the western dry parts as well as the central and eastern areas, near to the Sierras, to be irrigated. Farther down, the salt waters that used to push up the delta of the Sacramento and San Joaquin have been ponded back. The surplus water in the Sacramento has been carried across this delta into the San Joaquin, while a long canal up the dry western side of the San Joaquin, known as the Delta–Mendota channel, carries more water all the way up to the Fresno area. Meantime, the great Friant dam blocks the headwaters of the San Joaquin, and these waters are diverted along the Friant–Kern canal, a distance of 150 miles, to Bakersfield and the arid south. Hydro-electric power developed at the dams has been widely distributed. Here is one of the great works of man.

Urban development. Although agriculture is most important, it has not developed much of a rural population. California is, on the contrary, highly urbanized. 'More than in any other section save the "colonial" [i.e. north-east], the people are concentrated in urban districts. The population is very heterogeneous. There are all kinds and sorts of native Americans mingled

---

[1] Raup, H. F., 'Piedmont Plain Agriculture in Southern California', *Yearbook of Assoc. of Pacific Coast Geographers*, 1940, **6**, p. 27.

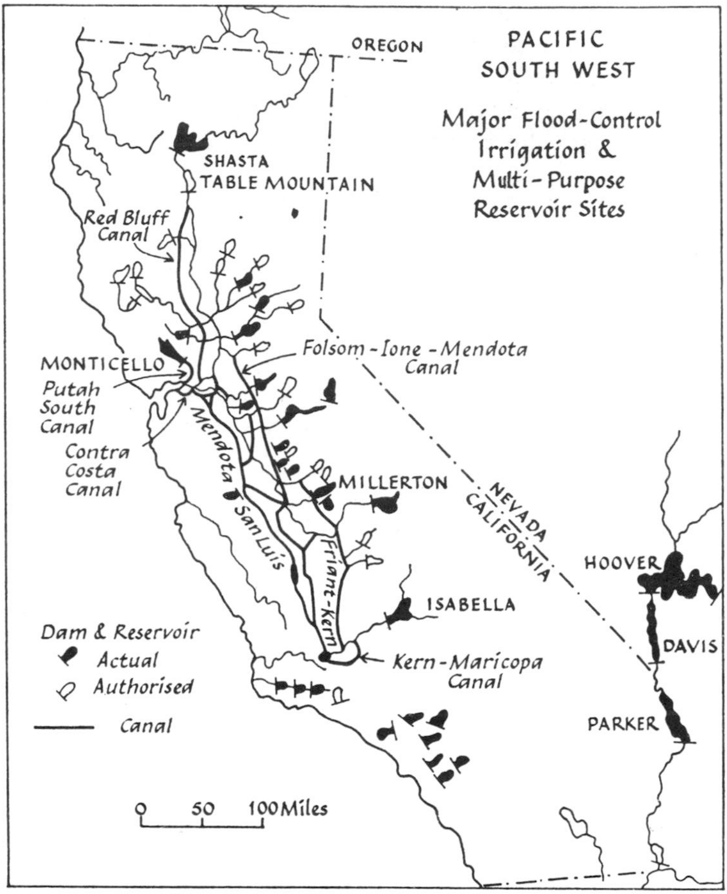

FIG. 182 Irrigation in the Pacific South-west. A transformation has been worked in the Central valley by trapping the water of the high, rain-swept and snowy mountains around. However, while the dams are primarily for irrigation, they also produce much power. In addition two large aqueducts from the Nevadas supply Los Angeles and the lower Colorado towns.

with a large foreign-born element. The widest variety of conditions are found. There is a definite trend of activities to the centers.'[1] Centred population is 20·4 times scattered. Urban-centred population is over 80 per cent of the total. Indeed, city growth has been unprecedented, and has so set its mark on the land that even the so-called rural areas are very 'citified', with city-style homes and amenities. This is the theme of Nelson's paper on 'The Spread of an Artificial Landscape over Southern California'. He points out that

[1] Sims, *Elements of Rural Sociology*, pp. 584–5.

The twentieth century may go down in history as an urban age. Urbanism is becoming increasingly significant throughout the world, and the United States, too, is strongly affected by this modern trend. California, perhaps better than other areas, epitomizes the recent dominance of the city. The area had few attractions for urban-industrial settlement during its early period of European settlement—its qualities have been recognized as assets for urban-industrial development only in recent decades. Once the proper stage was reached, however, the mature nature of the American economy and the advanced stage of industrial technology have made possible an extremely rapid growth. Today an artificial landscape of urban patterns dominates Southern California. The movement of people here during and since World War II ranks with the largest migrations in the history of the United States, and almost all the migrants have settled in the cities.

As a result, the coastal plain has been transformed. Sprawling subdivisions have been flung out, filling the valleys. Freeways, lacing old centers together, have spawned additional ribbon-like urban-industrial developments on newly accessible land along their rights-of-way. Orange groves and walnut orchards are yielding to the subdivider. Fields that were in beans or barley a few years ago are now occupied by houses or factories. Vegetables and flowers have been damaged by smog. Dry-lot dairies, directly serving the local population, are feeling urban pressures as a Planning Commission report, 'Where Now Brown Cow?' boldly testifies.

Although large areas of wild landscape remain on mountains and in some desert areas, the mark of urban man is heavy upon it. Eight million strong, he jams its roads and highways. He hikes through it, camps in it, and gets lost in it. In season he skis down its slopes and breaks his bones on them. He burns it and litters it, until the wild landscape, too, is . . . urbanized.[1]

In the south-west, San Diego, San Francisco, and its associated settlements, and, above all, Los Angeles are the chief centres.

San Diego (1,150,000) was discovered as early as 1542, but it was not occupied until 1769 when a fort was built at the mouth of the San Diego river. Fray Junipero Serra, one of the great Franciscan leaders of colonial Spain, set up a mission there, at the same time, and began to christianize the natives and induce them to take up agriculture. When the Americans pushed west, the site became one of the terminals of the Santa Fé and lower Colorado trail. Subsequently, the railway was built through to it. However,

[1] Nelson, H. J., 'The Spread of An Artificial Landscape Over Southern California , *Annals Assoc. American Geographers*, September 1959, **49**, no. 3, Part 2, pp. 80–81.

it was too removed from the bulk of California to be a main terminal. Most routes made for Los Angeles or San Francisco. On the other hand, this extreme southern position near to the Mexican border made it an excellent site for a naval station. From this advanced position U.S. ships could protect the approaches to the Pacific south-west. A wider role was possible when the Panama Canal was built. San Diego was the nearest American port, and thus enabled the U.S. fleet to protect the American life-lines from all over the Pacific which were centred in the canal. It thus became a most important naval base. But commercial interests have become more significant as the hinterland has developed, and the port handles many imported manufactured goods, and exports cotton and other local products. A large aircraft industry has developed, and the city has begun to expand industrially. The very mild winters have attracted a great influx of retired people, and the city is a growing residential site. It is said that one in ten of all retired naval officers in the United States have settled in the city or its surrounds. The population has expanded enormously from less than 20,000 at the beginning of the century. Between 1950 and 1952, alone, it grew by nearly 100,000.

San Francisco (3,084,000) has experienced a very different story. Founded in 1777 by a small company of officers, priests, and Spanish peasants, both as an administrative *presidio* and also as a Franciscan mission station, it leapt to fame in the 1849 gold rush, when over 25,000 people crowded its quays and thronged its hilly peninsula. This very sudden growth created a town that took the shape of its headlands, bays, and hills, giving the city a truly topographical character—something distinctive in the west, where so many cities have developed on such formal, geometrical lines.

San Francisco Bay is an extraordinary feature, where a deep depression let down between the San Andreas fault to the west and the Hayward fault to the east, backed by the Santa Cruz mountains and the Berkeley hills, has been extensively drowned by the sea. A very narrow entrance, the Golden Gate, leads to a most spacious reach of waters, enabling sea-going vessels not only to use the bay-side cities of San Francisco, Oakland, and Berkeley, but to sail inland as far as Stockton, in the Great Valley. Thus the bay area rapidly developed both as a maritime and an interior terminal, early used by Spanish and then by American ships engaged in the China trade and in trade with the Philippines, and also as the end of the road for overland trails from Mexico and from Denver and Salt Lake City. Its chief significance is still as America's main gateway to the Pacific and the Far East, with sailings and airplane flights to Hawaii, the Philippines, Hong Kong, and Japan in the west, and to New Zealand and Australia in the south-west. In addition, it has gained strength locally as the main focus of all the economic developments of the Great Valley of California.

San Francisco itself grew up around a market on a small flat on the east, or protected side, of its peninsula. The Spanish galleons rounded the gun-defended headland known as Fort Point to anchor by this flat, and the town spread slowly westward up the steep slope to the ridged spine of the peninsula. The port grew swiftly with the gold rush and with the building of the railway terminals, and a great number of quays were put up, north and south of the old harbour. The business area expanded by extending from lower Market Street outwards, but changed from mainly retail to mainly office functions as city population spread to the outskirts and suburban shopping centres. Residential expansion strode swiftly back up out of Chinatown, and the polyglot quarters behind the docks (filled with negroes, East Indians, and recent European immigrants); climbed above the more stable working-class areas of older immigrants to middle-class sectors on upper slopes, mainly of old American stock; and came to rest among the fine upper-class homes of Nob Hill. Further expansion came when the Golden Gate and the Bay bridges linked the city up with settlements to north and east. Of these the eastern connexions are by far the most important, since the main rail and trucking terminals are here, together with more flat land, on the bay and on Alameda Island, for quays, warehouses, and industries. The great Bay bridge has drawn out the skyscrapers of the business section towards it. The Bay region is growing at the rate of 23,000 people per month. In the vast metropolitan area, with over three million people, San Francisco is still the main port and business centre, Alameda the international air terminal, Oakland the chief rail terminal and industrial city, and Berkeley the university and residential town. Publishing, and the making of steel goods, ships, aeroplanes, and machinery in the Bay area have grown in importance, together with canning, wine making, and flour-milling. However, trading, transportation, and finance are still the main functions, and together employ three times as many as manufacturing.

Los Angeles (7,532,000) was founded in 1781 after San Diego, Monterey, and San Francisco, as a small *pueblo* near narrows in the Los Angeles river where Spanish settlers could easily tap irrigation water. Irrigated fruit, dry-farm wheat, and cattle gave the basin variety, and the *pueblo* slowly grew. However, it only achieved importance when the Old Spanish trail carried the trade of the interior to the coast, and later brought many American settlers. Subsequently, it became one of the terminals of the Southern Pacific from New Orleans and the Southern States; and of the Union Pacific from Salt Lake City, Omaha, and the Mid-West. The Aitchison, Topeka and Santa Fé also made it one of their Pacific terminals, connecting it with Santa Fé, Kansas City, and Chicago.

Its isolation alike from the Great Valley of California and from the American interior at first worked against it. Yet that very isolation induced its citizens to begin making products for themselves which they could obtain only at great expense from the east. In 1893 a steel industry was begun to supply Pacific coast shipyards, machinery for wheat elevators and flour mills, for packing houses and wineries, and other local needs. The development of oil in the immediate vicinity led to a phenomenal boom in the early 'twenties, creating further demands for steel derricks, pipes, pumps, oil-well tools, and the like. The oil boom also gave rise to an oil-refining and a large and varied chemical industry. The extraordinary variety of farming in the area, citrus orchards and nut orchards, vineyards, market gardens, wheat and hay farms, dairies, poultry ranches, and so on, further increased the market for chemical and other manufactured products. Aeroplane manufacture started up in the 'twenties, and became very important during the war. Machinery and rubber plants grew up in association. Steel-making expanded and the Kaiser, Bethlehem, and United Steel Companies enlarged or built new plants in Los Angeles and at the near-by towns of Torrance and Fontana, drawing iron from Eagle Mountain in California, and coking coal from Utah. Today, Los Angeles is America's third industrial city.

The really unique industry, of course, has been the making of 'movies' and Los Angeles is the film capital of the world. Climate has played a very large part in this. Bright sunshine was a great advantage in the early days when most motion pictures were shot outside. Movie makers also found the wide variety of scenery of great benefit, ranging from high snow-capped mountains to desert wastes, from a coast with magnificent cliffs and bays, to the open prairies of the drier interior plains, from woods to farms, the city to the sea. Thus almost any kind of drama could be appropriately staged within a hundred miles of Hollywood.

> Between 1913 when Cecil B. de Mille rented a barn at Vine and Selina Streets for his partners Jesse Lasky and Sam Goldwyn, and about 1920, all the outstanding film producers moved to Southern California. Here distance from the market was no problem; a can of film could be shipped relatively cheaply to any place in the country. Although some of the early climatic requirements are no longer of major importance, the early concentration of talent and skill remains to fix the industry in the area.[1]

California's climate also had much to do with the rise of the aircraft industry.

> Its mild winters and light winds (summed up by the term 'flying weather') found favor with early flying enthusiasts, who were also the early plane manufacturers. Again, distance from the major population centres was no

[1] Nelson, op. cit., p. 70.

handicap, as there is no locatable market for airplanes. In 1906 Glenn Martin built his first airplane in an abandoned Santa Ana church. An associate, Donald Douglas, began manufacturing airplanes in a former movie studio in Santa Monica in 1920. The Loughead brothers founded a company in Santa Barbara—the nucleus of the present Lockheed. By 1938, on the eve of the war, California was the undisputed leader in the manufacture of airplanes.[1]

Climate has also made Los Angeles a great residential as well as industrial site. 'Climate alone has attracted numerous people to the area, some in search of better health, some for sport and recreation, many looking for an easier and more comfortable life.'[2] Finally, climate has helped to make Los Angeles a great tourist and holiday centre.

To many the city seems rather formless and appears to be dominated more by the great express freeways, and through-parkways built for people who do not want to live in Los Angeles, than by the shopping centres and residential streets for the city dweller (Fig. 183). It has been described, indeed, as a huddle of suburbs looking for a city. There is much truth in this. Los Angeles appears to be a congeries of cities rather than a city in and by and for itself. There is no very definite downtown, midtown, and uptown as there is in New York. Indeed, one feels that it is more a part of the region than of the site. In other words, it has reached that stage already which some fear may become the ultimate in urban development: where the city as a whole is to its region, what the downtown is to the city, a highly specialized, highly competent, vital service centre for the community at large, but a centre somehow lacking in a life and personality of its own.

This may partly be because the Los Angeles city centre has migrated by degrees from the old plaza in front of the central church which dominated, and gave cohesion to, the original *pueblo* and the early American town. More probably it is due to the extraordinary way in which the promoters of settlement, following the big railway boom of the 1880s, created a great number of new subdivisions each laid out as a separate town. Over a hundred of these quasi-towns were 'platted' in Los Angeles county, and though most of them never materialized, nearly forty small nuclei remained, around which settlement grew. As Los Angeles expanded it took these over, one after the other, and thus became a wide network of little knots strung together in increasing dependence upon each other. City centre there is, and it is still important, but it has to vie with many other centres in the built-up area. Altogether, there are 102 incorporated cities in the L.A. area.

[1] Ibid., p. 91.

[2] Nelson, H. J., 'Urban Development and Major Centers', in Zierer, *California and the South-west*, p. 335.

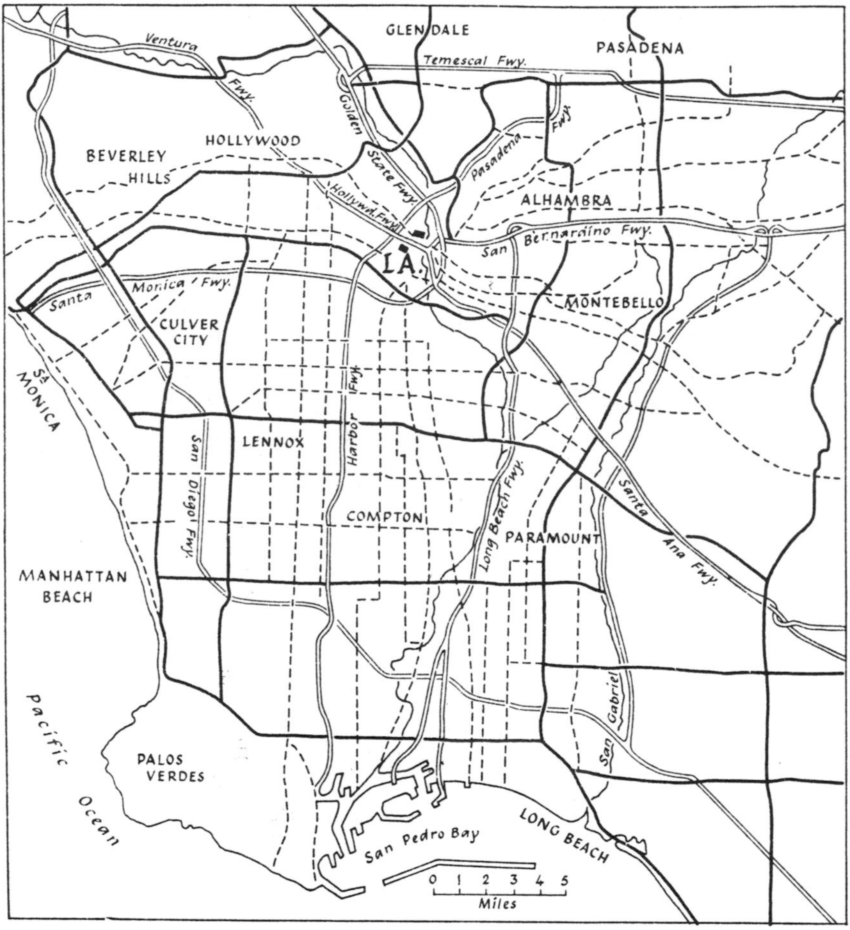

FIG 183 Los Angeles—City of Freeways, Model of the New American Metropolis. The town centre is literally lapped around in multi-level, multi-lane flyover expressways. Los Angeles has boldly tackled the problem of access to and exit from its central business and social area, by attempting to *make the car central*, rather than damping down central city activities. Since the car is the most vital and revolutionary thing in modern technology, and since it allows for the rapid spread of population into country-based suburbs of pleasant, high-value, low-density housing, the city must adjust to it. Whereas many cities try to cope by hindering the car and slowing down private traffic, Los Angeles has made a place for the car and flushes traffic through, giving millions the chance to 'work in' and 'live out' which they want. Major urban thoroughfares (in black) and principal city streets (in broken lines) tie in with the freeways (double lines).

Finally, it should be pointed out that by far the greatest growth of the city has occurred within the motor age. The seaways, the coach-roads, and the railways all had their part—but they had not acted with sufficient strength (as in New York, Boston, Philadelphia, or Chicago) to create a fixed pattern, on which the motorway would make but a mere embroidery. Here the motorway was itself a great creative force, and the commuter not someone to be made way for, through changes here and there in the basic pattern, but the very basis of the pattern—for whom the need to work in the city, yet live outside it, made the city conform to traffic requirements rather than traffic conform to the city. Average daily traffic into the city on the freeways is $1\frac{1}{2}$ million cars.[1] '7 out of 10 people entering the Central Business District come by auto.'[2] The automobile has permitted a truly extraordinary sprawl, made up not only of detached dwellings assembled in outlying communities, but also of scattered shopping and business districts and industries. The city has thus ceased to be a highly centralized, cohesive entity, but is instead a remarkably fluid series of cell-like growths linked to each other in ever-changing relationships. Does this make Los Angeles 'freak' or 'forerunner'—an exception to the rule, or the shape of things to come?

The Pacific North-west and Alaska

The second great subdivision of the Pacific Borderlands is the Pacific North-west. With this, Alaska may be linked. Both these areas are cooler, wetter, and much more wooded than the South-west. They are somewhat more dependent on the sea. They are rather more limited in their farming. Their external relations are with Canada, with whom they divide the Columbia and Yukon basins, rather than with Mexico.

The Pacific North-west is characterized by three 'f's'—forestry, fishing, and farming.

Forestry is especially important.

> The history and settlement of the Pacific North-west are inextricably linked with forests and the uses to which they have been put. Ever since the white men came to this region the forests have provided fuel, shelter, and a means of livelihood for much of the population. Simple logging and milling started with the first permanent settlement. Before long, lumber was shipped to California, the eastern states, and foreign countries, and lumber manufacture soon became (as it remains) the primary industry of the region. Other wood-using industries developed as time passed, and

[1] Telford, E. T., 'L. A. Area Freeways', *Cal. Highways and Public Works*, Mar.–Apr., 1962, Los Angeles, p. 15.

[2] Nelson, H. J., 'Significant Characteristics of the Los Angeles Metropolitan Growth Pattern for Transportation Planning', in *Transportation and Metropolitan Planning*, ed. Engelbert, B. A., Los Angeles, 1956, p. 10.

today forests contribute to the support of the major part of the population. Forests of the region are, in fact, one of the greatest natural resources in the United States. The Pacific North-west contains two thirds of the old-growth saw timber remaining in the entire country—a vast storehouse of raw materials for industries that provide jobs in many sections of the nation. If managed wisely for continuous production, the region's forests will remain a great economic asset.[1]

Seventy-two per cent of Washington is under forest, and 48 per cent of Oregon. An astonishing amount of this is merchantable—about 80 per cent in each state. Along the west coast, particularly, is an immense area, over 26 million acres, of commercial forestland. About half the cut consists of Douglas fir, one-seventh of ponderosa pine, and one-eighth western hemlock, a twentieth red cedar, and smaller amounts of Sitka spruce, lodgepole pine, and western larch. The Douglas fir, mixed with western hemlock, red cedar, and grand fir, is the chief forest of Puget Sound, the Willamette valley slopes, the bulk of the Coast Range, and the western slopes of the Cascade Range. A spruce-hemlock forest is found on the west slopes of the Olympics and of the northern part of the Coast Range, in very humid conditions. Often draped with hanging moss and carpeted with ferns, it has the dense, tall, rank growth of 'rain forest'. Balsam firs and hemlocks grow on the higher slopes of the Cascades, passing up through Engelmann spruce to alpine fir. The Douglas fir, ponderosa pine, and red cedar make excellent building material; the Douglas fir is also good for wood veneer; the better hemlocks are used for house or office finish, the poorer for pulp; while Engelmann and Sitka spruce, along with balsam fir, are made into pulp or plywood.

Lumber camps are numerous in both the Coast Range and the Cascades. They were formerly built at the heads of branch railway lines; today, they are more often set up beside good trucking roads. Highly mechanized means are used to cut down, trim, drag out, load, and unload the trees on their way from forest to mill. 'Modern falling is like machine-shop operation',[2] with power saws to rip through the huge tough trunks. Tractors 'snake out' the fallen trees, cleaned of their branches. The trunks are sawn into standard lengths, and swung by power cranes or claw-like loaders, on to giant eight-wheeler trailer trucks. These take their huge loads down to the railway, where the logs are reloaded on flat cars, and taken down the valley to the mill. If the distance to the mill is not great, trucks may haul the lumber there direct.

Many rivers have big sorting ponds, while calm stretches of coast shelter

[1] Wyckoff, S. N., 'Forests of the Pacific North-west', in Freeman and Martin, *The Pacific North-west*, p. 224.

[2] Stevens, J., 'Forest Utilization in the Pacific North-west', in Freeman and Martin, *The Pacific North-west*, p. 239.

large booming yards, into which trucks or trains tip the logs. Tugs herd groups of logs together, and sorters with long poles push logs of different woods and varied sizes and shapes into grading corrals. Peeler logs, suitable for veneer and plywood, are rafted together, as are logs best fitted for construction-lumber, shingle, or pulp and paper mills. The main collecting districts for log booms are the lower Columbia, upper Puget Sound, Willapa Bay, and Grays Harbor.

At the mills the logs are barked, often by being rolled round and round under highly forced jets of water, and then trimmed, before being put through the veneer peelers, the planking saws, or the pulp crushers. Formerly the bark, sawdust, and chips were thrown away, or burned in huge waste disposers. Now much of the waste—particularly the chips which are used in pulp making—is exploited for by-products, or burned up to make steam or electricity to help run the mill machines. Wood splinters are now crushed together into hardboard, or compressed into stiff 'container' paper. Since most of the mills are on or near the coast their products can be sent by the relatively cheap ocean haul round by the Panama Canal to the north-eastern industrial section of the United States; they can also be sent quite readily to Japan and other Pacific countries.

The wood-milling industry, in its many forms, is easily the largest in the Pacific North-west, employing about 100,000 men, which is more than twice as many as in the fish-canning, flour-milling, meat-packing, fruit-boxing, and other food industries; and as many as all other industries put together. Portland is the chief lumber, furniture, and paper-making centre, but the Seattle area is not far behind. Wood alcohol is important at Bellingham, and at Springfield, Oregon, and furniture making at Tacoma. Most of the towns of the Puget Sound have saw mills or paper factories.

Fishing has been of considerable value to the Pacific North-west, although the nearer fisheries are not now as important as those quite remote from the region. 'Just as the codfish is associated with New England, salmon has become one of the symbols of the Pacific North-west.'[1] The product has a nation-wide sale, and also goes out to world markets. The huge surplus, over and above local needs, is explained by the truly phenomenal run of salmon up the Columbia and other coastal rivers in their urge to spawn in the freshwater ponds and lakes in the mountains. Fishing is done from small boats often working out from little jetties in riverside hamlets. Sockeye salmon is the most popular, because it is a bright red. Coho or pink salmon fetches a lower price. King salmon are packed in ice and sold 'fresh' as well as being canned. At the height of the run, in late spring and early summer, the small boats dump their catch into large scows that then move on to the

[1] Martin, H. H., 'Fisheries of the North Pacific', in Freeman and Martin. *The Pacific North-west*, p. 179.

canneries. The salmon are scooped out and flung into chipped ice. From this mass they are fed into water-filled containers where machines remove head, fin and tail, and gut the fish. The trunkated bodies are then moved by conveyor belts under choppers that cut them up in sizes suitable for canning. The cans are sealed, cooked, cooled, and packed in large cases, ready for export. Astoria, on the Columbia, is a major port for the salmon fishing fleets, and also for freezing and canning salmon.

However, the over-fishing of the salmon runs has led to a marked decline in the salmon population since the early 'twenties. Washington State has now made the blockage of the rivers in spawning time by large salmon nets illegal, and special salmon runs have been built to help fish around falls, weirs, and dams, while parts of the rivers have been kept for propagation. None the less, the catch is only a third of what it was early in the century.

Fishing interests have therefore turned to remoter sources, particularly to the great halibut fisheries of the North Pacific, and to the herring and pilchard fisheries of the Inner Passage. The halibut had long been made a popular food by New Englanders fishing in the Atlantic. But the Atlantic fishery is shared by many nations and in any case is not as prolific as its Pacific counterpart and, as it waned, the Pacific fishery grew. Today the Pacific catch is forty times that in the Atlantic, and fast refrigerator cars carry the halibut from Seattle to all parts of the States. The fish are caught on long lines with many hooks baited with pieces of skate. The lines are paid out from the stern of quite large diesel-driven boats, with a fishing crew of eight to ten men. Halibut are caught off the edge of the continental shelf from California to Alaska, but mostly north of Queen Charlotte Isles. Fleets leave Astoria, Aberdeen, Bellingham, and Seattle to compete with Canadian fishermen for the catch. Again, over-fishing occurred, the halibut banks began to be depleted, and stern measures to control the fishery had to be instituted. A definite closed season, from fall to spring, was instituted; a limitation was made on the annual catch (a quota of just over 50 million pounds); and the fishing zone was divided into four areas—south of Willapa Harbour, from Willapa to Cape Spencer in Alaska, from this cape to the Aleutians, and in the Bering Sea; and a treaty was signed with Canada to set up the International Pacific Halibut Commission to supervise conservation measures. Taken all in all, Seattle is the main centre of the fishing trade; and the Fishermen's Terminal, with 84 acres of warehouses, yards, cleaning sheds, and market stalls, is the largest on the coast.

Farming early attracted settlers to the Pacific North-west. Most of the pioneers of the Oregon trail were looking for new land with good timber which, when cleared, would reveal a rich forest-brown soil. As early as 1847 an observer could write, 'Our citizens were forming prosperous settlements in the rich and beautiful valley of the Willamette and were thus giving

Lumbering and Mining in the American West

57. A huge lumber mill on White River, Wash. The dense forests on rainy slopes supply countless logs brought by rail and road to the big sorting pond outside the mill.

58. The largest open pit mine in the world is the Utah Copper Mine at Bingham Canyon, 30 miles southwest of Salt Lake City. Over 2 billion tons of rock and ore have been taken out of a pit over 900 acres in area.

59. Seattle is the focus of the Pacific Northwest. Dominating Puget Sound, it climbs over a rocky spur to L. Washington in the background. It is the chief terminal for Alaska.

Pacific Coast Metropoli—Pacific N.W. and S.W.

60. Los Angeles, twin focus, along with San Francisco, of the Pacific Southwest. The immense system of freeways, with flyover connections, provides rapid transport for nearly half a million cars per day into the heart of the city, occupied by administrative buildings, centres of art and music, and great offices and hotels.

strength to our [U.S.] title [to Oregon] resting upon occupancy.'[1] Indeed, it was this rush of homesteaders rather than fur traders that ensured the North-west for the United States.

However, thereafter the main wealth was found in the forests, and farming fell back to second place among the primary occupations. Nevertheless, its place is still important. Farming is most valuable in the interior plateaux and basins of the Columbia, where the ranching and wheat-farming, already described, have reached considerable proportions. Yet even in the western borderland it is significant. The humid and equable climate, with its mild winters, and with deep, humus-rich soils, are well suited to hay and forage crops, so that dairying is one of the major activities. The dairy farms are found chiefly in the Puget plains and the Willamette valley, but also in small plains at the head of coastal bays. Where the forest has been thinned or cut out by the lumbermen, good pasture is found for grazing beef or dual purpose cattle. Much butter, cheese, and dried milk are exported from the region, and also some meat. Many farms seed a field of wheat for a cash crop, and flour-milling is another thriving business. However, next to dairying in importance is fruit-farming. The temperate fruits, such as apples, plums, pears, and cherries flourish in the mild, moist climate with its long growing season of up to 200 days free from frost. The apple orchards of the Willamette valley are world-famous. Small fruits are also raised.

The settlements cluster where inlet and valley meet. In the north, Puget Sound pushes into Puget Lowland, and harbours the important cities of Seattle and Tacoma. The Columbia estuary makes contact with the Willamette valley at Portland. From these centres, railways run north and south, along the interior valleys, and also to central and eastern United States through mountain passes.

Portland, Oregon (900,000), is on the Willamette river, just above its confluence with the Columbia, about a hundred miles inland. The Columbia estuary allows large ocean-going ships to sail up to the valley: while the Columbia gorge, through the Cascades, provides an excellent route into the interior and across the continent. Near-by Bonneville Dam supplies large amounts of cheap electricity. Saw mills and canning factories are important. Portland packs and exports the fruit of its fertile hinterland.

Seattle (1,250,000) is the largest settlement and is one of the main centres of business and industry in the west. About a hundred miles from the sea, it lies about half-way up Puget Sound and is accessible alike to trans-oceanic and transcontinental terminals. It is on the shortest U.S. route to the Far East and is thus a major link between America and Asia (Fig. 184).

The city has an extraordinarily long water-front. Built at the head of Elliott Bay, itself a sizeable water body, the town straddles a peninsula in

[1] Brown, *Historical Geography of the United States*, p. 469.

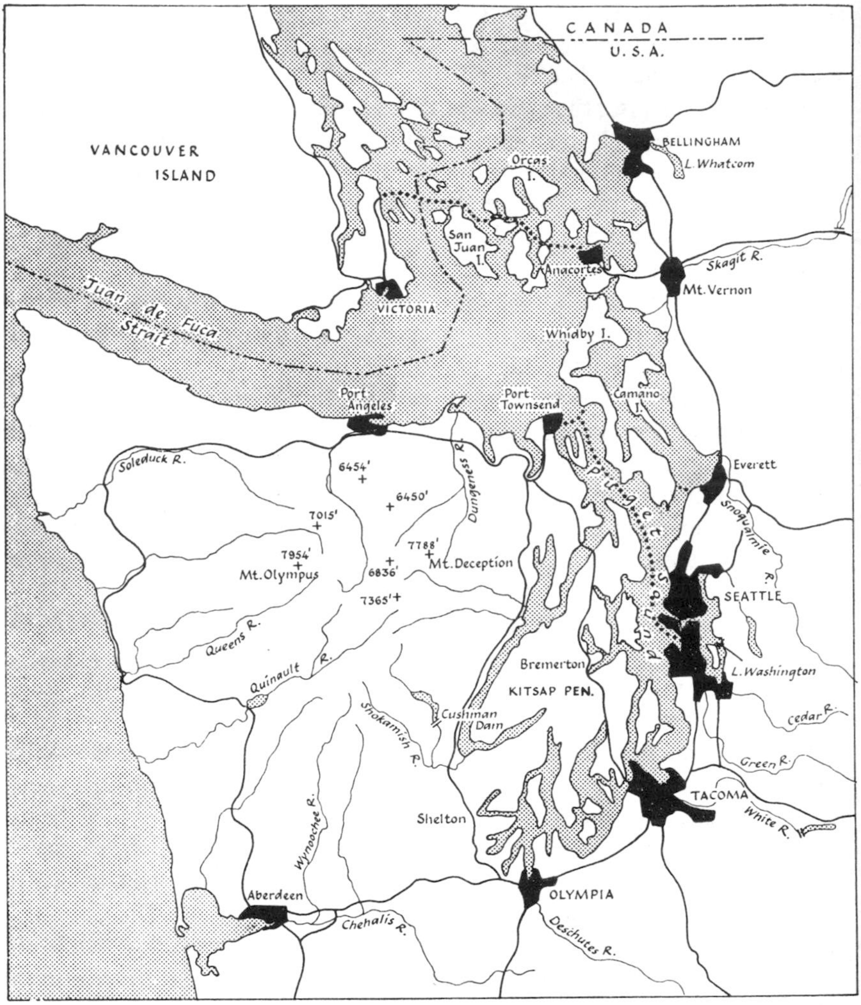

FIG. 184 Seattle and Puget Sound, heart of the Pacific North-west. A commanding site has been made use of to develop a commanding settlement. (Scale, 1:2 m.)

the middle of which is Lake Union, while it goes back to Washington Lake, a long, wide depression on the east. A canal has been cut between the three water bodies, allowing lake wharfage to be added to sea-front, and giving the town over fifty miles of water-front. The original nucleus was on a small flat which has proved far too small; it has been taken up by docks, ferries, and railway lines, pushing the town centre and the business district up on to old beach terraces and even the steep slopes of the rocky, hill-pricked peninsula. Space is at such a premium that along the back of the harbour there are raised railways and roads running above the dockside ones. The naval base in the south, the oceanic terminals and the Puget Sound ferries in the centre, the fish docks, lumber yards, oil 'farms', and the army base in the north use up most of the sea-front. Two main U.S. highways—5, running north and south, and 90 from the interior—make a T-junction at the heart of the city. Working-class homes crowd the lower slopes; upper-class homes have spread round the shores of Lake Washington. Industry has pushed up the Duwamish river in the south and spread around Salmon Bay and the canal in the northern-central part of the city. The town pattern responds very closely to the relief.

The chief industries are saw-milling, the making of window sashes and door frames, the manufacture of cedar shingles, and of many kinds of furniture; the processing of foods for export, particularly of fish, fruits, and fresh vegetables; flour-milling; the packing of imported tea, coffee, and spices; ship-building and ship repairs; the development of many kinds of machines, especially for the lumber industry; and the making of aeroplanes. The first two groups are based on local raw materials; the next on imported goods; and the last, on the city's important function as a transportation centre. However, industry as a whole is of less value than commerce. 'The waterfront rather than the factory dominates its urban personality. It is primarily a handler of cargoes.'[1] Also of great significance are its three universities, its museum, zoo, and art gallery: Seattle is a major cultural force in the west, and a notable 'conference centre'. Recently it was the site of a World Fair.

One of its chief functions has been to outfit and support developments in Alaska. 'On July 17, 1897, a steamer from Alaska arrived with the discovery shipment of gold. The following year the Klondike gold rush began, Seattle becoming the recognized gateway. Seattle and Alaska were linked together in the public mind.'[2] This relationship is still very real. Siddall, writing in 1957 of the hierarchy of settlements in Alaska, remarks: 'Two anomalies are found: first that Alaska does not have any true regional capital within its own borders, and second that the city which does serve as Alaska's regional capital is Seattle, which lies from 620 to over 2,700 miles away from the Territory.'[3] Even though Alaska has now become a state with a political capital of its own, Juneau, it is still dependent on Seattle from an economic, strategic, and social point of view (Fig. 185).

Alaska. This being the case, Alaska is in many ways an outlier of the Pacific North-west, and thus a sub-region of the Pacific Borderlands.

[1] Martin, H. H., 'Urban Pattern of Western Washington', in Freeman and Martin, *The Pacific North-west*, p. 461.

[2] Ibid., p. 459.

[3] Siddall, W. W., 'Seattle: Regional Capital of Alaska', *Annals Assoc. of American Geographers*, September 1957, **47**, no. 3, p. 277.

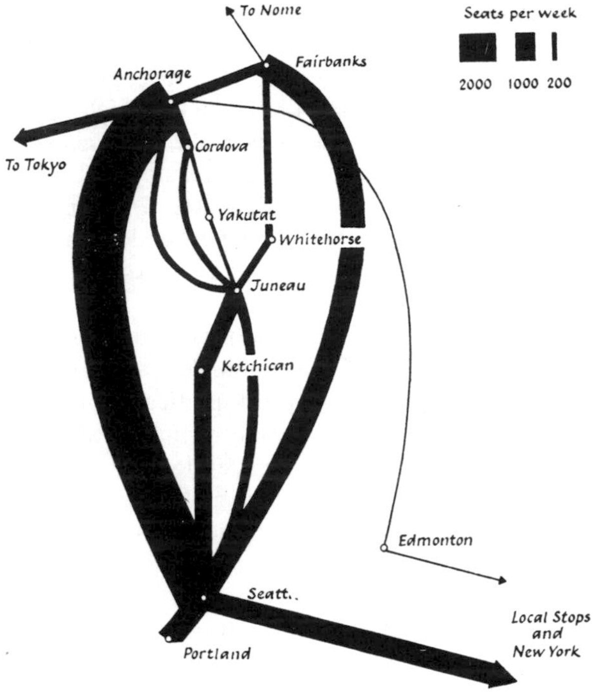

FIG. 185 Seattle, commercial capital of Alaska. (After Siddall.) Through command of the famous Inner Passage from Puget Sound to Juneau and beyond, and through its fortunate location on the short Arctic air-route from America to Japan, Seattle has become the metropolis for Alaska as well as for the Pacific North-west, thus linking the two regions intimately together. Most of Alaska is supplied directly from Seattle rather than Juneau, the official capital.

Although much of it is Arctic to sub-Arctic, and although it is connected by the Alaska Highway to northern Canada, it is in many ways less north than west. This is certainly so commercially, but it is even true, to a certain extent, physically. For Alaska is dominated by its Pacific mountain system and also by its Pacific climatic zone.

Western Alaska. The Pacific mountain system is continuous with the Coast Range of British Columbia and Canada's outer island arc. It is, however, much more massive, rising to over 18,000 feet in the Mt St Elias range and to over 20,000 feet in the Alaska range, clothed with eternal snows and feeding the continent's mightiest glaciers. Behind this huge barrier lies the Yukon plateau, indented with great basins, while beyond this again is a belt of low but continuous highlands, the Brooks range. Finally, north to the sea stretches the Arctic coastal plain.

The Pacific ranges look seaward to the vast Aleutian 'low', a centre of recurrent atmospheric depressions developed over a part of the North Pacific which has a strong positive temperature anomaly. The warm, moist, unstable air of this region forms the polar Pacific maritime air mass; and its invasion of the coast and deep penetration up fjords and valleys has turned what would otherwise have been a chilly waste into a green and living land. Here are the Aleutians, with their 'fog, heavy rainfall, dense clouds, storms, and uniform temperature';[1] the 'mild and equable, salubrious though damp' panhandle; and Cook Inlet where 'there are no extremes of heat or cold.'[2] Rainfall is all but exclusively of Pacific—that is, *western*—origin, and is heavy and continuous enough, coupled with a long growing season, to promote a dense and mature growth of forest. Sitka spruce, western hemlock, red cedar, and Alaska cedar are almost everywhere to be found except on slopes swept by strong winds, on high altitudes, or where the glaciers from great massifs push down to the coast. Western, too, are the currents that parallel or bathe the shore—the warm Kuro Siwo drift from the south-west Pacific moving in a great arc towards Alaska with an upwelling of cold waters along the actual edge of the land. This mingling of waters of different temperature and salinity around banks and islands off the mainland and up the great coastal fjords has produced a wealth of fish, with the largest salmon runs in the world, and the world's largest halibut fishery. Farther north is one of the world's chief sealing grounds in the Pribilof Islands.

These conditions call out the same activities and occupations that characterize the Pacific North-west; namely, lumbering, pulp and paper making, fishing, and trading by sea.

Northern Alaska. However, beyond the mighty barrier of the Alaska range conditions are different. The relief sinks down to low ranges, broad plateaux, and big basins through which the Yukon and other rivers thread their deeply incised but much-braided and shifting courses. The flatness of much of the land is made all the more apparent by its bareness. The hills and plateau tops are moorland or mossland. Even the forest in the river valleys is generally thin and low. Rainfall, which on the coast was 100 inches or more, falls off to 15 inches or less. Many parts are semi-arid and irrigation is required for summer agriculture. The climate, now dominated by polar continental—that is, northern interior—air is one of extremes, with short yet surprisingly warm summers and long dark bitter winters. Frost may strike even in the summer, and were it not for the very long days with their intense light, growth would not be even what it is.

---

[1] Miller, D. J., 'Gulf of Alaska Area', in Williams, H. (ed.), *Landscapes of Alaska*, Berkeley, 1958, p. 29.

[2] Teal, J. J., and Sharland, I., 'Alaska', in Kimble, G. H. T., and Good, D. (eds.), *Geography of the Northlands*, New York, 1955, pp. 294, 296.

This region is the 'golden heart' of Alaska, since, with little lumber or farm wealth to offer, it has relied mainly on its minerals, and above all on the placer gold of the Yukon basin and of the Seward peninsula. Mining is still important.

The Brooks range rapidly climbs above the tree-level to tundra and barren land. The climate is so dry that it could not supply enough moisture during the Ice Age to lead to the overall glaciation of the highlands; thus not a few broad areas stand out oddly unglaciated in an ice-swept, cold interior. Northward the Arctic plain is bleak and barren in the extreme, pock-marked by soil polygons and wrinkled by soil-flow and slumpage deposits.

Alaska, Population and Settlement. The whole vast area has only a population of a single good-sized town in mainland America—less than a quarter of a million. This is spread very unevenly, being concentrated here and there in a lot of little towns, with vast stretches of empty land between. It is still at a pioneer stage: Alaskans like to think of the region as the 'last American frontier'. It really has not had the time to develop. It was only discovered in 1741, when Vitus Bering, a Dane in Russian employ, came upon the peninsula in his explorations of the northern seas. Bering returned with a fortune in furs, particularly the much-prized pelt of the sea-otter, and a great fur-boom occurred, with the establishment of the Russian-American fur company. However, this was pretty ruthless in its dealings, and came near to exterminating seals and sea-otters, not to mention the Aleuts and the Indians! In fifty years the population of the Aleuts was reduced to a fifth of what it had been! The colony was written off as a loss and sold to the United States in 1867.

New England whalers were the first to use the new acquisition, together with New York fur traders or their agents, but very little happened until the Klondike gold rush of 1898. Gold was found at Fairbanks and Nome, and later at Juneau, and all of a sudden tent-towns and shack-towns mushroomed on the Alaska coast and in the lower Yukon basin, as the mining boom expanded. Population grew so rapidly that in 1912 Alaska became a Territory and began to administer many of its own affairs.

The main points of settlement are: the Panhandle, dominated by Ketchikan and Juneau; the Gulf of Alaska, or south-central region, marked out by Seward, Kenai, and Anchorage and the Matanuska valley; the Interior, centred in Fairbanks and the Tanana basin; and the western fringe, with a few scattered places, of which Nome is chief (Fig. 186).

Salmon and halibut fishing form the Panhandle's and, indeed, Alaska's main industry. This is carried out all along the south-east and south-central coast from quite a number of small centres. However, Ketchikan is the main base, in the midst of the fjord country where the salmon abound, easily accessible to the halibut fishery off the islands, and as near to main-

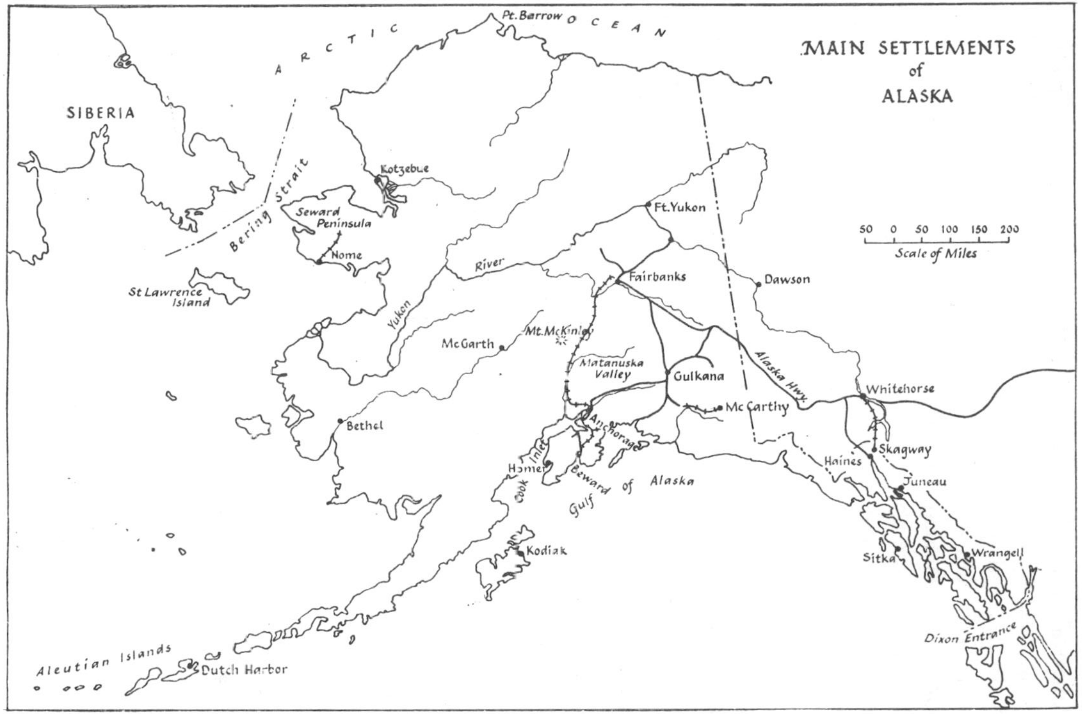

FIG. 186 The Main Settlements of Alaska. Note the central position of the Matanuska valley, chief site of pioneer agriculture.

land America as possible. It has large canneries and a freezing plant. A thriving pulp and paper mill has been opened to exploit the thick, old-growth forest of the rain-swept coast.

Farther north lies **Juneau,** the capital of the state. On the side of a long fjord, the Gastineau channel, it has developed on the gravel terraces of a glacial valley, the upper parts of which cut through a swarm of quartz veins in the Coast Range batholith, filled with gold. Beneath this famous ore area, which has produced much wealth in its time, are placer deposits in the loose post-glacial material by the coast. 'This is one of the few such deposits in south-eastern Alaska, for in most places glaciers have removed any older deposits that may have been present, and there has not been enough time since the ice retreated to allow new ones to accumulate.'[1] A large gold mine, on the side of the steep, glaciated fjord, still dominates the settlement, although Juneau's prosperity now lies in government activities.

Mining is also significant in south-central Alaska; for many years the Willow Creek area in the Talkeetna mountains was second in importance for lode gold, while the Chitina and Chitistone valleys became noted for their copper, the latter containing the rich Kennicott ores. The region is well-wooded on its lower slopes, especially in the Chugach National Forest, and some lumbering is carried on. Farming is quite important in the Matanuska valley at the head of Cook Inlet, which has some good soils on well-drained river terraces, a climate sheltered from keen winds, with 'on an average a growing season of 108 days',[2] where summer heat can develop, and with long hours of summer light, forcing growth. This valley was developed as a rehabilitation project in 1935 in which the U.S. government helped to settle unemployed. A road was built from Anchorage, the port, and money was loaned for clearing the land, building houses and farmsteads, and starting the farmers off. Oats, hay, potatoes, and peas are grown extensively, and dairies and poultry farms flourish. The valley also contains workable coal deposits.

Anchorage is the main town of the region, at the head of Cook Inlet and on the railway to the Matanuska and Susitna valleys and thence by Broad Pass across the Alaska range to the interior and Fairbanks. It is a thriving port and fishing centre, and the main warehousing depot for the lumber and mining towns around, and for agricultural settlements like Homer and Palmer. A modern highway runs eastward from it to the Copper valley, and thence north to Fairbanks.

Fairbanks is the only significant town north of the mountains. Situated on the Tanana, it is in an area where long tributaries from the lofty Alaskas

[1] Reed, J. C., 'South-eastern Alaska', in Williams, *Landscapes of Alaska*, p. 16.

[2] Hanson, H. C., *Agriculture in the Matanuska Valley*, U.S. Dept. of Interior, Washington, 1943, p. 3.

spread out huge fans of gravel and sand. These were found to be rich in placer gold, and as the Klondike gravels became worked out, prospectors pushed over into the Tanana valley and started mining there. Today massive dredges and hydraulic hoses work over the gravels systematically, still obtaining important amounts of precious metal. Pioneer farming has grown up along the lower terraces of the Tanana to produce eggs, milk, and potatoes for Fairbanks and the mining camps. However, agricultural development is at present 'spotty, unorganized, and generally ineffective'[1] compared with the Matanuska experiment. Nevertheless, it represents yet another stage in that great drama of the west that began with the Oregon trek.

CONCLUSION

What is known as the American West, today, is the last of many wests—from the Old West of the Appalachians to the Old North-west of Ohio and the Great Lakes, or the Old South-west through Alabama to Mississippi; from the Mid-West lying between Ohio and Missouri to the west of the Great Plains; until eventually the west of mountain, basin, and coast was reached, branching out to the farthest west of the Aleutians. The last of the wests, the region still has what first made the West; the invitation of space, the excitement of newness, the challenge of barriers, the chance of fulfilment. Here is a region where there is still room for development, where many resources still call for exploitation, where there are still great problems to be mastered, and where different horizons still open up. It is still, to a certain extent, the American dream. 'The West', said Lord Bryce, 'is the most American part of America. What Europe is to Asia, what England is to the rest of Europe, what America is to England, that the Western States and Territories are to the Atlantic States.'[2]

The West is still the region to be appraised, developed, and filled up. Although it covers a third of the national area it has less than a tenth of the population. Here is emptiness still to be used. The population density varies from less than one person per sq. mile in Nevada to about seventy people per sq. mile in California. This is far below the average for the North-eastern States, which is over 150 per sq. mile.

The low population is one of the characteristics of the West. It is due in part to the considerable amount of uninhabitable mountain or desert, but also to the general way of life. The West is still largely an area of primary production, that is, of farming, mining, lumbering, and fishing. It has not developed far as an industrial area, except in south-west California. It is characterized more by *extensive* development than by intensive.

[1] Dawson, *The New North-west*, p. 308.
[2] Bryce, *American Commonwealth*, 1895 edn., 2, p. 830.

Why is this the case? One of the reasons is its remoteness. The West is still remote from the chief markets in the United States and from Europe. Its nearness to Asia by no means makes up for this, because the United States trade with Asia is not nearly as important as with Europe.

Another reason is the terrain. The West is typically mountainous. It is corrugated by huge and difficult mountain ranges, faulted, deeply eroded, and lofty. The number of passes is limited and most of them are high. The cost of hauling raw material and fuel, and of distributing finished goods is so much higher than in the Central or North-eastern States that it is not economic to compete industrially, except along very special lines, where unique western products earn a national market, or goods of very high value can be produced.

Still another reason for the lack of intensive development in the west is the climate. The West is characterized by the desert. Every western state has some near-desert or true-desert area in it; even Alaska has its desert in the dry, cold barrens. Wide prairies of bunch grass or still wider plains of sage-brush abound. The sage might well be taken as the emblem of the West. Consequently, grazing and dry-farming are typical occupations. What intensive farming there is, apart from a few areas on the humid north-west coast, has had to rely on irrigation. This is another characteristically western feature; the great dams, the huge artificial lakes, the lines of conduits, the channelled water flashing through the deserts, the orchard laden with fruit, the rich alfalfa field, the gleaming plantation of cotton, the reclamation project. These projects have called for co-operation among the individuals using them, and for vast State or Federal expenditures. While we normally think of the West as a land of rugged individualism, it has also been a land of public or co-operative enterprise.

Since all this has had to be done without a great deal of man-power, all occupations in the West are highly mechanized. The landscape is full of machinery rather than men—of enormous dredges digging gold out of gravels; of giant 'cats' dragging out giant trees from the forest; huge combines reaping and threshing the wheat; massive diesel shovels cutting out irrigation ditches, big water tanks taken into the field to water stock, grids of gleaming sprinklers irrigating winter forage, or vegetable and fruits, mechanical sprayers passing down the orchard rows, and so forth: everywhere the hum and flash of machines.

Associated with this, almost all occupations are highly commercialized. They centre in cities. Thus although the wealth of the West is mainly from 'country' occupations, it is highly urbanized and the Pacific Borderland especially is characterized by large cities. It is the most highly urbanized region after the north-eastern states. Even the mountain states are fairly urban in their interests. They are more urbanized than the South. In these cities are centred the triumph over natural barriers and limitations, which is also typically western, and which has made the region so progressive and optimistic.

Thus the West has come to justify the prophecy that Hall Jackson Kelley made of it in 1839, when he was addressing Congress on the importance of acquiring Oregon and California, declaring that 'at no very distant day a swarming multitude of human beings will people the solitude, and monuments of civilization will throng along those streams whose waters now murmur to the desert'.

concept of "aristocracy". For these two virtues the system of plantations was a good school and . . . militated toward the early emergence of an *élite*.'[1]

Yet the paradox is—we know this was a small group, and in many ways an unrepresentative group. How did it achieve its influence? Whence the tremendous power of its sway, that the vast majority, who were anything but aristocrats, supported it—more, identified themselves with it? As Calhoun pointed out, his folk 'did not live in magnolia groves with tall white columns to hold up the front porches. We did not care for magnolias—they were swampy; and as for white columns, we considered them pretentious. We did not call our farms plantations in the upcountry, and we did not call ourselves old southern planters.' Yet the Calhouns turned out and fought for the Southern planters when the North demanded the abolition of slavery.

Why? Not because your upcountry farmer himself had a few slaves, or even hoped to have. At the time of the Civil War 'really prime field hands were selling for as high as $2,000'. The 4,000,000 negroes who lived in the south at the beginning of the Civil War 'were owned by only 384,000 whites of whom but 108,000 possessed more than 10. At least 6,000,000 southern whites had no direct interest in slavery.'[2] In fact, only 46,000 people could really call themselves major landowners and slave users—the people who owned more than one plantation, had over fifty slaves, and between them controlled 75 per cent of the wealth of the South. How is it that these people

> living upon great estates, managing the affairs of the colony, breeding their fine horses and racing them in good old English style, asserting and maintaining a lavish and lordly hospitality, their wives going about in coaches and four, dressed in satins and brocades brought from London, their daughters in fine raiment dancing, reading and marrying—and vying with their husbands and lovers in patriotism, sealing up their tea, and giving up all silk from England (except for hats and bonnets), their sons going to William and Mary, or across to Oxford or Cambridge, and growing up like their sires, gay, winning and losing wagers on garters, jealous of privilege, proud, assertive of their rights, and ready to fight and stake all on a point of principle',[3]

how did these people have behind them the southern merchants described as 'alert, enterprising, close-bargaining business men',[4] or, more amazing still, that vast endictment of the south, the poor white, who far outnumbered them?

---

[1] Gottman, J., *Virginia at Mid-Century*, p. 90.
[2] Faulkner, *Economic History of the United States*, p. 150.
[3] Page, T. N., *The Old South*.
[4] Wertenbaker, T. J., *Norfolk, Historic Southern Port*, Durham, N.C., 1931, p. 49.

Partly it was because, although like Sartoris they kept the South 'in a stew', they *finally succeeded in doing what all expected of them*: they had the essential qualities of leadership. Above all, as Odum points out, they knew how to 'play the great game of death'[1] amongst a 'frontiering people' whose character, as they moved farther and farther west, became 'welded in the white heat of a hunting economy' that included the hunting down not only of game but of the Indian!

This movement out was shared by everybody, from the younger sons of aristocratic planters to the indentured servant who had put in his servitude and was anxious to find his own bit of land. There is no question but that it produced a more individualistic, free, and democratic way of life. And the Southerner was as anxious to have his liberty as anyone. Indeed, he was more anxious than most to get off by himself and be free to fend for himself. And the warrant system of land procurement enabled him to push on and secure the best lot he could for himself: here was none of your New England dependence upon a township to be settled by a group. These westward moving people were relatively progressive and willing to take each other on merit. As Wish maintains, the frontier *did* act as a strong levelling force.

Yet the paradox arose that 'A westward-moving frontier of conservatism followed in the wake of the earlier westward-moving frontier of progress.' The southerner could not get away from his past. 'The past always casts its spell to a greater or a lesser degree upon the present, but in no other section of the United States is this quite so true as in the South.'[2] All observers agree about this. 'Many Virginians pride themselves', writes Gottmann, 'on belonging to a "conservative" group. This adjective has much more than a political connotation: it hints at a state of mind in matters of daily life.'[3]

This strong conservatism of the South—so strong that it caught up even with the frontier and persuaded the pioneer he could not escape the ways of his fathers—this playing of the game 'in the good old English style', this belief in the 'germs' of institutions and practices, tracing them back if possible not only to colonial precedents but to Teutonic roots, all helped to preserve the remarkable homogeneity of the Southern people. The more the people marched west, the more they rooted themselves in the east!

> The growth in numbers of the southern white people [writes Bruce] *was the growth of the original stock* of English, Scotch, and Scotch-Irish [Ulstermen]—a stock which, as early as 1800, had become as thoroughly homogeneous as the present population of France or England. This homogeneity of the whites was essentially complete. War [the Civil War]

---

[1] Odum, H. W., *The Way of the South*, New York, 1947, p. 19.
[2] Parkins, A. E., *The South*, New York, 1938, pp. 2, 4.
[3] Gottmann, J., *Virginia at Mid-Century*, p. 5.

elevated terraces rising above the swamps everywhere tend to control settlement.

The Appalachians also expand as they sweep into the south. The Piedmont broadens out, and isolated monadnocks rise above it, while several elongated triassic lowlands are enclosed within it. Thus it has had quite a lot to offer to farmers. The Blue Ridge heightens and broadens in the Smokies. They present more of a barrier to west–east communication than in the north. The Appalachian valley forms a long depression, about 600 miles in length, carrying sections of the Tennessee and Coosa rivers. Its rather drier conditions, the presence of prairies, and its limy soil made it most attractive to early settlers. Sharp ridges and narrow valleys run parallel to its western side. The Alabama coal and iron basins lie at the southern opening of the valley. The Cumberland plateau continues the Allegheny plateau in the south. It is largely limestone and is marked with sink holes, caves, and gorges. Smaller hollows became refuges for the 'poor whites'. Much of the region is difficult of access. The rivers flow through its gaps in profound and narrow defiles.

The Cumberland plateau passes west into the limestone plateau of Kentucky, with its rough rock-knob and cove surface, contrasting markedly with the fertile basins of Nashville and the Blue Grass region. These are the sites of wealthy stud farms and tobacco plantations. The West Virginia and West Kentucky coal fields lie in shallow depressions in the Appalachian interior plateaux.

The Interior Highlands run between the Gulf and the Central Lowlands. They are western extensions of the Appalachian system and consist mainly of the Ozark mountains, similar to the Cumberland plateau; the Boston mountains, corresponding to the Cumberland scarp; and the Arkansas valley and Ouachita ridges, which are like the valleys and ridges of the Appalachian valley. They, too, tended to become the refuge of the woodsman and 'poor white' farmer.

The Gulf Coastal Plain has well-marked belts. There is an outer belt of low marshy 'flatwoods' or coastal 'prairies', and of pine 'barrens' interspersed by marshy glades. This rises inland to low, sweeping escarpments. They overlook the Alabama Black Belt, the Jackson Prairie, and the Texas Black Prairies, which are low plains floored with a lime-rich, dark-coloured fertile soil. These plains pass into the Appalachians in the north, and the plateaux of western Texas. Through the centre of the Gulf Coastal Plain is the Mississippi Plain. It consists of swampy 'bottomlands' and fertile 'levees', and pushes out in a marshy delta to the Mexican Gulf.

Southern culture characterizes the Missouri region of the Central Lowland, and also the Texas and part of the Oklahoma districts of the Great Plains, and thus oversteps the Ozarks and the Balcones escarpment. These might be considered transitional areas, although linked more closely with the South than the West in terms of their land systems and institutional geography.

Climate and soils help to give unity to the South, because they run in east–west zones, in contradistinction to major physiographic trends, and thus give a similarity of life to regions as far apart as the Carolinas and Texas. The south is distinctive in that it has no month in which the monthly average falls below 42° F. The frost-free season is at least 180 days long, and in the Gulf and Atlantic coast plains it is from 210 to over 320 days long. In these plains the average July temperature is over 80° F. The Tropical Gulf and Atlantic air masses dominate. Lows are weak in winter and strong in summer. Thus, though there is rain at all seasons, the maximum period is in June–August. The total rainfall is over 40 inches throughout the South, often more than 60 inches on the coast.

This warm, wet climate, with a long growing season has developed a natural vegetation of dense forest. Typical forests are the oak-pine association of the Piedmont, Ozarks, and Ouachitas; the southern pineries of the sandy soils of the Gulf and Atlantic coastal plains; the cypress-gum forests of the Mississippi bottomlands. The black soils are covered with Tall Grass prairie, and the Mississippi delta and Florida ever-glades with salt-marsh vegetation. The pineries were useful for supplying naval stores, but were regarded as barriers by most settlers and scarcely worth clearing because of the sandy soils beneath. Oak forests meant deep, humid, loamy soils and were sought out and extensively cut into and replaced by farms. The widespread occurrence of natural or fire-made prairies in the south greatly attracted and assisted settlement.

The chief soil group is the yellow-red soil, a type with a thin organic layer, beneath which is a yellowish or red-coloured zone of leaching, and then a horizon of mottled yellow or red, with a considerable accumulation of clay. It is this soil which, perhaps more than any other, characterizes the south. However, there is a wide range of types; some, like the black prairies of the coastal vales, the red triassic soils, and the brown lime-based soils of the Great Valley and interior basins, have been more useful than the average. Although today this marked variety of soils is being matched by an ever-increasing diversification of farming, with crops to exploit the soils, for the first 250 years soil diversity was masked by the tendency to raise staples—except that rice did seek the swamps, tobacco the sandy soils, and cotton the better drained heavier soils. But the fever for growing cotton brought many soils under that crop that today are given up to truck farming, fruit farming, the production of beef or milk, or mixed farming. Thus soil variety had little effect on cultural homogeneity. Once that homogeneity was established, however, variety gave it economic strength, and is today of great import.

have led to soil exhaustion, to over-production, rising costs, and falling prices. Consequently, there is no longer the widespread dependence on cotton and tobacco that once obtained (Fig. 187). Mixed farming is coming in. Farmers raise corn and hogs, as well as cotton. Or they produce some dairy products. Or they go in for truck farming—so successful on the sandier soils that underlie the pine belts. There is a growing specialization on early vegetables and fruit, to make the most of the mild winters and quick springs of

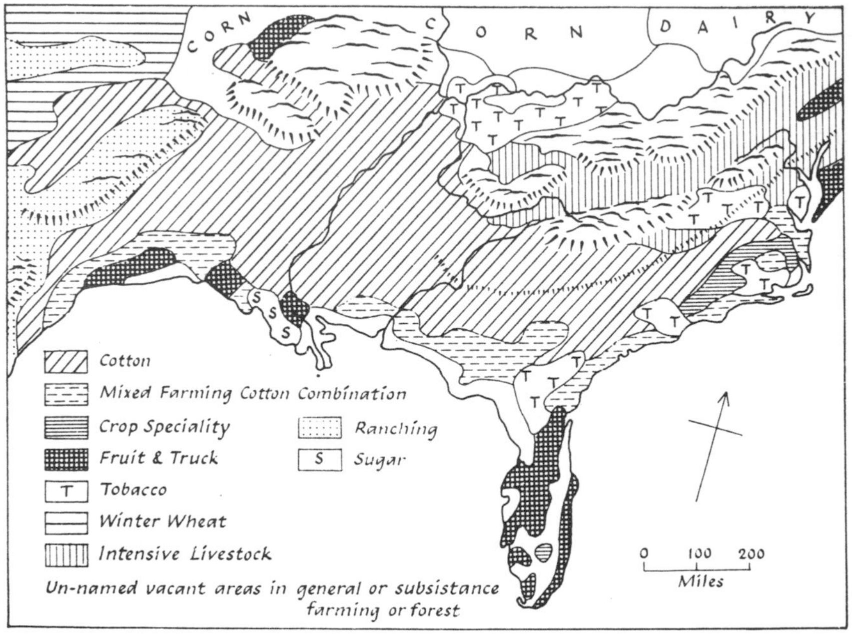

FIG. 187 Farming in the South—a truly diverse region. Although cotton is king, there are many extensive areas under other crops.

the South. In Virginia apples have been raised since 1885. In central Florida and the Rio Grande valley of Texas citrus fruits are produced in abundance. Peanuts, linseed, and groves of tung are grown for their oil. Small farms, worked by the owner, are giving very satisfactory returns, and are changing the rural pattern.

Other occupations are fishing, lumbering, mining, manufacturing, and the tourist trade. **Fishing** is not nearly as important as in the north-east, but is significant. The long coast, with its many estuaries, is an excellent base for small boats to go out each morning and return at night with a catch of oysters, shrimps, and in-shore fish. The continental shelf slopes gently out for a considerable distance, and offers good feeding and spawning grounds for the fish. Deep-water fish may be caught off the Bahamas and other Caribbean islands.

Lumbering has become one of the South's chief industries, particularly since northern forests started to be depleted. The southern pineries are now one of the chief sources of lumber for the nation. The pines are very tall and straight, with few lower branches and are ideal for sawing. A large trade in kerosene has sprung up. The kerosene is tapped from the pines, not unlike

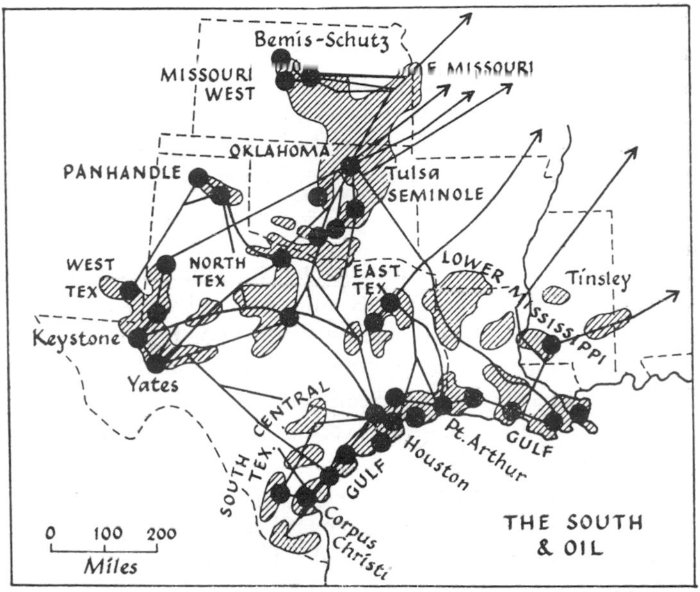

FIG. 188 The South and Oil. The South is by far the most important producer of oil in the United States—most of it going to the industrial North-east. Shaded areas are the oil fields; black circles, chief oil towns.

rubber latex from a rubber tree. Wood alcohol, paper, wall-board, and other by-products are increasingly important.

Mining is also on the increase. At the southern end of the Appalachians are the important coal and iron mines and limestone quarries of the Birmingham district. The Ozarks are especially rich in lead and zinc. Two-fifths of the United States production of lead comes from the Ozarks. West and south of the Ozarks dome are rich oil fields. Oil and natural gas also occur in large quantities in the coastal lowland of Texas and Louisiana (Fig. 188). Phosphates are mined in huge quantities in southern Florida.

The presence of coal in Alabama, the rich water-power developed along the Fall-line edge of the Piedmont, and the great amounts of oil in Texas supply large quantities of fuel or power which can be used for **manufacturing**.

Actually, industrialization was slow to start in the South, and even though it is growing rapidly at present, it is still behind agriculture in the value of its production. However, it has the advantage of being near to raw materials such as cotton and tobacco; of using relatively cheap labour; and of having recent equipment and modern factories. The South is now being more rapidly industrialized than any other part of America, except the Pacific south-west.

The tourist trade is another recent and booming occupation. The South has a sunny summer and mild winter to offer, together with beautiful beaches, warm water, and 'palm trees and Spanish moss'. It is different. The food, the clothes are different. The people are different. They speak with a southern accent. They are fond of history, and have maintained their old buildings and interesting traditions. Beyond them are the colourful folk and countries of the Caribbean. All this attracts the visitor from north and west.

Subdivisions of the South

The South falls into three great divisions: the Atlantic Coastal Plain; the Appalachians and Interior Highlands; and the Gulf Coastal Plain.

The Atlantic Coastal Plain is narrow in the north but broadens in the south. It is really a part of the continental shelf that has gradually risen above the waves. It is very flat. The only hills are where low escarpments of limestone or of sandstone stand above the sandy or clay vales. The outer edge has started to sink back into the sea, and is partially drowned. The sea has crept into valleys and turned them to bays and inlets. Waves have built bay bars and storm beaches along the coast, almost closing up the estuaries. Grassy 'prairies' occur on sandy knolls; luxuriant forest grows on the peninsulas between the swampy creeks.

This was the land which Raleigh's men saw in 1584 and reported as 'the fairest and sweetest spot of all the earth, a paradise of fruits and fish and game'. It was not until 1606, however, when Captain John Smith landed, that colonization was a success. The swamps had bred death and destruction to Raleigh's ventures. However, Africans came a few years later, and taking over the manual labour, worked the plantations of tobacco for the wealthy owners. Some of the plantations were over 5,000 acres in extent. They supported a luxurious and genteel society in Williamsburg, and other Tidewater communities.

The Coastal Plain today is still agricultural. In the north, tobacco is grown on the west shore of the Chesapeake, in the low interfluves between the swampy creeks. Truck farming is also popular, generally choosing the 'muck' soils of the swamp edges. Farther inland, the large cities of Washington and Richmond demand supplies of fresh milk from a belt of dairies that have sprung up to meet the need. Near the cities there is a good deal of 'station wagon' farming—grass parks for fattening stock, poultry raising, etc., done by city residents. In the Carolinas and Georgia, there is a lower Pine Belt, along the coast, and an upper Pine Belt, along the front of the Piedmont, which are rather infertile and undeveloped. Small general farms, often run by white tenants, raising corn and hogs, peanuts, and beans, are scattered in the forests. Almost invariably these are typified by board houses, one or one-and-a-half storeys high, and almost invariably unpainted. Lumbering is more important than farming. In between, along the better-drained and more fertile parts, are the now much-divided cotton plantations, usually with negro tenants and special-crop farms. This central zone carries most of the cities, roads, and railways.

Along the inner railway lines, such as the Richmond and Potomac, Southern, and Seaboard, are a series of market towns which have become industrial cities. These are the cities of the Fall Line. **Richmond** (455,000), capital of Virginia, is the most important. Its port facilities, though limited, are helpful, and it has good modern highways to Washington and Baltimore. It is at the edge of the Chesapeake Bay and Piedmont tobacco regions and has large cigar and cigarette factories. It is also at the north margin of the Cotton Belt and of the southern pineries. The local rivers have long ceased to supply enough power, but coal first from a near-by source in Chesterfield County and then from West Virginia became available, and steam-driven cotton mills, wood-working industries, and railway works occur. Richmond is rich in history, and was connected with Virginia's *élite*. This is seen in its stately buildings, one of which, the State Capitol, was designed by Jefferson: it is also observed in the 'ritual of the social season which is still maintained'.[1] The city organized the resistance of the South to the North, and became the capital of the Confederacy. It was the home of General Lee and of Edgar Allan Poe, two figures who typify the aristocratic and cultural traditions of the South. They would, however, scarcely recognize the town if they came back; it has become so extensively industrialized and modernized. Large new chemical plants, rayon and cellophane works, iron and steel foundries, and paper mills have concentrated at, or near, the city. The cigarette industry has expanded enormously, until today Richmond claims to be the cigarette capital of the world!

Other cities on the inner margin of the Coastal Plain are Raleigh, North Carolina; Columbia, South Carolina; Augusta, Macon, and Columbus, Georgia; and Montgomery, Alabama. These have all developed industries based on local water-power and raw materials. Modern developments depend on Piedmont hydro-electricity and coal from the Appalachians, and produce cottons, some tobacco goods, wood products, and canned goods.

---

[1] Mather, E., and Hart, J. F., *South-eastern Excursion*, I.G.U. XVIIth International Geographical Congress, Washington, 1952, p. 133.

An outer line of settlements occurs at the shore, some of which are linked up by the Atlantic coast-line. They consist of ports and resorts. The ports are at the heads of estuaries, or on sheltered arms. In Virginia are the three important ports: Norfolk and Portsmouth to the south of the James estuary, and Newport News to the north. They dominate the old historic entrance to James Bay, known as Hampton Roads. **Portsmouth** is a naval station and transatlantic cable terminal. **Newport News** is the chief coal exporting port for the coal of West Virginia, and has developed gigantic ship-building and repair yards. Here the giant liner the *United States* was built, which became the holder of the transatlantic blue riband. **Norfolk** also has shipyards, including a navy dock, but mainly exports cotton, tobacco, and peanuts. The three cities (910,000) have become Virginia's largest industrial-metropolitan area and are now linked together by a high-level toll bridge and by an expressway-tunnel. Working-class and residential suburbs are mingling with each other to make a single big built-up zone. Manufacturing, though important, is not as significant as trade. The harbours ship out more volume of material (mainly coal, but also tobacco and cotton) than New York, Philadelphia, and Baltimore combined. However, the trade is basically an export one. In-bound traffic is far below the great ports of the north, and in fact the area complains that many of Virginia's imports come through Baltimore or New York.

North Carolina has no really large port, since Pamlico and Albemarle Sounds are shallow and bordered by marshes. Also they are nearly cut off by the extraordinary off-shore bar that makes Cape Hatteras. However, the Cape Fear river makes a usable estuary, and here stands Wilmington on an interfluve crowded with farms between the Green Swamp and the Angola Swamp. South Carolina has the large port of **Charleston** (250,000), settled by the English as early as 1670. It serves as the main outlet for the State, but never succeeded in tapping the trans-Appalachian trade in a way that would permit it to compete with Baltimore or points north. Its fine harbour is, however, put to use as a large naval base. **Savannah** (210,000), on the estuary of the Savannah river, Georgia, is one of the chief cotton ports on the Atlantic. Considerable lumber is also exported, and factories making wood products and paper from the southern pineries have been developed. **Jacksonville**, Florida (600,000), is on the estuary of the St Johns, and exports naval stores and lumber from a hinterland of dense pine forest. It also makes cigars from the Cuba-type tobacco grown in the upper part of Florida.

The chief coastal resorts are found in Florida at Jacksonville Beach, Daytona Beach, and Miami Beach. These have outdistanced most of the older and even many modern industrial towns. As the U.S. standard of living has increased, more and more people have come to 'winter in Florida', and the servicing of these holiday-makers is now one of the South's major businesses. **Miami** (1,100,000) the chief tourist and 'convention' city, is also an international airport, being the jumping-off point for flights to the Caribbean, South America, southern Europe, and West Africa.

The Appalachians

When the Coastal Plain was largely taken over by the big planters, the small homesteader sold out wherever he could make a good profit and moved up-country. This was accelerated when the negroes came in, as many whites did not wish to be put in a position of having to compete with blacks. They could escape this by moving west. Many, of course, had ruined their own farms, and were leaving because the soil had become exhausted at their own hands. Many were simply of the roving kind, who, like Daniel Boone, 'moved on whenever a new neighbour settled close enough for him to hear his dogs bark'.[1] Most of these 'yeomen farmers' did very well in the comparative isolation and independence of the **Piedmont**, where they met other independent farmers moving down from the north. The low plateau attracted them by its oak forest, deep red soils, high dry interfluves, and deep valleys with water for running mills. Most villages and roads were built on the plateau crests, except where important crossings occurred in the valleys. The settlement still consists mainly of sparse, erratically scattered farmsteads. The soils are fairly thick, and are quite fertile, although they are easily eroded and need a lot of fertilizer. The climate is more humid than most of the Coastal Plain, with a rainfall of 40 to 60 inches. The rivers have a steady flow, and where rapids or falls occur can be dammed to provide cheap and abundant electricity. The forest cover, of oak, chestnut, beech, and poplar, which still remains in part, helps to maintain a regular stream flow.

In the western Piedmont of Virginia, farmers have replaced trees with fruit orchards, and between the Rappahannock and James rivers is one of the most famous apple regions in the United States. Dairy farming and the fattening of well-bred beef cattle (like Aberdeen Angus) are also common, especially near the big towns. South of the James river, tobacco has become the chief crop. Much of it is grown by individual operators on their own small farms. Garden crops and corn, pigs, and hens are raised for farm needs. The southern part of the Piedmont is under cotton. Here the plantation system became fairly firmly rooted, and large mansions occur side by side with negro shacks. Even after the slaves were freed, they lived on in their former quarters and worked the land for their masters on a share-crop basis.

As a result, the plantation-owners had to divide and subdivide their lands for suitable smallholdings such as could be worked by one man and his mule. Often, the plantation as the main unit of settlement has gone—all but

[1] Odum, *The Way of the South*, p. 30.

the house and servant quarters; and the mills, smithies, and carpenters' workshops have been set up in local hamlets, working for the scattered tenant-farmers around. So there has been a rise of 'service-centre' villages with the splitting up and decline of the plantation. 'The plantation spinner and weaver have disappeared and the crossroads storekeeper, with his cheap goods, has taken their place.'[1] But these 'villages' have not really flourished because Piedmont tenant-farming is poor. After a hundred years of inadequate attention, with little done for it except the application of lime, the soil has often become exhausted and washed out. Today 'most of the western Piedmont is poor farm land, and great acreages are wooded or lie vacant. Here, as in the mountains, the people seem to prefer industrial jobs to the harder work of farming. Mile after mile passes without fences or livestock, and an extraordinary absence of mechanized farm equipment is noticeable.'[2] However, better methods of farming are gradually being introduced, and many of the farmers have given up one-crop farming for a more diversified agriculture.

The Piedmont will probably always remain agricultural. The chief cities serving it are on its outermost edge, along the Fall Line, on the Coastal Plain. Thus its power resources and agricultural raw materials are used by the cities of the plain. It is only in the extreme south, where the Piedmont broadens out, that it has produced a city of major importance. This is **Atlanta** (1,320,000), the 'Gate City of the South', and capital of Georgia. It is mainly the creation of the railways, and draws together many lines from the Piedmont and from the Appalachian valley, around the massive Blue Ridge, and also the railways between the Atlantic coast and the Mississippi valley, thus commanding the broad gate between the South-east and the Old South-west. It has ample hydro-electric power and can also obtain coal cheaply from near-by Alabama, and has developed large cotton mills, lumber works, fertilizer plants, and agricultural-machine industries. During the Civil War it was the chief depot for the Southern armies. Its main functions, however, are as a commercial, communications, and cultural centre. It is one of the few great cities the South has thrown up that possesses wide metropolitan influence.

The Blue Ridge long formed a barrier to westward settlement. It is high, densely wooded, with deep, narrow valleys. However, some of the larger rivers cut right through it, and provide gaps to the Appalachian valley. The Potomac and James make important gaps, followed by road and railway. The Roanoke approaches the headwaters of the New, and the Carolina Broad approaches the French Broad in Tennessee. The Ridge itself is an important source of lumber, but more significant than that, it forms a major

---

[1] Bruce, *The Rise of the New South*, p. 23.
[2] Mather and Hart, *South-eastern Excursion*, pp. 125–6.

'summering' place where the peoples of the plain can get up to hill resorts away from the burning heat and great humidity of the lower cities. This has given the area new prosperity and compensated it for the dreadful decline of its farming communities, most of which had about reached the end of their tether. Farms ought, of course, never to have been cut out of the forest on the steep valley slopes. Soil erosion swiftly stepped in, especially because all the farmers continued to plough up and down the hill-face, as they had always done. They simply encouraged the soil to flow down their furrows and be swept away in the streams. Yet such was the appalling conservatism of the South, they did not change their ways even when faced with inescapable and growing penury. Many of them took to hunting and fishing for their main livelihood. Now they have a chance to act as guides for the tourists, or work in the summer hotels.

The Appalachian valley, west of the Blue Ridge, is a composite valley, containing the valley of the Shenandoah, Virginia; the upper Tennessee and its tributaries, Tennessee; and the Coosa and its tributaries, Alabama and Georgia. Except for the beautiful meander plain of the Shenandoah it is almost choked with ridges in Virginia. Farther south the valley widens, the ridges are not as conspicious as the valleys. The valley bottoms are at a level of about 1,000 feet, and the ridge tops about 2,000. Taken together, valley and ridge appear as a lowland between the Blue mountains (6,000 feet) and the Cumberland plateau (3,500 feet). The limestone rocks in the valley have weathered into many sink-holes, dry valleys, caves, and natural bridges, which have considerable tourist appeal. Much more important, they have produced a dark reddish-brown soil of considerable fertility. This came to be significant; for, as settlers did well on this kind of soil, they looked for it elsewhere, a search that led them on down to the dark, rich, calcareous plain of the Coosa, across to the limy and productive soils of the Tennessee valley, and so eventually to the grass-thick and game-rich limestone basins of Kentucky, which they turned into such lucrative areas. A major population stream in Southern settlement was thus guided into, down, and beyond the Great Valley by the attraction of lime-based earth.

The climate was also favourable, changing gradually from one with chilly winters and heavy snowfall north of Virginia to a sub-tropical climate in Tennessee and Alabama, with a mild, pleasant winter. The rainfall likewise increases southward from 35 inches to over 50 inches. It is evenly distributed throughout the year. In the winter it is mostly in the form of relief and cyclonic rain; in the summer, of convection rain. Adjustment to relief is well marked; the open floor has the lowest, the westward facing hill slopes the highest, amount of rain.

The warm, moist climate has produced a forest covering of oak and hickory. Beech, maple, birch, and hemlock climb up to clothe the ridges. In the south, many pines occur, along with oak. Fortunately for the pioneers, the Indians had already opened up the floor of the Great Valley. Consequently, 'At the first settling the valley was one vast prairie, and like the rich prairies of the west, afforded the finest possible pasturage. They had an artificial cause. At the close of each hunting season the Indians fired the open ground and thus kept it from reverting to woodland. This was done to attract the buffalo, an animal that shuns the forest. The progressive deforesting of the lowlands of the valley made settlement by the whites very easy and rapid.'[1]

However, the forest on the ridges above was so dense that it long prevented exploration and colonization. It was not until Daniel Boone discovered the Cumberland gap that the valley became one of the great routes to the west. Forest conditions have been ideal for tree crops. In Virginia the Shenandoah valley has long been a favoured apple district, the warmth of the valley ripening the fruit in summer, the hill slopes providing frost drainage in spring and fall. As the lowland area widens in the south, there is more room for crops of corn, cotton, and winter wheat. Some tobacco is grown, too. By the rivers are rich meadows pasturing sleek dairy cattle. Pigs are fattened on the corn.

Yet while the valley sections are well enough developed, the ridges are not. Small farms, carved out of the forest, provide a bare existence to the settlers. The families live in small wooden shacks, and get a living from garden crops, corn, pigs, and some fishing and lumbering. The story of the Blue Ridge has been repeated over again. As these ridge-farmers ploughed their steep slopes erosion began. This gradually stripped off the top soil; huge gullies opened up in the fields; land slips occurred; the farms became exhausted and poor. Meantime, the gullies carried the rainfall rapidly off the slopes down to the Tennessee and its tributaries. Floods started, which soon reached devastating proportions, ruining the rich meadows and spreading coarse sands and boulders over the flattened corn and wheat.

It was to meet this situation that in 1933 the Tennessee Valley Authority was established. Its primary aim has been to build dams, hold up the floodwater, improve navigation on the river, and provide hydro-electricity from a series of interlinked hydro plants. It realized from the first, however, that this could only be done successfully after attacking the soil erosion problem. Large areas of land have been bought up and reforested. An intensive educational drive is under way to teach farmers how to prevent erosion by building check dams across the gullies, by grassing the steeper slopes instead of ploughing them, and by cultivating the rest in strip-cropping; a strip of corn, a strip of grass, a strip of wheat, and a strip of grass—and so on. These strips are ploughed and cultivated along the contours of the land and prevent

[1] Kercheval, S., *A History of the Valley of Virginia*, Strasbourgh (Va.), 1925, p. 52.

sheet-erosion of the surface soil. Such practices are transforming the Appalachian valley in the south into a very progressive region (Fig. 189).

The development of hydro-electricity under the T.V.A. has quickened industrial developments. The valley had early used water-power for saw, flour, and cotton mills; but only on a small scale. Marble quarrying was a growing industry at Rome and Knoxville. Yet what made **Knoxville** (390,000) into the prosperous city it is, was the new sources of power released by T.V.A. Today this city, in addition to its important stone-dressing and cement works, has large cotton and woollen factories, flour mills, furniture works, potteries, and metal works. It refines zinc from near-by zinc mines, and has important iron and steel foundries. Its command of north–south routes through the Appalachian valley and of west–east gaps through the bordering uplands enables it to distribute goods over a wide area, and it is an important centre for gathering cotton together from the cotton farms of East Tennessee.

Unquestionably, a main result of the huge amounts of cheap electricity released by the very successful control of the waters of the Tennessee, has been the development at Oak Ridge of the giant U.S. research centre for nuclear energy, although the great quantity of water, dammed up in the many lakes the T.V.A. has made, is another important factor.

Farther south in the valley, **Chattanooga** (314,000) has also become an industrial and commercial city. But the largest industrial centre of all is **Birmingham** (700,000), at the end of the valley, where the Appalachian folds die out beneath the Alabama plains. In the gently folded rocks are large deposits of coal and iron. These are used, along with local limestone flux, for the large-scale manufacture of iron and steel, and steel machinery. It is said that Birmingham can make iron and steel more cheaply than any other centre in the United States, and this not merely because of negro low-price labour, but because of the geography of the place. For 'where else in the United States are good coking coal, fairly rich ore, and a suitable flux only from twenty to sixty minutes apart?'[1] There are about 800 mills, producing steel plate and pipes, nails, all-steel cars, car wheels; mill machinery for cotton gins; coal-mining machinery; textiles; fertilizers; chemicals; lumber products; and many lesser goods. The city is near to the Alabama Black Belt, where it draws its cotton and sells its machines and fertilizers. It commands still wider areas through excellent rail facilities to the Mississippi, Gulf and Atlantic plains, and has a wide sale for its goods.

Compared with the bustling progress of the valley, **the Cumberland plateau** still remains an isolated and backward district. The rocks consist of thick massive sheets of limestone, with some sandstone. They have been tilted up and faulted in the east to produce the Cumberland mountain, or escarpment.

[1] Parkins, *The South*, p. 477.

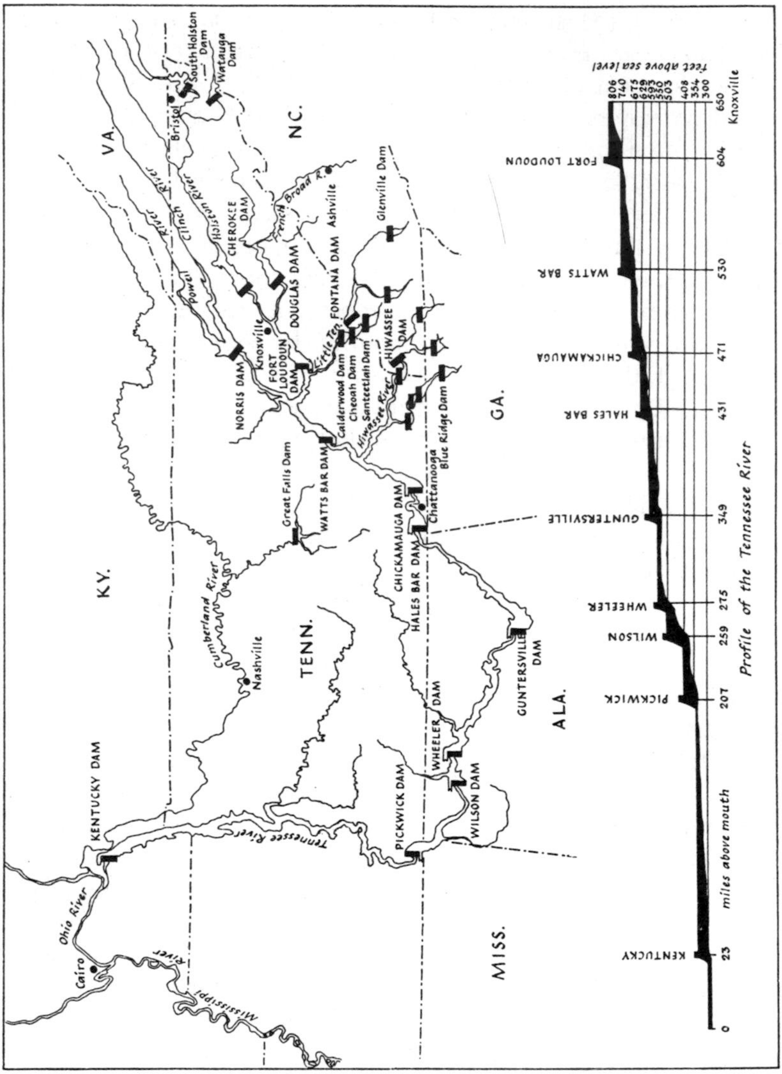

FIG. 189 The T.V.A.– The New South, where Conservation, Power, and Production go together. The Authority has power to make dams, halt erosion, reforest denuded slopes, encourage the modernization of agriculture, develop hydro-electricity and promote industrial growth. By this means it has helped to transform what once contained some of the poorest and most backward regions in America.

61. A sugar plantation in the hot moist climate of the Mississippi bottomlands, Baton Rouge.

The Agricultural South

62. Modernization of cotton farming has gone on apace. Here an automatic cotton-picker takes the place of forty men during a ten-hour working day.

63. The T.V.A. first began to transform the South. The Douglas Dam on the French Broad, Tenn., supplies hydro-electric power for a wide area. The Dam also controls erosion.

The Industrial South—Electricity and Oil

64. Petrochemical industries, such as this nylon and polyethylene plant on the Sabine River plain, Tex., have helped to revolutionize the geography of the Gulf Southwest, one of America's richest oil-bearing regions.

65. New Orleans, the queen of the South, still shows many of the French and Spanish influences of its early colonial days.

The Urban South, although by no means as urbanized as the North, Central or Pacific Southwest states, nevertheless accounts for a number of America's most historic and at the same time most rapidly expanding cities

66. Houston, Tex., claims to be America's fastest-growing city, and is mushrooming forth with great railyards, a flourishing port, big road transport terminals, and the skyscrapers of a rapidly expanding business area.

67. Amphitheatre of an old Aztec temple, with central half reconstructed, shows stepped-up pyramid surrounded by lesser altar platforms in a vast area set aside for religious festivities, near Mexico City.

Ancient Mexico—home of America's earliest civilizations

68. Ruins of a Mayan temple outside the still older Mayan town of Uxmal, in Yucatan.

They have a slight dip to the west, but are caught up in long, low folds which bring coal seams near to the surface. The rivers flowing through the plateau have cut very deep gorges; farther west they have coal seams on the valley sides. The plateau passes without much break into the Kentucky plateau to the west. The Tennessee river cuts back through the scarp and approaches the Cumberland, west of Knoxville, at several points, allowing railways to pierce the plateau. The Cumberland and Blue Ridge gaps had historic importance in permitting the South to unite the Mississippi and Atlantic plains across the whole Appalachian system.

Some lumbering and small-scale mining are carried on in the plateau, but agriculture is very limited, and is mainly for subsistence. The mines are usually small side-adit affairs, where a tunnel or gallery is opened up in the side of a valley, if the coal seam is exposed. The coal is brought easily to the surface, and then screened and shipped away by rail or truck. Because many of the companies are small they do not have much capital; their machinery is old-fashioned; some of the mining is still carried on by pick and shovel. The mining industry has been running down during the last few decades. Settlements are small and untidy. The miners, like the farmers of the region, are poor.

The poverty and isolation of the people of the Appalachian ridges and the Cumberland plateau explain why they are so conservative. They cling to old habits. A great deal of this has been due to isolation; yet not so much to an imposed isolation as to an isolation sought out. The mountains and plateaux were refuges where men preferred the struggle with nature to the competition with their fellow men. In their book on the *Hollow Folk*, Sherman and Henry indicate it was not relief alone, but psychology, as well, that shut people off in the hollows of the hills. While most of their contemporaries streamed into the plains after the many opportunities of the Old and New South-wests, the hollow folk got themselves deeper and deeper into their hollows. It was the refuge mentality that discovered a refuge in the hills. Even today when tourist roads go right by their houses and they have the opportunity to meet and mix with the world they still stay by themselves.

> Here isolation has been extreme; poverty, general; and living more primitive than in any other area of the United States. Outside the few 'industrial' villages, where a few foreigners and some negroes are found, the people are all of old Anglo-Celtic stock. Because of their retarded civilization they have sometimes been called 'our contemporaneous ancestors'. They are extremely individualistic, with characteristics and customs of early frontiersmen. The Church is even more Protestant than in the rest of the South . . . and the most Puritanic. 'There is much more Puritanism in the South today than remains in New England.' It is also

> highly emotional. Whole communities are swept by the blasts of frenzied revivalism into strange and weird emotional orgies. A typical case was the Cane Ridge meeting in Bourbon County, Kentucky, where a vast multitude of 20,000 or more came under the spell of wildest fanaticism. 'Many, very many fell down, and continued for hours together in an apparently breathless and motionless state, sometimes for a few moments reviving and exhibiting symptoms of life by a deep groan or piercing shriek. After lying there for hours . . . they would rise, shouting deliverance.'[1]

At the same time, 'by-products of this emotionalism are unrighteousness and immorality'. Crimes of violence are not infrequent. As Hooton observes, 'Rural residence puts a premium on hardihood and restricts the choice of crime. Life affords few opportunities for acquisitive offence. In general, one must rape, murder, or behave.'

Undoubtedly all this is due to a difficult and frustrating environment; but that environment has been altered, as for example by the T.V.A. Yet it took the people from outside to work the transformation. The hollow folk did not seem to have it in them to do it. Isolating themselves, they clung to old habits and old ideas. It is said that they still use many Elizabethan words and phrases and forms of pronunciation. Their folk songs are also very old; many of them Elizabethan. They also preserve the old-fashioned religious ideas of Elizabethan Puritans. They form part of what is known as 'The Bible Belt'; a belt of religious sects through the heart of the South that believe in the literal interpretation of the Bible. Tennessee is notorious for its fundamentalism, and once tried a teacher for teaching evolution. It is no wonder, then, that with these old attitudes they should preserve the old geography, and carry over into the landscape of today the landscape of all their yesterdays. This is the most important factor in the geography of their region, although it will be altered by mass Federal aid, now being applied.

The Interior Basins and Highlands

As the Cumberland plateau extends westward through Kentucky, it is more and more attacked by river-erosion, with the result that a new landscape arises; a broken, dissected plateau, enclosing wide, fertile basins. The plateau does not show many flat interfluves, but has been cut up into isolated ridges or knobs, with many dry valleys, sinks, and caves between them. This is rock-knob country, largely forested, or with only poor farms. It is not unlike the uplands already described. Consequently, attention will be focused on the basins.

The Blue Grass Basin, Kentucky, and the Nashville Basin, Tennessee, are fertile oases in the wilderness. As we have seen (Chapter Three), basins were once domes, but after the limestone cover was removed by erosion, the

[1] Sims, N. Le R., *Elements of Rural Sociology*, pp. 560–1, 579.

weaker shales beneath were carved away by rivers, leaving small plains, circled by ragged scarps. In contrast to the heavy forests of the rocky plateau, these basins were covered, in their natural state, by open prairies of tall blue grass. When settled by horse-loving Southerners they soon became famous for horse-breeding, and there are still many well-known studs.

The soils are derived from shale over limestone, and are very fertile and easy to till. Cultivated farms soon came to compete with 'grass parks', and tobacco plantations were started, using negro labour. The large plantations and rich horse-breeding ranchos brought a lot of wealth, which led to the building of very stately homes, and to beautiful cities like **Lexington** (157,000). There is not much industry, however. That has sprung up in West Kentucky around the coal field, one of the important interior fields, especially at **Louisville** (805,000), a river port on the Ohio and a busy railway junction, already described.

Again, here is a debatable area. From the physiographic viewpoint these basins, and possibly the valleys in lower West Virginia as well, belong to and are oriented towards the Mid-west. However, they were settled mainly by pioneers from the South. Those in West Virginia were mainly middle-class farmers and traders who had already been irked at the political and social domination of Tidewater Virginia and when the other Southern States seceded from the United States they 'seceded from Secession' and joined the North. Kentucky and Tennessee, however, with their great planters and with a well-entrenched system of slavery, stayed with the South. They have thus brought the South beyond the mountains into the Mid-west.

The interior basins give way westward to the plains of the Mississippi, beyond which rise the interior highlands associated with the Ozarks. Much the same sort of landscape is found as occurs in the southern Appalachians and Cumberland plateau. The great Ozarks plateau, underlain by gently swelling strata, builds up to a dissected surface, where rivers have cut down deeply, and broken it into a series of isolated knobs. It is crowned by the Boston mountains, representing the crest of the up-swell. These 'mountains' turn a long scarp to the north, but dip down in the south to the wide valley of the Arkansas. Beyond the valley is the ridge and valley country of the Ouachitas.

The climate is not unlike that of the Southern Appalachians. It is similarly moist, with 40 to 60 inches a year; but the chief amount of rain falls in spring rather than summer. This is because it comes more directly within the area of struggle between the Tropical Gulf and Polar Continental air masses—a struggle that is very intense in the spring. Both regions have between 180 days free of frost on their northern slopes and 200 on their southern ones. If anything, the Ozarks have a longer growing season. Their valleys escape sub-freezing weather in winter, and are equally hot in the

(50–60 inches) than in the western plain (40–50 inches). The highest rainfall (over 60 inches) occurs along the coast east of the Mississippi delta. A great number of 'lows' sweep along this coast and across northern Florida. The other chief track of the 'lows' is up the Mississippi.

The growing season is the longest in eastern America. The outer coastal plain has a frost-free season of generally ten months. In some years there is no frost. It never stays for more than a day or two. Nevertheless frost is important in the distribution of the tobacco and citrus areas. At Windsor, Florida, one severe frost in 1894 was enough to wipe out the citrus industry and change the landscape. Instead of flourishing orchards owned and operated by prosperous white families, there are now only deserted fields in what is virtually a ghost town. Coloured people and poor whites have moved in. They fish and hunt, raise corn, and keep pigs; a very different way of life.

The soils of the western and eastern Gulf plains are yellowish sandy loams, for the most part, with sands in south-east Texas and northern Florida. The Texas flatwoods have poorly drained dark-coloured limy soils. The Texas Black Prairies and Alabama Black Belt have well-drained highly calcareous black earths. They are very fertile. The Mississippi lowland is covered with fertile alluvials.

The vegetation is closely related to the soils. On the sands and sandy loams the mature vegetation is pine forest, of longleaf, loblolly, and slash pines. The black soils have a Tall Grass prairie vegetation. The Mississippi alluvials bear a river-bottom forest of cypress, tupelo, and red gum trees. The delta is carpeted with marsh grass.

The agriculture responds to the physical environment and shows two belts, an outer and an inner one. The outer belt is still largely undeveloped, and, where it is farmed, is characterized by rather poor general farms or cattle ranges. The rainfall is too high, and too much of it occurs in the late summer to permit the successful cultivation of cotton. The soils are sandy and not very fertile, though they can be adapted to tobacco, truck crops, and fruit. But with a high rainfall they are easily leached and need constant applications of fertilizer. Forest products compete on too favourable a basis with agriculture; many owners keep their land in timber, either for systematic cutting or tapping for turpentine. In many instances they combine lumbering with ranching, and turn range cattle loose in the timbers. The cattle find enough grazing in the underbrush and in the frequent little prairies that open out between the trees to need no forage crops. There is no problem of supplying them with special winter feeds. An interesting development has been the breeding of a special brand from Brahmin bulls and Jersey cows, who are able to withstand the heat, like their East Indian sires, but give good milk, like their European dams. In the vicinity of towns and harbours more specialized farms are found, with dairy herds and garden crops. In the marshes of the Mississippi delta thriving sugar-cane plantations have been established. Yet, on the whole, the outer plain is rather too isolated from markets and too infertile to promote highly specialized crops.

The inner coastal plain forms the heart of the Cotton Belt. Here the summers are long and hot. They are not too moist to spoil the boll; yet they are sufficiently moist to stimulate active growth. There are some excellent marly soils and fertile alluvials.

The chief problems are the exhaustion of the poorer sandy loams; the backward methods of farming, especially by coloured tenants; the recent spread of the boll weevil; and the fluctuations in price as other cotton regions in the world are beginning to compete with the United States. Some of the exhausted regions have now given up one-crop farming in favour of mixed farming, which is better for the soil.

The education of farmers is steadily going ahead. This is, however, a slow process. 'Of all the farmers to whom cotton is the chief source of income, more than two thirds are tenants.'[1] And most of the tenants are negroes. They have little means, and less education. It is difficult for them to understand about new techniques, or to secure the capital to make use of them. When the Gulf plains went in for plantation cotton in a big way, the number of negro labourers became very high. Only eighty years ago there were three states with more negroes than whites: South Carolina, Alabama, and Mississippi. Two of these were Gulf States, forming a part of the so-called 'Deep South'. The situation then gradually changed. Many negroes left to go north. By 1900 only Mississippi had a negro majority. This remained until as late as 1930, when the white population at last became preponderant. Nevertheless, the coloured population is still high. It lives at a low standard, and most of the negroes are share-croppers, who have little incentive to farm efficiently. They have suffered particularly badly from the boll weevil, because of lack of equipment and money to fight it. Many drift to cities.

Perhaps the chief problem in the Cotton Belt is the competition with California and Arizona, together with fluctuation in international prices. America no longer has the advantage it used to. Other countries like Egypt, India, Brazil, Uganda, Russia, Turkey, and even China are beginning to compete with it. Sometimes there is too much cotton put on the market and prices fall. The cotton 'pools' have tried to check this by storing a surplus from one year to sell later, when not as much cotton is produced, or prices improve. However, one of the best ways of meeting the problem has been to grow less cotton, and to raise alternative crops on the farm. Peanuts, beans, and winter wheat are favourites.

Specialized crops are becoming more common. They make a special

[1] Odum, *The Way of the South*, p. 156.

the immediate hinterland is still a very rich one. It is strategically situated above the claw-like delta of the Mississippi, about 100 miles from the coast, where sea-going vessels can anchor beside transcontinental railway terminals. It is beautifully sited between a broad loop of the river and Lake Pontchartrain to the north. The old town spread from the river inwards, like an antique fan: north of it the gridiron pattern of the normal American settlement begins but is interrupted by the beautiful Lakeview Park. The railways come in from west and east around the lake, and between it and the sea. The port became great through the exports to England and also to New England of cotton from the Mississippi plain. It is likewise a collecting and exporting centre for sugar, rice, and fish. Since the opening of the Panama Canal it has done a wide trade with the western states of South America. It is a great tourist attraction, thanks to its picturesque association with colonial days, its distinctly French appearance, and its mild winter climate. More than that, it is a metropolitan centre, with two major universities, and many leading business houses.

In the West Gulf plain are the important Black Prairie and Grand Prairie districts centred in Dallas, and the Coast Dark Prairie in Houston. These centres are noted for their high-grade cotton, early crops, and mineral products.

Dallas (1,350,000) is well situated where the Trinity river cuts a rather deep yet quite wide notch through the forested escarpment known as the Eastern Cross Timbers to connect up the scarp-foot vale to the north, the Grand Prairie (in which Fort Worth lies), with the major fertile tract of the dip-slope vale, the famous Black Prairie. Such a site attracted early pioneer routes and subsequently railways, and Dallas grew to importance as a railway town, with the St Louis and San Francisco railway coming in from the north-east, the Missouri and Kansas from the north-west, the Texas and Pacific from east and west, and the Southern Pacific from the south, besides several other lines. It is a major cotton market in Texas and also a jobbing centre for the oil industry. Oil from neighbouring fields is piped here, and then sent on to the North (Fig. 192). A great pyramid of skyscrapers soars up above its business area, including principal oil offices, banks, and hotels serving the south-west. The city has large oil refineries, textile mills, cotton-seed oil and fertilizer plants, and factories making agricultural implements and cotton-ginning machinery. It also has several large flour mills, a measure of the importance of winter wheat as the second crop in the region. **Fort Worth** (700,000), farther west, is also interested in cotton and petroleum, but, long having been a centre for the cattle trade of the ranchers on the high plains still farther west, it has retained this contact, and possesses large stock yards and meat-packing plants.

Houston (1,515,000) is one of the most rapidly growing towns in the South,

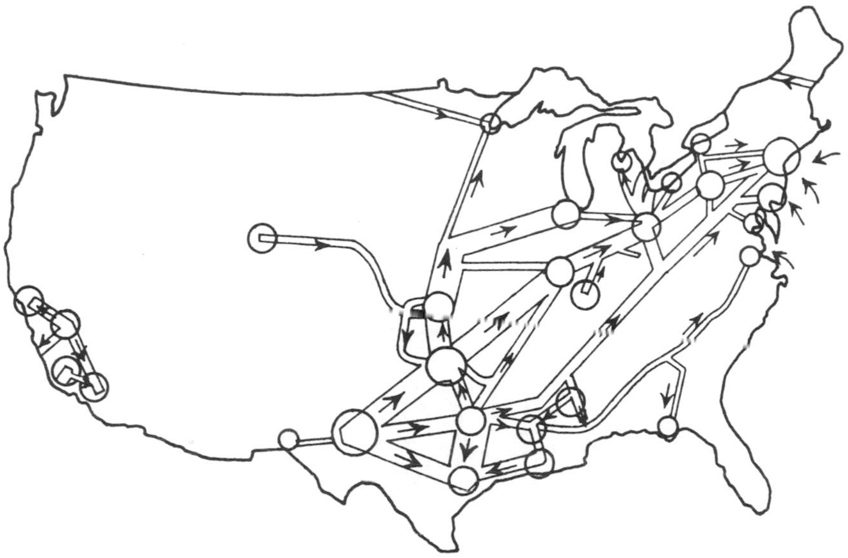

FIG. 192 The main system of United States Oil Pipe-lines. The concentration in the Dallas and southern–central region of Texas is noteworthy.

or for that matter in America. It is strangely non-Southern in appearance, with a tremendously busy, crowded, lofty, shiny, city centre (Fig. 193); a circle of low, horizontal, concrete-and-glass spread factories; and, beyond, a wonderful blossoming-forth of fine residential suburbs. It began as a small port for boats that could navigate into the inner reaches of Galveston Bay, and as a provisioning centre for the rapid expansion of the Cotton Belt into the coastal prairies. Railways gave it its first recognition and nine lines have built it up into the main coastal junction in Texas. Early in this century it constructed a ship-canal to the Gulf and is now a major port, taking away much of the trade of Galveston which used to be its out-port. (It is now eight times the size of Galveston, which grew up as the main port and settlement!) Its dynamic progress was further assisted by the oil boom of the Gulf oil fields, but above all by the great decentralization programme of war contracts and the post-war industrialization of the South. Here was a good port, lots of flat land for expansion, a local hinterland of some worth, surplus labour from an agricultural belt getting more mechanized and intensified, and all the amenities of a pleasant climate. It has large textile, chemical, and engineering works, and shares in exciting space-machine industries. It exports grain, cotton, and oil. It is one of the South's chief 'convention centres' and bids fair to be its chief metropolis.

In the East Gulf plain the leading centre is **Mobile** (350,000), which exports the cotton of the Black Belt in Alabama, and also many of the manufactured

Finally, transportation has been inadequate. The South depended too long on its rivers. The railways are few and far between, compared with the north. They also involve higher freight costs.

Nevertheless, there are certain industrial advantages in the South. It has an abundance of raw materials: cotton, tobacco, sugar, citrus fruits; lumber; lead, zinc, bauxite, iron, sulphur, petroleum, phosphates, and potash; cotton-seed, peanuts, and tung—for vegetable oils; and important fisheries. The South has an abundance of power—coal in the Appalachians and Ouachitas, oil in southern Texas and Louisiana, and hydro-electricity in the Ozarks, the Blue Ridge and Piedmont, and the Tennessee valley. It can start afresh and build modern factories, with much more efficient machinery than a lot of the obsolete stuff in Northern mills. It is nearest the expanding South American market.

As a result of all these things, the South is now developing new industries more rapidly than the older industrial parts of the United States. This will mean a new lease on life, giving the South a broader-based economy and a wider-structured society. If this should prove to be the case, then the prospects may very well help to resolve the problems. The voice of the South need not be, in the words of Faulkner, 'as proud and still as banners in the dust'. The banners have risen again.

CHAPTER TWENTY-THREE

Mexico

Mexico stands out from the other North American countries, Canada and the United States, in that it is more like South America. Mexico is, in fact, an outpost of the south against the north. It is Latin in outlook, custom, and practice, and this Latinization of life has been reflected in both rural and urban landscapes. This is important. A different America begins at the Rio Grande: an America that is both more native and yet in some ways strangely more European; an America that owes a great deal to the Indian and is still very Indian in blood and feeling, yet an America that, when it became Europeanized, kept to the European modes more than its northern counterparts.

At one time, of course, Latin influences were much wider, and Spain dominated the greater part of the continent west of the Mississippi. But the Spanish lost more and more territory, at first to France or England, and then to the United States. The loss of Louisiana took the Mississippi plains from them; the Mexican wars wrenched away Texas, California, and New Mexico. Mexico is a last remnant of Spanish culture in North America. It probably escaped complete absorption into the United States because of the barrier of desert between the two countries. South of the desert Mexico was safe, and could work out its own destiny.

The two countries are not unlike, where they join; but to north and south they differ considerably. The Spanish influence dies out in America; the Anglo-American influence in Mexico. At the southern edge of its plateau Mexico is thoroughly different and unique. It is a Latin outpost in what is largely an Anglo-American continent.

For this reason Mexico is often regarded as belonging to Central and South America rather than to North America. In all its reactions, its customs, and culture it is southern, not northern. It is a rural and in many ways still a peasant society; it has long been dominated by Church and Army; its wealth depends on the export of raw materials and not of finished goods; handicrafts and the neighbourhood market are still important; and the people are tied a great deal more to their own locality.

Yet physically the country is a part of North America. The Gulf Coast plain of the Southern States sweeps through Mexico to Campeche. The Rockies are represented in the Sierra Madre Oriental; the Sierra Nevada, in aboriginal times and continue to leave their mark on the geography of the country.

That the Mexican Indians were the most advanced on the continent set the region off from the beginning. The Spaniards were not dealing with the relatively primitive hunters and gardeners that the English came upon, or the yet more humble fishermen and hunters met with by the French. There

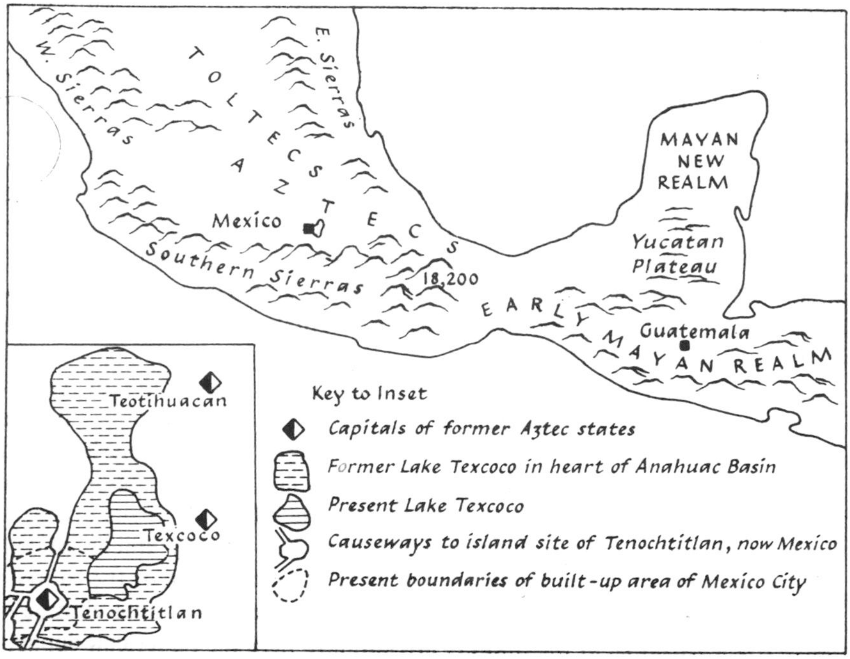

FIG. 195 Mexico and its Indian Past. Here where the continent narrowed down so that mountain, plateau, and plain, temperate and tropical climates, steppeland, and forest came close together, man paused in his long wanderings south through North America, and with a wealth of different conditions at his disposal, developed a sedentary, civilized way of life, with farms and villages, workshops, and cities. (Scale, 1:21 m.)

were, it is true, primitive slash-and-burn 'agriculturists' and nomadic hunters in the less accessible parts of Mexico, but farmers, miners, and city dwellers made up the bulk of the population in all the more favourable areas (Fig. 195).

Most of these were farmers, and the society was strongly rural, even though it supported several flourishing cities. Urban life was just a denser form, a condensation, of rural: cities were rooted and grounded in the country and, as we have seen, could rarely expand beyond what the immediate hinterland might supply. Trade in bulk commodities was very limited since there were no vehicles and no beasts of burden. Cities had to fend for themselves from their immediate neighbourhoods.

Although the Spaniards destroyed most of the Indian cities and then rebuilt them along Spanish lines, nevertheless they did find a city-building tradition in the land which greatly helped them. Moreover, that tradition oddly paralleled their own, and therefore lingered on in the Spanish efforts and helped to guide them. Aztec towns were dominated by temples; Spanish ones by great cathedrals. (In some cases small Christian chapels were actually built on top of the great flat-topped temple pyramids, and Indians could take the host where they had erstwhile watched their ancient sacrifices. Sometimes the temple was torn down to be replaced by a church, the Indian coming to the same *site* to worship.) Aztec towns had a central market-place, the Spanish their town *plaza*. Aztec buildings were low and flat-roofed; even nobles only had two-storey dwellings. Apart from their great churches and a few other public buildings, the Spaniards, too, liked low, flat dwellings. To this day Mexican towns contain a high proportion of one- or two-storey houses. Native houses abutted on the street, but 'each was provided with a court and garden'.[1] Writing of an Indian house in a town 'which must have changed little since the Conquest', Waldo Frank says: 'The sense of the place is that the *patios* come first, the walls and ceilings docilely follow.'[2] The *spaces*, not only the structures, of an Indian town came to matter. Spanish houses, likewise, lined the pavements but looked into pleasant courtyards, or *patios*, often with a pool and some flowering shrubs.

The Aztecs loved their sports. A kind of soccer, played with a small india-rubber ball, was very popular, and 'most towns of any size had special playing fields, a hundred feet long and fifty feet wide, inclosed by a smooth wall from nine to twelve feet high'.[3] Spaniards also took to football, but admired bull-fighting even more, and had their bull-fighting arenas. The Aztecs had a strong feeling for the community. Their streets were relieved at frequent intervals by little squares or parks, adorned with temples. The Spanish, too, had a love of fine public buildings, adequately displayed. This community feeling extended, in the Aztecs, to providing public hospitals for the poor. Spanish missions in the same way erected hospitals and alms-houses, orphanages, and rest-homes for the poor and afflicted, these buildings often forming a significant part of the town, built as they were around the high towers of the centrally placed church.

In many instances, then, the Spaniards simply revived and reinforced the ways and patterns of the Indians. Yet the Spanish were still more town-minded, and, as we have seen, persuaded the primitive nomadic Indians to live together in permanent villages, often associated with mission stations.

---

1 Bancroft, H. H., *The Native Races of the Pacific States of N. America*, New York, 2, p. 380.

2 Frank, W., 'Mexico', in Moseley, H. (ed.), *The Romance of North America*, Boston, 1958, p. 117.

3 Havemeyer, L., *Ethnography*, p. 383.

takes in the hot valleys of the Southern Sierra Madre and the Chiapas plateau. It is the region which the Spanish first encountered, as they sailed towards the coast, but which they quickly passed through to gain the more temperate and populous part of Mexico. Not many *creoles* live in the region, and indeed the Tierra Caliente would still be rather deserted, or left to Indians, were it not for the ports, the tropical agriculture, and the oil which it supplies. The east and south are very humid, as well as being hot; the west is very arid.

The Gulf Coastal Plain is like its American counterpart, a strip of marine terraces bordered by mangrove swamps, lagoons, and barrier beaches. It is a straight coast, since it parallels the mountains, and it does not possess many headlands or sheltered bays. This makes it a poor coast for ports, and the harbours are constantly in danger of being silted up or encroached on by spits and bars. The plain is only about twenty miles wide between Vera Cruz and Tampico, but broadens out northward at the Rio Grande and southward in the Gulf of Campeche.

The rivers have a sharp drop from the eastern Sierras to the shore, and in the wet season run very swiftly and strongly, often flooding their banks. They bring down great quantities of sediment and are steadily silting up their estuaries. In the northern drier parts they shrink to mere threads in the drought season and are not very reliable. It has been difficult to use them for irrigation.

This 'amphibious coast',[1] as Butland has called it, has really not proved very attractive, and is much less useful and distinctly less used than its counterpart in the United States. The northern part of the plain is warm and semi-arid. Most of it is a poor grassland or dry steppe suited only to ranching. Agriculture is limited. The southern section is hot and wet, clothed in dense forests. Here summer temperatures average 82°F. or more, and winter ones more than 70°F. The climate gives little relief from the prolonged heat, a heat made all the worse by the high humidity. The annual rainfall is over 60 inches, and though most of it falls between late May and October, sufficient occurs in the rest of the year to maintain a dense vegetation. The greater part of the humid plain is under forest, except in basins where burning by the Indians has allowed grasses to replace trees.

Both these extremities of the coast plain have been avoided. It is really only in the State of Vera Cruz that there has been much development and settlement. Here where the steppe thickens and the forest thins into savannah, the Spaniards lodged themselves, and, with the use of Indians, developed sugar plantations and established orange groves. Later in the shade of the orange trees they put in rows of coffee plants. A good deal of tobacco was also raised, while early this century bananas and other tropical fruits and

[1] Butland, G. J., *Latin America, A Regional Geography*, London, 1960, p. 30.

'winter' vegetables were produced on a commercial basis. A distinct land-use region was thus created, often called the Gulf Plantation Area.

Recent efforts to extend agriculture on the coast has led to a limited development of irrigated cotton in Tamaulipas, and of rice, cocoa, and coconuts in Tabasco. Around Villa Hermosa are found some of the largest banana plantations in Mexico. At the same time, the forest is beginning to be exploited for its hardwoods, dyes, and extracts. But the effort required to make the drier and wetter parts really productive or habitable has been so great that it has seemed more profitable to invest capital and labour in mineral exploitation and, particularly, in the extraction of oil (Fig. 198).

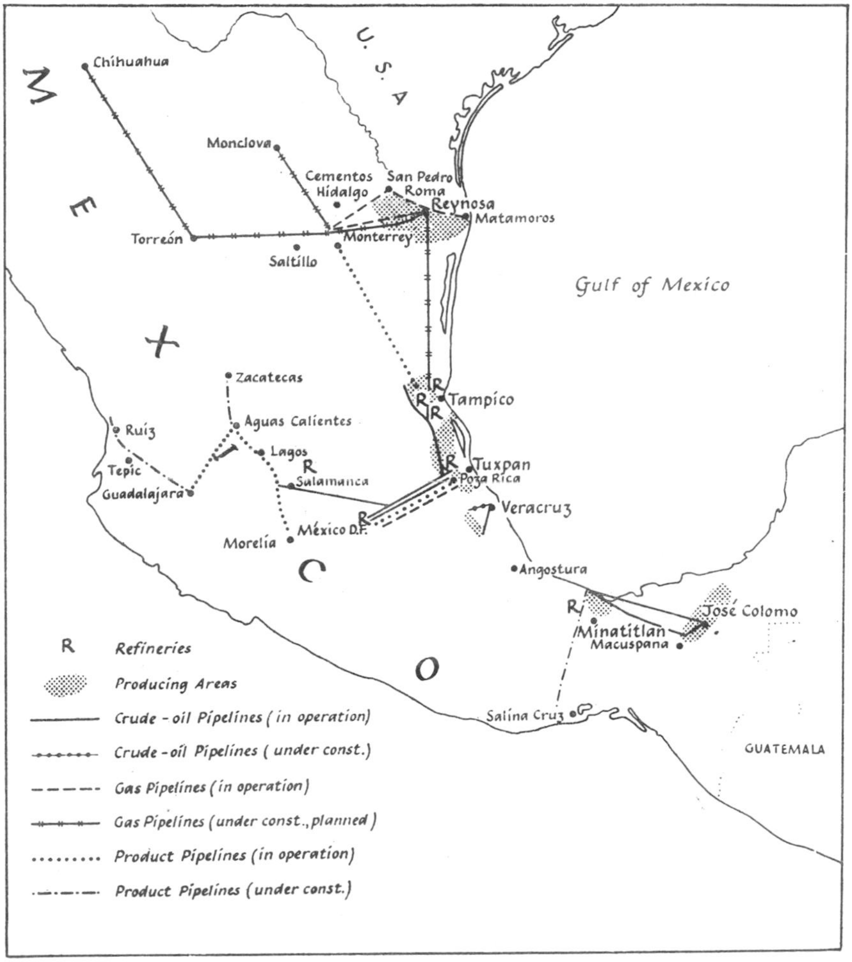

Fig. 198 Mexico and Oil—a Major National Resource. (Scale, 1:12·5 m.)

71. Spanish Mexico—Cathedral and Government Palace around the central plaza. Most of the buildings are low and look inward to pleasant, shaded patios.

Mexico City—Link between North and South America

72. American Mexico—great departmental stores and office blocks line the business sector between the central old-fashioned plaza and the railway station, in the distance.

Vera Cruz (165,000) is the chief outlet for the southern Mexico plateau, the most developed part of the country. It also has rail connexions to Oaxaca in the southern Sierras and to the Isthmus of Tehuantepec. Thus it draws on plateau, mountain, and lowland products. Its chief exports are silver and other metals, coffee and bananas, and Mexican handicraft products. It handles most of the imports of Mexico, including automobiles, machinery, hardware, textiles, and foodstuffs.

Eastward conditions change. The coast plain widens out in the *Yucatan peninsula.* Here there is rather less rain, since no mountains are present to force the winds to rise. The climate is well suited to henequin or sisal hemp, which is grown in the wet season. The Yucatan has a near monopoly of this useful fibre, from which hawsers and binder twine are manufactured. The region is, however, far too dependent on it, particularly as most of the crop is in foreign hands. Outside of the henequin area, very little is done. The peninsula is floored by limestone rocks which are rather soluble. The water does not collect in large rivers, but percolates down into the limestone and collects in pools, or caverns. The peninsula is much wetter where it slopes up to the *Chiapas mountains*, and is clothed with dense hardwood forests, or lush prairies. The Chiapas valley is a trough let down between two fault-split ranges. Cattle graze in its humid pastures, while coffee is raised on the hill-sides. Much of the farming is on a subsistence basis.

The South-west Pacific coast is rather different. Also hot, it is not so humid. It has not been as well developed as the Gulf coast because it is more remote, shut off by the southern Sierra, and looks away from America. The coastal plain is very narrow. Behind a fringe of graceful coco-nut palms, on the sandy beaches, there is a zone of marshy lagoon, or of grass-covered terrace. The plain is rather dry, up to about 500 feet, when rainfall increases, and jungle begins. Above 1,000 feet the region is densely forested. There are many valuable trees like cedar and mahogany. Plantations of rice, sugar, coco-nut palms, cocoa trees, and bananas dot the plain, but there is room for many more. Bush cattle roam much of the coastal lowland. In general most of the area is Indian and is thinly populated. Very primitive forms of 'shifting' agriculture still occur, the natives cutting down trees, burning them, spreading the ashes on the cleared land, and then raising their crops of maize and beans until the soil is exhausted. After that, they move on through the forest to another suitable site, open it up, and settle there, only to exhaust it in turn. The more advanced Indians and *mestizos* have moved up to the higher valleys and plateaux fringing the southern Sierras, in what is really a part of the Tierra Templada, or have drifted to a few favoured areas at the eastern and western extremities of the plain.

At the eastern end there is a narrow but fertile stretch underneath the Chiapas range, with very reliable rainfall, which, thanks mainly to the coastal railway connecting Mexico with Guatemala, has developed commercial plantations of cocoa, coffee, and bananas.

Farther west, mountain and plain become inextricably mixed. The great Balsas trough divides the Transverse Volcanics, at the southern extremity of the plateau, from the Sierra del Sur. The streams have brought down rich volcanic soils and spread them in fan after fan on the sides of the great trench. Many little Indian villages are found, the farmers growing tropical fruits and vegetables, maize and beans largely for their own use. The valley is so shut off that there is no real commercial outlet, and subsistence agriculture predominates. A major problem is the annual flooding following the melting of snows in the high mountains and the strong summer rains. An attempt is being made to control the floods, and use them for irrigation, especially in the Tepalcatepec basin. Sugar-cane is now being grown commercially.

The Balsas delta is not at all serviceable, and it is not until one comes to the small Colima basin, let into a ring of mountains, that there is much activity. Here are many banana plantations centred on the small port of Manzanillo, with its tortuous railway down from the Mexican plateau to the Pacific. Small amounts of copra are also produced for trade.

Still farther west is the great re-entrant of the Grande de Santiago. The lower part of the valley has hot summers of over 83° F. (July) and warm winters of over 70° F. (January), together with a moderate rainfall of between 30 and 35 inches. Irrigation helps to conserve and augment precipitation, and a fairly intensive agriculture, based on the *ejido* system, has developed. Small tobacco farms and market gardens, specializing in tomatoes, are much in evidence. Sugar cane is also important. Here the Indian peasant is lifting himself up to become a commercial producer; the old-style, large-scale plantations and ranches have lost their importance; more than half the population live on the newly divided smallholdings; and as a result the landscape is swiftly changing, with many scattered farmsteads, small fields, and irrigation ditches replacing the few large groups of houses about the great haciendas. There is, however, an undue concentration on winter vegetables, and over 90 per cent of the exports consist of tomatoes.

The West Coast, north of Mazatlan, witnesses a drier climate, until the Sonoran desert is reached, north of latitude 25°. The whole area is in the lee of the trade winds, cut off from rains. Three minor regions occur: the Sonoran district, the Colorado delta, and Lower California. *The Sonoran district* consists of a narrow plain, a piedmont plateau, and the west slopes of the Sierra Madre Occidental. The relief is rugged, the land having been broken up by severe faulting. The rainfall is less than 10 inches a year. Evaporation is very high. Only cactus, thorn bushes, and mesquite grass can grow, and there are large areas of bare rock between. The smaller rivers all die before they descend very far. They only flow for a few hours after the infrequent rainstorms. Yet they cause a lot of erosion. The larger rivers reach the coast. They have cut profound gorges, thousands of feet deep. Some of these are nearly as spectacular as the Grand Canyon. But they make travelling very difficult. Only one railway crosses from the coast to the interior. It runs from Guaymas to Tucson, Arizona. The district is so inaccessible that it has not been developed. Most of the land remains open range for scrub cattle. Irrigation is carried on in the larger, wider valleys, like the Fuerte and Yaqui, where permanent rivers supply just enough water. The Yaqui valley raises nearly half of all the rice grown in Mexico. But the difficulty is in selling the crops. Chick peas are sold to Spain; rice and wheat are sold in Mexico; early vegetables in the United States. Cattle are driven to Hermosillo, where there are large meat-packing plants. The mountains contain large amounts of gold, silver, lead, and copper. But most of the deposits have been buried deep under masses of lava. Placer mining has had a long and checkered career. Large-scale mining still awaits development, although copper mines at La Colorada and Nacozari are exceptions. Coal is mined in the Yaqui, but most of the deposits still remain untouched.

The Colorado delta has a small but important irrigation project which makes it the second most valuable cotton-producing area in Mexico. Here is one of the driest plains on earth, with only about 3 inches of rain a year. It is absolute desert; a complete waste, outside of irrigation. The Colorado river is its source of wealth. This river is 1,750 miles long, and is fed from the Wasatch and Rocky mountains. It is joined by the Gila river, just north of the international frontier. The delta area includes the Salton Sea depression. Here are several hundred square miles of very rich soil, not yet spoiled by the wanderings of a sand-choked river. It offers an ideal site for irrigation. Shortly after 1900, Americans thought of deflecting some of the Colorado water into the depression. Laguna Dam was built and the Imperial Canal was cut. The easiest route for this canal was via Mexico. Thus Mexico benefited by the United States enterprise. A treaty was drawn up in 1906 to give Mexico about 750,000 acre-feet of water from this canal. It was used to develop the fertile cotton plantations of Mexicali. Valuable long-staple cotton (the best variety in the world) is now produced, at about the rate of 60,000 bales a year. Wheat is another important cash crop. Silage corn, linseed, barley, and alfalfa are raised for fattening cattle.

Lower California is a peninsula about 750 miles long and 150 miles wide that extends south of California. It is a part of the Coast Ranges. It is very arid in the north; but the southern tip has some regular rainfall. The mountains are rocky and bare, except for the higher pine-clad peaks. They are broken by steep valleys, with desert plains at the bottom. Most rivers are intermittent. The region is the most inaccessible one in Mexico, and has no railway and but one road. The population of the peninsula is less than a medium-sized city. Some wheat and garden crops are grown in small irrigated plains, but not enough can be raised to feed the population. The largest town, Sta Rosalia, has only 9,000 people, but it cannot feed itself. It is a copper-mining town, which has to import fuel, supplies, and food to keep going. La Paz, the capital of the province, is on the wetter, better farmed southern coast, where cattle-raising is carried on. Fishing is of local importance.

The Tierra Caliente is, on the whole, the less developed and more backward part of Mexico. Few pure-bred Spaniards live in it; the *mestizo* in the better parts and the Indians in the drier or more isolated areas form the bulk of the population. Along the eastern coast are not a few negroes and *zambos*, from the days of slave labour. Although much has been done by giving the peasants land and by introducing irrigation, much more could be done through soil conservation, flood control, air-conditioning, and sanitation.

A major difficulty is physical isolation. The coast is cut off from the plateau by many ravines, dense forests, and high mountains. In the south and west it looks away from the continent. Neither by land nor sea is it in close contact with the populous parts, except in the Vera Cruz–Tamaulipas district. Trade has done little to quicken life, and many villages and small towns exist at a subsistence level.

The Tierra Templada

This is, without question, Mexico's most favoured region. It is represented primarily by the Mexican plateau. It also includes the intermediate slopes of the western and eastern Sierras: the upper slopes of the southern ranges and the meseta of Oaxaca. The Mexican plateau is the chief feature and has long come to form the heart of the country. The railways run out from it to all the other parts, like great arteries. It gives the country life, direction, and unity. Over two-thirds of the population live there. They produce the chief crops and mineral wealth and manufactured goods of Mexico.

The plateau is somewhat like the basin-and-range region of America. It consists of a number of short ridges, with a north-west–south-east strike. These are often fault blocks, or chains of volcanoes, with wide basins in between. The volcanoes have shot out masses of ash, which have been mixed with river alluvium to form a very fertile soil. Lava flows have occasionally blocked rivers to form lakes. Most of these have subsequently been drained, but have left fertile beaches and terraces. Thus, wherever it is rainy enough, or irrigation can be practised, agriculture flourishes. A great number of ridges lie together in the centre of the plateau, with outpourings of lava between them, forming rough terrain that divides the region into a northern low plateau and a southern high plateau.

The relief is asymmetric and consequently the rivers rise in the west and are shed to the east. Most of them, however, dry up or end in shallow or intermittent lakes. Much of the area is made up of enclosed drainage systems and only the river Conchos finds its way to the sea. Few streams are, therefore, of much use for irrigation, except in the southern plateau which is narrower and nearer to the high, snow-capped mountains.

The climate of the plateau is definitely temperate, and sub-humid to semi-arid. The winters have regular frosty spells, though the average temperature of the coldest month (54° F.) is not cold. The average for the hottest month, however, is distinctly mild. It is 65° F., which is lower than the average for Montreal, Toronto, or Winnipeg. Thus the Mexican plateau has an unusually temperate climate, with a fairly low range of temperature. Unfortunately, the rainfall is also low. A small rain-shadow area in the south-east, and a wide northern-central district, have less than 10 inches. The margins of the plateau have from 10 to 25 inches. Mexico City has an average of 23 inches a year. Most of this falls in the summer.

The mild, long summers are fairly well suited to corn and beans, the native crops of Mexico, and also to introduced crops such as wheat, barley, hay, and clover. In the sub-humid parts of the southern plateau the Indians have long been good farmers. Sheltered from foreign invasion by guardian mountains or the northern desert they had peace and protection to build little villages by the lakes, raise crops, and live a sedentary life. Thus they evolved much farther than the wandering nomads of the prairies in the drier, northern parts. Gradually they massed enough agricultural wealth to feed small towns and to support a population of artists and craftsmen, who were free to devote their time to cultural pursuits. Scientists studied the stars. Priests built beautiful temples. Scholars wrote books—carved on stone tablets. And merchants mined for gold and traded between one town and another.

However, the Aztec civilization, wonderful as it was, had not discovered the use of iron and coal, remained rather backward in its machines, and was inefficient in its organization. Consequently it fell before a little handful of Spanish conquerors. The courageous Spanish leaders, with horses, guns, and armour, and with their missionary zeal, soon defeated the wealthy but weak rulers of Mexico and planted the Cross above the deserted altars of Montezuma.

Although the native civilization was weaker, it was none the less a great civilization. The Spaniards found in the vicinity of Mexico City a tradition of sedentary and cultivated life, such as occurred nowhere else on the continent. This enabled the Spaniards to make much more progress, initially, than either the French or the British. If only the region itself had had greater physical resources and been more central in continental affairs it might have played a much greater role.

That its role was as significant as it turned out to be was largely a gift of the Mexican plateau. In this uplifted, pleasant region, wherever water and soil could be married together, the conditions existed for a genuinely significant contribution. Mexico not only started well—it built the first European school in the New World; set up the first printing press; and printed the first newspaper—it continued well, and, in many ways, it takes the lead in Spanish-American matters.

The northern plateau is lower, drier, and more thinly populated than the southern one. It has an average elevation of 4,000 feet. The rainfall varies from 5 to 18 inches. This is low in an area of hot summers (July, 72°–80° F.) and high evaporation. The trades are weak in this northern district. The eastern Sierras cut off the Gulf air mass. The region lies under the desert influence of the dry sub-tropical highs. However, the soils are quite fertile, if irrigated. Much of the plateau consists of lava tableland, which has weathered to produce a fine loamy fertile soil.

The water supply is the basic factor in development. But it is a problematical one. Most of the plateau has internal drainage. The rivers can never carry away their sand into the sea. They spread it in sheets over the plateau. In the wet season they come foaming from the mountains and dump masses of sand in the lakes. In the dry season the lakes shrink or dry up altogether. The sand blows about in dunes. There is now so much sand in the basins that rivers often lose themselves in it and disappear. It is difficult to use them for irrigation. The more permanent rivers, like the Nazos, are being harnessed for irrigation and water-power. The Nazos is the Nile of Mexico. It irrigates a low basin called the Laguna, which has become Mexico's chief source of cotton. About 250,000 bales are produced each year, which is enough for Mexican needs. Nearly half a million acres of land have been watered, and turned from desert to a veritable garden. Villages have sprung up by the score and village *ejidos*, or collectives, dominate the landscape. Population has increased tremendously, and so has prosperity. Here is truly a laboratory for Mexican progress.[1] The Rio Grande is also a source for irrigation, and in addition to cotton and wheat, citrus fruits and early vegetables are grown—many of which are exported as far as Canada.

However, most of the land is unsuited for irrigation and is used for grazing. This is the only economic activity available to the greater part of the region. Mexican sheep and cattle are raised in increasing numbers. The ranchers try to grow irrigated silage wherever possible to help eke out the rather poor mesquite grass, but the use of land is generally inefficient. This is partly because the area is still mainly under the old hacienda system, in which the land is divided up into huge estates, owned by a few wealthy

[1] Senior, C., 'The Laguna Region—Mexico's Agrarian Laboratory', *Q. Jour. of Inter-American Relations*, October 1939, pp. 67–78.

landlords. Some haciendas are over a million acres in extent, and include whole villages. They are like the vast feudal estates of Spain. Laws providing for private appropriation of idle lands[1] often let village lands pass to private hands.

The owner, or *haciendado*, has a large mansion on the estate, with stables and corrals, and houses for his servants and retainers. The overseer lives near by in another fine house. He looks after the estate in the absence of the owner, who invariably has a 'town house' where he spends most of the year on the profits of the hacienda. The great estate is worked by hundreds of peons, who live in little villages, built of mud. The peons have gardens and small fields from which they get enough bread and vegetables for their daily needs. But most of their work consists in ploughing the fields owned by their master, and in tending his cattle and sheep. The peons are paid for their work, but most of them owe more to the landlord than they get. This indebtedness is passed on from generation to generation, and ties them to the hacienda.

The hacienda system is very old. It goes back to Spain, and, in certain respects, even to Rome. It is characteristic of Latin America. However, recent land reforms in Mexico have tried to break up these estates and divide them between the peasants, so as to develop a class of 'owner operator' called *ejidatarios* who might have a stake in the land they operate. The *ejidatario* does not in fact own the land personally; ownership is vested in the community. But he is allotted a 'parcel' which he can develop. These reforms will probably lead to a more intensive and efficient use of the land, where that is feasible. But obviously most of the northern plateau is better suited to ranching than farming and will probably not witness the wide-spread adoption of the *ejido* system of land operation.

It has been said that the chief cash crops of the plateau are its *minerals*. Both the northern and southern plateaux are very rich in minerals, although the northern area depends on its mineral wealth to a greater extent. Metal-rich veins have formed in volcanic areas, or in fissures in faulted ranges, or on the edges of lava masses. Gold and silver first attracted the Spaniard, and led him north over the arid land. Copper and tin also occur in important quantities: sulphur, cinnabar, iron, and coal are likewise to be found (Fig. 199).

The State of Chihuahua is the chief mining area in Mexico. With rich silver, lead, zinc, copper, mercury, vanadium, and antimony mines it has attracted a great deal of American capital and, being on the U.S. border, can export its large surpluses at a reasonable cost to help feed the huge mineral industry of its northern neighbour. The three silver centres of Chihuahua, Parral, and Fresnillo produce over a quarter of the world's

[1] Highsmith, *The Ejido in Mexico*, Case Studies in World Geography, p. 18.

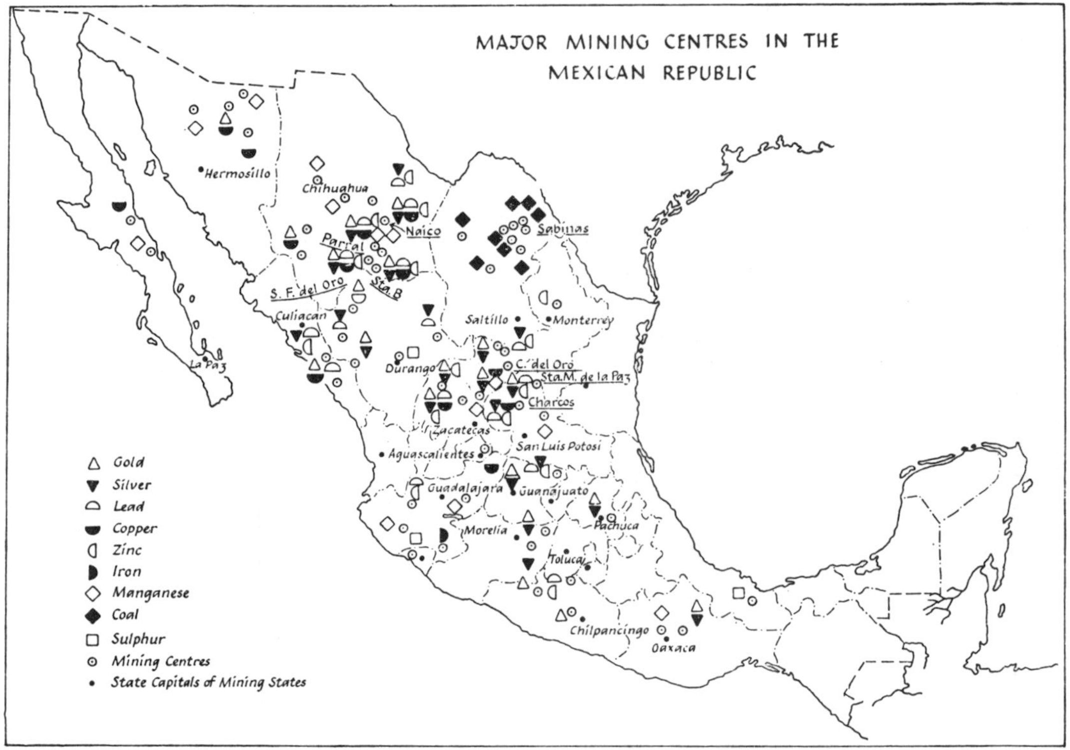

FIG. 199 The Mexican plateau and its wealth of minerals. This much-intruded area has one of the continent's highest concentrations of silver and base metals. Coal and iron, though not abundant, are situated fairly near to each other, affording the basis of a growing steel industry. (Scale, 1: 21 m.)

total. Between these is the very considerable iron field of Cerro de Mercado, near Durango. Also in the northern plateau a large coal field is worked, near the Sabinas river, in the State of Coahuila. It raises about two million tons of good steam coal a year, for use in Mexico's growing factories. Lead smelting and an active iron and steel-making industry have grown up at **Monterrey** (660,000), in the State of Nuevo Leon. This is not far from the Coahuila coal, nor too remote from Durango iron. Most important, it is near to United States capital and 'know how', and, dominating the gap in the eastern Sierras leading from the United States to the Mexican plateau, has risen to be Mexico's leading metallurgical centre. Many metal-using industries have flocked to the city, and other forms of manufacturing, like the making of beer and cigarettes, have been added. Monterrey is the most highly industrialized city in Mexico and as a result has lost most of its Spanish appearance to become an outpost of the Anglo-American way of life. Not only are there great factories, but there are also big car parks, numerous service stations, many motels and restaurants at every entry and exit, while streets of working-men's houses mount in density to the tall shops, offices, and hotels that have tended to take over the centre of the city.

Farther south, in the tangled landscape between the northern and southern plateaux, vulcanism and metamorphism led to a wide injection of rocks by silver, gold, and copper veins. Silver is chief of these. The centre of silver mining was long **San Luis Potosi**, but the ores here are exhausted and the town has continued to flourish as a railway and road junction and 'servicing' node. Mining has shifted farther south and is now concentrated mostly in the State of Hidalgo, where silver, gold, and copper are obtained. A great deal is exported to the United States and to Europe.

Mining cities such as Chihuahua, Durango, and San Luis Potosi have played a large part in the peopling and development of Mexico, and have had a long and distinguished career. Although to begin with they were often in isolation, with no supporting settlements, and were, in fact, but flash-points along what James has called 'the hollow frontier',[1] gradually they have attracted life and activity to their area, and so have helped to fill in the hollowness behind the original frontier, and give strength and support to the whole frontier movement and the occupation of the region. They may have rattled about in the emptiness of the early pioneer fringe, but they have now become the centres for the systematic and regular settlement of the country. They soon showed themselves to be good markets for the rancher and wheat farmer, and so invited the growth of rings of great haciendas about them. Later they became the hub of the railway network for their districts and helped the rise of small transportation and trading centres. They developed ever wider administrative and social services in the meantime,

[1] James, P., *Latin America*, New York, 1942, pp. 5–6, 9.

and helped in the organization of territories and states and of rural and urban districts. Eventually they knocked much of the hollowness out of the frontier and, even though they became the centre of nothing more vital than 'extensive' farming and wholesale trading, at least they 'centred' such developments, giving them stability, cohesion, and order. In doing so, they have stamped a strangely urban pattern of life on predominantly rural areas.

The southern plateau is more productive and populous than the north. It supports more than half of the population of Mexico—which is out of all proportion to its size. (The northern plateau by comparison, though a third of Mexico in size, only has one-eighth of the population.) The southern plateau is very beautiful. It has an average elevation of 6,000 feet, but far above it there gleam the lovely snow-clad peaks of Popocatepetl (17,734 feet) and Orizaba (18,242 feet), two of the grandest summits of the continent. Beneath the glow of everlasting snows is a dark green mantle of pines, while below this is a clothing of oak. The mountains are volcanoes. Much volcanic activity has pricked the plateau with cones, and spread a fine ash over the land, making a very fertile soil. Flat mesas, relics of basalt flows, and relict plugs give added variety to the relief. The southern plateau, thanks largely to this greater occurrence of volcanoes, has a greater variety of conditions to offer settlement than the north.

Unlike the situation in the north, most rivers drain to the sea; but some empty into basins of internal drainage. They are fed by eternal snows, and by the heavy rainfall of the mountains. They have cut deep gorges in the plateau, a few of which have been dammed up to form great hydro-electric projects. Not a few rivers were choked by eruptive material in their lower courses, and now come down into beautiful blue lakes, that mirror the clear skies and the distant peaks. The Rio Santiago flows into the large Lake Chapala, beneath the Tancitario range. Mexico City is built by the side of Lake Texcoco. These lakes help to keep away frosts and make the climate more humid. Most of them have fallen in level, and have thus exposed broad terraces around their margins, covered with a deep mantle of silt. Where this is not encrusted with saline deposits, it is intensively cultivated.

The high altitude of the southern plateau makes it cooler than the north, and more pleasant for white people to live in. Here is the real 'tierra templada'. Monthly means in the height of summer rarely exceed 70° F. On the other hand, winter means rarely fall below 50° F.—there is usually a pleasant range of from 68° F. to 54° F. (Mexico City, 63° F. July, 57° F. January; Puebla, 63° F. July, 60° F. January; Leon, 69° F. July, 57° F. January; Guadalajara, 69° F. July, 60° F. January). This régime gives enough variety to avoid monotony and to provide stimulus, yet the range is not so great as to cause discomfort or distress. The Spaniards found it most attractive, and made their home in the district if at all possible. About 80 per cent of all the *creole* population is concentrated here—surely a measure of climatic control.

High altitude has also helped to make the plateau more moist. The rainfall is from 20 to 25 inches. This is quite sufficient for the extensive cultivation of wheat, beans, and maguey (the crop from which Mexico's national beverage, Pulque, is made), and other 'temperate' crops. In a way, without frost or drought, with warm summers and mild winters, and a tolerable supply of water, conditions have been ideal for agriculture, and it is little wonder that here was, in all likelihood, the *hearthland* of seed cultivation in North America, and particularly of the cultivation of maize.[1] It certainly became the hearthland for the Teotihuacan, Toltec, and Aztec cultures that proved a strong support for Spanish power.

Some general conditions are common to the whole southern plateau, although there are noteworthy differences between its eastern and western basins. Population tends to gather in little clusters on the fertile aprons of volcanic soils on the lower slopes of old volcanoes, or else on the margins of the many intermontane depressions—above the flats, but below the steeps. Almost everywhere there is a zoning of activity with altitude. (i) The forested slopes of the mountains are centres of lumbering, and the manufacture of charcoal. This is the chief locally produced fuel, since there is no coal or oil in the southern plateau. Grass parks stretching between the stands of trees make excellent summer grazing. (ii) The sub-humid plateau is a good ranching area, grazing many cattle which are generally fattened in the valleys. It is also the zone of grains. (iii) The slopes from the plateau down to the valley bottoms are fairly moist and are rather hotter. They often form a plantation zone, where coffee, maguey, olives, figs, peaches, and apples have been planted out in hill-side plantations or orchards. (iv) The valleys and lake basins have rather little rainfall, but are well watered by living streams. They are the hottest parts of the region, and grow irrigated crops such as corn, alfalfa, sugar-cane, and tobacco. They fatten cattle and raise hogs, and have many dairy and poultry farms. They form a zone of intensive cultivation. (v) Below this, on the Short Grass prairie of the slightly saline terraces about shrunken lakes, is a zone of grazing. Finally, on really saline flats, is a waste zone—on to which, however, roads and industries may sometimes encroach.

Regional differences between the several parts of the plateau are quite significant. In the west is a series of basins lower than the average level, forming the *el bajio* or 'flat' which thrusts out from the main mass of the plateau like a great shelf. The Lerma river links up the little depressions on this shelf and gives the district a certain degree of unity. Agriculture is

[1] Sauer, C. *Agricultural Origins and Dispersals* p. 64.

surprisingly diverse, with orchards of peaches and pears on the gentle slopes, fields of potatoes and tomatoes on the basin floors, and maize and chick-peas everywhere. On the rimlands, now much denuded of trees, there graze many small herds of cattle, and flocks of sheep, and goats. Population is quite dense and is largely concentrated in many little villages. Leon and Morelia are two important market towns.

Lower down still, but still within the temperate (albeit warm temperate) zone, is the basin of Jalisco, dominated by volcanoes and centred in Lake Chapala. While maize is again the main crop, obviously raised for home consumption, good cash crops of oranges, linseed, and chili pepper are grown. **Guadalajara** (775,000) is the outstanding town. It is Mexico's second city and reflects the density of rural population in the western basins. It is on the principal route from the plateau to the Pacific and has important textile, clothing, and shoe-making factories.

The eastern part of the southern plateau of Mexico is rather higher than the western; it also has more areas of internal drainage; above all, it is dominated by the great peaks of the Southern Transverse Volcanic Range. The highest basin, that of Toluca, stands at about 8,600 feet. With distinctly cool summers it does not have much variety in agriculture, but this is made up for by the intensity with which the traditional type of peasant farming has come to work the land. Somewhat lower is the Puebla basin between the great volcanoes of Ixtaccihuatl and Malinche. Once more, with a rather cool summer, it has gone in for 'temperate' grains, and specializes in barley and wheat production. The lofty peaks feed plunging streams whose waters have been forced into power plants. Here is one of the few centres of ample hydro-electric power in Mexico. Most of it is used to run the textile and other mills of **Puebla** (315,000), the country's fourth largest city.

The most famous of the eastern depressions is the Valley of Mexico, or, as it was called in ancient times, the Anáhuac or 'well-watered' vale. It only occupies about 150 sq. miles and yet it contains 5 million people, or about 1 in 7 of all the people in the nation. This is an extraordinary concentration and bespeaks the remarkable centrality and productivity of this basin!

Into the narrow confines of this beautiful and fertile little lowland there drifted in various peoples from the north, the last of which were the Nahuas. As they arrived here they were so hemmed in by majestic heights they could not go any farther. They had to give up their nomadic habits and settle down and become fishermen by the lakes and farmers along the lakeshore plain. Their differences led to competition and to conflict, but this in turn stimulated them to co-operation and eventually federation. Competition sparked off new ideas; co-operation allowed them to share and synthesize and systematize these ideas, and so civilization emerged and developed. Mexico's central position permitted them to carry civilization down from the plateau to the Atlantic and Pacific, until the Aztecs mastered the Central American world.

Today the maize, beans, and maguey which were developed in those ancient times are still widely cultivated, and indeed form staples of food and drink. It is astonishing, indeed, how much land is given to maize, which under the conditions in which it is grown, does not have a high yield. But there is, of course, an almost religious attachment to the plant; this is the oldest cereal in the Western Hemisphere, and has featured in various folk festivals, dances, symbols, and the like. Thus even although the summers are really too cool to produce the better varieties and yields the mean July average of 68° F. to 69° F. being well below the 77° F. found in the heart of the American Corn Belt—the peasants continue to rely on the crop. However, diversification of agriculture has begun and there are now many market gardens, orchards, dairies, and poultry farms. As Platt points out, reclaimed land from the swampy margins of the lakes is of increasing importance. Most of it is used for alfalfa, of which eight crops may be raised in a year. The alfalfa is sold to the dairies.[1]

One of the main drawbacks to agricultural expansion is the tremendous expansion of the cities. Here is the heart of the whole commercial, financial, administrative, and cultural life of Mexico: there are no rivals, and consequently an unusual concentration of people and activity has built itself up. This is not only large for its region, or for the state; it is one of the largest in Latin America, surpassed only by Buenos Aires and, for that matter, it is one of the larger concentrations in North America, surpassing anything in Canada, and coming after New York, Chicago, Los Angeles, and Philadelphia.

Mexico City (5,300,000) is, then, one of the great works of man. And *man* it is that has made it. As Butland points out, it has no geographical merits of local site that make it obviously much better than other sites. True, it is in one of the most attractive situations in Mexico, on a fertile basin at the end of the plateau and fairly near to the great flanking oceans, but within that situation there were several sites that might have done equally well for a great capital. As Havemeyer reminds us:

> Various peoples settled around the valley of Anáhuac on the shores of the lake. The three principal groups were the Acolhuas, the Aztecs, and the Tepanecs, and their respective capitals were Texcuco, Mexico, and Tlacopan. Within the valley the eastern portion belonged to Texcuco, the southern and western to Mexico, and a small territory in the north-west to Tlacopan. These three people eventually founded a federation, but the most powerful state was that of the Aztecs.[2]

[1] Platt, R. S., *Latin America*, New York, 1943, p. 36, 'Reclaimed fields'.

[2] Havemeyer, *Ethnography*, p. 356.

Bancroft underlines this idea.

While keeping within the boundaries of their respective provinces, so far as the Valley of Mexico (i.e. Anáhuac) was concerned [he writes], these three chief powers united their forces to extend their conquests beyond the limits of the valley in every direction. Under the leadership of a line of warlike kings, Mexico extended her domain to the shores of either ocean. During this period of foreign conquest, Aztec kings, more energetic, ambitious, warlike, and unscrupulous than their allies, acquired a decided preponderance in the confederate councils and possessions.[1]

It was the human factor, therefore, which by making the most out of this particular site, as compared with other no less favourable sites, established the pre-eminence of Mexico City. The place grew to have a population variously estimated at between 200,000 to 300,000 before the Spaniards arrived. The Spanish conquerors accepted the value and prestige of the site, and, although they razed much of the town, they rebuilt it *in situ*, making it even greater and more spectacular than it had been. For long it was the largest city in the Americas; it is still the largest for that vast tract between Los Angeles and São Paulo (Fig. 200).

The town has both an excellent situation and site. It lies in a sheltered basin, in which six beautiful lakes occur, under a group of towering, snowy-breasted mountains, of which 'The White Lady' is queen. The city was built on the high plateau for health and protection; also because it was accessible to western, southern, and eastern lowlands. The main lake was saline and its immediate borders were not suited to agriculture. But the Indians chose it because of an island in Lake Mexico, near enough to be accessible over several short causeways, yet sufficiently isolated to be defensible. After Cortez conquered it, in 1522, he made the centre of the ancient city into a spacious *plaza*. Most of the lake was drained and filled in. A lofty cathedral was erected, appropriately, on the site of Montezuma's temple. Today tall offices, an opera house, theatres, and large multiple-stores crowd the centre of the city. Like most Latin cities, Mexico is built on a rectangular system, with key intersections opening out into large squares and beautiful parks, with fine public buildings. The houses are built right to the sidewalk. There are no front gardens, although shade-giving trees along the streets provide a bosky appearance. But the houses give back to charming *patios*, or courtyards, with plots of grass, palm trees, and flowers. The rooms are built around these quiet *patios*, where people can take their afternoon siesta away from the noises of the street.

The capital is in every way the centre of the nation. It has large central

[1] Bancroft, *Native Races of the Pacific States*, **2**, pp. 92–93.

institutions like the national university, the national theatre, the national library, and the national museum. Its offices are the headquarters of industry throughout the nation. Its shops are used by people who come there from all over the country. Its residential districts have *haciendados* from all the leading estates. Its manufactured articles feature in well over a half of all the homes of Mexico.

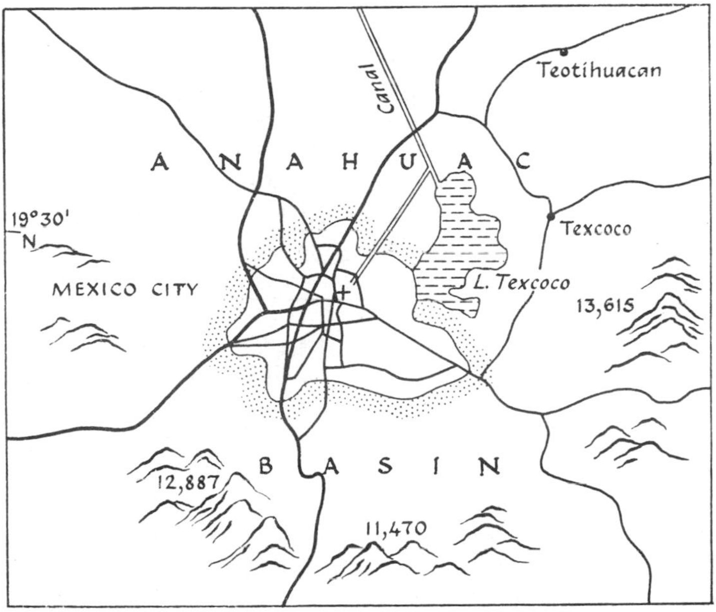

FIG. 200 Mexico City—giant of the Latin South. The early rival of Texcoco and Teotihuacan, Mexico rose swiftly to power in Indian times, and was maintained as the chief settlement of the Anáhuac basin by the Spaniards. Although originally on an island in Lake Texcoco it has now drained much of the lake away and found room to expand on lake-bed flats. It has grown to be the centre of all Mexico and, in a sense, of Central America. (Scale 1:0·75 m.)

This is a very high concentration of leadership and control. It shows the great ease with which the city—through its central, commanding situation as the hub of national railways—can assemble raw materials from many different areas and zones. This same situation enables it to distribute goods over a wide area. There is an abundance of cheap electricity from the hydro-electric projects in the mountains. Petroleum is pumped fairly cheaply from the Gulf field. Manufactures that can use these fuels, and agricultural raw materials, flourish. However, there is a great drawback in not having coal or iron in the vicinity. It is doubtful whether Mexico can develop really large-scale heavy industries, or supply the country with the automobiles and machinery it needs. A useful experiment has been the building of a steel mill to make steel from scrap; and this is promising. The chief industries of the city are foodstuffs, textiles, tobacco, brewing, printing and publishing. Cornmeal and flour mills use the wheat and maize of the plateau. Packers sell local coffee throughout the nation. Large breweries produce enormous quantities of pulque, on which, it is claimed, the worker will spend nearly a third of his earnings. Textile mills use cotton grown in the Laguna district and wool from the drier parts of the plateau.

Industrial growth now characterizes Mexico City, which is responsible for nearly two-fifths of all the manufactures of the country. This has meant a great change in the landscape. Factories and factory chimneys hold the eye as much as, if not more than, church towers. There is a wide and irregular and largely unplanned sprawl to the factory areas, very different from the compact, regular, and strongly traditional layout of the old commercial residential city. Big industrial housing estates offer a marked and sometimes unhappy contrast to the older residential areas. New suburbs are growing up, pushing well into the countryside. The villages and small towns round about, such as Ixtacalco, Ixtapalpa, Coyoacán, Obregón, and Atzcapotzalco, have been largely engulfed, and strings of motels, service stations, small restaurants, and shops line the main roads out of town. Urbanization has increasingly taken over the basin. A major canal was cut from Lake Texcoco to the upper Panuco to drain its excess waters to the sea, and as the waters fell the marshy or shallow sections along the edge were taken in for urban expansion, the building of a large airfield, and for big new factories and warehouses. Thus the salty wastes of the flats that mark the old lake-bed, long bare of use and devoid even of vegetation, but the source of many unpleasant summer duststorms, have been given a new and beneficial role. They are in many ways ideal for industry, and help to draw it away from taking up good agricultural land.

The importance of Mexico as the hub of all the main routes in the country may be gauged by the fact that the five principal railroads and highways coming in from north-east (Tampico), north (Monterrey, Chihuahua), east (Puebla and Vera Cruz), south (Balsas), and west (Guadalara and Pacific ports), have drawn the city into the form of a great star, its growth radiating out to the chief parts of the country. Without question, it has come to dominate the whole of southern Mexico, and its influence, transgressing the old self-contained plateau basins, the high mountain rim, the valleys leading down to the coast, and segments of the coast (between Vera Cruz and Tampico), has created a *human, city-centred region* (urbanized, commercialized, industrialized, linked up with flashing railways and strident roads) that in large measure overrides, displaces, and even replaces the physiographic or climatic divisions that were formerly so significant.

To a certain extent this has long been true; Mexico dominated the Aztec Empire, and it was the unquestioned centre of Spanish North America. But its place has grown physically more significant with the great national revolution of modern times which has gone hand in hand with modern industrialization. The new industrialism, centred as it is in a series of super-plants surrounded by satellite factories, dependent on broad highways, and associated with workmen's amenities like big car parks, football or baseball parks, new open-space housing suburbs and horizontally designed schools, hospitals, and social centres—all this tends to concentrate itself more and more in the few really favoured areas, and, since all this takes up a great deal of space, it expands those areas and links them up with other nuclei of development.

This kind of thing has begun to revolutionize Mexico—country and city.

> Anyone who knew Mexico three decades ago, and then drove down the Pan America Highway today . . . would not believe he was in the same country. Factories, filling stations, garages, motels, truck assembly plants, housing projects with running water in each unit and schools in the center —all these things so unlike the colonial towns . . . hit the eye as he drives south, while traffic becomes congested and buses and trucks almost push him off the road. It is Mexico City with its factories and new suburbs and ultra-modern freeways that surprises him most, capital of a nation that owns its own oil industry and railroads, that is building up its consumer-goods manufacturing, and that hopes to be self-sufficient in all but the heaviest industry.[1]

Mexico City is, then, with its modern factories and quiet *patios*, with its popular movie theatres, and still more popular bull-rings, with its old Spanish cathedrals and modern State schools, one of the most cosmopolitan cities, truly Latin, and yet unmistakably American. It typifies a country which is the oldest on the continent, and yet is striving to be its youngest. The modern reforms have swept many of the old traditions away; nevertheless, there are enough of these left to mark Mexico off as a distinct cultural area in North America. Actually, the new reforms have arisen from the most ancient of urges, the desire of the peasant for land of his own, and has therefore released an upsurge of Indian creativity, which, together with the Spanish spirit, has led to the rise of a new culture; a culture that, since it is both native and European, is in many ways most truly American. In this, Mexico may find a new importance. One of its writers, who was also for a

[1] Bailey, H. M., and Nasatir, A. P., *Latin America, The Development of its Civilization*, New Jersey, 1960, p. 508.

me a member of its government, José Vasconcelos, proudly affirmed: 'We wish to make Mexico the cultural centre of the Western Hemisphere as the United States is the industrial centre.' Seen in this way the country's role will be to interpret Anglo-America and Indo-Hispanic America to each other; it is the bridge between these two great New World regions.

Bibliography

of references cited, and additional works

NOTE: The American Guide Series, and Rivers of America, publications on the individual, States and rivers of the U.S.A. are not included.

NORTH AMERICA—*General*

JAMES, P. E., & JONES, C. F. (eds.), *American Geography*, Inventory and Prospect, Syracuse, 1954.

MAYER, H. M., & KOHN, C. F., *Readings in Urban Geography*, Chicago, 1959.

Readings in the Geography of North America, Amer. Geog. Soc. Pubn., New York, 1952.

VINCE, C. L. & GRACE, A., U.S. Government Publications for Teaching and Research in Geography, Norman, Oklahoma, 1962.

GOTTMANN, J., *L'Amérique*, 3e edn., Paris, 1960.

GRIFFIN, P. F., YOUNG, R. N., & CHATHAM, R. L., *Anglo-America*, a regional geography of the United States and Canada, San Francisco, 1962.

JONES, L. R., & BRYAN, P. W., *North America:* an historical, economic and regional geography, London, 10th edn., 1957.

KIEFFER, J. E., *North America*, London, 1950.

MEAD, W. R., & BROWN, E. H., *The United States and Canada*, a regional geography London, 1962.

MILLER, G. L., PARKINS, A. E.,.& HUDGINS, B., *The Geography of North America*, New York, 3rd edn., 1954.

MOSELEY, H. (ed.), *The Romance of North America*, Boston, 1958.

PARKER, W. H., *Anglo-America*, a systematic regional geography, London, 1962.

PATERSON, J. H., *North America*, a regional geography, London, 1960.

POUNDS, N. J. G., *North America*, 2nd ed., London, 1964.

PRESTON, R. G. & TOTTLE, J., *United States and Canada, a Geography*, Boston, 1966.

SHAW, E. B., *Anglo-America*, a regional geography, New York, 1959.

SMITH, J. R., & PHILLIPS, M. D., *North America*, New York, 1942.

TOMKINS, G. S., *A Regional Geography of North America*, Toronto, 1961.

WATSON, J. W., 'North America in the changing world', *Journ. Geog.*, Vol. 57, No. 8, 1958.

WHITE, C. L., & FOSCUE, E. J., & MCKNIGHT, T. *Regional Geography of Anglo-America*, Englewood Cliffs, N.J., 1964.

NORTH AMERICA—*Physical*

ANTEVS, E., *The Quaternary of North America*, New York, 1941.

—— 'Wisconsin glacial maxima', *Amer. Jour. Sci.* 239A, 1945.

ATWOOD, W. W., *The Physiographic Provinces of North America*, New York, 1940.

—— *The Rocky Mountains*, New York, 1945.

BROOKS, C. F., & CONNOR, A. J., *Climatic Maps of North America*, Cambridge (Mass.), 1936.

BRUNNSCHWEILER, 'Geographical distribution of air masses in North America', *Geographische Mitteilungen*, Jahr 97, 1952.

CLARK, T. H., *The Geological Evolution of North America*, New York, 1960.

EARDLEY, A. J., *Structural Geology of North America*, New York, 1951.

FLINT, R. F., *Glacial Geology and the Pleistocene Epoch*, New York, 1957.

—— 'New radio-carbon dates and late-pleistocene stratigraphy', *Amer. Jour. Sci.*, Vol. 254, May 1956.

—— & DEEVEY, E. S., 'Postglacial hypsithermal interval', *Sci.*, Vol. 125, No. 3240, Feb. 1957.

FLINT, R. F., & BRANTDER, F., 'Climatic changes since the last interglacial', *Amer. Jour. Sci.*, Vol. 259, No. 5, 1961.
HARE, F. K., 'The boreal conifer zone', *Geog. Studies*, Vol. 1, No. 1, 1954.
IVES, J. D., 'Glacial Drainage Channels as indicators of late-glacial conditions . . . a discussion', *Cah. de Géog. de Québec*, 3me, Ann. No. 5, 1959.
KAY, M. *North American Geosynclines*, Geol. Soc. Amer., Mem. 48, 1951.
KIMBLE, G. H. T., *Our American Weather*, New York, 1955.
KING, P. B., *The Evolution of North America*, New York, 1959.
—— *The Tectonics of Middle North America*, Princeton, 1951.
LOUGEE, R. L., 'A chronology of postglacial time in eastern North America', *Sci. Monthly*, Vol. 76, No. 6, May 1953.
PALMER, *Mammals of North America North of Mexico*, New York, 1954.
PEATTIE, R., *The Pacific Coast Ranges*, New York, 1946.
PRESTON, R. J., *North American Trees*, Iowa State University 1961
RIEHL, H., *The Jet Stream*, Meteor. Monographs, Vol. 2, No. 7, 1954.
SHAPLEY, H. (ed.), *Climatic Change*, Cambridge (Mass.), 1960.
SHELFORD, V. E., *The Ecology of North America*, Urbana, Illinois, 1963.
SHIMER, J. A., *This Sculptured Earth, the Landscape of America*, New York, 1959.
SOCIETY AMER. FORESTERS, *Forest Cover Types of North America*, Washington, 1954.
STARRETT, L. G., 'Relation of Precipitation Patterns in North America to . . . jet streams' *Jour. Met.*, Vol. 6, 1949.
THORNBURY, W. D., *Regional Geomorphology of the United States*, New York, 1965.

NORTH AMERICA—*Economic*

AMES, O., *Economic Annuals and Human Cultures*, Cambridge (Mass.), 1939.
BEETLE, A. A. (ed.), *Agricultural Problems in Arid and Semi-arid Environments*, Amer. Assoc. Advancement of Science, Symposium, Laramie, 1960.
CLARK, J. S., *The Oil Century*, Norman, 1958.
HOOVER, E. M., *Location of Economic Activity*, New York, 1948.
ROSENBLUTH, G., 'Industrial concentration in Canada and the United States', *Can. Jour. Econ. & Pol. Sci.*, Vol. 20, No. 3, Aug. 1954.
WRIGHT, A. J., *United States and Canada, an Economic Geography*, New York, 1950.

NORTH AMERICA—*Social*

BARNARD, B. T., 'The impacts on land from metropolitan growth', Urban Land Instit. Bul., No. 31, Nov. 1957.
BERRY, B. J. L., & GARRISON, W. L., 'Cities and freeways', *Landscape*, Vol. 10, No. 3, Spring 1961.
BOGUE, J. D., *The Structure of the Metropolitan Community*, Ann Arbor, 1949.
DUNCAN, O. D., *Metropolis and Region*, New York, 1960.
ENGELBERT, B. A. (ed.), *Transportation and Metropolitan Planning*, Los Angeles, 1956.
FUTTERMAN, R. A., *The Future of our Cities*, New York, 1961.
HANSEN, M. L., *The Atlantic Migration*, 1607–1860, Cambridge (Mass.), 1940.
MCKENZIE, R. D., *The Metropolitan Community*, New York, 1933.
PARK, R. E., BURGESS, E. W., & MCKENZIE, R. D., *The City* Chicago, 1925.
STAFFORD, H. A., 'The dispersed city', *Profl. Geogr.*, Vol. 14, No. 4, July 1962.
THORNTHWAITE, C. W., *et al.*, *Migration and Economic Opportunity*, Philadelphia, 1936.

ABORIGINAL AMERICA—*Eskimoes*

BIRKET-SMITH, K., *The Eskimos*, London, 1936.
COLLINS, H. B., *The Arctic Area*, indigenous period, Mexico, 1953.
—— 'The origin and antiquity of the Eskimo', Smithsonian Ann. Rept., 1950.
—— 'Eskimo archaeology and its bearings on the problem of man's antiquity in America', *Proc. Amer. Phil. Soc.*, Philadelphia, 86, No. 2, 1943.
GIBSON, W., 'Prehistoric wanderings of the Eskimo', *The Beaver*, Winnipeg, Dec. 1939.

IGLAUER, E., *The New People*, the Eskimo's journey into our time, New York, 1966.
MELDGAARD, J., 'Origin and evolution of Eskimo cultures in the eastern arctic', *Can. Geog. Jour.*, Vol. 60, No. 2, Feb. 1960.
ROWLEY, G., 'The Dorset culture of the eastern arctic', *Amer. Anthrop.*, Vol. 42, No. 3, 1940.
URQUHART, J. A., 'Eskimos of the Canadian Western Arctic', in *The New North-West*, ed. Dawson, Toronto, 1947.

ABORIGINAL AMERICA—*Indians*

General

AMER. ACAD. POL. & SOC. SCI., 'American Indians & American life', *The Annals*, Vol. 311, May 1957.
BIRDSELL, J. B., *The Problems of the Early Peopling of the Americas as viewed from Asia*, New York, 1951.
DRIVER, H. E., *Indians of North America*, Chicago, 1961.
FLETCHER, S. E., *The American Indian*, New York, 1954.
FORDE, D., *Habitat, Economy and Society*, London, 1934.
GIFFIN, J. B., *The United States and Canada*, indigenous period, Mexico, 1953.
GLADWIN, H. S., *Men out of Asia*, New York, 1947.
HIBBEN, F. C., *Treasure in the Dust*, exploring ancient North America, Philadelphia, 1951.
JENNESS, D., 'Prehistoric culture waves from Asia to America', *Wash. Acad. Sci. Journ.*, Vol. 30, No. 1, 1940.
KROEBER, A. L., *Cultural and Natural Areas of Native North America*, Berkeley, 1939.
LEECHMAN, D., 'The first men in the New World', *Can. Geog. Jour.*, Vol. 39, No. 5, 1949.
LORAIN, C. T., & MCILWRAITH, T. F., *The North American Indian Today*, Toronto, 1943.
OSWALT, W. H., *This Land was Theirs*, a study of the North American Indian, New York, 1966.
SAUER, C. O., *Man in Nature*, America before the days of the white man, New York, 1939.
—— *Agricultural Origins and Dispersals*, New York, 1952.
SOUSTELLE, J., *Daily Life of the Aztecs*, London, 1961.
SPENCER, R. F., & JENNINGS, J. D., *The Native American's Prehistory*, an Ethnology of the American Indian, New York, 1965.
WORMINGTON, H. M., *Origins*, Vol. 1 of Ser. 1, Hist. of the Americas, Pan. Am. Inst. Hist & Geog., Mexico, 1953.

Canada

CAN. CITIZENSHIP & IMMIGRATION, *The Canadian Indian*, Ottawa, 1961.
—— *Census of Indians in Canada, 1961.*
JENNESS, D., *Indians of Canada*, 5th ed., Ottawa, 1960.
—— 'Canada's debt to the Indians', *Can. Geog. Jour.*, Vol. 65, No. 4, Oct. 1962.
LEECHMAN, D., *Native Tribes of Canada*, Toronto, 1956.
KIDD, K. E., *Canadians of Long Ago*, the story of the Canadian Indians, Toronto, 1951.

United States

ATKINSON, M. J., *Indians of the Southwest*, Naylor, 1958.
CARTER, G. F., 'Evidence for pleistocene man in southern California', *Geo. Rev.*, Vol. 40, 1950.
DAIFUKU, H. 'A new conceptual scheme for prehistoric cultures in the southwestern United States', *Amer. Anthrop.*, Vol. 54. No. 2, pt. 1, 1952.
DALE, E. E., *The Indians of the Southwest*, a century of development under the United States, Norman, Univ. of Oklahoma, 1949.
GLADWIN, H. S., *A History of the Ancient Southwest*, 1957.
GODDARD, P. E., 'Indians of the northwest coast', in *Amer. Mus. Nat. Hist. Handbook.*
GUNTHER, E., *Early Man in the Pacific Northwest*, 8th Ann. Biol. Colloquium, Oregon State College, Corvallis.
JOHNSON, F. (ed.), *Man in Northeastern North America*, Andover, 1944.

LOWIE, R. H., *Indians of the Plains*, New York, 1954.
WISSLER, C., *Indians of the United States*, four centuries of their history and culture, New York, 1946.

COLONIAL AMERICA—*Exploration*

BAKELESS, J., *The Eyes of Discovery*, New York, 1950.
BARTLETT, R. A., *Great Surveys of the American West*, Norman, Oklahoma, 1962.
BOLTON, C. K., *Terra Nova*, the northeast coast of America before 1602, Boston, 1935.
BOLTON, H. E., *Spanish Exploration in the Southwest, 1542–1706*, New York, 1946.
BRADSHAW, G., *A Collection of Travel in America*, New York, 1948.
BREBNER, J. B., *The Explorers of North America, 1492–1806*, London, 1933.
CAMPBELL, P., *Travels in the Interior Inhabitated Parts of North America, 1791–92*, Toronto, 1937.
DAVIES, A., *The Discovery of America*, Univ. Coll. S.W. England, Exeter, 1949.
GILBERT, E. W., *Exploration of Western North America*, London, 1933.
GRANT, W. L., *Voyages of S. de Champlain*, New York, 1907.
GUILLET, E. C., *The Pathfinders of North America* (rev. ed.), Toronto, 1957.
HOFFMAN, B. G., *Cabot to Cartier*, Toronto, 1961.
JOST, J. P., *Portuguese Activity Along the Canadian Shore at the Beginning of Modern Times*, Ottawa, 1960.
KENTON, E., *Black Gown and Redskins*—the early Jesuit missionaries in North America, 1610–1791, London, 1956.
LEADER, H., 'Hudson Bay Company in California', *The Beaver*, No. 279, Mar. 1949.
LUNNY, R. M., *Early Maps of North America*, New Jersey, 1961.
MIRSKY, J., *The Westward Crossings—Balboa, Mackenzie, Lewis and Clark*, New York, 1946.
SHEPPE, W., *First Man West* (*Alexander Mackenzie*), Berkeley, 1962.
STEPHENS, H. B., *Jacques Cartier*, his four voyages to Canada, Toronto, 1890.
THWAITES, R. G., *Early Western Travel, 1748–1846*, Cleveland, 1905.
—— *The Jesuit Relations and Allied Documents*, London, 1926.
WAGNER, H. R., *Cartography of the Northwest Coast of America to 1800*, Berkeley, 1937.

COLONIZATION—*Settlement of U.S. colonies and contested areas*

ANDREWS, C. M., *Our Earliest Colonial Settlements, Their Diversity of Origin, and Later Characteristics*, New York, 1933.
BOLTON, H. E., *New Spain and the Anglo-American West*, 2 vols., Los Angeles, 1932.
BROWN, R. H., *Historical Geography of the United States*, New York, 1948.
CARMAN, H. (ed.), *American Husbandry, 1775*, New York, 1939.
DORN, W., *Competition for Empire, 1740–63*, New York, 1939.
DOUGLAS, J., *New England and New France*, contrasts and parallels in colonial history, New York, 1913.
FINLEY, J. H., *The French in the Heart of America*, New York, 1915.
GRAHAM, G. S., *Empire of the North Atlantic*, the maritime struggle for North America, Toronto, 1950.
HARING, C. H., *The Spanish Empire in America*, New York, 1947.
HARLOW, R. V., *The Growth of the United States*, New York, 1938.
IRELAND, G., *Boundaries, Possessions and Conflicts in Central and North America and the Caribbean*, Cambridge (Mass.), 1941.
KALM, P., *The America of 1750*, New York, 1937.
NOTESTEIN, W., *The English People on the Eve of Colonization, 1603–30*, New York, 1954.
PATTISON, W. D., *Beginnings of the American Rectangular Land Survey System*, 1784–1800, Chicago, 1957.
THWAITES, R. G., *France in America, 1497–1763*, New York, 1905.
TREWARTHA, G. T., 'Types of rural settlement in colonial America', *Geog. Rev.*, 1946.
TURNER, F. J., *The Frontier in American History*, reprint, New York, 1949.

DE VOTO, B. A., *The Course of Empire*, Boston, 1952.
DE VORSEY, L. *The Southern Indian Boundary Line*, Chapel Hill, 1966.
WERTENBAKER, T. J., *The Founding of American Civilization*, the Middle Colonies, New York, 1938.
—— *The Founding of American Civilization*, the Old South, New York, 1942.
—— *The Founding of American Civilization*, the Puritan Oligarchy, New York, 1957
WISH, H., *Society and Thought in Early America*, London, 1950.

American colonies—Individual
ADAMS, J. T., *The Founding of New England*, Boston, 1921.
ANDREWS, M. P., *The Founding of Maryland*, New York, 1933.
CRANE, V. M., *The Southern Frontier, 1670–1732*, Univ. of Michigan, 1956.
CRAVEN, W. F., *The Southern Colonies in the 17th Century, 1607–89*, Baton Rouge, 1949.
DONTON, D., *A Brief Description of New York in 1670*, New York, 1937.
GOODWIN, M. W., *Dutch and English on the Hudson*, New Haven, 1920.
JOHNSON, H. B., 'French Canada and the Ohio country', *Can. Geogr.*, No. 12, 1958.
SHEPHERD, W. R., *The Story of New Amsterdam*, New York, 1926.
WARD, C., *The Dutch and Swedes on the Delaware, 1609–64*, Philadelphia, 1930.

Canada
BURPEE, L. J., *The Discovery of Canada*, Toronto, 1944.
BURT, A. L., *The Old Province of Quebec*, Minneapolis, 1933.
ENGLAND, R., *The Colonization of Western Canada, 1896–1934*, London, 1936.
GALBRAITH, J. S., *The Hudson's Bay Company as an Imperial Factor, 1821–69*, Toronto, 1957.
HUGO-BRUNT, M., 'The origin of colonial settlements in the Maritimes', Plan, Vol. 1, No. 2, June 1960.
LANDON, F., *Western Ontario and the American frontier*, New Haven, 1941.
LANCTOT, G., *Les Canadiens français et leur voisin du sud*, New Haven, 1941.
MACKAY, R. A., *The Honourable Company* (H.B.C.), Toronto, 1936.
MORTON, W. L., *The critical years: the union of British North America*, 1857–1873, Toronto, 1964.
MUNRO, W. B., *The Seignioral System in Canada*, New York, 1927.
RICH, E. E., *The History of the Hudson's Bay Company, 1670–1870*, Vol. 1, 1670–1763, London, 1958.
TRUDEL, M., *Le régime seigneural*, Can. Hist. Assoc. Brochure 6, Ottawa, 1956.
WRIGHT, E. C., *The Loyalists of New Brunswick*, Ottawa, 1955.
WADE, MASON, ed., *Canadian dualism: studies of French-English relations*, Toronto, 1960.
—— *The French Canadians, 1760–1945*, Toronto, 1955.

CANADA—*Physical*
CAN. GEOL. SURV., Econ. Geol. Ser. 1, *Geology and economic minerals of Canada*, Ottawa, 1947.
CAN. INST. MIN. & MET., *Structural Geology of Canadian Ore Deposits*, Montreal, 1948.
CAN. FORESTRY DEPT., Native Trees of Canada (6th edn.), Ottawa, 1961.
CAN. DEPT. TRANSPORT, Met. Div., *The Climate of Canada*, Ottawa, 1962.
COLEMAN, A. P., *The Last Million Years*, a history of the Pleistocene in North America, rev. ed., Toronto, 1958.
CONNOR, A. J., 'The Climate of Canada', in *Can. Yrbk*, Dom. Bur. Stat., Ottawa, 1949.
COOKE, H. C., 'The Canadian Shield', in *Geology & Economic Minerals of Canada*, Ottawa, 1947.
GADJA, R. T., 'The Canadian Ecumene—inhabited and uninhabited areas', *Geog. Bul.* No. 15, 1960.
GILL, J. E., 'Natural divisions of the Canadian Shield', *Trans. Roy. Soc. Can.*, Vol. 43, Ser. 3, Sec. 4.
HALLIDAY, W. E. D., 'A forest classification for Canada', Can., Dept. Res. & Dev., For. Serv., Bul. 89, 1952.

HALLIDAY, W. E. D., 'Climate, soils, and forests of Canada', *Forestry Chron.*, Vol. 26, No. 4, April 1941.
HUME, G. S., *Petroleum Geology of Canada*, Ottawa, 1955.
JENNESS, J. L., 'Permafrost in Canada', *Arctic*, 2, 1949.
KOEPPE, C. E., *The Canadian Climate*, Bloomington, 1931.
LANG, A. H., *On the Relation of Metal Occurrences to Tectonic Divisions of the Canadian Shield*, Roy. Soc. Can. Special Pubn., 1962.
LEAHEY, A., 'Agricultural soil resources of Canada', *Agric. Inst. Rev.*, Vol. 1, No. 5, May 1946.
LEGGETT, R. F., *Soils in Canada*, Roy. Soc. Can. Spec. Pubn., 1961.
MOORE, E. S., *Canada's Mineral Resources*, Toronto, 1933.
—— *Elementary Geology for Canada*, Toronto, 1944.
OSBORNE, J. F., ed., *Geochronology in Canada*, Ottawa, 1961.
PORSILD, A. E., 'Geographical distribution of some elements in the flora of Canada', *Geog. Bul.*, No. 11, 1958.
PUTNAM, D. F., 'Pedogeography of Canada', *Geog. Bul.*, No. 1, 1951.
STEVENSON, J. S., *The Tectonics of the Canadian Shield*, Toronto, 1962.
STOBBE, P. C., 'The Major soil zones and regions of Canada', *Can. Yrbk.*, Dom. Bur. Stat., Ottawa, 1951.
TAVENER, *The Birds of Canada*, Toronto, 1949.
THOMAS, M. K., *Climatological Atlas of Canada*, Can. Nat. Res. Counc., Ottawa, 1953.
WATSON, J. W., 'The Land of Canada', *Can. Geog. Jour.*, April, 1956.

CANADA—*Economic*

VAN ALLEN, W. H., 'Canal systems of Canada', *Can. Geog. Journ.*, Vol. 61, No. 5, Nov. 1960.
BROUILLETTE, B., *Les principales industries manufacturières du Canada*, Montreal, 1957.
—— 'L'approvisionnement régional du Canada en combustibles; houille, petrol, gaz natural', *L'Actualité Économique*, Jan.–Mar., 1961.
BUCK, W. K., 'Preliminary survey of the Canadian mineral industry in 1961', *Can. Mining Jour.*, Feb. 1962.
CAMU, P., WEEKS, E. P., & SAMETZ, Z. W., *Economic Geography of Canada*, Toronto, 1964.
CAN. DEPT. MINES & TECH. SURV., *The Canadian Mineral Industry*, Ottawa, 1966.
CAN. DEPT. N. AFFAIRS & NAT. RESOURCES, *Resources for Tomorrow*, Vols. 1 and 2, Ottawa, 1961.
CURRIE, A. W., *An Economic Geography of Canada*, Toronto, 1945.
—— *Canadian Economic Development*, Toronto, 1951.
—— *Economics of Canadian transportation*, 2nd ed., Toronto, 1959.
DAVIS, M. B., 'Canada's fruit industry', *Can. Geog. Jour.*, Sept. 1955.
EASTERBROOK, W. T., & AITKEN, G. J., *Canadian Economic History*, Toronto, 1956.
ELVER, R. B., *Survey of the Canadian Iron Ore Industry*, Can. Dept. of Mines, Mineral Infor. Bul. Ottawa, 1966.
GENTILCORE, L., ed., *Canada's Changing Geography*, Toronto, 1967.
GLAZEBROOK, G. P. DE T., *History of Transportation in Canada*, New ed., Toronto, 1964.
GROSS, G. A., *Iron Deposits in Canada*, Ottawa, 1965.
INNIS, H. A., *The Fur Trade in Canada*, 2nd edn., Toronto, 1956.
—— (ed. M. Q. Innis), *Essays in Canadian Economic History*, Toronto, 1956.
JANES, T. H., & WITTUR, G. E., *The Primary Iron and Steel Industry in Canada*, Ottawa, 1962.
HUDSON, S. C., *et al.*, *Types of Farming in Canada*, Can. Agric. Dept., Pubn. 825, Ottawa, 1949.
KERR, D., 'Industrial location in Canada', *Annals Assoc. Amer. Geogrs.*, Vol. 43, June 1953.
LOUNSBURY, J. P., *The Canadian Petroleum Industry*—the next five years, Toronto, 1962.
LOWER, A. R. M., *The North American Assault on the Canadian Forest*, New Haven, 1936.
MILLER, E. W., 'Mineral regionalism of the Canadian Shield', *Can. Geogr.*, No. 13, 1959.
SHOTWELL, J. S. G., 'Canada's energy sources to 1989—a forecast', *Eng. Jour.*, Vol. 43, No. 10, Oct. 1960.

SIMPSON, R. A., NOWLAN, D. M., & RUTLEDGE, D. W., *The Natural Gas Industry in Canada*, Ottawa, 1961.
—— *A Survey of the Petroleum Industry in Canada*, Ottawa, 1961.
STEVENS, G. R., *Canadian National Railways*, Toronto, 1962.

CANADA—*social and political*

BLISHEN, B. R., *et al.*, *Canadian Society*, Glencoe, 1961.
BREBNER, J. B., *North Atlantic Triangle*, New Haven, 1947.
CLARK, S. D., *The Social History of Canada*, Toronto, 1942.
—— *The developing Canadian community*, Toronto, 1962. (*Note:* this is a second publication of S. D. Clark's).
DEFFONTAINES, P., *L'homme et l'hiver au Canada*, Paris, 1957.
FORTIN, G., 'Social effects of the evolution of Canadian agriculture', in *Resources for Tomorrow*, Ottawa, 1961.
HEDGES, J. B., *Building the Canadian West, the Land and Colonization Policies of the Canadian Pacific Railway*, New York, 1939.
INNIS, D. Q., *Canada*, a geographic study, Toronto, 1966.
LOWER, A. R. M., *Colony to Nation*, 2nd ed., Toronto, 1957.
MACDONALD, N., *Canada, 1763–1841*, immigration and settlement, London, 1929.
NICHOLSON, N. L., *The Boundaries of Canada*, its provinces and territories, Ottawa, 1954.
—— *Canada in the American community*, Princeton, 1963.
PUTNAM, D. F., *et al.*, *Canadian regions*, Toronto, 1952.
ROBINSON, J. L. & M. J., *The Geography of Canada*, London, 1950.
—— 'The problem of geographical regions in Canada', *Can. Georg.*, No. 7, 1956.
SAVELLE, M., *Diplomatic History of the Canadian Boundary, 1749–63*, New Haven, 1940.
VEYRET, P., 'La population du Canada', *Rev. de Géog. Alpine*, Vol. 41.
WARKENTIN, J., ed., *Canada*, a geographical interpretation, Toronto, 1967.
WATSON, J. W., 'The geography of Canada', in *Canada*, ed. Brown, G., Univ. of Calif. P., 1949.
—— 'Canada, geographic bridgehead', *Public Affairs*, Vol. 13, No. 2, Winter 1950.
—— 'Basic problems of regional planning in Canada', *Community Plan. Rev.*, Vol. 4, 1954.
—— 'Canada and its regions', *Scot. Geog. Mag.*, Vol. 78, No. 3, Dec. 1962.
WOOD, W. D., & THOMAN, R. S., *Areas of Economic Stress in Canada*, Kingston, 1965.

MAJOR REGIONS OF CANADA—*Atlantic Region*

ALCOCK, F. J., 'The Appalachian region', in *Geology & Economic Minerals of Canada*, Ottawa, 1947.
ATLANTIC PROVINCES ECONOMIC COUNCIL, *The Economy of the Atlantic region in perspective*, Halifax, 1960.
BIRD, J. B., 'Settlement patterns in Maritime Canada, 1687–1756', *Geog., Rev.*, 45, No. 3, 1955.
BLACK, W. A., 'Population distribution of the Labrador coast, Nfd.', *Geog. Bul.*, No. 9, 1956.
CAMERON, H. L., 'Tectonics of the Maritimes area', *Trans. Roy. Soc. Can.*, Ser. 3, Sec. 4, June, 1956.
CAMPBELL, G. G., 'Mining in Nova Scotia', *Can. Geog. Journ.*, Vol. 59, No. 1, July 1959.
CAN. GOVT. HANDBK., *Newfoundland*, an Introduction to Canada's New Province, Ottawa, 1951.
CLARK, A. H., *Three Centuries and the Island* (P.E.I.), Toronto, 1959.
DOUGLAS, G. V., 'The Structure of Ungava', *Trans. Roy. Soc. Can.*, 43, Ser. 3, Sec. 4.
DUNFIELD, SIR B., 'Urban growth in Newfoundland', *Habitat*, Vol. 4, No. 1, Jan.-Feb., 1961.
GOLDTHWAIT, J. W., 'Physiography of Nova Scotia', Can. Geol. Surv., Mem. 140, Ottawa, 1924.
GRANT, R. F., *The Canadian Atlantic Fishery*, Toronto, 1934.
GREENING, W. E., 'Some recent changes in the economy of Newfoundland', *Can. Geog. Jour.*, Vol. 55, No. 4, Oct. 1957.
GUTSELL, B., *An Introduction to the Geography of Newfoundland*, Ottawa, 1949.

HARE, F. K., 'The climate of the island of Newfoundland', *Geog. Bul.*, No. 2, 1952.
HAWBOLDT, L. S., 'Forestry in Nova Scotia', *Can. Geog. Jour.*, Vol. 51, No. 2, Aug. 1955.
HUMPHRYS, G., 'Mining Activity in Labrador-Ungava', Trans., I.B.G., 1961.
HUSTICH, J., *On the Forest Geography of the Labrador Peninsula*, Helsinki, 1949.
LOUCKS, O. L., 'A forest classification for the Maritime provinces', Proc. N.S. Inst. of Sci., Halifax, Vol. 25, pt. 2, 1960.
MACNUTT, W. S., *The Making of the Maritime Provinces, 1713–84*, Can. Hist. Assoc. Brochure 4, Ottawa, 1955.
MATHESON, M. H., 'The Hinterlands of Saint John, N.B.', *Geog. Bul.*, No. 7, 1955.
PARENT, R. C., 'Agriculture in the Atlantic Provinces, its Present Status and Future Possibilities', *Atlantic Advocate*, Vol. 79, No. 9, June 1957.
PUTNAM, D. F., 'The climate of the Maritime provinces', *Can. Geog. Jour.*, Vol. 21, No. 3, Sept. 1940.
—— 'Agricultural development of New Brunswick', *Econ. Geog.*, Vol. 15, No. 4, Oct. 1939; Vol. 15, No. 1, Jan. 1939.
—— 'Farm distribution in Nova Scotia', *Econ. Geog.*, Vol. 15, No. 1.
RAYMOND, C. W., MCLELLAN, J. B., & RAYBURN, J. A., *Land Utilization in Prince Edward Island*, Ottawa, 1963.
SUMMERS, W. F., & SUMMERS, M. E., *Geography of Newfoundland*, Toronto, 1965.
TANNER, V., 'Outline of the geography, life and customs of Newfoundland–Labrador', *Acta Geoga.*, 8, No. 1, 1944.
TROTTER, R. G., 'The Appalachian barrier in Canadian history', *Can. Hist. Assoc. Rept.*, May, 1939.
WALSH, F. W., 'Changes in the pattern of agricultural development in the Maritimes', *Proc. Inst. Pub. Admin. Can.*, 7th Ann. Conference, Sept. 1955.
WATSON, J. W., 'Halifax, Nova Scotia; relict geography in an urban community', in *Geographical Essays*, eds. Miller, R., & Watson, J. W., London, 1959.
WOODFINE, W. J., 'Canada's Atlantic provinces, a study in regional retardation', *Commerce Jour.*, Feb., 1962.

MAJOR REGIONS OF CANADA—*Southern Central Provinces*

BLANCHARD, R., 'Québec, esquisse de géographie urbaine', *Rev. de Géog. Alpine*, Tome 22, 1934.
—— *L'Est du Canada français*, Paris, 1935.
—— 'La région du fleuve Saint-Laurent entre Québec et Montréal', *Rev. de Géog. Alpine*, 1936.
—— *Le centre du Canada français*, Montréal, 1947.
—— 'Montréal, esquisse de géographie urbaine', *Rev. Can. de Géog.*, Vol. 4, Nos. 1–2, Jan.–Avr., 1950.
—— *L'Ouest du Canada français*, Montréal, Vol. 1, 1953, Vol. 2, 1954.
—— *Le Canada Français*, province de Québec, Paris, 1960.
BONKOFF, E. J., *The Canadian Asbestos Industry*, Toronto, 1960.
BROUILLETTE, B., 'Les régions géographiques et économiques de la province de Québec', *Can. Geogr.*, No. 3, 1953.
BRUCE, E. L., 'The Canadian Shield, and its geographic effects', *Geog. Jour.*, Vol. 93, 1939.
CAMU, P., 'The St Lawrence Seaway from Quebec city to Cornwall', *Can. Geogr.*, No. 7, 1956.
—— 'Le paysage urbain de Québec', *Geog. Bul.*, No. 10, 1957.
—— 'Types de maisons dans la région suburbaine de Montréal', *Can. Geogr.*, No. 9, 1957.
—— *Étude du port de Québec*, Geog. Br. Paper No. 17, Ottawa, 1959.
CARTER, DE W., *The Welland Canal*, a history, Pt. Colborne, 1960.
CHAPMAN, L. J., 'Adaptation of crops in Ontario', *Can. Geog. Jour.*, Vol. 24, No. 5, May 1942.
—— & PUTNAM, D. F., *The Physiography of Southern Ontario*, Toronto, 1951.
CREIGHTON, D. G., *The Commercial Empire of the St Lawrence*, New Haven, 1937.
DAVIES, B., *Ottawa*, portrait of a capital, New York, 1954.

DEACON N. A. H., 'Geographical factors and land use in Toronto', *Can. Geog. Journ.*, Vol. 29, No. 2, 1944.
DRESSER, J. A., & DENIS, T. C., *Geology of Quebec*, P.Q. Dept. Mines, Geol., Rept. 20, 1944.
DUFRESNE, A. O., 'Significance of mining in the province of Quebec', *Can. Geog. Jour.*, Vol. 60, No. 6, June, 1960.
FALARDEAU, J. C., *Croissance et physionomie de la ville de Québec*, L'Univ. Laval Pubn., Quebec, 1943.
FONTAINE, C. A., 'Les sols du Québec', *Actualité Économique*, 17, Vol. 1, No. 5, Mar. 1942.
GARDINER, F. G., 'Metropolitan Toronto', *Industrial Canada*, Vol. 54, No. 3, July 1953.
GARIQUE, P., 'Change and continuity in rural French-Canada', *Culture*, Vol. 18, Dec. 1957.
HILLS, G. A., 'Pedology . . . and agricultural settlement in Ontario', *Can. Geog. Jour.*, Vol. 29, No. 3, Sept. 1944.
—— 'Soil-Forest relationships in the site regions of Ontario', *Proc. Forest Soils Conference*, Ontario, Sept. 1958.
HILLS, T. L., *The St Lawrence Seaway*, London 1959.
KERR, D., & SPELT, J., 'Manufacturing in Downtown Toronto', *Geog. Bul.*, No. 10, 1957.
—— 'Some aspects of industrial location in Southern Ontario', *Can. Geogr.*, No. 15, 1960.
KRUEGER, R. R., 'Changing land use patterns in the Niagara Fruit belt', *Trans. Roy. Can. Inst.*, Vol. 32, No. 67, 1959.
LACOSTE, N., *Les caractéristiques sociales de la population du grand Montréal*, Louvain, 1958.
LANGLOIS, C., 'Problems of urban growth in Greater Montreal', *Can. Geogr.*, Vol. 5, No. 3, Autumn 1961.
MCGUIRE, B. J., 'Water power in Quebec', *Can. Geog. Jour.*, Vol. 64, No. 6.
MACKAY, J. ROSS, 'Physiography of the lower Ottawa valley', *Rev. Can. de Géog.*, Vol. 3, Nos. 1–4, Jan.–Dec. 1949.
MINVILLE, E. (ed.), *Notre Milieu*, Montreal, 1942.
—— (ed.), *Montreal économique*, Montreal, 1943.
MORRIS, K. W., 'The St Lawrence Seaway—its development and economic significance', *Jour. Geog.*, Vol. 55, No. 9, 1956.
MORWICK, F. J., 'Soils of Southern Ontario', *Sci. Agric.*, Vol. 13, No. 7, 1953.
ONT. AGRIC. DEPT., *Farm life in Ontario*, Toronto, 1961.
QUEBEC, NAT. RES. DEPT., *Mining Industry of the Province*, Quebec, 1962.
PARDÉ, M., 'Hydrologie du Saint-Laurent et de ses affluents', *Rev. Can. de Géog.*, Vol. 12, Nos. 2–4, Sept.–Dec., 1948.
PARKER, W. H., 'A revolution in the agricultural geography of Lower Canada', *Rev. Can. de Géog.*, Vol. 11, No. 4, 1957.
PUTNAM, D. F., 'Changes in rural land use patterns on the Central Lake Ontario plain', *Can. Geogr.*, Vol. 6, No. 2, 1962.
RAY, D. M., *A Quantitative Analysis of Industrial Location in S. Ontario*, Chicago, 1965.
REEDS, L. G., 'Agricultural regions of Southern Ontario, 1880–1951', *Econ. Geog.*, Vol. 35, 1959.
RICH, E. E., *Montreal and the Fur Trade*, Leicester, 1966.
RICHARDS, J. H., 'Land types in the precambrian Shield area of S. Ontario', *Geog. Bul.*, No. 13, 1959.
ROBINSON, J. L., 'Windsor, Ontario, a study in Urban Geography', *Can. Geog. Journ.*, Vol. 27, No. 3, Sept. 1943.
ROY, J. M., 'Quelques aperçus géographiques de la région de Québec', *Can. Geogr.*, Vol. 1, No. 1, 1952.
—— 'Québec, esquisse de géographie urbaine', *Can. Geogr.*, Vol. 2, 1953.
SIMMONS, J. W., *Toronto's Changing Retail Complex*, Chicago, 1966.
SPELT, J., *The Urban Development in South Central Ontario*, Utrecht, 1955.
—— & KERR, D., *The Changing Face of Toronto*, Ottawa, 1965.
TRÉPANIER, R., 'Modern trends in agriculture—Quebec', *Can. Geog. Jour.*, Vol. 58, No. 6, June 1959.

VILLENEUVE, G. O., *Climatic Conditions of the Province of Quebec and their Relationship to the Forest*, Dept. Lands and Forest, Quebec, 1946.

WADE, M., *The French-Canadian Outlook*, New York, 1946.

WATSON, J. W., 'Urban developments in the Niagara Peninsula', *Can. Jour. Econ. & Pol. Sci.*, Vol. 9, No. 4, Nov. 1943.

—— 'Hamilton (Ontario) and its environs', *Can. Geog. Jour.*, Vol. 30, No. 5, May 1945.

—— 'Mapping a hundred years of change in the Niagara Peninsula', *Can. Geog. Jour.*, Vol. 32, No. 6, June 1946.

—— 'The Changing industrial pattern of the Niagara Peninsula', *Ont. Hist. Soc. Papers & Records*, Vol. 37, 1947.

—— 'Rural Depopulation in S.W. Ontario', *Annals Assoc. Amer. Geogr.*, Vol. 37, No. 3, Sept. 1947.

MAJOR REGIONS OF CANADA—*Southern Prairies*

ALBERTA DEPT. OF AGRIC., *Farming in Alberta*, Pubn. No. 40, 1957.

BAKER, W. B., 'Changing community patterns in Saskatchewan', *Can. Geog. Jour.*, Vol. 56, No. 2, Feb. 1958.

CARD, B. Y., *The Canadian Prairie Provinces from 1870–1950*, Toronto, 1960.

CURRIE, B. W., 'The vegetation & frost-free seasons of the Prairie provinces & N.W.T.', *Can. Jour. Research*, Vol. 26, No. 1, 1948.

DAWSON, C. A., *Group Settlement*, Ethnic Communities in Western Canada, Toronto, 1936.

EGGLESTON, W., 'The short grass prairies of Western Canada', *Can. Geog. Jour.*, Vol. 50, No. 4, April 1955.

ENGLAND, R., 'The emergent west', *Queen's Q.*, Vol. 41, Autumn, 1934.

ENGLISH, R. E., *Farming in Alberta*, Edmonton, 1961.

HEDGES, J. B., *Building the Canadian West*, Toronto, 1939.

HEWSON, L. C., 'History of the Lake Winnipeg fishery', *Jour. Fisheries Res. Bd., Can.*, Vol. 17, No. 5, Sept., 1960.

HOPKINS, E. S., *et al.*, *Soil Drifting in the Prairie Provinces*, Ottawa, 1937.

HUME, G. S., 'The interior plains', in *Geology & Economic Minerals of Canada*, Ottawa, 1947.

JOEL, A. H., 'Diversity of soil types in the Prairie provinces', *Sci., Agric.*, Vol. 8, June, 1928.

LLOYD, T., 'Mapping Western Canada', *Can. Geog. Jour.*, Vol. 26, No. 5, 1943.

MACKINTOSH, W. A., *Prairie Settlement*, the Geographical Setting, Toronto, 1934.

—— *Economic Problems of the Prairie Provinces*, Toronto, 1935.

MACNEILL, P., 'They are changing the face of Saskatchewan' (Irrigation), *Can. Geog. Jour.*, Vol. 60, May 1960.

MORTON, A. S., *A History of the Canadian West*, London, 1939.

—— & MARTIN, C., *History of Prairie Settlement and Dominion Lands Policy*, Toronto, 1938.

MORTON, W. L., *Manitoba*, a history, Toronto, 1957.

NICHOLSON, N. L., 'Regions in S. Alberta', *Rev. Can. de Géog.*, Vol. 8, Nos. 3–4, 1954.

PALMER, A. E., 'Irrigation in western Canada, its possible effects on industry and population', *Engin. Jour.*, Vol. 31, No. 9, 1948.

PICKERSGILL, T. B., 'The vanishing prairie village', *Habitat*, 4, No. 3, 1961.

ROE, F. G., 'Early opinions on the fertile belt of western Canada', *Can. Hist. Rev.*, Vol. 27, No. 2, June 1946.

—— 'Early agriculture in western Canada in relation to climatic stability', *Agric. Hist.*, Vol. 26, No. 3, July 1952.

SMITH, P. J., 'Calgary, a study in urban pattern', *Econ. Geog.*, Vol. 38, No. 4, Oct. 1962.

SPENCE, G., 'Water for the Prairies', *Can. Geog. Jour.*, June 1952.

STUART, D., *The Canadian Desert*, Toronto, 1938.

VANDERHILL, B. G., 'The farming frontier of western Canada, 1950–60', *Jour. Geog.*, Vol. 61, No. 1, Jan. 1962.

VILLMOW, J. R., 'The nature & origin of the Canadian dry belt', *Annals Assoc. Amer. Geogrs.*, Vol. 46, No. 2, June 1956.

WAINES, W. J., *Prairie Population Possibilities*, Ottawa, 1939.

WARKENTIN, J., ed., *The Western Interior of Canada*, a record of Geographical Discovery, 1612–1917, Toronto, 1964.

WATT, A. B., 'Edmonton', *Can. Geog. Jour.*, Vol. 33, No. 6, Dec. 1946.

WEIR, T., 'Land use and population characteristics of central Winnipeg', *Geog. Bul.*, No. 9, 1956.

MAJOR REGIONS OF CANADA—*British Columbia*

ATAMENENKO, G. T., *et al.*, *The Port of Vancouver*, Vancouver, 1961.

BOSTOCK, H. S., *Physiography of the Canadian Cordillera*, Geol. Surv. Can., Mem. 247. Ottawa, 1948.

B.C. POWER COMMISSION, *Power in British Columbia*, Victoria, 1961.

CLEMENS, W. A., & WILBY, G. V., *Fishes of the Pacific coast of Canada*, Ottawa, 1961.

DENTON, V. L., *The Far West Coast*, Toronto, 1924.

HARDWICK, W. G., *Geography of the Forest Industry of Coastal British Columbia*, U.B.C., Vancouver, 1963.

KERR, D., 'The physical basis of agriculture in British Columbia', *Econ. Geog.*, Vol. 28, No. 3, July 1952.

—— & KENDREW, W. G., *The Climate of British Columbia and the Yukon Territory*, Ottawa, 1955.

LANG, A. H., 'The cordilleran region of W. Canada', in *Structural Geology of Canadian Ore Deposits*, Can. Inst. Min. & Met., Montreal, 1948.

LESLIE, E. A., 'Vancouver, Canada's second port', *Foreign Trade*, Vol. 101, No. 2, Feb. 1954.

MCGOVERN, P. D., 'Industrial development in the Vancouver area', *Econ. Geog.*, Vol. 37 No. 3, July 1961.

MCMATH, R. A., *Manufacturing Industry in the Lower Mainland of British Columbia*, Vancouver, 1960.

MARR, N., 'The Columbia river basin', *Can. Geog. Jour.*, Vol. 45, No. 2, 1952.

MATTHEWS, W. H., 'Climate & physiography of British Columbia', in *Proc. 9th Can. Soil Mechanics Conference*, Ottawa, 1956.

ORMSBY, M., *British Columbia*, a history, Toronto, 1958.

PEACOCK, M. A., 'Fjord-land of British Columbia', *Bul. Geol. Soc. Amer.*, Vol. 46.

ROBINSON, I. M., 'Growth and distribution of the population of B.C.', in *Trans. 9th Brit. Col. Nat. Resources Conf.*, Victoria, 1956.

ROBINSON, J. L., 'Population trends and distribution in British Columbia', *Can. Geogr.*, No. 4, 1954.

SAGE, W. N., 'Vancouver, the rise of a city', *Dalhousie Rev.*, Vol. 17, No. 1.

SPILLSBURY, R. H., 'Land utilization on Vancouver island', *Forestry Chron.*, Vol. 19, No. 3, Sept. 1943.

——— & TISDALE, E. W., 'Soil-plant relationships and vertical zonation in southern interior B.C.', *Sci. Agric.*, No. 24, 1944.

TAYLOR, GRIFFITH, 'British Columbia, a study in topographical control', *Geog. Rev.*, Vol. 32, July 1942.

TISDALE, E. W., 'The grasslands of the southern interior of B.C.', *Ecology*, Vol. 28, No. 4, Oct. 1947.

WALKER, J. F., 'Mining development in British Columbia', *Can. Geog. Jour.*, Vol. 45, No. 3, Sept. 1952.

WARREN, P. S., 'The Rocky Mountain geosyncline in Canada', *Trans. Roy. Soc. Can.*, 45, Ser. 3, Sec. 4.

WEIR, T. R., 'The physical basis of ranching in the interior plateau of British Columbia', *Geog. Bul.*, No. 3, 1953.

MAJOR REGIONS OF CANADA—*The Canadian North*

AHRENS, J. T. (ed.), *Canadian North*, Washington, 1956.
ARCHIBALD, E. S., 'Agricultural lands in the Canadian northwest', *Can. Geog. Jour.* Vol. 29, No. 1, July 1944.
BIRD, J. B., 'Terrain conditions in the central Canadian arctic', *Geog. Bul.*, No. 7, 1955.
BLADEN, V. W. (ed.), *Canadian Population and Northern Colonization*, Roy. Soc. Can. Spec. Pubn., Toronto, 1962.
CAMPBELL, T. C., 'Quebec–Labrador Ore', *Iron Age*, No. 166, 1950.
CANADA, NORTHERN AFFAIRS & NATURAL RESOURCES DEPT., *Mining in the North*, Ottawa, 1961.
—— *Yukon*, its Riches and Romance, Ottawa, 1962.
CHRISTIE, K. J., *Known Mineralized Areas and Mining Development*, Yukon Territory & Northwest Territories, Ottawa, 1960.
DAWSON, C. A., *The Settlement of the Peace River Country*, Toronto, 1934.
—— *The New North-West*, Toronto, 1947.
DOUGLAS, R. J. W., ed., *Geology and Petroleum Possibilities of Northern Canada*, Ottawa, 1963.
DRINNAN, R. H., & PRIOR, L., 'Physical characteristics of the Ungava Bay area', *Geog. Bul.*, No. 7, 1955.
DURRELL, W. H., 'Labrador iron ore and the St Lawrence Seaway', *Eng. & Min. Jour.*, No. 151, 1950.
FINNIE, R., *Canada Moves North*, London, 1945.
FLINT, R. F., 'The ice age in the North American arctic', *Arctic*, Vol. 5, No. 3, Oct. 1952.
HAMELIN, L. E., "Typologie de l'écoumène canadien', Roy. Soc. Can., 4th Ser., Vol. IV, June, 1966.
HARE, F. K., 'The Labrador frontier', *Geog. Rev.*, Vol. 42, No. 3, 1952.
—— 'Weather and climate of the Northlands', in *Geography of the Northlands*, eds. Kimble, G. H. T., & Good, D., New York, 1955.
HERBERT, C. H., 'The development of transportation in the Canadian North', *Can. Geog. Jour.*, Vol. 53, No. 5, Nov. 1956.
KEENLEYSIDE, H. L., 'The human problems and resources of the Canadian North', *Roy. Soc. Can.*, Vol. 44, Ser. 3, App. B.
KIMBLE, G. H. T., & GOOD, D., *Geography of the Northlands*, New York, 1955.
KIRBY, R. P., 'Deglaciation in Central Labrador–Ungava', *Geo. Bul.*, No. 16, Nov. 1961.
LAIRD, D. G., 'Differentiation of forest and agricultural lands', *Sci. Agric.*, Vol. 15, No. 5, Jan. 1940.
LANG, A. H., & DOUGLAS, R. J. W., 'Minerals and fuels', in *The Canadian Northwest, its potentialities*, ed. Underhill, F., Toronto, 1959.
LLOYD, T., "The Future Colonization of Northern Canada", in *Canadian Population and Northern Colonization*, ed. Bladen, V. W., Toronto, 1962.
MACDONALD, R. S., ed., *The Arctic Frontier*, Toronto, 1966.
MCGUIRE, B. H., & WILD, R., 'Kitimat, tomorrow's city today', *Can. Geog. Jour.*, Nov. 1959.
MERRILL, G. C., 'Human geography of the Lesser Slave Lake area', *Geog. Bul.*, No. 3, 1953.
MILLER, E. W., 'Mineral regionalism of the Canadian Shield', *Can. Geogr.*, Vol. 13, 1949.
NICHOLSON, N. L., 'The face of the north', *Can. Geog. Jour.*, Vol. 57, No. 3, 1958.
—— 'The North-west Territories, geographical aspects', *Can. Geog. Jour.*, Vol. 60, No. 1, Jan. 1960.
PORSILD, A. E., 'Plant life in the Arctic', *Can. Geog. Jour.*, Vol. 42, 1951.
—— 'Land use in the Arctic, I–II', *Can. Geog. Jour.*, Vol. 48, No. 6, June 1954; 49, No. 1, July 1954.
QUIRIN, G. D., *Economics of Oil and Gas Development in Northern Canada*, Ottawa, 1962.
RAE, R. W., *Climate of the Canadian Arctic Archipelago*, Can. Dept. of Transport, Met. Div., Ottawa, 1951.
ROBINSON, I. M., *New Industrial Towns on Canada's Resource Frontier* (Kitimat & Schefferville), Chicago, 1962.

ROBINSON, J. L., 'Land use possibilities in Mackenzie district', *Can. Geog. Jour.*, July 1945.
—— 'Agriculture and forests of Yukon Territory', *Can. Geog. Jour.*, Aug. 1945.
—— 'Exploration and settlement of Mackenzie district, Northwest Territories', *Can. Geog. Jour.*, July 1946.
—— 'Canada's western arctic', *Can. Geog. Jour.*, Dec. 1948.
—— *et al.*, *The Canadian Arctic*, Ottawa, 1951.
ROBINSON, J. M., 'Forest resources of the Mackenzie river basin, N.W.T.', *Polar Record*, Vol. 10, No. 66, Sept. 1960.
SANDERSON, M., 'Drought in the Canadian Northwest', *Geog. Rev.*, Vol. 38, No. 2, Apr. 1948.
STAGER, J. K., 'Fur trading posts in the Mackenzie region up to 1850', *Can. Assoc. Geogr.*, B.C. Div., Occasl. Papers, No. 3, May 1962.
STONE, K. H., 'Human geographic research in the North American Northern lands', *Arctic*, Vol. 7, Nos. 3 & 4, 1954.
TAYLOR, GRIFFITH, 'A Mackenzie Domesday', in *The New North-West*, ed. Dawson, C. A., Toronto, 1947.
THORSTEINSSON, R., & TOZER, E. T., *Summary Account of Structural History of the Canadian Arctic Archipelago Since Precambrian Time*, Ottawa, 1960.
UNDERHILL, F. H. (ed.), *The Canadian Northwest*, its potentialities, Ottawa, 1959.
WATSON, JESSIE W., 'The Mackenzie Basin', *Geog. Mag.*, Vol. 24, No. 10, 1952.
WATSON, J. W., 'Canada, power vacuum or pivot area', in *New Compass of the World*, eds. Weigert, H. W., Stefansson, V., & Harrison, R. E., New York, 1949.
—— 'Population pressure and marginal lands', *Scot. Geog. Mag.*, Vol. 72, No. 2, 1956.
WILSON, J. TUZO, 'Geology of Northern Canada', in *Canadian North*, ed. Ahrens, J. T. Washington, 1956.
WONDERS, W. C., 'Assessment of the Northwest Territories by a geographer', in *The Canadian Northwest*, ed. Underhill, F., Ottawa, 1959.

UNITED STATES—*Physical*

ALLEN, S. W., *An Introduction to American Forestry*, New York, 1960.
BRAUN, E. L., *Deciduous Forests of Eastern North America*, New York, 1950.
BROWN, E. H., 'Britain and Appalachia, a study in the correlation and dating of plantation surfaces'; Trans., I.B.G., No. 29, 1961.
FENNEMAN, N. M., *Physiography of Western United States*, New York, 1931.
—— *Physiography of Eastern United States*, New York, 1938.
FROST, R. E., & WOODS, K. B., *Airphoto Patterns of Soils of the Western United States*, U.S. Dept. of Comm. Civ. Aeronautics Admin., Tech. Devel. Rept. 85, Washington, 1948.
HIGHSMITH, R., *et al.*, *Conservation in the United States*, Chicago, 1962.
HITCHCOCK, A. S., *Manual of the grasses of the United States*, Washington, 1935.
JAEGER, E. C., *North American Deserts*, Stanford, 1957.
JENKINS, D. S., *et al.*, *The Origin, Distribution and Airphoto Identification of U.S. Soils*, Tech. Devel. Rept. 52, Washington, 1946.
KELLOG, C. E., *Development and Significance of the Great Soil Groups in the U.S.*, Washington, 1936.
LOOMIS, F. B., *Physiography of the United States*, New York, 1938.
MANNERS, G., 'Natural Gas in the U.S.A.', *Coke and Gas*, May 1961.
MARBUT, C. F., *Soils of the United States*, Washington, 1935.
MEIGS, P., 'Water Problems in the United States', *Geog. Rev.*, 1952.
PALEY, W. S., *et al.*, *The Outlook for Key Commodities*, President's Materials Policy Commission, Vol. 2, Washington, 1952.
PARSON, R. L., *Conserving American Resources*, New York, 1956.
RENNER, G. T., *Conservation of National Resources*, New York, 1942.
RUSSELL, R. J., *Dry Climates of the United States*, I & II, U. of Cal. Pubns. in Geogy., Vol. 5, No. 1, Vol. 5, No. 5.
SMITH, G. H. (ed.), *Conservation of Natural Resources*, New York, 1950.

U.S. DEPT. OF AGRIC., *Yearbook of Agriculture*: 1938—Soils and men; 1941—Climate and man; 1948—Grass; 1949—Trees; 1958—Land.
—— *Timber Resources for America's Future*, 1958.
U.S. DEPT. OF INTERIOR, *Minerals Yearbook*, 1967 (Annual).
VISHER, S. S., *Climatic Atlas of the United States*, Cambridge, Harvard, 1954.
WOLFANGER, L. A., *Major Soil Divisions of the United States*, New York, 1929.

UNITED STATES—*General, Economic and Social*

ALEXANDER, J. W., 'The basic-nonbasic concept of urban economic functions', *Econ. Geog.*, Vol. 30, July 1954.
ALEXANDERSSON, G., *The Industrial Structure of American Cities*, New Haven, 1956.
BAKER, O. E., *Atlas of American Agriculture*, Washington, 1918–36.
—— 'Agricultural regions of the United States', *Econ. Geog.*, 1926.
BARACH, A. B., *U.S.A. and its Economic Future*, New York, 1964.
BARTHOLOMEW, H., *Land Use in American Cities*, London, 1956.
BERRY, B. J. L., & HANKINS, T. D., *A Bibliographic Guide to the Economic Regions of the U.S.A.*, Chicago, 1963.
BOESCH., H., *Die Vereinigten Staaten* v. *Amerika*, Bern, 1949.
BOGUE, D. J., *The Population of the U.S.A.*, Glencoe, Illinois, 1959.
——, & BEALE, C. L., *Economic Areas of the U.S.*, New York, 1961.
BROWN, I. C., *The Story of the American Negro*, New York, 1957.
BRUNNER, E. S., & KOLB, J. H., *Rural Social Trends*, New York, 1933.
CHITTENDEN, H. M., *The American Fur Trade*, Vols. 1 & 2, Stanford, 1954.
CLAWSON, M., *Land for Americans: Trends, Prospects and Problems*, Chicago, 1963.
COMMAGER, H. S., *Immigration and American History*, Minneapolis, 1961.
CONWAY, A., *The Welsh in America*, Minneapolis, 1961.
CREVELING, H. F., 'Mapping cultural groups in an American city', *Econ. Geog.*, Vol. 31, 1955.
DICKINSON, R. E., 'Metropolitan Regions of the United States', *Geog. Rev.*, Vol. 24, 1934.
DUCKHAM, A. N., *American Agriculture*, its background and its lessons, London, 1959.
DUNN, E. S., *The Location of Agricultural Production*, Gainesville, 1954.
FAULKNER, H. U., *Economic History of the United States*, New York, 1937.
FORD, H. J., *The Scotch-Irish in America*, London, 1951.
FRANK, A. B., *The German Element in the United States*, 2 vols., Boston, 1927.
FUCHS, V. R., *Changes in the location of U.S. manufacturing since 1929*, New Haven, 1962.
GEDDES, A., 'Variability in change of population in the United States and Canada, 1900–51', *Geog. Rev.*, Vol. 44, No. 1, 1954.
GLOVER, J. G., *The Development of American Industries*, 4th ed., New York, 1959.
GOTTMANN, J., *Megalopolis*, New York, 1961.
GREEN, C. MCL., *American Cities in the Growth of the Nation*, London, 1957.
HALLENBECK, W. C., *American Urban Communities*, New York, 1951.
HARRIS, C. D., 'A functional classification of cities in the United States', *Geog. Rev.*, Vol. 33, Jan. 1943.
—— 'The market as a factor in the localization of industry', *Annals Amer. Assoc. Geogrs.*, Vol. 44, No. 4, 1954.
—— 'Agricultural production in the United States—the past fifty years and the next', *Geog. Rev.*, Vol. 37, 1957.
HATT, P. K., & REISS, A. J., *Cities and Society*, Glencoe, 1957.
HAWLEY, A. H., *The Changing Shape of Metropolitan America*, Glencoe, 1956.
—— *Population Distribution within Metropolitan areas of U.S., 1900–50*, Oxford (Ohio) 1952.
HAYSTEAD, L., & FITE, G. C., *Agricultural Regions of the United States*, New York, 1955.
HIGBEE, E., *American Agriculture*, New York, 1958.
—— *The American Oasis, the Land and its Uses*, New York, 1957.
HOYT, H., *Structure and Growth of Residential Areas in American Cities*, Washington, 1939.
—— 'Structure of American cities in the post-war era', *Amer. Jour. Soc.*, Vol. 48, 1943.

ISARD, W., 'Some locational factors in the iron and steel industry', *Jour. Pol. Econ.*, Vol. 56.
JENSEN, M., *Regionalism in America*, Madison, 1951
KLOVE, R. C., 'The growing population of the United States', *Jour. Geog.*, Vol. 60, No. 5, May 1961.
LORD, C. L. & E. H., *Historical Atlas of the United States*, New York, 1944.
MCCARTY, H. H., *The Geographic Basis of American Economic Life*, New York, 1940.
MARSCHNER, F., *Land Use and Its Patterns in the United States*, 1959.
MIGHELL, R. L., *American Agriculture*, New York, 1955.
MILLER, E. W., 'Changing patterns in the mineral economy of the United States', *Profl. Geogr.*, Vol. 13, No. 3, May 1961.
MURPHY, R., 'A comparative study of nine central business districts', *Econ. Geog.*, Vol. 30, 1954.
MURPHY, R. E., *The American City*, New York, 1965.
NELSON, H. J., 'A Service classification of American cities', *Econ. Geog.*, Vol. 31, 1955.
ODUM, W. H., & MOORE, H. E., *American Regionalism*, New York, 1928.
PAULLIN, C. O., & WRIGHT, J. K., *Historical Geography of the United States*, New York, 1932.
PAULLIN, C. O., *Atlas of the Historical Geography of the U.S.A.*, New York, 1932.
PERLOFF, H. S., *Regions, Resources and Economic Growth*, Baltimore, 1960.
PERRY, G. S., *Cities of America*, New York, 1947.
PIERSON, G. W., 'The Frontier and American institutions', in *The Turner Thesis*, ed. Taylor, Boston, 1949.
POWERS, W. E., & LOGAN, R. F., *Transcontinental Excursion Guide*, I.G.U. XVIIth Internat. Geogl. Congress, Washington, 1952.
RAUP, P. M., 'Economic Development and Competition for land use in the United States', *Jour. Farm Econ.*, Vol. 39, 1957.
RODGERS, A., 'Industrial inertia—a major factor in the location of the steel industry of the United States', *Geog. Rev.*, Vol. 42, 1952.
ROSE, A. & C., *America Divided*, New York, 1948.
SAVELLE, M., *United States, Colonial Period*, Mexico, 1953.
SCHLESINGER, A. M., *History of American Life*, Vol. 10, 'Rise of the City', New York, 1933.
SCHRIER, A., *Ireland and the American Emigration, 1850–1900*, Minneapolis, 1958.
SEMPLE, E. C., *American History and Its Geographic Conditions*, New York, 1933.
SHEPPERSON, W. S., *British Emigration to North America*, Oxford, 1957.
STOVER, J. F., *American Railroads*, Chicago, 1961.
TAUEBER, C. & I. B., *The Changing Population of the U.S.*, New York, 1958.
TAYLOR, C. C., *et al.*, *Rural Life in the United States*, New York, 1949.
TAYLOR, G. R., *The Turner Thesis Concerning the Role of the Frontier in American History*, Boston, 1949.
THOMPSON, W. S., *The Growth of Metropolitan Districts in the U.S., 1900–40*, Washington, 1948.
TREWARTHA, G. T., 'Some regional characteristics of American farmlands', *Annals Assoc. Amer. Geogrs.*, Vol. 38, 1948.
TURNER, F. J., *Rise of the New West*, New York, 1906.
ULLMAN, E., 'Railroad patterns of the United States', *Geog. Rev.*, 1949.
U.S. DEPT. OF AGRIC., *Generalized Types of Farming in the United States*, Bur. Agric. Econ., Inf. Bul. No. 3, Washington, 1950.
—— *Changes in the American Textile Industry*, 1959.
U.S. INFORMATION SERVICE, *U.S.A., Its Geography and Growth*, London, 1955.
VANCE, S., *American Industries*, New York, 1955.
WADE, R. C., *The Urban Frontier*, Cambridge (Mass.), 1959.
WHITTLESEY, D., 'The United States, expansion and consolidation', in *The Changing World*, eds. East, G., & Moodie, A. E., London, 1956.
WISSINK, G. A., *American Cities in Perspective*, Utrecht, 1962.
WITTKE, C., *The Irish in America*, Louisiana, 1956.

ZELINSKY, W., 'Changes in the geographic patterns of rural population in the United States', *Geog. Rev.*, Vol. 52, No. 4, Oct. 1962.

MAJOR UNITED STATES REGIONS—*Industrialized North and Northeast*

ALEXANDER, J. W., *Industrial Expansion in the United States*, New York, 1952.
BALLERT, E. G., 'The Great Lakes coal trade, present and future', *Econ. Geog.*, 1953.
BLACK, J. D., *The Rural Life of New England*, Cambridge (Mass.), 1950.
BLOOD, P., 'Factors in the economic development of Baltimore', *Econ. Geog.*, 1937.
BREESE, G. W., *The Daytime Population of the Central Business District of Chicago*, Chicago, 1949.
BRIDENBAUGH, *The New England Town, Worcester*, 1947.
BRIGHT, A. A., & ELLIS, G. H., *The Economic State of New England*, New Haven, 1954.
BURGY, J. H., *The New England Cotton Textile Industry*, Baltimore, 1932.
CAMER, C., *The Hudson*, New York, 1939.
CHAMBERLAIN, S., *Ever New England*, New York, 1945.
COFFIN, R. P. T., *Life in America—New England*, Grand Rapides, 1951.
ESTALL, R. C., *New England*, A Study in Industrial Adjustment, London, 1966.
FEININGER, A., *The Face of New York*, New York, 1954.
FIREY, W., *Land Use in Central Boston*, Cambridge (Mass.), 1947.
GARBER, J. P., *The Valley of the Delaware, its Place in American History*, Philadelphia, 1934.
GREELEY, R. B., 'Part-time farming and recreational land use in New England', *Econ. Geog.*, 1942.
HAMBURG, J. R., & SHARKEY, R., 'Chicago's changing land use and population structure', *Jour. Amer. Inst. Planning*, Vol. 26, No. 4, Nov. 1960.
HARPER, F. C., *Pittsburgh, Forge of the Universe*, New York, 1957.
HEPBURN, A., *New York City*, New York, 1957.
HIGBEE, E. C., 'The three earths of New England', *Geog. Rev.*, 1952.
HOOVER, E. M., & VERNON, R., *The Anatomy of a Metropolis*, the changing distribution of people and jobs within N.Y., Cambridge, Harvard U.P., 1959.
HOYT, H., *One Hundred Years of Land Values in Chicago*, Chicago, 1933.
HUDGINS, B., 'The evolution of metropolitan Detroit', *Econ. Geog.*, 1940.
HUNGERFORD, E., *Pathway of Empire* (New York State), New York, 1935.
JENNINGS, *Boston, Cradle of Liberty, 1630–1776*, New York, 1947.
KELLY, R. S., & BRIGHT, A. A., 'The forests of New England', in *Economic State of New England*, eds. Ellis & Bright, New Haven, 1954.
KENT, L., *Village Greens of New England*, New York, 1948.
KLIMM, L. E., 'The empty areas of the Northeastern United States', *Geog. Rev.*, Vol. 44, 1954.
—— 'Philadelphia, its site and situation', *Bul. Geog. Soc. Phil.*, Vol. 33.
KOHN, C. F., 'Detroit', in *Industrial Cities Excursion*, eds. Mayer & Philbrick, I.G.U. XVIIth Internat. Congress, Washington, 1952.
MANNERS, G., 'Decentralization in Metropolitan Boston', *Geog.*, 45, 1960.
MAYER, H. M., *The Port of Chicago and the St Lawrence Seaway*, Chicago, 1957.
MAYER, H. M., & PHILBRICK, A. Q., 'Chicago', in *Industrial Cities Excursion*, eds. Mayer & Philbrick, Washington, 1955.
MEIRLEIR, M. J., 'Manufactural occupance in the west central area of Chicago', Res. Pap. 11, Geog. Dept., Chicago U.P., 1950.
Metropolis in Maps, the Boston Area, Cambridge (Mass.), 1946.
MILLER, E. W., 'Industrial development of the Allegheny Valley', *Econ. Geog.*, 1943.
MURPHY, R. E. & M., *Pennsylvania*, a Regional Geography, Harrisburg, 1937.
NATL. PLANNING ASSOC. REPT., *Economic State of New England*, New Haven, 1955.
NEVINS, A., & KROUT, J. A., *The Greater City, New York, 1898–1948*, New York, 1948.
N.Y. METROPOLITAN REGION STUDIES: *Anatomy of a Metropolis*, Cambridge (Mass.), 1959.
NYSTROM, J., *et al.*, 'Pittsburgh', in *Industrial Cities Excursion*, eds. Mayer & Philbrick, Washington, 1952.

PATTON, D. J., 'General cargo hinterlands of New York, Philadelphia, Baltimore, and New Orleans', *Annals Assoc. Amer. Geogrs.*, Vol. 48, 1958.
QUAIFE, M. M., *This is Detroit*, Wayne, 1951.
RODGERS, C., & RANKINS, R. B., *New York*, The World's Capital City, New York, 1948.
ROHRER, W. C., & HIRZEL, R. K., *Population Change and Urbanization in the Northeast*, Md. Agric. Exper. Stn., College Pk., 1959.
SCOFIELD, E., *Origin of Settlement Patterns in Rural New England*, 1938.
SMITH, T., *The Cotton Textile Industry of Fall River, Mass.*, a study in industrial location, New York, 1944.
SOLOMON, E., & BILBIJA, Z. G., *Metropolitan Chicago*, Glencoe, 1959.
THOMPSON, J. H., & HIGBEE, E. C., *New England Excursion*, I.G.U. XVIIth Internat. Congress, Washington, 1952.
—— ed., *The Geography of New York State*, Syracuse, 1966.
WARNER, L., & LUNT, P. F., *Yankee City*, Social Life of a Modern Community, New Haven, 1941.
WEBSTER, C. M., *Town Meeting Country*, Boston, 1945.
WHITE, D. J., *New England Fishing Industry*, Cambridge (Mass.), 1954.
WHITEHILL, W. M., *Boston*, a Topographical History, Belknap P., Harvard, 1959.
WRIGHT, J. K. (ed.), *New England's Prospect*, New York, 1933.
—— 'The diversity of New York City', *Geog. Rev.*, Vol. 26, 1936.

MAJOR REGIONS of the UNITED STATES—The Mid-West

AIKMAN, D., *The Taming of the Frontier*, New York, 1925.
ATHERTON, L., *Main Street on the Middle Border*, Bloomington, 1954.
ALEXANDER, W. H., & PATTON, C. A., *The Climate of Ohio*, Ohio Agric. Exper. Stn., Bul. 445, Wooster, 1929.
BANTA, R. E., *The Ohio*, New York, 1949.
BOOTH, A. W., 'Trade and transportation', in *The North American Mid-West*, ed. Garland, 195–.
BORCHERT, J. R., 'The climate of the central North American grassland', *Annals Assoc. Amer. Geogrs.*, Vol. 40, No. 1, Mar. 1950.
—— 'The Twin Cities' urbanized area; past, present and future', *Geog. Rev.*, Vol. 51, No. 1, Jan. 1961.
BURGHARDT, A. F., 'The location of river towns in the Central Lowlands of the U.S.', *Annals Assoc. Amer. Geogrs.*, Vol. 49, 1959.
CLARK, D. E., *The West in American History*, New York, 1937.
CROY, H., *Corn Country*, New York, 1947.
CUMMING, G. A., 'The Upper Mississippi waterway', *Scot. Geog. Mag.*, Vol. 71, No. 3, 1955.
DURAND, L., 'The American dairy region', *Jour. Geog.*, 1949.
DURY, J., *Midwest Heritage*, New York, 1948.
FREEMAN, O. W., 'Indianapolis: Hoosier Metropolis', *Jour. Geog.*, 1945.
GARLAND, H. *The Western March of American Settlement*, Chicago, 1927.
GARLAND, J. H. (ed)., *The North American Mid-west*, New York, 1955.
HARTSHORNE, R., 'The Twin City district, a unique form of urban landscape', *Geog. Rev.*, 1932.
HEWES, L., 'Some features of early woodland and prairie settlement in a Central Iowa county', *Annals Assoc. Amer. Geogrs.*, 1950.
—— 'The northern wet prairie of the United States', *Annals Assoc. Amer. Geogrs.*, Vol. 41, No. 4, Dec. 1951.
—— 'Causes of Wheat Failure in the Dry Farming Region, Central Great Plains, 1939–1957', Economic Geography, Vol. 41, No. 4, 1965.
HUTTON, G., *Midwest at Noon*, Chicago, 1946.
KOHN, C. F., 'Settlement forms and patterns', in *The North American Mid-West*, ed. Garland, New York, 1955.
MCCARTY, H. H., 'Structure of industry', in *The North American Mid-West*, 1955.

MCMANIS, D. R., *The Initial Evaluation and Utilization of the Illinois Prairies, 1815–1840*, Chicago, 1964.
MALIN, J. C., *The Grassland of North America; Prolegomena to its History*, Lawrence, Kansas, 1956.
MURRAY, J. J., *The Heritage of the Middle West*, Norman, Oklahoma, 1958.
NOLAN, *Hoosier City*, the story of Indianapolis, New York, 1943.
PATTON, D., 'The traffic pattern on American inland waterways', *Econ. Geog.*, Vol. 32, 1956.
ROSE, J. K., 'Corn yield and climate in the corn belt', *Geog. Rev.*, 1936.
SAUER, C. O., 'The settlement of the humid east', in *Climate and Man*, U.S. Yrbk. of Agric., 1941.
—— 'Homestead and community on the Middle Border', *Landscape*, Vol. 12, No. 1, Autumn 1962.
SCHMID, C. F., *Social Saga of Two Cities* (Minneapolis–St Paul), Minneapolis, 1937.
SEYMOUR, R. F., *Our Midwest*, Chicago, 1954.
SHANTZ, H. L., 'The natural vegetation of the Great Plains region', *Annals Assoc. Amer. Geogrs.*, Vol. 13.
SHAW, E., 'Swine production in the corn belt of the United States', *Econ. Geog.*, 1936.
WALKER, C. R., *American City—Minneapolis*, New York, 1937.
WEAVER, J. C., 'Crop combination regions in the Middle West', *Geog. Rev.*, Vol. 44, 1954.
—— 'Changing patterns of cropland use in the Middle West', *Econ. Geog.*, Vol. 30, No. 1, Jan. 1954.
——, LEVERTT, P. H., & FENTON, B. L., 'Livestock units and combinations in the Middle West', *Econ. Geog.*, Vol. 32, 1956.

MAJOR REGIONS OF THE UNITED STATES—*The West*

ALTROCCHI, J., *The Old California Trail*, Caldwell, 1945.
ANNALS ASSOC. AMER. GEOGRS., 'Symposium on the Great Plains', 1923.
ATHERTON, L., *The Cattle Kings*, Bloomington, 1961.
BAKER, O. E., 'The grazing and irrigated crops region', *Econ. Geog.*, 1931.
—— 'North Pacific hay and pasture region', *Econ. Geog.*, 1931.
—— 'The Pacific subtropical crops region', *Econ. Geog.*, 1930.
BALCHIN, W. G. V., & PYE, N., 'Climate and Culture in S. Arizona', *Weather*, Vol. X, No. 12, December, 1955.
BELKNAP, H. O., *The Church of the Changing Frontier*, New York, 1922.
BEYER, J. L., 'The integration of grazing and crop agriculture', Chicago, 1957.
BILLINGTON, R. A., *Westward Expansion*, New York, 1949.
BLACKWELDER, E., 'Origin of the Colorado', *Bul. Geol. Soc. Amer.*, Vol. 45.
BOGARDUS, J. F., 'The Great Basin', *Econ. Geog.*, 1930.
BROCK, J. M., *The Santa Clara Valley, California*; a study in landscape changes, Berkeley, 1932.
BUTLER, E. I., *Alaska, the Land and the People*, New York, 1957.
CAUGHEY, J. W., *History of the Pacific Coast*, New York, 1938.
CLAWSON, M., *The Western Range Livestock Industry*, New York, 1950.
COX, R., *The Columbia River*, Norman, 1957.
DEBO, A., *Prairie City*, New York, 1944.
DENISON, B. W., *Alaska Today*, Coldwell, Idaho, 1950.
DICK, *The Sod-house Frontier*, New York.
DODGE, N. N., & ZIM, H. S., *The American Southwest*, New York, 1955.
DODGE, R. I., *The Plains of the West and Their Inhabitants*, New York, 1959.
FLANAGAN, J. T., *America is West*, Minneapolis, 1945.
FREEMAN, O. W., 'Salmon industry of the Pacific coast', *Econ. Geog.*, 1935.
—— & RAYS, H. F., 'Industrial trends in the Pacific Northwest', *Jour. Geog.*, 1944.
—— & MARTIN, H. H. (eds.), *The Pacific Northwest*, New York, 1954.
GARNSEY, M. E., *America's New Frontier*, the Mountain West, New York, 1950
GHENT, W. J., *The Road to Oregon*, London, 1929.

GHENT, W. J., *The Early Far West*, New York, 1936.
GREGOR, H. F., 'A sample study of the California ranch', *Annals Assoc. Amer. Geogrs.*, 1951.
—— 'The Plantation in California', *Profl. Geogr.*, Vol. 14, No. 2, 1962.
HAFEN, LE R., *Overland Routes to the Goldfields*, Glendale, 1942.
—— *Western America*, the exploration . . . beyond the Mississippi, 2nd edn., New York, 1950.
HANSON, H. C., *Agriculture in the Matanuska Valley*, Alaska, Washington, 1943.
HERRON, E. A., *Alaska, Land of Tomorrow*, New York, 1947.
HEWES, G. W., 'The Fisheries of Northwestern North America', *Econ. Geog.*, Vol. 28.
HIGBEE, E., *The American Oasis*, New York, 1957.
HIGHSMITH, R. M., 'Irrigation in the Willamette Valley', *Geog. Rev.*, Vol. 46, 1956.
HOOVER, J. W., 'The littoral of California as a geographic province', *Geog. Rev.*, 1933.
HORAN, J. D., *The Great American West*, Crown, 1959.
HOUGH, E., *The Passing of the Frontier*, New Haven, 1918.
HUNGERFORD, E., *Wells Fargo Advancing the Frontier*, New York, 1949.
HUTCHISON, C. B., *California Agriculture*, Berkeley, 1946.
JAEGER, E. C., *The California Deserts*, Stanford, 1933.
—— *The North American Deserts*, Stanford, 1957.
KESSELI, J. E., 'Climates of California', *Geog. Rev.*, Vol. 32.
KRAENZEL, C. F., *The Great Plains in Transition*, Norman, 1955.
LAUBER, P., *Dust Bowl*, New York, 1958.
MATHER, E., 'The production and marketing of Wyoming beef cattle', *Econ. Geog.*, 1930.
MEIGS, P., 'Water problems in the United States', *Geog. Rev.*, Vol. 42.
—— 'Water planning in the Great Central Valley, California', *Geog. Rev.*, 1939.
—— 'Current trends in California orchards and vineyards', *Econ. Geog.*, 1941.
MORRIS, R. C., 'The Notion of a "Great American Desert" East of the Rockies', *Mississippi Val. Hist. Rev.*, Sept. 1926.
MORTON, W. L., 'The significance of site in the settlement of the American and Canadian Wests', *Agric. Hist.*, Vol. 25, No. 3, July 1951.
MUENCH, *Salt Lake City*, New York, 1947.
NELSON, H. J., 'Significant characteristics of the Los Angeles metropolitan growth pattern', in *Transportation and Metropolitan Planning*, ed. Engelbert, Los Angeles, 1956.
—— 'The spread of an artificial landscape over Southern California', *Annals Assoc. Amer. Geogrs.*, Vol. 49, No. 3, Pt. 2, 1959.
PARKMAN, F., *The Oregon Trail*, New York, 1849.
PARSONS, J. J., 'California manufacturing', *Geog. Rev.*, Vol. 39, 1949.
PEATTIE, R., *The Sierra Nevada*, New York, 1949.
—— *The Cascades*, Mountains of the Pacific Northwest, New York, 1949.
RAUP, H. F., 'Piedmont plain agriculture in Southern California', *Yrbk., Assoc. Pacific Coast Geogrs.*, No. 6, 1940.
RISTER, C. C., *Southern Plainsmen*, Norman, 1934.
ROBINSON, W. W., *Los Angeles from the Days of the Pueblo*, Los Angeles, 1959.
RUXTON, G. T. A., *Life in the Far West*, Norman, 1951.
SANDOZ, MARI, *The Buffalo Hunters*, New York, 1954.
—— *The Cattle Men*, New York, 1958.
SCHMITT, M. F., *The Settlers' West*, New York, 1955.
SEEMAN, A. L., 'Seattle as a port city', *Econ. Geog.*, 1935.
SEEMAN, A. L., & TENANT, H. E., 'Changing frontier in the Columbia basin', *Econ. Geog.*, 1938.
SIDDALL, W. W., 'Seattle, regional capital of Alaska', *Annals Amer. Assoc. Geogrs.*, Vol. 47, No. 3, 1957.
SPAULDING, K. A., *On the Oregon Trail*, Norman, 1953.
STONE, K. H., 'Populating Alaska: the United States phase', *Geog. Rev.*, 1952.
—— *Alaskan group settlement*, U.S. Dept. Int., Washington, 1950.

TEAL, J. J., & SHARLAND, I., 'Alaska', in *Geography of the Northlands*, eds. Kimble & Good, New York, 1955.
THOMAS, W. S. (ed.), 'Man, Time and Space in Southern California, a Symposium', *Annals Assoc. Amer. Geogrs.*, Vol. 49, 1959.
THOMPSON, W. S., *Growth and Changes in California's Population*, Los Angeles, 1955.
THORNTHWAITE, C. W., 'Climate and settlement in the Great Plains', in *Climate and Man*, Washington, 1941.
TOUSLEY, R. D., & LEMONS, H., 'The Washington apple industry', *Econ. Geog.*, 1945.
VESTAL, S., *Short Grass Country*, New York, 1941.
WARD, R. C., 'The northern Great Plains as a producer of wheat', *Econ. Geog.*, 1946.
WEAVER, J. E., *North American Prairie*, Lincoln, Nebraska, 1954.
—— & ALBERTSON, F. W., *Grasslands of the Great Plains; their Nature and Use*, Lincoln, Nebraska, 1956.
WEBB, W. P., *The Great Plains*, New York, 1931.
WILLIAMS, A. N., *Rocky Mountain Country*, New York, 1950.
WILLIAMS, H. (ed.), *Landscapes of Alaska*, Berkeley, 1958.
WOESTEMEYER, I. F., *The Westward Movement*, New York, 1939.
WYMAN, W. D., & KROEBER, C. B., *The Frontier in Perspective*, Madison, 1957.
YI-FU TUAN, 'Structure, climate and basin land forms in Arizona and New Mexico', *Annals Assoc. Amer. Geogrs.*, Vol. 52, 1962.
ZIERER, C. M. (ed.), *California and the Southwest*, New York, 1956.

MAJOR REGIONS of the UNITED STATES—*The South*

BONHAM, H. D., 'The Prospects for heavy industry in the South', *Southern Econ. Jour.*, 1947.
BOWMAN, M. J., & HAYNES, W. W., *Resources and people in East Kentucky; Problems and Potentials of a Lagging Economy*, Baltimore, 1963.
BROWN, G., *The Lower South in American History*, New York, 1930.
CALEF, W., & NELSON, H. J., 'Distribution of Negro population in the United States', *Geog. Rev.*, Vol. 46.
CARSON, R. B., 'The Florida tropics', *Econ. Geog.*, 1951.
CARSON, W. J. (ed.), *The Coming of Industry to the South*, Amer. Acad. Pol. Sci. Pubn., 1931.
CARTER, H., *Gulf coast country*, New York, 1951.
CARUSO, J. A., *The Appalachian Frontier*, New York, 1959.
CASH, W. J., *The Mind of the South*, New York, 1941.
CHAMBERS, W. T., 'Life in a cotton farming community', *Jour. Geog.*, 1930.
—— 'The Gulf port city region of Texas', *Econ. Geog.*, 1931.
—— 'Kilgore Texas, an oil boom town', *Econ. Geog.*, 1933.
CLARK, *Travels in the Old South, 1527–1825*, 3 vols., Norman, Oklahoma, 1952.
COTTERILL, R. S., *The Old South*, Glendale, California, 1939.
CRANE, V. W., *The Southern Frontier, 1670–1732*, Ann Arbor, 1956.
DAVIS, *et al.*, *The Deep South*, Chicago, 1946.
DOLLARD, J., *Caste and Class in a Southern Town*, New York, 1949.
DOWDEY, C., *The Great Plantation*, New York, 1957.
DURAND, L., & BIRD, E. T., 'The Burley tobacco region of the mountain South', *Econ. Geog.*, 1950.
ERICKSON, F. C., 'The tobacco belt of N. Carolina', *Econ. Geog.*, 1945.
FISKE, J., *Old Virginia and Her Neighbours*, 2 vols., Boston, 1925.
FOSCUE, E. J., 'Industrialization of the Texas Gulf Coast', *S.W. Soc. Sci. Q.*, Vol. 31, 1950.
—— 'Gatlinburg, a mountain community', *Econ. Geog.*, 1945.
FRIEDMANN, J. R. P., *The Spatial Structure of Economic Development in the Tennessee Valley*, Chicago, 1955.
GIBSON, J. S., 'The Alabama "black belt", its geographic status', *Econ. Geog.*, 1941.
GOTTMANN, J., *Virginia at Mid-Century*, New York, 1955.
GRAY, L., *History of Agriculture in the Southern United States*, 2 vols., Washington, 1933.

HART, J. F., 'The Changing distribution of the American Negro', *Annals Assoc. Amer. Geogrs.*, Vol. 50, 1960.
HAWK, E. Q., *The Economic History of the South*, New York, 1934.
HESSELTINE, W. B., *The South in American History*, New York, 1951.
HOBBS, S. H., *North Carolina, a Social and Economic Profile*, Chapel Hill, 1947.
HOLLEY, W. C., *The Plantation South*, Washington, 1940.
HOLLON, W. E., *The Southwest, Old and New*, New York, 1961.
HOOVER, C. B., *The Economy of the South*, Washington, 1950.
—— & RATCHFORD, B. U., *Economic Resources and Policies of the South*, New York, 1951.
HOWARD, R. W. (ed.), *This is the South*, Chicago, 1959.
JOHNSON, R. W., 'Land use in the bluegrass basins', *Econ. Geog.*, 1940.
JONES, K. M., *The Plantation South*, Bobbs Merrill, Indianopolis, 1957.
LAND, M., *The Changing South*, Coward McCann, New York, 1959.
LILENTHAL, D. F., *T.V.A.—Democracy on the March*, 1944.
LYNN, S. M., *New Orleans*, New York, 1949.
MCLAUGHLIN, G. E., *Why Industry Moves South*, Washington, 1950.
MCKNIGHT, E. L., 'The distribution of manufacturing in Texas', *Annals Assoc. Amer. Geogrs.*, Vol. 47, No. 4, 1947.
MATHER, E., & HART, J. F., *Southeastern Excursion*, I.G.U. XVIIth Internat. Congress, Washington, 1952.
MERRENS, H. R., *Colonial N. Carolina in the Eighteenth Century; a study in Historical Geography*, Chapel Hill, 1964.
MEZERIK, A. G., *The Revolt of the South and West*, New York, 1946.
NIXON, H. C., *Lower Piedmont County*, New York, 1946.
ODUM, H. W., *The Way of the South*, New York, 1947.
—— & BROOKS, L. M., *Southern Regions of the United States*, Chapel Hill, 1936.
OLMSTED, F. L., *The Cotton Kingdom*, New York, 1953.
PARKINS, A. E., *The South*, New York, 1938.
PARSONS, J. J., 'Recent industrial development in the Gulf South , *Geog. Rev.*, Vol. 40.
PEATTIE, R. (ed.), *The Great Smokies and the Blue Ridge*, New York, 1943.
PHILLIPS, U. B. *Life and Labor in the Old South*, Boston, 1929.
POST, L. C., 'The rice country of Southwestern Louisiana', *Jour. Geog.*, 1934.
PRUNTY, M., 'The renaissance of the Southern plantations', *Geog. Rev.*, Vol. 45.
—— 'Recent quantitative changes in the cotton regions of the South-eastern States' *Econ. Geog.*, Vol. 27, 1951.
STONEY, S., *Plantations of the Carolina Low Country*, 4th edn. by Albert Simons and Samuel Lapham, Carolina Art Assoc., Charleston, 1955.
STRAIN, W., 'The Florida citrus crop', *Econ. Geog.*, 1942.
—— 'The Florida phosphate industry', *Jour. Geog.*, 1945.
STREET, J. H., *The New Revolution in the Cotton Economy*, North Carolina, Durham, 1956.
VANCE, R. B., *Human Geography of the South*, Chapel Hill, 2nd edn., 1935.
VAN SICKLE, J. U., 'Industrialization and the South', *Southern Econ. Jour.*, 1949.
WERTENBAKER, T. J., *The Old South*, New York, 1942.
WHITE, L., 'The iron and steel industry of Birmingham, Alabama', *Econ. Geog.*, 1928.

MEXICO

ALEXANDER, R. J., 'Agrarian reform in Latin America', *Foreign Affairs*, Vol. 41, No. 1, 1962.
ARELLAND, A. R. V., 'Datos geológicos sobre la antigüedad del hombre en la cuenca de México', 2nd Cong. Mex. de Ciencias Sociales, 5, 1946.
BAILEY, H. M., & NASATIR, A. P., *Latin America, the Development of Its Civilization*, New Jersey, 1960.
BASAURI, C., *La población indigena de México*, Mexico, 1940.
BENHAM, F., & HALLEY, H. A., *A Short Introduction to the Economy of Latin America*, Oxford, 1960.
BUTLAND, G. J., *Latin America, a Regional Geography*, London, 1960.

CARLSON, F. A., *Geography of Late America*, New York, 1953.
CHEVALIER, FR., *La formation des grandes domaines au Mexique*, 1952.
COE, M. D., *Mexico*, London, 1962.
COLE, J. P., *Notes on the Towns of Latin America*, Univ. Nottingham Dept. Geog. Pubn., Oct. 1962.
COVARRUBIAS, M., *Mexico South, the Isthmus of Tehuantepec*, 1954.
DELGADILLO, D., *La républica mexicana, geografia elemental*, Mexico, 1947.
DICKEN, S. N., 'Monterrey and Northeastern Mexico', *Annals Assoc. Amer. Geogrs.*, Vol. 29, 1939.
FONSECA, M. M., *Monografia de la républica mexicana*, Mexico, 1946.
FRANK, W., 'Mexico', in *The Romance of North America*, ed. Moseley, 1958.
GALLENKAMP, C., 'The cities of ancient Mexico', *Can. Geog. Jour.*, Vol. 49, No. 4, 1959.
GILL, T., *Land Hunger in Mexico*, Washington, 1951.
HANSON, S. G., *Economic Development in Latin America*, Washington, 1951.
HAYNES, N. S., 'Mexico City, its growth and configuration', *Amer. Jour. Soc.*, Vol. 50, 1945.
HYMPHREYS, R. A., *The Evolution of Modern Latin America*, Oxford, 1945.
JAMES, P., *Latin America*, New York, 1942.
LEOPOLD, A. S., *Zonas de vegetación en México*, Bol. Soc. Mex. Geog. Estadistica, Vol. 73, 1952.
LEWIS, O., 'Social and economic changes in a Mexican village: Tepoztlan, 1928–44', *Amer. Indigina*, Vol. 4, 1944.
MCBRIDE, G. M., *The Land Systems of Mexico*, New York, 1923.
MEGEE, M., 'Some post-war aspects of industrial development in Monterrey, Mexico', *Revista Geografica*, No. 54, Tomo 28, 1961.
MEIGS, P., 'The Dominican mission frontier of Lower California', Univ. of Cal. Pubns. in *Geog.*, Vol. 7, 1935.
MIRANDA, F., 'Estudios sobre la vegetacion de México', *Anales Inst. Biol.*, Vol. 1, 1942.
MOORE, D. R., *A History of Latin America*, New York, 1942.
MORLEY, S. G., *The Ancient Maya*, revd. by Brainerd, G. W., London, 1956.
ORDONEZ, E., 'Las profincias fisiograficas de México', *Revista Geog.*, Vol. 1, 1941.
PETERSON, F., *Ancient Mexico*, London, 1959.
PLATT, R. S., *Latin America*, New York, 1943.
RINCÓN, F. Z., *La républica mexicana, geografia atlas*, Mexico, 1941.
RIPPY, J. F., *Latin America*, Ann Arbor, 1958.
ROBINSON, H., *Latin America*, London, 1961.
SAUER, C. O., *The Aboriginal Population of Northwestern Mexico*, Berkeley, 1935.
—— 'The personality of Mexico', *Geog. Rev.*, Vol. 31, 1941.
SENIOR, C., 'The Laguna region—Mexico's agrarian laboratory', *Q. Jour. Inter-Amer. Relations*, Oct. 1939.
SIMPSON, E. N., *The Ejido, Mexico's way out*, Chapel Hill, 1937.
SORRE, M., *Mexique, Amérique centrale*, Paris, 1928.
STANISLOWSKI, D., 'Early Spanish town planning in the New World', *Geog. Rev.*, Vol. 37, 1947.
DE TERRA, *et al.*, *Tepexpan Man*, New York, 1949.
UNESCO, *Urbanization in Latin America*, Paris, 1961.
VAILLANT, G. C., *The Aztecs of Mexico*, London, 1950.
VIOLICH, F., 'Evolution of the Spanish city; issues basic to planning today', *Jour. Amer. Inst. Planners*, Vol. 28, No. 3, 1962.
VIVO, J. A., *Geografia de México*, (rev). ed., Mexico, 1958.
WHETTEN, N. L., *Rural Mexico*, Chicago, 1948.
WYTHE, G., *Industry in Latin America*, New York, 1946.

General Index

Principal references are shown in **bold type**;
Maps, charts, etc, are shown in *italics*.

Index of Authors Cited